Grade 5 NCTM Focal Points Alignment

Math Triumphs,* Grade 5 provides the prerequisite concepts and skills necessary for success with the Grade 5 NCTM Focal Points. Horizontal alignment ensures successful transitions between *Math Connects* and *Math Triumphs.

Preparation for NCTM Grade 5 Focal Points	*Math Triumphs,* Grade 5	Targeted Prerequisite Skills and Concepts	Preparation for *Math Connects,* Grade 5
Focal Point 1 Number and Operations and Algebra *Math Triumphs* Book 1	Chapter 1 **Place Value and Number Relationships**	Compare and order whole numbers.	Chapter 1
		Add and subtract whole numbers.	Chapter 2
		Identify and use basic patterns and sequences.	Chapters 6 and 7
	Chapter 2 **Multiplication**	Understand basic multiplication and repeated addition.	Chapter 3
		Use patterns and sequences.	Chapter 3
		Add and multiply whole numbers.	Chapter 3
	Chapter 3 **Division**	Understand basic division and repeated subtraction.	Chapter 4
		Use patterns and sequences.	Chapter 4
		Subtract and divide numbers.	Chapter 4
	Chapter 4 **Properties of Operations**	Add, subtract, multiply, and divide whole numbers.	Chapters 3 and 5
Focal Point 2 Number and Operations *Math Triumphs* Book 2	Chapter 5 **Fractions**	Understand basic division.	Chapter 8
		Understand parts of whole, parts of a set.	Chapters 8, 9, and 15
	Chapter 6 **Add and Subtract Fractions**	Understand and use equivalent fractions.	Chapter 10
		Use factors and multiples of numbers to add and subtract fractions.	Chapter 10
	Chapter 7 **Decimals**	Understand place value through the thousandths.	Chapters 1 and 2
Focal Point 3 Geometry, Measurement, and Algebra *Math Triumphs* Book 3	Chapter 8 **Geometry**	Classify two-dimensional and three-dimensional figures.	Chapters 13 and 14
	Chapter 9 **Area**	Estimate area using a grid.	Chapter 14
		Find the area of a two-dimensional figure, such as a rectangle, parallelogram, and triangle.	Chapter 14
	Chapter 10 **Surface Area, Volume, and Measurement**	Understand units of metric and customary measure.	Chapters 11, 12, and 14
		Find the surface area of a rectangular solid.	Chapters 11, 12, and 14
		Find the volume of a rectangular solid.	Chapters 11, 12, and 14

For a complete correlation to the NCTM Curriculum Focal Points, go to www.macmillanmh.com and select **Math,** then **Teacher View.** The complete Curriculum Focal Points may be viewed at www.nctm.org/focalpoints.

NCTM Focal Points	Preparation in *Math Triumphs,* Grade 5
***Number and Operations* and *Algebra* (G5-FP1) Developing an understanding of and fluency with division of whole numbers** Students apply their understanding of models for division, place value, properties, and the relationship of division to multiplication as they develop, discuss, and use efficient, accurate, and generalizable procedures to find quotients involving multidigit dividends. They select appropriate methods and apply them accurately to estimate quotients or calculate them mentally, depending on the context and numbers involved. They develop fluency with efficient procedures, including the standard algorithm, for dividing whole numbers, understand why the procedures work (on the basis of place value and properties of operations), and use them to solve problems. They consider the context in which a problem is situated to select the most useful form of the quotient for the solution, and they interpret it appropriately.	**Chapter 1: Place Value and Number Relationships** **Chapter 2: Multiplication** **Chapter 3: Division** **Chapter 4: Properties of Operations**
***Number and Operations* (G5-FP2) Developing an understanding of and fluency with addition and subtraction of fractions and decimals** Students apply their understandings of fractions and fraction models to represent the addition and subtraction of fractions with unlike denominators as equivalent calculations with like denominators. They apply their understandings of decimal models, place value, and properties to add and subtract decimals. They develop fluency with standard procedures for adding and subtracting fractions and decimals. They make reasonable estimates of fraction and decimal sums and differences. Students add and subtract fractions and decimals to solve problems, including problems involving measurement.	**Chapter 5: Fractions** **Chapter 6: Add and Subtract Fractions** **Chapter 7: Decimals**
***Geometry* and *Measurement* and *Algebra* (G5-FP3) Describing three-dimensional shapes and analyzing their properties, including volume and surface area** Students relate two-dimensional shapes to three-dimensional shapes and analyze properties of polyhedral solids, describing them by the number of edges, faces, or vertices as well as they types of faces. Students recognize volume as an attribute of three-dimensional space. They understand that they can quantify volume by finding the total number of same-sized units of volume that they need to fill the space without gaps or overlaps. They understand that a cube that is 1 unit on an edge is the standard unit for measuring volume. They select appropriate units, strategies, and tools for solving problems that involve estimating or measuring volume. They decompose three-dimensional shapes and find surface areas and volumes of prisms. As they work with surface area, they find and justify relationships among the formulas for the areas of different polygons. They measure necessary attributes of shapes to use area formulas to solve problems.	**Chapter 8: Geometry** **Chapter 9: Area** **Chapter 10: Surface Area, Volume, and Measurement**

Focal Points Connections	Preparation in *Math Triumphs,* Grade 5
Algebra (G5-FP4C) Students use patterns, models, and relationships as contexts for writing and solving simple equations and inequalities. They create graphs of simple equations. They explore prime and composite numbers and discover concepts related to the addition and subtraction of fractions as they use factors and multiples, including applications of common factors and common multiples. They develop an understanding of the order of operations and use it for all operations.	**Chapter 4: Properties of Operations** **Chapter 5: Fractions** **Chapter 6: Add and Subtract Fractions**
Measurement (G5-FP5C) Students' experiences connect their work with solids and volume to their earlier work with capacity and weight or mass. They solve problems that require attention to both approximation and precision of measurement.	**Chapter 9: Area** **Chapter 10: Surface Area, Volume, and Measurement**
Data Analysis (G5-FP6C) Students apply their understanding of whole numbers, fractions, and decimals as they construct and analyze double-bar and line graphs and use ordered pairs on coordinate grids.	**Chapter 1: Place Value and Number Relationships** **Chapter 5: Fractions** **Chapter 6: Add and Subtract Fractions** **Chapter 7: Decimals**
Number and Operations (G5-FP7C) Building on their work in grade 4, students extend their understanding of place value to numbers through millions and millionths in various context. They apply what they know about multiplication of whole numbers to larger numbers. Students also explore contexts that they can describe with negative numbers (e.g., situations of owing money or measuring elevations above and below sea level.)	**Chapter 1: Place Value and Number Relationships** **Chapter 2: Multiplication**

For a complete correlation to the NCTM Curriculum Focal Points, go to www.macmillanmh.com and select **Math,** then **Teacher View.** The complete Curriculum Focal Points may be viewed at www.nctm.org/focalpoints.

Contents in Brief

Preparation for Focal Points and Connections
See front cover folder for key.

Student Study Guide: Book 1

Student Study Guide: Book 2

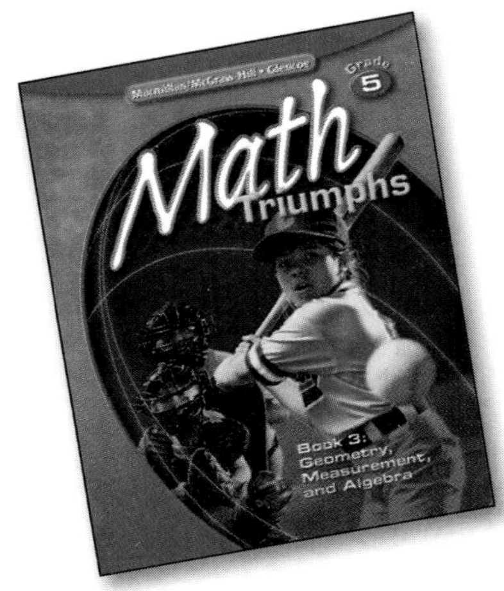

Student Study Guide: Book 3

T60622

Authors and Consultants

AUTHORS

Frances Basich Whitney
Project Director, Mathematics K–12
Santa Cruz County Office of Education
Capitola, California

Kathleen M. Brown
Math Curriculum Staff Developer
Washington Middle School
Long Beach, California

Dixie Dawson
Math Curriculum Leader
Long Beach Unified
Long Beach, California

Philip Gonsalves
Mathematics Coordinator
Alameda County Office of Education
Hayward, California

Robyn Silbey
Math Specialist
Montgomery County Public Schools
Gaithersburg, Maryland

Kathy Vielhaber
Mathematics Consultant
St. Louis, Missouri

CONTRIBUTING AUTHORS

Viken Hovsepian
Professor of Mathematics
Rio Hondo College
Whittier, California

FOLDABLES Study Organizer

Dinah Zike
Educational Consultant,
Dinah-Might Activities, Inc.
San Antonio, Texas

CONSULTANTS

Assessment

Donna M. Kopenski, Ed.D.
Math Coordinator K–5
City Heights Educational Collaborative
San Diego, California

Instructional Planning and Support

Beatrice Luchin
Mathematics Consultant
League City, Texas

ELL Support and Vocabulary

ReLeah Cossett Lent
Author/Educational Consultant
Alford, Florida

Reviewers

Each person below reviewed at least two chapters of the Student Study Guide, providing feedback and suggestions for improving the effectiveness of the mathematics instruction.

Dana M. Addis
Teacher Leader
Dearborn Public Schools
Dearborn, MI

Renee M. Blanchard
Elementary Math Facilitator
Erie School District
Erie, PA

Jeanette Collins Cantrell
5th and 6th Grade Math Teacher
W.R. Castle Memorial Elementary
Wittensville, KY

Helen L. Cheek
K-5 Mathematics Specialist
Durham Public Schools
Durham, NCI

Mercy Cosper
1st Grade Teacher
Pershing Park Elementary
Killeen, TX

Bonnie H. Ennis
Mathematics Coordinator
Wicomico County Public Schools
Salisbury, MD

Sheila A. Evans
Instructional Support Teacher – Math
Glenmount Elementary/Middle School
Baltimore, MD

Lisa B. Golub
Curriculum Resource Teacher
Millennia Elementary
Orlando, FL

Donna Hagan
Program Specialist – Special Programs Department
Weatherford ISD
Weatherford, TX

Russell Hinson
Teacher
Belleview Elementary
Rock Hill, SC

Tania Shepherd Holbrook
Teacher
Central Elementary School
Paintsville, KY

Stephanie J. Howard
3rd Grade Teacher
Preston Smith Elementary
Lubbock, TX

Rhonda T. Inskeep
Math Support Teacher
Stevens Forest Elementary School
Columbia, MD

Albert Gregory Knights
Teacher/4th Grade/Math Lead Teacher
Cornelius Elementary
Houston, TX

Barbara Langley
Math/Science Coach
Poinciana Elementary School
Kissimmee, FL

David Ennis McBroom
Math/Science Facilitator
John Motley Morehead Elementary
Charlotte, NC

Jan Mercer, MA; NBCT
K-5 Math Lab Facilitator
Meadow Woods Elementary
Orlando, FL

Rosalind R. Mohamed
Instructional Support Teacher – Mathematics
Furley Elementary School
Baltimore, MD

Patricia Penafiel
Teacher
Phyllis Miller Elementary
Miami, FL

Lindsey R. Petlak
2nd Grade Instructor
Prairieview Elementary School
Hainesville, IL

Lana A. Prichard
District Math Resource Teacher K-8
Lawrence Co. School District
Louisa, KY

Stacy L. Riggle
3rd Grade Spanish Magnet Teacher
Phillips Elementary
Pittsburgh, PA

Wendy Scheleur
5th Grade Teacher
Piney Orchard Elementary
Odenton, MD

Stacey L. Shapiro
Teacher
Zilker Elementary
Austin, TX

Kim Wilkerson Smith
4th Grade Teacher
Casey Elementary School
Austin, TX

Wyolonda M. Smith, NBCT
4th Grade Teacher
Pilot Elementary School
Greensboro, NC

Kristen M. Stone
3rd Grade Teacher
Tanglewood Elementary
Lumberton, NC

Jamie M. Williams
Math Specialist
New York Mills Union Free School District
New York Mills, NY

Mathematics Teacher Handbook

Table of Contents

Welcome to Macmillan/McGraw-Hill Mathematics

Concepts • Skills • Problem Solving

The only true vertically aligned PreK–12 Mathematics Curriculum

Math Connects offers three dimensions of vertical alignment.

❶ Content Design

Vertical content alignment is a process that ensures you and your students experience an articulated, coherent sequence of content from grade level to grade level. This provides you with the assurance that content is introduced, reinforced, and assessed at appropriate times in the series, eliminating gaps and unnecessary duplication. You are able to target your instruction to student needs because you are not teaching content intended to be covered later or that students have previously mastered.

❷ Instructional Design

Our strong vertical alignment in instructional approach from PreKindergarten through Algebra 2 provides a smooth transition for students from elementary to middle school to high school. Our common vocabulary, technology, manipulatives, lesson planning, and Data-Driven Decision Making reduce the confusion students often encounter when transitioning between grade levels without this built-in articulation.

❸ Visual Design

The student pages of ***Math Connects*** have a consistent visual design from grade to grade. This aids students' transition from elementary school to middle school and from middle school to Algebra 1. Students are more likely to succeed when they are already familiar with how to navigate student pages.

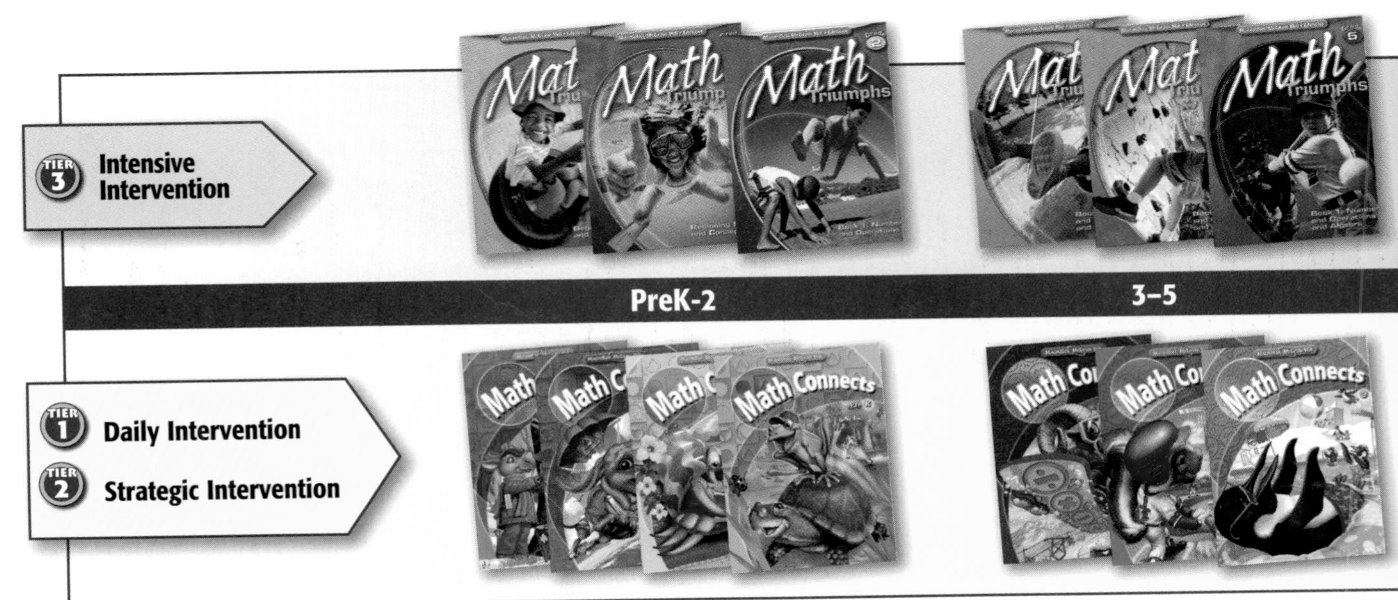

5 Keys to Success

1 Backmapping

According to College Board research, about 80% of students who successfully complete Algebra 1 and Geometry by 10th grade attend and succeed in college. (Changing the Odds: Factors Increasing Access to College, 1990) ***Math Connects*** was conceived and developed by backmapping with the final result in mind–student success in Algebra 1 and beyond.

2 Balanced, In-Depth Content

Math Connects was developed to specifically target the skills and topics that give students the most difficulty, such as Problem Solving, in each grade span.

Grades K–2	Grades 3–5
1. Problem Solving 2. Money 3. Time 4. Measurement 5. Fractions 6. Computation	1. Problem Solving 2. Fractions 3. Measurement 4. Decimals 5. Time 6. Algebra
Grades 6–8	**Grades 9–12**
1. Fractions 2. Problem Solving 3. Measurement 4. Algebra 5. Computation	1. Problem Solving 2. Fractions 3. Algebra 4. Geometry 5. Computation 6. Probability

– *K–12 Math Market Analysis Survey,* Open Book Publishing, 2006

3 Ongoing Assessment

Math Connects includes diagnostic, formative, and summative assessment; data-driven instruction; intervention options; and performance tracking, as well as remediation, acceleration, and enrichment tools throughout the program.

4 Intervention and Differentiated Instruction

A three-tiered Response To Intervention (RTI) is provided.

TIER 1 **Daily Intervention** Reteach masters and Alternative Strategy suggestions address concepts from a different modality or learning style.

TIER 2 **Strategic Intervention** Teachers can use the myriad of intervention tips and ancillary materials, such as the Strategic Intervention Guide (1–5) and Study Guide and Intervention (6–8).

TIER 3 **Intensive Intervention** For students who are two or more years below grade level, ***Math Triumphs*** provides step-by-step instruction, vocabulary support, and data-driven decision making to help students succeed.

5 Professional Development

Math Connects includes many opportunities for teacher professional development. Additional learning opportunities in various formats–video, online, and on-site instruction–are fully aligned and articulated from Kindergarten through Algebra 2.

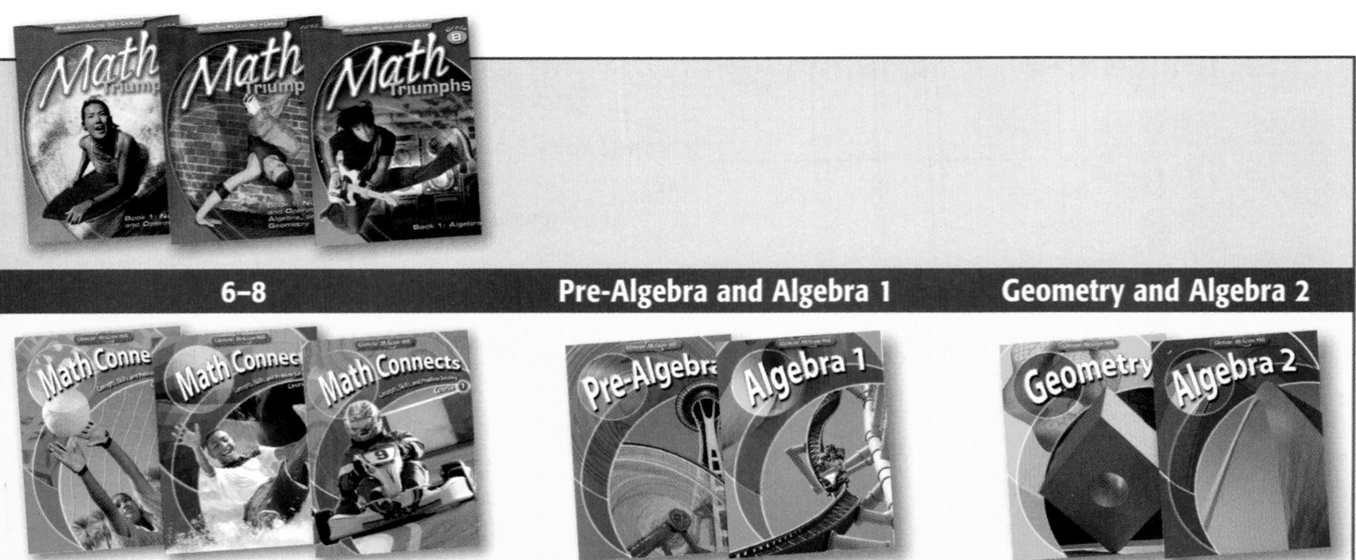

Implementing Intensive Intervention

Data-Driven Intensive Intervention

Ongoing assessment aids the teacher in student placement, progress monitoring, and exit.

Instructional Design	Classroom Implementation
1 Diagnose and Prescribe • Course Placement Test • Online Readiness Quiz • Chapter Preview • Chapter Pretest • Book Pretest	Teacher prepares individual or group intervention plan(s).
2 Teach and Practice • Student Study Guide • Teacher Edition Strategies • Vocabulary Cards • Manipulatives	Teacher modifies instruction based on results of formative assessments.
3 Advance and Exit • Assessment Masters • Chapter Test • Book Test	Test success indicates that a student can progress to another *Math Triumphs* chapter (if needed) or exit the intervention program.

Alignment to NCTM Focal Points

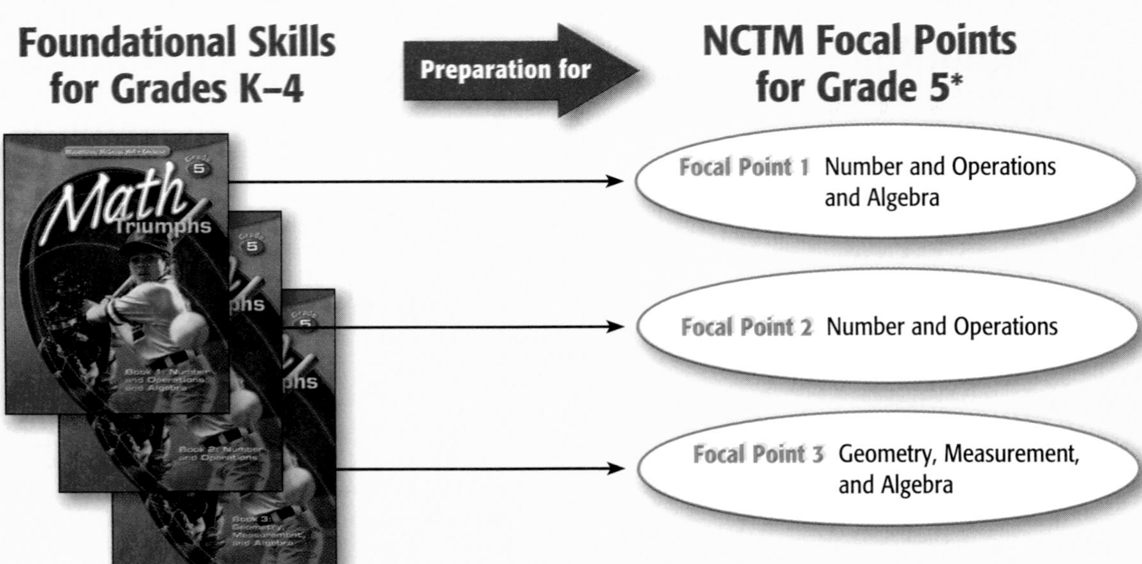

*See front cover folder for key and complete NCTM Focal Points.

Program Organization

Provide Personalized Instruction

Consumable volumes and minimal preparation requirements allow for flexibility and personalized instruction in any setting.

- After school
- Before school
- Tutoring
- Summer school
- Intersession
- Pull-out/Resource room

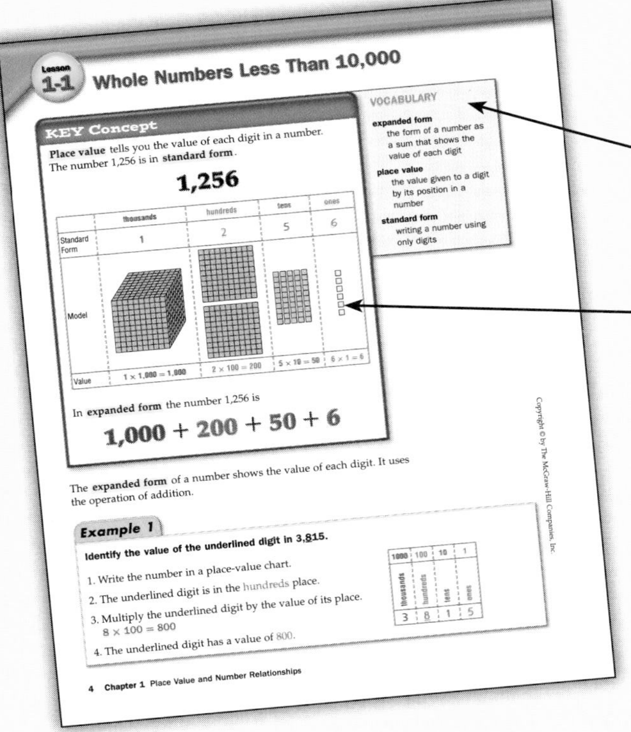

Vocabulary

Vocabulary helps students identify terms presented in the lesson.

Key Concepts

Key Concepts introduce and break mathematics into conceptual steps. Multiple representations demonstrate the skills being presented.

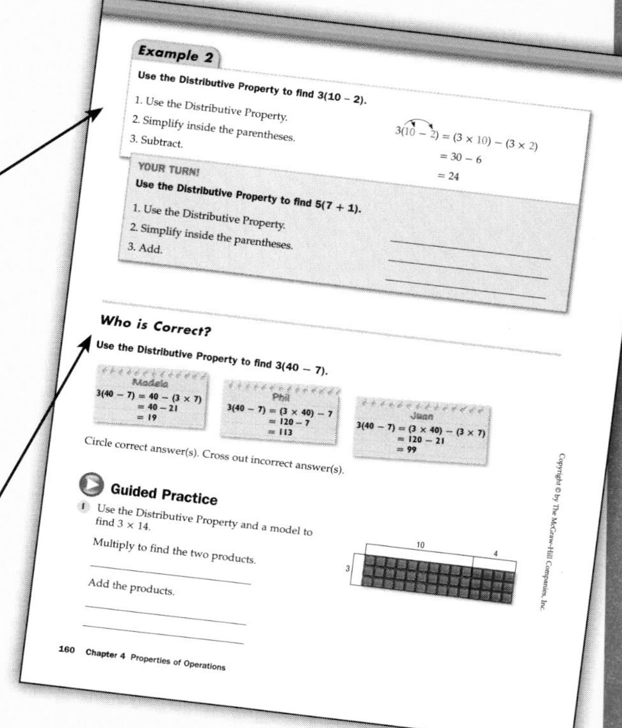

Examples

Fully worked-out **Examples** enable students and parents to see how to solve problems step by step. **Your Turn!** gives students an opportunity to practice skills immediately.

Who is Correct?

Students "grade" sample answers. This formative assessment opportunity generates meaningful classroom discussion and highlights possible misconceptions.

Guided Practice

Guided Practice exercises provide computational practice. They can be used as formative assessment to monitor student progress and guide your instruction.

Step-by-Step Practice guides students to complete a computational problem through a series of conceptual steps. Instructional aids are provided to students in the exercises that follow.

Step-by-Step Problem-Solving Practice walks the student through a four-step problem-solving strategy (Understand, Plan, Solve, Check) that is relevant to the word problem. Aids help the student break down and visualize what the problem is asking and how to solve it.

A **Reflect** question requires the student to think and write about the process of completing a problem.

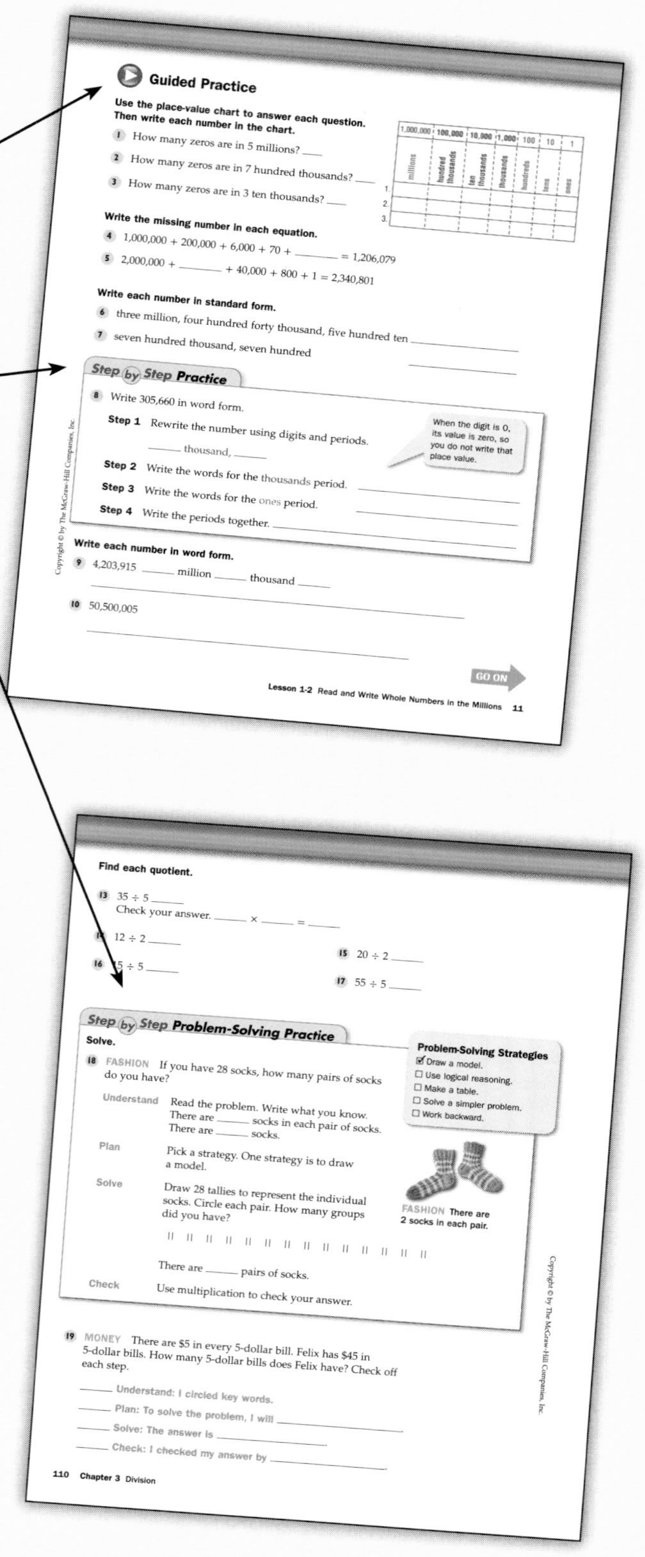

Guided Practice

Use the place-value chart to answer each question. Then write each number in the chart.

1 How many zeros are in 5 millions? ____

2 How many zeros are in 7 hundred thousands? ____

3 How many zeros are in 3 ten thousands? ____

	1,000,000	100,000	10,000	1,000	100	10	1
	millions	hundred thousands	ten thousands	thousands	hundreds	tens	ones
1.							
2.							
3.							

Write the missing number in each equation.

4 1,000,000 + 200,000 + 6,000 + 70 + ______ = 1,206,079

5 2,000,000 + ______ + 40,000 + 800 + 1 = 2,340,801

Write each number in standard form.

6 three million, four hundred forty thousand, five hundred ten ______

7 seven hundred thousand, seven hundred ______

Step by Step Practice

8 Write 305,660 in word form.

Step 1 Rewrite the number using digits and periods.
______ thousand, ______

When the digit is 0, its value is zero, so you do not write that place value.

Step 2 Write the words for the thousands period. ______

Step 3 Write the words for the ones period. ______

Step 4 Write the periods together. ______

Write each number in word form.

9 4,203,915 ______ million ______ thousand ______

10 50,500,005 ______

GO ON

Copyright © by The McGraw-Hill Companies, Inc.

Lesson 1-2 Read and Write Whole Numbers in the Millions 11

Find each quotient.

13 35 ÷ 5 ______
Check your answer. ______ × ______ = ______

14 12 ÷ 2 ______

15 20 ÷ 2 ______

16 15 ÷ 5 ______

17 55 ÷ 5 ______

Step by Step Problem-Solving Practice

Solve.

18 FASHION If you have 28 socks, how many pairs of socks do you have?

Problem-Solving Strategies
☑ Draw a model.
☐ Use logical reasoning.
☐ Make a table.
☐ Solve a simpler problem.
☐ Work backward.

Understand Read the problem. Write what you know.
There are ______ socks in each pair of socks.
There are ______ socks.

Plan Pick a strategy. One strategy is to draw a model.

Solve Draw 28 tallies to represent the individual socks. Circle each pair. How many groups did you have?

|| || || || || || || || || || || || || ||

There are ______ pairs of socks.

Check Use multiplication to check your answer.

FASHION There are 2 socks in each pair.

19 MONEY There are $5 in every 5-dollar bill. Felix has $45 in 5-dollar bills. How many 5-dollar bills does Felix have? Check off each step.

______ Understand: I circled key words.
______ Plan: To solve the problem, I will ______
______ Solve: The answer is ______.
______ Check: I checked my answer by ______

Copyright © by The McGraw-Hill Companies, Inc.

110 Chapter 3 Division

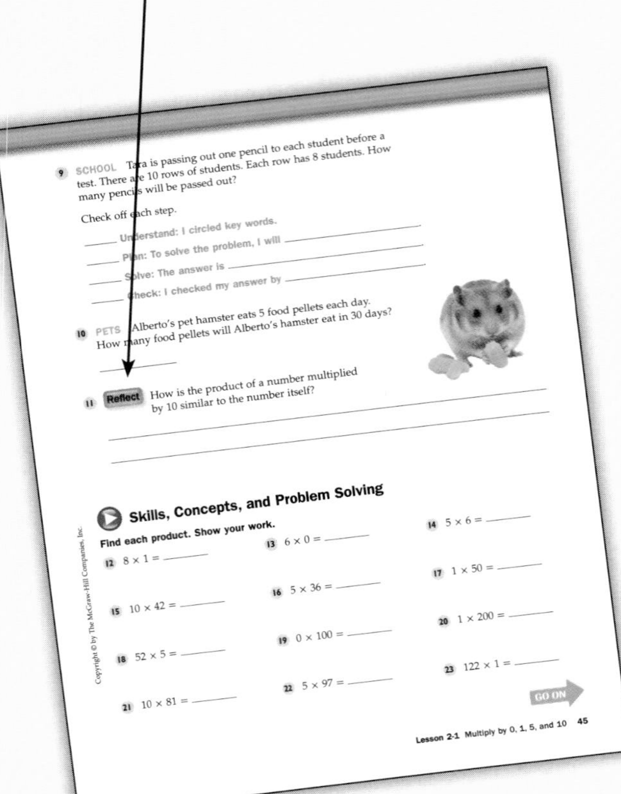

9 SCHOOL Tara is passing out one pencil to each student before a test. There are 10 rows of students. Each row has 8 students. How many pencils will be passed out?

Check off each step.

______ Understand: I circled key words.
______ Plan: To solve the problem, I will ______
______ Solve: The answer is ______
______ Check: I checked my answer by ______

10 PETS Alberto's pet hamster eats 5 food pellets each day. How many food pellets will Alberto's hamster eat in 30 days?

11 **Reflect** How is the product of a number multiplied by 10 similar to the number itself?

Skills, Concepts, and Problem Solving

Find each product. Show your work.

12 8 × 1 = ______

13 6 × 0 = ______

14 5 × 6 = ______

15 10 × 42 = ______

16 5 × 36 = ______

17 1 × 50 = ______

18 52 × 5 = ______

19 0 × 100 = ______

20 1 × 200 = ______

21 10 × 81 = ______

22 5 × 97 = ______

23 122 × 1 = ______

GO ON

Copyright © by The McGraw-Hill Companies, Inc.

Lesson 2-1 Multiply by 0, 1, 5, and 10 45

Balance

McGraw-Hill's ***Math Triumphs*** is designed to provide students a balanced approach to mathematics learning by offering them the opportunity to:

- investigate concepts and build their conceptual understanding;
- review, learn, and practice basic computational and procedural skills; and
- apply mathematics to problem solving in real-world situations.

Independent Practice

Skill, Concepts, and Problem Solving provide homework opportunities and independent practice.

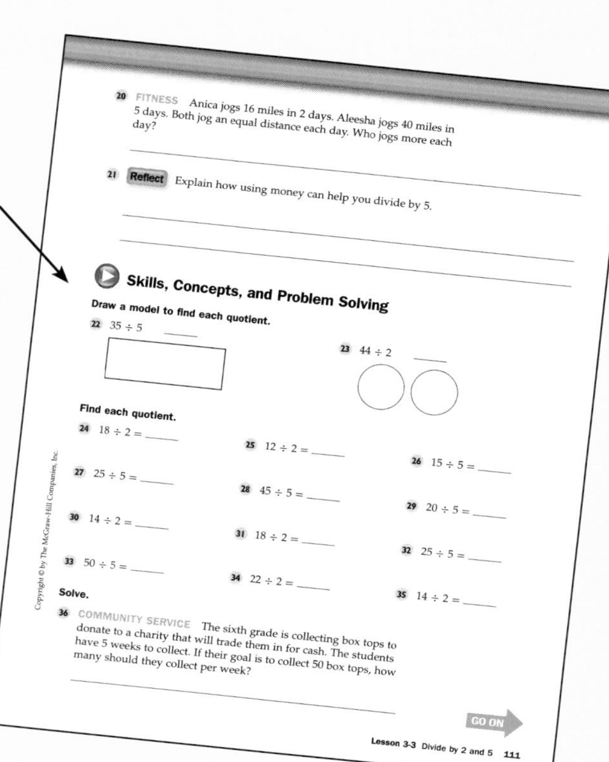

20 FITNESS Anica jogs 16 miles in 2 days. Aleesha jogs 40 miles in 5 days. Both jog an equal distance each day. Who jogs more each day?

21 Reflect Explain how using money can help you divide by 5.

Skills, Concepts, and Problem Solving

Draw a model to find each quotient.

22 35 ÷ 5 ____

23 44 ÷ 2 ____

Find each quotient.

24 18 ÷ 2 = ____
25 12 ÷ 2 = ____
26 15 ÷ 5 = ____
27 25 ÷ 5 = ____
28 45 ÷ 5 = ____
29 20 ÷ 5 = ____
30 14 ÷ 2 = ____
31 18 ÷ 2 = ____
32 25 ÷ 5 = ____
33 50 ÷ 5 = ____
34 22 ÷ 2 = ____
35 14 ÷ 2 = ____

Solve.

36 COMMUNITY SERVICE The sixth grade is collecting box tops to donate to a charity that will trade them in for cash. The students have 5 weeks to collect. If their goal is to collect 50 box tops, how many should they collect per week?

GO ON

Copyright © by The McGraw-Hill Companies, Inc.

Lesson 3-3 Divide by 2 and 5 111

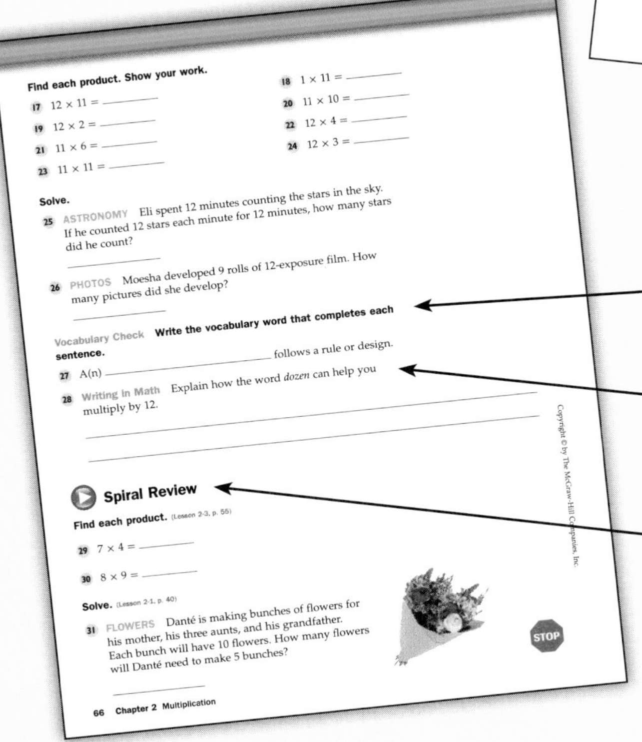

Find each product. Show your work.

17 12 × 11 = ____
18 1 × 11 = ____
19 12 × 2 = ____
20 11 × 10 = ____
21 11 × 6 = ____
22 12 × 4 = ____
23 11 × 11 = ____
24 12 × 3 = ____

Solve.

25 ASTRONOMY Eli spent 12 minutes counting the stars in the sky. If he counted 12 stars each minute for 12 minutes, how many stars did he count?

26 PHOTOS Moesha developed 9 rolls of 12-exposure film. How many pictures did she develop?

Vocabulary Check **Write the vocabulary word that completes each sentence.**

27 A(n) ____ follows a rule or design.

28 Writing in Math Explain how the word *dozen* can help you multiply by 12.

Spiral Review

Find each product. (Lesson 2-3, p. 55)

29 7 × 4 = ____

30 8 × 9 = ____

Solve. (Lesson 2-1, p. 40)

31 FLOWERS Danté is making bunches of flowers for his mother, his three aunts, and his grandfather. Each bunch will have 10 flowers. How many flowers will Danté need to make 5 bunches?

STOP

Copyright © by The McGraw-Hill Companies, Inc.

66 Chapter 2 Multiplication

Vocabulary Check exercises relate directly to the core vocabulary introduced in each lesson.

The **Writing in Math** question requires students to describe, explain, summarize, or otherwise write an answer.

Spiral Review

Spiral Review provides constant reinforcement of skills from previous lessons.

Comprehensive Assessment System

Data-Driven Decision Making

Math Triumphs offers frequent and meaningful assessment of student progress within the curriculum structure and teacher support materials.

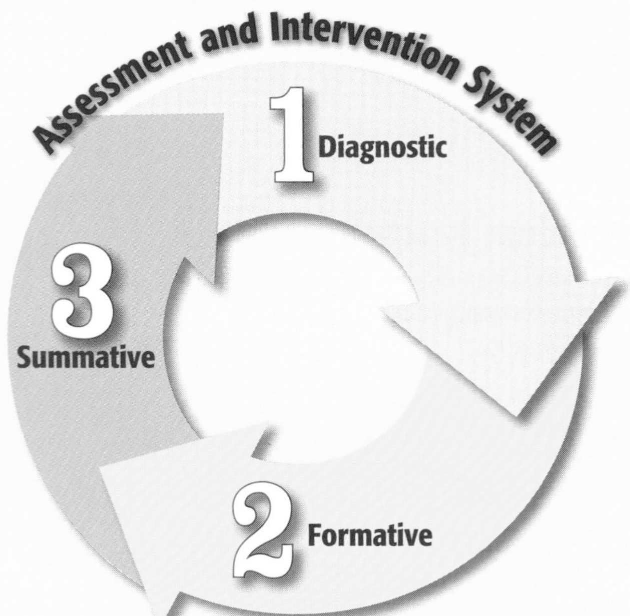

1 Diagnostic

Initial Assessment Assess students' knowledge **at the beginning of the year** with the *Diagnostic and Placement Tests*.

Entry–Level Assessment Assess students' prior knowledge **at the beginning of a chapter** with one of the following options.

Student Study Guide

- Preview

Print Resources

- Assessment Masters, Chapter Pretest

Teacher Edition

- Vocabulary Preview

Technology Resources

ExamView Assessment Suite

 Online Readiness Quiz

Advance Tracker

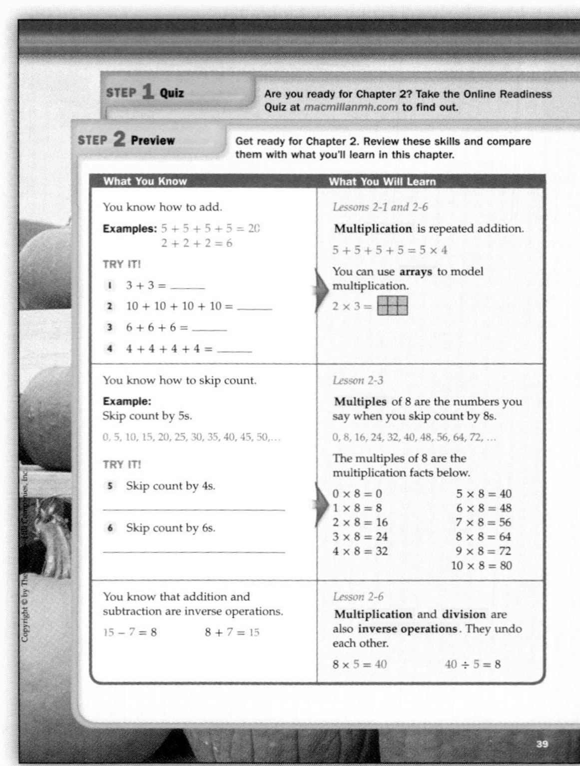

STEP 1 Quiz — Are you ready for Chapter 2? Take the Online Readiness Quiz at macmillanmh.com to find out.

STEP 2 Preview — Get ready for Chapter 2. Review these skills and compare them with what you'll learn in this chapter.

What You Know	What You Will Learn
You know how to add. **Examples:** $5 + 5 + 5 + 5 = 20$ $2 + 2 + 2 = 6$ TRY IT! 1 $3 + 3 =$ ____ 2 $10 + 10 + 10 + 10 =$ ____ 3 $6 + 6 + 6 =$ ____ 4 $4 + 4 + 4 + 4 =$ ____	*Lessons 2-1 and 2-6* **Multiplication** is repeated addition. $5 + 5 + 5 + 5 = 5 \times 4$ You can use **arrays** to model multiplication. $2 \times 3 =$
You know how to skip count. **Example:** Skip count by 5s. 0, 5, 10, 15, 20, 25, 30, 35, 40, 45, 50,... TRY IT! 5 Skip count by 4s. ____ 6 Skip count by 6s. ____	*Lesson 2-3* **Multiples** of 8 are the numbers you say when you skip count by 8s. 0, 8, 16, 24, 32, 40, 48, 56, 64, 72, ... The multiples of 8 are the multiplication facts below. $0 \times 8 = 0$, $1 \times 8 = 8$, $2 \times 8 = 16$, $3 \times 8 = 24$, $4 \times 8 = 32$ $5 \times 8 = 40$, $6 \times 8 = 48$, $7 \times 8 = 56$, $8 \times 8 = 64$, $9 \times 8 = 72$, $10 \times 8 = 80$
You know that addition and subtraction are inverse operations. $15 - 7 = 8$ $8 + 7 = 15$	*Lesson 2-6* **Multiplication** and **division** are also **inverse operations**. They undo each other. $8 \times 5 = 40$ $40 \div 5 = 8$

39

Formative

Progress Monitoring Determine if students are progressing adequately as you teach each lesson. Use the assessments to differentiate lesson instruction and practice.

Student Study Guide
- Progress Check
- Who is Correct?
- Study Guide
- Foldables®

Teacher Edition
- Intervention Strategy
- Are They Getting It?
- Ticket Out the Door
- See It, Do It, Say It, Write It
- Data-Driven Decision Making

Print Resources
- Assessment Masters
- Chapter Resource Masters

Technology Resources

Math Online My Math Zone

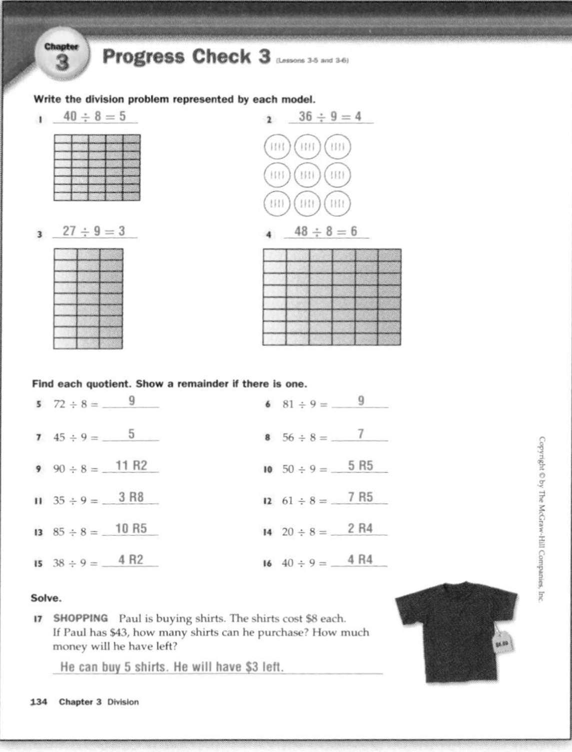

Chapter 3 **Progress Check 3** (Lessons 3-5 and 3-6)

Write the division problem represented by each model.

1. 40 ÷ 8 = 5
2. 36 ÷ 9 = 4
3. 27 ÷ 9 = 3
4. 48 ÷ 8 = 6

Find each quotient. Show a remainder if there is one.

5. 72 ÷ 8 = 9
6. 81 ÷ 9 = 9
7. 45 ÷ 9 = 5
8. 56 ÷ 8 = 7
9. 90 ÷ 8 = 11 R2
10. 50 ÷ 9 = 5 R5
11. 35 ÷ 9 = 3 R8
12. 61 ÷ 8 = 7 R5
13. 85 ÷ 8 = 10 R5
14. 20 ÷ 8 = 2 R4
15. 38 ÷ 9 = 4 R2
16. 40 ÷ 9 = 4 R4

Solve.

17. SHOPPING Paul is buying shirts. The shirts cost $8 each. If Paul has $43, how many shirts can he purchase? How much money will he have left?
He can buy 5 shirts. He will have $3 left.

Copyright © by The McGraw-Hill Companies, Inc.

134 Chapter 3 Division

Summative

Summative Evaluation Assess student success in learning the concepts in each chapter.

Student Study Guide
- Chapter Test
- Test Practice
- Foldables®

Teacher Edition
- Data-Driven Decision Making

Print Resources
- Assessment Masters
- Chapter Resource Masters

Technology Resources

Math Online

Advance

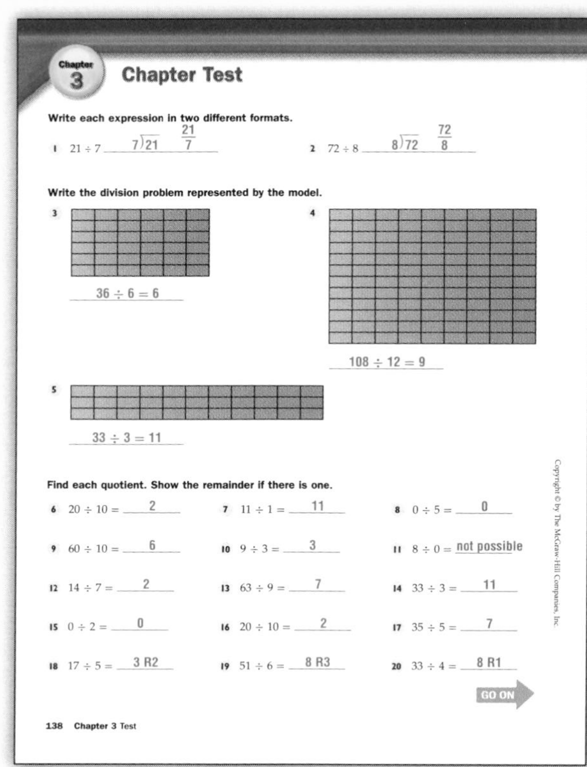

Chapter 3 **Chapter Test**

Write each expression in two different formats.

1. 21 ÷ 7 $7\overline{)21}$ $\frac{21}{7}$
2. 72 ÷ 8 $8\overline{)72}$ $\frac{72}{8}$

Write the division problem represented by the model.

3. 36 ÷ 6 = 6
4. 108 ÷ 12 = 9
5. 33 ÷ 3 = 11

Find each quotient. Show the remainder if there is one.

6. 20 ÷ 10 = 2
7. 11 ÷ 1 = 11
8. 0 ÷ 5 = 0
9. 60 ÷ 10 = 6
10. 9 ÷ 3 = 3
11. 8 ÷ 0 = not possible
12. 14 ÷ 7 = 2
13. 63 ÷ 9 = 7
14. 33 ÷ 3 = 11
15. 0 ÷ 2 = 0
16. 20 ÷ 10 = 2
17. 35 ÷ 5 = 7
18. 17 ÷ 5 = 3 R2
19. 51 ÷ 6 = 8 R3
20. 33 ÷ 4 = 8 R1

GO ON

Copyright © by The McGraw-Hill Companies, Inc.

138 Chapter 3 Test

PreK-12 Data-Driven Professional Development

McGraw-Hill Professional Development (MHPD) provides a comprehensive plan for mathematics that is fully aligned and articulated with ***Math Connects K–8*** and the ***Glencoe Mathematics*** high school series.

Professional Development Needs	Online Courses	DVD Workshops	Video Library	Teach-Use-Succeed	Ready-Access Math
Has immediate classroom application	✓	✓	✓	✓	✓
Builds content knowledge	✓	✓			✓
Promotes best teaching practices		✓	✓		
Supports new and experienced teachers	✓	✓	✓	✓	✓
Allows customization of courses	✓	✓			✓
Can be self-paced	✓	✓		✓	✓
Adaptable for various timeframes	✓	✓	✓	✓	✓
Is grade-level specific			✓	✓	✓
Promotes a learning community	✓	✓			✓
Provides vertically-aligned content	✓	✓	✓		✓
Helps with RTI (Response to Intervention), Tiers 1–3	✓	✓	✓		✓

Use students' mathematics achievement data to help develop a targeted Professional Development Plan.

Accredited Online Courses
(available for purchase)

- Watch video clips of math classrooms.
- Complete interactive exercises.
- Develop electronic portfolios.
- Complete each 3- to 5-hour online module one segment at a time.
- Earn university credit (additional tuition).

DVD Workshops

- Watch video clips of classroom mathematics lessons and commentaries by leading educators.
- Complete lessons and activities.

MHPD Online

- Access this online Professional Development resource for K–12 educators.
- Link to relevant Web sites.
- Download grade-level student resources.

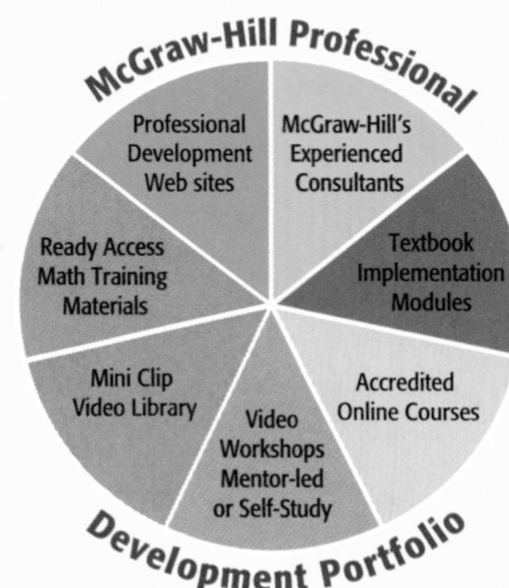

Video Library Math Online

- Access hundreds of K–12 video clips.
- See clips that illustrate mathematics content and instructional strategies.
- Watch demonstrations or commentaries.

Teach-Use-Succeed Textbook Implementation Modules

- Watch an experienced teacher demonstrate the *Math Connects* K–8 Student Editions, Teacher Editions, and program ancillaries–Online or DVD.

Ready-Access Math, Personalized Professional Development

- Access training materials for nearly 300 lessons.
- Create a customized sequence of professional development sessions.
- Deliver 45–60 minute after-school professional development sessions.

Place Value and Number Relationships

Preparation for Focal Points and Connections
See front cover folder for key.

Central Park, New York, New York

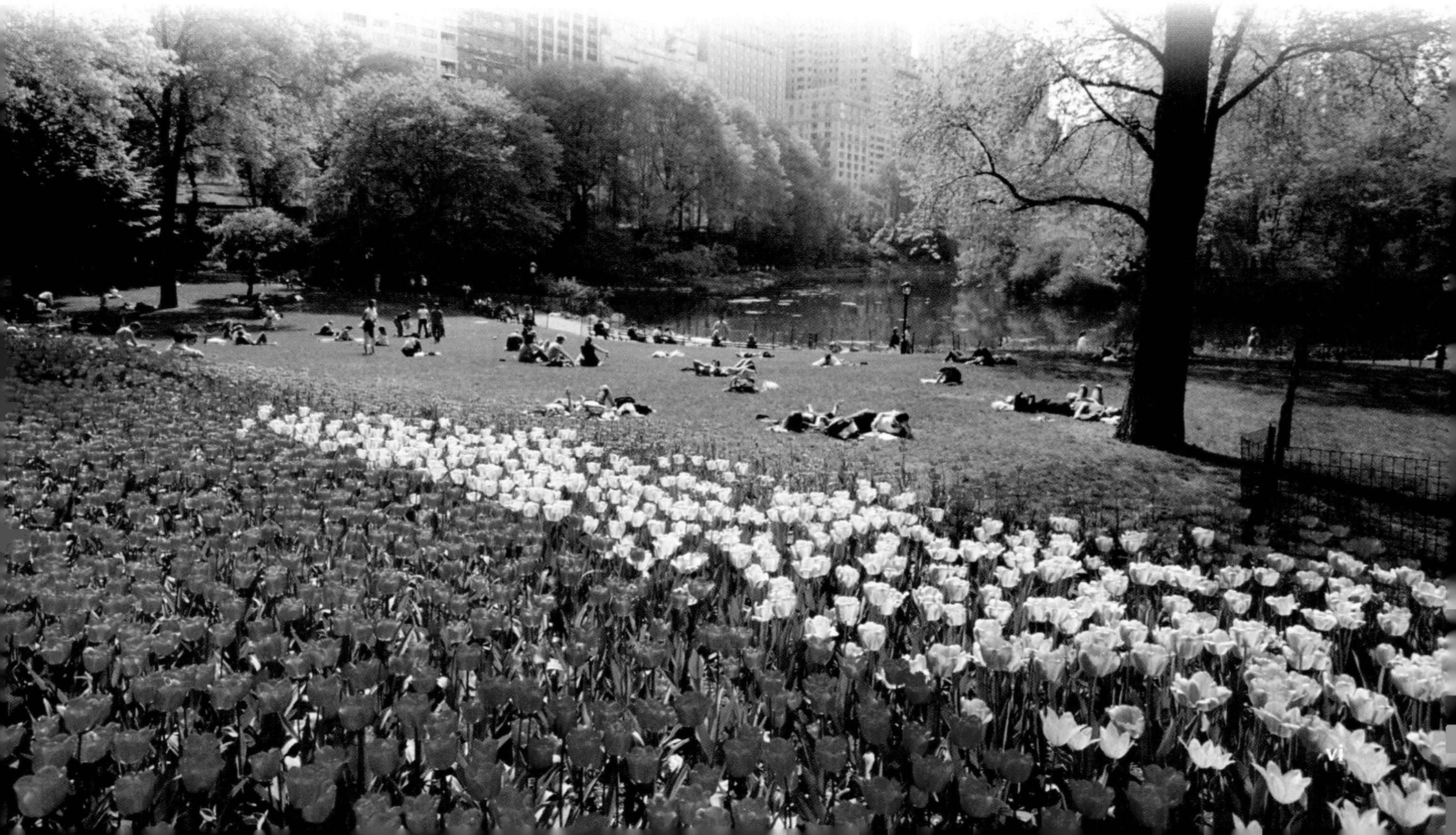

Contents

Chapter 2 Multiplication

Preparation for Focal Points and Connections
See front cover folder for key.

Cypress Trees, Lake Bradford, Tallahassee, Florida

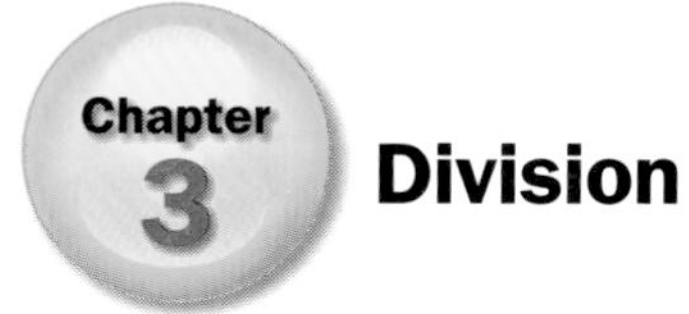

Division

Preparation for Focal Points and Connections
See front cover folder for key.

Cape Fear, Wilmington, North Carolina

Contents

Properties of Operations

Preparation for Focal Points and Connections
See front cover folder for key.

Guadalupe Mountains, Salt Flat, Texas

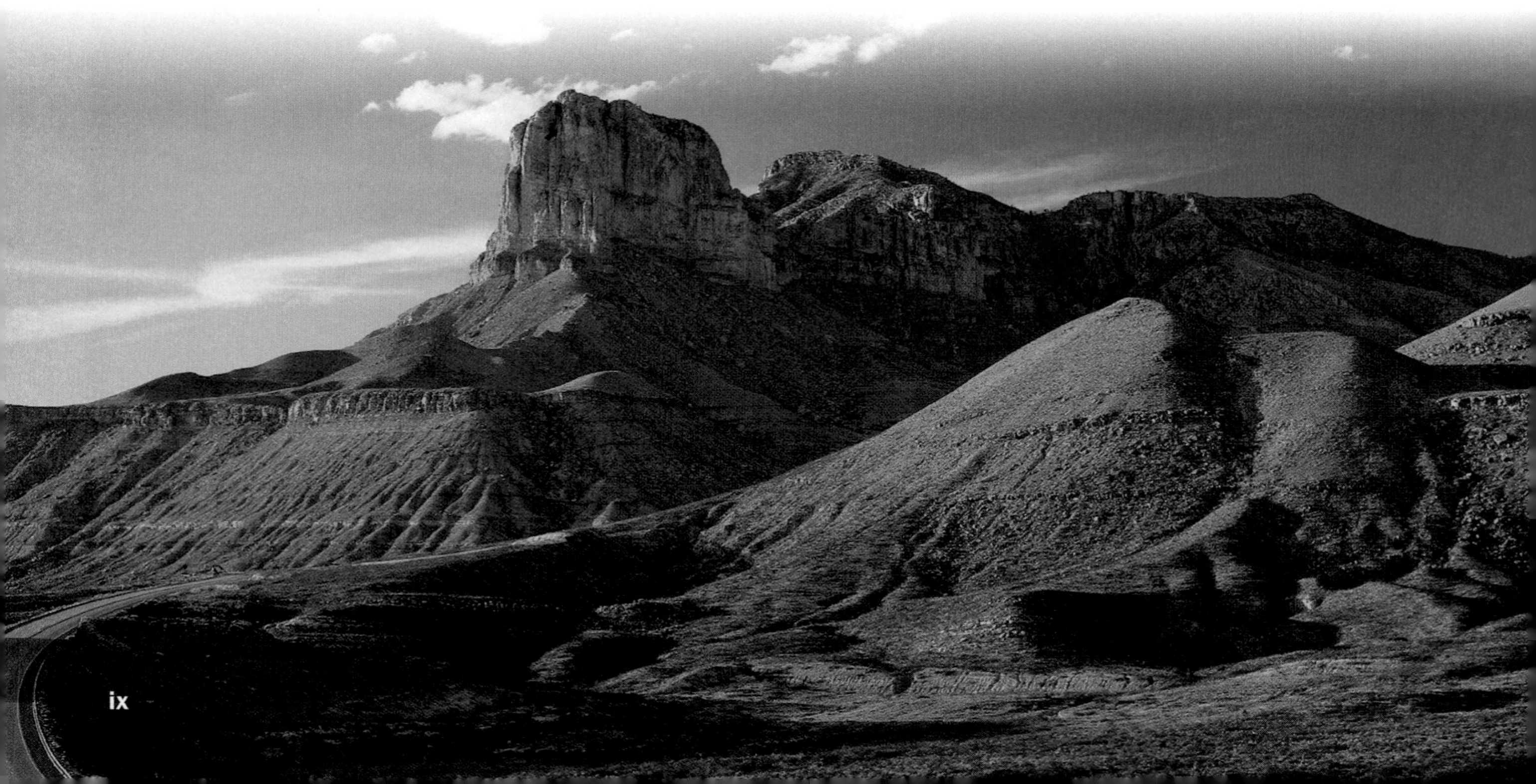

Chapter 5 Fractions

Preparation for Focal Points and Connections
See front cover folder for key.

Row Houses, Charleston, South Carolina

Contents

Chapter 6 Add and Subtract Fractions

Preparation for Focal Points and Connections
See front cover folder for key.

Yellowstone Falls, Yellowstone National Park, Wyoming

Chapter 7 Decimals

Preparation for Focal Points and Connections
See front cover folder for key.

French Quarter, New Orleans, Louisiana

Contents

Chapter 8 Geometry

Preparation for Focal Points and Connections
See front cover folder for key.

Badlands National Park, Interior, South Dakota

Area

Preparation for Focal Points and Connections
See front cover folder for key.

City Hall, Philadelphia, Pennsylvania

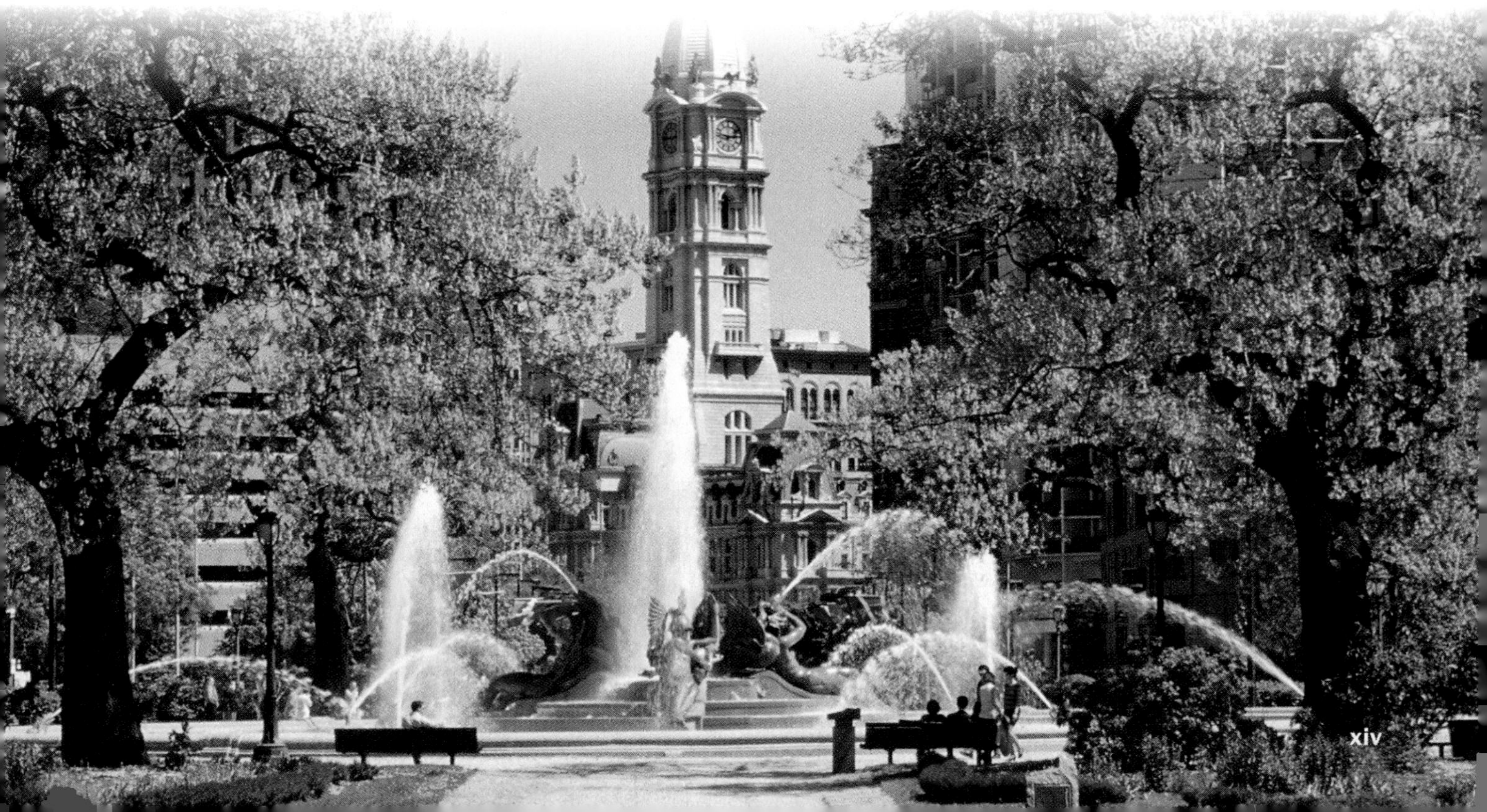

Contents

Chapter 10 Surface Area, Volume, and Measurement

Preparation for Focal Points and Connections
See front cover folder for key.

The Alamo, San Antonio, Texas

Let's Get Started

Use the Scavenger Hunt below to learn where things are located in each chapter.

1. What is the title of Chapter 9?
   Area
2. What is the Key Concept of Lesson 8-4?
   three dimensional shapes
3. What is the definition of a parallelogram on page 334?
   a quadrilateral with four sides in which each pair of opposite sides are parallel and equal in length
4. What are the vocabulary words for Lesson 10-2?
   customary system, capacity, weight, benchmark
5. How many examples are presented in the Chapter 8 Study Guide? 4
6. What figure is used as a model in Example 1 on page 368?
   rectangle
7. According to Lesson 10-2, how many ounces are in one gallon? 128 fl oz
8. What do you think is the purpose of the Progress Check 1 on page 348? It allows you to practice naming the shapes found in lessons 1 and 2 of Chapter 8.
9. On what pages will you find the study guide for Chapter 10?
   pages 441–445
10. In Chapter 9, find the internet address that tells you where you can take the Online Readiness Quiz. It is found on page 367. The URL is macmillanmh.com.

SCAVENGER HUNT

CHAPTER 1

Let's Get Started

Use the Scavenger Hunt below to learn where things are located in each chapter.

1. What is the title of Chapter 6?
   Add and Subtract Fractions
2. What is the Key Concept of Lesson 7-3?
   comparing and ordering decimals
3. What is the definition of a numerator on page 182?
   the number above the bar in a fraction that tells how many equal parts are being used
4. What are the vocabulary words for Lesson 6-3? least common denominator, prime factorization, unlike fractions
5. How many examples are presented in the Chapter 7 Study Guide? 6
6. What shapes are used as models in Example 1 on page 215? circles
7. According to Example 1 of Lesson 6-1, how many equal parts are in the circle? 8 equal parts
8. What do you think is the purpose of the Progress Check 3 on page 231? It allows you to practice problems from the last two lessons.
9. On what pages will you find the study guide for Chapter 7?
   pages 325–327
10. In Chapter 6, find the internet address that tells you where you can take the Online Readiness Quiz. It is found on page 241. The URL is macmillanmh.com.

Chapter 1

Chapter Overview

Chapter-at-a-Glance

Lesson	Math Objective	State/Local Standards
1-1 Whole Numbers Less Than 10,000 (pp. 4–8)	Identify place values to 10,000 and use expanded form.	
1-2 Read and Write Whole Numbers in the Millions (pp. 9–14)	Write and expand whole numbers in the millions and be able to identify place value.	
Progress Check 1 (p. 15)		
1-3 Number Relationships (pp. 16–22)	Identify, describe, and continue various number patterns.	
1-4 Linear Patterns (pp. 23–29)	Extend linear patterns.	
Progress Check 2 (p. 30)		

Content-at-a-Glance

The diagram below summarizes and unpacks Chapter 1 content.

Read and Write Numbers to 10,000 → Read and Write Numbers in the Millions → Identify Number Relationships → Linear Patterns

Chapter Assessment Manager

Diagnostic

Diagnose students' readiness.

	Student Study Guide/ Teacher Edition	Assessment Masters	Technology
Course Placement Test		1	ExamView® Assessment Suite
Book 1 Pretest		8	ExamView® Assessment Suite
Chapter 1 Pretest		11	ExamView® Assessment Suite
Quiz/Preview	SSG 3		Math Online macmillanmh.com StudentWorks™ Plus

Formative

Identify students' misconceptions of content knowledge.

	Student Study Guide/ Teacher Edition	Assessment Masters	Technology
Progress Checks	SSG 15, 30		Math Online macmillanmh.com StudentWorks™ Plus
Vocabulary Review	SSG 31		Math Online macmillanmh.com
Lesson Assessments			ExamView® Assessment Suite
Are They Getting It?	TE 6, 11, 18, 26		

Summative

Determine student success in learning the concepts in the lesson, chapter, or book.

	Student Study Guide/ Teacher Edition	Assessment Masters	Technology
Chapter 1 Test	SSG 34	14	ExamView® Assessment Suite
Test Practice	SSG 36	17	ExamView® Assessment Suite
Alternative Assessment	TE 34	20	
See It, Do It, Say It, Write It	TE 8, 14, 22, 29		
Book 1 Test		55	ExamView® Assessment Suite

Back-mapping and Vertical Alignment **McGraw-Hill's *Math Triumphs*** intervention program was conceived and developed with the final result in mind: student success in grade-level mathematics, including Algebra 1 and beyond. The authors, using the **NCTM Focal Points and Focal Connections** as their guide, developed this brand-new series by backmapping from grade-level and Algebra 1 concepts, and vertically aligning the topics so that they build upon prior skills and concepts and serve as a foundation for future topics.

Chapter Resource Manager

	Lesson 1-1	Lesson 1-2	Lesson 1-3	Lesson 1-4
Concept	Whole Numbers Less Than 10,000	Read and Write Whole Numbers in the Millions	Number Relationships	Linear Patterns
Objective	Identify place values to 10,000 and use expanded form.	Write and expand whole numbers in the millions and be able to identify place value.	Identify, describe, and continue various number patterns.	Extend linear patterns.
Math Vocabulary	expanded form place value standard form	period standard form word form	pattern rule	pattern rule
Lesson Resources	**Materials** • Place-value chart **Manipulatives** • Base-ten blocks • Counters • Money **Other Resources** CRM Vocabulary and English Language Development CRM Skills Practice CRM Problem-Solving Practice CRM Homework Practice	**Materials** • Construction paper • Number line • Place-value chart **Manipulatives** • Base-ten blocks **Other Resources** CRM Vocabulary and English Language Development CRM Skills Practice CRM Problem-Solving Practice CRM Homework Practice	**Materials** • Classroom objects • Construction paper • Graph paper **Manipulatives** • Base-ten blocks • Connecting cubes • Two-color counters **Other Resources** CRM Vocabulary and English Language Development CRM Skills Practice CRM Problem-Solving Practice CRM Homework Practice	**Materials** • Classroom objects • Index cards **Manipulatives** • Base-ten blocks • Connecting cubes **Other Resources** CRM Vocabulary and English Language Development CRM Skills Practice CRM Problem-Solving Practice CRM Homework Practice
Technology	Math Online macmillanmh.com StudentWorks™ Plus ExamView® Assessment Suite	Math Online macmillanmh.com StudentWorks™ Plus ExamView® Assessment Suite	Math Online macmillanmh.com StudentWorks™ Plus ExamView® Assessment Suite	Math Online macmillanmh.com StudentWorks™ Plus ExamView® Assessment Suite

Intervention Strategy

Writing Numbers from Verbal Statements

Listening carefully when numbers are read out loud is a skill that may require much practice for some students.

Step 1 Instruct students to number a sheet of paper from 1 to 10.

Step 2 Slowly say the following 10 numbers and give students time to write the number in standard form on the appropriate line on their papers.

Number List

1. three hundred five 305
2. four thousand, one hundred fifty 4,150
3. fifteen thousand, six hundred thirty-three 15,633
4. sixty-seven thousand, one hundred 67,100
5. two hundred twelve thousand, nine hundred eleven 212,911
6. eight hundred five thousand, seventy-four 805,074
7. three hundred twenty-five thousand, four hundred ninety-one 325,491
8. one million, three hundred thousand, fourteen 1,300,014
9. three million, two hundred fifty-two thousand, six hundred forty-five 3,252,645
10. one million, five hundred six thousand, one 1,506,001

Step 3 After all of the numbers have been read, give students time to review their answers and ask for any to be repeated.

Step 4 When students are satisfied with their numbers, review the answers and answer any questions that students have.

Chapter 1 Chapter Notes

Real-World Applications

Round Numbers According to the U.S. Census Bureau, the United States had a population of over 302 million people in 2007. Large numbers like state and country populations are often written with words like "million" or "thousand." Ask students to name other situations in which numbers are stated with word names. Sample answers: exports, imports, surveys, and so on

Intervention Strategy

Place Value

Step 1 Divide students into small groups.

Step 2 Have each group create a poster that displays a place-value chart covering the ones place through the millions place and insert numbers in the chart to illustrate the value of each digit.

Step 3 Give each group the following set of five numbers:

5,463,261	1,962,034	610,335
8,225,000	7,050,891	

Step 4 Using the set of numbers from above, each group should identify the value of each number in the tens place, hundreds place, thousands place, ten-thousands place, hundred-thousands place, and millions place.

Chapter 1
Place Value and Number Relationships
Would you rather have $100,000 or $1,000,000?
To make that decision, you compare and order the numbers. You determine the value of the digits in each number.
2 Chapter 1 Place Value and Number Relationships

Key Vocabulary

Find interactive definitions in 13 languages in the **eGlossary** at macmillanmh.com.

English **Español** *Introduce the most important vocabulary terms from Chapter 1.*

expanded form **forma desarrollada**
writing a number as a sum that shows the value of each digit (p. 4)
The expanded form of 15 is 10 + 5.

place value **valor de posición**
the value given to a digit by its position in a number (p. 4)

standard form **forma estándar**
writing a number using only digits (p. 4)
The standard form of 10 + 5 is 15.

period **período**
a group of three digits in the place-value chart (p. 9)

word form **en palabras**
a way to write numbers using only words (p. 9)
The word form of 15 is fifteen.

pattern **patrón**
a sequence of numbers, figures, or symbols that follows a rule or design (p. 16)

rule **regla**
tells how numbers are related to each other (p. 16)
Examples:
There are 12 inches in 1 foot.
Add 4 to the previous number.

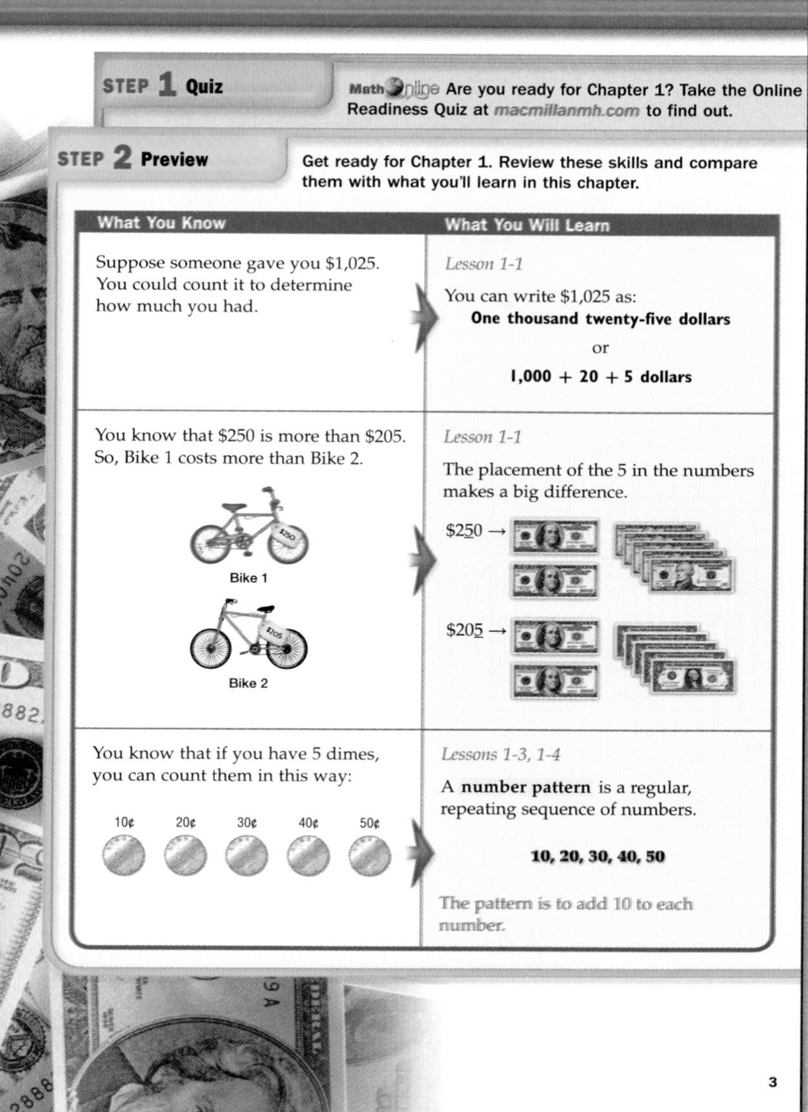

STEP 1 Quiz

Math Online Are you ready for Chapter 1? Take the Online Readiness Quiz at macmillanmh.com to find out.

STEP 2 Preview

Get ready for Chapter 1. Review these skills and compare them with what you'll learn in this chapter.

What You Know	What You Will Learn
Suppose someone gave you $1,025. You could count it to determine how much you had.	*Lesson 1-1* You can write $1,025 as: **One thousand twenty-five dollars** or **1,000 + 20 + 5 dollars**
You know that $250 is more than $205. So, Bike 1 costs more than Bike 2. Bike 1 Bike 2	*Lesson 1-1* The placement of the 5 in the numbers makes a big difference. $250 → $205 →
You know that if you have 5 dimes, you can count them in this way: 10¢ 20¢ 30¢ 40¢ 50¢	*Lessons 1-3, 1-4* A **number pattern** is a regular, repeating sequence of numbers. **10, 20, 30, 40, 50** The pattern is to add 10 to each number.

3

Step 1 Quiz

Pretest/Prescribe Students can take the Online Readiness Quiz or the Diagnostic Pretest in the Assessment Masters.

Step 2 Preview

Use this pre-chapter activity to activate students' prior knowledge, build confidence, and help students preview the lessons.

Dinah Zike's Foldables®

Guide students through the directions on p. A1 in the Chapter Resource Masters to create their own Foldable graphic organizer to use with this chapter.

Home Connections

- Have students find items in their homes that contain, hold, or have about 10; 100; 1,000; or 10,000 of something.
- Have students name three things in which the order is very important to the overall outcome.

Vocabulary Preview

- As students complete the Chapter Preview, have them make a list of important terms throughout the chapter.
- Relate the importance of the location of a digit in place value to the location of a letter in a crossword puzzle. Pass out graph paper and have students make a crossword puzzle that includes the key words and any other important terms throughout the chapter.
- The clues used for the puzzle should be given using definitions and examples.
- Once students are finished, have them trade and complete each other's crossword puzzles.

Mc Graw Hill **Professional Development**

Targeted professional development has been articulated throughout **McGraw-Hill's *Math Triumphs*** intervention program. **The McGraw-Hill Professional Development Video Library** provides short videos that support the **NCTM Focal Points and Focal Connections.** For more information, visit macmillanmh.com.

Model Lessons

Instructional Strategies

Lesson 1-1

Lesson Notes

Lesson Planner

Objective Identify place values to 10,000 and use expanded form.

Vocabulary **expanded form**, **place value**, **standard form**

Materials/Manipulatives base-ten blocks, counters, money, place-value chart

Chapter Resource Masters

- CRM Vocabulary and English Language Development (p. A4)
- CRM Skills Practice (p. A5)
- CRM Problem-Solving Practice (p. A6)
- CRM Homework Practice (p. A7)

Vocabulary

Think Vocabulary Write 4,803 on the board. Call on volunteers to define *place value.* What is the value of the 8? Ask for the differences between *standard* and *expanded forms.* Challenge students to write a number in as many ways as they can.

Nonexamples Write 4,800 + 3 on the board. What form is this? Show students other nonexamples. Is 21 a digit? Ask students to come up with other nonexamples.

Key Concept

Foundational Skills and Concepts After students have read through the Key Concept box, have them try these exercises.

1. Write 1,256 in expanded form. 1,000 + 200 + 50 + 6
2. What is the value of the 2 in 1,256? 200
3. What form is 1,256? standard form

Lesson 1-1

Whole Numbers Less Than 10,000

KEY Concept

Place value tells you the value of each digit in a number. The number 1,256 is in **standard form**.

1,256

	thousands	hundreds	tens	ones
Standard Form	1	2	5	6
Model				
Value	1 × 1,000 = 1,000	2 × 100 = 200	5 × 10 = 50	6 × 1 = 6

In **expanded form** the number 1,256 is

1,000 + 200 + 50 + 6

VOCABULARY

expanded form the form of a number as a sum that shows the value of each digit

place value the value given to a digit by its position in a number

standard form writing a number using only digits

The **expanded form** of a number shows the value of each digit. It uses the operation of addition.

Example 1

Identify the value of the underlined digit in 3,8̲15.

1. Write the number in a place-value chart.
2. The underlined digit is in the hundreds place.
3. Multiply the underlined digit by the value of its place. 8 × 100 = 800
4. The underlined digit has a value of 800.

1000	100	10	1
thousands	hundreds	tens	ones
3	8̲	1	5

4 **Chapter 1** Place Value and Number Relationships

Additional Example 1

Identify the value of the underlined digit in 2,7̲18.

1. Write the number in the place-value chart.

1,000	100	10	1
thousands	hundreds	tens	ones
2	7̲	1	8

2. The underlined digit is in the hundreds place.
3. Multiply the underlined digit by the value of its place. 7 × 100 = 700
4. The underlined digit has a value of 700.

YOUR TURN!

Identify the value of the underlined digit in 6,525.

1. Write the number in a place-value chart.
2. In what place is the underlined digit? tens
3. Multiply the underlined digit by the value of its place.
   2 × 10 = 20
4. What is the value of the underlined digit? 20

1000	100	10	1
thousands	hundreds	tens	ones
6	5	2	5

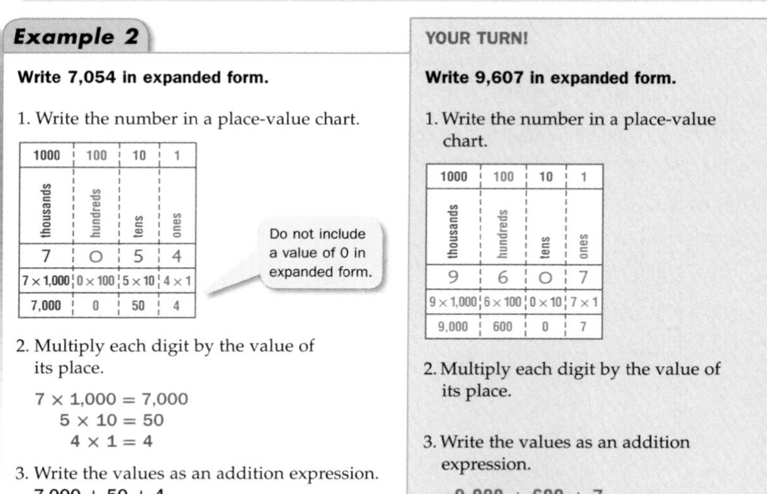

Example 2

Write 7,054 in expanded form.

1. Write the number in a place-value chart.

1000	100	10	1
thousands	hundreds	tens	ones
7	0	5	4
7 × 1,000	0 × 100	5 × 10	4 × 1
7,000	0	50	4

Do not include a value of 0 in expanded form.

2. Multiply each digit by the value of its place.
   7 × 1,000 = 7,000
   5 × 10 = 50
   4 × 1 = 4
3. Write the values as an addition expression.
   7,000 + 50 + 4

YOUR TURN!

Write 9,607 in expanded form.

1. Write the number in a place-value chart.

1000	100	10	1
thousands	hundreds	tens	ones
9	6	0	7
9 × 1,000	6 × 100	0 × 10	7 × 1
9,000	600	0	7

2. Multiply each digit by the value of its place.
3. Write the values as an addition expression.
   9,000 + 600 + 7

Who is Correct?

What is the value of the underlined digit in 5,085?

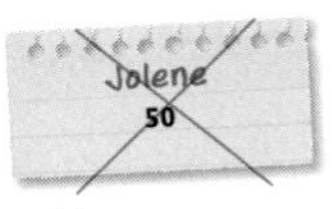

GO ON

Circle correct answer(s). Cross out incorrect answer(s).

Additional Example 2

Write 6,082 in expanded form.

1. Write the number in a place-value chart.

1,000	100	10	1
thousands	hundreds	tens	ones
6 × 1,000	0 × 100	8 × 10	2 × 1
6	0	8	2

2. Multiply each digit by the value of its place.

   6 × 1,000 = 6,000

   8 × 10 = 80

   2 × 1 = 2

3. Write the values as an addition expression.

   6,000 + 80 + 2

Note This!

Take Notes Encourage students to take notes while they listen. Tell them that even if something is said that makes sense, it is still a good idea to write it down. Later when they review their notes, there will be more continuity, and they are less likely to forget.

Who *is Correct?*

Diagnostic Teaching

- LaBron wrote 5,000. This is correct.
- Adita wrote 500. This is incorrect because the 5 is in the thousands place.
- Jolene wrote 50. This is incorrect.

Students who make these types of mistakes should practice writing numbers within a place-value chart.

Math Coach Notes

Place Value The consequence of our base-ten number system is place value. Expanded form shows students that a number such as 9,453 is the sum of 9,000 + 400 + 50 + 3. Place-value charts show the concept that numbers are the *sum* of products of powers of ten. For instance, 9,453 can be written as 9 × 1,000 + 4 × 100 + 5 × 10 + 3 × 1.

3 Practice

Using Manipulatives

Base-Ten Blocks When presenting Example 1, model the number using base-ten blocks.

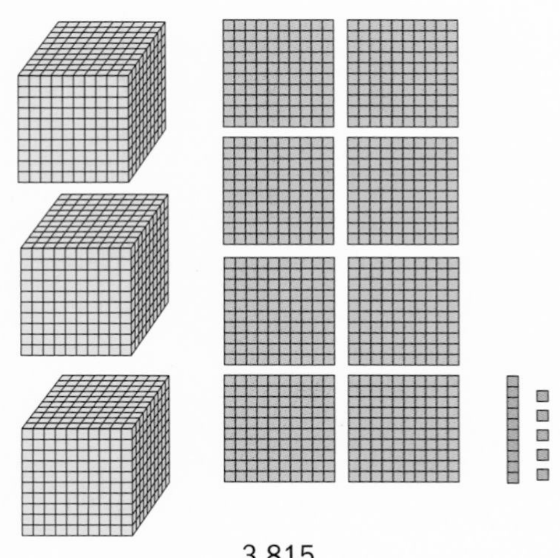

3,815

Money Use 38 dollars + 15 cents to represent 3,815.

On-Hand Manipulatives Use drawings or counters to represent different place values.

Math Coach Notes

Connect Concepts

1. Connect the concepts in this lesson with the other lessons in this chapter. Ask students for examples of numbers that are in the thousands in their everyday lives.
2. Scaffold from the ones place to the thousands place with expanded form. Continue to represent numbers as the sum of products, i.e., $134 = 100 + 30 + 4 =$ $1 \times 100 + 3 \times 10 + 4 \times 1$

Guided Practice

Identify the digit in the thousands place-value position of each number.

1 4,908 4 2 2,005 2

Step by Step Practice

3 Identify the value of the underlined digit in 5,470.

Step 1 Write the number in a place-value chart.

Step 2 The place value of the 5 is thousands.

Step 3 Multiply 5 × 1,000.

Step 4 The underlined digit has a value of 5,000.

1000 thousands	100 hundreds	10 tens	1 ones
5	4	7	0

Identify the value of each underlined digit.

4 2,087 80

1000 thousands	100 hundreds	10 tens	1 ones
2	0	8	7

5 8,362 300 6 3,491 400 7 984 80

8 322 20 9 9,873 9,000 10 5,060 5,000

Write each number in expanded form.

11 6,915 6,000 + 900 + 10 + 5

12 3,654 3,000 + 600 + 50 + 4

13 5,107 5,000 + 100 + 7

14 3,806 3,000 + 800 + 6

15 6,300 6,000 + 300

16 2,500 2,000 + 500

Write each number in standard form.

17 1,000 + 700 + 50 + 2 1,752 18 4,000 + 700 + 10 + 7 4,717

19 3,000 + 6 3,006 20 5,000 + 5 5,005

Are They Getting It?

Check students' understanding of whole numbers less than 10,000 by writing these problems on the board. Ask students to point out wrong answers. Tell them to use base-ten blocks or a place-value chart to show why the answers are correct or incorrect.

1. 8,053 in expanded form is 8,000 + 100 + 50 + 3. This is incorrect, because there is a 0 in the hundreds place.
2. The value of the underlined digit in 5,981 is 80. This is correct.
3. The model shows 2,906. This is incorrect. The model shows 2,096.

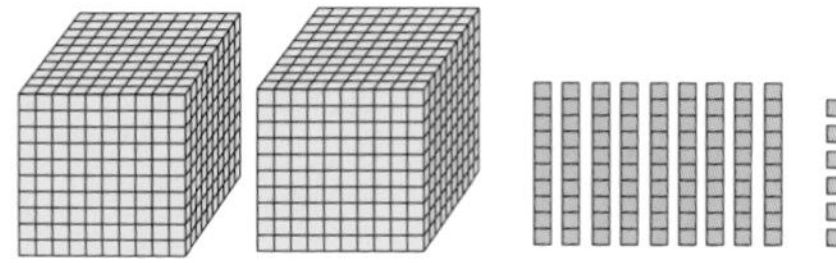

Step by Step Problem-Solving Practice

Problem-Solving Strategies
- ☐ Act it out.
- ☑ Make a table.
- ☐ Work backward.
- ☐ Solve a simpler problem.
- ☐ Look for a pattern.

21 BASEBALL An umpire picks four players with single-digit uniform numbers from each team. The team with the greatest number value will bat first. The Ravens' numbers are 2, 6, 9, and 5. The Hawks' numbers are 1, 8, 5, and 7. Which team will bat first?

Understand Read the problem. Write what you know.

The numbers for the Ravens are 2, 6, 9, and 5.

The numbers for the Hawks are 1, 8, 5, and 7.

Plan Pick a strategy. One strategy is to make a table. Use place-value charts to make each team's greatest number.

1000	100	10	1
thousands	hundreds	tens	ones

Cardinals

Solve Pick a number from each team that will give the highest value in the thousands place.

Ravens 9 Hawks 8

Pick a number from the remaining digits for each team that will give the highest value in the hundreds, tens, and ones places.

The Ravens' greatest number is 9,652.

The Hawks' greatest number is 8,751.

The Ravens will bat first.

1000	100	10	1
thousands	hundreds	tens	ones

Hawks

Check Rearrange each team's number using a new thousands-place digit. Are the new numbers greater than the original numbers?

22 COMPUTERS Corinna has to change her current computer password. In order to remember it, she wants to keep the same digits, but lower the value of the numbers altogether. Her current password is 3762. What will be her new password? Check off each step.

✔ Understand: I circled key words.

✔ Plan: To solve the problem, I will make a table.

✔ Solve: Her new password will be Sample answers: 2376, 2736, 2673.

✔ Check: I checked my answer by rearranging the digits.

GO ON

Intervention Strategy

Visual/ Kinesthetic Learners

Model Value

1. Draw a place-value chart on the board.
2. Place a number in the chart. Tell students to model the number with base-ten blocks.
3. Using the same number, switch place values. Discuss how their models will now change. Guide students to see that it is the place value or position of the digit, and not the digit, that determines its value.

Common Error *Alert*

Multi-Step Problem If a student has trouble with Exercise 21, he or she may not have read and understood all the clues for the solution. Tell the student to underline or circle each key word. Then tell the student to make a list of what criteria the solution must have. Once the problem is broken into steps, the student can go through the list and find the solution.

Math Coach Notes

Test-Taking Tips Tell students that when taking multiple-choice tests, it is best to read each answer before choosing a response. They can underline key words in the question and cross out any answer choices they know are incorrect. Never choose *all* or *none of the above* unless they are certain that every answer choice qualifies.

English Learner Strategy

Guiding Questions Ask students the following questions to ensure that they understand the concept.

- Which digit is in the thousands place in 8,093? 8
- What is the value of the underlined digit in 5,6̲80? 600
- How do you write 9,423 in expanded form? 9,000 + 400 + 20 + 3
- How can place value be written as a sum of products? Sample answer: Numbers are the *sum* of products of powers of ten.

Odd/Even Assignments

Exercises 24–36 are structured so that students practice the same concepts whether they are assigned the odd or even problems.

In-Class Assignment

Have students complete Exercises 25, 30, 32, 36, and 39 to ensure that they understand the concept.

See It, Do It, Say It, Write It

Step 1 Write a few examples on the board of four-digit numbers. Discuss the place values of the digits. With help from students, write the numbers in expanded form.

Step 2 Write more examples on the board. Have students write the examples in expanded form.

Step 3 Have students work in pairs. Give them numbers to model. Then ask them to share and discuss answers.

Step 4 Have students spend some time writing the definitions of *standard* and *expanded forms.* Include examples.

Looking Ahead: Pre-teach

Read and Write Whole Numbers in the Millions In the next lesson, students will learn how to read and write whole numbers in the millions. The same rules for using a place-value chart will apply.

Example

Write three million, four hundred thousand, one hundred in standard form. 3,400,100

Write each number in standard form.

1. six million, three hundred eight thousand 6,308,000
2. one million, sixty thousand, four 1,060,004
3. nine million, eighty-two thousand, three hundred 9,082,300

---

23 **Reflect** Write a four-digit number. Identify the place of each digit and its value.

Sample answer: 3,265. The 3 is in the thousands place and has a value of 3,000. The 2 is in the hundreds place and has a value of 200. The 6 is in the tens place and has a value of 60. The 5 is in the ones place and has a value of 5.

Skills, Concepts, and Problem Solving

Identify the value of the underlined digit.

24 4,78<u>6</u> 6

25 8,<u>3</u>33 300

26 2,1<u>4</u>7 40

27 <u>5</u>,740 5,000

Write each number in expanded form.

28 4,312 4,000 + 300 + 10 + 2

29 6,753 6,000 + 700 + 50 + 3

30 7,007 7,000 + 7

31 3,100 3,000 + 100

Write each number in standard form.

32 4,000 + 500 + 6 4,506

33 6,000 + 700 + 70 + 7 6,777

34 9,000 + 20 9,020

35 5,000 + 400 + 4 5,404

Solve.

36 PUZZLES Use the digits 7, 9, and 8 to write the greatest possible even number. Use each digit only once. 978

Vocabulary Check **Write the vocabulary word that completes each sentence.**

37 The operation of addition is used in expanded form.

38 The thousands place is to the left of the hundreds place.

39 Writing in Math Create a place-value chart for 9,762. Be sure to put in the titles for the place values used. Explain why you placed each digit in its location on the chart.

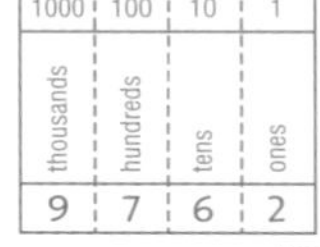

1000	100	10	1
thousands	hundreds	tens	ones
9	7	6	2

Each digit is placed according to its place-value position: 9,000 + 700 + 60 + 2.

8 Chapter 1 Place Value and Number Relationships

Ticket Out the Door

Puzzles Write a description of a number on the board. Example: *This odd number has the digits 8, 1, 0, and 6. The number is no higher than 7,000. What is the number?* 6,801 Change the puzzle to include different digits and details. Do this several times before students hand in their papers as they exit the classroom.

Lesson 1-2

Read and Write Whole Numbers in the Millions

KEY Concept

Place values are grouped into **periods**.

2,436,819

millions	thousands			ones		
1,000,000	100,000	10,000	1,000	100	10	1
millions	hundred thousands	ten thousands	thousands	hundreds	tens	ones
2	4	3	6	8	1	9

Say: two million, four hundred thirty-six thousand, eight hundred nineteen.

VOCABULARY

period
a group of three digits in the place-value chart

standard form
writing a number using only digits

word form
a way to write numbers using only words

Periods are separated by commas. The word "one" is not said at the end of the ones period.

Example 1

Write two million, six hundred five thousand, one hundred seventy-three in standard form.

1. Rewrite the number using digits and periods.
   2 million, 605 thousand, 173
2. Fill in each period of a place-value chart.
   Write the number. 2,605,173

millions	thousands			ones		
1,000,000	100,000	10,000	1,000	100	10	1
millions	hundred thousands	ten thousands	thousands	hundreds	tens	ones
2	6	0	5	1	7	3

YOUR TURN!

Write seven million, five hundred seventy-five thousand, two in standard form.

1. Rewrite the number using digits and periods.
   7 million, 575 thousand, 2
2. Fill in each period of a place-value chart.
   Write the number. 7,575,002

millions	thousands			ones		
1,000,000	100,000	10,000	1,000	100	10	1
millions	hundred thousands	ten thousands	thousands	hundreds	tens	ones
7	5	7	5	0	0	2

GO ON

Lesson 1-2 Read and Write Whole Numbers in the Millions 9

Additional *Example 1*

Write five million, two hundred three thousand, six hundred thirty-four in standard form.

1. Rewrite the number using digits and periods.
   5 million, 203 thousand, 634
2. Fill in each period of a place-value chart.
   Write the number. 5,203,634

1,000,000	100,000	10,000	1,000	100	10	1
millions	hundred thousands	ten thousands	thousands	hundreds	tens	ones
5	2	0	3	6	3	4

Lesson Notes

Lesson 1-2

Lesson Planner

Objective Write and expand whole numbers in the millions and be able to identify place value.

Vocabulary **period**, **standard form**, **word form**

Materials/Manipulatives base-ten blocks, construction paper, number line, place-value chart

Chapter Resource Masters

- CRM Vocabulary and English Language Development (p. A8)
- CRM Skills Practice (p. A9)
- CRM Problem-Solving Practice (p. A10)
- CRM Homework Practice (p. A11)

1 Introduce

Vocabulary

Communicate Vocabulary Begin by reviewing a number less than 10,000 and its place value. Draw a place-value chart on the board that includes *millions, hundred thousands,* and *ten thousands.* Write a number in the millions on the board. Use your fingers to show the periods in the number. Have students help place each digit in the chart.

Key Concept

Foundational Skills and Concepts After students have read through the Key Concept box, have them try these exercises.

1. How are place values grouped? into periods
2. What is the value of the 3 in 2,436,819? 30,000
3. What is the value of the 2 in 2,436,819? 2,000,000

Additional **Example 2**

Write 8,096,114 in word form.

1. Rewrite the number using digits and periods.
   8 million, 96 thousand, 114
2. Write the words for the millions period.
   eight million
3. Write the words for the thousands period.
   ninety-six thousand
4. Write the words for the ones period.
   one hundred fourteen
5. Write the periods in order. Separate each period with a comma.
   eight million, ninety-six thousand, one hundred fourteen

Math Coach Notes

Number Tip It is easy to skip a number when writing large numbers. Tell students to make certain they include the commas that separate the periods in large numbers and check the number of digits to make certain they have written the number down correctly.

English Learner Strategy

Guiding Questions Ask these questions to ensure that students understand the concept.

- Which digit is in the ten-thousands place in 14,514,669? 1
- How many millions are in 11,892,745? 11
- How do you write four million, three hundred thirty-two thousand, six hundred seventy-three in standard form? 4,332,673
- How do you write 1,892,745 in word form? one million, eight hundred ninety-two thousand, seven hundred forty-five
- How would you describe the place value of each digit in the number 7,802,906? 7 million, 8 hundred thousands, 0 ten thousands, 2 thousands, 9 hundreds, 0 tens, 6 ones

Example 2

Write 4,560,326 in word form.

1. Rewrite the number using digits and periods.
   4 million, 560 thousand, 326
2. Write the words for the millions period.
   four million
3. Write the words for the thousands period.
   five hundred sixty thousand
4. Write the words for the ones period.
   three hundred twenty-six
5. Write the periods in order. Separate each period with a comma.
   four million, five hundred sixty thousand, three hundred twenty-six

YOUR TURN!

Write 9,592,030 in word form.

1. Rewrite the number using digits and periods. 9 million, 592 thousand, 30
2. Write the words for the millions period. nine million
3. Write the words for the thousands period. five hundred ninety-two thousand
4. Write the words for the ones period. thirty
5. Write the periods in order. Separate each period with a comma.
   nine million, five hundred ninety-two thousand, thirty

Who is Correct?

Write 2,200,002 in word form.

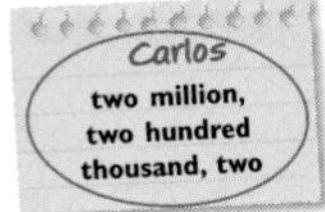

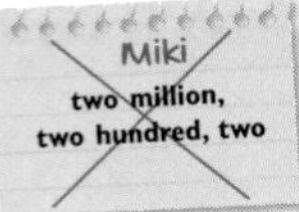

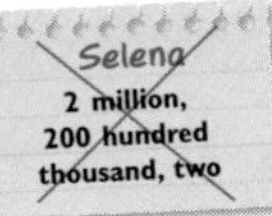

Circle correct answer(s). Cross out incorrect answer(s).

10 **Chapter 1** Place Value and Number Relationships

Who *is Correct?*

Diagnostic Teaching

- Carlos wrote two million, two hundred thousand, two. This is correct.
- Miki wrote two million, two hundred, two. This is incorrect because there are two hundred thousands, not two hundred.
- Selena wrote 2 million, 200 hundred thousand, two. This is incorrect because there are numbers and words in her answer.

Remind students to use place-value charts to help them read numbers.

Guided Practice

Use the place-value chart to answer each question. Then write each number in the chart.

1. How many zeros are in 5 millions? 6
2. How many zeros are in 7 hundred thousands? 5
3. How many zeros are in 3 ten thousands? 4

	1,000,000	100,000	10,000	1,000	100	10	1
	millions	hundred thousands	ten thousands	thousands	hundreds	tens	ones
1.	5	0	0	0	0	0	0
2.		7	0	0	0	0	0
3.			3	0	0	0	0

Write the missing number in each equation.

4. 1,000,000 + 200,000 + 6,000 + 70 + 9 = 1,206,079
5. 2,000,000 + 300,000 + 40,000 + 800 + 1 = 2,340,801

Write each number in standard form.

6. three million, four hundred forty thousand, five hundred ten 3,440,510
7. seven hundred thousand, seven hundred 700,700

Step by Step Practice

8. Write 305,660 in word form.

When the digit is 0, its value is zero, so you do not write that place value.

Step 1 Rewrite the number using digits and periods.
305 thousand, 660

Step 2 Write the words for the thousands period. three hundred five thousand

Step 3 Write the words for the ones period. six hundred sixty

Step 4 Write the periods together. three hundred five thousand, six hundred sixty

Write each number in word form.

9. 4,203,915 4 million 203 thousand 915
four million, two hundred three thousand, nine hundred fifteen

10. 50,500,005
fifty million, five hundred thousand, five

Lesson 1-2 Read and Write Whole Numbers in the Millions 11

Are They Getting It?

Check students' understanding of whole numbers to 1,000,000 by writing these problems on the board. Have students explain the incorrect information in each problem. Tell them to use a number line or a place-value chart to show why the answers are correct or incorrect.

1. The value of the 3 in the number 2,391,056 is thirty thousand. This is incorrect, because the 3 is in the hundred thousands place. The value of the 3 is 300,000.
2. 2,391,056 is two million, three hundred ninety-one thousand, fifty-six in word form. This is correct.
3. The number line shows 740,000. This is correct.

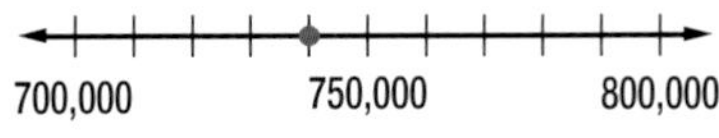

3 Practice

Using Manipulatives

Base-Ten Blocks Put the 10 cubes together from the base-ten block kits and ask how much they represent. If there are 100 cubes available, repeat with differing amounts.

On-Hand Manipulatives Have students create place-value holders out of construction paper. For example, one red block equals 1,000.

Math Coach Notes

Million Strategies

1. Ask students to provide ideas for some large numbers. Use Web sites and books that can help students visualize a million. Begin the lesson by reading one of the books about a million.
2. Concrete materials are not practical to model large numbers, but visual aids such as place-value charts and number lines can be used.
3. To give students opportunities to work with large numbers, use the distances between planets, populations, or areas of states and countries as sources of real-world large numbers. Have students research a million on the Internet. Share the results.
4. Have students skip count by 1,000s for 1 minute. How far along did they get? Calculate how long it would take to count to a million.

Common Error *Alert*

Multi-Step Problem If a student has trouble with Exercises 11 and 12, he or she may be confused when reading a large number in words. Tell the student to draw a place-value chart. Then have him or her concentrate on translating the periods into numbers. Ask him or her to name the greatest place value mentioned. Once the word is translated into digits in the place-value chart, tell the student to read the standard form of the number to make certain it is the same as the problem.

Note This!

Study Tip Tell students that when they study it helps to use visual images, either drawn on paper or in their minds to help them connect with a concept. When learning large numbers, they might visualize a 6 to remember how many zeros there are in a million, or a cup of sand to imagine a million grains filling the cup.

Step by Step Problem-Solving Practice

Problem-Solving Strategies
- ☐ Draw a diagram.
- ☐ Make a table.
- ☐ Work backward.
- ☑ Solve a simpler problem.
- ☐ Look for a pattern.

Solve.

11 PHYSICS The speed of light is one hundred eighty-six thousand, two hundred eighty-two miles per second. What is this number in standard form?

Understand	Read the problem. Write what you know. What is the greatest period in the speed of light?	thousands
Plan	Pick a strategy. One strategy is to solve a simpler problem.	
Solve	Break the number into the thousands period and the ones period.	
	Write the thousands period in digits.	186
	Write the ones period in digits.	282
	Write the periods together, separated by a comma.	186,282
Check	Read the standard form aloud. Follow along with the word form to make sure the forms match.	

12 SPACE The distance between two asteroids is three hundred eighty-four thousand, three hundred eighty-five kilometers. Write this distance in standard form. Check off each step.

✔ Understand: I circled key words.

✔ Plan: To solve the problem, I will solve a simpler problem.

✔ Solve: The answer is 384,385.

✔ Check: I checked my answer by reading it aloud.

13 GEOGRAPHY Look at the photo at the right. Write the height of Mount Everest in word form.

twenty-nine thousand, thirty-five feet

Mount Everest

14 EARTH SCIENCE The Mariana Trench in the Pacific Ocean is the deepest part at 36,198 feet below sea level. Write this number in word form.

thirty-six thousand, one hundred ninety-eight

12 Chapter 1 Place Value and Number Relationships

Intervention Strategy

Linguistic/ Kinesthetic Learners

Real-World Numbers

1. Separate the class into small groups. Assign each group ten thousands, hundred thousands, or millions. Have students review magazines, newspapers, and other printed materials to find numbers in the place values that they have been assigned. Tell them to find at least five numbers.
2. Ask students to write the numbers in word form (or standard form if already in word form). Have them graph the numbers on a number line and place the numbers into a place-value chart.
3. Ask students to present their results to the class.

5 **Reflect** Place commas in the number 3710392. Then write the number in word form.

3,710,392; three million, seven hundred ten thousand, three hundred ninety-two

Skills, Concepts, and Problem Solving

se the place-value chart to answer each question. hen write each number in the chart.

6 How many zeros are in 7 ten thousands?

4; 70,000

7 How many zeros are in 2 millions?

6; 2,000,000

8 How many zeros are in 4 hundred thousands?

5; 400,000

	1,000,000	100,000	10,000	1,000	100	10	1
	millions	hundred thousands	ten thousands	thousands	hundreds	tens	ones
16.			7	0	0	0	0
17.	2	0	0	0	0	0	0
18.		4	0	0	0	0	0

rite the missing number in each equation.

9 2,000,000 + 400,000 + 30,000 + 6,000 + 800 + 10 + 4 = 2,436,814

1,000,000	100,000	10,000	1,000	100	10	1
millions	hundred thousands	ten thousands	thousands	hundreds	tens	ones
2	4	3	6	8	1	?

) 1,000,000 + 60,000 + 500 + 5 = 1,060,505

rite each number in standard form.

three hundred eight thousand, six hundred fifty-three 308,653

six hundred six thousand, four hundred sixty-five 606,465

one hundred one thousand, one hundred one 101,101

five hundred five thousand, five hundred 505,500

GO ON

Intervention Strategy

Logical Learners

Place Value The consequence of our base-ten number system is place value. Make sure students realize that each digit to the left has a place value that is 10 times larger. Use the expanded form, such as $1 \times 1{,}000{,}000 + 1 \times 100{,}000 + 1 \times 10{,}000$ and so on, until students are sure of the abbreviated form.

Odd/Even Assignments

Exercises 16–29 are structured so that students practice the same concepts whether they are assigned the odd or even problems.

In-Class Assignment

Have students complete Exercises 17, 20, 22, 27, 28, and 32 to ensure that they understand the concept.

Common Error Alert

Large Numbers If students struggle with Exercises 16–18, they might not know how to read a place-value chart with large numbers correctly. Draw a place-value chart on the board, but separate the columns with some space. Beginning with the ones place, ask how much larger the tens place is than the ones place. Move to the left, demonstrating that each column represents a value that is 10 times larger.

See It, Do It, Say It, Write It

Step 1 Write a number line on the board that begins at 400,000 and ends at 500,000. Divide it evenly into tens. Ask students what each interval names. Label the number line and graph 450,000. After students can name the plotted number, change the labeling and ask students to help you graph numbers.

Step 2 Tell students to draw a place-value chart to the millions with long columns for multiple numbers. One at a time, write numbers on the board that are in the hundred thousands, and then in the millions. Tell students to use their place-value charts and place the digits of each number into the charts.

Step 3 Ask students to discuss the results with a partner.

Step 4 Now ask students to write each of the numbers from the step above in word form. Discuss the results.

Looking Ahead: Pre-Teach

Number Relationships In the next lesson, students will learn how to identify patterns, determine the rule, and use the rule to determine the next few terms for the pattern.

Example

What is the rule and the next three terms for the pattern: 4, 11, 18, 25, _______, _______, _______
add 7; 32, 39, 46

Find the next three terms for each pattern.

1. 1,458, 486, 162, 54, _____, _____, _____ 18, 6, 2
2. 3, 6, 9, 12, ____, ____, ____ 15, 18, 21
3. 1, 5, 25, 125, ____, ____, ____ 625; 3,125; 15,625

Write each number in word form.

25 1,305,450
one million, three hundred five thousand, four hundred fifty

26 3,407,690
three million, four hundred seven thousand, six hundred ninety

27 8,211,099
eight million, two hundred eleven thousand, ninety-nine

Solve.

28 GEOGRAPHY Greenland is the largest island in the world. Its area is eight hundred forty thousand square miles. Write this number in standard form.
840,000 sq mi

29 GEOGRAPHY Write the area of the state of New York in standard form, using the map at the right.
141,205 sq km

Area = one hundred forty-one thousand, two hundred five square kilometers

New York

Vocabulary Check **Write the vocabulary word that completes each sentence.**

30 Commas are used to separate periods in a number.

31 A number that has a 1 followed by six 0s is called one million.

32 Writing in Math Divide a sheet of paper into four sections. Write the number 5,345,600 in one section of the paper. Use the other three sections to represent the number in three other ways.
Sample answer: 5,000,000 + 300,000 + 40,000 + 5,000 + 600; five million, three hundred forty-five thousand, six hundred; 5 millions, 345 thousands, 6 hundreds

Spiral Review

Identify the place-value position of each underlined digit. (Lesson 1-1, p. 4)

33 2,702 700
34 300,594 300,000
35 203,000 3,000
36 9,260 60

STOP

14 **Chapter 1** Place Value and Number Relationships

Ticket Out the Door

Write Numbers Write 489,056 and 9,019,704 on the board. Tell students to write both numbers in word form on paper. Then write three million, ninety-nine thousand, two hundred three on the board. Remind students to place their commas correctly. Tell students to write the number in standard form. Students will turn in their papers as they exit the classroom.

four hundred eighty-nine thousand, fifty-six; nine million, nineteen thousand, seven hundred four; 3,099,203

Progress Check 1 (Lessons 1-1 and 1-2)

Write each number in expanded form.

1 1,802 1,000 + 800 + 2

2 3,461 3,000 + 400 + 60 + 1

3 7,015 7,000 + 10 + 5

4 9,060 9,000 + 60

5 2,544 2,000 + 500 + 40 + 4

6 7,178 7,000 + 100 + 70 + 8

7 4,881 4,000 + 800 + 80 + 1

8 6,836 6,000 + 800 + 30 + 6

Write each number in word form.

9 8,324,015 eight million, three hundred twenty-four thousand, fifteen

10 1,447,398 one million, four hundred forty-seven thousand, three hundred ninety-eight

11 6,700,000 six million, seven hundred thousand

Write each number in standard form.

12 three million, four hundred five thousand 3,405,000

13 five million, one hundred twelve thousand 5,112,000

Solve.

14 **PUZZLES** Use the digits 1, 2, and 4 to write the least possible odd number. Use each digit once.

241

15 **PUZZLES** Use the digits 6, 8, and 5 to write the least possible odd number. Use each digit once.

685

16 **POPULATION** The population of Chicago in 2010 is estimated to become two million, eight-hundred thousand. Write this number in standard form.

2,800,000

Progress Check 1

Chapter 1

Formative Assessment

Use the Progress Check to assess students' mastery of the previous lessons. Have students review the lesson indicated for the problems they answered incorrectly.

Odd/Even Assignments

Exercises are structured so that students practice the same concepts whether they are assigned the odd or even problems.

Common Error *Alert*

Check Answers Students can think of writing numbers in expanded form as an addition problem. They can add their answers to verify the expanded form was written correctly.

Exercises 1–8 If students are having difficulty with this section, be sure they recall the concept of expanded form. If they are still having difficulty, have them use a place-value chart to show the composition of the numbers.

Exercises 9–13 Remind students to pay careful attention to commas in the numbers.

Data-Driven Decision Making

Students missing Exercises . . .	Have trouble with . . .	Should review and practice . . .
1–8	writing numbers in expanded form.	SSG Lesson 1-1, p. 4 CRM Skills Practice, p. A5
9–13	writing numbers in word form and standard form.	SSG Lesson 1-2, p. 9 CRM Skills Practice, p. A9
14–16	solving word problems involving writing specific types of numbers by comparing the values of the digits.	CRM Problem-Solving Practice, pp. A6 and A10

Lesson 1-3 Lesson Notes

Lesson Planner

Objective Identify, describe, and continue various number patterns.

Vocabulary **pattern**, **rule**

Materials/Manipulatives base-ten blocks, classroom objects, connecting cubes, construction paper, graph paper, two-color counters

Chapter Resource Masters

- CRM Vocabulary and English Language Development (p. A12)
- CRM Skills Practice (p. A13)
- CRM Problem-Solving Practice (p. A14)
- CRM Homework Practice (p. A15)

Vocabulary

Speak Vocabulary Write this number pattern on the board: 1, 3, 5, 7, . . . Ask what the *rule* is. Have students read the *pattern* aloud, continuing on through the next few terms. Ask students to give an example of a number *pattern* with a rule of "Subtract 1." Do the same exercise with the number pattern: 10, 8, 7, 5, 4, 3, . . . This is a nonexample for the rule "Subtract 1." Ask students to think of other nonexamples.

Key Concept

Foundational Skills and Concepts After students have read through the Key Concept box, have them try these exercises.

1. What is the rule? Add 12.
2. What are the next three terms? 96, 108, 120
3. What is a rule? words that tell relationships between numbers

Lesson 1-3 Number Relationships

KEY Concept

Number **patterns** follow a rule.

You can use a **rule** to answer questions about the pattern and to predict what comes next.

12, 24, 36, 48, 60, 72, 84, ... The rule is "Add 12."

To continue the pattern, add 12 to the last term.

$84 + 12 = 96$

$96 + 12 = 108$

$108 + 12 = 120$

So, the next three terms in the pattern are 96, 108, and 120.

Rules define relationships between numbers. For example, there are 12 inches in 1 foot. So, there are 24 inches in 2 feet (12×2), 36 inches in 3 feet (12×3), 48 inches in 4 feet (12×4), and so on.

VOCABULARY

pattern
a sequence of numbers, figures, or symbols that follows a rule or design

rule
tells how numbers are related to each other

Sometimes patterns can follow more than one rule.

Example 1

A car has 4 wheels. How many wheels are on 6 cars?

1. Each car has 4 wheels.
2. One rule is "add 4 for each car."
   $4 + 4 + 4 + 4 + 4 + 4 = 24$
3. Another rule is "multiply the number of cars by 4."
   $6 \times 4 = 24$
4. No matter which rule is used, there are 24 wheels on 6 cars.

YOUR TURN!

A spider has 8 legs. How many legs are on 5 spiders?

1. Each spider has _8_ legs.
2. One rule is _add 8 for each spider_.
   _8_ + _8_ + _8_ + _8_ + _8_ = _40_.
3. Another rule is _multiply the number of spiders by 8_.
   _5_ × 8 = _40_
4. There are _40_ legs on 5 spiders.

16 Chapter 1 Place Value and Number Relationships

Additional Example 1

A car has 4 wheels. How many wheels are on 7 cars?

1. Each car has 4 wheels.
2. One rule is to "add 4 for each car."
   $4 + 4 + 4 + 4 + 4 + 4 + 4 = 28$
3. Another rule is "multiply the number of cars by 4."
   $7 \times 4 = 28$
4. No matter which rule is used, there are 28 wheels on 7 cars.

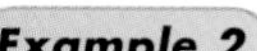

Example 2

Write the next three terms in the pattern.

1, 3, 7, 15

1. Find the rule.
   The rule is multiply by 2, and then add 1.
   $1 \times 2 = 2 + 1 = 3$
   $3 \times 2 = 6 + 1 = 7$
   $7 \times 2 = 14 + 1 = 15$
2. Continue the pattern.
   $15 \times 2 = 30 + 1 = 31$
   $31 \times 2 = 62 + 1 = 63$
   $63 \times 2 = 126 + 1 = 127$

The next three terms are 31, 63, 127.

YOUR TURN!

Write the next three terms in the pattern.

4, 7, 13, 25

1. Find the rule.
   The rule is multiply by 2, and then subtract 1.
   $4 \times 2 = 8 - 1 = 7$
   $7 \times 2 = 14 - 1 = 13$
   $13 \times 2 = 26 - 1 = 25$
2. Continue the pattern.
   $25 \times 2 = 50 - 1 = 49$
   $49 \times 2 = 98 - 1 = 97$
   $97 \times 2 = 194 - 1 = 193$

The next three terms are 49, 97, and 193.

Who is Correct?

How many cups are in 5 pints?

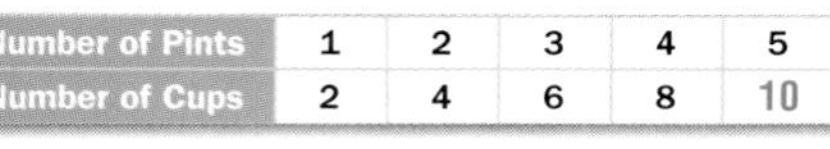

Number of Pints	1	2	3	4	5
Number of Cups	2	4	6	8	10

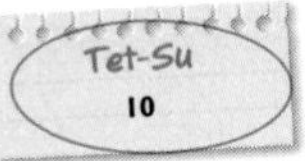

Circle correct answer(s). Cross out incorrect answer(s).

Guided Practice

Find a rule for each pattern.

1. 20, 15, 10, 5 subtract 5
2. 10, 17, 24, 31 add 7
3. 200, 100, 50, 25 divide by 2
4. 3, 9, 27, 81 multiply by 3

GO ON

Lesson 1-3 Number Relationships 17

Who is Correct?

Diagnostic Teaching

- Eduardo wrote 12. This is incorrect. Skip count to find that the next number is 10.
- Tet-su wrote 10. This is correct.
- Patrick wrote 100. This is incorrect because if you extend the table, you can see that there are 20 cups in 10 pints.

Show students how to extend the table.

Number of Pints	6	7	8	9	10
Number of Cups	12	14	16	18	20

Additional Example 2

Write the next three terms in the pattern.
1, 4, 13, 40

1. Find the rule.
   The rule is multiply by 3, and then add 1.
   $1 \times 3 = 3 + 1 = 4$
   $4 \times 3 = 12 + 1 = 13$
   $13 \times 3 = 39 + 1 = 40$
2. Continue the pattern.
   $40 \times 3 = 120 + 1 = 121$
   $121 \times 3 = 363 + 1 = 364$
   $364 \times 3 = 1{,}092 + 1 = 1{,}093$

The next three terms are 121, 364, and 1,093.

3 Practice

Using Manipulatives

Base-Ten Blocks Use base-ten blocks to represent numbers in a number pattern. For Example 1, represent the numbers using base-ten blocks.

Number of Cars	1	2	3	4	5	6
Number of Wheels						

Two-Color Counters Counters can also be used to represent numbers in patterns.

On-Hand Manipulatives Collect various classroom objects for students to represent numbers in a pattern, such as pencils, pens, erasers, different-colored pieces of chalk, squares of construction paper, and so on.

Math Coach Notes

Comprehension Strategies

1. Begin this lesson by modeling examples using base-ten blocks. Then put the numbers the blocks represent into a table. You can also use counters to model simple addition and subtraction rules.
2. Encourage students to use tables and write the rule underneath. Make certain they test the rule between all sets of numbers. Because patterns can be difficult to see, use visual aids like graphs to help students see the linear, predictable relationship between the quantities.
3. Encourage students to find more than one rule that applies to a given problem. For example, repeated addition can be used in place of multiplication.

Step by Step Practice

5 There are 36 inches in 1 yard and 72 inches in 2 yards. Continue the pattern to find how many inches are in 3, 4, and 5 yards.

Step 1 Write the pattern with the missing terms

36, 72, ____, ____, ____

Step 2 Find a rule: Multiply by the number of yards.

Step 3 Multiply the number of yards by 36 to continue the pattern.

3 × 36 = 108 4 × 36 = 144

5 × 36 = 180

The next three terms are 108, 144, and 180.

Find a rule in each sequence. Then write the next three terms.

6 19, 16, 13, 10, ____, ____, ____

Rule: subtract 3

10 − 3 = 7

7 − 3 = 4

4 − 3 = 1

The next three terms are:

7, 4, and 1.

7 320, 160, 80, 40, ____, ____, ____

Rule: divide by 2

40 ÷ 2 = 20

20 ÷ 2 = 10

10 ÷ 2 = 5

The next three terms are:

20, 10, and 5.

8 1, 3, 9, 27, ____, ____, ____

Rule: multiply by 3

The next three terms are:

81, 243, and 729.

9 153, 162, 171, 180, ____, ____, ____

Rule: add 9

The next three terms are:

189, 198, and 207.

Are They Getting It?

Check students' understanding of number relationships by writing these problems on the board. Ask students to point out the wrong answers. Instruct students to use a model or drawing to show why each answer is correct or incorrect.

1. In the pattern, 18, 16, 14, 12, the rule is "Add 2."
   This is incorrect. The rule is "Subtract 2."
2. In the pattern, 5, 10, 20, 40, the rule is "Add 5."
   This is incorrect. The rule is "Multiply by 2."
3. Jake bought 6 books for $3 each. He spent $12.
   This is incorrect. He spent $18.
4. In the pattern, 8, 12, 16, 20, the next three terms are 24, 28, 32.
   This is correct.

Write the next three conversions in each pattern.

10

Number of Pounds	1	2	3	4
Number of Ounces	16	32	48	64

11

Number of Feet	1	2	3	4
Number of Inches	12	24	36	48

Step by Step Problem-Solving Practice

Problem-Solving Strategies
- ☑ Make a table.
- ☐ Guess and check.
- ☐ Act it out.
- ☐ Solve a simpler problem.
- ☐ Work backward.

Solve.

12 BOOKS Fidel bought 6 books. The first book cost \$5. Each additional book cost \$1 more than the previous book. How much did Fidel spend on books in all?

Understand Read the problem. Write what you know.
The first book costs _\$5_.
Each additional book costs _\$1_ more than the previous book.
Fidel bought _6_ books.

Plan Pick a strategy. One strategy is to make a table. Label the rows Book and Cost.

Solve One book costs _\$5_. The cost increases by _\$1_ for each additional book.
The rule is _add 1_.

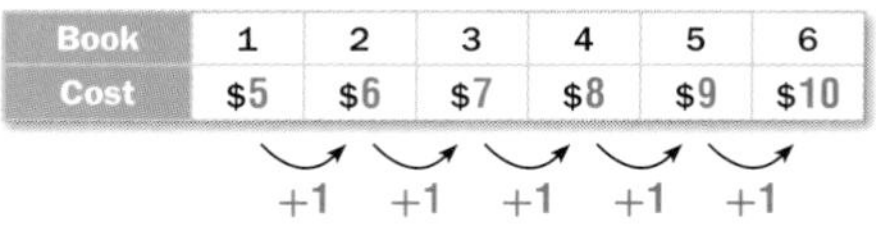

Book	1	2	3	4	5	6
Cost	\$5	\$6	\$7	\$8	\$9	\$10

To find the total cost, add the cost of each book.

_\$5_ + _\$6_ + _\$7_ + _\$8_ + _\$9_ + _\$10_ = _\$45_
Book 1 Book 2 Book 3 Book 4 Book 5 Book 6 Total

Fidel spent _\$45_ on books.

Check Does your answer make sense?

GO ON

Intervention Strategy

Visual/ Logical Learners

Use a Table Ask students to make a table to solve the following: *Each hexagon has 6 sides. How many sides do 5 hexagons have?* 30 sides

Note This!

Pre-reading In order to know what the lesson is about, encourage students to read the lessons before coming to class. This will give them an opportunity to anticipate the new material, as well as to be prepared to ask questions.

Math Coach Notes

Conversions Take a moment to explain the word *conversions*. Students will learn more about using conversions in systems of measurement in Chapter 10.

English Learner Strategy

Guiding Questions Use base-ten blocks. Place 3, 6, 9, and 12 in separate piles. Then ask students the following questions to ensure they understand the concept.

- What is the next number of blocks? 15 blocks
- Write the numbers for the blocks on paper. What are the next three terms? The next three terms are 15, 18, and 21.
- What is the pattern in 3, 6, 9, 12? Add 3.
- How would you find the rule for the number pattern 13, 26, 52, 104? You would find the pattern between the numbers (multiply by 2).
- Make a table to solve the following: Ella jogged 2 miles in 15 minutes. How far did she jog in 60 minutes?

Minutes	15	30	45	60
Miles Jogged	2	4	6	8

; 8 mi

Odd/Even Assignments

Exercises 16–31 are structured so that students practice the same concepts whether they are assigned the odd or even problems.

In-Class Assignment

Have students complete Exercises 19, 22, 28, 30, and 34 to ensure that they understand the concept.

Intervention Strategy

Kinesthetic/ Visual Learners

Use a Table Students may have difficulty finding a pattern. Have students make a table that includes the rule. The table below represents Exercise 13. Students can place the table into a page protector and use a dry-erase marker to fill it in, then reuse it for other functions.

Position	Rule	Value of Term
1	+14	14
2	+14	28
3	+14	42
4	+14	56
5	+14	70
6	+14	84

13 FISH A swordfish grows at a regular rate for the first year of life. Suppose it weighs 14 pounds at the age of 1 month, 28 pounds at the age of 2 months, and 42 pounds at the age of 3 months. What is the weight of a swordfish at the age of 6 months? Check off each step.

✓ Understand: I circled key words.

✓ Plan: To solve the problem, I will make a table.

✓ Solve: The answer is 84 pounds.

✓ Check: I checked my answer by skip counting.

14 FITNESS Martha runs for 30 minutes each day except for Saturday and Sunday. After 2 weeks, how much time will Martha have spent running?

300 minutes or 5 hours

15 **Reflect** Explain a rule for the pattern 10, 20, 40, 80.

One rule is multiply by 2. $10 \times 2 = 20$; $20 \times 2 = 40$; $40 \times 2 = 80$

Skills, Concepts, and Problem Solving

Find a rule for each pattern.

16 625, 125, 25, 5 divide by 5

17 561, 574, 587, 600 add 13

18 2, 6, 18, 54 multiply by 3

19 482, 346, 210, 74 subtract 136

20 9, 36, 144, 576 multiply by 4

21 1080, 180, 30, 5 divide by 6

Math Challenge

Flip-and-Roll Rules Write an assortment of rules on index cards, such as "Add 4," "Subtract 7," "Divide by 3," and "Multiply by 2." One student will flip a card for the rule and then each student will take turns rolling a number cube. Using the rolled number as the first or last number, each student will write a number pattern with five terms using the rule from the flipped card.

To score: Students will find the sum of their five terms. Whoever gets to 100 points first, wins.

In each sequence, find a rule. Then write the next three terms.

22 18, 30, 42, 54

Rule: add 12

Next terms: 66, 78, 90

23 321, 310, 299, 288

Rule: subtract 11

Next terms: 277, 266, 255

24 7, 14, 28, 56

Rule: multiply by 2

Next terms: 112, 224, 448

25 31,250; 6,250; 1,250; 250

Rule: divide by 5

Next terms: 50, 10, 2

26 101, 110, 119, 128

Rule: add 9

Next terms: 137, 146, 155

27 5103, 1701, 567, 189

Rule: divide by 3

Next terms: 63, 21, 7

28 Write the next three conversions in the pattern.

Number of Gallons	1	2	3	4
Number of Quarts	4	8	12	16

29 Write the next three conversions in the pattern.

Number of Meters	1	2	3	4
Number of Centimeters	100	200	300	400

Solve.

30 BOOKS Dimitri placed boxes of books on 5 shelves in the library. He put 1 box on the top shelf, 3 boxes on the second shelf, and 5 boxes on the third shelf. If he continues this pattern, how many boxes will he put on the fifth shelf? 9 boxes

31 MUSIC For a band concert, chairs were set up for the musicians. There were 4 chairs in every row. How many chairs are there in 5 rows? 20 chairs

1st row	2nd row	3rd row	4th row	5th row
4 chairs	8 chairs	12 chairs	16 chairs	20 chairs

GO ON

Math Coach Notes

Varied Rules Keep in mind that students may be able to find more than one rule that applies to a given problem. For example, repeated addition can be used in place of multiplication in many instances. Repeated subtraction can be used in place of division. Accept all reasonable responses when students are prompted to provide the rule. Encourage students who are stating the rules as repeated addition to find the related mutiplication rules, because multiplication is a better, faster approach for standardized testing. Likewise, students who are using repeated subtraction should be encouraged to find the division rule instead.

Math Challenge

Use Graphs Provide students with graph paper. Label the *x*-axis to 10. Label the *y*-axis to 50. Practice solving other problems using the coordinates from tables in the lesson. Guide students to see how the graph is a straight line and how they can use the line to make predictions.

See It, Do It, Say It, Write It

Step 1 Write a number pattern on the board. Have a student volunteer state the rule. Another volunteer can help define the next three terms. Repeat this activity several times.

Step 2 Write a rule on the board. Ask students to say five terms that fit the rule. Have students make a table on the board so that others can see their methods.

Step 3 Ask students to discuss their methods with a partner.

Step 4 Tell students they have three minutes to write as much as they can about number patterns and rules. Tell them to include definitions and examples. Have them describe their method for finding a rule in a number pattern.

Looking Ahead: Pre-Teach

Linear Patterns In the next lesson, students will learn how to determine values in a linear pattern. A linear pattern is a rule for a sequence of numbers that changes by the same rate from one term to the next.

Example

Miguel read 3 books in one month. How many books will Miguel read in 4 months?
Miguel will read 12 books in 4 months.

Have students determine the requested piece from the linear pattern.

1. Cari swims 10 laps in her pool in the morning. How many laps does Cari swim in 6 days?
Cari swims 60 laps.

2. Seoung can bake 5 loaves of bread in an hour. How many loaves of bread does Seoung bake in 6 hours? Seoung bakes 30 loaves of bread.

3. Kamal builds 13 bird houses in a weekend. How many birdhouses did Kamal build in 4 weekends?
Kamal built 52 birdhouses.

Vocabulary Check **Write the vocabulary word that completes each sentence.**

32 A(n) rule tells how numbers are related to each other.

33 A(n) pattern is a sequence of numbers, figures, or symbols that follows a rule or design.

34 **Writing in Math** Explain how to find the next three terms in the sequence 2, 4, 8, 16 using two different rules.
One rule is to multiply by 2. The next three terms are 32, 64, 128.
Another rule is to add each term to itself to find the next term.

Spiral Review

Identify the value of the underlined digit. (Lesson 1-1, p. 4)

35 6,391 90

36 8,404 8,000

37 9,008 8

38 1,982 900

Write each number in standard form. (Lesson 1-2, p. 9)

39 nine hundred two thousand, three hundred sixty-one 902,361

40 four hundred thirty-two thousand, one hundred five 432,105

Write each number in word form. (Lesson 1-2, p. 9)

41 2,492,102 two million, four hundred ninety-two thousand, one hundred two

42 1,973,923 one million, nine hundred seventy-three thousand, nine hundred twenty-three

Solve. (Lesson 1-2, p. 9)

43 SCHOOL Daniel wrote 5,305,707 in words on his homework paper. He wrote "five million, three hundred five thousand, seven hundred." What mistake did Daniel make?
Daniel forgot the last 7 in the ones period. The number is five million, three hundred five thousand, seven hundred seven.

STOP

Ticket Out the Door

Tell students to write the first seven terms of a pattern so that 24 is the first term and the pattern is to subtract 3 from the previous term. Students will hand in their papers as they exit the classroom.

24, 21, 18, 15, 12, 9, 6

Lesson 1-4 Linear Patterns

KEY Concept

Patterns follow a **rule**. A rule describes the relationship that one element of a sequence has with the next element of the sequence. A rule can also describe the relationship an element has with its position in the sequence.

A table can help you identify and extend a pattern by its rules.

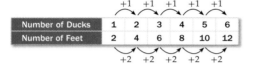

	+1	+1	+1	+1	+1
Number of Ducks	1	2	3	4	5	6
Number of Feet	2	4	6	8	10	12

+2 +2 +2 +2 +2

For each additional duck, the number of feet increases by 2.

Another way to describe the pattern is the number of ducks multiplied by 2 is the number of feet.

VOCABULARY

pattern
a sequence of numbers, figures, or symbols that follows a rule or design

rule
tells how numbers, figures, or symbols in a pattern are related to each other

GO ON

Intervention Strategy Logical Learners

Functional Relationships A functional relationship occurs when the value of the second variable is determined by the value of the first variable. A functional relationship can be written as ordered pairs. Write this table on the board, then ask students to explain the relationship.

Number of Minutes	1	2	3	4
Number of Seconds	60	120	180	240

Help students to recognize that the information can be written as ordered pairs (number of minutes, number of seconds).

(1, 60) (2, 120) (3, 180) (4, 240)

Each minute has 60 seconds.

Lesson Notes

Chapter 1-4

Lesson Planner

Objective Extend linear patterns.

Vocabulary **pattern**, **rule**

Materials/Manipulatives base-ten blocks, classroom objects, connecting cubes, index cards

Chapter Resource Masters

- CRM Vocabulary and English Language Development (p. A16)
- CRM Skills Practice (p. A17)
- CRM Problem-Solving Practice (p. A18)
- CRM Homework Practice (p. A19)

1 Introduce

Vocabulary

Access Vocabulary Write a few word problems that reflect a linear pattern on the board. Ask for volunteers to go to the board and identify the *patterns.* Ask the students to identify the *rule* for each pattern. Also ask students to give examples of patterns and rules that are not linear.

2 Teach

Key Concept

Foundational Skills and Concepts After students have read through the Key Concept box, have them try these exercises.

1. List another part of the body that could be used in the table to fit the pattern. wings
2. Describe the pattern in the Key Concept box in your own words. Sample answer: The number of feet is equal to the number of ducks multiplied by 2.

Additional ***Example 1***

How many points do six stars have?

1. Make a table.
2. Each star has 5 points, so the number of points increases by 5 for each additional star. The rule is add 5 for each star.
3. Add 5 to each term to obtain the next term in the pattern.

+1 +1 +1 +1 +1

Number of Stars	1	2	3	4	5	6
Number of Points	5	10	15	20	25	30

+5 +5 +5 +5 +5

Six stars have 30 points.

Additional ***Example 2***

There are 24 students in Mr. Rivera's class. He divided the students into groups of three. Then he handed four sheets of paper to each group. How many sheets of paper were handed out altogether?

1. For every 1 group of students, there are 4 sheets of paper. The number of sheets of paper increases by 4 for each additional group. The rule is multiply by 4.
2. Multiply the number of student groups by the number of sheets of paper given to each group.
   $24 \div 3 = 8$ groups of students
   $8 \times 4 = 32$

Mr. Rivera handed out 32 sheets of paper to 8 student groups in the class.

Example 1

Margo rides her bike at 6 miles per hour. How many miles can she travel in 4 hours?

1. Make a table.
2. For every 1 hour traveled, Margo rides 6 miles. So the number of miles traveled increases by 6 for each additional hour. The rule is add 6 for each hour traveled.
3. Add 6 to a term to obtain the next term in the pattern.

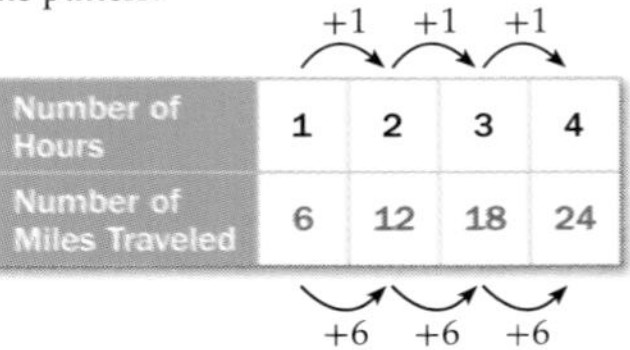

+1 +1 +1

Number of Hours	1	2	3	4
Number of Miles Traveled	6	12	18	24

+6 +6 +6

Margo can ride 24 miles in 4 hours.

YOUR TURN!

Dawn's Diner serves 9 cheesesticks in 1 order. How many cheesesticks are in 6 orders?

1. Make a table.
2. Each order has 9 cheesesticks. The number of cheesesticks increases by 9 for each additional order. The rule is add 9 for each order.
3. Add 9 to a term to obtain the next term in the pattern.

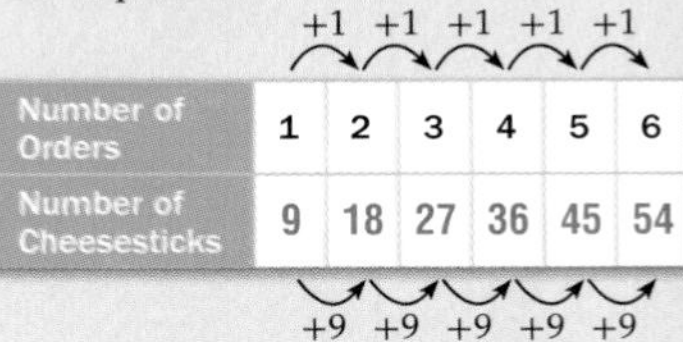

+1 +1 +1 +1 +1

Number of Orders	1	2	3	4	5	6
Number of Cheesesticks	9	18	27	36	45	54

+9 +9 +9 +9 +9

There are 54 cheesesticks in 6 orders.

Example 2

For each block, there are 5 apartment buildings. How many apartment buildings are in 8 blocks?

1. For each 1 block, there are 5 apartment buildings. The number of buildings increases by 5 for each additional block. The rule is multiply by 5.
2. Multiply the number of blocks by the number of apartment buildings in each block.
   $8 \times 5 = 40$

There are 40 apartment buildings in 8 blocks.

YOUR TURN!

For each car, there are 4 wheels. How many wheels do 10 cars have?

1. For each 1 car, there are 4 wheels. The number of wheels increases by 4 for each additional car. The rule is multiply by 4.
2. Multiply the number of cars by the number of wheels on each car.
   10 (number of cars) × 4 (number of wheels) = 40

There are 40 wheels on 10 cars.

English Learner Strategy

Prior Knowledge Use a highlighter or colored pencil to highlight, circle, or underline key words in word problems. Have English learners keep a list of key words from earlier vocabulary boxes and color-code those words with words in contextual problems.

Who is Correct?

How many fingers (including the thumb) do 3 people have?

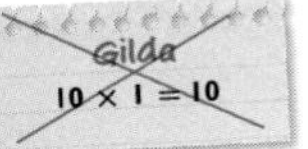

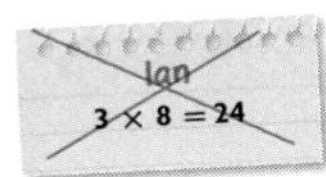

Circle correct answer(s). Cross out incorrect answer(s).

Guided Practice

Write a possible situation for each rule.

1 Add 2 for each additional person.

Possible answer: the number of ears people have

2 Multiply by 4 for each additional animal.

Possible answer: the number of legs on a dog or horse

3 EXERCISE John jogs 2 miles in 20 minutes. How long will it take John to jog 8 miles?

The rule is add 20 for every 2 miles.

It will take John 80 minutes to jog 8 miles.

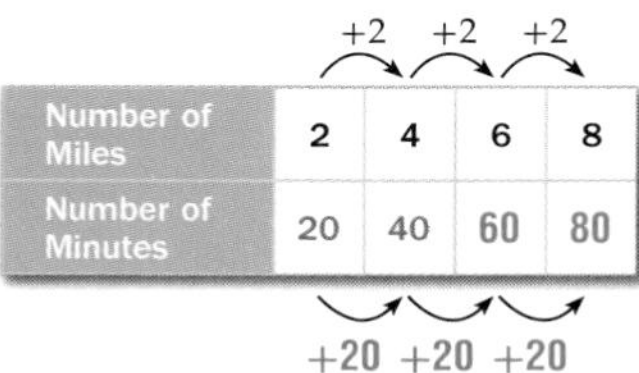

Number of Miles	2	4	6	8
Number of Minutes	20	40	60	80

Step by Step Practice

4 There are 3 feet in a yard. How many feet are there in 5 yards?

Step 1 Each yard has 3 feet. The number of feet increases by 3 for each additional yard. The rule is multiply by 3.

Step 2 Multiply the number of yards by the number of feet in each yard.

5 × 3 = 15

There are 15 feet in 5 yards.

GO ON

Who *is Correct?*

Diagnostic Teaching

- Gilda is incorrect. She shows how many fingers 1 person has.
- Ian is incorrect. He shows how many fingers (excluding the thumb) 3 people have.
- Marni is correct.

Remind students to figure out the rule and then apply it to 3 people.

3 Practice

Using Manipulatives

Base-Ten Blocks/Connecting Cubes

When presenting Example 1, use unit cubes to give students a visual concept of the linear pattern used to make a rule. Use the base-ten blocks to show how many miles Margo rode per hour, then show 6 miles. Count the number of unit cubes to get the total.

□□□□□□ = 1 hour

□□□□□□
□□□□□□
□□□□□□
□□□□□□ = 4 hours

On-Hand Manipulatives When presenting the examples, represent the objects in the question with classroom objects, such as pencils, pens, and chalk to give students a visual concept of the linear pattern used to make the rule.

Math Coach Notes

1. Begin this lesson by using base-ten blocks to show patterns in numbers. Show 1, 3, 5, 7 with blocks and have students add more blocks to the pattern.
2. Encourage students to use tables with the rule underneath. Then ask them to use blocks to make their own patterns. Ask them to describe the rule.

Common Error *Alert*

Patterns If students are having difficulty understanding the pattern, give students a pattern to work with. Ask students to write a linear word problem to fit the pattern. Have students write a rule in their own words that fits the pattern.

Note This!

Formatting Notes Show students how to write notes within the body of their notebook paper and leave wide margins to add notes in the future. Tell students that as they study, they can write important points, concepts they need to review, or items that were stressed in class in the margins. When it is time for a quick review, they need only focus on the margins instead of their entire notes.

Intervention Strategy — Visual Learners

Three Steps Have students show three parts to each problem when they are not sure about a rule. The first step is to draw a picture that shows enough to establish a pattern. The second step is to transfer the information from the picture into a table. The final step is to write a rule that describes the relationship.

5 READING Francisco can read at a rate of 30 pages for every 2 hours. How many pages can Francisco read in 4 hours?

Francisco can read __60__ pages in 4 hours.

6 SWIMMING Liz swam at a rate of 18 laps per hour. How many laps will Liz swim in 3 hours?

Liz will swim __54__ laps in 3 hours.

Step by Step Problem-Solving Practice

Problem-Solving Strategies
- ☑ Use logical reasoning.
- ☐ Guess and check.
- ☐ Act it out.
- ☐ Solve a simpler problem.
- ☐ Work backward.

Solve.

7 FUNDRAISING Larisa sold raffle tickets for a fundraiser. She sold the tickets at a rate of 6 tickets each hour. How many tickets did Larisa sell in 5 hours?

Understand: Read the problem. Write what you know.

Larisa sold __6__ tickets each hour.

Plan: Pick a strategy. One strategy is to use logical reasoning. Multiply the number of tickets Larisa sold each hour by the number of hours.

Solve: Multiply.

__6__ (number of tickets) × __5__ (number of hours) = __30__ (total tickets)

Larisa sold __30__ tickets in 5 hours.

Check: Skip count by 6 five times.

__6__ + __6__ + __6__ + __6__ + __6__ = __30__

8 NATURE How many minutes will it take for Lupé to climb out of a hole that is 27 inches deep? Check off each step.

NATURE Lupé the Ladybug is able to climb 9 inches every 3 minutes.

- __✔__ Understand: I circled key words.
- __✔__ Plan: To solve the problem, I will __use logical reasoning__.
- __✔__ Solve: The answer is __9 minutes__.
- __✔__ Check: I checked my answer by __skip counting__.

Are They Getting It?

Check students' understanding of linear patterns by writing these problems on the board. Ask students to point out wrong answers. Encourage students to use manipulatives or a table in their explanations.

1. Tyler takes 40 steps in 1 minute. How many steps will Tyler take in 3 minutes?
   Tyler will take __80__ steps in 3 minutes.
   This is incorrect. Tyler will take 120 steps in 3 minutes.
2. Hailey takes 15 minutes to solve one puzzle. How many minutes will it take Hailey to solve 4 puzzles?
   It will take Hailey __60__ minutes to solve 4 puzzles.
   This is correct.
3. Noah uses 5 scoops of drink mix to make one pitcher. How many scoops will Noah use to make 3 pitchers?
   Noah will use __10__ scoops to make 3 pitchers.
   This is incorrect. Noah will use 15 scoops to make 3 pitchers.

9 FOOD Kenyon and 5 friends went to the ice cream parlor. They each ordered 2 scoops of ice cream. How many scoops of ice cream were served to Kenyon and his 5 friends?

12 scoops

10 **Reflect** Explain two ways to find the number of ears on 5 students.

The rule is to add 2: $2 + 2 + 2 + 2 + 2 = 10$ or the rule is to multiply by 2: $5 \times 2 = 10$. Five students have 10 ears.

Skills, Concepts, and Problem Solving

Write a possible situation for each rule.

11 Add 6 for each additional desk.

Sample answer: the number of pencils in each desk

12 Multiply by 9 for each additional tree.

Sample answer: the number of apples on each tree

13 TRACK Jeremy walked at a rate of 6 laps per hour on the track. How many laps did Jeremy walk in 4 hours?

The rule is add 6 laps for every 1 hour(s).

Jeremy walked 24 laps in 4 hours.

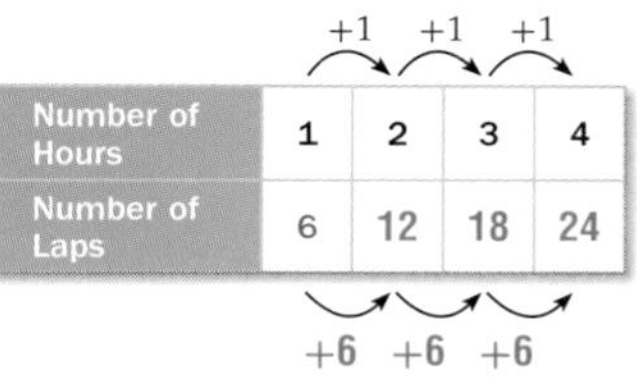

Number of Hours	1	2	3	4
Number of Laps	6	12	18	24

GO ON

Intervention Strategy

Auditory Learners

Use Songs Use songs as a way to help students learn linear patterns. Arrange students into pairs and have each group create a song that uses the facts from a linear-pattern word problem. Each group can present a song to the rest of the class. Have the students pick the best two songs. Print the songs and give each student a copy for reference.

Odd/Even Assignments

Exercises 11–18 are structured so that students practice the same concepts whether they are assigned the odd or even problems.

In-Class Assignment

Have students complete Exercises 12, 14, 17, and 21 to ensure that they understand the concept.

Math Coach Notes

Strategies

1. When students are identifying linear patterns, review repeated addition and multiplication. Show how both of these number strategies result in the same answer. The pattern "3 groups of 6" can be shown the following two ways:
   $6 + 6 + 6 = 18$
   $6 \times 3 = 18$
2. Write other real-world examples on the board to help students see the pattern.

Common Error *Alert*

Using Multiplication If students are having difficulty with linear patterns, remind them of the concept of multiplication. If one shirt costs \$15, how much would 6 cost? Have them set up a table indicating the cost for 1, 2, 3, 4, 5, and 6 shirts. Have them check their answers using multiplication.

Note This!

Study Strategies As students encounter linear patterns, have them start with an index card file. Cards should include the word problem, a brief description (students write what they know), and a table that reflects the pattern. As they re-encounter a pattern, they can revisit their index cards to refresh their memories.

14 TRAVEL Careta traveled at a rate of 70 miles for every 2 hours. How many miles did Careta travel in 8 hours? 280 miles

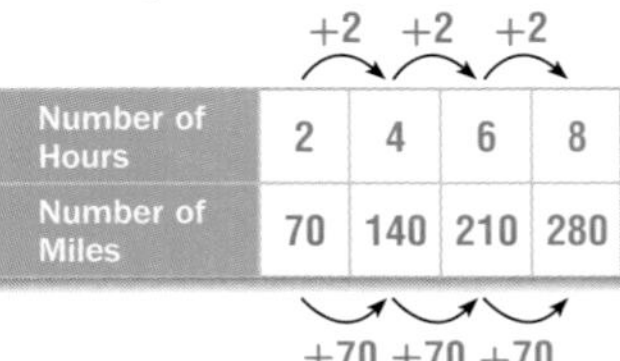

+2 +2 +2

Number of Hours	2	4	6	8
Number of Miles	70	140	210	280

+70 +70 +70

Solve.

15 FOOD Sherita is selling lemonade for \$1 per glass. In the first hour of business, she sold 10 glasses. How much money did Sherita make?

\$10

16 GEOMETRY Aiden had to cut 7 triangles out of a sheet of construction paper. How many sides did Aiden cut out of the construction paper?

21 sides

A triangle has 3 sides.

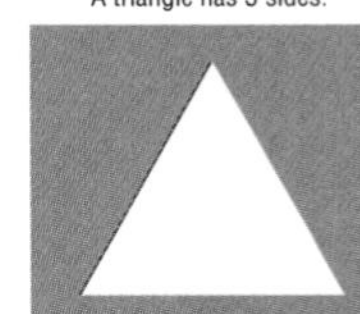

17 FOOD The chicken-finger appetizer at the Chick Pantry comes with 4 pieces of chicken. The cooks had 6 orders at the same time. How many pieces of chicken did they have to prepare?

24 pieces

18 SLEEP It is recommended that a person should get at least 8 hours of sleep each night. What is the least number of hours a person should sleep in 1 week?

56 hours

Vocabulary Check **Write the vocabulary word that completes each sentence.**

19 A(n) rule tells how numbers are related to each other.

20 A(n) pattern is a sequence of numbers, figures, or symbols that follows a rule or design.

28 **Chapter 1** Place Value and Number Relationships

Math Challenge

Rules by the Numbers Review linear patterns such as each person has two ears and each carton of a dozen eggs has 12 eggs. Arrange students into pairs. Challenge the pair to find a situation for the numbers from 1 to 10. Examples are 1 person has 1 mouth, 1 person has 2 feet, 1 tricycle has 3 wheels, and so on through 10.

21 Writing in Math Explain how to find the number of legs that 6 octopuses have by using the photo at the right.

Each octopus has 8 legs and $8 \times 6 = 48$.

Six octopuses have 48 legs.

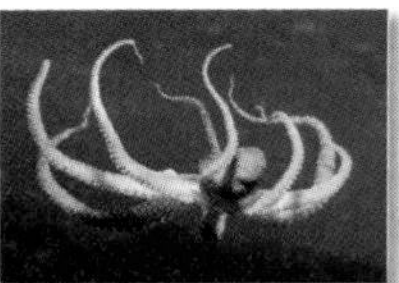
An octopus has 8 legs.

Spiral Review

Write each number in expanded form. (Lesson 1-1, p. 4)

22 908 900 + 8

23 204 200 + 4

24 1,367 1,000 + 300 + 60 + 7

25 4,972 4,000 + 900 + 70 + 2

Write each number in standard form. (Lesson 1-2, p. 9)

26 two hundred seven

207

27 one million, forty-five

1,000,045

28 two million, one hundred eighty

2,000,180

29 nine hundred thousand, six hundred

900,600

Solve. (Lesson 1-3, p. 16)

30 PICTURES Emil made a pyramid of pictures for a school project. He put 3 pictures in the top row, 6 pictures in the second row, and 9 pictures in the third row. If the pattern continues, how many pictures will be in the fifth row?

15 pictures

Ticket Out the Door

Capacity Rules Write these tables on the board.

Number of Gallons	1	2	3	4
Number of Quarts	4	8	12	16

Number of Pints	1	2	3	4
Number of Cups	2	4	6	8

Have the students line up at the door single file. As each student approaches the door, ask a question about the data in the table or data that is found by extending the table. Example: How many cups are equal to 6 pints? Continue until all students have exited the classroom.

4 Assess

See It, Do It, Say It, Write It

Step 1 Write multiple linear-pattern word problems on the board.

Step 2 Have students make a table that shows the relationship of one element of a sequence with the next element of the sequence.

Step 3 Arrange students in pairs and have them explain to each other how they found the pattern that fits each situation.

Step 4 Have students write in their own words the definitions of each of the vocabulary words and how they solve a linear pattern in their math journal.

Chapter 1

Progress Check 2

Formative Assessment

Use the Progress Check to assess students' mastery of the previous lessons. Have students review the lesson indicated for the problems they answered incorrectly.

Odd/Even Assignments

Exercises are structured so that students practice the same concepts whether they are assigned the odd or even problems.

Common Error *Alert*

Using Rules If students are having difficulty with these problems, remind them that when continuing these patterns, they should be looking for a *rule* that is recurring.

Exercises 1–4 Have students ask themselves: "What amount would have to be added, subtracted, multiplied, or divided to get from one number in this sequence to the next number?" Once they arrive at a potential rule, test to see if this is the case throughout the entire list.

Exercises 5–8 The most difficult part of these exercises is for students to analyze the wording in order to really know what the problem is asking them to find. You might have to "jump-start" them.

Chapter 1

Progress Check 2 (Lessons 1-3 and 1-4)

In each sequence, find a rule. Then write the next three terms.

1 315, 296, 277, 258, ______, ______, ______

Rule: subtract 19

Next terms: 239, 220, 201

2 9, 18, 36, 72, ______, ______, ______

Rule: multiply by 2

Next terms: 144, 288, 576

Write the next three conversions in each pattern.

3

Number of Milliliters	1,000	2,000	3,000	4,000
Number of Liters	1	2	3	4

4

Number of Hours	1	2	3	4
Number of Minutes	60	120	180	240

Solve.

5 **HEALTH** Tyree sleeps 9 hours each night. How many hours does he sleep in 1 week?

Tyree sleeps 63 hours in one week.

6 **MEASUREMENT** One bucket can hold 8 gallons of water. How many gallons of water can 7 buckets hold?

Seven buckets can hold 56 gallons of water.

7 **FITNESS** Steve exercises 0.75 hour each day. How many hours will he exercise in 8 days?

Steve will exercise 6 hours in 8 days.

8 **SHARKS** Refer to the photo at the right. About how many inches does a great white shark grow in 7 years?

A great white shark grows about 70 inches in 7 years.

SHARKS Great white sharks grow about 10 inches per year.

30 **Chapter 1** Place Value and Number Relationships

Data-Driven Decision Making

Students missing Exercises . . .	Have trouble with . . .	Should review and practice . . .
1-2	writing the next three terms in a pattern.	SSG Lesson 1-3, p. 16 CRM Skills Practice, p. A13
3-4	writing the next three conversions in a pattern.	SSG Lesson 1-4, p. 23 CRM Skills Practice, p. A17
5-8	solving word problems with number patterns.	CRM Problem-Solving Practice, pp. A14 and A18

Study Guide

Vocabulary and Concept Check

expanded form, *p. 4*
pattern, *p. 16*
period, *p. 9*
rule, *p. 16*
standard form, *p. 4*
word form, *p. 9*

Write the vocabulary word that completes each sentence.

1. A number is written in standard form using only digits.
2. A(n) rule tells how the numbers, figures, or symbols in a pattern are related to each other.
3. A group of three digits in the place-value chart is known as a period.
4. Expanded form shows a number as a sum of the value of each digit.

Label each diagram below. Write the correct place value in each blank.

5. ten thousands
23,496

6. million
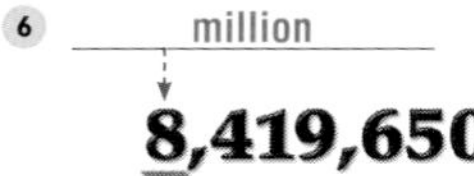
8,419,650

Lesson Review

1-1 Whole Numbers Less Than 10,000 (pp. 4-8)

Identify the value of each underlined digit.

7. 4,853 4,000
8. 7,090 90
9. 9,248 200
10. 6,092 90
11. 3,381 3,000
12. 5,305 300

Example 1

Identify the value of the underlined digit in 3,506.

Write each digit in the place-value chart.

The underlined digit is in the hundreds place.

1000	100	10	1
thousands	hundreds	tens	ones
3	5	0	6

Multiply the underlined digit by the value of its place. 5 × 100 = 500

The underlined digit has a value of 500.

Study Guide
Formative Assessment

Chapter 1

Vocabulary and Concept Check

If students have difficulty answering Exercises 1–6, remind them that they can use the page references to refresh their memories about the vocabulary terms.

Vocabulary Review Strategies

Puzzles Have students make a crossword puzzle to help them review key vocabulary words. They should interlock the words in the Vocabulary and Concept Check and then write clues that are used to determine the correct word. (Example: In the number 4,783, the digit 7 is in the ______________ place. *Answer: hundreds)* Have them trade puzzles with another student for additional practice.

Lesson Review

Each example walks students through the main concepts of the chapter. If the given examples are not sufficient to review the primary concepts of the chapter, remind students that the page references tell them where to review that topic in their textbooks.

Find **Extra Practice** for these concepts in the Practice Worksheets, pages A4–A19.

Classroom Management

Group Time Have students who finish the review problems for each example create additional problems, for which they also develop a solution. Then have them gather in small groups to discuss their problems and explain the corresponding solutions.

Dinah Zike's Foldables®

Review Remind students to complete and refer to their Foldables as they progress through the Chapter 1 Study Guide. Suggest that students share the examples they have written with a partner. Students should explain their examples to each other. (For complete instructions, see Chapter Resource Masters p. A1.)

1,000	100	10	1

Note This!

Create Place-Value Charts Help students create place-value charts to go with each type of example in this study guide. Give them a *skeletal* outline of the chart and have the students fill in the missing parts/ places.

1-2 Read and Write Whole Numbers in the Millions (pp. 9-14)

Write each number in word form.

13 5,854,120
five million, eight hundred fifty-four thousand, one hundred twenty

14 258,764
two hundred fifty-eight thousand, seven hundred sixty-four

15 3,400,250
three million, four hundred thousand, two hundred fifty

16 14,273
fourteen thousand, two hundred seventy-three

Example 2

Write 2,375,608 in word form.

Rewrite the number using digits and words (using period names).

Write the millions period. two million

Write the thousands period. three hundred seventy-five thousand

Write the ones period. six hundred eight

Write the periods together.
two million, three hundred seventy-five thousand, six hundred eight

1-3 Number Relationships (pp. 16-22)

What is the rule for each pattern?

17 185, 179, 173, 167 subtract 6

18 4, 8, 16, 32 multiply by 2

19 2, 6, 18, 54 multiply by 3

Write the next three terms in the pattern.

20 18, 30, 42, 54, 66, 78, 90

21 3, 10, 17, 24, 31, 38

22 856, 736, 616, 496, 376, 256, 136

Example 3

Write the next three terms in the pattern. 2, 5, 11, 23, ____, ____, ____

Find the rule.

$2 \times 2 = 4 + 1 = 5$

$5 \times 2 = 10 + 1 = 11$

$11 \times 2 = 22 + 1 = 23$

The rule is multiply by 2, and then add 1.

Continue the pattern.

$23 \times 2 = 46 + 1 = 47$

$47 \times 2 = 94 + 1 = 95$

$95 \times 2 = 190 + 1 = 191$

The next three terms are 47, 95, 191.

32 Chapter 1 Study Guide

Intervention Strategy Kinesthetic Learners

Number Cards Have students play a game using two sets of cards. One stack of cards will be numbered from 1 to 9. The other stack of cards will include the directions, such as, "Draw four number cards and make the greatest number possible with them." This game could be played alone or in small groups with students taking turns.

Solve.

23 **SHAPES** A pentagon has 5 sides. How many sides do 7 pentagons have?

35 sides

24 **HOMEWORK** Regina needs to read 3 chapters this week. Each chapter has 23 pages. How many pages does Regina need to read?

69 pages

25 **TRAVEL** Cesar's dad drives 8 miles to work and 8 miles home 5 days a week. How many miles does his dad drive to and from work each week?

80 miles

Example 4

How many toes are on 6 feet?

Each foot has 5 toes.

One rule is "add 5 for each foot."

$$5 + 5 + 5 + 5 + 5 + 5 = 30$$

Another rule is "multiply the number of feet by 5."

$$6 \times 5 = 30$$

There are 30 toes on 6 feet.

1-4 Linear Patterns (pp. 23-29)

Solve.

26 A spider has 8 legs. How many legs do 4 spiders have?

32 legs

27 Joselyn can run 1 mile in 7 minutes. If she keeps a constant pace, how many miles can she run in 35 minutes?

5 miles

28 Ross and his 5 friends each bought 3 comic books. How many comic books did they buy in all?

18 comic books

Example 5

Janice works at her father's business for $8 per hour. How much money will Janice earn if she works for 5 hours? Make a table.

For every 1 hour worked, Janice earns $8. So the amount of money earned increases by $8 for each additional hour. The rule is add 8 for each hour worked.

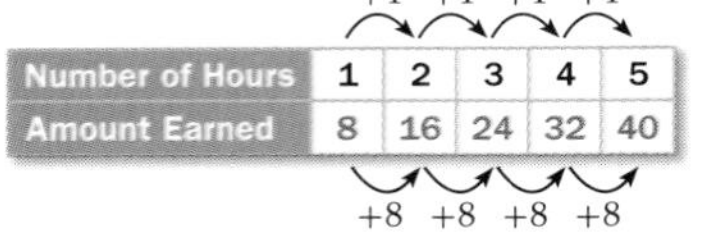

+1 +1 +1 +1

Number of Hours	1	2	3	4	5
Amount Earned	8	16	24	32	40

+8 +8 +8 +8

Janice will earn $40 for working 5 hours.

Math Coach Notes

If students are having trouble understanding what operations to perform to get to the answers in Exercises 26–28, have the students create a table of values. Once the table is created, show the students that the values increase using multiplication.

Ticket Out the Door

Write Problems Have students write an example of a problem for each of the four following topics: whole numbers in expanded form, numbers as high as one million, numbers in a number pattern, and numbers with a linear pattern. Have them turn in their papers as they exit the classroom.

Chapter 1 Chapter Test

Chapter Resource Masters

Additional forms of the Chapter 1 Tests are available.

Test Format	Where to Find it
Chapter 1 Test	Math Online macmillanmh.com
Blackline Masters	Assessment Masters, p. 14

Customize and create multiple versions of your chapter tests and their answer keys. All of these questions from the chapter tests are available on ExamView® Assessment Suite.

Online Assessment and Reporting
macmillanmh.com

This online assessment tool allows teachers to track student progress with easily accessible comprehensive reports available for every student. Assess students using any internet-ready computer.

Alternative Assessment

Use Portfolios Ask students to write examples of all the different forms of a number in their portfolios. Also have them include some examples of numbers in a place-value chart. Have them identify the value of each place.

Chapter 1 Chapter Test

Write each number in standard form.

1 seven hundred forty-six thousand, two hundred eight 746,208

2 one hundred fifty-two thousand, six hundred eleven 152,611

3 2,000 + 800 + 50 + 9 2,859

4 8,000 + 500 + 20 + 1 8,521

Write each number in expanded form.

5 9,764 9,000 + 700 + 60 + 4

6 2,505 2,000 + 500 + 5

7 3,491 3,000 + 400 + 90 + 1

8 6,700 6,000 + 700

Identify the value of each underlined digit.

9 7,890 800

10 3,080 3,000

11 5,492 5,000

12 3,081 80

13 6,919 10

14 2,304 300

Write each number in word form.

15 2,378,490
two million, three hundred seventy-eight thousand, four hundred ninety

16 254,300
two hundred fifty-four thousand, three hundred

17 3,511,780
three million, five hundred eleven thousand, seven hundred eighty

18 8,211,099
eight million, two hundred eleven thousand, ninety-nine

34 Chapter 1 Test

English Learner Strategy

Assessment Allow students time to look over the assessment. Have students take a close look at all the problem directions, as well as any terms in the word problems. Provide an opportunity for students to clarify any words they think they do not understand by conducting a brief question-and-answer period or by allowing them to look them up in their textbooks.

Write the next three terms.

19 11, 18, 25, 32
39, 46, 53

20 3, 9, 27, 81
243, 729, 2,187

21 100, 85, 70, 55
40, 25, 10

Write the next three conversions in each pattern.

22

Number of Yards	1	2	3	4
Number of Inches	36	72	108	144

23

Number of Kilometers	1	2	3	4
Number of Meters	1,000	2,000	3,000	4,000

State the rule. Then find the solution for each of the following.

24 How many tires do four "18-wheeler" tractor-trailer trucks have?

Sample answer: Add 18: $18 + 18 + 18 + 18 = 72$ wheels.

25 How many legs do 7 cats have?

Sample answer: Multiply by 4: $7 \times 4 = 28$ legs.

Solve.

26 **TRAVEL** During each day of her 1 week vacation in the mountains, Monica biked a distance of 15 miles. Over the entire vacation, how many miles did Monica bike?

105 miles

Correct the mistakes.

27 **BANKING** When writing a check, you must write both the standard form and word form of the dollar amount of the check. Mr. Krueger made a purchase at Kid Creations for $375. He wrote the check shown below. Explain what Mr. Krueger did wrong.

The word form should be written as: three *hundred* seventy-five.

Kelsey Krueger
123 High Street,
Santa Cruz, CA 95064
001
DATE 9/14/2007
PAYEE Kid Creations
$ 375.00
Three seventy-five
/00 DOLLARS
BANK •
Kelsey Krueger
⑈001⑈12345⑆123⑆ 123456⑆123⑈

Learning from Mistakes

Review Review commonly missed questions as a small group or class. Ask students to share their methods of answering each question. Try to point out when any errors occur and take corrective measures.

Data-Driven Decision Making

Students missing Exercises . . .	Have trouble with . . .	Should review and practice . . .
1-8, 15-18	writing numbers in alternate forms.	SSG Lessons 1-1, 1-2, pp. 4, 9 CRM Skills Practice, pp. A5 and A9
9-14	identifying the value of the underlined digit of a given number.	CRM Skills Practice, p. A5
19-23	identifying the next values in a pattern.	SSG Lessons 1-3, 1-4 pp. 16, 23 CRM Skills Practice, pp. A13 and A17
24-25	determining the rule for a pattern and then utilizing the rule to create more pieces for the pattern.	SSG Lessons 1-3, 1-4 pp. 16, 23 CRM Skills Practice, pp. A13 and A17
26-27	solving word problems involving patterns.	SSG Lessons 1-3, 1-4, pp. 16, 23 CRM Problem-Solving Practice, pp. A14 and A18

Chapter 1 Test Practice

Diagnose Student Errors

Survey student responses for each item. Class trends may indicate common errors and misconceptions.

1. Ⓐ correct
B used 1 instead of 0 as placeholder
C used wrong place value for the number 3
D placed 3 in both place values instead of just the ones place

2. A missing thousands place
Ⓑ correct
C misinterpreted tens place
D misinterpreted hundreds place

3. A guess
B place value misinterpreted; this is the tens place
Ⓒ correct
D place value misinterpreted; this is the millions place

4. A wrong place value of 7
B wrong place values of 6 and 7
C wrong place value of 6
Ⓓ correct

5. A misinterpreted pattern
Ⓑ correct
C miscalculated next number
D misinterpreted pattern

6. A divided instead of multiplied
B misinterpreted question
C multiplied by incorrect rate
Ⓓ correct

7. A numbers are decreasing, not increasing
Ⓑ correct
C miscalculated pattern
D numbers are decreasing, not increasing

8. A miscalculated pattern
B miscalculated pattern
Ⓒ correct
D doubled instead of divided

Chapter 1 Test Practice

Choose the best answer and fill in the corresponding circle on the sheet at right.

1 Which number shows nine thousand three written in standard form?

Ⓐ 9,003 C 9,300
B 9,013 D 9,330

2 $7{,}000 + 60 + 2 =$

A 762 C 7,602
Ⓑ 7,062 D 7,662

3 Which digit is in the thousands place in 7,005,012?

A 0 Ⓒ 5
B 1 D 7

4 Which of these is the number 6,007,017?

A six million, seven hundred, seventeen
B six thousand, seven hundred, seventeen
C six billion, seven million, seventeen
Ⓓ six million, seven thousand, seventeen

5 What is the next number in the sequence?

9, 18, 27, 36, 45, ____

A 50 C 58
Ⓑ 54 D 60

6 Samson can run 2 miles in 10 minutes. If he keeps this pace, how long will it take him to run 4 miles?

A 5 minutes C 15 minutes
B 10 minutes Ⓓ 20 minutes

7 What is the rule for this pattern?

22, 19, 16, 13, 10, 7, 4, 1

A add 4 C subtract 4
Ⓑ subtract 3 D add 5

8 Ducks have 2 legs. Rico is feeding ducks at the pond. He counts 28 duck legs. How many ducks are there?

A 7 ducks Ⓒ 14 ducks
B 28 ducks D 56 ducks

9 The numbers in the pattern increase by the same amount each time. What are the next three numbers in the pattern?

23, 40, 57, 74, ____, ____, ____

A 99, 124, 149
B 86, 98, 110
Ⓒ 91, 108, 125
D 93, 112, 131

GO ON

36 Chapter 1 Test Practice

9. A incorrectly added 25 to previous term
B incorrectly added 12 to previous term
Ⓒ correct
D incorrectly added 9 to previous term

10. Ⓐ correct
B miscalculated, 4 humans + 2 dogs = 16 legs
C miscalculated, 3 humans + 6 dogs = 30 legs
D miscalculated, 5 humans + 4 dogs = 26 legs

11. A guess
B guess
Ⓒ correct
D guess

12. A miscalculation
Ⓑ correct
C miscalculation
D miscalculation

Paige's family is gathered in the living room for family game night. She has a large family and a few dogs. If there is a total of 24 legs in this room, how many humans and how many dogs are there?

- (A) 6 humans, 3 dogs
- B 4 humans, 2 dogs
- C 3 humans, 6 dogs
- D 5 humans, 4 dogs

Stacey bought 5 bottles of hairspray. Each bottle of hairspray cost $2. How much did Stacey spend?

- A $8
- B $12
- (C) $10
- D $14

Valerie bought a watch that was 4 times as much as the hat Bea bought. Bea spent $22. How much did Valerie spend?

- A $80
- (B) $88
- C $84
- D $100

ANSWER SHEET

Directions: Fill in the circle of each correct answer.

1	**A**	B	C	D
2	A	**B**	C	D
3	A	B	**C**	D
4	A	B	C	**D**
5	A	**B**	C	D
6	A	B	C	**D**
7	A	**B**	C	D
8	A	B	**C**	D
9	A	B	**C**	D
10	**A**	B	C	D
11	A	B	**C**	D
12	A	**B**	C	D

Success Strategy

Double check your answers after you finish. Read each problem and all of the answer choices. Put your finger on each bubble you filled in to make sure it matches the answer for each problem.

Diagnosing Student Errors and Misconceptions

Review Understanding place value is the foundation for being able to order numbers. If students are consistently missing problems about place value, have them review the place-value chart and expanded form.

Chapter 2

Chapter Overview

Chapter-at-a-Glance

Lesson	Math Objective	State/Local Standards
2-1 Multiply by 0, 1, 5, and 10 (p. 40-46)	Multiply when one of the factors is 0, 1, 5, or 10.	
2-2 Multiply by 2, 3, 4, and 6 (p. 47-53)	Multiply when one of the factors is 2, 3, 4, or 6.	
Progress Check (p. 54)		
2-3 Multiply by 7, 8, and 9 (p. 55-60)	Multiply when one of the factors is 7, 8, or 9.	
2-4 Multiply by 11 and 12 (p. 61-66)	Multiply when one of the factors is 11 or 12.	
Progress Check (p. 67)		
2-5 Multiply Greater Numbers (p. 68-74)	Multiply when factors have more than one digit.	
2-6 Multiplication and Division (p. 75-80)	Understand that multiplication and division are inverse operations of each other.	
Progress Check (p. 81)		

Content-at-a-Glance

The diagram below summarizes and unpacks Chapter 2 content.

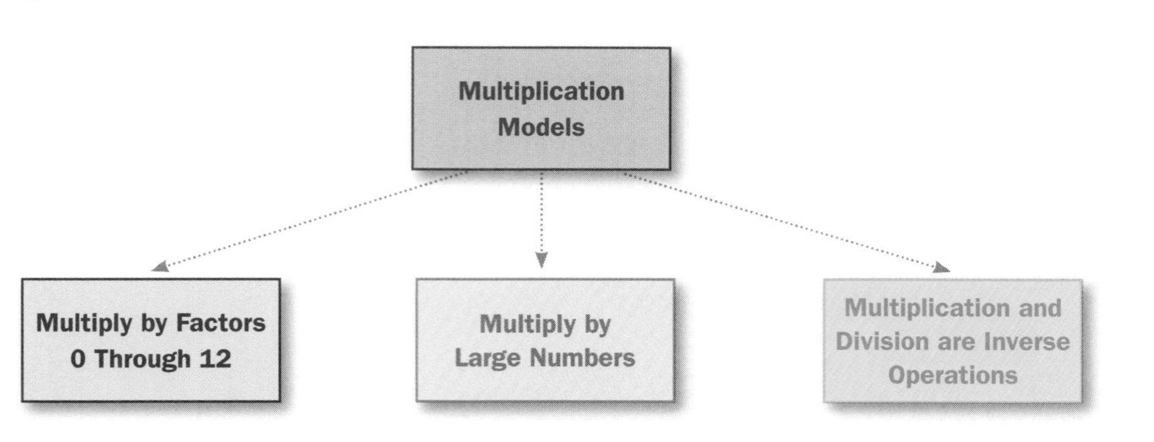

Online Assessment and Reporting
macmillanmh.com

Chapter Assessment Manager

Diagnostic Diagnose students' readiness.

	Student Study Guide/ Teacher Edition	Assessment Masters	Technology
Course Placement Test		1	ExamView® Assessment Suite
Book 1 Pretest		8	ExamView® Assessment Suite
Chapter 2 Pretest		22	ExamView® Assessment Suite
Quiz/Preview	SSG 39		Math Online macmillanmh.com StudentWorks™ Plus

Formative Identify students' misconceptions of content knowledge.

	Student Study Guide/ Teacher Edition	Assessment Masters	Technology
Progress Checks	SSG 54, 67, 81		Math Online macmillanmh.com StudentWorks™ Plus
Vocabulary Review	SSG 82		Math Online macmillanmh.com
Lesson Assessments			ExamView® Assessment Suite
Are They Getting It?	TE 41, 50, 58, 64, 71, 77		

Summative Determine student success in learning the concepts in the lesson, chapter, or book.

	Student Study Guide/ Teacher Edition	Assessment Masters	Technology
Chapter 2 Test	SSG 86	25	ExamView® Assessment Suite
Test Practice	SSG 88	28	ExamView® Assessment Suite
Alternative Assessment	TE 86	31	
See It, Do It, Say It, Write It	TE 46, 53, 60, 66, 74, 80		
Book 1 Test		55	ExamView® Assessment Suite

Back-mapping and Vertical Alignment **McGraw-Hill's *Math Triumphs*** intervention program was conceived and developed with the final result in mind: student success in grade-level mathematics, including Algebra 1 and beyond. The authors, using the **NCTM Focal Points and Focal Connections** as their guide, developed this brand-new series by backmapping from grade-level and Algebra 1 concepts, and vertically aligning the topics so that they build upon prior skills and concepts and serve as a foundation for future topics.

Chapter Resource Manager

	Lesson 2-1	Lesson 2-2	Lesson 2-3	Lesson 2-4
Concept	Multiply by 0, 1, 5, and 10	Multiply by 2, 3, 4, and 6	Multiply by 7, 8, and 9	Multiply by 11 and 12
Objective	Multiply when one of the factors is 0, 1, 5, or 10.	Multiply when one of the factors is 2, 3, 4, or 6.	Multiply when one of the factors is 7, 8, or 9.	Multiply when one of the factors is 11 or 12.
Math Vocabulary	factor Identity Property of Multiplication multiplication product Zero Property of Multiplication	array Commutative Property of Multiplication factor multiplication product	factor multiple product	array Distributive Property of Multiplication pattern(s) product
Lesson Resources	**Materials** • Construction paper • Grid paper **Manipulatives** • Base-ten blocks • Two-color counters **Other Resources** CRM Vocabulary and English Language Development CRM Skills Practice CRM Problem-Solving Practice CRM Homework Practice	**Materials** • Classroom objects • Construction Paper **Manipulatives** • Geoboard • Money • Two-color counters **Other Resources** CRM Vocabulary and English Language Development CRM Skills Practice CRM Problem-Solving Practice CRM Homework Practice	**Materials** • Everyday objects **Manipulatives** • Algebra tiles • Base-ten blocks • Money • Two-color counters **Other Resources** CRM Vocabulary and English Language Development CRM Skills Practice CRM Problem-Solving Practice CRM Homework Practice	**Materials** • Items that come in dozens **Manipulatives** • Algebra tiles • Base-ten blocks • Two-color counters **Other Resources** CRM Vocabulary and English Language Development CRM Skills Practice CRM Problem-Solving Practice CRM Homework Practice
Technology	Math Online macmillanmh.com StudentWorks™ Plus ExamView® Assessment Suite	Math Online macmillanmh.com StudentWorks™ Plus ExamView® Assessment Suite	Math Online macmillanmh.com StudentWorks™ Plus ExamView® Assessment Suite	Math Online macmillanmh.com StudentWorks™ Plus ExamView® Assessment Suite

Student Study Guide
Chapter Resource Masters
Teacher Edition
DVD

	Lesson 2-5	Lesson 2-6
Concept	Multiply Greater Numbers	Multiplication and Division
Objective	Multiply when factors have more than one digit.	Understand that multiplication and division are inverse operations of each other.
Math Vocabulary	estimate partial products method	division fact family inverse operations multiplication
Lesson Resources	**Materials** • Egg cartons • Grid paper • Index cards • Straightedge • Things that come in dozens **Manipulatives** • Base-ten blocks **Other Resources** CRM Vocabulary and English Language Development CRM Skills Practice CRM Problem-Solving Practice CRM Homework Practice	**Materials** • Construction paper • Number line **Manipulatives** • Base-ten blocks • Number cubes • Two-color counters **Other Resources** CRM Vocabulary and English Language Development CRM Skills Practice CRM Problem-Solving Practice CRM Homework Practice
Technology	Math Online macmillanmh.com StudentWorks™ Plus ExamView® Assessment Suite	Math Online macmillanmh.com StudentWorks™ Plus ExamView® Assessment Suite

Intervention Strategy

Multiplication Rolls

Materials needed Multiplication table, Number cube

Step 1

Create a large multiplication table as shown below.

×	1	2	3	4	5	6	7	8	9	10
1	1	2	3	4	5	6	7	8	9	10
2	2	4	6	8	10	12	14	16	18	20
3	3	6	9	12	15	18	21	24	27	30
4	4	8	12	16	20	24	28	32	36	40
5	5	10	15	20	25	30	35	40	45	50
6	6	12	18	24	30	36	42	48	54	60
7	7	14	21	28	35	42	49	56	63	70
8	8	16	24	32	40	48	56	64	72	80
9	9	18	27	36	45	54	63	72	81	90
10	10	20	30	40	50	60	70	80	90	100

Step 2

Students will work in partners or with small groups. One student rolls a number cube. The number rolled is the number of spaces that should be counted on the top horizontal line of the multiplication chart.

Step 3

Another student rolls a number cube. The number rolled is the number of spaces that should be counted down the left vertical column.

Step 4

The two students should say the multiplication problem produced from the rolls out loud. Example: 3×10

Step 5

A third students states the product without looking at the multiplication table. The other students verify the answer.

Step 6

Continue play for several rounds.

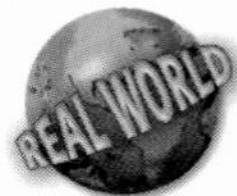

Chapter 2 Chapter Notes

Real-World Applications

Bowling Mr. and Mrs. Rodriguez are opening bowling lanes next to the local post office. They are trying to decide how many bowling pins are needed to fill the lanes. If there are 12 lanes and each lane needs 10 pins, how many pins should they order? They should order 120 pins.

Intervention Strategy

Multiplication Bingo

Step 1 Divide students into pairs.

Step 2 Have students create four bingo cards or provide students with four copies of a bingo card. In each square they must write a product of a multiplication fact. No repeats per card.

Step 3 Each student will need 156 index cards. They will each make a set of multiplication-fact flashcards.

Step 4 As groups finish, combine pairs into groups of four students. Within each game, there will be one caller and three players. Have students take turns using each other's bingo cards and flashcards. Allow each student to be the flashcard caller.

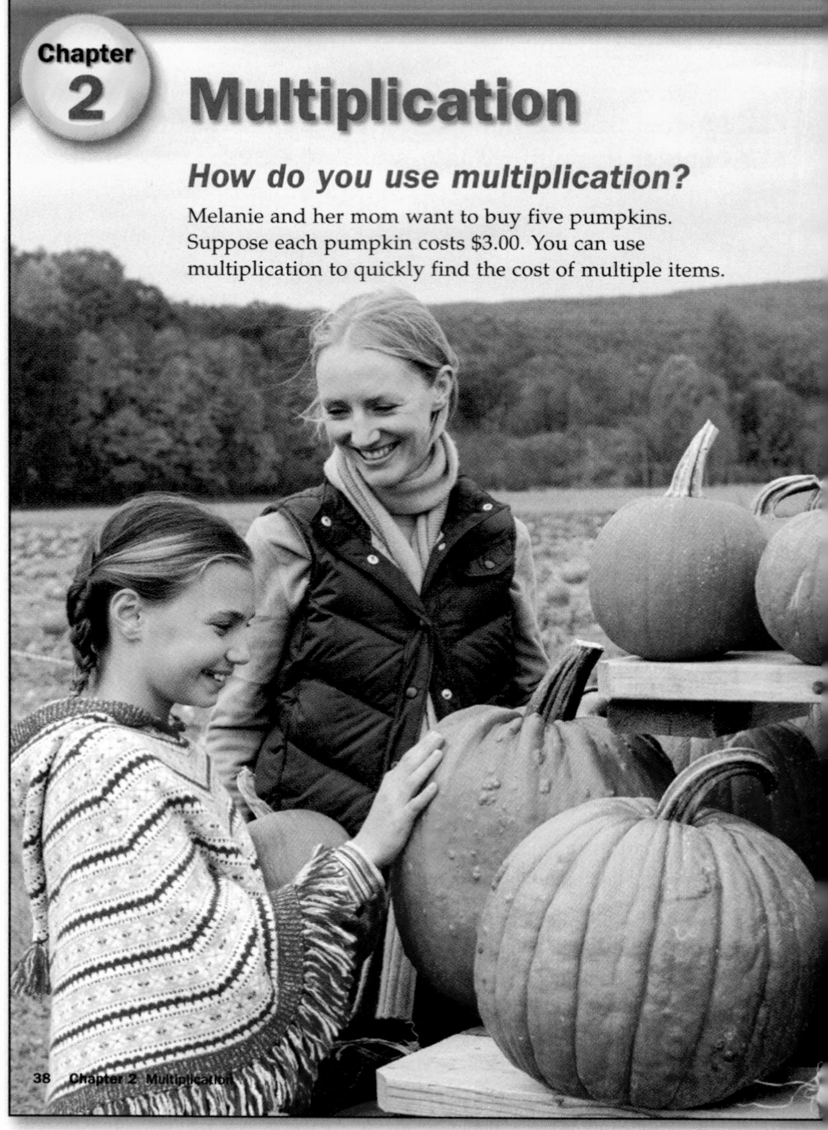

Chapter 2
Multiplication
How do you use multiplication?
Melanie and her mom want to buy five pumpkins. Suppose each pumpkin costs $3.00. You can use multiplication to quickly find the cost of multiple items.
38 Chapter 2 Multiplication

Key Vocabulary

Find interactive definitions in 13 languages in the **eGlossary** at macmillanmh.com.

English **Español** *Introduce the most important vocabulary terms from Chapter 2.*

multiplication **multiplicación**

an operation on two numbers to find their product; it can be thought of as repeated addition (p. 40)

$4 \times 3 = 3 + 3 + 3 + 3$

factor **factor**

a number that divides into a whole number evenly; also a number that is multiplied by another number (p. 40)

$4 \times 3 = 12$ — 4 and 3: factors; 12: product

product **producto**

the answer or result of a multiplication problem; it also refers to expressing a number as the product of its factors (p. 40)

fact family **familia de operaciones**

a group of related facts using the same numbers (p. 75)

$2 + 3 = 5$ $3 + 2 = 5$
$5 - 3 = 2$ $5 - 2 = 3$

$4 \times 3 = 12$ $3 \times 4 = 12$
$12 \div 4 = 3$ $12 \div 3 = 4$

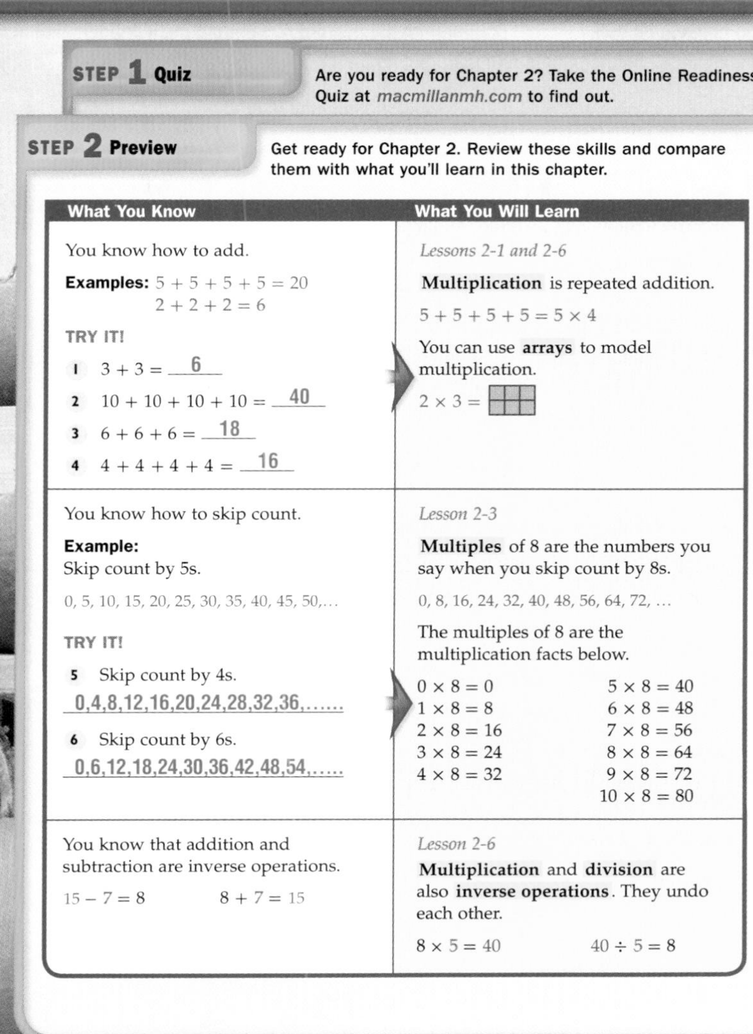

STEP 1 Quiz

Are you ready for Chapter 2? Take the Online Readiness Quiz at *macmillanmh.com* to find out.

STEP 2 Preview

Get ready for Chapter 2. Review these skills and compare them with what you'll learn in this chapter.

What You Know	What You Will Learn
You know how to add. **Examples:** $5 + 5 + 5 + 5 = 20$ $2 + 2 + 2 = 6$ **TRY IT!** **1** $3 + 3 =$ 6 **2** $10 + 10 + 10 + 10 =$ 40 **3** $6 + 6 + 6 =$ 18 **4** $4 + 4 + 4 + 4 =$ 16	*Lessons 2-1 and 2-6* **Multiplication** is repeated addition. $5 + 5 + 5 + 5 = 5 \times 4$ You can use **arrays** to model multiplication. $2 \times 3 =$
You know how to skip count. **Example:** Skip count by 5s. 0, 5, 10, 15, 20, 25, 30, 35, 40, 45, 50,… **TRY IT!** **5** Skip count by 4s. 0,4,8,12,16,20,24,28,32,36,…… **6** Skip count by 6s. 0,6,12,18,24,30,36,42,48,54,…..	*Lesson 2-3* **Multiples** of 8 are the numbers you say when you skip count by 8s. 0, 8, 16, 24, 32, 40, 48, 56, 64, 72, … The multiples of 8 are the multiplication facts below. $0 \times 8 = 0$ $5 \times 8 = 40$ $1 \times 8 = 8$ $6 \times 8 = 48$ $2 \times 8 = 16$ $7 \times 8 = 56$ $3 \times 8 = 24$ $8 \times 8 = 64$ $4 \times 8 = 32$ $9 \times 8 = 72$ $10 \times 8 = 80$
You know that addition and subtraction are inverse operations. $15 - 7 = 8$ $8 + 7 = 15$	*Lesson 2-6* **Multiplication** and **division** are also **inverse operations**. They undo each other. $8 \times 5 = 40$ $40 \div 5 = 8$

39

Vocabulary Preview

- As students complete the Chapter Preview, have each write down five of the key vocabulary words on a strip of paper.
- Students will then fold their strips of paper and place them into a jar called the "Word Jar."
- Walk around the classroom and have students pull strips from the Word Jar. The student should say the word out loud and state the definition. The class should correct any mistakes in the definition.
- Continue the process until the terms become familiar to the students.

Step 1 Quiz

Pretest/Prescribe Students can take the Online Readiness Quiz or the Diagnostic Pretest in the Assessment Masters.

Step 2 Preview

Use this pre-chapter activity to activate students' prior knowledge, build confidence, and help students preview the lessons

Dinah Zike's Foldables®

Guide students through the directions on p. A20 in the Chapter Resource Masters to create their own Foldable graphic organizer to use with this chapter.

Home Connections

- Count the number of pairs of shoes in your closet at home. Multiply the number of pairs by 2 in order to find the total number of shoes in your closet.
- Make a list of all of the perfect squares between 1 and 100.

Professional Development

Targeted professional development has been articulated throughout **McGraw-Hill's *Math Triumphs*** intervention program. **The McGraw-Hill Professional Development Video Library** provides short videos that support the **NCTM Focal Points and Focal Connections.** For more information, visit macmillanmh.com.

Model Lessons

Instructional Strategies

Lesson 2-1 Lesson Notes

Lesson Planner

Objective Multiply when one of the factors is 0, 1, 5, or 10.

Vocabulary **factor**, **Identity Property of Multiplication**, **multiplication**, **product**, **Zero Property of Multiplication**

Materials/Manipulatives base-ten blocks, construction paper, grid paper, two-color counters

Chapter Resource Masters

- CRM Vocabulary and English Language Development (p. A23)
- CRM Skills Practice (p. A24)
- CRM Problem-Solving Practice (p. A25)
- CRM Homework Practice (p. A26)

1 Introduce

Vocabulary

Match Vocabulary Write four problems on the board with one each that requires the Zero Property of Multiplication, the Identity Property of Multiplication, a factor of 5 and a factor of 10. Ask for student volunteers to determine which problem matches each concept.

2 Teach

Key Concept

Foundational Skills and Concepts After students have read through the Key Concept box, have them try these exercises.

1. Why is $12 \times 0 = 0$? because 12 groups of zero is zero
2. How can the Identity Property of Multiplication be used to say $12 \times 1 = 12$? The Identify Property states that any number times one is that number.

Lesson 2-1 Multiply by 0, 1, 5, and 10

KEY Concept

The **Zero Property of Multiplication** states that any number multiplied by zero is zero.

$12 \times 0 = 0$ because 12 groups of zero is zero.

The **Identity Property of Multiplication** states that any number multiplied by 1 is equal to that number.

$12 \times 1 = 12$ because 12 groups of 1 is 12.

Skip count by 5s to say the multiples of 5.

1	2	3	4	5	6	7	8	9	10
5,	10,	15,	20,	25,	30,	35,	40,	45,	50

15 is the third multiple of 5, so $3 \times 5 = 15$.

Skip count by 10s to say the multiples of 10.

$1 \times 10 = 10$	$2 \times 10 = 20$	$3 \times 10 = 30$
$4 \times 10 = 40$	$5 \times 10 = 50$	$6 \times 10 = 60$
$7 \times 10 = 70$	$8 \times 10 = 80$	$9 \times 10 = 90$
$10 \times 10 = 100$		

To multiply by 10, write a 0 to the place on the right of the number.

VOCABULARY

factor
a number that divides into a whole number evenly; also a number that is multiplied by another number

Identity Property of Multiplication
when a number is multiplied by 1, the product is the same as the given number
Example: $8 \times 1 = 8$

multiplication
an operation on two numbers to find their product; it can be thought of as repeated addition

product
the answer or result of a multiplication problem; it also refers to expressing a number as the product of its factors

Zero Property of Multiplication
property that states any number multiplied by zero is zero

The Identity and Zero Properties hold true for numbers of any size. Use skip counting to learn multiplication facts with 5 or 10 as factors.

Example 1

Find the product of 8 and 0.

1. What is the first factor? 8
   What is the second factor? 0
2. Use the Zero Property of Multiplication. Any number multiplied by zero is zero.
3. Write the product.
   $8 \times 0 = 0$

YOUR TURN!

Find the product of 2 and 0.

1. What is the first factor? 2
   What is the second factor? 0
2. Use the Zero Property of Multiplication.
3. Write the product.
   $2 \times 0 = 0$

40 **Chapter 2** Multiplication

Additional Example 1

Find the product of 9 and 0.

1. What is the first factor? 9
   What is the second factor? 0
2. Use the Zero Property of Multiplication. Any number multiplied by zero is zero.
3. Write the product.
   $9 \times 0 = 0$

Example 2

Find the product of 46 and 1.

1. What is the first factor? 46

   What is the second factor? 1
2. Use the Identity Property of Multiplication. Any number multiplied by 1 is equal to the given number.
3. Write the product.

   $46 \times 1 = 46$

YOUR TURN!

Find the product of 69 and 1.

1. What is the first factor? ___69___

   What is the second factor? ___1___
2. Use the Identity Property of Multiplication. Any number multiplied by ___1___ is equal to the given number.
3. Write the product.

   ___$69 \times 1 = 69$___

Example 3

Find the product of 10 and 73.

1. Use the rule for multiplying by 10.

   To multiply by 10, write a 0 to the place on the right of the number.
2. $10 \times 73 = 730$
3. Estimate to check.

   73 is close to 70.

   $10 \times 70 = 700$

   700 is close to 730, so the answer makes sense.

YOUR TURN!

Find the product of 10 and 16.

1. Use the rule for multiplying by 10.

   To multiply by 10, write a ___0___ to the place on the right of the number.
2. $10 \times 16 =$ ___160___
3. Estimate to check.

   16 is close to ___20___.

   $10 \times$ ___20___ $=$ ___200___

   ___200___ is close to ___160___, so the answer makes sense.

GO ON

Additional Example 2

Find the product of 23 and 1.

1. What is the first factor? 23

   What is the second factor? 1
2. Use the Identity Property of Multiplication. Any number multiplied by 1 is equal to the given number.
3. Write the product.

   $23 \times 1 = 23$

Additional Example 3

Find the product of 10 and 57.

1. Use the rule for multiplying by 10.

   To multiply by 10, add 0 to the place on the right of the number.
2. $10 \times 57 = 570$
3. Estimate to check.

   57 is close to 60.

   $10 \times 60 = 600$

   600 is close to 570, so the answer makes sense.

Are They Getting It?

Check students' understanding by writing these problems on the board. Ask the students to point out the wrong answers and explain why they are wrong. Encourage students to include a justification for each step or mistake.

1. $33 \times 0 = 0$ — Zero Product Property of Multiplication
2. $95 \times 1 = 95$ — Identity Property of Multiplication
3. $4 \times 5 = 20$ — Skip count by 5s: 5, 10, 15, 20, 25... . The fourth 5 is 20.
4. $18 \times 10 = 180$ — Add 0 to the place on the right of the number.

Intervention Strategy

Kinesthetic Learners

Use Manipulatives Students may have difficulty visualizing that multiplication is a short form of addition. Prompt students to use coins, beans, and other similar materials to represent the factors, and then solve using the manipulatives.

Additional **Example 4**

Find the product of 5 and 29.

1. Rewrite the problem in a vertical format.

2. Multiply the number in the ones column by 5.

   $5 \times 9 = 45$

   Write the tens digit above the tens column.

   $$\begin{array}{r} {\scriptstyle 4} \\ 29 \\ \times\ 5 \\ \hline 5 \end{array}$$

   Write the ones digit under the ones column as part of the product.

3. Multiply 5 times the digit in the ten column.

   $5 \times 2 = 10$

   Add the 4 regrouped tens for a total of 14 tens.

   $$\begin{array}{r} {\scriptstyle 4} \\ 29 \\ \times\ 5 \\ \hline 145 \end{array}$$

   The product is 145.

4. Skip count to check.

   29×5 is the 29th multiple of 5.

   1 2 3 4 5 .... 27 28 29
   5, 10, 15, 20, 25, ...135, 140, 145

   The 29th multiple of 5 is 145, so the answer makes sense.

Example 4

Find the product of 5 and 15.

1. Rewrite the problem in a vertical format.
2. Multiply the number in the ones column by 5. $5 \times 5 = 25$
   Write the tens digit above the tens column.
   Write the ones digit under the ones column as part of the product.

   $$\begin{array}{r} {\scriptstyle 2} \\ 15 \\ \times\ 5 \\ \hline 5 \end{array}$$

3. Multiply 5 times the digit in the tens column. $5 \times 1 = 5$
   Add the 2 regrouped tens for a total of 7 tens.
   The product is 75.

   $$\begin{array}{r} {\scriptstyle 2} \\ 15 \\ \times\ 5 \\ \hline 75 \end{array}$$

4. Skip count to check. 15×5 is the 15th multiple of 5.
   1 2 3 4 5 6 7 8 9 10 11 12 13 14 15
   5, 10, 15, 20, 25, 30, 35, 40, 45, 50, 55, 60, 65, 70, 75

The 15th multiple of 5 is 75, so the answer makes sense.

YOUR TURN!

Find the product of 5 and 32.

1. Rewrite the problem in a vertical format.
2. Multiply the number in the ones column by 5. $5 \times 2 =$ __10__
   Write the tens digit above the tens column.
   Write the ones digit under the ones column as part of the product.

   $$\begin{array}{r} {\scriptstyle 1} \\ 32 \\ \times\ 5 \\ \hline 0 \end{array}$$

3. Multiply 5 times the digit in the tens column. $5 \times 3 =$ __15__
   Add in the 1 regrouped ten for a total of __16__ tens.
   The product is __160__.

   $$\begin{array}{r} {\scriptstyle 1} \\ 32 \\ \times\ 5 \\ \hline 160 \end{array}$$

4. Skip count to check. 32×5 is the __32nd__ multiple of 5.
   1 2 3 4 5... 29 30 31 32
   5, 10, 15, 20, 25,... 145, 150, __155__, __160__

The 32nd multiple of 5 is __160__, so the answer makes sense.

Who is Correct?

Find the product of 10 and 21.

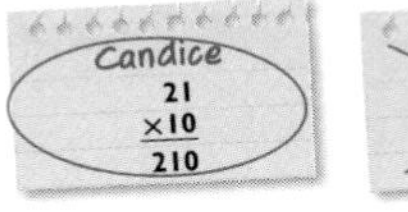

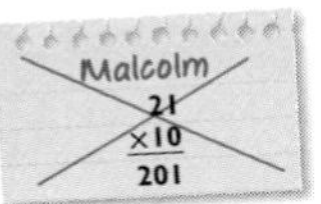

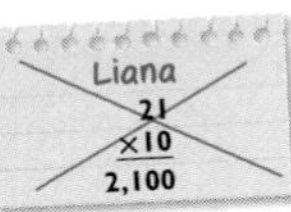

Circle correct answer(s). Cross out incorrect answer(s).

42 Chapter 2 Multiplication

Who *is Correct?*

Diagnostic Teaching

- Candice's answer is correct.
- Malcolm's answer is incorrect. Malcolm did not multiply by 10 correctly.
- Liana's answer is incorrect. She did not multiply by 10 correctly. The answer has one extra 0.

Intervention Strategy Auditory

Solve Out Loud Have the students break up into pairs. Instruct the students to take turns where one partner creates a multiplication problem with one of the factors being 0, 1, 5, or 10 and the other partner solves the problem and justifies his or her answer. Then have the partners switch roles. Encourage the students to listen carefully to each other.

Guided Practice

Use the Zero Property or the Identity Property of Multiplication to find each product.

1. Find the product of 62 × 0.
   What is the first factor? 62
   What is the second factor? 0
   Which property should you use?
   Zero Property of Multiplication
   Write the product. 62 × 0 = 0

2. Find the product of 832 × 1.
   What is the first factor? 832
   What is the second factor? 1
   Which property should you use?
   Identity Property of Multiplication
   Write the product. 832 × 1 = 832

Step by Step Practice

3. Find the product of 5 and 407.

Step 1 Rewrite the problem in a vertical format.

Step 2 Multiply the number in the ones column by 5.
5 × 7 = 35
Write the tens digit above the tens column.
Write the ones digit under the ones column as part of the product.

$$\begin{array}{r} ^{3} \\ 407 \\ \times\ 5 \\ \hline 5 \end{array}$$

Step 3 Multiply 5 times the digit in the tens column.
5 × 0 = 0
Add the 3 regrouped tens for a total of 3 tens.

$$\begin{array}{r} ^{3} \\ 407 \\ \times\ 5 \\ \hline 35 \end{array}$$

Step 4 Multiply 5 times the digit in the hundreds column.
5 × 400 = 2,000

$$\begin{array}{r} ^{3} \\ 407 \\ \times\ 5 \\ \hline 2{,}035 \end{array}$$

Step 5 5 × 407 = 2,035

Common Error *Alert*

Alignment When multiplying larger numbers, many students have difficulty keeping the values in their proper vertical position. To prevent students from making mistakes, suggest that they use grid paper or a straightedge to assist in lining up the factors.

Using Manipulatives

Base-Ten Blocks Use base-ten blocks as a way to show multiplying by 10.

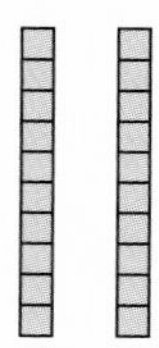

2 × 10

Two-Color Counters Use two colored counters to show multiplication by 3 and 5.

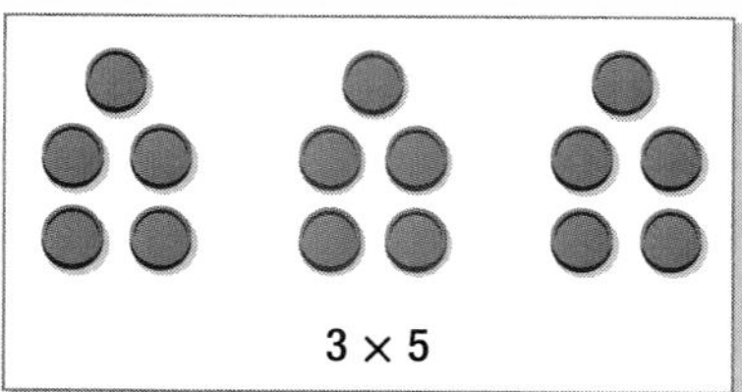

3 × 5

On-Hand Manipulatives Use squares cut out from construction paper as algebra tiles. Grid paper can be used to help students line up their vertical multiplication problems.

Math Coach Notes

Vertical Method Encourage students to line the problem up vertically when multiplying large numbers. This method shows all of the information that the student needs. Remind the students that they need to make sure to carry digits for regrouping when needed.

Note This!

Estimation Stress to students that estimation is an important tool to use to verify the validity of their answers. They should note that this tool is not a substitute for the answer, but it gives them a way to check if their answer is reasonable.

Intervention Strategy
Visual Learners

Drawing Students working in small groups can use drawings to model multiplication problems. Assign each group a product that has 5 or 10 as a factor. Make sure to assign the same product to at least two groups. Have the students complete a drawing to illustrate their product, and then have the groups share their drawing with the class. Show students that the result is the same in each drawing.

Math Coach Notes

Study Tips When memorizing the facts for 5 and 10 encourage students to draw on their experience with skip counting.

English Learner Strategy

Vocabulary In pairs, have the students verbalize a multiplication problem. Have the partner write down the problem, solve it, identify the factors and product, and write the related multiplication fact. Continue by trading roles during the time allotted.

Note This!

Trouble Spots Encourage students to make a notation on their papers whenever they come across a problem that causes them difficulty. They can write a quick note reminding them of what was troublesome. This will help them remember to ask questions when reviewing the work in class.

Find each product. Show your work.

4. $193 \times 0 =$ 0
5. $774 \times 1 =$ 774
6. $10 \times 86 =$ 860
7. $5 \times 34 =$ 170
8. $1 \times 15 =$ 15
9. $0 \times 42 =$ 0
10. $5 \times 20 =$ 100
11. $10 \times 30 =$ 300

Step by Step Problem-Solving Practice

Problem-Solving Strategies
- ☐ Draw a model.
- ☐ Use logical reasoning.
- ☐ Make a table.
- ☑ Solve a simpler problem.
- ☐ Work backward.

Solve.

12. HOUSING A housing development has 5 houses on each acre of land. The development sits on 26 acres of land. How many houses are in the development?

Understand Read the problem. Write what you know.

There are 5 houses on each acre of land.

There are 26 acres of land.

Plan Pick a strategy. One strategy is to solve a simpler problem.

Solve You need to find the product of 5 and 26.
Think: $26 = 20 + 6$. Multiply 5×20 and 5×6.

Multiply 5 times the ones place value. $5 \times 6 = 30$

Multiply 5 times the tens place value. $5 \times 20 = 100$

Add the products. $30 + 100 = 130$

A total of 130 houses are built.

Check You can multiply 5×26 vertically to check.

$$\begin{array}{r} 26 \\ \times\ 5 \\ \hline 130 \end{array}$$

44 Chapter 2 Multiplication

Math Challenge

Divide students into pairs. Each student writes a number that is a multiple of 10 and trades papers with his or her partner. Each student should then write a product with a factor of 5 and a factor of 10 to represent the written number.

Example:

Student 1 writes	Student 2 writes
140 =	14×10 and 28×5

13 SCHOOL Tara is passing out one pencil to each student before a test. There are 10 rows of students. Each row has 8 students. How many pencils will be passed out?

Check off each step.

✓ Understand: I circled key words.

✓ Plan: To solve the problem, I will solve a simpler problem.

✓ Solve: The answer is 80 pencils.

✓ Check: I checked my answer by using repeated addition.

14 PETS Alberto's pet hamster eats 5 food pellets each day. How many food pellets will Alberto's hamster eat in 30 days?

150 pellets

15 **Reflect** How is the product of a number multiplied by 10 similar to the number itself?

It is 10 times the number, so it is the number with a 0 in the place to the right of the original number.

Skills, Concepts, and Problem Solving

Find each product. Show your work.

16 $8 \times 1 =$ 8 17 $6 \times 0 =$ 0 18 $5 \times 6 =$ 30

19 $10 \times 42 =$ 420 20 $5 \times 36 =$ 180 21 $1 \times 50 =$ 50

22 $52 \times 5 =$ 260 23 $0 \times 100 =$ 0 24 $1 \times 200 =$ 200

25 $10 \times 81 =$ 810 26 $5 \times 97 =$ 485 27 $122 \times 1 =$ 122

GO ON

English Learner Strategy

Flash Cards Have students write the English term for the each of the parts of a multiplication problem. On the other side of the card, have students write the words in their native language. Allow students to use these flash cards until they are comfortable with the English words.

Note This!

Use Color Students may be able to retain the concepts better if they are allowed to use color in their notebooks. Explain to them that they should pick a color for, say the Zero Property of Multiplication. All through the section, if they use this color in their notes when referencing the Zero Property of Multiplication, they may remember the concept better.

Odd/Even Assignments

Exercises 16–38 are structured so that students practice the same concepts whether they are assigned the odd or even problems.

In-Class Assignment

Have students complete Exercises 19, 22, 35, 37, and 41 to ensure that they understand the concept.

Intervention Strategy

Interpersonal Learning

Cooperative Learning Form groups of four and assign each person a number from 1 to 4. Have each person supply a sheet of paper that is to be folded in half, twice so that when unfolded, he or she has a sheet of paper with four sections. On the board write the following four questions:

1. $10 \times 37 = ?$ 370
2. $5 \times 18 = ?$ 90
3. $363 \times 1 = ?$ 363
4. $76 \times 0 = ?$ 0

Everyone begins by solving Question 1 on the first section of the paper. Now pass the paper to the right, check the first question, and make corrections where necessary. Then work Question 2 in the second section. Continue this process until all four questions are complete. To ensure that everyone has the correct answers, put the answers on the board and answer any questions.

See It, Do It, Say It, Write It

Step 1 On the board, write 47 × 5 and ask for volunteers to tell you how to evaluate the expression.

Step 2 Give each student a multiplication problem involving factors of 0, 1, 5, and 10. Make sure several students have the same question. Ask students to find the solution, justify their problem, and be prepared to present their problem to the class.

Step 3 Once the students have presented their problem discuss the similarities and differences in the approaches that students took.

Step 4 Ask students to write an explanation of how to multiply when one of the factors is 0, 1, 5, or 10. Have them show sample problems and give a detailed explanation for each.

Looking Ahead: Pre-teach

Multiply by 2, 3, 4, and 6 In the next lesson, students will learn how to multiply by 2, 3, 4, and 6.

Example

Draw an array to model the expression 2 × 3. Find the product.

1. The first factor is 2, so there will be 2 rows. The second factor is 3, so there will be 3 columns, or 3 in each row.

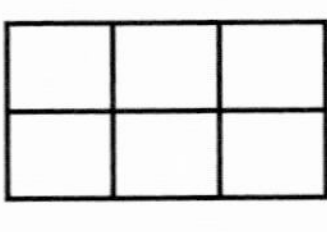

2. Label the array 2 × 3. Count the rectangles. 6
3. Write the multiplication fact. 2 × 3 = 6

Draw an array to model each expression.

1. 4 × 2 8
2. 6 × 3 18
3. 3 × 5 15
4. 2 × 7 14

Find each product. Show your work.

28 26 × 0 = 0

29 98 × 1 = 98

30 14 × 5 = 70

31 73 × 10 = 730

32 1 × 573 = 573

33 10 × 206 = 2,060

34 0 × 841 = 0

35 5 × 190 = 950

36 45 × 1 = 45

Solve.

37 PIANO Julius practices the piano for 45 minutes each day. How many minutes will Julius practice in 10 days?

450 minutes

38 SCHOOL SUPPLIES Ying is buying school supplies. She buys 5 packs of paper. There are 250 pages of paper in each pack. How many pages of paper did Ying buy?

1,250 pages

Vocabulary Check **Write the vocabulary word that completes each sentence.**

39 Multiplication can be thought of as repeated addition.

40 The answer or result of a multiplication problem is the product.

41 Writing in Math When might you need to multiply a number by zero? Give an example and explain.

Sample answer: You multiply a number by 0 when solving a multiplication problem such as 5 × 1,000. You need to know that 5 × 0 = 0 in order to get the answer (5,000).

Ticket Out the Door

Multiply by 0, 1, 5, and 10 As students are leaving the classroom, ask them to give you a multiplication problem whose product uses the Zero Product Property of Multiplication, the Identity Property of Multiplication, or skip counting by 5s or 10s. Alternate these four types of questions. Students will hand in their papers as they exit the classroom.

1. 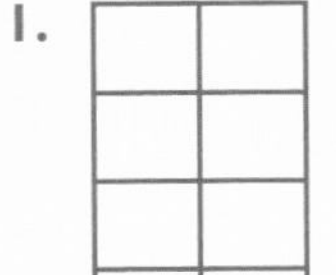
2. 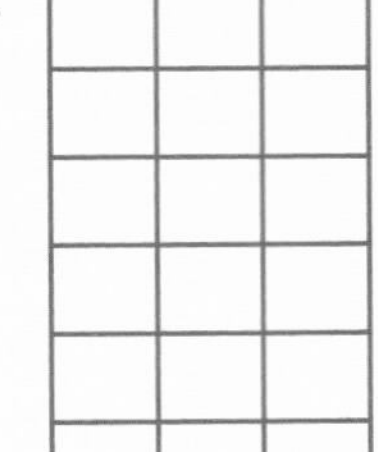
3. 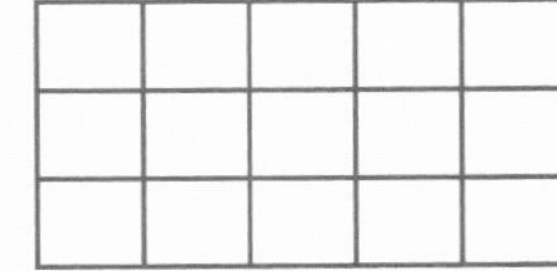
4. 

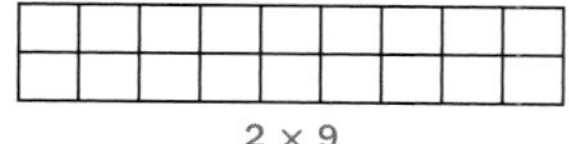

Lesson 2-2 Multiply by 2, 3, 4, and 6

KEY Concept

Multiples are the numbers you say when you skip count.

- Multiples of 2: 2, 4, 6, 8, 10, 12, 14, 16, 18, 20
- Multiples of 3: 3, 6, 9, 12, 15, 18, 21, 24, 27, 30
- Multiples of 4: 4, 8, 12, 16, 20, 24, 28, 32, 36, 40
- Multiples of 6: 6, 12, 18, 24, 30, 36, 42, 48, 54, 60

The **Commutative Property of Multiplication** states that the order of factors does not change the product.

$4 \times 6 = 24$ $6 \times 4 = 24$

You can find 25×6 in different ways.

$$\begin{array}{r} 20 + 5 \\ \times \quad 6 \\ \hline 120 + 30 \\ 150 \end{array} \qquad \begin{array}{r} \overset{3}{2}5 \\ \times 6 \\ \hline 150 \end{array}$$

VOCABULARY

array
objects or symbols displayed in rows of the same length and columns of the same length; the length of a row might be different from the length of a column

Commutative Property of Multiplication
the order in which two numbers are multiplied does not change the product

factor
a number that divides into a whole number evenly; also a number that is multiplied by another number

multiplication
an operation on two numbers to find their product; it can be thought of as repeated addition

product
the answer or result of a multiplication problem; it also refers to expressing a number as the product of its factors

You should practice memorizing the multiplication facts of 2, 3, 4, and 6.

Example 1

Draw an array to model the expression 2×9. Find the product.

1. The first factor is 2, so there will be 2 rows. The second factor is 9, so there will be 9 columns, or 9 in each row.

2×9

2. Label the array 2×9. Count the rectangles. 18
3. Write the multiplication fact. $2 \times 9 = 18$

Additional *Example 1*

Draw an array to model the expression 2×4. Find the product.

1. The first factor is 2, so there will be 2 rows. The second factor is 4, so there will be 4 columns, or 4 in each row.

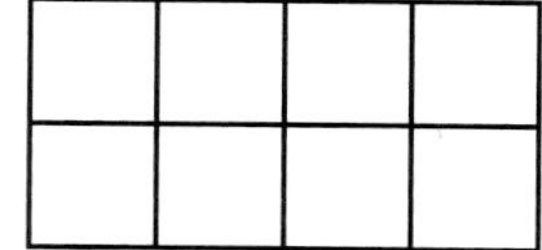

2×4

2. Label the array 2×4. Count the rectangles. 8
3. Write the multiplication fact. $2 \times 4 = 8$

Lesson Notes

Lesson Planner

Objective Multiply when one of the factors is 2, 3, 4, or 6.

Vocabulary **array**, **Commutative Property of Multiplication**, **factor**, **multiplication**, **product**

Materials/Manipulatives classroom objects, construction paper, geoboard, money, two-color counters

Chapter Resource Masters

- CRM Vocabulary and English Language Development (p. A27)
- CRM Skills Practice (p. A28)
- CRM Problem-Solving Practice (p. A29)
- CRM Homework Practice (p. A30)

1 Introduce

Vocabulary

Compare Vocabulary Students should be familiar with many of the words in this lesson. Write the vocabulary words on the board. Have the students form groups and compare the words in the list. Have the students list the commonality of the words.

2 Teach

Key Concept

Foundational Skills and Concepts After students have read through the Key Concept box, have them try these exercises.

1. What are the first 6 multiples of 4 if you are skip counting? 4, 8, 12, 16, 20, 24
2. Using the Commutative Property of Multiplication, how do you write $4 \times 6 = 24$ in another way. $6 \times 4 = 24$
3. What does the Commutative Property of Multiplication say? the order of factors does not change the product

Additional **Example 2**

Find the product of 2 and 76.

1. Rewrite the problem in a vertical format.
2. Multiply the number in the ones column by 2.
   $2 \times 6 = 12$

   Write the ones digit under the ones column as part of the product.

   $$\begin{array}{r} {}^{1} \\ 76 \\ \times\ 2 \\ \hline 2 \end{array}$$

   Write the tens digit above the tens column.
3. Multiply 2 times the digit in the tens column.
   $2 \times 7 = 14$

   $$\begin{array}{r} {}^{1} \\ 76 \\ \times\ 2 \\ \hline 152 \end{array}$$

   Add the 1 regrouped ten for a total of 15 tens.
4. $2 \times 76 = 152$

YOUR TURN!

Draw an array to model the expression 3×8. Find the product.

1. The first factor is 3, so there will be 3 rows.
   The second factor is 8, so there will be 8 columns.

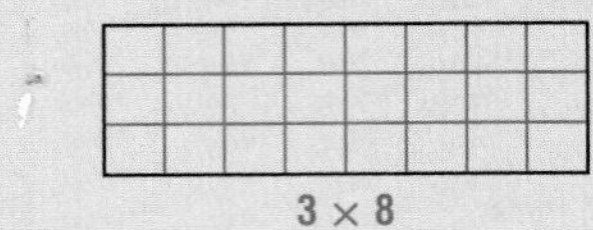

3×8

2. Label the array 3×8. There are 24 rectangles.
3. Write the multiplication fact. 3 × 8 = 24

Example 2

Find the product of 3 and 59.

1. Rewrite the problem in a vertical format.
2. Multiply the number in the ones column by 3. $3 \times 9 = 27$
   Write the ones digit under the ones column as part of the product.
   Write the tens digit above the tens column.

   $$\begin{array}{r} {}^{2} \\ 59 \\ \times\ 3 \\ \hline 7 \end{array}$$
3. Multiply 3 times the digit in the tens column. $3 \times 5 = 15$
   Add the 2 regrouped tens for a total of 17 tens.

   $$\begin{array}{r} {}^{2} \\ 59 \\ \times\ 3 \\ \hline 177 \end{array}$$
4. $3 \times 59 = 177$

YOUR TURN!

Find the product of 4 and 37.

1. Rewrite the problem in a vertical format.
2. Multiply the number in the ones column by 4. $4 \times 7 = 28$
   Write the ones digit under the ones column as part of the product.
   Write the tens digit above the tens column.

   $$\begin{array}{r} {}^{2} \\ 37 \\ \times\ 4 \\ \hline 8 \end{array}$$
3. Multiply 4 times the digit in the tens column.
   $4 \times 3 =$ 12
   Add the 2 regrouped tens for a total of 14 tens.

   $$\begin{array}{r} {}^{2} \\ 37 \\ \times\ 4 \\ \hline 148 \end{array}$$
4. $4 \times 37 =$ 148

48 Chapter 2 Multiplication

Intervention Strategy — Kinesthetic Learners

Repeated Addition If students are having difficulty seeing the connection between repeated addition and multiplication, tell them to use some type of manipulative to illustrate what is occurring.

For example: $4 + 4 + 4 + 4 + 4 + 4$ can be represented by 6 groups of 4 items. If they count all of the items, there will be 24 items. Show students that this is the same as the product 4×6.

Who is Correct?

Find the product of 83 and 6.

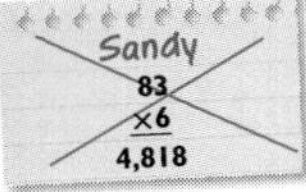

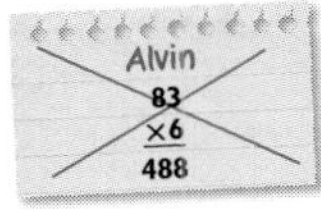

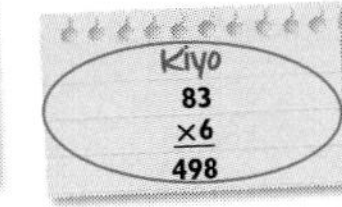

Circle correct answer(s). Cross out incorrect answer(s).

Guided Practice

Draw an array to model each expression. Find each product.

1 $3 \times 6 =$ 18

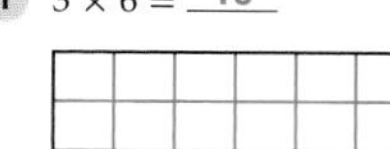

2 $2 \times 4 =$ 8

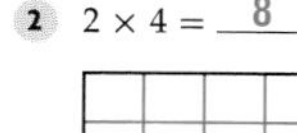

Step by Step Practice

3 Find the product of 77 and 6.

Step 1 Rewrite the problem in a vertical format.

Step 2 Multiply the number in the ones column by 6. $6 \times 7 =$ 42
Write the tens digit above the tens column.
Write the ones digit under the ones column as part of the product.

$$\begin{array}{r} {}^{4} \\ 77 \\ \times\ 6 \\ \hline 2 \end{array}$$

Step 3 Multiply 6 times the digit in the tens column.
$6 \times 7 =$ 42
Add the 4 regrouped tens for a total of 46 tens.

$$\begin{array}{r} {}^{4} \\ 77 \\ \times\ 6 \\ \hline 462 \end{array}$$

Step 4 The product is 462.

Who *is Correct?*

Diagnostic Teaching

- Sandy is incorrect. She did not add the regrouped ten to the product for the tens column; she just wrote the digit after the product.
- Alvin is incorrect. He did not add the regrouped ten to the product for the tens column.
- Kiyo wrote 498. This is correct.

Remind students that when you multiply the ones digits together and you carry a tens digit, you must add that digit to the product that you get from multiplying the ones digit by the tens digit.

Common Error *Alert*

If students are having difficulty seeing the correct solution in the Who is Correct activity, have students start from the beginning and work out the problem themselves. Then compare their work to what is shown to determine the correct solution. This may also help the students who are wrong find their mistakes.

3 Practice

Using Manipulatives

Money Illustrate multiplication with money to help students relate to their everyday lives.

3×2

Geoboards Show how a geoboard can be used to illustrate multiplication.

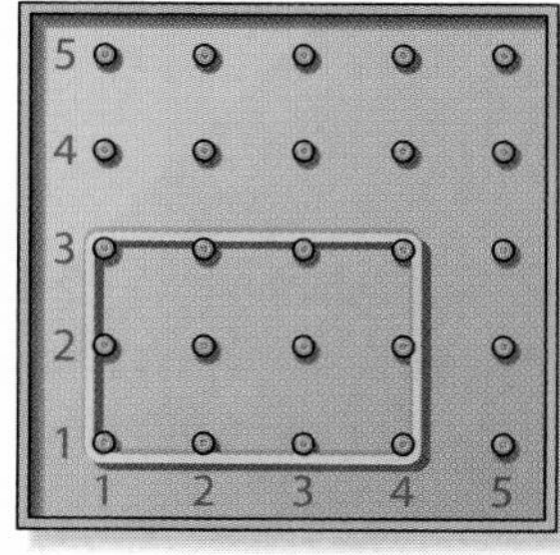

4×3

Two-Colored Counters

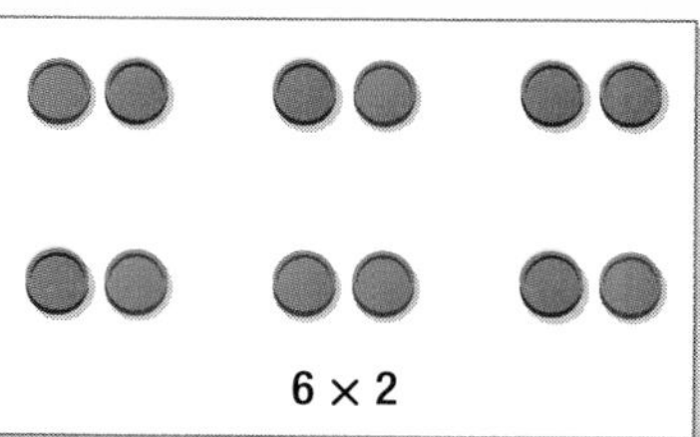

6×2

On-Hand Manipulatives Allow students to use construction paper, beans, or other objects around the classroom as counters.

Note This!

Highlighting It is often helpful for students to highlight important topics in their notes to assist them in studying. Important topics that may be highlighted are definitions, examples, and key words or phrases that may not be familiar.

Intervention Strategy

Visual/Interpersonal Learners

Multiplication Facts Stress to students that memorizing the facts for the multiples of 2, 3, 4, and 6 will help solve multiplication problems more rapidly. Have students make flashcards of the multiples. Then have the students work in pairs to quiz each other using the flashcards.

Math Coach Notes

Strategies Begin the lesson by reviewing the vocabulary *factor*, *multiplication*, and *product*. Recite several multiplication problems involving factors of 2, 3, 4, and 6 and have students write down what they hear. Have students find the correct answer to the problem, and identify the factors and products. Discuss how the students completed the work.

Common Error Alert

Word Problems Students may have a difficult time visualizing what is happening in a word problem. Encourage these students to use manipulatives of any type to model the situation. For example, in Exercise 13 the student could make 19 groups of 4 beans to illustrate the tires needed for the cars.

Find each product. Show your work.

4 $12 \times 2 =$ 24

5 $9 \times 3 =$ 27

6 $7 \times 4 =$ 28

7 $6 \times 6 =$ 36

8 $2 \times 25 =$ 50

9 $3 \times 16 =$ 48

10 $4 \times 51 =$ 204

11 $6 \times 33 =$ 198

12 $3 \times 21 =$ 63

Step by Step Problem-Solving Practice

Solve.

13 CARS A car factory is shipped 19 new car bodies for assembly. With 4 tires needed per car, how many tires are needed to assemble the entire shipment?

Problem-Solving Strategies
- ☐ Draw a model.
- ☑ Use a logical reasoning.
- ☐ Make a table.
- ☐ Solve a simpler problem.
- ☐ Work backward.

Understand Read the problem. Write what you know.
There are 4 tires for each car.
There were 19 car bodies shipped.

Plan Pick a strategy. One strategy is to use logical reasoning.

Solve Think: 19 is close to 20.
$4 \times 20 =$ 80, so the product should be close to 80.

$$\begin{array}{r} 19 \\ \times\ 4 \\ \hline 76 \end{array}$$

76 tires are needed to assemble the entire shipment.

Check Compare the answer to the estimate.

Are They Getting It?

Put the following problems on the board and have the students determine if the answers are correct. If the answers are wrong, have the students explain why the answer is wrong.

1. $5 \times 6 = 30$ This is correct.
2. $2 \times 79 = 160$ This is incorrect. The correct answer is 158.
3. $\begin{array}{r} 54 \\ \times\ 3 \\ \hline 1512 \end{array}$ This is incorrect. The regrouped ten was not added to the product from the tens digits. The correct answer is 162.

14 BIRDS There are 12 bird nests in a tree. There are 6 eggs in each nest. What is the total number of eggs in the tree?

Check off each step.

✔ Understand: I circled key words.

✔ Plan: To solve the problem, I will use logical reasoning.

✔ Solve: The answer is 72 eggs.

✔ Check: I checked my answer by using repeated addition.

15 SCHOOL Mrs. Romero gives stickers to her students when they do well on exams. She estimates that she will need 4 stickers for each student. There are 33 students in Mrs. Romero's class. How many stickers will Mrs. Romero need?

132 stickers

16 **Reflect** How is multiplication like repeated addition? Give an example and explain.

Sample answer: When you multiply, you are repeating one factor the number of times given by the other factor. For example, when you multiply 3×5, you are repeating 3 five times: $3 + 3 + 3 + 3 + 3 = 15$.

Skills, Concepts, and Problem Solving

Draw an array to model each expression. Find each product.

17 $4 \times 5 =$ 20

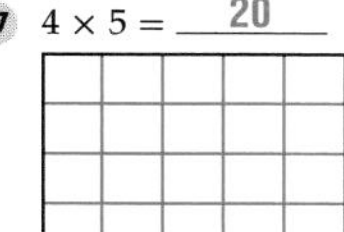

18 $2 \times 5 =$ 10

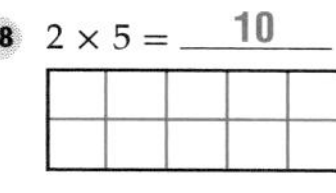

19 $6 \times 3 =$ 18

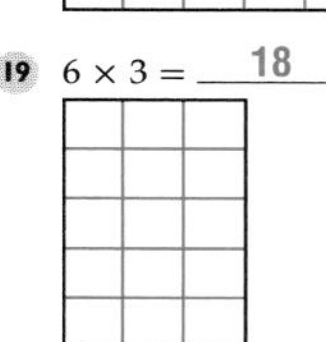

20 $3 \times 4 =$ 12

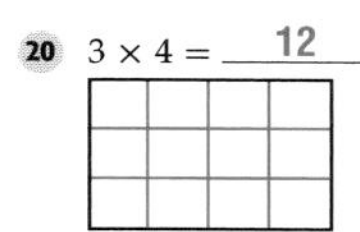

Math Challenge

Money to Multiply Use money to practice multiples of 4. Have students work in pairs. One student will give another student one or more single dollars, which the second student will exchange for quarters. Each time, tell them to write the number sentence that represents the exchange.

Math Coach Notes

Patterns In order to help students to see the patterns that occur with the different multiples, point out the following facts:

1. All multiples of 2 will end in an even number.
2. A number is a multiple of 3 when the sum of its digits is a multiple of 3.
3. All multiples of 4 and 6 are also multiples of 2 and are therefore even.

Odd/Even Assignments

Exercises 17–41 are structured so that students practice the same concepts whether they are assigned the odd or even problems.

In-Class Assignment

Have students complete Exercises 17, 22, 25, 40, and 44 to ensure that they understand the concept.

English Learner Strategy

Guiding Questions Have a large rectangle to use as an array available. Then ask students the following questions.

- What array will show the product 3×7?
- What is the related fact for this product? 7×3
- What is a number sentence for the product of four and thirty-nine? 4×39
- What is the answer to this problem? $4 \times 40 = 160$

Math Coach Notes

Multiplication facts Students should memorize the multiplication facts from this lesson. For example, the multiplication facts for 6 are:

$0 \times 6 = 0$	
$1 \times 6 = 6$	$6 \times 6 = 36$
$2 \times 6 = 12$	$7 \times 6 = 42$
$3 \times 6 = 18$	$8 \times 6 = 48$
$4 \times 6 = 24$	$9 \times 6 = 54$
$5 \times 6 = 30$	$10 \times 6 = 60$

Have them create flashcards for these multiples and for the multiples of 2, 3, and 4, and have students get into pairs and quiz each other.

Draw an array to model each expression. Find each product.

21 $2 \times 4 =$ 8

22 $4 \times 4 =$ 16

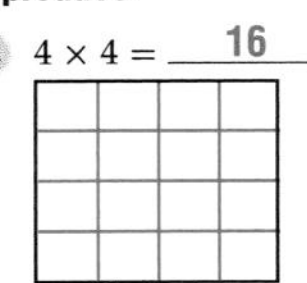

23 $3 \times 3 =$ 9

24 $2 \times 6 =$ 12

Find each product. Show your work.

25 $6 \times 4 =$ 24

26 $3 \times 2 =$ 6

27 $8 \times 2 =$ 16

28 $4 \times 23 =$ 92

29 $3 \times 46 =$ 138

30 $6 \times 63 =$ 378

31 $2 \times 98 =$ 196

32 $73 \times 3 =$ 219

33 $19 \times 4 =$ 76

34 $6 \times 200 =$ 1,200

35 $3 \times 40 =$ 120

36 $55 \times 2 =$ 110

37 $4 \times 493 =$ 1,972

38 $222 \times 6 =$ 1,332

39 $2 \times 99 =$ 198

Intervention Strategy

Auditory Learners It may be difficult for students to memorize the multiplication facts. Encourage students to record themselves reciting the facts and then play back the results when studying. Also suggest to these students that they quietly recite their facts during tests and quizzes if necessary.

40 BICYCLES Mr. Wilson's bicycle shop has 234 bicycles in stock. Each bicycle has 2 wheels. How many wheels are in Mr. Wilson's bicycle shop?

468 wheels

41 TREES Each day, 315 trees are planted in Westin Woods. How many trees will be planted in 6 days?

1,890 trees

Vocabulary Check **Write the vocabulary word that completes each sentence.**

42 Multiplication is an operation on two numbers to find their product.

43 A(n) array is objects or symbols displayed in rows of the same length and columns of the same length.

44 Writing in Math Explain how to use the Commutative Property to write $6 \times 2 \times 3$ three different ways. Solve the problem.

Sample answer: The Commutative Property states that the order of factors does not change the product. So, $6 \times 2 \times 3$ can be written as $2 \times 3 \times 6$, $3 \times 2 \times 6$, or $6 \times 3 \times 2$. The product will be 36.

Spiral Review (Lesson 2-1, p. 40)

Solve.

45 $5 \times 264 =$ 1,320

46 $0 \times 26 =$ 0

47 57×10 570

48 NEWSPAPERS Kerri is delivering newspapers on her paper route. There are 72 houses on Kerri's route. Each house gets 1 newspaper. How many newspapers will Kerri deliver?

72 newspapers

Ticket Out the Door

Commutative Sentences As the students are walking out the door verbally state a product involving a factor of 2, 3, 4, and 6. Ask them to tell you the related facts for the statement. Continue until all of the students have left the classroom.

Common Error *Alert*

Exercise 44 Students may have a difficult time explaining how the Commutative Property applies to a multiplication expression. Encourage them to explain the property in words as if they were explaining the property to a fellow student who missed the lesson.

See It, Do It, Say It, Write It

Step 1 Draw an array on the board. Ask students to determine what two factors the array represents. Write their response as a product. Discuss possible strategies to find the answer.

Step 2 Now give students a number sentence and ask them to create a model that shows the product. Remind students that they can use money, counters, or any other concrete item.

Step 3 Have students discuss the results. Make sure they discuss the related facts for the number sentence.

Step 4 Have students write a summary of the lesson that they could give to a student who is absent. Make sure to remind the students of the importance of illustrations and definitions.

Looking Ahead: Pre-teach

Multiply by 7, 8, and 9 In the next lesson, students will learn how to multiply by 7, 8, and 9.

Example

Use skip counting to find the product of 5×8.

Multiples of 8: 8, 16, 24, 32, 40, 48, 56

$5 \times 8 = 40$ since the 5th multiple of 8 is 40.

Use skip counting by seven to find the products.

1. Multiples of 7: __, __, __, __, __, __, __, __, __, __.
7, 14, 21, 28, 35, 42, 49, 56, 63, 70

2. 2×7 $2 \times 7 = 14$

3. 7×7 $7 \times 7 = 49$

4. 10×7 $10 \times 7 = 70$

Chapter 2 Progress Check 1

Formative Assessment

Use the Progress Check to assess students' mastery of the previous lessons. Have students review the lesson indicated for the problems they answered incorrectly.

Odd/Even Assignments

Exercises are structured so that students practice the same concepts whether they are assigned the odd or even problems.

Common Error Alert

Vertical Alignment It is important for students to remember the proper way to align multiplication problems vertically. In addition, remind students to carry any regrouped tens that occur when multiplying the ones column to the top of the tens column.

Chapter 2 Progress Check 1 (Lessons 2-1 and 2-2)

Find each product. Show your work.

1. $5 \times 7 =$ 35
2. $10 \times 4 =$ 40
3. $2 \times 9 =$ 18
4. $3 \times 4 =$ 12
5. $4 \times 6 =$ 24
6. $6 \times 8 =$ 48
7. $29 \times 0 =$ 0
8. $98 \times 1 =$ 98
9. $5 \times 41 =$ 205
10. $10 \times 17 =$ 170
11. $19 \times 2 =$ 38
12. $27 \times 3 =$ 81
13. $36 \times 4 =$ 144
14. $71 \times 6 =$ 426
15. $92 \times 10 =$ 920

Use the Identity Property of Multiplication to solve.

16. $32 \times$ 1 $=$ 32
17. 1 $\times 192 =$ 192

Use the Zero Property of Multiplication to solve.

18. $418 \times$ 0 $=$ 0
19. 0 $\times 22 =$ 0

Solve.

20. **LUNCH** Tamara eats 5 grapes every day for lunch. How many grapes will Tamara eat in 97 days?
485 grapes

21. **SCHOOL** There are 10 students in Mr. Castillo's class. Each student has 10 fingers. How many fingers do these students have altogether?
100 fingers

54 Chapter 2 Multiplication

Data-Driven Decision Making

Students missing Exercises . . .	Have trouble with . . .	Should review and practice . . .
1–15	finding the product of two numbers.	SSG Lessons 2-1 and 2-2, pp. 40 and 47 CRM Skills Practice p. A24 and A28
16–17	using the Identity Property of Multiplication.	SSG Lesson 2–1 p. 40 CRM Skills Practice, p. A24
18–19	using the Zero Property of Multiplication.	SSG Lesson 2–1 p. 40 CRM Skills Practice, p. A24
20–21	solving word problems involving multiplication.	SSG Lessons 2-1 and 2-2, pp. 40 and 47 CRM Problem-Solving Practice, pp. A25 and A29

Lesson 2-3

Multiply by 7, 8, and 9

KEY Concept

Multiples are the numbers you say when you skip count.

- Multiples of 7: 7, 14, 21, 28, 35, 42, 49, 56, 63, 70
- Multiples of 8: 8, 16, 24, 32, 40, 48, 56, 64, 72, 80
- Multiples of 9: 9, 18, 27, 36, 45, 54, 63, 72, 81, 90

You can find 35×8 in several ways.

30	5	30 + 5	$\overset{4}{35}$
×8	×8	× 8	×8
240	40	240 + 40	280
280		280	

VOCABULARY

factor
a number that divides into a whole number evenly; also a number that is multiplied by another number

multiple
a multiple of a number is the product of that number and any whole number.
Example: 30 is a multiple of 10 because $3 \times 10 = 30$.

product
the answer or result of a multiplication problem; it also refers to expressing a number as the product of its factors

ractice memorizing the multiplication facts f 7, 8, and 9. This will make multiplying wo- and three-digit numbers easier.

Example 1

Use a pattern to find the product of 9 × 9.

1. Skip count by 9s to write the multiples of 9. Facts with 9 make a pattern.
2. Multiples of 9:
   9, 18, 27, 36, 45, 54, 63, 72, 81, 90

$1 \times 9 = 9$	$6 \times 9 = 54$
$2 \times 9 = 18$	$7 \times 9 = 63$
$3 \times 9 = 27$	$8 \times 9 = 72$
$4 \times 9 = 36$	$9 \times 9 = 81$
$5 \times 9 = 45$	$10 \times 9 = 90$

3. $9 \times 9 = 81$

YOUR TURN!

Use a pattern to find the product of 6 × 7.

1. Skip count by 7s to write the multiples of 7.
2. Multiples of 7: 7, 14, 21, 28, 35, 42

$1 \times 7 =$ 7	$6 \times 7 =$ 42
$2 \times 7 =$ 14	$7 \times 7 =$ 49
$3 \times 7 =$ 21	$8 \times 7 =$ 56
$4 \times 7 =$ 28	$9 \times 7 =$ 63
$5 \times 7 =$ 35	$10 \times 7 =$ 70

3. $6 \times 7 =$ 42

GO ON

Additional *Example 1*

Use a pattern to find the product of 8 × 8.

1. Skip count by 8s to write the multiples of 8. Facts with 8 make a pattern.
2. Multiples of 8: 8, 16, 24, 32, 40, 48, 56, 64, 72, 80

$1 \times 8 = 8$	$6 \times 8 = 48$
$2 \times 8 = 16$	$7 \times 8 = 56$
$3 \times 8 = 24$	$8 \times 8 = 64$
$4 \times 8 = 32$	$9 \times 8 = 72$
$5 \times 8 = 40$	$10 \times 8 = 80$

3. $8 \times 8 = 64$

Lesson Notes

Lesson 2-3

Lesson Planner

Objective Multiply when one of the factors is 7, 8, or 9.

Vocabulary **factor**, **multiple**, **product**

Materials/Manipulatives algebra tiles, base-ten blocks, everyday objects, money, two-color counters

Chapter Resource Masters

- CRM Vocabulary and English Language Development (p. A31)
- CRM Skills Practice (p. A32)
- CRM Problem-Solving Practice (p. A33)
- CRM Homework Practice (p. A34)

1 Introduce

Vocabulary

Review Vocabulary Write an expression on the board that contains a factor of 7, 8, or 9. Ask students to identify the factors and the product. Discuss how to use arrays to illustrate a product.

Nonexamples Write an expression on the board and then draw an array that does not represent the product. Discuss how to recognize when an array does not match the product.

2 Teach

Key Concept

Foundational Skills and Concepts After students have read through the Key Concept box, have them try these exercises.

1. If you skip count by 7s, what is the 8th term? What factors would you use to write this product? 56; $7 \times 8 = 56$
2. In how many ways can you find 35×8? 3

Additional **Example 2**

Find the product of 8 and 37. Use doubling.

Double 1 and you have 2. Double 2 and you have 4. Double 4 and you have 8. You can find the product of any number and 8 by doubling the number three times.

1. Double 37. $37 \times 2 = 74$

2. Double the product. $74 \times 2 = 148$

3. Double the product again. $148 \times 2 = 296$

$8 \times 37 = 296$

Common Error *Alert*

Students may have difficulty with the factors of 8 when it comes to doubling. Remind students that they need to double three times to get the correct product. This holds true no matter what the second factor is. For example, to find 8×13, they should find $13 \times 2 = 26$; $26 \times 2 = 52$; and finally $52 \times 2 = 104$. If they check this using the vertical method, they should also get 104.

Example 2

Find the product of 8 and 35. Use doubling.

Double 1 and you have 2.
Double 2 and you have 4.
Double 4 and you have 8.
You can find the product of any number and 8 by doubling the number three times.

1. Double 35. $35 \times 2 = 70$

2. Double the product. $70 \times 2 = 140$

3. Double the product again. $140 \times 2 = 280$

$8 \times 35 = 280$

YOUR TURN!

Find the product of 8 and 49. Use doubling.

Double 1 and you have 2.

Double 2 and you have 4.

Double 4 and you have 8.

1. Double 49. $49 \times 2 = 98$

2. Double the product. $98 \times 2 = 196$

3. Double the product again. $196 \times 2 = 392$

$8 \times 49 = 392$

Who is Correct?

Find the product of 24 and 9.

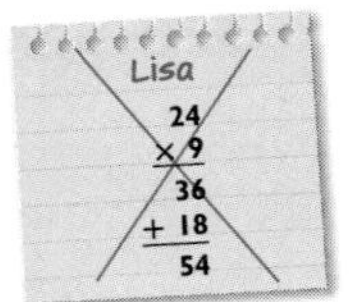

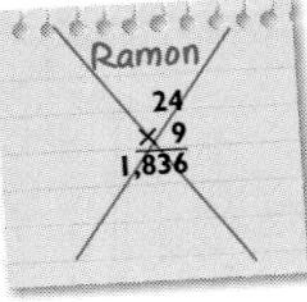

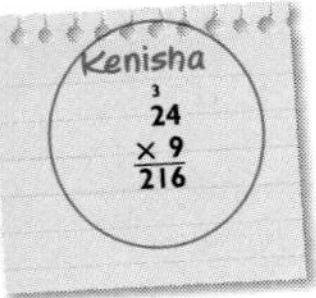

Circle correct answer(s). Cross out incorrect answer(s).

Guided Practice

Use a pattern to find each product.

1. $6 \times 8 =$ 48
   Multiples of 8: 8, 16, 24, 32, 40, 48, 56, 64, 72, 80

2. $7 \times 7 =$ 49
   Multiples of 7: 7, 14, 21, 28, 35, 42, 49, 56, 63, 70

56 **Chapter 2** Multiplication

Math Coach Notes

Multiplication facts Students should memorize the facts from this lesson. For example:

$1 \times 7 = 7$	$6 \times 7 = 42$
$2 \times 7 = 14$	$7 \times 7 = 49$
$3 \times 7 = 21$	$8 \times 7 = 56$
$4 \times 7 = 28$	$9 \times 7 = 63$
$5 \times 7 = 35$	$10 \times 7 = 70$

Have the students create flashcards for the multiples of 7. Then have the students get into pairs and quiz each other.

Who *is Correct?*

Diagnostic Teaching

- Lisa is incorrect. She did not carry the regrouped ones to the top of the tens column.
- Ramon is incorrect. He did not carry the regrouped ones to the top of the tens column.
- Kenisha is correct. She found the product $24 \times 9 = 216$.

Remind students to carefully align the numbers when you multiply large numbers. If the product of the ones column is ten or larger, you write the ones digit of the number under the product and carry the tens digit to the top of the tens column. Then when you multiply the tens digit you add the regrouped value to the product.

Step by Step Practice

3 Find the product of 109 × 8. Use doubling.

Step 1 Double 109.
$$\begin{array}{r} 109 \\ \times\ 2 \\ \hline 218 \end{array}$$

Step 2 Double the product.
$$\begin{array}{r} 218 \\ \times\ 2 \\ \hline 436 \end{array}$$

Step 3 Double the product again.
$$\begin{array}{r} 436 \\ \times\ 2 \\ \hline 872 \end{array}$$

Step 4 109 × 8 = 872

Find each product. Show your work.

4 7 × 5 = 35

5 8 × 7 = 56

6 9 × 6 = 54

7 14 × 7 = 98

8 22 × 8 = 176

9 30 × 9 = 270

10 7 × 501 = 3,507

11 8 × 234 = 1,872

12 9 × 111 = 999

GO ON

Math Challenge

Memory Game Have students work in pairs. One student will write the expressions for the multiples of 8 from 0 through 4 on index cards. The other student will write the expressions for the multiples of 8 from 5 to 10. The products of each expression will be written on separate index cards, so there is a total of 20 cards. Students can shuffle and lay the cards facedown in a 5 by 4 array to make a memory game. One student will turn two cards. If they are equal, the student keeps the card. If they are not equal, the cards are turned facedown. When all the cards are removed, the student with the most cards wins.

3 Practice

Using Manipulatives

Algebra Tiles Use algebra tiles to show multiples.

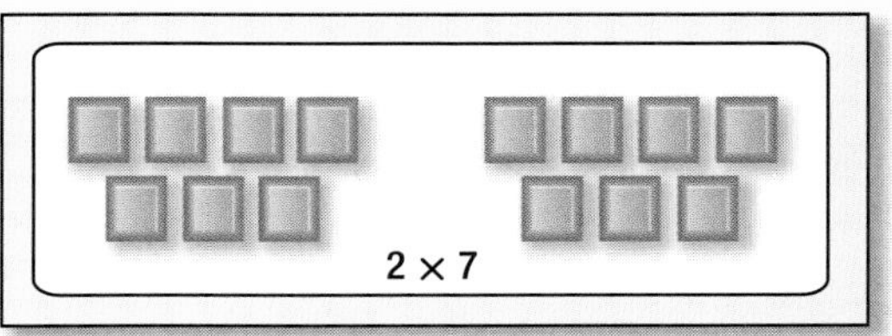

Base-Ten Blocks

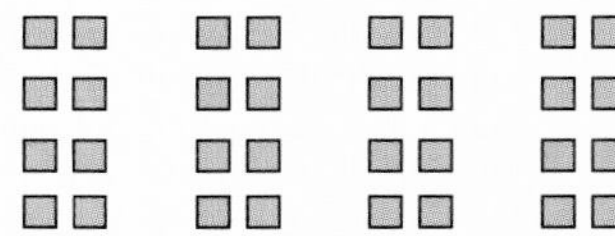

4 × 8

Two-Color Counters Counters or other everyday objects can be used to show the multiples of 7, 8, and 9

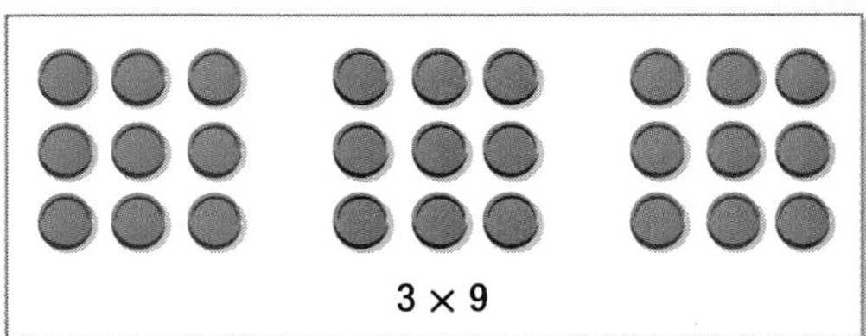

On-Hand Manipulatives Use coins, beans, or other everyday objects as counters.

Note This!

Word Diagram Tell students to write the word *multiplication* in the center of a sheet of paper. Then ask them to draw rays off the word and write all the words that they can think of that relate to *multiplication*. The words they choose should include *factor*, *multiple*, *product*, *multiplication fact*, *Commutative Property*, and so on. Ask students to discuss the meaning of each.

Intervention Strategy

Logical/ Visual Learners

Patterns In addition to memorizing the facts for the multiples of 9, it is important for students to recognize that a unique pattern exists. Have the students write the multiples of 9 from 1 through 10. Now have students add the digits in each product together. Ask the students to describe what they find. They should see each sum is 9. This is always true for any multiple of 9.

Note This!

Taking Notes One of the biggest obstacles for students taking good notes is distractions. When they are distracted, they may miss important information. Suggest that these students take steps to ensure their notes are complete. One strategy is to tape the discussion. They can review their notes later while listening to make certain their notes are complete.

English Learner Strategy

Products of Pennies Use pennies as counters. Have 90 pennies available. Count out 9 pennies. Write $9 \times 1 = 9$ on the board. Say "one group of 9 pennies is 9 cents." Repeat with 18 pennies, saying "two groups of 9 pennies is 18 cents." Then ask students to represent 9×3 with the pennies. Guide students to see that the factor 9 is the number of pennies in each group. The other factor is the number of groups. The product is the total number of pennies.

Intervention Strategy

Linguistic/ Interpersonal Learners

Multiplication Strategies Have students work in groups of four. Give a problem to each group, such as 391×7. Ask them to find the product using a strategy discussed in class. Tell them to use concrete materials or illustrations. Then have each group present their strategies and answers to the rest of the class.

Step by Step Problem-Solving Practice

Problem-Solving Strategies
- ☐ Draw a model.
- ☐ Use logical reasoning.
- ☑ Make a table.
- ☐ Solve a simpler problem.
- ☐ Work backward.

Solve.

13 BASKETBALL The Rockville City basketball league ends their season with an awards banquet. There are 14 teams in the league, each with 9 players. How many players will be invited to the awards banquet?

Understand Read the problem. Write what you know.
There are 14 basketball teams.
There are 9 players on each team.

Plan Pick a strategy. One strategy is to make a table. Make a table with two rows. Title one row "teams" and the other row "players."

Solve Write 1 through 14 for teams, because there are 14 teams in the league. There are 9 players on each team, so add 9 each time.

Teams	1	2	3	4	5	6	7	8	9	10	11	12	13	14
Players	9	18	27	36	45	54	63	72	81	90	99	108	117	126

Check Multiply 14×9 to check your answer.

$$\begin{array}{r} 14 \\ \times\ 9 \\ \hline 126 \end{array}$$

14 SCHOOL The lunch room at Central School has 7 tables. Eight students can sit at each table. If all the seats are filled, how many students will be sitting in the lunch room?

Check off each step.

✓ Understand: I circled key words.

✓ Plan: To solve this problem, I will make a table.

✓ Solve: The answer is 56 students.

✓ Check: I checked my answer by using a pattern.

58 Chapter 2 Multiplication

Are They Getting It?

Check students' understanding of multiplying by 7, 8, and 9 by writing these problems on the board. Ask them to point out wrong answers and explain why they are wrong.

1. $7 \times 8 = 56$ This is correct.
2. When using doubling to find the product of 8 and 14, you get 16, then 32 and finally 64. So $8 \times 14 = 64$. This is incorrect. You need to double 14, three times, not 8. You should get 28, 56, and 112. $8 \times 14 = 112$
3. $9 \times 6 = 45$ This is incorrect. The product is 54, not 45.

15 WALKING Nawat walks 4 miles per hour. If Nawat walks for 7 hours, how far will he have walked? Show your work.

28 miles

16 **Reflect** Explain the Commutative Property. Use the example $7 \times 8 = 56$ in your explanation.

Sample answer: According to the Commutative Property, the product is the same regardless of the order of the factors. So, the equation 7×8 can be written as 8×7 without changing the answer, 56.

Skills, Concepts, and Problem Solving

Use patterns to find each product.

17 $7 \times 10 =$ 70
Multiples of 7: 7, 14, 21, 28, 35, 42, 49, 56, 63, 70

18 $8 \times 8 =$ 64
Multiples of 8: 8, 16, 24, 32, 40, 48, 56, 64, 72, 80

19 $9 \times 9 =$ 81
Multiples of 9: 9, 18, 27, 36, 45, 54, 63, 72, 81, 90

Find each product. Show your work.

20 $7 \times 3 =$ 21
21 $8 \times 5 =$ 40
22 $9 \times 4 =$ 36

23 $2 \times 7 =$ 14
24 $6 \times 8 =$ 48
25 $3 \times 9 =$ 27

26 $9 \times 20 =$ 180
27 $7 \times 11 =$ 77
28 $8 \times 26 =$ 208

29 $49 \times 8 =$ 392
30 $29 \times 7 =$ 203
31 $99 \times 9 =$ 891

32 $880 \times 8 =$ 7,040
33 $211 \times 7 =$ 1,477
34 $6 \times 109 =$ 654

Lesson 2-3 Multiply by 7, 8, and 9 59

Intervention Strategy

Interpersonal/ Naturalist Learners

Real-World Problems There are many products whose price includes the digit 9. Groceries and gasoline are two common examples. Have students gather information on items that include one or more 9s in their price. If possible have students bring in the products. Using these products, have them write a variety of number sentences that require multiplying the prices by single- and double-digits numbers. For example, a student brings in a box of cereal that costs $1.99. She writes a word problem that says, "There are 12 boxes of cereal that cost $1.99 each. How much is the total cost?" Have students trade and solve their word problems with another group.

Math Coach Notes

Multiplication facts Students should memorize the facts from this lesson.

$1 \times 8 = 8$	$6 \times 8 = 48$
$2 \times 8 = 16$	$7 \times 8 = 56$
$3 \times 8 = 24$	$8 \times 8 = 64$
$4 \times 8 = 32$	$9 \times 8 = 72$
$5 \times 8 = 40$	$10 \times 8 = 80$

Have the students create flashcards for the multiples of 8. Then have the students get into pairs and quiz each other.

Note This!

Note-Taking Strategies Some students write so carelessly that they are unable to read their notes when they study. These students need to slow down. Have them practice writing legibly. Then help them focus on key words and concepts so that they can eliminate extra note-taking. Remind them that the secret to taking good notes is to write as little as possible to express the information clearly.

Odd/Even Assignments

Exercises 17–36 are structured so that students practice the same concepts whether they are assigned the odd or even problems.

In-Class Assignment

Have students complete Exercises 17, 20, 21, 29, 36, and 39 to ensure that they understand the concept.

4 Assess

See It, Do It, Say It, Write It

Step 1 Write 63 on the board. What factor along with 9 has a product of 63? Do this several times with the multiples of 7, 8, and 9 and have the students find the missing factor.

Step 2 Give each pair of students a multiplication fact for 7, 8, or 9. Tell them to model the expression using concrete materials or pictorial models.

Step 3 Ask students to share their work. Discuss their results.

Step 4 Tell students to write the multiples of 7 as quickly as possible. Repeat with the multiples of 8 and 9.

Looking Ahead: Pre-teach

Multiplying by 11 and 12 In the next lesson, students will learn how to multiply by 11 and 12.

Example

Use a table to complete the pattern for the factors of 11.

1	× 11 =	11
2	× 11 =	22
3	× 11 =	33
4	× 11 =	44

The pattern for 11s is the digit repeated.

Use the pattern for 11s to find each product.

1. 5 × 11 55

2. 8 × 11 88

3. 7 × 11 77

35 BABYSITTING Camellia earns $8 an hour babysitting. If Camellia works for 6 hours, how much will she have earned?

$48

36 BAKING Al's bakery has 35 baskets full of rolls. Each basket has 9 rolls inside. How many rolls are there all together?

315 rolls

Vocabulary Check **Write the vocabulary word or words that complete each sentence.**

37 A(n) multiple of a number is the product of that number and any whole number.

38 The answer or result of a multiplication problem is called the product.

39 Writing in Math Write the multiples of 9 from 1 to 10. Explain any pattern in the products.

Sample answer: Multiples of 9: 9, 18, 27, 36, 45, 54, 63, 72, 81, 90. As the number in the tens place of each two-digit product increases by 1, the number in the ones place decreases by 1.

Spiral Review (Lessons 2-1, p. 40 and 2-2, p. 47)

Find each product.

40 5 × 44 = 220

41 0 × 999 = 0

42 92 × 3 = 276

Solve. (Lesson 2-2, p. 47)

43 BASEBALL CARDS Luther bought 6 packs of baseball trading cards. There are 4 cards in each pack. How many cards did Luther buy?

24 cards

STOP

60 **Chapter 2** Multiplication

Ticket Out the Door

A-B Matchup Take a stack of index cards, one for each student. Write an equal number of As and Bs on the back of each card. Then write expressions for the multiples of 7, 8, and 9 on the A cards and the products on the B cards. Hand them out randomly. Tell students to find their partner (i.e., the student with an equivalent half of the equation). Now have each pair of students come to the front and say a word problem that could be solved with their equation. For example, if the students' equation is 8 × 2 = 16, their problem may be, "There are 8 candles in each package; how many candles are in 2 packages?" After the last pair of students presents, they may exit the classroom.

Multiply by 11 and 12

KEY Concept

When multiplying by 11 and 12, you can use **patterns** and **array** models.

Multiply by 11		
1	× **11** =	11
2	× **11** =	22
3	× **11** =	33
4	× **11** =	44
5	× **11** =	55
6	× **11** =	66
7	× **11** =	77
8	× **11** =	88
9	× **11** =	99

The table shows that when a single-digit number is multiplied by 11, the **product** is the digit repeated.

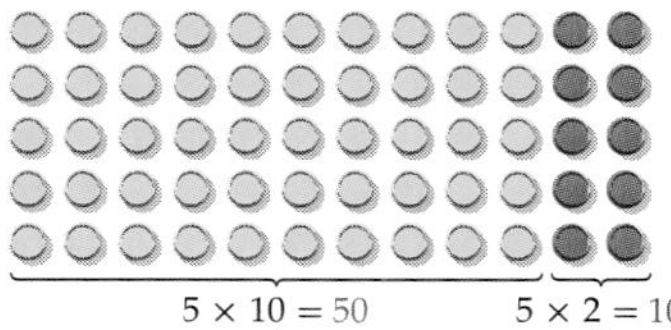

The array model shows that you can think of 12 × 5 as (10 × 5) + (2 × 5). This is the **Distributive Property of Multiplication**.

VOCABULARY

array
a display of objects or symbols in rows of the same length and columns of the same length

Distributive Property of Multiplication
to multiply a sum by a number, multiply each addend by the number and add the products

pattern(s)
a sequence of numbers, figures, or symbols that follows a rule or design

product
the answer to a multiplication problem; it also refers to expressing a number as the product of its factors

Use array models, patterns, or the Distributive Property of Multiplication to multiply by 11 and 12.

GO ON

English Learner Strategy

Guiding Questions Write 6 × 11 on the board. Then ask students the following questions to check if they understand how to use the pattern.

- What are the factors?
- How would you use the table to complete the pattern?

1	× 11 =	11
2	× 11 =	22
3	× 11 =	33
4	× 11 =	44
5	× 11 =	55
6	× 11 =	66

- What is the pattern for 11s? the digit is repeated

Lesson Notes

Lesson 2-4

Lesson Planner

Objective Multiply when one of the factors is 11 or 12.

Vocabulary **array**, **Distributive Property of Multiplication**, **pattern(s)**, **product**

Materials/Manipulatives algebra tiles, base-ten blocks, items that come in dozens, two-color counters

Chapter Resource Masters

- CRM Vocabulary and English Language Development (p. A35)
- CRM Skills Practice (p. A36)
- CRM Problem-Solving Practice (p. A37)
- CRM Homework Practice (p. A38)

1 Introduce

Vocabulary

Interaction Vocabulary Write 12 × 2 on the board. What is the product? Then write 12 × 10 and ask the product. Now write 12 × 12 on the board. What is the product? Show students that 12 × 12 can be written in distributive form as (10 × 12) + (2 × 12). This gives you 120 + 24 = 144. Explain that by creating a simpler problem and using the Distributive Property, the end result draws on what the students already know.

2 Teach

Key Concept

Foundational Skills and Concepts After students have read through the Key Concept box, have them try these exercises.

1. What is the product of 7 and 11? 77
2. What is the product of 5 and 12? 60
3. How do you remember the pattern for 11s? The pattern for 11s is the digit repeated.

Additional **Example 1**

Use a pattern to find 5 × 11.

1. Use a table to complete the pattern.

1	× 11 =	11
2	× 11 =	22
3	× 11 =	33
4	× 11 =	44
5	× 11 =	55
6	× 11 =	66
7	× 11 =	77
8	× 11 =	88
9	× 11 =	99

2. 5 × 11 = 55

Additional **Example 2**

Use an array model to find 12 × 9.

1. Rewrite 12 × 9 as (10 × 9) + (2 × 9). Then use the Distributive Property.

2. Draw an array using two sets of counters.

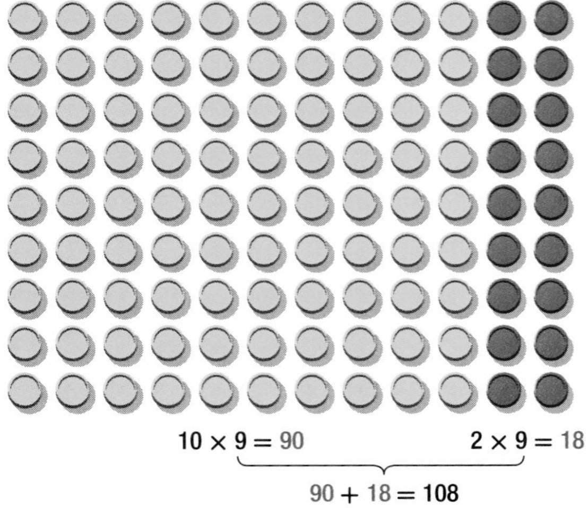

3. The array shows 10 × 9 = 90 and 2 × 9 = 18. So, 90 + 18 = 108.

4. 12 × 9 = 108

Example 1

Use a pattern to find 8 × 11.

1. Use a table to complete the pattern.

1	× 11 =	11
2	× 11 =	22
3	× 11 =	33
4	× 11 =	44
5	× 11 =	55
6	× 11 =	66
7	× 11 =	77
8	× 11 =	88

2. 8 × 11 = **88**

YOUR TURN!

Use a pattern to find 8 × 12.

1. Use a table to complete the pattern.

1	× 12 =	12
2	× 12 =	24
3	× 12 =	36
4	× 12 =	48
5	× 12 =	60
6	× 12 =	72
7	× 12 =	84
8	× 12 =	96

2. 8 × 12 = 96

Example 2

Use an array model to find 12 × 7.

1. Rewrite 12 × 7 as (10 × 7) + (2 × 7). Then use the Distributive Property.
2. Draw an array using two sets of counters.

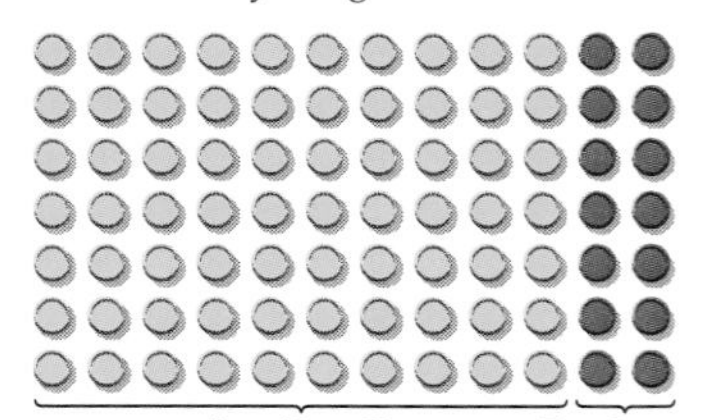

70 + 14 = **84**

3. The array shows 10 × 7 = 70 and 2 × 7 = 14. So, 70 + 14 = 84.
4. 12 × 7 = 84

YOUR TURN!

Use an array model to find 12 × 4.

1. Rewrite 12 × 4.
   (10 × 4) + (2 × 4)
2. Draw an array using two sets of counters.

3. The array shows 10 × 4 = 40 and 2 × 4 = 8. So, 40 + 8 = 48.
4. 12 × 4 = 48

Intervention Strategy

Interpersonal/ Visual Learners

Distributive Form Students can work in small groups. Assign each group two products; one that is a factor of 11 and one that is a factor of 12. Have each group rewrite the products using distributive form. Then have the groups use two sets of counters to show their product. Ask a member of each group to draw one of their models on the board. When all of the groups have completed their work, ask the class to determine what product each model represents.

Who is Correct?

Find the product of 11 and 10.

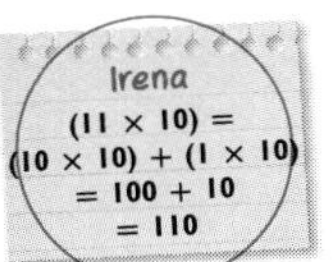

Circle correct answer(s). Cross out incorrect answer(s).

Guided Practice

Rewrite the factors in distributive form.

1. 12×3
   $12 \times 3 = (10 \times 3) + (2 \times 3)$
2. 12×6
   $12 \times 6 = (10 \times 6) + (2 \times 6)$

Step by Step Practice

3. Use an array model to find 11×5.

Step 1 Rewrite 11×5.
(10 × 5) + (1 × 5)

Step 2 Draw an array using two sets of counters.

Step 3 $11 \times 5 = (10 \times 5) + (1 \times 5)$
$= 50 + 5$
$= 55$

GO ON

Lesson 2-4 Multiply by 11 and 12 63

Who *is Correct?*

Diagnostic Teaching

- Irena wrote 110. This is correct.
- Amos is incorrect. When he multiplied 10 by 0 instead of 1.
- Gabe is incorrect. He multiplied 10 by 1 and got 100 instead of 10.

Remind students to write products carefully when using distributive form.

Common Error *Alert*

Distributive Form Students may become confused about which factor to split into a sum and which factor stays the same in each piece of the distributive form. The 11 or 12 term is the one that should be split into a sum of 10 and either 1 or 2. The other factor should remain the same in each piece of the distributive form.

3 Practice

Using Manipulatives

On-Hand Manipulatives Use containers of items that come in a dozen, such as eggs, bakery items, and pencils.

2 × 12

Algebra Tiles

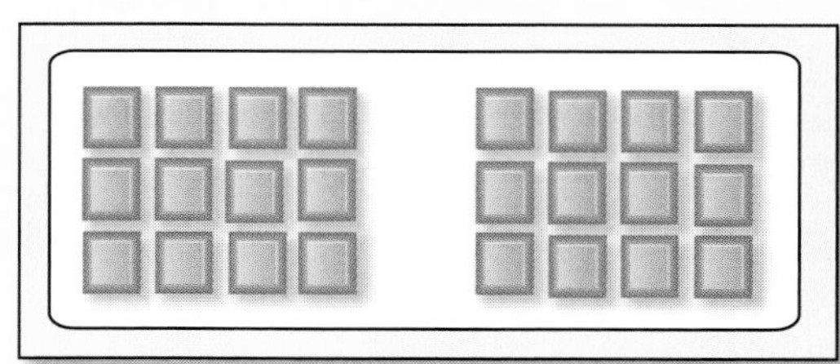

2 × 12

Two-Color Counters

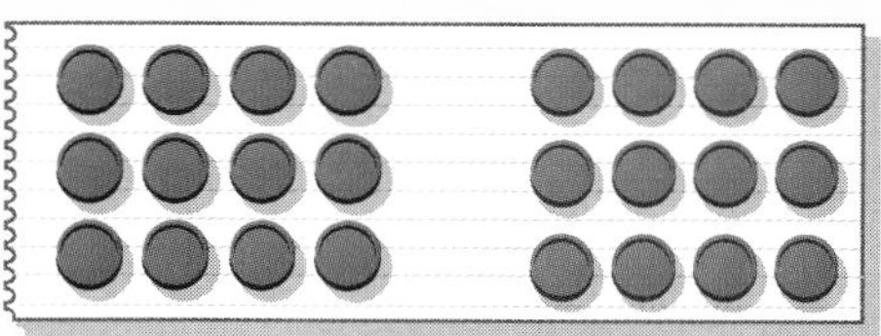

2 × 12

Base-Ten Blocks

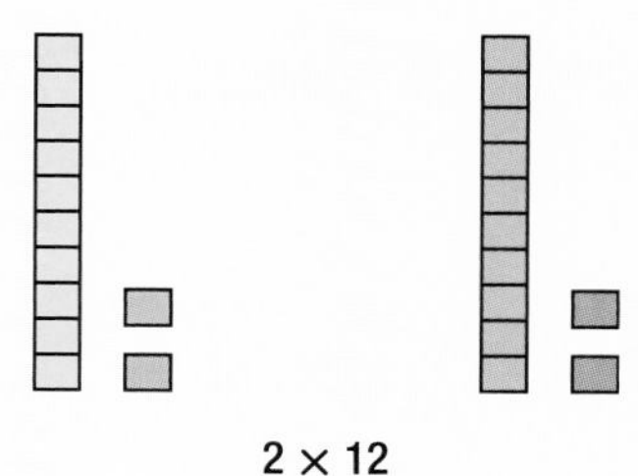

2 × 12

Math Coach Notes

Multiplication Facts Encourage students to memorize these facts for this lesson.

Multiplication Facts for 11

$1 \times 11 = 11$	$6 \times 11 = 66$
$2 \times 11 = 22$	$7 \times 11 = 77$
$3 \times 11 = 33$	$8 \times 11 = 88$
$4 \times 11 = 44$	$9 \times 11 = 99$
$5 \times 11 = 55$	$10 \times 11 = 110$

Multiplication Facts for 12

$1 \times 12 = 12$	$6 \times 12 = 72$
$2 \times 12 = 24$	$7 \times 12 = 84$
$3 \times 12 = 36$	$8 \times 12 = 96$
$4 \times 12 = 48$	$9 \times 12 = 108$
$5 \times 12 = 60$	$10 \times 12 = 120$

Intervention Strategy

Kinesthetic/ Naturalist Learners

Egg Carton Math Have students bring in empty egg cartons. Use the cartons to model the multiples of 12. Hold up two cartons and ask: How many eggs would there be if these were full? Practice with a different number of cartons each time. Use the cartons to set up missing number sentences on the board. For example, write $6 \times \square = 72$. What is $\square$, if $\square$ = the number of eggs in a carton? Have students write their own number sentences and present them to the class.

Common Error *Alert*

Exercise 5 Students may have difficulty with Exercise 5 because they have not seen a problem where both factors contain two digits. Stress that the process is the same. It may be useful for students to use an array model for this problem if they are having difficulty finding the solution.

Use an array model to find the product.

4. $12 \times 9 =$ 108

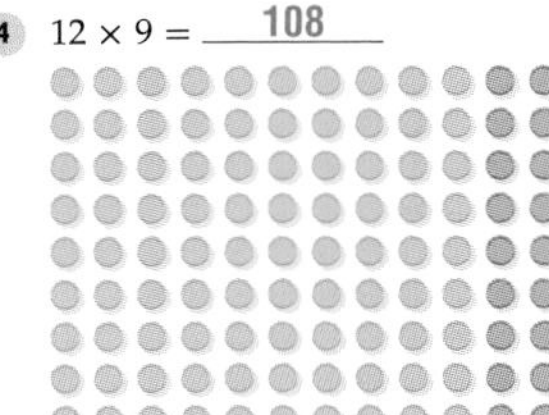

5. $11 \times 12 =$ 132

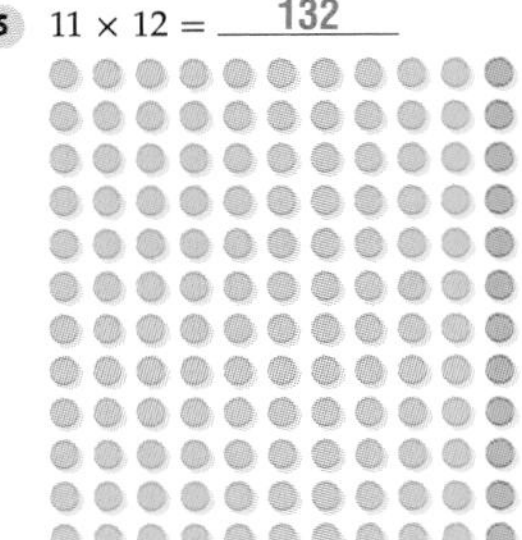

Find each product. Show your work.

6. $8 \times 11 =$ 88

7. $6 \times 12 =$ 72

8. $12 \times 10 =$ 120

9. $11 \times 7 =$ 77

Step by Step Problem-Solving Practice

Problem-Solving Strategies
- ☐ Draw a picture.
- ☐ Use logical reasoning.
- ☑ Solve a simpler problem.
- ☐ Work backward.
- ☐ Make a table.

Solve.

10. INTERIOR DESIGN Derrick's room is 11 feet by 10 feet. How many square feet of carpeting does Derrick need to carpet his room?

Understand — Read the problem. Write what you know.

The room is 11 by 10 feet.

Plan — Pick a strategy. One strategy is solve a simpler problem.

Solve — Write 11×10 using the Distributive Property.

$(10 \times 10) + (1 \times 10)$

Add the products. $100 + 10 = 110$

Derrick needs 110 square feet of carpet.

Check — You can skip count by 10s to the 11th number.

64 Chapter 2 Multiplication

Are They Getting It?

Check students' understanding of multiplying by 11 and 12 by writing these problems on the board. Ask students to point out wrong answers and explain why they are wrong.

1. The distributive form of 12×4 is $(10 + 4) \times (2 + 4)$. This is incorrect. The addition and multiplication symbols are switched. The correct distributive form is $(10 \times 4) + (2 \times 4)$.
2. The array model for 2×11 is

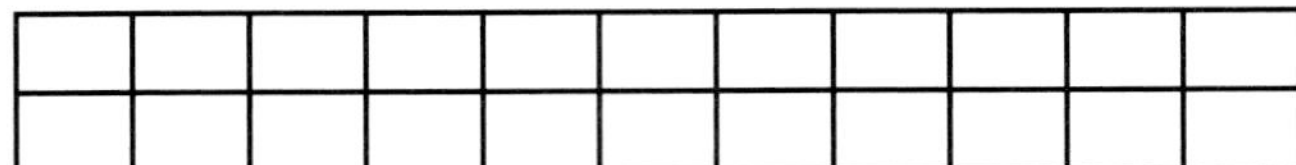

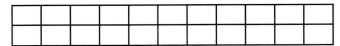

This is correct.

3. $11 \times 3 = 23$ This is incorrect. The pattern for multiplying by 11 is that the digit is repeated. 2 and 3 are not the same digits. The correct answer is 33.

11 HOBBIES There were 12 beads in a handmade bracelet. If Carla made 3 bracelets, how many beads did she use? Check off each step.

✓ Understand: I circled key words.

✓ Plan: To solve the problem, I will solve a simpler problem.

✓ Solve: The answer is 36 beads.

✓ Check: I checked my answer by Sample answer: Skip counting by 12s.

12 **Reflect** Why does the pattern for multiplying by 11 only work for single digits?

Sample answer: When you multiply 11×10, it is not the digit repeated. In other words, 11×10 does not equal 1,010.

Skills, Concepts, and Problem Solving

Use patterns or array models to find the product.

13 $11 \times 9 =$ 99

14 $12 \times 5 =$ 60

15 $12 \times 7 =$ 84

16 $11 \times 7 =$ 77

GO ON

Math Challenge

Product Practice Arrange students into pairs. One student is "A" and the other is "B." Give each pair of students a number cube. Begin by telling the class the A's represent the 11s and the Bs represent the 12s. Now have each student toss the cube. The number that they get is their second factor. Their task is to construct an array to represent their product. Have students check each other's work. Now have the pairs switch factors and toss the cube to get a new second factor. This time have students write their factor using the distributive form and then find the product. Continue switching methods and factors until the students feel comfortable with the process.

Odd/Even Assignments

Exercises 13–26 are structured so that students practice the same concepts whether they are assigned the odd or even problems.

In-Class Assignment

Have students complete Exercises 14, 17, 21, 26, and 28 to ensure that they understand the concept.

Math Coach Notes

Strategies

1. Start this lesson by asking for examples of things that come in sets of 12. Their suggestions might include eggs, books, markers, golf balls, and sports teams. Choose one example and say, "If there are 12 markers in a box, how many markers are there total in 7 boxes?" Use both words and real-world examples to pique interest and create relevant examples.

2. Ask students to name the multiples of 11, using a number line if possible. Ask what the pattern is. Students should easily see that the product of a 1-digit number multiplied by 11 is that number twice.

Intervention Strategy

Kinesthetic/ Visual Learners

Vertical Method When the products of 11 involve factors that are greater than 9, the pattern of the digit repeated is no longer applicable. Place the students in groups of 3 or 4. Have each student take out a sheet of paper. Ask the students to determine the product of 11 and 17 using the vertical method. Each person should write the problem in vertical form and perform the first step (11×7 or 17×1). When each person is finished, he or she should pass his or her paper to the right and check what was done. If the work is correct, complete the next step. If the work is incorrect, discuss how to correct it and then complete the next step. Continue until the problem is complete. You may need to model this for students before setting them to work.

See It, Do It, Say It, Write It

Step 1 Using two-color counters, show 12 × 10. Now show (10 × 10) + (2 × 10). Ask students if the distributive form and the array model represent the same product. Have students justify their response.

Step 2 Give each student pair a product using 11 or 12 where the other factor is also a two-digit number. Tell students that they can use either method to find their product. Ask students to present their work and tell which method they prefer and why.

Step 3 Ask students to group themselves according to whether they found a product of 11 or 12. Ask them to discuss their findings in the group.

Step 4 Tell students to write the multiples of 11 and 12. Then tell them the pattern for the multiplication facts of 11. Ask if they notice any pattern for the facts for 12.

Looking Ahead: Pre-teach

Multiply Large Numbers In the next lesson, students will learn about multiplying large numbers using the traditional method and the partial products method.

Example: Find 41 × 37.

Put the product in vertical form.

Break each digit into its pieces; 41 becomes 40 and 1 and 37 becomes 30 and 7.

Begin by multiplying 7 times the ones column.
7 × 1 = 7

$$\begin{array}{r} 41 \\ \times\ 37 \\ \hline 7 \\ 280 \\ 30 \\ +\ 1{,}200 \\ \hline 1{,}517 \end{array}$$

Next multiply 7 times the tens column.
7 × 40 = 280

Then multiply 30 by the ones column.
30 × 1 = 30

Now multiply 30 by the tens column.
30 × 40 = 1,200

Finally add the partial products.
7 + 280 + 30 + 1,200 = 1,517

Find each product. Show your work.

17 12 × 11 = 132

18 1 × 11 = 11

19 12 × 2 = 24

20 11 × 10 = 110

21 11 × 6 = 66

22 12 × 4 = 48

23 11 × 11 = 121

24 12 × 3 = 36

Solve.

25 ASTRONOMY Eli spent 12 minutes counting the stars in the sky. If he counted 12 stars each minute for 12 minutes, how many stars did he count?
144 stars

26 PHOTOS Moesha developed 9 rolls of 12-exposure film. How many pictures did she develop?
108 pictures

Vocabulary Check **Write the vocabulary word that completes each sentence.**

27 A(n) pattern follows a rule or design.

28 Writing in Math Explain how the word *dozen* can help you multiply by 12.
Sample answer: A dozen is equal to 12. I can picture a dozen eggs for each set of 12.

Spiral Review

Find each product. (Lesson 2-3, p. 55)

29 7 × 4 = 28

30 8 × 9 = 72

Solve. (Lesson 2-1, p. 40)

31 FLOWERS Danté is making bunches of flowers for his mother, his three aunts, and his grandfather. Each bunch will have 10 flowers. How many flowers will Danté need to make 5 bunches?
50 flowers

STOP

66 Chapter 2 Multiplication

Ticket Out the Door

Products Write the products 11 × 10 and 12 × 12 on the board. Tell students to draw an array model for one of the products and to put the other product in distributive form to determine the product. Students can hand in their papers as they exit the classroom.

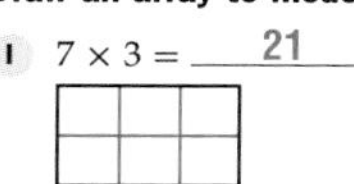

Progress Check 2 (Lessons 2-3 and 2-4)

Draw an array to model each expression.

1. 7 × 3 = 21
2. 8 × 6 = 48

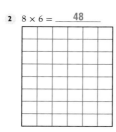

Rewrite the factors in distributive form. Find each product.

3. 5 × 12 = (5 × 10) + (5 × 2) = 50 + 10 = 60
4. 12 × 7 = (10 × 7) + (2 × 7) = 70 + 14 = 84
5. 11 × 4 = (10 × 4) + (1 × 4) = 40 + 4 = 44
6. 11 × 8 = (10 × 8) + (1 × 8) = 80 + 8 = 88

Find each product. Show your work.

7. 6 × 11 = 66
8. 8 × 9 = 72
9. 7 × 4 = 28
10. 11 × 2 = 22
11. 8 × 12 = 96
12. 5 × 9 = 45

Solve.

13. **ZOO** On Saturday 12 school groups visited the zoo. Each group had 20 students. How many students visited the zoo on Saturday? 240 students
14. **SUPPLIES** Oscar bought 9 packs of pencils. There are 12 pencils in each pack. How many pencils did Oscar buy? 108 pencils

Lesson 2-4 Multiply by 11 and 12 67

Progress Check 2

Chapter 2

Formative Assessment

Use the Progress Check to assess students' mastery of the previous lessons. Have students review the lesson indicated for the problems they answered incorrectly.

Odd/Even Assignments

Exercises are structured so that students practice the same concepts whether they are assigned the odd or even problems.

Common Error Alert

Identify Patterns Skip counting is a way to use patterns of multiples to find products. If the students memorize the patterns, the information will be more readily available to them when solving multiplication problems.

Exercises 3–6 Be sure that students know that they need to have as many distributive pieces as the digits in the largest number. Estimation will help them to check the reasonableness of their solutions.

Data-Driven Decision Making

Students missing Exercises . . .	Have trouble with . . .	Should review and practice . . .
1–2	drawing an array to represent a product.	SSG Lesson 2-3 p. 55
3–6	finding a product by rewriting the factors in distributive form.	SSG Lesson 2-4 p. 61 CRM Skills Practice, p. A36
7–12	finding a product.	SSG Lesson 2-4 p. 61 CRM Skills Practice, p. A36
13–14	solving word problems involving multiplication.	SSG Lessons 2-3 and 2-4 pp. 55 and 61 CRM Problem-Solving Practice, pp. A33 and A37

Lesson 2-5

Lesson Notes

Lesson Planner

Objective Multiply when factors have more than one digit.

Vocabulary **estimate**, **partial products method**

Materials/Manipulatives base-ten blocks, egg cartons, grid paper, index cards, straightedges, things that come in dozens

Chapter Resource Masters

- CRM Vocabulary and English Language Development (p. A39)
- CRM Skills Practice (p. A40)
- CRM Problem-Solving Practice (p. A41)
- CRM Homework Practice (p. A42)

Vocabulary

Vocabulary Interlace Connect previous lessons with this lesson by reviewing the meanings of *factor, product,* and *estimate.* Then ask what methods of multiplication students have learned. Write $2 \times 7 = 2 \times (5 + 2) = (2 \times 5) + (2 \times 2)$ on the board.

Key Concept

Foundational Skills and Concepts After students have read through the Key Concept box, have them try these exercises.

1. If you used the partial products method to multiply 43×35, what four equations would you write? $5 \times 3 = 15$; $5 \times 40 = 200$; $30 \times 3 = 90$, $30 \times 40 = 1{,}200$
2. What is another method to find the product of 43 and 35? multiplication method

---

Lesson 2-5

Multiply Greater Numbers

KEY Concept

Traditional Multiplication Method	Partial Products Method	
1		
43	43	
× 35	× 35	
215	15	$5 \times 3 = 15$
+ 1 290	200	$5 \times 40 = 200$
1,505	90	$30 \times 3 = 90$
	+ 1,200	$30 \times 40 = 1{,}200$
	1,505	

estimate a number close to an exact value; an estimate indicates *about* how much

partial products method a way to multiply; the value of each digit in one factor is multiplied by the value of each digit in the other factor; the product is the sum of its partial products

Before you multiply, you should **estimate** your answer. Then check your actual answer for reasonableness.

Example 1

Find the product of 36 and 82. Use the partial products method.

1. Estimate. $40 \times 80 = 3{,}200$
2. Rewrite the problem in a vertical format.
3. Multiply 2 times the ones column. $2 \times 6 = 12$
4. Multiply 2 times the tens column. $2 \times 30 = 60$
5. Multiply 80 times the ones column. $80 \times 6 = 480$
6. Multiply 80 times the tens column. $80 \times 30 = 2{,}400$
7. Add the partial products. $12 + 60 + 480 + 2{,}400 = 2{,}952$
8. $36 \times 82 = 2{,}952$

$$\begin{array}{r} 36 \\ \times\ 82 \\ \hline 12 \\ 60 \\ 480 \\ +2{,}400 \\ \hline 2{,}952 \end{array}$$

YOUR TURN!

Find the product of 28 and 57. Use the partial products method.

1. Estimate. $30 \times 60 =$ 1,800
2. Rewrite the problem in a vertical format.
3. Multiply 7 times the ones column. $7 \times 8 =$ 56
4. Multiply 7 times the tens column. $7 \times 20 =$ 140
5. Multiply 50 times the ones column. $50 \times 8 =$ 400
6. Multiply 50 times the tens column. $50 \times 20 =$ 1,000
7. Add the partial products. 56 + 140 + 400 + 1,000 = 1,596
8. $28 \times 57 =$ 1,596

$$\begin{array}{r} 28 \\ \times\ 57 \\ \hline 56 \\ 140 \\ 400 \\ +1{,}000 \\ \hline 1{,}596 \end{array}$$

68 Chapter 2 Multiplication

Additional Example 1

Find the product of 29 and 68. Use the partial products method.

1. Estimate. $30 \times 70 = 2{,}100$
2. Rewrite the problem in a vertical format.
$$\begin{array}{r} 29 \\ \times\ 68 \\ \hline \end{array}$$
3. Multiply 8 times the ones column. $8 \times 9 = 72$
4. Multiply 8 times the tens column. $8 \times 20 = 160$
5. Multiply 60 times the ones column. $60 \times 9 = 540$
6. Multiply 60 times the tens column. $60 \times 20 = 1{,}200$
7. Add the partial products. $72 + 160 + 540 + 1{,}200 = 1{,}972$
8. $29 \times 68 = 1{,}972$

Example 2

Find the product of 76 and 14. Use the traditional multiplication method.

1. Estimate.
   $80 \times 10 = 800$
2. Rewrite the problem in a vertical format.
3. Multiply 4 times the digit in the ones column.
   $4 \times 6 = 24$
   Write the tens digit above the tens column. Write the ones digit in the product under the ones column.
   $$\begin{array}{r} {}^{2} \\ 76 \\ \times\ 14 \\ \hline 4 \end{array}$$
4. Multiply 4 times the tens column.
   $4 \times 7 = 28$
   Add the two tens to get 30.
   $$\begin{array}{r} {}^{2} \\ 76 \\ \times\ 14 \\ \hline 304 \end{array}$$
5. Multiply the value of the digit in the tens place times 6.
   $10 \times 6 = 60$
   $$\begin{array}{r} 76 \\ \times\ 14 \\ \hline 304 \\ 60 \end{array}$$
6. Multiply the value in the tens column by 10.
   $10 \times 70 = 700$
   Write the 7 in the hundreds place.
   $$\begin{array}{r} 76 \\ \times\ 14 \\ \hline 304 \\ +\ 760 \\ \hline 1{,}064 \end{array}$$
7. Find the sum of the two products.
8. $76 \times 14 = 1{,}064$

   Compare to your estimate for reasonableness.

YOUR TURN!

Find the product of 56 and 32. Use the traditional multiplication method.

1. Estimate.
   60 × 30 = 1,800
2. Rewrite the problem in a vertical format.
3. Multiply 2 times the digit in the ones column.
   2 × 6 = 12
4. Multiply 2 times the tens column.
   2 × 5 = 10
   Add the 1 ten(s) to get 11.
5. Multiply each place value by the tens digit.
   30 × 6 = 180
6. Multiply the value in the tens column by 30.
   30 × 50 = 1,500
   Add 1 hundred(s) for 1,600.
7. Find the sum of the two products.
8. 56 × 32 = 1,792

   Compare to your estimate for reasonableness.

$$\begin{array}{r} 56 \\ \times\ 32 \\ \hline 112 \\ +\ 1{,}680 \\ \hline 1{,}792 \end{array}$$

English Learner Strategy

Use Models Use base-ten blocks to extend the concepts learned in previous lessons. The objective is to connect to previous lessons and to demonstrate to students that multiplying large numbers is still repeated addition. Write 3 × 10 on the board, then place 3 rods in a row and say, "Here are three groups of ten." Point to the 3 and 10 in the expression and repeat, and then write the product. Do the same with the expression 3 × 13 and represent 3 groups of 13 with the blocks. Progress to 2 two-digit factors like 12 × 14 using blocks. Then allow students to model expressions and find the products. Have students write what the expressions and equations represent and verbally state each model and number sentence.

Additional Example 2

Find the product of 47 and 13. Use the traditional multiplication method.

1. Estimate. 50 × 10 = 500
2. Rewrite the problem in a vertical format.
   $$\begin{array}{r} {}^{2} \\ 47 \\ \times\ 13 \\ \hline 141 \\ 470 \\ \hline 611 \end{array}$$
3. Multiply 3 times the digit in the ones column. 3 × 7 = 21 Write the tens digit above the tens column and the ones digit in the product under the ones column.
4. Multiply 3 times the tens column. 3 × 4 = 12 Add the two tens to get 14.
5. Multiply the value of the digit in the tens place times 7. 10 × 7 = 70
6. Multiply the value in the tens column by 10. 10 × 40 = 400 Write the 4 in the hundreds place.
7. Find the sum of the two products.
8. 47 × 13 = 611 Compare to your estimate for reasonableness.

Common Error *Alert*

Partial Products Method Students who have difficulty with the partial products method may not be following a set procedure and therefore may be confusing the numbers. Suggest these students draw arrows from the digits that are to be multiplied as a visual clue. Instead of writing just the product under the vertical problem, these students might benefit from writing each equation that their arrows indicate from digit to digit. In Example 1,

$$\begin{array}{r} 36 \\ \times\ 82 \\ \hline \end{array} \qquad \left.\begin{array}{r} 2 \times 6 = 12 \\ 2 \times 30 = 60 \\ 80 \times 6 = 480 \\ 80 \times 30 = 2{,}400 \end{array}\right\} \quad \begin{array}{l} 12 + 60 + \\ 480 + 2{,}400 \\ = 2{,}952 \end{array}$$

Filling the Spaces If students are having difficulty multiplying large numbers, have them fill in the unused place values in the problem with 0s or with Xs to use as placeholders.

3 Practice 

Using Manipulatives

Base-Ten Blocks Show students how to represent numbers in expanded form using base-ten blocks. In Example 1, the place values of the factors will be easier to see using rods and units.

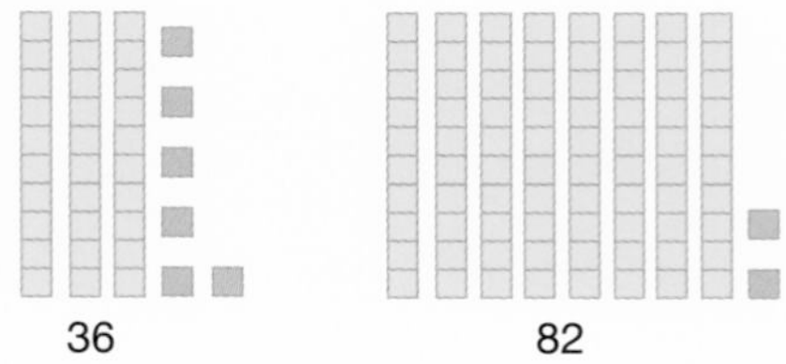

 **On-Hand Manipulatives** Give students straightedges or grid paper to help them line up the digits when multiplying large numbers.

Common Error *Alert*

Who is Correct? If students continue to have difficulty multiplying large numbers, such as in Who is Correct? make certain students are proficient at estimating and that they estimate *every* time. Estimating first will ensure that students have an idea of the relative magnitude of the product. In Who is Correct?, if Vivian had estimated first, she would have known that the product would be about $30 \times 50 = 1{,}500$. Her answer would then not be reasonable.

Who is Correct?

Find the product of 26 and 47.

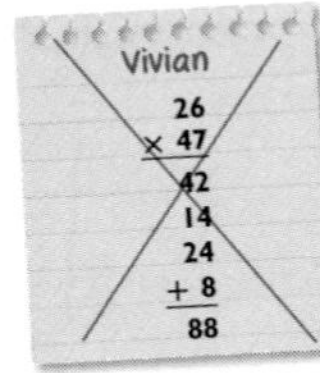

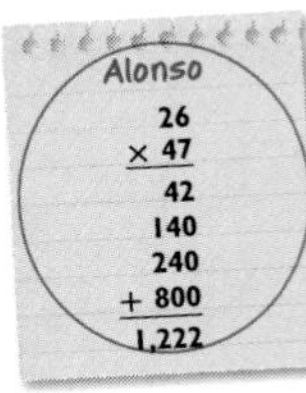

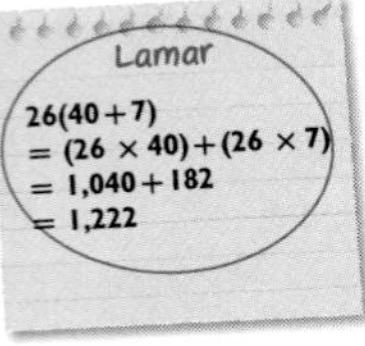

Circle correct answer(s). Cross out incorrect answer(s).

Guided Practice

Estimate each product.

1. 95×47
   Round each factor to the greatest place value.
   Find the estimated product.
   90 × 50 = 4,500

2. 70×32
   Round each factor to the greatest place value.
   Find the estimated product.
   70 × 30 = 2,100

Step by Step Practice

3. Find the product of 14 and 89. Use the traditional multiplication method.

Step 1 Rewrite the problem in a vertical format.

Step 2 Multiply each place value by the ones digit.

Step 3 Multiply each place value by the tens digit.

Step 4 Find the sum of the two products.

Step 5 $14 \times 89 =$ 1,246

```
   3
  14
× 89
 126
1 12
1,246
```


Who *is Correct?*

Diagnostic Teaching

- Vivian is incorrect. She did not use the correct place value for the digits.
- Alonso wrote 1,222. This is correct.
- Lamar wrote 1,222. This is correct.

Remind students to learn both methods and to use the one that feels most comfortable.

Find each product. Use the traditional multiplication method.

4 $11 \times 71 =$ 781

$$\begin{array}{r} 11 \\ \times\ 71 \\ \hline 11 \\ 77\ \\ \hline 781 \end{array}$$

5 $12 \times 101 =$ 1,212

Find each product. Use the partial products method.

6 $39 \times 83 =$ 3,237

7 $28 \times 94 =$ 2,632

Step by Step Problem-Solving Practice

Problem-Solving Strategies

- ☐ Draw a diagram.
- ☑ Use logical reasoning.
- ☐ Solve a simpler problem.
- ☐ Work backward.
- ☐ Make a table.

Solve.

8 SCHOOL The teacher's aide is grading tests. Each test has 45 questions. Each student took 4 tests. If there are 28 students in the class, how many test questions are there in all?

Understand Read the problem. Write what you know.
Each student took 4 tests.
Each test has 45 questions.
There are 28 students in the class.

Plan Pick a strategy. One strategy is to use logical reasoning. Find the number of questions on 4 tests. Then multiply by the number of students to find the number of test questions in all.

Solve number of questions × number of tests = questions on 4 tests
questions on 4 tests × number of students = test questions in all

Use the values from the problem to solve.

45 × 4 = 180

180 × 28 = 5,040

There are 5,040 test questions in all.

Check Look at your solution. Did you answer the question?

GO ON

Are They Getting It?

Check students' understanding of multiplying large numbers by writing these problems on the board. Ask students to point out wrong answers and explain why they are wrong.

1. When you multiply 24 × 36, the four expressions that are made using the partial products method are 4 × 6, 4 × 30, 2 × 6, 2 × 3. This is incorrect. The correct answer is 4 × 6, 4 × 30, 20 × 6, and 20 × 30.
2. The product of 23 × 82 is 1,886. This is correct.
3. The product of 13 × 67 is 771. This is incorrect. The product is 871.

English Learner Strategy

Guiding Questions Write 54 × 33 on the board. Then ask students the following questions.

- Which are the factors?
- How do you write 54 in expanded form?
- How would you use the partial products method to solve a multiplication problem?
- What is 54 × 33 using the partial products method?
- What steps do you take to find the product of 54 and 33 using the traditional method?

Intervention Strategy

Linguistic/Interpersonal Learners

Use Different Methods Have students go through printed material and cut out two- and three-digit numbers. Take the numbers and glue them onto index cards. Then hand two cards randomly to each student pair. Divide the class in half and assign each half a different method to use to solve their problem. Student pairs can share their work.

Common Error Alert

Exercises 8 and 9 If students have difficulty finding the solution to Exercises 8 and 9, it may be because they cannot visualize the situation. Tell students to draw a picture if they have a hard time "seeing" a problem. For Exercise 8, tell students to divide a square into four quadrants and write 45 in each quadrant. How many squares are in each graph total? In Exercise 9, students can draw a square and write 16 in it. This is one shovel of sand. If there are 27 of these shovels, how many clams are there?

Odd/Even Assignments

Exercises 12–35 are structured so that students practice the same concepts whether they are assigned the odd or even problems.

In-Class Assignment

Have students complete Exercises 16, 20, 28, 34, and 37 to ensure that they understand the concept.

Note This!

Vocabulary Table When a lesson has several new vocabulary words, such as this lesson, encourage students to make a three-column vocabulary table. The first column is for the vocabulary word, the second is for the definition and the third column is for illustrations and examples.

9 BUSINESS Ginny is digging for clams to sell to a local seafood store. For every shovel of sand she digs up, she finds 16 small clams. If she digs 27 shovels of sand, how many clams could she expect to find?

Check off each step.

✔ Understand: I circled key words.

✔ Plan: To solve the problem, I will use logical reasoning.

✔ Solve: The answer is 432 clams.

✔ Check: I checked my answer by using repeated addition.

10 COOKING When making meat loaf, Ruben uses 12 ounces of breadcrumbs. His mother uses the same recipe at her restaurant, but she multiplies the recipe to make 32 meat loaves. How many ounces of breadcrumbs will his mother use?

384 ounces

11 **Reflect** Compare two different ways of multiplying 13 × 17.

Answers will vary. Students should compare two of the following methods: traditional, partial products, Distributive Property, or expanded form.

Skills, Concepts, and Problem Solving

Find each product. Use the traditional multiplication method.

12 45 × 87 = 3,915

13 56 × 91 = 5,096

14 11 × 15 = 165

15 13 × 14 = 182

16 28 × 51 = 1,428

17 32 × 60 = 1,920

72 Chapter 2 Multiplication

English Learner Strategy

Use Models Use counters or pattern blocks to create models of multiplication problems. Model how to explain a sentence the model represents. Ask the students to echo you. Then practice with sentences you write and sentences the student writes. Alternate between modeling and explaining.

Find each product. Use the partial products method.

18 $39 \times 63 =$ 2,457

19 $18 \times 22 =$ 396

20 $32 \times 16 =$ 512

21 $32 \times 31 =$ 992

22 $42 \times 14 =$ 588

23 $58 \times 22 =$ 1,276

Find each product. Show your work.

24 $19 \times 19 =$ 361

25 $29 \times 21 =$ 609

26 $48 \times 77 =$ 3,696

27 $25 \times 87 =$ 2,175

28 $26 \times 31 =$ 806

29 $44 \times 62 =$ 2,728

30 $17 \times 45 =$ 765

31 $51 \times 23 =$ 1,173

Solve

32 COOKING Ricky is making sandwiches for a banquet. Each package of cheese has 16 slices. He uses 14 packages. How many slices of cheese did he use in all?

224 slices of cheese

33 PHOTOGRAPHY Tessa's online photo album holds 50 pictures. She has 18 photo albums. How many pictures does she have in all?

900 pictures

GO ON

Intervention Strategy

Logical/ Interpersonal Learners

Secret Problems Students will work in pairs. Each student will secretly write a multiplication problem with 2 two-digit factors. The same student will write the four partial product expressions that are created. The students will then trade these four expressions. The other students will use those expressions as clues to write the original problem. For example, a student secretly writes 45×16 on paper. The four expressions she will give to her partner are 6×5, 6×40, 10×5, and 10×40. Student volunteers can share their work with the class.

Math Challenge

Greatest Wins Give each student pair or group a set of cards numbered from 0 to 9. One student is the dealer and hands out four cards to each player. Players will use the four cards to create 2 two-digit numbers that will multiply to yield the greatest product possible. They multiply those numbers together, and this is their score. Students continue playing rounds until they have played five rounds or time is up. The student with the highest score wins.

4 Assess

See It, Do It, Say It, Write It

Step 1 Multiply 2 two-digit numbers on the board using the traditional method. Use a different colored marker or chalk for the numbers that are carried to the next place value. Then ask a student to explain how you would use the partial products method to solve the same problem. Repeat with 2- and 3-digit factors.

Step 2 Assign each student pair two multiplication problems. Tell them to use two different methods to solve them.

Step 3 Ask students to discuss the results with the rest of the class by volunteering to write their problems on the board or overhead.

Step 4 Now tell students to explain in writing the two methods of multiplying large numbers from the lesson.

Additional Answer

Exercise 37 Sophie forgot to place a 0 in the ones column. When she multiplied the top number by 10 it should have been 450 not 345. The correct answer is 810.

Looking Ahead: Pre-teach

Multiplication and Division In the next lesson, students will learn that multiplication and division are opposite or inverse operations.

Example

$9 \times 3 = 27 \qquad 27 \div 3 = 9$

Find the product and then write a division fact from each product.

1. 3×4 12; $12 \div 3 = 4$ or $12 \div 4 = 3$
2. 8×6 48; $48 \div 6 = 8$ or $48 \div 8 = 6$
3. 11×7 77; $77 \div 11 = 7$ or $77 \div 7 = 11$
4. 5×9 45; $45 \div 5 = 9$ or $45 \div 9 = 5$

Solve.

34 MUSIC Look at the photo at the right. If Martino has 63 CDs, how many total songs does Martino have?

693 songs

35 FITNESS Lawana runs 3 miles every day. Michelle runs 4 miles a day on weekdays. Michelle does not run on the weekends. After 45 weeks, who will have run more? By how much?

Lawana will have run 45 miles more in 45 weeks than Michelle.

MUSIC Each CD has 11 songs.

Vocabulary Check **Write the vocabulary word that completes each sentence.**

36 A number close to an exact value is called a(n) estimate.

37 Writing in Math Sophie multiplied 45 × 18. What mistake did she make?

$$\begin{array}{r} {}^{4}\\ 45 \\ \times\ 18 \\ \hline 360 \\ +345 \\ \hline 705 \end{array}$$

See margin.

$$\begin{array}{r} {}^{4}\\ 45 \\ \times\ 18 \\ \hline 360 \\ +450 \\ \hline 810 \end{array}$$

Or using the distributive method:

$45 \times 18 = 45\,(10 + 8)$
$= (45 \times 10) + (45 \times 8)$
$= 450 + 360$
$= 810$

Spiral Review

Solve. (Lesson 2-3, p. 55)

38 GROCERY There are 7 egg cartons on the shelf at the corner market. Each egg carton contains 1 dozen eggs. What is the total number of eggs on the shelf?

84 eggs

Find each product. (Lesson 2-4, p. 61)

39 $11 \times 8 =$ 88
40 $12 \times 7 =$ 84
41 $12 \times 13 =$ 156
42 $11 \times 46 =$ 506
43 $12 \times 31 =$ 372
44 $11 \times 52 =$ 572

STOP

74 Chapter 2 Multiplication

Ticket Out the Door

Birth-Year Math Tell students to write the last 2 digits of the years they were born on paper. So, if their year of birth is 1997, they write 97. Now tell them to multiply their ages by that two-digit number. Students will hand in their papers as they exit the classroom.

Lesson 2-6

Multiplication and Division

KEY Concept

Multiplication and **division** are opposite, or **inverse operations**. They undo each other.

There are 4 cartons of eggs. Each carton has 12 eggs. There are 48 eggs in all.

4	×	12	=	48
factor		factor		product

There are 48 eggs in all. Each carton has 12 eggs. There are 4 cartons.

48	÷	12	=	4
product		factor		factor

In multiplication, the product is the missing number. In division, one of the factors is the missing number.

A **fact family** is a group of related facts using the same numbers.

$4 \times 12 = 48$
$12 \times 4 = 48$
$48 \div 12 = 4$
$48 \div 4 = 12$

VOCABULARY

division
an operation on two numbers in which the first number is split into the same number of equal groups as the second number
Example: $6 \div 3$ means 6 is divided into 3 groups of equal size.

fact family
a group of related facts using the same numbers
Example: $5 \times 3 = 15$; $3 \times 5 = 15$; $15 \div 3 = 5$; $15 \div 5 = 3$

inverse operations
operations that undo each other
Example: Multiplication and division are inverse operations.

multiplication
an operation on two numbers to find their product; it can be thought of as repeated addition

You can use what you know about multiplication to help you learn more about division.

Intervention Strategy

Kinesthetic/ Interpersonal Learners

Building Division Skills

1. Begin the lesson by using concrete materials to illustrate various products. Build the model and ask for student volunteers to determine what product the model represents. Have students break into pairs and continue this process.
2. Now discuss how you would undo the multiplication. Remind students that division is the inverse of multiplication. Put a model of a product up and ask students to identify the model. Now change the multiplication problem to division of the same model. Ask students if the model still fits. Have students create some more models using division.

Lesson Notes

Lesson 2-6

Lesson Planner

Objective Understand that multiplication and division are inverse operations of each other.

Vocabulary **division**, **fact family**, **inverse operations**, **multiplication**

Materials/Manipulatives base-ten blocks, construction paper, number line, number cubes, two-color counters

Chapter Resource Masters

- CRM Vocabulary and English Language Development (p. A43)
- CRM Skills Practice (p. A44)
- CRM Problem-Solving Practice (p. A45)
- CRM Homework Practice (p. A46)

1 Introduce

Vocabulary

Connect Vocabulary Connect the vocabulary from previous lessons with this lesson. What are the 11s called in the expression 11×11? factors What is the answer to a multiplication problem called? product What is the product of 11 and 11? 121

2 Teach

Key Concept

Foundational Skills and Concepts After students have read through the Key Concept box, have them try these exercises.

1. What is a fact family? a group of related facts using the same numbers
2. In the equation $48 \div 12 = 4$, which number is the product in the related multiplication fact? 48

Additional **Example 1**

Write the fact family for the array.

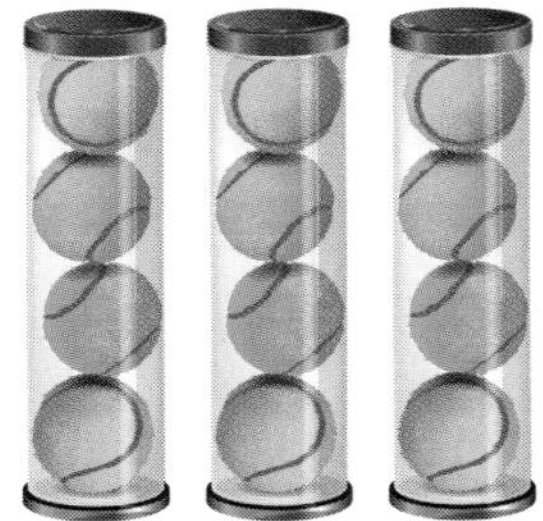

1. Write two multiplication sentences shown by the array. $3 \times 4 = 12$; $4 \times 3 = 12$
2. Write two division sentences using the same numbers. $12 \div 4 = 3$; $12 \div 3 = 4$

Intervention Strategy

Auditory/ Interpersonal Learners

Comic Strip Have students work in pairs or in small groups. Ask students to create a comic strip about a fact family. The comic strip should involve an array or a model to help illustrate the fact family and how it operates.

Common Error *Alert*

Commutative Property Students may have difficulty understanding that the order in which they write the pieces for multiplication does not matter. Remind them that multiplication is commutative. Since division is the inverse of multiplication, it works in a similar manner. As long as the product becomes the dividend, it does not matter which factor is used as the divisor. The remaining factor is always the quotient.

Example 1

Write the fact family for the array.

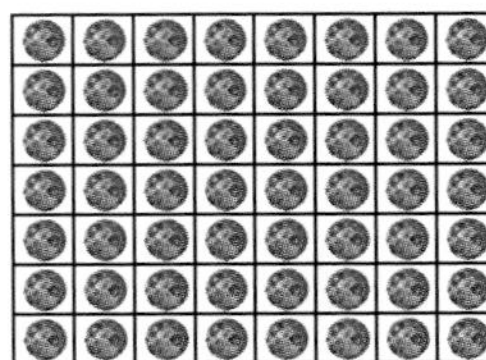

1. Write two multiplication sentences shown by the array.

   $7 \times 8 = 56$ $8 \times 7 = 56$

2. Write two division sentences using the same numbers.

   $56 \div 7 = 8$ $56 \div 8 = 7$

YOUR TURN!

Write the fact family for the array.

1. Write two multiplication sentences shown by the array.

   $9 \times 6 = 54$ $6 \times 9 = 54$

2. Write two division sentences using the same numbers.

   $54 \div 6 = 9$ $56 \div 9 = 6$

Who is Correct?

Write a division sentence related to $45 \times 9 = 405$.

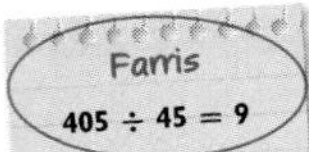

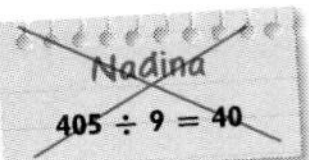

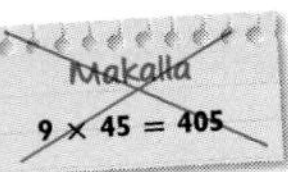

Circle correct answer(s). Cross out incorrect answer(s).

76 **Chapter 2** Multiplication

Who *is Correct?*

Diagnostic Teaching

- Ferris' work is correct. He took the quotient and made it the dividend. Factors then became the divisor and the quotient.
- Nadina's work is incorrect. $405 \div 9 = 45$. She did not use the other factor as the quotient.
- Makalla's work is incorrect. She used the Commutative Property to write another multiplication sentence instead of a division sentence.

Guided Practice

Write a number family for the array.

1 Write two multiplication sentences shown by the array.

$9 \times 8 = 72$

$8 \times 9 = 72$

2 Write two division sentences with the same numbers.

$72 \div 8 = 9$

$72 \div 9 = 8$

Step by Step Practice

3 Complete each equation. Write the numbers in the fact family.

13 × 20 = 260

20 × 13 **= 260**

260 ÷ 20 **= 13**

260 ÷ 13 **= 20**

13, 20, 260

HINT: Each equation is missing one number.
- Find the missing number in one equation.
- Use your answer to complete the remaining equations.

Step 1 Find the third number in the first equation. Find the product of 13 and 20.

Step 2 What is the missing factor in the second equation?

Step 3 Which number completes the third equation? 20

Step 4 Which number completes the fourth equation? 13

Step 5 Write the numbers in the fact family.

Step 6 Skip count by 20s to check.

1	2	3	4	5	6	7	8	9	10	11	12	13
20	40	60	80	100	120	140	160	180	200	220	240	260

Are They Getting It?

Check students' understanding of multiplication and division by writing these problems on the board. Ask them to point out wrong answers and explain why they are wrong.

1. The array represents $2 \times 9 = 18$. This is correct.

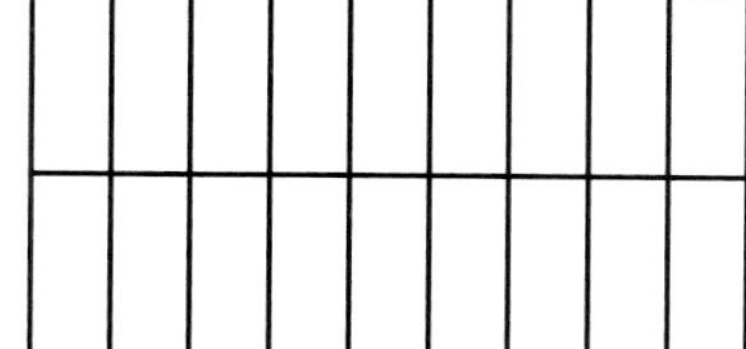

2. Another way to represent the array is $18 \div 2 = 7$. This is incorrect. The division problem should use both factors from the family. 7 is not part of the family.

Using Manipulatives

Two-Color Counters Counters, base-ten blocks, or other objects can be used to show multiplication and division fact families.

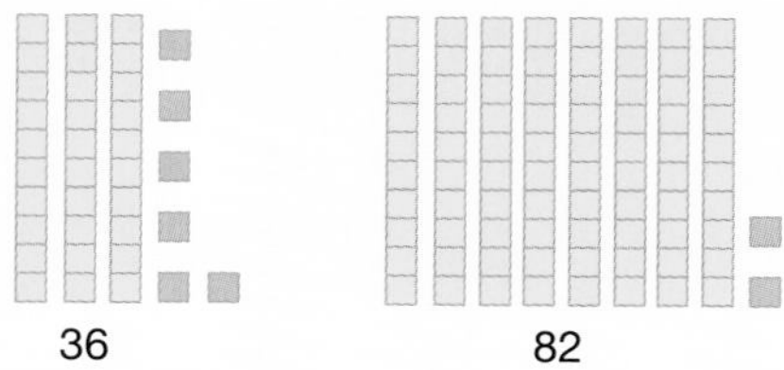

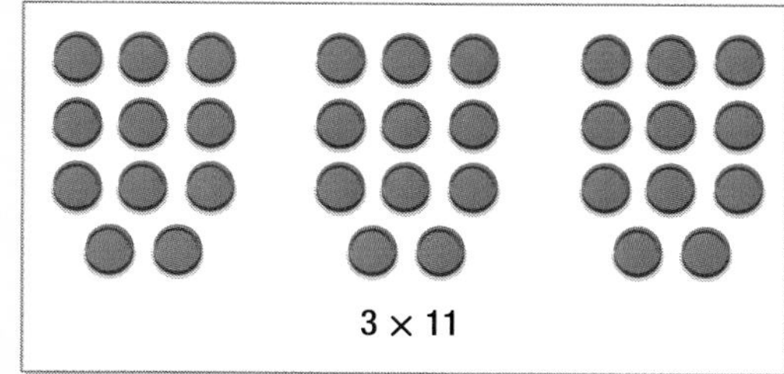

Number Line

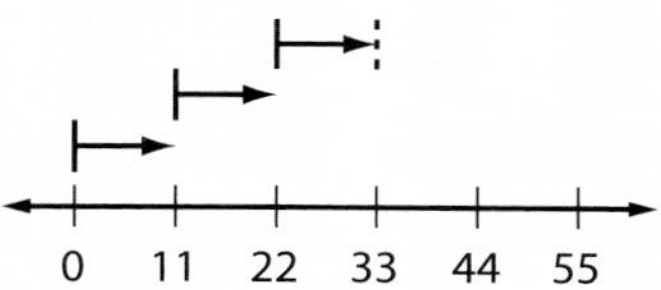

On-Hand Manipulatives Use two different colors of construction paper. Cut out squares to use as counters.

English Learner Strategy

Guiding Questions Draw a 5 × 7 array on a sheet of paper. Then ask the following questions to ensure that students understand the concepts.

- How many rows are in the array?
- How many columns are in the array?
- What is a multiplication sentence that describes the array?
- How can you use the Commutative Property of Multiplication to write another multiplication sentence?
- What is a division sentence that also describes the array?
- Why are you able to do this? Make sure you use inverse operations in your explanation.

Math Coach Notes

Multiplication Facts Tell students to make sure they continue to work on their multiplication facts. The better they know their facts, the easier the division will be and the more readily the fact families will become apparent.

Common Error *Alert*

Fact Families Students may have trouble understanding fact families. Remind students that once they have a fact, the three numbers involved are the only three numbers they need. The fact family just rearranges the numbers using multiplication or division to make different statements.

Note This!

Summarize Notes Help students summarize their notes. Hand out index cards towards the end of a lesson. Tell students to write a summary of their notes on one side of a card. Once they are finished, have students compare their work. Which card summarized the information best? Why? Help students explain what is effective when using limited space and words to convey the lesson.

Complete each equation using the numbers in the fact family.

4. $8 \times 17 =$ 136
   $17 \times$ 8 $= 136$
   $136 \div 8 =$ 17
   $136 \div$ 17 $= 8$

5. $36 \times 5 =$ 180
   $5 \times$ 36 $= 180$
   $180 \div 5 =$ 36
   $180 \div$ 36 $= 5$

6. $24 \times 19 =$ 456
   $19 \times$ 24 $= 456$
   $456 \div 24 =$ 19
   $456 \div$ 19 $= 24$

Step by Step Problem-Solving Practice

Problem-Solving Strategies
- ☑ Draw a model.
- ☐ Use logical reasoning.
- ☐ Make a table.
- ☐ Solve a simpler problem.
- ☐ Work backward.

7. SCHOOL The auditorium chairs are set up for a school performance. There are 4 sections, each with 128 chairs. How many chairs are set up in the auditorium?

Understand Read the problem. Write what you know.
There are 4 sections of chairs.
Each section has 128 chairs.

Plan Pick a strategy. One strategy is to draw a model. Draw 4 sections. Show that each section contains 128 chairs.

Solve There are 4 sections. Each section has 128 chairs.

128 chairs	128 chairs	128 chairs	128 chairs

Multiply 128 by 4 to find the total number of chairs.

$$\begin{array}{r} 128 \\ \times\ 4 \\ \hline 512 \end{array}$$

There are 512 chairs set up in the auditorium.

Check Use a related multiplication or division equation to check your work.

8. MAP Jin is making a map of Junction City. There are 6 neighborhoods on the map. Each neighborhood has 145 houses. How many houses will be shown on Jin's map? Check off each step.

✔ Understand: I circled key words.
✔ Plan: To solve this problem, I will draw a model.
✔ Solve: The answer is 870 houses.
✔ Check: I checked my answer by using a related division fact.

Math Challenge

Number Cubes Have students work in pairs to practice their fact families. Give each team a pair of number cubes. Each student should toss a number cube and use the two digits that come up as two of the digits in their fact family. Each student should write a fact family using the digits. Once they have written the family, have them compare results. If the students have different fact families using the same numbers, they each get 2 points; if they have the same family, they get 1 point. At the end of the allotted time, the student with the most points wins.

9 CAMPING 72 children are spending a week at camp. There are 12 cabins at the camp. An equal number of campers will sleep in each cabin. How many campers will sleep in each cabin?
6 campers

10 **Reflect** What does it mean to say that multiplication and division are *inverse operations*? Give an example.
Sample answer: Multiplication and division operations that have the same product undo each other. For example, $72 \div 9 = 8$ and $8 \times 9 = 72$ have the same product, 72, but the operations undo each other.

Skills, Concepts, and Problem Solving

Write a number family for the array.

11 Write two multiplication sentences.
$15 \times 5 = 75$
$5 \times 15 = 75$

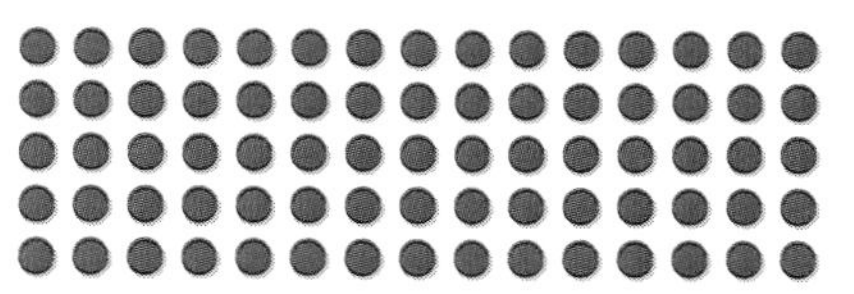

Write two division sentences.
$75 \div 15 = 5$ $75 \div 5 = 15$

Complete each equation. Write the numbers in the fact family.

12 $6 \times 45 = 270$
$45 \times 6 = 270$
$270 \div 45 = 6$
$270 \div 6 = 45$
The numbers in the fact family are: 6, 45, 270.

13 $13 \times 7 = 91$
$7 \times 13 = 91$
$91 \div 7 = 13$
$91 \div 13 = 7$
The numbers in the fact family are: 7, 13, 91.

Fill in the blanks to make each equation correct.

14 $21 \times 43 = 903$
15 $9 \times 50 = 450$
16 $88 \times 7 = 616$
17 $888 \div 4 = 222$
18 $45 \div 3 = 15$
19 $132 \div 2 = 66$

Intervention Strategy

Kinesthetic/ Interpersonal Learners

Hand Factor Begin by having two students stand in front of the class. Tell them to hide their hands behind their backs. Tell them that when you say "Now!" they should show one, both, or none of their hands as quickly as they can. Their classmates will raise their hands and call out a multiplication or division fact involving these numbers. For instance, if one student holds out 2 hands and the other student holds out 1 hand, one fact that can be used is $5 \times 3 = 15$. The first factor is the number of fingers on one hand (5) and the second factor is the number of hands presented (this number varies). Once a fact is stated, have other students state the rest of the facts in the fact family until all four facts are stated. Increase the number of students up to 6. Rotate students so that everybody has a chance to play.

Odd/Even Assignments

Exercises 11–21 are structured so that students practice the same concepts whether they are assigned the odd or even problems.

In-Class Assignment

Have students complete Exercises 11, 13, 16, 21, and 23 to ensure that they understand the concept.

English Learner Strategy

Fact Families Draw a model of 7 groups of 4 marbles. Have students write a multiplication or division fact about the model. Take volunteers to state their facts out loud. Keep taking volunteers until all 4 facts have been stated. Now have students draw a model of some type (array, drawings, etc.). Instruct students to write the fact family that their model represents. Have students share their models with each other.

Note This!

Homework Tell students that it is best to do their math homework the same day it is assigned so that it can reinforce new concepts. As they work out problems, encourage them to try more than one strategy to test if their answers are correct. The more they practice, the more comfortable students will become with solving math problems.

See It, Do It, Say It, Write It

Step 1 Draw a model or an array on the board. Ask for volunteers to each give you one part of the fact family that matches the model.

Step 2 Next write a division or multiplication fact on the board. Ask for more student volunteers to first draw a model to represent the fact and then to find the other facts for the family.

Step 3 Now ask students to draw a model or array. Have them exchange papers with a person near them. Write the fact family that corresponds to the drawing.

Step 4 Finally have students write a multiplication or division sentence on the paper and hand it back to its owner. The owner of the paper should then write the rest of the fact family. If needed, students can draw a model to represent the family.

Common Error *Alert*

Exercise 23 If students are having difficulty thinking of an everyday situation. Use questioning techniques to help them think about tasks they perform that have multiple steps, (i.e., playing a game, setting the table). Talk them through using the whole amount as the dividend and then breaking the whole into the appropriate pieces to give you the divisor and the quotient. If they still have difficulty with the concept, have them think of a situation involving multiplication. Then relate this concept with division.

Use either multiplication or division to solve each problem. Use a related multiplication or division equation to check your work.

20 PAINT It takes 5 gallons of paint to paint each room in a school. The school has 26 rooms. How many gallons of paint will be needed to paint all the rooms? 130 gallons

Check: $130 \div 5 = 26$ or $130 \div 26 = 5$

21 LIBRARY The public library has 900 new books. There are 20 empty shelves where the books will be displayed. If the same number of books must be put on each shelf, how many books will go on each shelf? 45 books

Check: $20 \times 45 = 900$ or $45 \times 20 = 900$

Vocabulary Check **Write the vocabulary word that completes each sentence.**

22 A group of related facts using the same numbers is called a(n) fact family.

23 Writing in Math Describe an everyday situation where you would use division. Give an example.

Sample answer: If you had 24 game pieces to share equally between 8 friends, you could use division to find that each friend would get 3 pieces.

Spiral Review

Find each product. Show your work. (Lesson 2-5, p. 68)

24 14×99 1,386

25 62×23 1,426

Solve. (Lesson 2-4, p. 61)

26 HORSES Mr. Ortega is putting horseshoes on his 12 horses. Each horse needs 4 horseshoes. How many horseshoes will Mr. Ortega need for all of his horses?

48 horseshoes

STOP

80 Chapter 2 Multiplication

Ticket Out the Door

Quick Quiz Write the following on the board:

1. What fact family is represented by the model? $3 \times 7 = 21$; $7 \times 3 = 21$; $21 \div 3 = 7$; $21 \div 7 = 3$

2. What is the product of 9 and 6? $9 \times 6 = 54$

3. What are the remaining statements for the fact family including 9 and 6? $6 \times 9 = 54$; $54 \div 9 = 6$; $54 \div 6 = 9$

Progress Check 3 (Lessons 2-5 and 2-6)

Find each product. Use the partial products method.

1.
```
    27
  × 16
    42   = 6 × 7
   120   = 6 × 20
    70   = 10 × 7
+  200   = 10 × 20
   432
```

2.
```
    46
  × 32
    12   = 2 × 6
    80   = 2 × 40
   180   = 30 × 6
+  120   = 30 × 40
 1,200
```

Find each product. Use the traditional multiplication method.

3.
```
   56
 × 17
  952
```

4.
```
   64
 × 23
1,472
```

Complete each equation. Write the numbers in the fact family.

5. $15 \times 27 =$ 405
$27 \times$ 15 $= 405$
$405 \div$ 27 $= 15$
$405 \div 15 =$ 27
15, 27, 405

6. $49 \times$ 11 $= 539$
11 $\times 49 = 539$
$539 \div$ 11 $= 49$
$539 \div 49 =$ 11
11, 49, 539

Solve.

7. **BUSES** Ridgewood Middle School uses buses to take fifth graders on a field trip. One bus can hold 40 students. How many buses will be needed to take 320 fifth graders on a field trip?
8 buses

8. **BEADS** Tammy wants to make a bracelet for all 18 girls on her softball team. It takes 12 beads to make a bracelet. How many beads does Tammy need?
216 beads

Lesson 2-6 Multiplication and Division 81

Progress Check 3

Chapter 2

Formative Assessment

Use the Progress Check to assess students' mastery of the previous lessons. Have students review the lesson indicated for the problems they answered incorrectly.

Odd/Even Assignments

Exercises are structured so that students practice the same concepts whether they are assigned the odd or even problems.

Common Error *Alert*

Partial Products Remind students that the partial products method consists of 4 steps of multiplication. Each step comes from writing the factors in their extended form.

Exercises 3-4 Students may want to estimate the answer prior to solving. This will give them a basis to determine if their answer is reasonable.

Exercises 7-8 If students are having a difficult time determining which operation to perform, instruct the students to create a model. This will help them to visualize the context of each problem.

Data-Driven Decision Making

Students missing Exercises . . .	Have trouble with . . .	Should review and practice . . .
1-2	using the partial products method to find a product.	SSG Lesson 2-5, p. 68 CRM Skills Practice, p. A40
3-4	multiplying large numbers using the traditional method.	SSG Lesson 2-5, p. 68 CRM Skills Practice, p. A40
5-6	finding all of the parts to a fact family.	SSG Lesson 2-6, p. 75 CRM Skills Practice, p. A44
7-8	solving word problems involving multiplication and division.	SSG Lessons 2-5 and 2-6, pp. 68 and 75 CRM Problem-Solving Practice, pp. A41 and A45

Chapter 2

Study Guide
Formative Assessment

Vocabulary and Concept Check

If students have difficulty answering Exercises 1–7, remind them that they can use the page references to refresh their memories about the vocabulary terms.

Vocabulary Review Strategies

Puzzles Have students make a crossword puzzle to help them review key vocabulary words. They should interlock the words in the Vocabulary and Concept Check and then write clues that are used to determine the correct word. (For instance: $4 + 3 = 3 + 4$ is an example of the ________ Property of ________. *Answer: Commutative, Addition)* Have them exchange puzzles with other students for additional practice.

Lesson Review

Each example walks the students through the main concepts of this chapter. If the given examples are not sufficient to review the questions, remind students that the page references tell them where to review that topic in their textbooks.

Find **Extra Practice** for these concepts in the Practice Worksheets, pages A23–A46.

Classroom Management

Early Finishers Some students will not require as much time to complete their study guides. For those students who seem to have a solid understanding of the materials from the chapter, suggest they write another example for each lesson. They can present these examples to other members of the class who could use the additional practice.

Chapter 2

Study Guide

Vocabulary and Concept Check

array, *p. 47*
Commutative Property of Multiplication, *p. 47*
Distributive Property of Multiplication, *p. 61*
division, *p. 75*
estimate, *p. 68*
fact family, *p. 75*
factor, *p. 40*
Identity Property of Multiplication, *p. 40*
inverse operations, *p. 75*
multiple, *p. 55*
multiplication, *p. 40*
partial products method, *p. 68*
pattern, *p. 61*
product, *p. 40*
Zero Property of Multiplication, *p. 40*

Write the vocabulary word that completes each sentence.

1. A number that is multiplied by another number to find a product is called a(n) ___factor___.
2. The ___Zero Property of Multiplication___ states that any number multiplied by zero is zero.
3. ___Inverse operations___ are operations that undo each other.
4. A number close to an exact value is a(n) ___estimate___.
5. A group of related facts using the same numbers is called a(n) ___fact family___.

Label each diagram below. Write the correct vocabulary term in each blank.

6. ___multiples___

4: 4, 8, 12, 16, 20, 24

7. ___array___

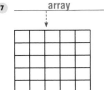

Lesson Review

2-1 Multiply by 0, 1, 5, and 10 (pp. 40–46)

Find each product.

8. 16 × 0 = 0
9. 92 × 10 = 920
10. 5 × 15 = 75
11. 1 × 310 = 310
12. 0 × 402 = 0
13. 71 × 10 = 710
14. 48 × 1 = 48
15. 20 × 5 = 100

Example 1

Find the product of 5 and 13.

1. Rewrite the problem in a vertical format.
2. Multiply the number in the ones column by 5.
   3 × 5 = 15
   Write the tens digit above the tens column. Write the ones digit under the ones column.

$$\begin{array}{r} ^{1} \\ 13 \\ \times\ 5 \\ \hline 5 \end{array}$$

3. Multiply 5 times the digit in the tens column.
   5 × 1 = 5
   Add one regrouped tens for a total of 6 tens.

$$\begin{array}{r} ^{1} \\ 13 \\ \times\ 5 \\ \hline 65 \end{array}$$

4. **5 × 13 = 65**

2-2 Multiply by 2, 3, 4, and 6 (pp. 47–53)

Find each product.

16. 2 × 28 = 56
17. 3 × 17 = 51
18. 51 × 4 = 204
19. 36 × 6 = 216
20. 17 × 2 = 34
21. 12 × 6 = 72
22. 4 × 30 = 120
23. 21 × 3 = 63

Example 2

Find the product of 4 and 32.

1. Rewrite the problem in a vertical format.
2. Multiply the number in the ones column by 4. **4 × 2 = 8**
   Write the ones digit under the ones column.

$$\begin{array}{r} 32 \\ \times\ 4 \\ \hline 8 \end{array}$$

3. Multiply 4 times the digit in the tens column.
   4 × 3 = 12
   Write the tens digits under the tens column.

$$\begin{array}{r} 32 \\ \times\ 4 \\ \hline 128 \end{array}$$

4. **4 × 32 = 128**

Chapter 2 Study Guide 83

Intervention Strategy — Visual Learners

Use Models Have students use arrays more often if they are in need of more visualization of modeling multiplication expressions. Also, the same students may benefit from using arrays to find the missing number in a multiplication expression.

Dinah Zike's Foldables®

Review Have students quiz themselves by reviewing their Foldables and stating each product without looking under the tab. Students can also work with partners by quizzing each other until they know the multiplication facts with automaticity. (For complete instructions, see Chapter Resource Masters, p. A20.)

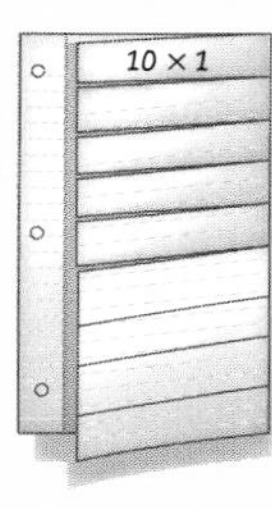

Math Coach Notes

Create a Checklist Help students create a study checklist. The checklist should include the following items:

- know how to create an array to model multiplication expressions;
- know how to find a missing number in a multiplication expression with the use of an array;
- know how to find a missing number in a multiplication expression without the use of an array;
- know your multiplication facts (digits 0 through 12) from memory;
- know the algorithm for multiplying larger numbers (not from memory);
- know how to estimate a product and understand the significance an estimate offers in determining the reasonableness of an answer.

Students should put a checkmark next to each topic when they feel they have a good grasp of the process.

Common Error *Alert*

Repeated Addition Remind students when writing the multiplication expressions as repeated addition that the first factor is the number being added. The second factor is the number of times you add the number.

2-3 Multiply by 7, 8, and 9 (pp. 55–60)

Find each product.

24 $7 \times 6 =$ 42

25 $8 \times 8 =$ 64

26 $9 \times 7 =$ 63

27 $31 \times 8 =$ 248

28 $56 \times 9 =$ 504

29 $19 \times 7 =$ 133

30 $8 \times 15 =$ 120

31 $9 \times 12 =$ 108

Example 3

Use a pattern to find the product of 5 × 8.

1. Skip count by 8s to write the multiples of 8.
2. Multiples of 8: 8, 16, 24, 32, 40, 48, 56, 64
   $1 \times 8 = 8$ $2 \times 8 = 16$ $3 \times 8 = 24$
   $4 \times 8 = 32$ $5 \times 8 = 40$ $6 \times 8 = 48$
   $7 \times 8 = 56$ $8 \times 8 = 64$ $9 \times 8 = 72$
   $10 \times 8 = 80$
3. $5 \times 8 = 40$

2-4 Multiply by 11 and 12 (pp. 61–66)

Find each product.

32 $4 \times 11 =$ 44

33 $12 \times 6 =$ 72

34 $11 \times 12 =$ 132

35 $3 \times 12 =$ 36

36 $11 \times 8 =$ 88

37 $12 \times 7 =$ 84

38 $3 \times 11 =$ 33

39 $9 \times 12 =$ 108

Example 4

Use an array model to find 12 × 8.

1. Rewrite 12×8 in distributive form.
   $(10 \times 8) + (2 \times 8)$
2. Draw an array using two sets of counters.

3. The array shows $10 \times 8 = 80$ and $2 \times 8 = 16$. So, $80 + 16 = 96$.
4. $12 \times 8 = 96$

Intervention Strategy

Naturalist/ Visual Learners

Real-World Examples Tell students that six of one thing is also called half a dozen. Ask students to think of real-world examples of items that come in sets of a half-dozen. Examples could be eggs, fruit, bagels, doughnuts, and roses. Use concrete materials, such as an egg carton with six plastic eggs. Ask: How many half-dozens are in 30 egg cartons? Students can draw or cut out pictures of their items and place them on poster board.

2-5 Multiply Greater Numbers (pp. 68–73)

Find each product.

40 $\begin{array}{r} 13 \\ \times\ 18 \\ \hline 234 \end{array}$

41 $\begin{array}{r} 47 \\ \times\ 62 \\ \hline 2{,}914 \end{array}$

42 $\begin{array}{r} 26 \\ \times\ 53 \\ \hline 1{,}378 \end{array}$

43 $\begin{array}{r} 71 \\ \times\ 29 \\ \hline 2{,}059 \end{array}$

Example 5

Find the product of 31 and 42. Use the partial products method.

1. Rewrite the problem in a vertical format.
2. Multiply 2 times the ones column.
   $2 \times 1 = 2$
3. Multiply 2 times the tens column.
   $2 \times 30 = 60$
4. Multiply 40 times the ones column.
   $40 \times 1 = 40$
5. Multiply 40 times the tens column.
   $40 \times 30 = 1{,}200$
6. Add the partial products.
   $2 + 60 + 40 + 1{,}200 = 1{,}302$
7. $31 \times 42 = 1{,}302$.

$$\begin{array}{r} 31 \\ \times\ 42 \\ \hline 2 \\ 60 \\ 40 \\ 1{,}200 \\ \hline 1{,}302 \end{array}$$

2-6 Multiplication and Division (pp. 75–80)

Complete each equation. Write the numbers in the number family.

44 $18 \times 62 =$ 1,116

$62 \times$ 18 $= 1{,}116$

$1{,}116 \div$ 18 $= 62$

$1{,}116 \div$ 62 $= 18$

18, 62, 1,116

45 $45 \times$ 10 $= 450$

10 $\times 45 = 450$

$450 \div 10 =$ 45

$450 \div$ 45 $= 10$

10, 45, 450

Example 6

Write the fact family for the array.

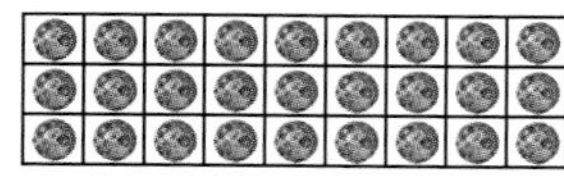

1. Write two multiplication sentences shown by the array.
   $9 \times 3 = 27$
   $3 \times 9 = 27$
2. Write two division sentences with the same numbers.
   $27 \div 9 = 3$
   $27 \div 3 = 9$

Ticket Out the Door

Quizzes Have every student create a 10-question quiz on various topics from this chapter. Then during the following day of class, have students trade quizzes with a partner or look at the quizzes and present some of the better questions to the class.

Math Coach Notes

Commutative Property Have students define the *Commutative Property.* Have them state the operations for which the Commutative Property applies. Explore whether or not the Commutative Property applies to subtraction and division.

Intervention Strategy — Interpersonal Learners

Pair-and-Share Examples Have students write down some simple multiplication expressions and ask their partner to make an array that models the expression. Tell them to be prepared to check the work of their partner, and if a mistake is made, they will have to demonstrate the steps needed to get the correct answer.

English Learner Strategy

Multiply Students Have one student stand in front of the class. Count his or her arms and legs. The fact is $4 \times 1 = 4$. Have another student come forward. How many arms and legs are there total? Write $4 \times \_\_ = 8$ on the board. What fact do the two students represent? $4 \times 2 = 8$ Practice first writing the fact on the board, and then having the students write the fact. Have 8 students stand in front and repeat the process.

Chapter 2 Chapter Test

Chapter Resource Masters

Additional forms of the Chapter 2 Tests are available.

Test Format	Where to Find it
Chapter 2 Test	Math Online macmillanmh.com
Blackline Masters	Assessment Masters, p. 25

Customize and create multiple versions of your chapter tests and their answer keys. All of these questions from the chapter tests are available on ExamView® Assessment Suite.

Online Assessment and Reporting
macmillanmh.com

This online assessment tool allows teachers to track student progress with easily accessible, comprehensive reports available for every student. Assess students using any internet-ready computer.

Alternative Assessment

Use Portfolios Ask students to write examples of each type of problem from this chapter in their portfolios. Ask them to include an array or a factor tree with the examples, where appropriate. Also, have the students find the answer to each example in their portfolio. Stress that they show all of the work required to arrive at the answer.

Chapter Test

Draw an array to model each expression.

1 $9 \times 3 =$ 27

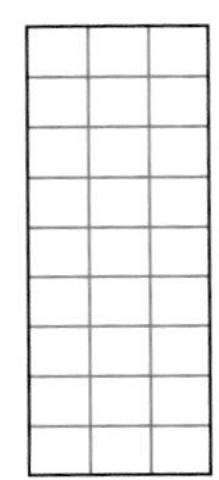

2 $8 \times 8 =$ 64

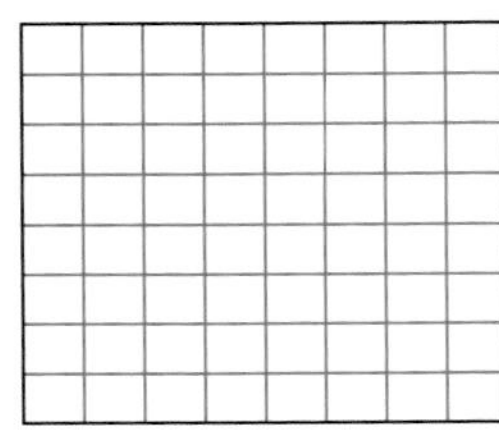

Find each product. Show your work.

3 $0 \times 481 =$ 0

4 $97 \times 1 =$ 97

5 $7 \times 5 =$ 35

6 $18 \times 10 =$ 180

7 $13 \times 2 =$ 26

8 $3 \times 18 =$ 54

9 $21 \times 4 =$ 84

10 $6 \times 14 =$ 84

11 $16 \times 7 =$ 112

12 $28 \times 8 =$ 224

13 $9 \times 20 =$ 180

14 $11 \times 6 =$ 66

15 $12 \times 4 =$ 48

16 $17 \times 5 =$ 85

17 $12 \times 8 =$ 96

GO ON

English Learner Strategy

Assessment Allow students time to look over the assessment. Have the students take a close look at the problem directions. Since much of this chapter uses repetitive directions, students should understand the directions. However, if a student does not remember what a word(s) means, such as *related fact,* provide an opportunity for students to clarify any misunderstandings they may have. You can do this by offering further explanation or you can refer them to the pages in their text where the topic was presented.

Use partial products to find the product.

18

$$\begin{array}{r} 29 \\ \times\ 38 \\ \hline 72 \\ 160 \\ 270 \\ +\ 600 \\ \hline 1{,}102 \end{array}$$

19

$$\begin{array}{r} 44 \\ \times\ 57 \\ \hline 28 \\ 280 \\ 200 \\ +\ 2000 \\ \hline 2{,}508 \end{array}$$

Solve.

20 **FRUIT** Brooke is picking strawberries from her garden. She picked 9 pints and 15 fit into a pint. How many strawberries will Brooke have?

135 strawberries

21 **FITNESS** Ricco is lifting weights at the gym. Ricco has 4 weights on the barbell he is bench pressing. Each weight is 20 pounds. How much can Ricco bench press?

80 pounds

Correct the mistakes.

22 **SNACKS** Charles wanted to share his box of raisins with Mila and Miles. He counted 36 raisins altogether. He said, "We can each have 14 raisins." Is Charles' statement correct? How do you know?

No; Sample answer: 36 raisins divided by 3 is 12 raisins.

Each person should get 12 raisins, not 14 raisins.

Learning from Mistakes

Review Review commonly missed questions as a small group or class. Ask students to share their methods of answering each question. Try to point out when any errors occur and take corrective measures.

Data-Driven Decision Making

Students missing Exercises . . .	Have trouble with . . .	Should review and practice . . .
1–2	drawing an array to model a multiplication expression.	SSG Lesson 2-1, p. 40
4–17	finding products.	SSG Lessons 2-1 to 2-5, pp. 40, 47, 55, 61 and 68 Skills Practice, pp. A24, A32, A36, and A40
18–19	use partial products to find a product.	SSG Lesson 2-5, p. 68 CRM Skills Practice, p. A42
20–22	solving word problems involving division.	SSG Lessons 2-6, pp. 68 and 75 CRM Problem-Solving Practice, pp. A41 and A45

Chapter 2 Test Practice

Diagnose Student Errors

Survey student responses for each item. Class trends may indicate common errors and misconceptions.

1. A misunderstood Distributive Property
B misunderstood Zero Property of Multiplication
(C) correct
D misunderstood Commutative Property of Multiplication

2. A added instead of multiplied
(B) correct
C wrote numbers in the wrong order
D divided instead of multiplied

3. (A) correct
B added instead of multiplied
C transposed digits
D multiplied wrong

4. A wrong property, this is an example of the Distributive Property
B wrong property, this is an example of the Zero Property of Multiplication
C wrong property, this is an example of the Identity Property of Multiplication
(D) correct

5. A these are factors, not multiples
(B) correct
C product of 4 and 9
D not multiples of 9

6. A guess
(B) correct
C added 7 and 91
D added 13 and 91

7. A confused division with multiplication
B this is the product
(C) correct
D total items multiplied by 4, should be the number of rows by the number of columns

8. (A) correct
B divided by 18, not 4
C divided by 9, not 4
D divided by 3, not 4

Chapter 2 Test Practice

Choose the best answer and fill in the corresponding circle on the sheet at right.

1 $36 \times 1 = 36$ is an example of which property?

A Distributive Property
B Zero Property of Multiplication
(C) Identity Property of Multiplication
D Commutative Property of Multiplication

2 $68 \times 2 =$

A 70 C 163
(B) 136 D 34

3 Find the product of 12 and 52.

(A) 624 C 246
B 64 D 46

4 Which is an example of Commutative Property of Multiplication?

A $6(4 + 1) = (6 \times 4) + (6 \times 1) = 24 + 6 = 30$
B $6 \times 0 = 0$
C $6 \times 1 = 6$
(D) $6 \times 4 = 24$ and $4 \times 6 = 24$

5 The first four multiples of 9 are...

A 1, 3, 3, 9 C 36
(B) 9, 18, 27, 36 D 9, 10, 11, 12

6 Grace cut a rope into 7 pieces. Each piece is 13 ft long. How long was the original rope?

A 21 feet C 98 feet
(B) 91 feet D 104 feet

7 Which expression does this array model?

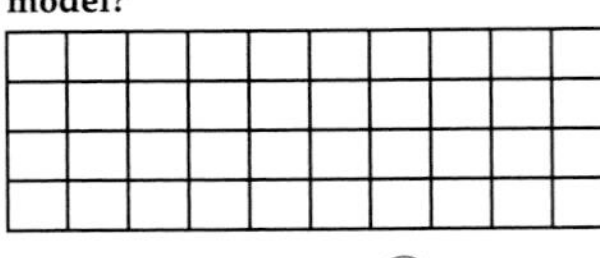

A $10 \div 4$ (C) 4×10
B 40 D 40×4

8 Bruno is walking dogs for his dog walking business. If he counts 36 dog legs, how many dogs is he walking?

(A) 9 dogs C 4 dogs
B 2 dogs D 12 dogs

9 $86 \times 7 =$

A 93 C 206
B 522 (D) 602

GO ON

9. A added instead of multiplied
B subtracted the regrouped tens instead of adding
C guess
(D) correct

10. A misunderstood inverse operations
(B) correct
C misunderstood inverse operations
D misunderstood inverse operations

11. A guess
B guess
(C) correct
D guess

12. A added instead of multiplied
B subtracted instead of multiplied
C divided instead of multiplied
(D) correct

10 Which is an example of an inverse operation?

A addition and multiplication

(B) multiplication and division

C subtraction and division

D addition and division

11 The cafeteria has 5 long tables. Each table can seat 10 students. How many students can sit at all of the tables?

A 2

B 20

(C) 50

D 55

12 The product of 77 and 7 is ____.

A 84

B 70

C 11

(D) 539

ANSWER SHEET

Directions: Fill in the circle of each correct answer.

1	(A)	(B)	● C	(D)
2	(A)	● B	(C)	(D)
3	● A	(B)	(C)	(D)
4	(A)	(B)	(C)	● D
5	(A)	● B	(C)	(D)
6	(A)	● B	(C)	(D)
7	(A)	(B)	● C	(D)
8	● A	(B)	(C)	(D)
9	(A)	(B)	(C)	● D
10	(A)	● B	(C)	(D)
11	(A)	(B)	● C	(D)
12	(A)	(B)	(C)	● D

Success Strategy

Double check your answers after you finish. Read each problem and all of the answer choices. Put your finger on each bubble you filled in to make sure it matches the answer for each problem.

STOP

Diagnosing Student Errors and Misconceptions

Find Mistakes Have students try to find where they made their mistakes and correct them. If some students are still having trouble, pair them with those who have a good grasp of the material. Have the student who is comfortable with the material "teach" the concept. Partners should take turns teaching the same concept.

Eliminate Wrong Answers If students are not able to successfully eliminate wrong answer choices, maybe it would be helpful for you to point out the following:

Exercises 2 and 3 Students should estimate the answers to give them an idea of which answers can be eliminated.

Exercise 8 Students should read the problem carefully. The question asks for the use of division, not multiplication.

Chapter 3

Chapter Overview

Chapter-at-a-Glance

Lesson	Math Objective	State/Local Standards
3-1 Model Division (pp. 92–98)	Understand the meaning of division.	
3-2 Divide by 0, 1, and 10 (pp. 99–105)	Divide when the divisor is 0, 1, or 10.	
Progress Check 1 (p. 106)		
3-3 Divide by 2 and 5 (pp. 107–112)	Divide when the divisor is 2 or 5.	
3-4 Divide by 3 and 4 (pp. 113–119)	Divide when the divisor is 3 or 4.	
Progress Check 2 (p. 120)		
3-5 Divide by 6 and 7 (pp. 121–126)	Divide when the divisor is 6 or 7.	
3-6 Divide by 8 and 9 (pp. 127–133)	Divide when the divisor is 8 or 9.	
Progress Check 3 (p. 134)		

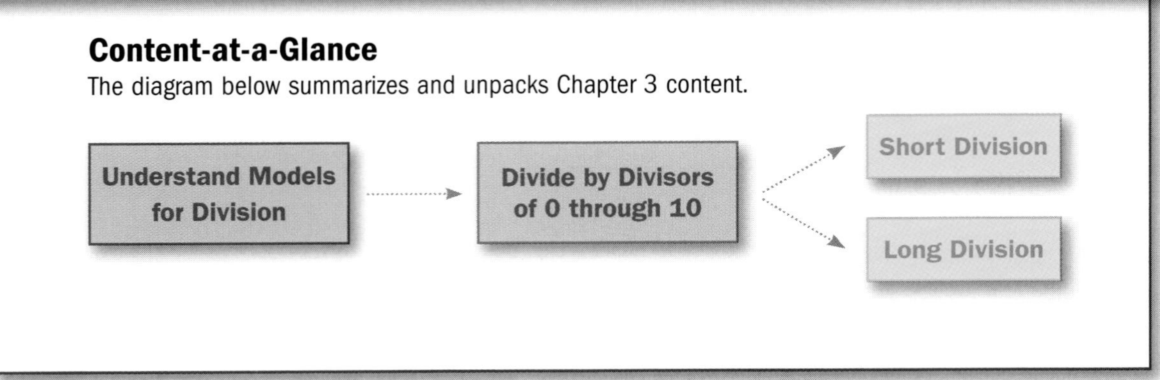

Chapter Assessment Manager

Diagnostic Diagnose students' readiness.

	Student/Teacher Editions	Assessment Masters	Technology
Course Placement Test		1	ExamView® Assessment Suite
Book 1 Pretest		8	ExamView® Assessment Suite
Chapter 3 Pretest		33	ExamView® Assessment Suite
Quiz/Preview	SSG 91		Math Online macmillanmh.com StudentWorks™ Plus

Formative Identify students' misconceptions of content knowledge.

	Student/Teacher Editions	Assessment Masters	Technology
Progress Checks	SSG 106, 120, 134		Math Online macmillanmh.com StudentWorks™ Plus
Vocabulary Review	SSG 135		Math Online macmillanmh.com
Lesson Assessments			ExamView® Assessment Suite
Are They Getting It?	TE 96, 102, 110, 115, 124, 129		Math Online macmillanmh.com

Summative Determine student success in learning the concepts in the lesson, chapter, or book.

	Student/Teacher Editions	Assessment Masters	Technology
Chapter 3 Test	SSG 138	36	ExamView® Assessment Suite
Test Practice	SSG 140	39	
Alternative Assessment	TE 138	42	ExamView® Assessment Suite
See It, Do It, Say It, Write It	TE 98, 105, 112, 119, 126, 133		
Book 1 Test		55	ExamView® Assessment Suite

Backmapping and Vertical Alignment **McGraw-Hill's *Math Triumphs*** intervention program was conceived and developed with the final result in mind: student success in grade-level mathematics, including Algebra 1 and beyond. The authors, using the **NCTM Focal Points and Focal Connections** as their guide, developed this brand-new series by backmapping from grade-level and Algebra 1 concepts, and vertically aligning the topics so that they build upon prior skills and concepts and serve as a foundation for future topics.

Chapter Resource Manager

	Lesson 3-1	Lesson 3-2	Lesson 3-3	Lesson 3-4
Concept	Model Division	Divide by 0, 1, and 10	Divide by 2 and 5	Divide by 3 and 4
Objective	Understand the meaning of division.	Divide when the divisor is 0, 1, or 10.	Divide when the divisor is 2 or 5.	Divide when the divisor is 3 or 4.
Math Vocabulary	array dividend division divisor inverse operations quotient	dividend divisor quotient	dividend divisor quotient	multiple remainder
Lesson Resources	**Materials** • Construction paper **Manipulatives** • Algebra tiles • Connecting cubes • Geoboard **Other Resources** CRM Vocabulary and English Language Development CRM Skills Practice CRM Problem-Solving Practice CRM Homework Practice	**Materials** • Construction paper • Index cards • Multiplication chart **Manipulatives** • Algebra tiles • Base-ten blocks • Geoboard **Other Resources** CRM Vocabulary and English Language Development CRM Skills Practice CRM Problem-Solving Practice CRM Homework Practice	**Materials** • Everyday objects • Grid paper **Manipulatives** • Algebra tiles • Connecting cubes • Counters • Geoboard **Other Resources** CRM Vocabulary and English Language Development CRM Skills Practice CRM Problem-Solving Practice CRM Homework Practice	**Materials** • Construction paper • Multiplication chart • Number line **Manipulatives** • Geoboard • Number line • Two-color counters **Other Resources** CRM Vocabulary and English Language Development CRM Skills Practice CRM Problem-Solving Practice CRM Homework Practice
Technology	Math Online macmillanmh.com StudentWorks™ Plus ExamView® Assessment Suite	Math Online macmillanmh.com StudentWorks™ Plus ExamView® Assessment Suite	Math Online macmillanmh.com StudentWorks™ Plus ExamView® Assessment Suite	Math Online macmillanmh.com StudentWorks™ Plus ExamView® Assessment Suite

Teacher Edition
DVD

Lesson 3-5	Lesson 3-6	
Divide by 6 and 7	Divide by 8 and 9	**Concept**
Divide when the divisor is 6 or 7.	Divide when the divisor is 8 or 9.	**Objective**
multiple remainder	mental math multiple short division	**Math Vocabulary**
Materials • Hundred chart • Multiplication chart • Number line **Manipulatives** • Pattern blocks • Two-color counters **Other Resources** CRM Vocabulary and English Language Development CRM Skills Practice CRM Problem-Solving Practice CRM Homework Practice	**Materials** • Grid paper • Number line **Manipulatives** • Algebra tiles • Two-color counters **Other Resources** CRM Vocabulary and English Language Development CRM Skills Practice CRM Problem-Solving Practice CRM Homework Practice	**Lesson Resources**
Math Online macmillanmh.com StudentWorks™ Plus ExamView® Assessment Suite	Math Online macmillanmh.com StudentWorks™ Plus ExamView® Assessment Suite	**Technology**

Intervention Strategy

Flashcard Practice

Arrange students into pairs. Students should mix up the order of their own set of flashcards.

Have students take turns being the one who shows the cards and the one who gives the quotients.

Discuss with students that practicing flashcards is necessary to memorize these facts.

Flashcard Suggestions

- Have students go through the flashcards and make two piles as they go. One pile is of the division facts they know. The other pile contains the facts that they do not know automatically. Have them spend some time with the second pile.
- Suggest that students practice at home with their parents/caregivers, friends, or siblings.
- Use the flashcards as students enter or exit the classroom. Students must say the quotient before coming or going.
- Students can make one set of flashcards to keep in the classroom and another set to keep at home.

Chapter 3 Chapter Notes

Real-World Applications

Classes San Bernido Middle School has 234 incoming sixth graders. If there are 9 sixth-grade teachers and the students are evenly divided, how many students will there be in each class? There will be 26 students in each class.

Intervention Strategy

Direction Presentations

Step 1 Divide students into small groups.

Step 2 Have each group create step-by-step directions on how to complete a long-division problem.

Step 3 Then have them simplify each step by using only a few words to describe the step. They will also need to come up with an acronym for their directions to help them remember each step.

Step 4 Each group will be responsible for sharing its directions and using an example to help it illustrate the steps even better.

Step 5 After every group has shared its directions, have students raise their hands for which acronym they will use to help them remember the steps of long division.

Chapter 3 Division

Let's play a game of soccer.

Division helps us make up the teams. If there are 18 people who want to play, you would divide 18 by 2 to get 2 teams of 9 people.

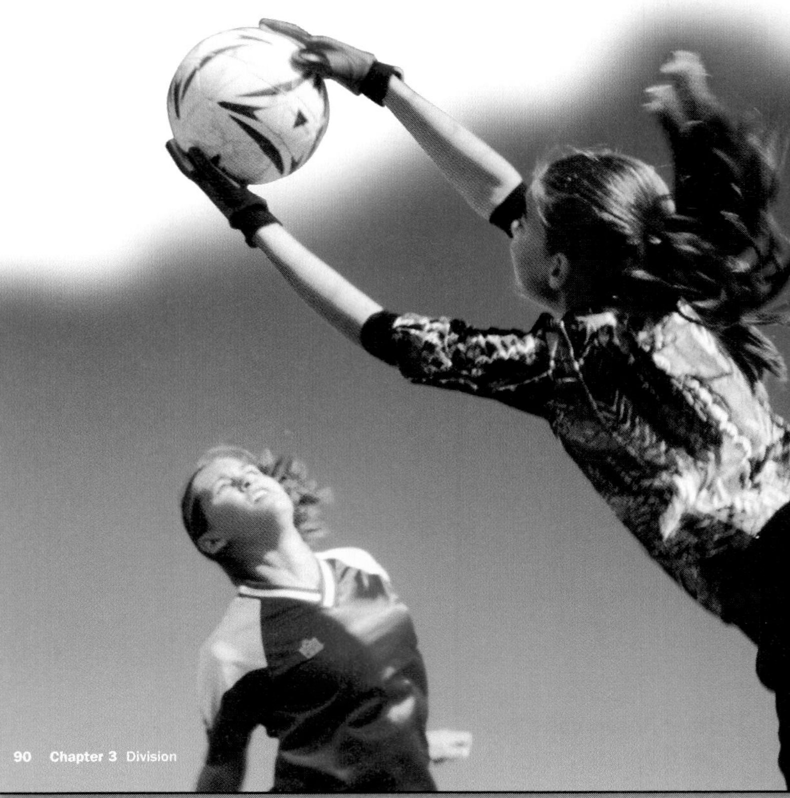

90 Chapter 3 Division

Key Vocabulary

Find interactive definitions in 13 languages in the **eGlossary** at macmillanmh.com

English **Español** *Introduce the most important vocabulary terms from Chapter 3.*

array **arreglo**

objects or symbols displayed in rows of the same length and columns of the same length; the length of a row might be different from the length of a column (p. 92)

dividend **dividendo**

the number that is being divided (p. 92)

division **división**

an operation on two numbers in which the first number is split into the same number of equal groups as the second number (p. 92)

$6 \div 3$ means 6 divided into 3 groups of equal size

divisor **divisor**

the number by which the dividend is being divided (p. 92)

divisor ↘ $5\overline{)15}$ with quotient 3 above; dividend ↖ 15

$15 \div 5 = 3$ (15 = dividend, 5 = divisor, 3 = quotient)

quotient **cociente**

the answer or result of a division problem (p. 92)

remainder **residuo**

the number that is left after one whole number is divided by another (p. 113)

STEP 1 Quiz Are you ready for Chapter 3? Take the Online Readiness Quiz at *macmillanmh.com* to find out.

STEP 2 Preview Get ready for Chapter 3. Review these skills and compare them with what you'll learn in this chapter.

What You Know	What You Will Learn
You know how to subtract. **Examples:** 8 − 2 = 6 6 − 2 = 4 4 − 2 = 2 2 − 2 = 0 **TRY IT!** 1 32 − 8 = 24 2 40 − 10 = 30 3 16 − 4 = 12 4 20 − 1 = 19	*Lesson 3-1* **Division** is repeated subtraction. 8 ÷ 2 = ? 8 − 2 = 6 Subtract 2 one time. 6 − 2 = 4 Subtract 2 two times. 4 − 2 = 2 Subtract 2 three times. 2 − 2 = 0 Subtract 2 four times. So, 8 ÷ 2 = 4.
You know that addition and subtraction are inverse operations. **Example:** 5 + 7 = 12 12 − 7 = 5 **TRY IT!** Rewrite each equation using an inverse operation. 5 9 − 5 = 4 4 + 5 = 9 or 5 + 4 = 9 6 15 + 10 = 25 25 − 10 = 15 or 25 − 15 = 10 7 64 − 31 = 33 33 + 31 = 64 or 31 + 33 = 64 8 22 + 76 = 98 98 − 76 = 22 or 98 − 22 = 76	*Lessons 3-2 through 3-8* Multiplication and division are **inverse operations**. 5 × 7 = 35 35 ÷ 7 = 5 9 × 3 = 27 27 ÷ 3 = 9

91

Vocabulary Preview

- As a class, make a list of important terms throughout the chapter on the board.
- Divide students into pairs. Have students identify any words that are new or unfamiliar to them.
- Students will then discuss possible definitions of the new terms, as well as the other terms.
- Have student pairs present two or three terms with definitions to the rest of the class.

Step 1 Quiz

Pretest/Prescribe Students can take the Online Readiness Quiz or the Diagnostic Pretest in the Assessment Masters.

Step 2 Preview

Use this pre-chapter activity to activate students' prior knowledge, build confidence, and help students preview the lessons.

Dinah Zike's Foldables®

Guide students through the directions on p. A47 in the Chapter Resource Masters to create their own Foldable graphic organizer for use with this chapter.

Home Connections

- Take a bag or box that has numerous small items such as buttons or paper clips. Count the total number of items. Divide the total number by 3, 5, and 8. Then double-check your work by manually dividing the items into 3, 5, and 8.

Professional Development

Targeted professional development has been articulated throughout McGraw-Hill's ***Math Triumphs intervention*** program. **The McGraw-Hill Professional Development Video Library** provides short videos that support the **NCTM Focal Points and Focal Connections.** For more information, visit www.macmillanmh.com.

Lesson 3-1 Lesson Notes

Lesson Planner

Objective Understand the meaning of division.

Vocabulary **array, dividend, division, divisor, inverse operations, quotient**

Materials/Manipulatives algebra tiles, connecting cubes, construction paper, geoboard

Chapter Resource Masters

- CRM Vocabulary and English Language Development (p. A50)
- CRM Skills Practice (p. A51)
- CRM Problem-Solving Practice (p. A52)
- CRM Homework Practice (p. A53)

1 Introduce

Vocabulary

Models Write several division expressions on the board. Ask for volunteers to write the *quotient* for each expression. Have students identify the *dividends* and *divisors.* See if students can draw *arrays* to represent the sentences. Invite other volunteers to write the rest of the fact families for each division sentence.

2 Teach

Key Concept

Foundational Skills and Concepts After students have read through the Key Concept box, have them try these exercises.

1. What are the 3 ways a division sentence can be written? horizontal, vertical, fraction method
2. When you draw an array, the number of rows = __divisor__. The number of columns = __quotient__.
3. How do you know $8 \div 2 = 4$? $2 \times 4 = 8$

Lesson 3-1 Model Division

KEY Concept

Division is the **inverse operation** of multiplication. You use multiplication facts when you divide. Division is used to make groups of equal size.

If you had eight pretzels and wanted to share them with a friend, you would divide the pretzels into two groups.

The division can be written three ways.

horizontal method	vertical method	fraction method
$8 \div 2 = 4$	$2\overline{)8}$ with 4 above	$\frac{8}{2} = 4$

- The **dividend** in these problems is 8.
- The **divisor** in these problems is 2.
- The **quotient** in these problems is 4.

Arrays can help you find the quotient of a division problem.

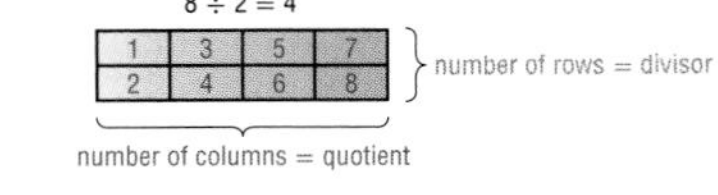

number in all		number of rows		number of columns
8	÷	2	=	4
dividend		divisor		quotient

Use multiplication to check your division.

$8 \div 2 = 4$ is correct because $2 \times 4 = 8$.

VOCABULARY

array
objects or symbols displayed in rows of the same length and columns of the same length; the length of a row might be different from the length of a column

dividend
the number that is being divided

division
to separate into equal groups
Example: $6 \div 3$ means 6 is divided into 3 groups of equal size.

divisor
the number by which the dividend is being divided

inverse operations
operations that undo each other
Example: Multiplication and division are inverse operations.

quotient
the answer or result of a division problem

Think of fact families when dividing. A fact family has two multiplication sentences and two division sentences.

$4 \times 2 = 8$	$8 \div 2 = 4$
$2 \times 4 = 8$	$8 \div 4 = 2$

Intervention Strategy — Kinesthetic/Logical/Visual Learners

Share Models Have students work in pairs using geoboards. One student creates an array on a geoboard. The partner has to explain the division sentence the array represents. The partner writes down the sentence and draws the corresponding array. Together, the pair writes that division sentence in three different formats and writes the rest of the members of its fact family. Students reverse roles and continue practice. Pairs can share the sentences they created with other groups or with the class.

Example 1

Draw an array to model the expression $6 \div 3$.

1. Identify the dividend (the first number). This is the *total number of rectangles* in the array. 6
2. Identify the divisor (the second number). This represents the number of *rows*. 3
3. Draw an array with 6 rectangles in 3 rows.

1	4
2	5
3	6

2 columns = quotient

4. The number of columns in the array is the quotient. 2
5. Check by multiplying the quotient by the divisor. The product should be the dividend. $3 \times 2 = 6$

YOUR TURN!

Draw an array to model the expression $12 \div 4$.

1. Identify the dividend. 12
   This is the total number of rectangles in the array.
2. Identify the divisor. 4
   This represents the number of rows.
3. Draw an array with 12 rectangles in 4 rows.

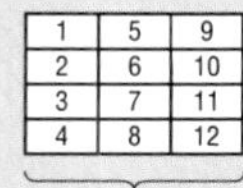

1	5	9
2	6	10
3	7	11
4	8	12

3 columns = quotient

4. The number of columns in the array is the quotient.
   3
5. Check by multiplying the quotient by the divisor.
   $3 \times 4 = 12$

Example 2

Draw a model of $10 \div 2$ using circles and tally marks.

1. What is the divisor? 2
   Draw 2 circles.

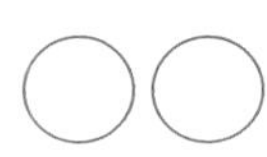

2. What is the dividend? 10
   Use tally marks to divide the 10 into 2 groups.
   Place a tally mark in each circle as you count until you have drawn 10 tally marks.

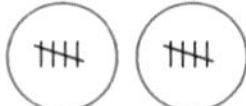

3. How many tally marks are in each circle? 5
   Write the problem with the quotient. $10 \div 2 = 5$
4. Check. $2 \times 5 = 10$ ✓

GO ON

English Learner Strategy

Guiding Questions Write $10 \div 2 = 5$ on a sheet of paper. Then ask the following questions to ensure that students understand the concept.

- Read this math sentence aloud. What shows you this is a division problem?
- How do you write this sentence in two other ways?
- Which is the dividend, divisor, and quotient?
- How do you find the other members of this fact family?
- Use counters to build an array for this sentence. How is this array different from the array for $10 \div 5 = 2$?

Additional *Example 1*

Draw an array to model the expression $18 \div 3$.

1. Identify the dividend (the first number). This is the *total number of rectangles* in the array. 18
2. Identify the divisor (the second number). This represents the number of *rows*. 3
3. Draw an array with 18 rectangles in 3 rows.

1	4	7	10	13	16
2	5	8	11	14	17
3	6	9	12	15	18

6 columns = quotient

4. The number of columns in the array is the quotient. 6
5. Check by multiplying the quotient by the divisor. The product should be the dividend. $3 \times 6 = 18$

Additional *Example 2*

Draw a model of $16 \div 4$ using circles and tally marks.

1. What is the divisor? 4
   Draw 4 circles.

2. What is the dividend? 16
   Use tally marks to divide the 16 into 4 groups. Place a tally mark in each circle as you count until you have drawn 16 tally marks.
3. How many tally marks are in each circle? 4
   Write the problem with the quotient.
   $16 \div 4 = 4$
4. Check. $4 \times 4 = 16$ ✓

Additional **Example 3**

Write 24 ÷ 6 in two different formats.

1. What number is the divisor? 6
   The divisor goes in front of the division bracket.
2. Write the vertical format. $6\overline{)24}$
   Read as, "Twenty-four divided by six."
3. Write as a fraction. $\frac{24}{6}$
   Read as, "Twenty-four divided by six."

Additional **Example 4**

Write the division facts from the fact family of 7 × 4 = 28.

1. Write the division fact using the first factor as the divisor.
   28 ÷ 7 = 4
2. Write another division fact using the second factor as the divisor.
   28 ÷ 4 = 7

YOUR TURN!

Draw a model of 15 ÷ 3 using circles and tally marks.

1. What is the divisor? 3 Draw 3 circles.
2. What is the dividend? 15
   Use tally marks to divide the 15 into 3 groups.
   Place a tally mark in each circle as you count until you have drawn 15 tally marks.
3. How many tally marks are in each circle? 5
   Write the problem with the quotient. 15 ÷ 3 = 5
4. Check. 3 × 5 = 15

Example 3

Write 6 ÷ 3 in two different formats.

1. What number is the divisor? 3
   The divisor goes in front of the division bracket.
2. Write the vertical format. $3\overline{)6}$
   Read as, "Six divided by three."
3. Write as a fraction. $\frac{6}{3}$
   Read as, "Six divided by three."

YOUR TURN!

Write 15 ÷ 5 in two different formats.

1. What number is the divisor? 5
2. Write the vertical format. $5\overline{)15}$
   Read as,
   "Fifteen divided by five."
3. Write as a fraction. $\frac{15}{5}$
   Read as,
   "Fifteen divided by five."

Example 4

Write the division facts from the fact family of 5 × 2 = 10.

1. Write the division fact using the first factor as the divisor.
   10 ÷ 5 = 2
2. Write another division fact using the second factor as the divisor.
   10 ÷ 2 = 5

YOUR TURN!

Write the division facts from the fact family of 7 × 2 = 14.

1. Write the division fact using the first factor as the divisor.
   14 ÷ 7 = 2
2. Write another division fact using the second factor as the divisor.
   14 ÷ 2 = 7

Intervention Strategy

Linguistic/ Interpersonal Learners

Word Problems Have students create division word problems in pairs or small groups. Ask students to write and draw their division word problems, including the solutions and a written explanation. Allow time for students to share their problems with the class.

Who is Correct?

Write 16 ÷ 4 in two different formats.

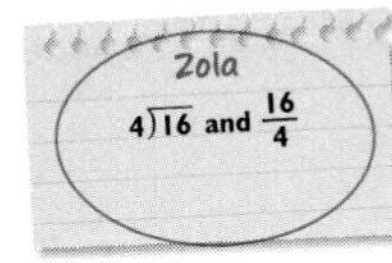

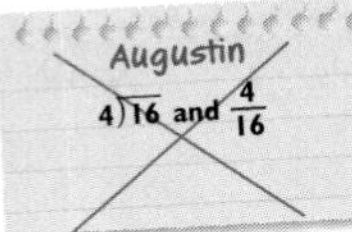

Circle correct answer(s). Cross out incorrect answer(s).

Guided Practice

1 Draw an array to model the expression 12 ÷ 3.

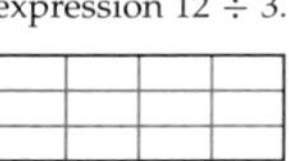

2 Draw a model of 12 ÷ 2 using circles and tally marks.

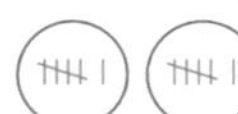

Step by Step Practice

3 Draw an array to model the expression 12 ÷ 6.

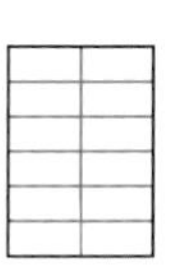

Step 1 Identify the dividend. 12

This is the total number of rectangles in the array.

Create an array that has 12 rectangles in 6 rows.

Step 2 Identify the divisor. 6

This represents the number of rows.

Step 3 The number of columns in the array is the quotient.

2

Step 4 Check your division by multiplying the quotient by the divisor.

$2 \times 6 = 12$.

GO ON

Lesson 3-1 Model Division **95**

Who ***is Correct?***

Diagnostic Teaching

- Paulita's work is incorrect. The divisor and dividend are switched in the vertical format.
- Zola's work is correct. Both formats are written properly.
- Augustin's work is incorrect. The fraction is written in reverse order.

Remind students that the number following the division sign is the divisor.

3 Practice

Using Manipulatives

Geoboards When presenting Example 1, use concrete materials such as geoboards to make the arrays.

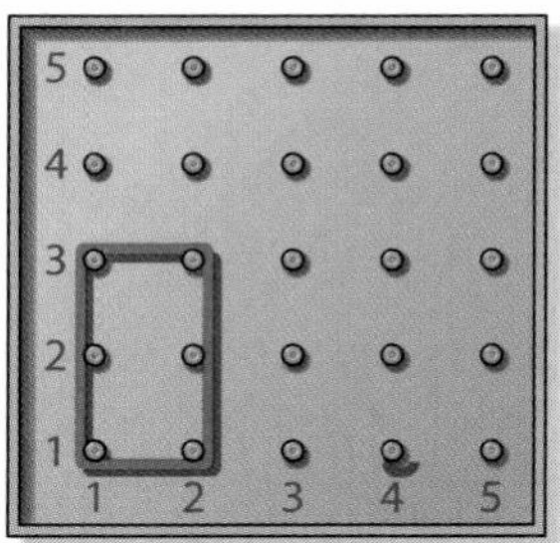

$6 \div 3 = 2$

Algebra Tiles Use algebra tiles to form arrays or use as counters to solve multiplication and division problems.

Connecting Cubes Use connecting cubes to move into groups to solve multiplication and division problems.

On-Hand Manipulatives Use beans or squares of different-colored construction paper as counters.

Math Coach Notes

Strategies

1. Begin this lesson by reviewing multiplication facts. Reinforcing the relationship between fact families of multiplication and division will increase automaticity.
2. Discuss real-world examples of division in students' daily routines. Recognizing the importance of these concepts may help increase the motivation to learn the algorithms.

Common Error *Alert*

Exercises 4–8 If students have difficulty with Exercises 4–8, they might be confused about which number represents the number of rows and which represents the number of columns. Demonstrate how an array for 12 ÷ 3 is different from an array for 12 ÷ 4.

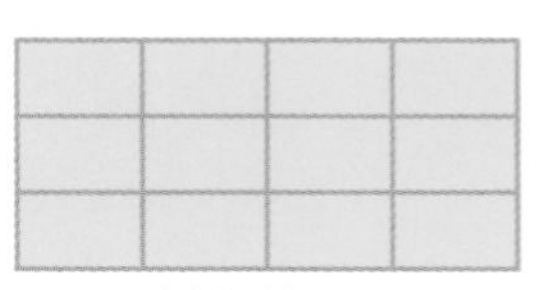

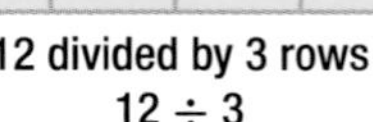

12 divided by 3 rows
12 ÷ 3

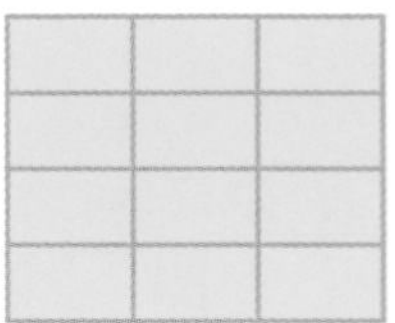

12 divided by 4 rows
12 ÷ 4

Note This!

Color Coding Encourage students to use different colors to match terms with examples in their math journals. For instance, have students write and define the term *dividend.* Write the name in red. Then in the examples, write the division sentence in a variety of forms showing the dividend in red each time. This will help students link the definition with its application.

Draw an array to model each expression.

4. 9 ÷ 3 How many rows? 3
How many rectangles? 9
How many columns? 3

5. 8 ÷ 4

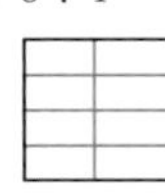

6. 14 ÷ 7

7. 6 ÷ 3

8. 16 ÷ 2

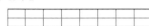

Step by Step Problem-Solving Practice

Problem-Solving Strategies
☑ Draw a diagram.
☐ Use logical reasoning.
☐ Solve a simpler problem.
☐ Work backward.
☐ Guess and check.

Solve.

9. GARDENS Berto is planting a garden with 18 seeds. He wants to have 3 rows of seeds with the same number of seeds in each row. How many seeds will be in each row?

Understand Read the problem. Write what you know.
There are 18 seeds. There will be 3 rows.

Plan Pick a strategy. One strategy is to draw a diagram.

Solve Make an array with the correct number of rows.
Continue making columns until there are 18 rectangles.
The diagram shows how the seeds will be planted.
There are 3 rows and 6 columns.
The number of columns represents the quotient.
There will be 6 seeds in each row.

Check Think about the fact family. Is the division fact part of the family? Yes; 18 ÷ 3 = 6.

96 Chapter 3 Division

Are They Getting It?

Check students' understanding of division operations by writing these problems on the board. Ask students to point out wrong answers and explain why they are wrong.

1. 18 ÷ 3 can be expressed as $3\overline{)18}$ with quotient 6 and $\frac{18}{3} = 6$. This is correct.

2. The following is an array for 6 ÷ 3. 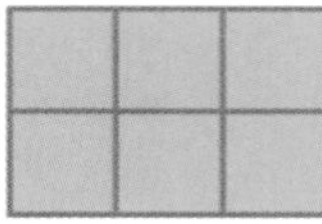 This is incorrect. 6 divided by 3 rows is 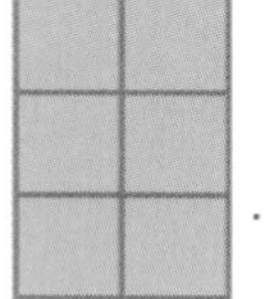.

3. A model of 14 ÷ 2 is .
This is incorrect. The circle and tally model of 14 ÷ 2 is .

10 PROJECT Vito and 3 of his classmates are to study the 12 animals from the Chinese calendar. How many animals will each of them have to study? Check off each step.

✔ Understand: I circled key words.

✔ Plan: To solve the problem, I will draw a diagram.

✔ Solve: The answer is 3 animals.

✔ Check: I checked my answer by using fact families.

PROJECT
Chinese calendar

11 ENTERTAINMENT José is arranging 20 chairs for a party. He wants to have 5 rows of chairs with the same number of chairs in each row. How many chairs will he put in each row?
4 chairs

12 **Reflect** Explain how multiplication is the inverse operation for division.

Sample answer: An inverse operation undoes another operation. When you divide by a number, you are dividing a number into groups. To undo this, multiply the number of groups (divisor) by the quotient to get the dividend.

Skills, Concepts, and Problem Solving

Draw an array to model each expression.

13 $20 \div 5$

14 $8 \div 4$

Draw a model using circles and tally marks for each expression.

15 $18 \div 3$

16 $9 \div 3$

17 $3 \div 1$

18 $8 \div 2$

GO ON

Math Challenge

Write Division Sentences Challenge students to use 36 counters to write as many division sentences as they can. Have them include a drawing of the array for each sentence they create. For more proficient students, challenge them to use other materials for their arrays, such as base-ten blocks, geoboards, number lines, algebra tiles, or drawings.

Odd/Even Assignments

Exercises 13–30 are structured so that students practice the same concepts whether they are assigned the odd or even problems.

In-Class Assignment

Have students complete Exercises 13, 16, 18, 22, 24, 27, and 33 to ensure that they understand the concept.

Intervention Strategy

Auditory/Kinesthetic Learners

Model Problems Ask students to practice explaining how to model division expressions to one another. Working in pairs, have each student use correct terms and clear language to model a division problem and find its quotient. Students can use any concrete materials for the models, including counters, base-ten blocks, algebra tiles, geoboards, or drawings. For proficient learners, challenge the pairs to make errors during the explanations to see if the listeners can catch the mistakes.

4 Assess

See It, Do It, Say It, Write It

Step 1 Write two division problems on the board, one vertically and the other horizontally. Ask two student volunteers to solve them.

Step 2 Ask students to model the problems using manipulatives or drawings.

Step 3 Ask students to share their drawings with a partner. Have them explain the differences in what they drew.

Step 4 Write a third division problem on the board. Have students work in pairs. Tell them to write a brief word problem for the sentence. Problems should include a quotient and a model that represents the situation. Have students share their word problems in small groups or with the class.

Looking Ahead: Pre-teach

Divide by 0, 1, and 10 In the next lesson, students will learn how to divide by 0, 1, and 10.

Example

What number times 7 will give you 7? Consider the multiplication fact this question represents: ____ $\times$ 7 = 7. Use fact families to fill in the missing number. 1 $\times$ 7 = 7 so 1 is the missing number.

Find each missing number.

1. 5 × ____ = 50 10
2. 9 × ____ = 0 0
3. 8 ÷ ____ = 8 1
4. 30 ÷ ____ = 10 3
5. 0 ÷ 3 = ____ 0
6. 40 ÷ ____ = 40 1

Write each expression in two different formats.

19 25 ÷ 5 $5\overline{)25}$ $\frac{25}{5}$

20 16 ÷ 8 $8\overline{)16}$ $\frac{16}{8}$

Write the division facts from each fact family.

21 6 × 3 = 18 18 ÷ 6 = 3; 18 ÷ 3 = 6

22 7 × 4 = 28 28 ÷ 7 = 4; 28 ÷ 4 = 7

23 4 × 5 = 20 20 ÷ 4 = 5; 20 ÷ 5 = 4

24 2 × 8 = 16 16 ÷ 2 = 8; 16 ÷ 8 = 2

25 6 × 4 = 24 24 ÷ 6 = 4; 24 ÷ 4 = 6

26 3 × 9 = 27 27 ÷ 3 = 9; 27 ÷ 9 = 3

27 2 × 11 = 22 22 ÷ 2 = 11; 22 ÷ 11 = 2

28 10 × 5 = 50 50 ÷ 10 = 5; 50 ÷ 5 = 10

Solve.

29 PACKAGING Three packages contain 36 golf balls in all. How many golf balls are in each package if there are the same number of balls in each?
12 golf balls

30 MOVIES Eleanor received 18 movie passes for her birthday. How many times can she and 2 friends go to see a movie?
6 times

Vocabulary Check **Write the vocabulary word that completes each sentence.**

31 Division is the same as repeated subtraction.

32 The inverse operation for division is multiplication.

33 Writing in Math Karen wrote the division facts from the fact family 4 × 5 = 20. What mistake did Karen make?

20 ÷ 5 = 5 20 ÷ 4 = 4

Karen forgot to use both factors. She should have written 20 ÷ 5 = 4 and 20 ÷ 4 = 5.

98 **Chapter 3** Division

Ticket Out the Door

Write, Model, and Solve Write the following on the board: 20 ÷ 5 = ?

Ask students to:

1. Write the expression in two other formats. Include the quotient in each format.
2. Draw an array to model the expression.

Students will hand in their papers as they exit the classroom.

Lesson 3-2

Divide by 0, 1, and 10

KEY Concept

There are special division rules to use when you divide.

Any number divided by itself is equal to 1.

$3 \div 3 = 1$

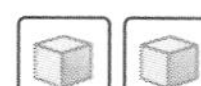

Any number divided by 1 is the same number.

$3 \div 1 = 3$

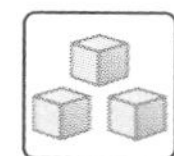

Zero divided by any number (except 0) equals 0.

You cannot divide by 0. It is not possible.

You can use models to divide by ten.

$30 \div 10 = 3$

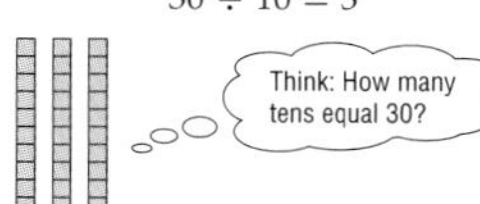
Think: How many tens equal 30?

VOCABULARY

dividend
a number that is being divided

divisor
the number by which the dividend is being divided

quotient
the answer or result of a division problem

You should memorize the division rules for 0, 1, and 10.

- 0: Zero divided by any number equals zero.
- 1: Any number divided by one is the same number.
- 10: Models can be used to divide by ten.

GO ON

Math Coach Notes

Division Facts Have students memorize these facts during the study of this lesson.

$0 \div 10 = 0$	
$10 \div 10 = 1$	$60 \div 10 = 6$
$20 \div 10 = 2$	$70 \div 10 = 7$
$30 \div 10 = 3$	$80 \div 10 = 8$
$40 \div 10 = 4$	$90 \div 10 = 9$
$50 \div 10 = 5$	$100 \div 10 = 10$

Encourage students to practice both multiplication and division facts. Use flashcards, tables, or frequent timed skill drills to assess progress. The more comfortable and automatic these basic facts become, the less difficulty students will encounter when the numbers and processes become more complex.

Lesson Notes

Lesson 3-2

Lesson Planner

Objective Divide when the divisor is 0, 1, or 10.

Vocabulary **dividend, divisor, quotient**

Materials/Manipulatives algebra tiles, base-ten blocks, construction paper, index cards, geoboard, multiplication chart

Chapter Resource Masters

- CRM Vocabulary and English Language Development (p. A54)
- CRM Skills Practice (p. A55)
- CRM Problem-Solving Practice (p. A56)
- CRM Homework Practice (p. A57)

1 Introduce

Vocabulary

Division Operations Write several division expressions on the board, using 1 and 10 as divisors. Ask for volunteers to write the *quotient* for each expression. Have students identify the *dividends* and *divisors*. Ask for other volunteers to write the *inverse operation* for each division sentence on the board. Challenge students to draw *models* to represent the sentences.

2 Teach

Key Concept

Foundational Skills and Concepts After students have read through the Key Concept box, have them try these exercises.

1. What is true about any number divided by itself? equal to 1
2. What is 0 divided by any number except 0? 0
3. What is any number divided by 1? the same number

Additional **Example 1**

Use a model to find 5 ÷ 1.

1. Draw a model.
2. How many groups will be there? 1
3. How many in each group? 5

  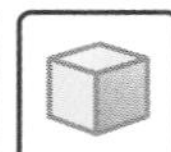  

4. Write the quotient. $5 \div 1 = 5$
5. Check. $1 \times 5 = 5$

Additional **Example 2**

Find 60 ÷ 10.

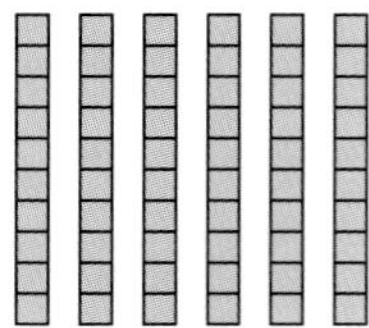

1. What number is the divisor? 10
2. How many tens equal 60? 6
3. Write the quotient. $60 \div 10 = 6$
4. Check. $6 \times 10 = 60$

Example 1

Use a model to find 6 ÷ 1.

1. Draw a model.
2. How many groups will there be? 1
3. How many in each group? 6
4. Write the quotient. $6 \div 1 = 6$
5. Check. $1 \times 6 = 6$

YOUR TURN!

Use a model to find 7 ÷ 1.

1. Draw a model.
2. How many groups will there be? 1
3. How many in each group? 7
4. Write the quotient. $7 \div 1 =$ 7
5. Check. $1 \times 7 =$ 7

Example 2

Find 40 ÷ 10.

1. What number is the divisor? 10

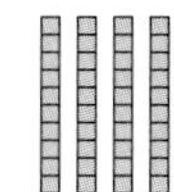

2. How many tens equal 40? 4
3. Write the quotient. $40 \div 10 = 4$
4. Check. $4 \times 10 = 40$

YOUR TURN!

Find 80 ÷ 10.

1. What number is the divisor? 10

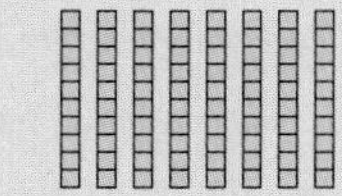

2. How many tens equal 80? 8
3. Write the quotient. $80 \div 10 =$ 8
4. Check. $8 \times 10 =$ 80

100 **Chapter 3** Division

Intervention Strategy — Logical/Visual Learners

Multiplication and Division

1. Begin this lesson by using a multiplication chart to identify and practice finding the multiples of 10.
2. Discuss the difference between the arrays of 60 ÷ 10 and 60 ÷ 6. It is important for students to recognize how the groupings change. Discuss fact families and the related facts.

Who is Correct?

Find 100 ÷ 10.

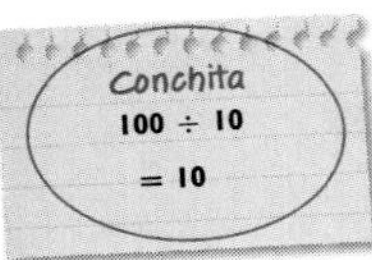

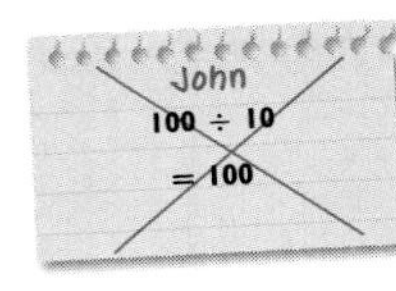

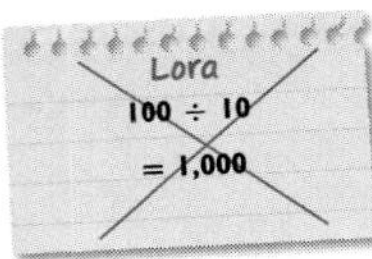

Circle correct answer(s). Cross out incorrect answer(s).

Guided Practice

Use a model to find each quotient.

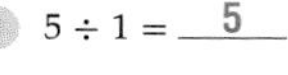

1. $5 \div 1 =$ <u>5</u>

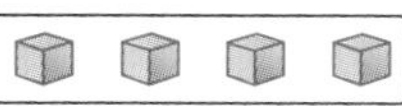

2. $60 \div 10 =$ <u>6</u>

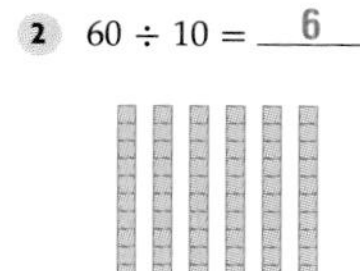

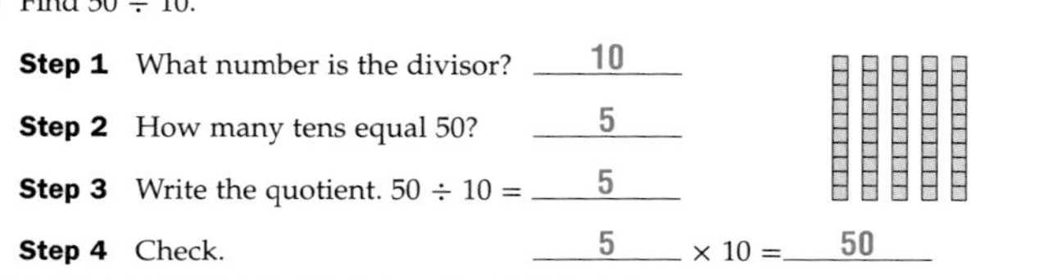

Step by Step Practice

3. Find $50 \div 10$.

Step 1 What number is the divisor? <u>10</u>

Step 2 How many tens equal 50? <u>5</u>

Step 3 Write the quotient. $50 \div 10 =$ <u>5</u>

Step 4 Check. <u>5</u> $\times 10 =$ <u>50</u>

GO ON

Who *is Correct?*

Diagnostic Teaching

- Conchita's work is correct. $10 \times 10 = 100$
- John's work is incorrect. $10 \times 100 = 1{,}000$, not 100.
- Lora's work is incorrect. $10 \times 1{,}000 = 10{,}000$, not 100.

Remind students that dividing by 10 means there is one less zero in these answers than in the dividend.

Intervention Strategy

Kinesthetic/ Linguistic Learners

Group Work Write several division expressions on the board, such as $30 \div 10$, $8 \div 1$, and $0 \div 4$. Have students work in pairs or small groups. Ask students to practice explaining how to find the quotient for each expression. Students should use correct terms and clear language for their explanations. Next, have students prove their quotients are correct by providing the other members of the fact family and building or drawing a model for each division sentence. Encourage students to use concrete materials such as counters, base-ten blocks, algebra tiles, geoboards, number lines, or drawings. Groups can share their explanations and models with the class.

3 Practice

Using Manipulatives

Geoboards When presenting models of division sentences, use concrete materials such as geoboards to make arrays.

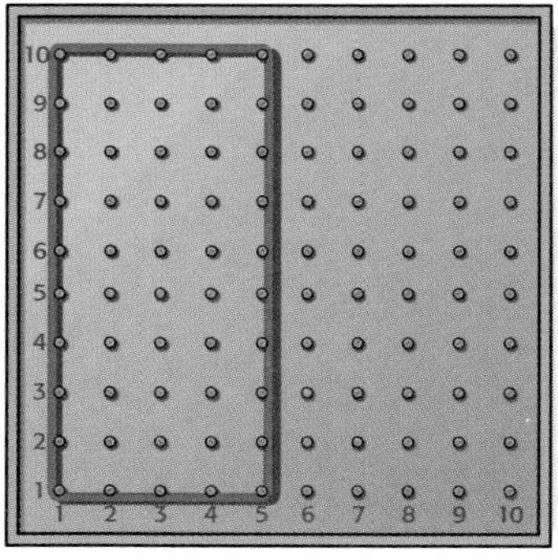

$50 \div 10 = 5$

Algebra Tiles Use algebra tiles to form arrays or use as counters to solve division problems.

Base-Ten Blocks Use rods to move into groups to solve division problems with divisors of 10.

On-Hand Manipulatives Use beans or squares of different-colored construction paper as counters.

Common Error *Alert*

Exercises 11–12 If students have difficulty with Exercises 11–12, they might be confused about zero as the divisor versus zero as the dividend. Have students practice reading the problem as "___ groups of ___" to see if they understand what is being divided by what. For instance, 0 divided into 7 equal groups is 0. But 7 divided into 0 groups is not possible. Use concrete materials such as counters to create a visual and help students see that no number can be divided by 0, but that 0 can be divided by any number.

English Learner Strategy

Color Code Use different colors to write vocabulary words such as *divisor, dividend,* and *quotient* on index cards. When modeling division sentences, use the same color of the matching vocabulary word to write the numbers. Model saying the number and the name of the term for each division sentence. Ask students to echo you. Practice with sentences you write and sentences the student writes.

Find each quotient. If the quotient is not possible, write *not possible*.

4. $90 \div 10 =$ 9

   Check. 9 × 10 = 90

5. $10 \div 10 =$ 1
6. $70 \div 10 =$ 7
7. $60 \div 10 =$ 6
8. $40 \div 10 =$ 4
9. $6 \div 1 =$ 6
10. $9 \div 1 =$ 9
11. $15 \div 0 =$ not possible
12. $4 \div 0 =$ not possible
13. $12 \div 1 =$ 12
14. $3 \div 1 =$ 3
15. $0 \div 7 =$ 0
16. $0 \div 2 =$ 0
17. $11 \div 11 =$ 1
18. $8 \div 8 =$ 1

Step by Step Problem-Solving Practice

Problem-Solving Strategies
- ☐ Draw a model.
- ☐ Use logical reasoning.
- ☑ Make a table.
- ☐ Solve a simpler problem.
- ☐ Work backward.

Solve.

19. MONEY There are 10 pennies in each dime. If you have 60 pennies, for how many dimes could you trade?

Understand Read the problem. Write what you know.

There are 10 pennies in a dime.
There are 60 pennies altogether.

Plan Pick a strategy. One strategy is to make a table.

Solve Complete the table.

The table shows that 60 pennies equal 6 dimes.

Check Does the answer make sense? Look over your solution. Did you answer the question?

Pennies	Dimes
10	1
20	2
30	3
40	4
50	5
60	6

102 Chapter 3 Division

Are They Getting It?

Check students' understanding of division operations by writing these problems on the board. Have students state which are correct and which are incorrect. Make certain they provide reasons. Encourage them to use drawings or examples in their explanations.

1. 30 ÷ 10 is 3 because 10 × 3 is 30. This is correct.
2. 10 ÷ 0 is 0 because 0 × 10 is 10. This is incorrect. Any number divided by 0 is not possible because any number times 0 is 0.
3. 0 ÷ 7 is 0 because 0 × 7 is 0. This is correct.

20 CONSTRUCTION There are 10 rolls of paper towels in every jumbo package. If a shopper wants 80 rolls of paper towels, how many packages should he purchase? Check off each step.

✔ Understand: I circled key words.

✔ Plan: To solve the problem, I will make a table.

✔ Solve: The answer is 8 packages.

✔ Check: I checked my answer by multiplying.

21 FOOD The cafeteria used 120 eggs for a recipe. How many dozens of eggs did they use? Hint: use base-ten blocks.

10 dozen

A dozen is 12 eggs.

22 Reflect Explain why you cannot divide by zero.

Sample answer: Multiplication is used to check division. For example, in $6 \div 0$, ask what times 0 is 6. No number times 0 is equal to 6, so division by 0 does not work. $6 \div 0$ is undefined or impossible.

Skills, Concepts, and Problem Solving

Use a model to find each quotient.

23 $8 \div 8 =$ 1

24 $50 \div 10 =$ 5

25 $60 \div 10 =$ 6

26 $40 \div 10 =$ 4

GO ON

Intervention Strategy

Visual/ Kinesthetic Learners

Model Problems Have students use geoboards and grid paper to model division sentences. Write several division expressions on the board. Ask students to model each expression on their geoboards and find the quotient. On grid paper, students should draw the array they made on the geoboard and explain how this demonstrates the division sentence and proves their quotient is correct. Encourage students to use correct vocabulary terms and clear language in their explanations.

Odd/Even Assignments

Exercises 23–46 are structured so that students practice the same concepts whether they are assigned the odd or even problems.

In-Class Assignment

Have students complete Exercises 24, 27, 33, 37, 42, and 49 to ensure that they understand the concept.

Math Coach Notes

Related Facts Emphasize related facts when teaching multiplication and division facts. Reinforcing that the division algorithm is simply another way to write the multiplication algorithm will help students identify fact families more easily and increase automaticity.

Intervention Strategy

Logical/ Visual Learners

Division Bingo

Materials needed: index cards, writing utensils, paper, markers, or counters

Have students create flashcards to play a division bingo game. Tell students to write division expressions using 1 and 10 as the divisors and 0 as the dividend on index cards. Write one expression per card. Students should create a bingo board and write the quotients for the expressions in random squares. Have students shuffle the cards together and place them facedown. Students take turns drawing a card and using markers to cover any squares with that expression's quotient on their game board. When students get a bingo or five covered squares in a row, they must recite the division sentences for the other players to check.

Common Error *Alert*

Multi-Step Problem If students struggle with Exercises 43–46, they may have difficulty determining what they need to know. Ask students to read the problem aloud and rephrase the given information in their own words. Review the strategies they could use to find the missing information. Have them determine which strategy would best help them find the solution. Encourage students to use concrete materials to model the problem. Reread the questions to make sure the answers are complete and reasonable.

Intervention Strategy

Auditory/ Logical Learners

Correct or Not? Recite several division sentences. Include a few incorrect quotients in the list of sentences. Ask students to write down the sentences you recite. Challenge students to determine which ones are correct. Have students provide proof for those sentences that are correct and explanations for those that are not correct.

Math Coach Notes

Review When studying for tests or quizzes, encourage students to review the problems they struggled with on their homework. Practice breaking those problems down and explaining them out loud and in writing. Have students try to write similar problems to solve, and invite a family member or classmate to check their work.

Find each quotient. If the quotient is not possible, write *not possible*.

27 $60 \div 10 =$ 6

28 $90 \div 1 =$ 90

29 $12 \div 1 =$ 12

30 $15 \div 1 =$ 15

31 $40 \div 0 =$ not possible

32 $40 \div 1 =$ 40

33 $30 \div 10 =$ 3

34 $0 \div 80 =$ 0

35 $3 \div 0 =$ not possible

36 $0 \div 7 =$ 0

37 $1 \div 1 =$ 1

38 $2 \div 1 =$ 2

39 $8 \div 1 =$ 8

40 $4 \div 1 =$ 4

41 $3 \div 3 =$ 1

42 $5 \div 5 =$ 1

Solve.

43 MODELS Alana uses base-ten blocks to model a division problem. She takes the one-blocks and groups them into 10 piles of 9 blocks. What division sentence models her actions?

$90 \div 10 = 9$

44 INTERIOR DESIGN Larry is laying tiles on the kitchen floor. The tiles come in boxes of 10. If each tile is 1 square foot, how many boxes will Larry need to tile a floor that is 80 square feet?

8 boxes

45 STORAGE Each storage rack in the school gym can hold 12 basketballs. Mrs. Booker has 12 basketballs. How many storage racks does Mrs. Booker need? What division sentence models her actions?

$12 \div 12 = 1$; Mrs. Booker needs 1 storage rack.

104 Chapter 3 Division

Math Challenge

Division Gaming Challenge students to create a game using division problems with divisors of 1 and 10, and 0 as a dividend. Ask students to write out rules and instructions for the game they create. If students design a board game, provide materials for them to create the board, markers, number cubes, or cards. Encourage students to play the game themselves and to work out any problems before sharing it with the class. Then provide time for students to demonstrate their games and a space for students to play the game with classmates when their class work is completed.

46 FITNESS Jake's grandfather started training on an exercise machine. By the third month, he trained 10 times longer each day than he did the first month. He trained for 60 minutes a day the third month. How many minutes a day did he train when he began?

6 minutes

Vocabulary Check **Write the vocabulary word that completes each sentence.**

47 In a division problem, the number being divided is the dividend.

48 Zero cannot be a divisor because you cannot divide by zero.

49 Writing in Math Explain why division can be thought of as repeated subtraction.

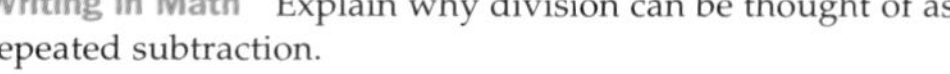

Sample answer: To find the answer to a problem such as $12 \div 3$, keep subtracting until you get to 0. $12 - 3 = 9$, $9 - 3 = 6$, $6 - 3 = 3$, $3 - 3 = 0$. Then count the number of times you subtracted 3:4.

Spiral Review

Solve. (Lesson 3-1, p. 92)

50 HOBBIES Ti is planting 35 flowers. He wants to have 5 rows of flowers. How many flowers will he put in each row?

$35 \div 5 = 7$ flowers

51 BOOKS Stella read a total of 6 books over the 12 weeks of summer. Terrance read a total of 20 books during the 40 weeks of the school year. Who read faster? Explain your answer.

Stella read 1 book every 2 weeks. Terrance read 1 book every 2 weeks. So, they read at the same pace.

Ticket Out the Door

Word Problem

Write the following on the board.

One medium pizza is cut into 10 slices. How many medium pizzas were ordered if students ate 80 slices of pizza? 8 pizzas

Have students write a division sentence that represents the word problem and then find the quotient. Tell them to provide proof or support that their answers are correct. Students will hand in their papers as they exit the classroom.

See It, Do It, Say It, Write It

Step 1 Write several division expressions on the board with 1 and 10 as divisors and 0 as the dividend. Ask student volunteers to find the quotients.

Step 2 Ask students to model the problems using manipulatives or drawings.

Step 3 Write another division expression on the board. Have students work in pairs. Tell them to write a brief word problem for the expression. Problems should include a quotient and a model that represents the situation. Have students share their word problems in small groups or with the class.

Step 4 Ask students to write their own division expressions. Ask them to write a brief word problem for the expression. Tell them to include a quotient and a model to represent the situation in the word problem.

Looking Ahead: Pre-teach

Divide by 2 and 5 In the next lesson, students will learn about dividing by 2 and 5. Students will use multiples and multiplication fact families to find missing terms.

Example

Draw an array to model $6 \div 2$. Find the quotient.

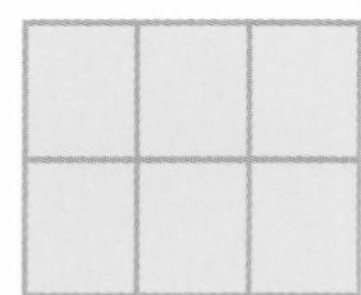

$6 \div 2 = 3$

Find each quotient.

1. $18 \div 2$ 9

2. $20 \div 5$ 4

3. $60 \div 2$ 30

Chapter 3

Progress Check 1

Formative Assessment

Use the Progress Check to assess students' mastery of the previous lessons. Have students review the lesson indicated for the problems they answered incorrectly.

Odd/Even Assignments

Exercises are structured so that students practice the same concepts whether they are assigned the odd or even problems.

Common Error *Alert*

Check Your Work to Eliminate Errors If students have time, they can check their answers on many of these exercises since division is the inverse operation of multiplication.

Exercises 5–14 These exercises are developed to stress the following significant division facts:
(1) Any number (except zero) divided by itself is 1.
(2) Zero divided by any number (except zero) is 0.
(3) Any number divided by 1 is itself.
(4) Any number divided by 0 is *not possible.*

Exercises 5–6 These exercises focus on dividing a multiple of 10 by 10. To find the quotient, students should drop the 0 from the dividend.

Chapter 3

Progress Check 1 (Lessons 3-1 and 3-2)

Draw a model for each expression.

1 $8 \div 2$

2 $15 \div 5$

Write the division expression represented by each model.

3 $40 \div 10 = 4$

4 $14 \div 2 = 7$

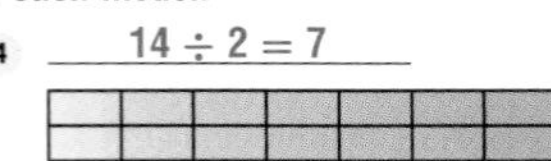

Find each quotient. If the quotient is not possible, write *not possible*.

5 $60 \div 10 =$ 6

6 $70 \div 10 =$ 7

7 $10 \div 1 =$ 10

8 $30 \div 1 =$ 30

9 $20 \div 0 =$ not possible

10 $70 \div 0 =$ not possible

11 $50 \div 50 =$ 1

12 $35 \div 35 =$ 1

13 $0 \div 6 =$ 0

14 $0 \div 10 =$ 0

Solve.

15 **MUSIC** Tina plays a series of 7 notes over and over. If she plays a total of 70 notes, how many times does Tina play the series? 10 times

16 **PARTIES** Jeannine placed 30 items into 3 favor bags. She placed the same number of items in each bag. How many items did she place in each bag? 10 items

17 **HISTORY** Refer to the photo caption at the right. A decade is 10 years. How many decades ago was the Declaration of Independence signed? 23 decades

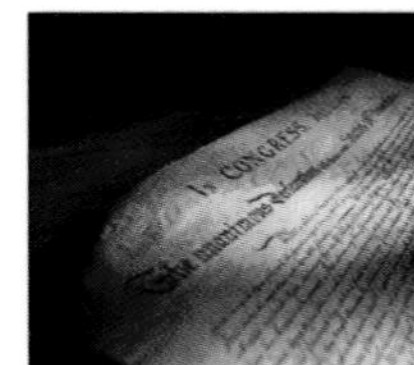

HISTORY The Declaration of Independence was signed about 230 years ago

106 Chapter 3 Division

Data-Driven Decision Making

Students missing Exercises . . .	Have trouble with . . .	Should review and practice . . .
1-2	drawing models for division expressions.	SSG Lesson 3-1, p. 92 CRM Skills Practice, p. A51
3-4	writing division expressions represented by models.	SSG Lesson 3-1, p. 92 CRM Homework Practice, p. A53
5-14	finding quotients, if possible, and recognizing when it is not possible.	SSG Lesson 3-2, p. 99 CRM Skills Practice, p. A55
15-17	solving word problems involving division.	CRM Problem-Solving Practice, pp. A52 and A56

Lesson 3-3 Divide by 2 and 5

KEY Concept

There are several phrases that represent dividing by 2. For example, 8 ÷ 2 can mean:

- the quotient of 8 and 2
- 8 divided by 2
- half of 8

You can use money and related multiplication facts when dividing by 5.

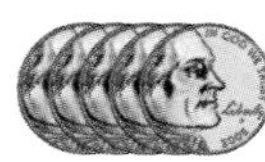

There is 25¢ in nickels shown. Each nickel is worth 5¢. There are 5 nickels. So, 25 ÷ 5 = 5. You can check using multiplication. 5 × 5 = 25.

VOCABULARY

dividend
the number that is being divided

divisor
the number by which the dividend is being divided

quotient
the answer or result of a division problem

Memorize the related multiplication facts of 2 and 5.

Example 1

Draw an array to find 8 ÷ 2.

1. Draw an array.

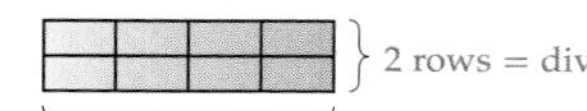

2. How many rectangles will be in the array? 8
3. How many rows? 2
4. Count the number of columns. 4
5. Write the quotient. 8 ÷ 2 = 4
6. Check. 4 × 2 = 8

GO ON

Additional *Example 1*

Draw an array to find 14 ÷ 2.

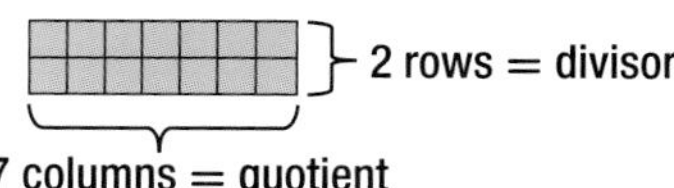

1. Draw an array.
2. How many rectangles will be in the array? 14
3. How many rows? 2
4. Count the number of columns. 7
5. Write the quotient. 14 ÷ 2 = 7
6. Check. 7 × 2 = 14

Lesson Notes

Lesson 3-3

Lesson Planner

Objective Divide when the divisor is 2 or 5.

Vocabulary **dividend, divisor, quotient**

Materials/Manipulatives algebra tiles, connecting cubes, counters, everyday objects, geoboard, grid paper

Chapter Resource Masters

- CRM Vocabulary and English Language Development (p. A58)
- CRM Skills Practice (p. A59)
- CRM Problem-Solving Practice (p. A60)
- CRM Homework Practice (p. A61)

1 Introduce

Vocabulary

Division Terms Write several division sentences with divisors of 2 or 5 on the board. Ask student volunteers to go to the board and find the solutions. Have students identify the *quotient, dividend,* and *divisor* for each sentence. Ask volunteers to explain how to use counters to model each division sentence.

2 Teach

Key Concept

Foundational Skills and Concepts After students have read through the Key Concept box, have them try these exercises.

1. Write *eight divided by two* in both vertical and horizontal formats. Find the quotient.
   8 ÷ 2 = 4 $\quad 2\overline{)8}$ with quotient 4
2. What are some phrases that represent dividing by 2?
   half of a number; a number divided by 2; the quotient of a number and 2
3. How do you know 25 ÷ 5 = 5 is correct?
   5 × 5 = 25

Additional **Example 2**

Find 35 ÷ 5.

1. Write the answer if you know it. Otherwise, solve using related multiplication.
2. What number multiplied by 5 equals 35? 7
3. Write the quotient: 35 ÷ 5 = 7
4. Check. How many nickels equal 35¢? 7 nickels

Math Coach Notes

Divide Larger Numbers By initially using arrays and drawings to teach division, students will soon recognize that this will not be a realistic method once the numbers become larger. Then students will be more receptive to learning the multiplication and division algorithms.

Intervention Strategy

Naturalist/ Kinesthetic Learners

Use Models Have students practice building models to represent division facts. Ask students to write division sentences with 2 or 5 as a divisor. Tell students to construct a model for each sentence. The models can include concrete materials such as counters, base-ten blocks, geoboards, algebra tiles, money, pattern blocks, or connecting cubes. Encourage students to also try using grid paper, drawings, number lines, or other materials they find in their environment. Allow time for students to share their sentences and models with the class.

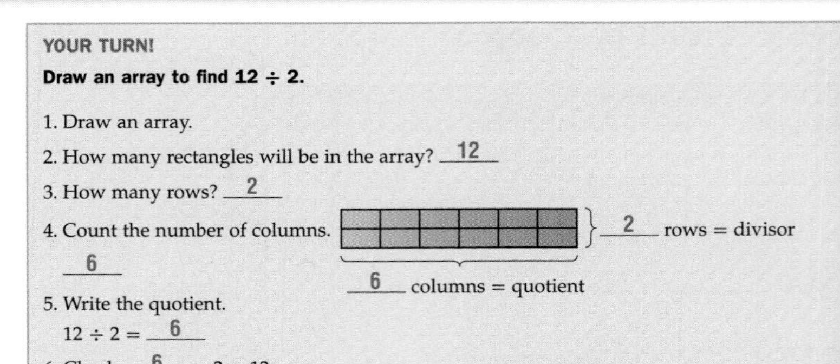

YOUR TURN!

Draw an array to find 12 ÷ 2.

1. Draw an array.
2. How many rectangles will be in the array? 12
3. How many rows? 2
4. Count the number of columns. 6 — 2 rows = divisor; 6 columns = quotient
5. Write the quotient. 12 ÷ 2 = 6
6. Check. 6 × 2 = 12

Example 2

Find 40 ÷ 5.

1. Write the answer if you know it. Otherwise, solve using related multiplication.
2. What number multiplied by 5 equals 40? 8
3. Write the quotient. **40 ÷ 5 =** 8
4. Check. How many nickels equal 40¢? 8 nickels

YOUR TURN!

Find 35 ÷ 5.

1. Write the answer if you know it. Otherwise, solve using related multiplication.
2. What number multiplied by 5 equals 35? 7
3. Write the quotient. 35 ÷ 5 = 7
4. Check. How many nickels equal 35¢? 7 nickels

Who is Correct?

Find 45 ÷ 5.

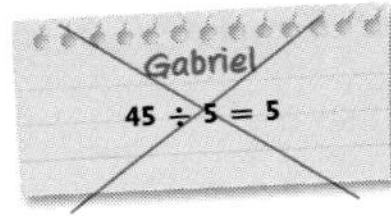

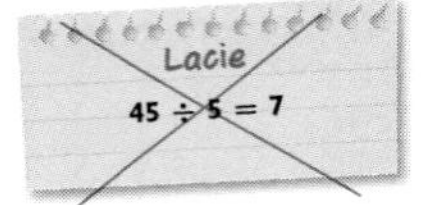

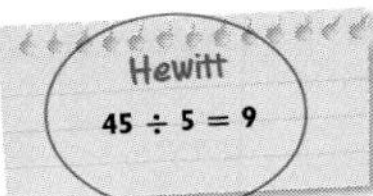

Circle correct answer(s). Cross out incorrect answer(s).

Who *is Correct?*

Diagnostic Teaching

- Gabriel's work is incorrect. He incorrectly divided by 5. 5 × 5 = 25, not 45.
- Lacie's work is incorrect. She incorrectly divided by 5. 5 × 7 = 35, not 45.
- Hewitt's work is correct.

Remind students to find the related multiplication fact correctly.

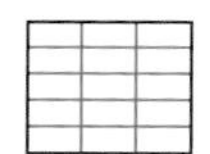

Guided Practice

Draw a model and find each quotient.

1. 15 ÷ 5 = 3 　　　　2. 12 ÷ 2 = 6

number of columns = 3 = quotient 　　　　number of columns = 6 = quotient

Find each quotient. (Use multiplication facts to help you.)

3. 30 ÷ 5 = 6	4. 45 ÷ 5 = 9	5. 18 ÷ 2 = 9
6. 14 ÷ 2 = 7	7. 50 ÷ 5 = 10	8. 20 ÷ 2 = 10
9. 20 ÷ 5 = 4	10. 16 ÷ 2 = 8	11. 8 ÷ 2 = 4

Step by Step Practice

12. Find 60 ÷ 5.

Step 1 Write the answer if you know it. Otherwise, solve using related multiplication.

Step 2 Write the related multiplication fact.

5 × 12 = 60

Step 3 Write the quotient.

60 ÷ 5 = 12

Step 4 Check.

12 × 5 = 60

Intervention Strategy — Auditory/ Logical Learners

Solve Aloud Write division problems with two-digit dividends and a 2 or 5 as divisors on the board. Make sure the quotients are whole numbers. Ask students to work in pairs to explain how to find the quotients. Have one student write a problem in vertical format and explain step by step how to solve it. Encourage students to use correct vocabulary terms and clear language. Then have students switch roles with a different problem. For more proficient students, challenge them to make errors in their explanations and ask their partners to find the mistakes.

Using Manipulatives

Geoboards When presenting Example 1, use concrete materials such as geoboards to make arrays.

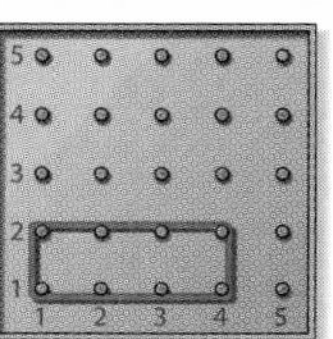

Algebra Tiles Use algebra tiles to form arrays or use as counters to solve division problems.

Connecting Cubes Use connecting cubes to move into groups and build arrays to model division problems.

On-Hand Manipulatives Use beans or squares of different-colored construction paper as counters.

Math Coach Notes

Strategies

1. Begin this lesson by using concrete materials. Model some division sentences with 2 or 5 as the divisor. Have students find the difference using manipulatives. Encourage the correct language. Have students write the numeric forms of these models on paper.
2. Practice division facts with flashcards that show vertical format. Students will need to become comfortable with this format before the numbers become larger and long division is required.

English Learner Strategy

Guiding Questions Write $40 \div 5 = 8$ on a sheet of paper. Then ask the following questions to ensure that students understand the concept.

- Read the sentence out loud. What kind of sentence is this? What lets you know that?
- Which numbers are the dividend, divisor, and quotient?
- How do you write this sentence in vertical format?
- How do you find the quotient?
- Use counters to build an array for this sentence. How is this array different from the array for $40 \div 8 = 5$?

Math Coach Notes

Study Tip Encourage students to practice their division facts with a friend or family member. Use flashcards, timed skill drill sheets, or a multiplication chart. Regularly practicing basic multiplication and division facts will facilitate students' automaticity. This will increase speed and accuracy as students move into long division.

Common Error *Alert*

Exercises 13–17 If students have difficulty with Exercises 13–17, check if students are writing the problems in vertical format and correctly aligning the corresponding place values. Ask students to use grid paper and write only one number per square. This will help the column alignment and keep the numbers brought down in the correct place.

Find each quotient.

13 $35 \div 5$ 7
Check your answer. 5 × 7 = 35

14 $12 \div 2$ 6

15 $20 \div 2$ 10

16 $15 \div 5$ 3

17 $55 \div 5$ 11

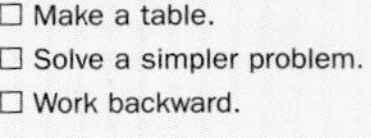

Step by Step Problem-Solving Practice

Problem-Solving Strategies
- ☑ Draw a model.
- ☐ Use logical reasoning.
- ☐ Make a table.
- ☐ Solve a simpler problem.
- ☐ Work backward.

Solve.

18 FASHION If you have 28 socks, how many pairs of socks do you have?

Understand: Read the problem. Write what you know.
There are 2 socks in each pair of socks.
There are 28 socks.

Plan: Pick a strategy. One strategy is to draw a model.

Solve: Draw 28 tallies to represent the individual socks. Circle each pair. How many groups did you have?

(||)(||)(||)(||)(||)(||)(||)(||)(||)(||)(||)(||)(||)(||)

There are 14 pairs of socks.

Check: Use multiplication to check your answer.

FASHION There are 2 socks in each pair.

19 MONEY There are $5 in every 5-dollar bill. Felix has $45 in 5-dollar bills. How many 5-dollar bills does Felix have? Check off each step.

✓ Understand: I circled key words.
✓ Plan: To solve the problem, I will draw a model.
✓ Solve: The answer is nine 5-dollar bills.
✓ Check: I checked my answer by multiplying.

110 Chapter 3 Division

Are They Getting It?

Check students' understanding of division operations by writing these problems on the board. Ask students to point out wrong answers and explain why they are wrong.

1. The quotient of $58 \div 2$ is 28. This is incorrect. $58 \div 2 = 29$
2. An array of $45 \div 5$ looks like: This is incorrect.

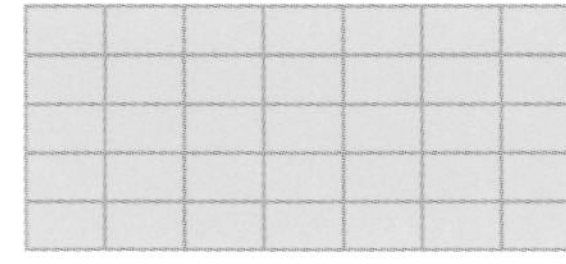

The array for $45 \div 5$ is:

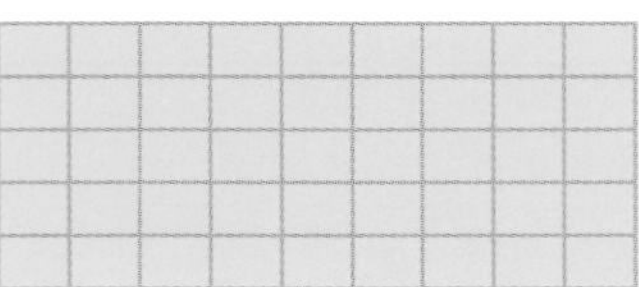

3. The quotient of $85 \div 5$ is 17. This is correct.

20 FITNESS Anica jogs 16 miles in 2 days. Aleesha jogs 40 miles in 5 days. Both jog an equal distance each day. Who jogs more each day?

They both jogged the same distance each day.

21 **Reflect** Explain how using money can help you divide by 5.

Nickels are worth 5¢. To divide a number by 5, think of the number of nickels you need to come up with that amount of money.

Skills, Concepts, and Problem Solving

Draw a model to find each quotient.

22 $35 \div 5$ 7

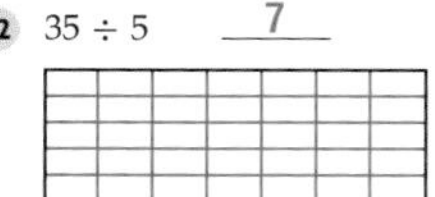

23 $44 \div 2$ 22

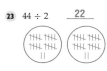

Find each quotient.

24 $18 \div 2 =$ 9	25 $12 \div 2 =$ 6	26 $15 \div 5 =$ 3
27 $25 \div 5 =$ 5	28 $45 \div 5 =$ 9	29 $20 \div 5 =$ 4
30 $14 \div 2 =$ 7	31 $18 \div 2 =$ 9	32 $25 \div 5 =$ 5
33 $50 \div 5 =$ 10	34 $22 \div 2 =$ 11	35 $14 \div 2 =$ 7

Solve.

36 COMMUNITY SERVICE The sixth grade is collecting box tops to donate to a charity that will trade them in for cash. The students have 5 weeks to collect. If their goal is to collect 50 box tops, how many should they collect per week?

10 box tops per week

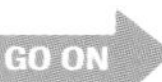

Math Challenge

True or False Have students determine if each sentence is *true* or *false*. For each false sentence, students should write an example that proves the falsehood.

1. Any number that can be divided by 10 can be divided by both 2 and 5. true
2. Any number evenly divisible by 2 is also evenly divisible by 5. False; 12 is evenly divisible by 2 but not 5.
3. A number that can be evenly divided by 5 cannot also be evenly divided by 2. False; 10 can be evenly divided by both 2 and 5.
4. There are four whole numbers between 30 and 40 (not including 30 and 40) that are divisible by 2. true

Odd/Even Assignments

Exercises 22–38 are structured so that students practice the same concepts whether they are assigned the odd or even problems.

In-Class Assignment

Have students complete Exercises 22, 29, 35, 36, and 41 to ensure that they understand the concept.

Common Error *Alert*

Multi-Step Problem If students struggle with Exercises 36–38, they might be confused about how to use the given pieces of information. Ask students to first read the problem out loud. Then have them summarize the information in their own words. Encourage students to draw a diagram or illustration to help keep the information straight. Help them determine what they need to know. Brainstorm strategies that could help them find the solution to their problem. When students have an answer, reread the problem to make sure the solution is reasonable and complete.

Intervention Strategy

Linguistic/ Interpersonal Learners

Solve and Write Write the following on the board:

$78 \div 2 = ?$ $35 \div 5 = ?$ $16 \div 2 = ?$

Have students work in pairs. Ask students to find the quotients and then write a brief word problem that represents each division sentence. Encourage pairs to share their word problems with the class. For more proficient students, ask them to prove their solutions are correct using two different strategies.

4 Assess

See It, Do It, Say It, Write It

Step 1 Write several division expressions with 2 and 5 as divisors on the board. Vary the problems, including some that require short division. Ask student volunteers to find the quotients.

Step 2 Ask students to model the problems using manipulatives or drawings.

Step 3 Write another short division expression on the board. Have students work in pairs. Tell them to write a brief word problem for the expression. Problems should include a quotient and a model that represents the situation. Have students share their word problems in small groups or with the class.

Step 4 Ask students to write a word problem involving division by 2 or 5. Have them include a quotient and a model to represent the situation in the word problem.

Looking Ahead: Pre-teach

Divide by 3 and 4 In the next lesson, students will learn about dividing by 3 and 4. Sometimes numbers do not divide evenly, which leaves a leftover amount, called a *remainder.*

Example

Find $16 \div 3$. Show the remainder.

$$\begin{array}{r} 5 \\ 3\overline{)16} \\ -15 \\ \hline 1 \end{array} \qquad 16 \div 3 = 5 \text{ R1}$$

Find each quotient. Show the remainder.

1. $13 \div 4$ 3 R1
2. $23 \div 3$ 7 R2
3. $27 \div 4$ 6 R3

37 FOOD Mrs. Foster made 2 pans of meatloaf and 5 pans of macaroni and cheese to serve for lunch. The meatloaf is cut so that there are 20 servings altogether. The macaroni and cheese is cut so there are 30 servings total. Which item has more servings in 1 pan?

The meatloaf has more servings in 1 pan.

38 SPORTS The after-school sports club rented the gym. It cost $60. If 5 sponsors donated an equal amount of money to cover the rental fees, then how much did each sponsor contribute?

Each sponsor donated $12.

Vocabulary Check **Write the vocabulary word that completes each sentence.**

39 If you divide something in half, it is divided into two equal parts.

40 In a division problem, the number you divide by is the divisor.

41 Writing in Math What mistake did Mario make in dividing 17 by 2 and getting 9?

Sample answer: 17 cannot be divided equally in half.

Spiral Review

Solve. (Lesson 3-2, p. 99)

42 GRAPHING While making a scale for her graph, Sarah wants each side of each square to represent 10 years. If she plots a point that represents 70 years, how many squares high will it be?

$70 \div 10 = 7$; 7 squares high

43 FOOD The cafeteria manager wants to ensure there is 1 piece of pizza for every student. If he cuts each pizza into 10 slices, how many whole pizzas will he need to have enough for 120 students?

12 pizzas

44 PACKAGING Cinnamon rolls come in packages of 7 or 8. What combination of packages is needed for exactly 30 cinnamon rolls?

2 of each package

112 Chapter 3 Division

Ticket Out the Door

Word Problem

Write the following on the board.

Joaquin earned $40 mowing lawns on Friday. He worked for 5 hours. How much did he earn per hour? $8

Have students write a division sentence that represents the word problem and find the quotient. Tell them to provide proof or support that their answers are correct. Students will hand in their papers as they exit the classroom.

Lesson 3-4 Divide by 3 and 4

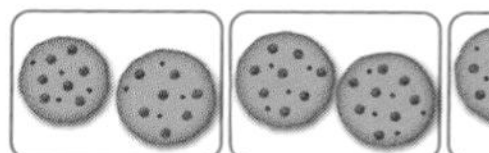

KEY Concept

When a number does not divide evenly, the part left over is called the **remainder**. Suppose 3 friends share 7 cookies.

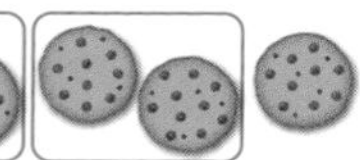

There is 1 cookie left over. This is the remainder.

When there are remainders, **multiples** help you find the number closest to the dividend.

The cookie example shows 7 ÷ 3. The closest multiple of 3 is 6, leaving 1 left over.

VOCABULARY

multiple
a multiple of a number is the *product* of that number and any whole number
Example: 30 is a multiple of 10 because 3 × 10 = 30.

remainder
the number that is left after one whole number is divided by another

Practice memorizing the division facts for 3 and 4.

Example 1

Draw an array to model 8 ÷ 4.

1. Write the answer if you know it. Otherwise, draw an array.
2. How many rectangles will be in the array? 8
3. How many rows? 4

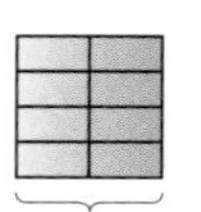

2 columns = quotient

4. Count the number of columns. 2
5. Write the quotient. 8 ÷ 4 = 2
6. Check. 2 × 4 = 8

YOUR TURN!

Draw an array to model 20 ÷ 4.

1. Write the answer if you know it. Otherwise, draw an array.
2. How many rectangles will be in the array? 20
3. How many rows? 4

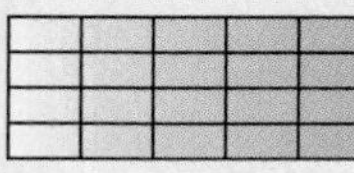

4. Count the number of columns. 5
5. Write the quotient. 20 ÷ 4 = 5
6. Check. 5 × 4 = 20

GO ON

Additional *Example 1*

Draw an array to model 20 ÷ 4.

1. Write the answer if you know it. Otherwise, draw an array.

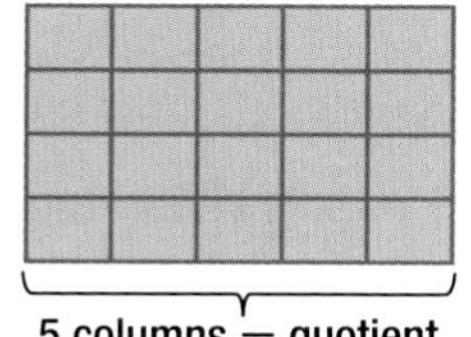

5 columns = quotient

2. How many rectangles will be in the array? 20
3. How many rows? 4
4. Count the number of columns. 5
5. Write the quotient. 20 ÷ 4 = 5
6. Check. 5 × 4 = 20

Lesson Notes

Lesson 3-4

Lesson Planner

Objective Divide when the divisor is 3 or 4.

Vocabulary **multiple**, **remainder**

Materials/Manipulatives construction paper, geoboard, multiplication chart, number line, two-color counters

Chapter Resource Masters

- CRM Vocabulary and English Language Development (p. A62)
- CRM Skills Practice (p. A63)
- CRM Problem-Solving Practice (p. A64)
- CRM Homework Practice (p. A65)

1 Introduce

Vocabulary

Multiples Write several short division expressions on the board, with 3 and 4 as divisors. Model how to explain one of the expressions using the word *multiple*. For instance, 24 ÷ 4 can be read as: "How many multiples of 4 are in 24?" Ask for student volunteers to practice this wording on other expressions.

2 Teach

Key Concept

Foundational Skills and Concepts After students have read through the Key Concept box, have them try these exercises.

1. How many multiples of 3 are less than 7? Write a division sentence and find the quotient.
   2; 7 ÷ 3 = 2, with 1 left
2. Explain why the 7 cookies were divided into 3 groups.
   Three friends shared the cookies. Each got 2 cookies.

Additional **Example 2**

Find 23 ÷ 3. Show the remainder.

1. Rewrite the problem in vertical format. $3\overline{)23}$
2. What number multiplied by 3 is close to 23? $\begin{array}{r} 7 \\ 3\overline{)23} \\ -21 \\ \hline 2 \end{array}$
   3 × 8 = 24. That is too much.
   3 × 7 = 21. This is close without going over.
   Multiply. Write the product under the dividend.
3. Subtract.
4. There are no more digits. The quotient is 7 with a remainder of 2. Write 7R2. $\begin{array}{r} 7\text{ R2} \\ 3\overline{)23} \\ -21 \\ \hline 2 \end{array}$
5. Check your answer. Multiply the quotient by the divisor. Then add the remainder.

   7 × 3 = 21
   21 + 2 = 23

Math Coach Notes

Division with Remainders Using a number line to teach division with remainders will enable students to understand the concept of greatest possible multiple without exceeding the dividend. Number lines create a visual for students to relate the difference, or remainder, to the amount remaining after the multiples.

Example 2

Find 8 ÷ 3. Show the remainder.

1. Rewrite the problem in vertical format. $3\overline{)8}$
2. What number multiplied by 3 is close to 8? $\begin{array}{r} 2 \\ 3\overline{)8} \end{array}$
   3 × 3 is 9. That is too much.
   3 × 2 is 6. This is close without going over.
   Multiply. Write the product under the dividend. $\begin{array}{r} 2 \\ 3\overline{)8} \\ -6 \\ \hline 2 \end{array}$
3. Subtract.
4. There are no more digits. The quotient is 2 with a remainder of 2. Write 2 R2. $\begin{array}{r} 2\text{ R2} \\ 3\overline{)8} \\ -6 \\ \hline 2 \end{array}$
5. Check your answer. Multiply the quotient by the divisor. Then add the remainder.

   2 × 3 = 6
   6 + 2 = 8

YOUR TURN!

Find 13 ÷ 4. Show the remainder.

1. Rewrite the problem in vertical format. $4\overline{)13}$
2. What number multiplied by 4 is close to 13? $\begin{array}{r} 3 \\ 4\overline{)13} \end{array}$
   4 × __3__ = __12__
   Multiply. Write the product under the dividend. $\begin{array}{r} 3 \\ 4\overline{)13} \\ -12 \\ \hline 1 \end{array}$
3. Subtract.
4. The quotient is __3__ with a remainder of __1__. $\begin{array}{r} 3\text{R1} \\ 4\overline{)13} \\ -12 \\ \hline 1 \end{array}$
5. Check your answer.
   __4 × 3 = 12__
   __12 + 1 = 13__

Who is Correct?

Find 22 ÷ 3. Show the remainder.

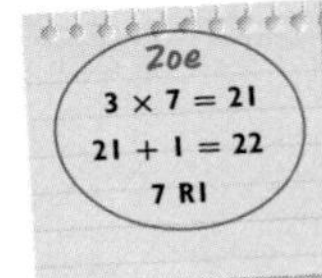

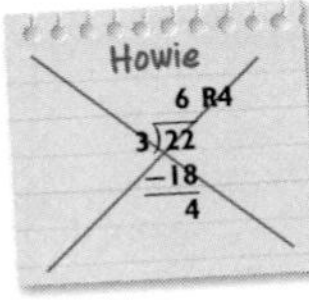

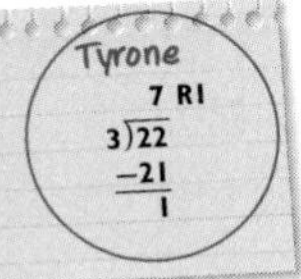

Circle correct answer(s). Cross out incorrect answer(s).

Who *is Correct?*

Diagnostic Teaching

- Zoe's work is correct. She multiplied and added correctly.
- Howie's work is incorrect. The remainder is greater than the divisor.
- Tyrone's work is correct. He multiplied and added correctly.

Remind students that the notation for remainder is an uppercase R.

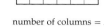

Guided Practice

Draw an array to model each quotient.

1. $18 \div 3$

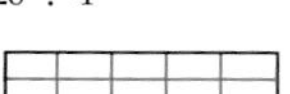

number of columns = 6 = quotient

2. $12 \div 4$

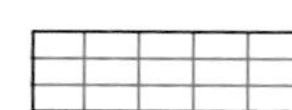

number of columns = 3 = quotient

3. $20 \div 4$

number of columns = 5 = quotient

4. $15 \div 3$

number of columns = 5 = quotient

Step by Step Practice

5. Find $13 \div 3$. Show the remainder.

Step 1 Rewrite the problem in vertical format.

Look at the first digit in the dividend. Since the divisor is more than the first digit, look at the first two digits.

$$3\overline{)13}\ \text{quotient } 4$$

Step 2 What number multiplied by 3 is equal to or less than 13? 4

Multiply 3 × 4.

Write the answer under the dividend.

$$\begin{array}{r} 4 \\ 3\overline{)13} \\ -12 \\ \hline 1 \end{array}$$

Step 3 Subtract.

Step 4 There are no more digits. Write the quotient.

$13 \div 3 =$ 4 R1

Step 5 Check your answer.

4 × 3 = 12
12 + 1 = 13

GO ON

Are They Getting It?

Check students' understanding of division operations by writing these problems on the board. Have students state which are correct and which are incorrect. Make certain they provide reasons. Encourage them to use drawings or examples in their explanations.

1. $15 \div 3 = 5$ means there are 5 multiples of 3 in 15. This is correct.
2. The array for $12 \div 4$ is: This is incorrect. The array should have 4 rows of 3, showing 3 multiples of 4.

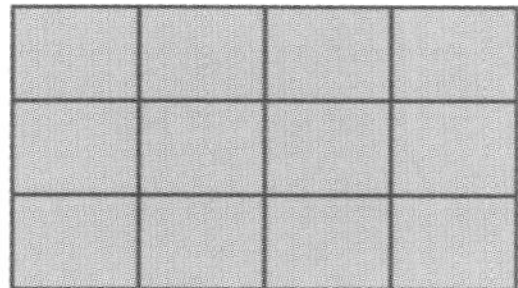

3. The quotient for $38 \div 4$ is 8 R6. This is incorrect. The remainder is greater than the divisor. The quotient of $38 \div 4$ is 9 R2.

Intervention Strategy

Logical/Auditory Learners

Practice Facts Have students make a multiplication chart to practice finding multiples and quotients. Ask students to create a 10 by 10 grid. Write the numbers 1–10 in the top row and down the first column. Have students work in pairs to write in the multiples of each number, both horizontally and vertically. Model how to find quotients using the grid. For instance, write $24 \div 4$ on the board. Tell students to find row 4 and count how many multiples of 4 are in 24. Reinforce the relationship by making a proof statement: "There are 6 multiples of 4 in 24, so $24 \div 4 = 6$ because $4 \times 6 = 24$." Ask students to work in pairs to practice multiples and division facts.

3 Practice

Using Manipulatives

Geoboards When presenting models of division sentences, use concrete materials such as geoboards to make arrays.

Two-Color Counters Use counters to move into groups or to form arrays to solve division problems.

On-Hand Manipulatives Use beans or squares of different-colored construction paper as counters.

Number Line Draw a number line to show multiples and determine the remainder.

Math Coach Notes

Strategies Begin this lesson by using a multiplication chart to identify and practice finding the multiples of 3 and 4. Use concrete materials such as counters or a number line to determine multiples and quotients.

English Learner Strategy

Guiding Questions Write 22 ÷ 3 on a sheet of paper. Then ask students the following questions to ensure that they understand the concept.

- Read this expression aloud. Which operation is required?
- How can you represent this expression with counters?
- Using a multiplication chart, what are multiples of 3?
- What are the dividend, divisor, quotient, and remainder of this expression?
- How do inverse operations prove your quotient is correct?

Common Error *Alert*

Exercise 6–10 If students have difficulty with Exercises 6–10, they might not be comparing the difference to the divisor after dividing. This could result in missing multiples. Remind students that remainders should be less than the divisor. If they get a difference that is greater than the divisor, the number of multiples is too small. Encourage students to pause after they subtract during division and make this comparison. This will increase accuracy when they move into long division.

Find each quotient. Show the remainder.

6. 14 ÷ 4 <u>3 R2</u>

$$\begin{array}{r} 3 \\ 4\overline{)14} \\ -12 \\ \hline 2 \end{array}$$

Check your answer. <u>3</u> × <u>4</u> = <u>12</u>

<u>12</u> + <u>2</u> = <u>14</u>

7. 11 ÷ 3 = <u>3 R2</u>

8. 23 ÷ 3 = <u>7 R2</u>

9. 18 ÷ 4 = <u>4 R2</u>

10. 21 ÷ 4 = <u>5 R1</u>

Step by Step Problem-Solving Practice

Problem-Solving Strategies
- ☐ Draw a diagram.
- ☑ Use logical reasoning.
- ☐ Make a table.
- ☐ Solve a simpler problem.
- ☐ Work backward.

Solve.

11. TRIPS Twenty-one students are going on a field trip in three vans. One-third of the students will ride in each van. How many students will ride in each van?

One-third means to divide by 3.

Understand Read the problem. Write what you know.

There are <u>21</u> students.

$\frac{1}{3}$ of <u>21</u> will ride in each van.

Plan Pick a strategy. One strategy is to use logical reasoning.

One-third means that a whole is divided into <u>3</u> equal parts.

Solve Divide 21 by 3.
<u>7</u> students will ride in each van.

Check Check your answer with repeated addition.

<u>7</u> + <u>7</u> + <u>7</u> = <u>21</u>

TRIPS Twenty-one students will go on the field trip.

Intervention Strategy

Naturalist/ Interpersonal Learners

Real-World Division Ask students to work in small groups and brainstorm ways they use division in their everyday routines. Encourage them to think of when and where in their school and environments they break down information or objects into smaller chunks. Have them write a list on a large piece of easel or newsprint paper. Groups can share their lists with the class. Post the lists somewhere in the room for students to reference. As students recognize the relevance and application of division in their daily lives, they may be more willing to learn and practice the division algorithm.

12 EGGS A farmer collected 8 eggs from 4 of his chickens. If each chicken produced the same number of eggs, how many eggs did each chicken produce? Check off each step.

✓ Understand: I circled key words.

✓ Plan: To solve the problem, I will use logical reasoning.

✓ Solve: The answer is 2 eggs.

✓ Check: I checked my answer by using repeated addition.

13 MONEY If Andre has 20 quarters, how many dollars does he have? (There are 4 quarters in a dollar.)

5 dollars

14 **Reflect** There are different ways to interpret a remainder. Suppose there are 25 students who are to sit in chairs that will be arranged in rows with 4 seats.

25 ÷ 4 = 6 R1.

How would you interpret the remainder?

Sample answer: The remainder is 1 student. If there are 6 rows, there would be 24 seats, which is not enough. If there are 7 rows, there will be 28 seats.

Skills, Concepts, and Problem Solving

Draw an array to model each quotient.

15 44 ÷ 4

16 24 ÷ 3

17 15 ÷ 3

18 16 ÷ 4

GO ON

Intervention Strategy Visual/Linguistic Learners

Explain Division Draw two arrays without labels on the board. Ask students to draw the arrays and write the division sentence each represents. Have them find each quotient and then write an explanation of how each array represents its division sentence. Encourage students to use correct vocabulary terms and clear language in their explanations, including proof statements to show how they know their division sentences are correct. Have students share their explanations in small groups.

Odd/Even Assignments

Exercises 15–39 are structured so that students practice the same concepts whether they are assigned the odd or even problems.

In-Class Assignment

Have students complete Exercises 16, 18, 22, 32, 36, and 42 to ensure that they understand the concept.

Math Coach Notes

Study Tips Encourage students to study math in a way that best suits their learning style. Students usually have a good idea of how they learn best—seeing a problem and writing it down, saying it out loud and talking it out, building a model or drawing an illustration, and so on. Discuss how to study for quizzes and tests in the way that works best for them. This may include using flashcards or charts, verbally quizzing one another in pairs or small groups, or using objects in their environment such as paper clips to create arrays or models. Emphasize that studying will look different depending on learning styles but can be equally as effective. This may help students prepare better and find success while boosting their confidence.

Common Error *Alert*

Multi-Step Problem If students struggle with Exercises 37–39, they may have difficulty comprehending the given information. Encourage students to draw a diagram or build a model to represent the given facts. Then ask them to summarize what their diagrams or models show and have them verbalize what they need to know to solve the problem. Separating and focusing on one piece of information at a time can sometimes make the problem more manageable.

Intervention Strategy

Auditory/ Intrapersonal Learners

Correct or Not? Recite several short division sentences that require remainders. Include a few incorrect quotients in the list of sentences. Ask students to write down the sentences you recite. Challenge students to determine which ones are correct. Have students provide proof for those sentences that are correct and explanations for those that are not.

Note This!

Previous Knowledge Encourage students to relate new material to previously learned concepts. As they write vocabulary terms or examples in their math journals, model how to jot a note in the margin that shows how this is similar to something else. Similarly, if students have questions about concepts or problems, they can write a note so they remember to ask for more help in particular areas.

Find each quotient. Show the remainder if there is one.

19. $16 \div 4 =$ 4
20. $9 \div 3 =$ 3
21. $12 \div 3 =$ 4
22. $20 \div 4 =$ 5
23. $27 \div 3 =$ 9
24. $36 \div 4 =$ 9
25. $6 \div 3 =$ 2
26. $32 \div 4 =$ 8
27. $15 \div 3 =$ 5
28. $40 \div 4 =$ 10
29. $12 \div 4 =$ 3
30. $8 \div 4 =$ 2
31. $8 \div 3 =$ 2 R2
32. $10 \div 3 =$ 3 R1
33. $9 \div 4 =$ 2 R1
34. $20 \div 3 =$ 6 R2
35. $35 \div 4 =$ 8 R3
36. $28 \div 3 =$ 9 R1

Solve.

37. PETS Four friends visit a pet store. They each buy the same number of fish. If they bought 28 fish altogether, how many did each friend buy?

    7 fish

38. BUSINESS There are 10 packs of paper in a case. Three teachers share a case evenly. How much paper will each teacher get?

    3 packs with 1 pack remaining.

39. FITNESS In 10 days, Alan walked a total of 30 miles. In the same number of days, Jennifer walked 40 miles. How much more did Jennifer walk per day than Alan?

    1 mile

118 **Chapter 3** Division

Math Challenge

Card Game Have students shuffle together sets of cards numbered from 1 to 10. Students draw two cards to create a two-digit number. Practice dividing by 3 and 4 with these drawn numbers. Students should write the division sentence and show all of their work to find the quotient. Then return the cards to the bottom of the pack and draw again. Have more proficient students draw three or four cards to create larger dividends and challenge them to practice dividing by divisors 1 through 5.

Vocabulary Check **Write the vocabulary word that completes each sentence.**

40 A multiple of a number is the product of that number and any whole number.

41 The remainder is the number left after one whole number is divided by another.

42 Writing in Math Explain how to check a division problem when it has a remainder. Use the division problem $15 \div 4$ to show the work.

When you multiply the quotient by the divisor and add the remainder, the answer should equal the dividend. The quotient is 3. The divisor is 4 and the remainder is 3. $3 \times 4 + 3 = 12 + 3 = 15$.

$$\begin{array}{r} 3R3 \\ 4\overline{)15} \\ -12 \\ \hline 3 \end{array}$$

Spiral Review

Find each quotient.

Solve. (Lesson 3-3, p. 107)

43 $30 \div 5 =$ 6

44 $18 \div 2 =$ 9

45 $20 \div 2 =$ 10

46 $60 \div 5 =$ 12

47 BOOKS Together, Karina and her friend read 18 books over the summer. If they each read the same number of books, how many books did they read?

9 books

48 FOOD Sheila's manager asked her to take a survey of the customers in the pizza parlor. She was to ask customers at every other table to name their favorite pizza. If there were 16 tables with customers in the restaurant, how many tables did she go to?

8 tables

Ticket Out the Door

Word Problem

Write the following on the board.

Jonah has 62 books to divide evenly among 4 shelves. If all but 2 books fit in the bookcase, how many books are on each shelf?

$62 \div 4 = 15$ R2, because $4 \times 15 = 60$ and $60 + 2 = 62$.

Have students write a division sentence that represents the word problem and find the quotient. Tell them to write a proof statement that supports their quotients. Students will hand in their papers as they exit the classroom.

See It, Do It, Say It, Write It

Step 1 Write several division expressions on the board, with 3 and 4 as divisors. Ask student volunteers to find the quotients.

Step 2 Ask students to model the problems using manipulatives or drawings.

Step 3 Write another division expression on the board. Have students work in pairs. Tell them to write a brief word problem for the expression. Problems should include a quotient and a model that represents the situation. Have students share their word problems in small groups or with the class.

Step 4 Ask students to write an explanation of how to model $28 \div 7$ using manipulatives. Ask them to describe how they found the quotient.

Looking Ahead: Pre-teach

Divide by 6 and 7 In the next lesson, students will learn about dividing by 6 and 7. Students will use multiples and multiplication fact families to find missing terms.

Example

Draw an array to model $30 \div 6$. Find the quotient.

$30 \div 6 = 5$

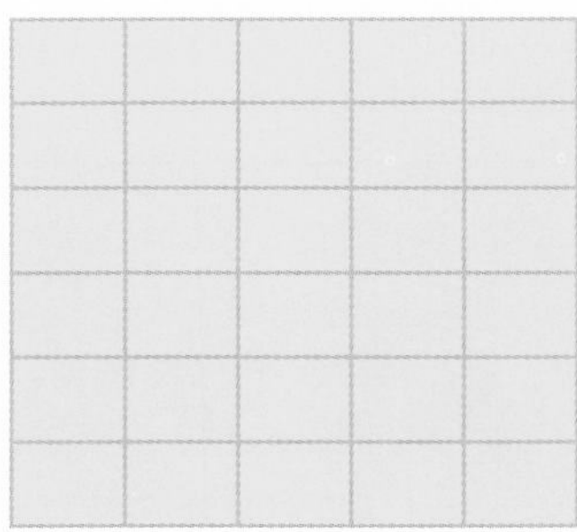

Find each quotient.

1. $35 \div 7$ 5
2. $42 \div 6$ 7
3. $60 \div 6$ 10

Chapter 3 Progress Check 2

Formative Assessment

Use the Progress Check to assess students' mastery of the previous lessons. Have students review the lesson indicated for the problems they answered incorrectly.

Odd/Even Assignments

Exercises are structured so that students practice the same concepts whether they are assigned the odd or even problems.

> **Note This!**
>
> **Remainders** When finding a quotient, the divisor does not always necessarily divide into the dividend a whole number of times. Tell students to come up with the greatest number of times the divisor can divide into the dividend, recording anything "left over" as the remainder.

Common Error *Alert*

Remainders Larger than the Divisor? It is important to point out to students that if their remainder is greater than the problem's divisor, then they need to work the problem again because the quotient should be a larger number.

Chapter 3 Progress Check 2 (Lessons 3-3 and 3-4)

Draw a model to find each quotient.

1. 14 ÷ 2 7
2. 18 ÷ 3 6

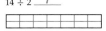

Write the division expression represented by each model.

3. 24 ÷ 4

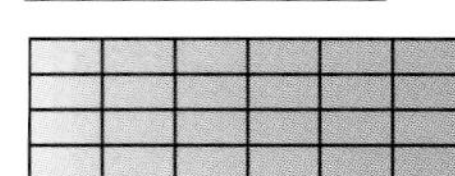

4. 21 ÷ 3

Find each quotient. Show the remainder if there is one.

5. 35 ÷ 5 = 7
6. 4 ÷ 2 = 2
7. 4 ÷ 4 = 1
8. 30 ÷ 3 = 10
9. 50 ÷ 5 = 10
10. 18 ÷ 3 = 6
11. 36 ÷ 4 = 9
12. 24 ÷ 3 = 8
13. 30 ÷ 4 = 7 R2
14. 31 ÷ 5 = 6 R1
15. 11 ÷ 3 = 3 R2
16. 37 ÷ 4 = 9 R1

Solve.

17. **FARMS** A dairy farmer has 40 cows. She began with 16 cows and bought the rest of her herd over the next 4 years. Not including her initial herd, how many cows did she buy each year?

    6 cows

18. **BIRDS** The bird club counted 27 birds on an outing to the nature center. There are 3 acres in the nature center. How many birds are there per acre?

    9 birds

19. **PHOTOS** Gordon's digital camera holds 43 pictures. Suppose he takes the same number of pictures each day. How many pictures can he take on a 4-day vacation? How many pictures will he have left?

    He can take 10 pictures a day, and he will have 3 pictures left.

120 Chapter 3 Division

Data-Driven Decision Making

Students missing Exercises . . .	Have trouble with . . .	Should review and practice . . .
1–2	drawing models and finding quotients.	SSG Lesson 3-3, p. 107 CRM Skills Practice, p. A59
3–4	writing division expressions represented by models.	SSG Lesson 3-3, p. 107
5–16	finding quotients and showing remainders.	SSG Lessons 3-3 and 3-4, pp. 107 and 113 CRM Skills Practice, pp. A59 and A63
17–19	solving word problems involving division (with and without remainders).	CRM Problem-Solving Practice, pp. A60 and A64

Divide by 6 and 7

KEY Concept

You use the same process to divide by all single-digit numbers. Sometimes you will have remainders and sometimes you will not have remainders.

$$6\overline{)754} = 125 \text{ R4}$$
-6, $1 \times 6 = 6$; 15; -12, $2 \times 6 = 12$; 34; -30, $5 \times 6 = 30$; 4

$$7\overline{)784} = 112$$
-7, $1 \times 7 = 7$; 8; -7, $1 \times 7 = 7$; 14; -14, $2 \times 7 = 14$; 0

A remainder must always be less than the divisor.

VOCABULARY

multiple
a multiple of a number is the *product* of that number and any whole number
Example: 30 is a multiple of 10 because
3 × 10 = 30.

remainder
the number that is left after one whole number is divided by another

Memorize the division facts for 6 and 7.

Example 1

Write the division problem represented by the model.

1. How many rectangles are in the array? **18**
2. How many rows? **6**

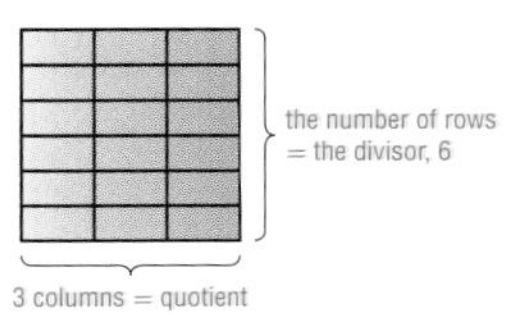

3. Count the number of columns. This is the quotient. **3**
4. Write the division problem. **18 ÷ 6 = 3**
5. Check. **3 × 6 = 18**

YOUR TURN!

Write the division problem represented by the model.

1. How many rectangles are in the array? 42
2. How many rows? 7

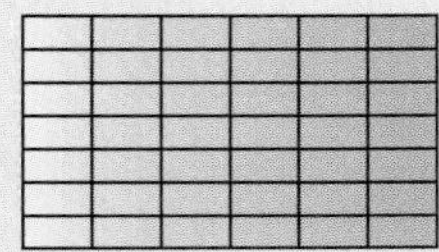

3. Count the number of columns. This is the quotient. 6
4. Write the division problem. 42 ÷ 7 = 6
5. Check. 6 × 7 = 42

GO ON

Additional Example 1

Write the division problem represented by the model.

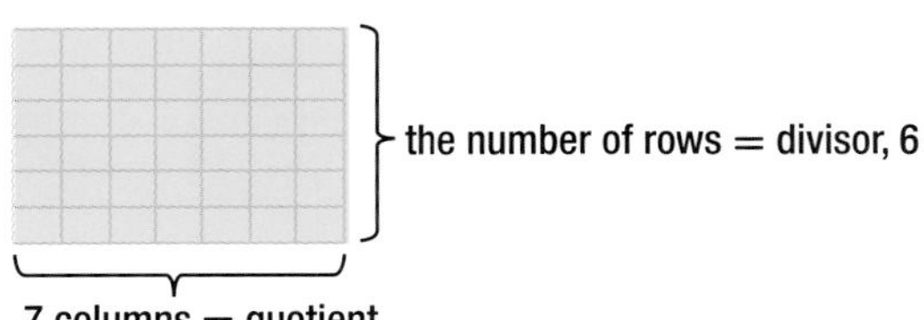

1. How many rectangles are in the array? 42
2. How many rows? 6
3. Count the number of columns. This is the quotient. 7
4. Write the division problem. 42 ÷ 6 = 7
5. Check. 7 × 6 = 42

Lesson Notes

Lesson 3-5

Lesson Planner

Objective Divide when the divisor is 6 or 7.

Vocabulary **multiple, remainder**

Materials/Manipulatives hundred chart, multiplication chart, number line, pattern blocks, two-color counters

Chapter Resource Masters

- CRM Vocabulary and English Language Development (p. A66)
- CRM Skills Practice (p. A67)
- CRM Problem-Solving Practice (p. A68)
- CRM Homework Practice (p. A69)

1 Introduce

Vocabulary

Division Facts Write several division sentences with divisors of 6 or 7 on the board. Ask student volunteers to go to the board and find the solutions. Have volunteers provide the fact family for each division sentence to prove their quotients are correct. Ask students to explain how to use counters to model each division sentence.

Ask students to guess the meaning of *remainder.* Students should conclude that it is parts left over.

2 Teach

Key Concept

Foundational Skills and Concepts After students have read through the Key Concept box, have them try these exercises.

1. What is the remainder when you divide 754 by 6? 4
2. Can the remainder of $7\overline{)784}$ be 7? no
3. Can the remainder be equal to the divisor? no

Additional **Example 2**

Find 624 ÷ 6.

1. Rewrite the problem in vertical format.

   $6\overline{)624}$

2. Look at the first digit. What number multiplied by 6 is 6?
   1 × 6 = 6 Write 1 in the hundreds place in the quotient.

   $\begin{array}{r} 1 \\ 6\overline{)624} \end{array}$

3. Multiply. Write the product under the hundreds place in the dividend.
4. Subtract. Bring down the next number in the dividend.

   $\begin{array}{r} 1 \\ 6\overline{)624} \\ -6\downarrow \\ \hline 2 \end{array}$

5. Since 2 < 6, there is not enough to divide. So, put 0 in the tens place.

   $\begin{array}{r} 10 \\ 6\overline{)624} \\ -6 \\ \hline 2 \end{array}$

6. Bring down the next number in the dividend.

   $\begin{array}{r} 10 \\ 6\overline{)624} \\ -6\ \downarrow \\ \hline 24 \end{array}$

7. What number multiplied by 6 is 24? 4
   Multiply. Write the product under the dividend.

   $\begin{array}{r} 104 \\ 6\overline{)624} \\ -6 \\ \hline 24 \\ -24 \\ \hline 0 \end{array}$

8. Subtract.
9. The quotient is 104.

Math Coach Notes

Division Algorithm While teaching division of larger numbers, emphasize that this process is simply a sequence of divisions by a one-digit number. By practicing the multiplication table, students will gain confidence and automaticity with these fundamental relationships.

Example 2

Find 696 ÷ 6.

1. Rewrite the problem in vertical format. $6\overline{)696}$
2. Look at the first digit. What number multiplied by 6 is 6? 1 × 6 = 6 Write 1 in the hundreds place in the quotient. $\begin{array}{r} 1 \\ 6\overline{)696} \end{array}$
3. Multiply. Write the product under the hundreds place in the dividend.
4. Subtract. Bring down the next number in the dividend. $\begin{array}{r} 1 \\ 6\overline{)696} \\ -6\downarrow \\ \hline 9 \end{array}$
5. What number multiplied by 6 is close to 9, but not more than 9? 1 × 6 = 6 Write 1 in the tens place in the quotient. $\begin{array}{r} 11 \\ 6\overline{)696} \\ -6 \\ \hline 9 \\ -6 \\ \hline 3 \end{array}$
6. Multiply. Write the product under the dividend.
7. Subtract. Bring down the 6 in the ones place of the dividend.
8. What number multiplied by 6 is 36? 6
   Multiply.
   Write the product under the dividend.
9. Subtract.
10. The quotient is 116. $\begin{array}{r} 116 \\ 6\overline{)696} \\ -6 \\ \hline 9 \\ -6\downarrow \\ \hline 36 \\ -36 \\ \hline 0 \end{array}$

YOUR TURN!

Find 784 ÷ 7.

1. Rewrite the problem in vertical format. $7\overline{)784}$
2. Look at the first digit. What number multiplied by 7 is 7? __1__ Write __1__ in the hundreds place of the quotient. $\begin{array}{r} 1 \\ 7\overline{)784} \end{array}$
3. Multiply. Write the product under the hundreds place in the dividend.
4. Subtract. Bring down the next number in the dividend. $\begin{array}{r} 1 \\ 7\overline{)784} \\ -7\downarrow \\ \hline 8 \end{array}$
5. What number multiplied by 7 is close to 8, but not more than 8? __1__ Write __1__ in the tens place in the quotient. $\begin{array}{r} 11 \\ 7\overline{)784} \\ -7\downarrow \\ \hline 8 \\ -7 \\ \hline 1 \end{array}$
6. Multiply. Write the product under the dividend.
7. Subtract. Bring down the next number in the ones place of the dividend.
8. What number multiplied by 7 is 14? __2__.
   Multiply.
   Write the product under the dividend.
9. Subtract.
10. The quotient is __112__. $\begin{array}{r} 112 \\ 7\overline{)784} \\ -7 \\ \hline 8 \\ -7\downarrow \\ \hline 14 \\ -14 \\ \hline 0 \end{array}$

122 Chapter 3 Division

Intervention Strategy — Kinesthetic/Logical Learners

Create Models Have students create models representing division sentences with 6 or 7 as the divisor. Encourage students to use concrete materials such as counters, base-ten blocks, geoboards, algebra tiles, money, pattern blocks, or connecting cubes. Students could also try using grid paper, drawings, number lines, or other materials they find in their environment. Assign each model a number and have students rotate around the room solving one another's division models. Ask students to write the sentence modeled and find the quotient. Review the sentences and quotients together.

Who is Correct?

Find 636 ÷ 7. Show the remainder.

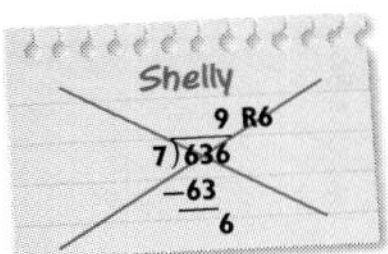

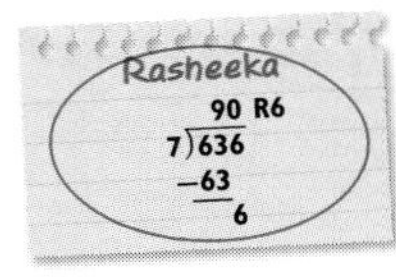

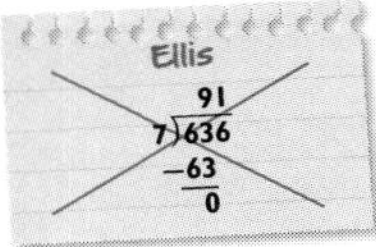

Circle correct answer(s). Cross out incorrect answer(s).

Guided Practice

Write the division problem represented by the model.

1 $12 \div 6 = 2$

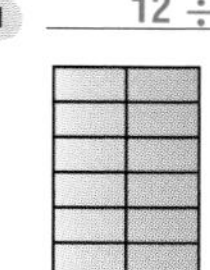

2 $49 \div 7 = 7$

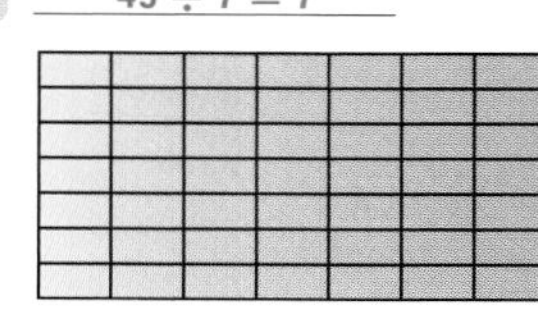

Step by Step Practice

3 Find 20 ÷ 6. Show the remainder.

Step 1 Rewrite the problem in vertical format.

Step 2 Look at the first digit in the dividend. Since the divisor is greater than the first digit, look at the first two digits. What number multiplied by 6 is close to 20? 3

Step 3 Multiply. Write the product under the dividend.

Step 4 Subtract.

Step 5 There are no more digits. Write the quotient. $20 \div 6 =$ 3 R2

Step 6 Check.

$3 \times 6 = 18$

$18 + 2 = 20$

$$\begin{array}{r} 3\text{ R2} \\ 6\overline{)20} \\ -18 \\ \hline 2 \end{array}$$

GO ON

Lesson 3-5 Divide by 6 and 7 123

Who is Correct?

Diagnostic Teaching

- Shelly's work is incorrect. She did not correctly line up the 9 in her quotient, which moved all her other place values over.
- Rasheeka's work is correct. She divided and subtracted each column correctly.
- Ellis's work is incorrect. The ones place in the quotient was multiplied incorrectly.

Remind students that a remainder must be less than the divisor.

Math Coach Notes

Strategies

1. Begin this lesson by using concrete materials. Model some division sentences with 1 through 5 as the divisors. Have students draw or build arrays for the sentences. Ask them to explain how each array represents its sentence, using the correct vocabulary and clear language. Then move into division sentences with 6 or 7 as the divisor.

2. Practice dividing in vertical format using divisors of 6 or 7 that require a remainder. Keep problems to one or two steps each. Model a few problems and then have students practice in pairs.

Using Manipulatives

Pattern Blocks Use pattern blocks to form arrays or use as counters to move into groups to find multiples.

On-Hand Manipulatives Use a hundred chart to determine multiples and remainders in division problems.

Number Line When presenting division using multiples, use concrete materials such as number lines to find multiples.

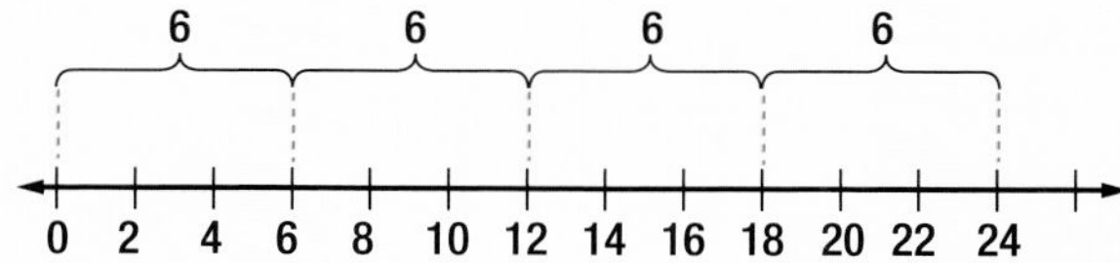

Common Error *Alert*

Exercises 4–10 If students have difficulty with Exercises 4-10, check if students are writing a multiple that is greater than the dividend. Sometimes students do not understand they need to get as close as possible without going over the dividend. Have students work with counters to reinforce that they cannot use more than they have to find the quotient.

Intervention Strategy

Visual/ Logical Learners

Find Quotients Have students use laminated hundreds charts and wipe-off markers to practice finding quotients with remainders. On the board, write several division expressions with divisors of 6 or 7 that are not evenly divisible. Ask students to circle the multiples of each divisor on their charts and determine the quotient for each expression. Have students write the division sentences with their quotients on a sheet of paper. For more proficient students, write division expressions with larger dividends and ask them to find the quotients showing all of their work.

English Learner Strategy

Use Models Use number lines, counters, or pattern blocks to create models of division sentences. Model how to explain the sentence a model represents, using the terms *divisor, dividend, quotient,* and *remainder.* Ask the student to echo you. Then practice with sentences you write and sentences the student writes, alternating the modeling and the explaining.

Find each quotient. Show the remainder if there is one.

4. $15 \div 7$ 2R1

$$\begin{array}{r} 2\text{ R1} \\ 7\overline{)15} \\ -14 \\ \hline 1 \end{array}$$

5. $19 \div 6 =$ 3 R1
6. $35 \div 7 =$ 5
7. $45 \div 7 =$ 6 R3
8. $39 \div 6 =$ 6 R3
9. $50 \div 7 =$ 7 R1
10. $54 \div 6 =$ 9

Step by Step Problem-Solving Practice

Problem-Solving Strategies
- ☐ Draw a diagram.
- ☐ Use logical reasoning.
- ☐ Make a table.
- ☑ Solve a simpler problem.
- ☐ Work backward.

Solve.

11. HOBBIES Han makes jewelry. He bought beads to make 7 necklaces. He will use an equal number of beads for each necklace. If he purchased 400 beads, how many beads can he use to make each necklace?

Understand Read the problem. Write what you know. There are 400 beads to make 7 identical necklaces.

Plan Pick a strategy. One strategy is to solve a simpler problem.

Solve When you multiply 7 by 5, the product is 35. When you multiply 7 by 50, the product is 350. Subtract this from 400. 50

What number multiplied by 7 is close to 50 without going over? 7
Multiply this by 7 and subtract the product from 50. What is left is the remainder.

Add the factors you multiplied by 7. Along with the remainder, this is the answer.

50 + 7 = 57 R 1

So, Han can use 57 beads per necklace.

Check Does the answer make sense? Look over your solution. Did you answer the question?

Are They Getting It?

Check students' understanding of division operations by writing these problems on the board. Have students state which are correct and which are incorrect. Make certain they provide reasons. Encourage them to use drawings or examples in their explanations.

1. The quotient of $56 \div 7$ is 9. This is incorrect. $56 \div 7 = 8$
2. This array represents $36 \div 6$. This is correct.

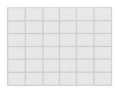

3. The quotient of $63 \div 8$ is 8 R1. This is incorrect. The quotient of $63 \div 8$ is 7 R7.

12 ART The art museum has 532 pieces to place into 6 exhibit halls. How many pieces will go into each exhibit hall? Check off each step.

✓ Understand: I circled key words.

✓ Plan: To solve the problem, I will solve a simpler problem.

✓ Solve: The answer is 88 with 4 extra pieces.

✓ Check: I checked my answer by making sure it makes sense.

13 HEALTH There are 90 vitamins in a bottle. If Janelle takes 1 vitamin a day, how many weeks will a bottle of vitamins last?

12 weeks and 6 days

14 **Reflect** Complete the four sections below for $28 \div 7 = 4$.

Write the fact family.

$7 \times 4 = 28$

$4 \times 7 = 28$

$28 \div 4 = 7$

$28 \div 7 = 4$

Draw an array to model the division fact.

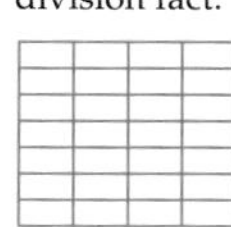

Write the fact in vertical and fraction forms.

$7\overline{)28}$ with quotient 4 $\quad \frac{28}{7} = 4$

Draw circles and tally marks to model the division fact.

Skills, Concepts, and Problem Solving

Write the division problem represented by each model.

15 $21 \div 3 = 7$

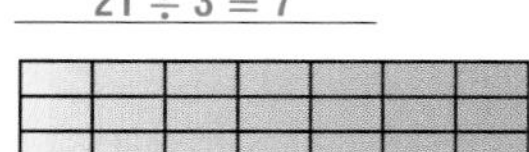

16 $24 \div 4 = 6$

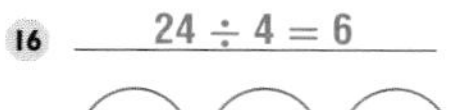

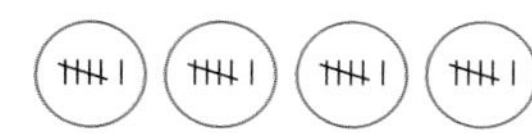

Write each quotient. Show the remainder if there is one.

17 $42 \div 6 =$ 7	18 $28 \div 7 =$ 4	19 $36 \div 6 =$ 6
20 $21 \div 7 =$ 3	21 $12 \div 6 =$ 2	22 $56 \div 7 =$ 8

Math Challenge

Division Flashcards Challenge students to create a game board for a division flashcard game. Use counters as game pieces to move across the board. Ask students to use or make division flashcards with 6 or 7 as the divisor and problems that yield whole-number quotients. Students can play in pairs or small groups. Each student draws a flashcard from the pile of facedown flashcards. He or she finds the quotient and moves a game piece that number of spaces along the game board. To make the game more interesting, have students make cards that direct the players to move ahead or backward a number of places or send them to a specific location on the game board. The first person to reach the end of the game board wins.

Odd/Even Assignments

Exercises 15–32 are structured so that students practice the same concepts whether they are assigned the odd or even problems.

In-Class Assignment

Have students complete Exercises 15, 18, 22, 30, 32, and 35 to ensure that they understand the concept.

Math Coach Notes

Use Inverse Operations Encourage students to practice checking quotients using inverse operations. Have them explain to a peer or family member how to work backward to prove their answers are correct. This will help build confidence in their problem-solving and logical reasoning skills.

Intervention Strategy

Linguistic/Interpersonal Learners

Solve and Write Write the following on the board: $58 \div 7 = ?$ 8 R2

Have students work in pairs. Ask students to find the quotient and then write a brief word problem that represents the division sentence. Encourage pairs to share their word problems with the class. Ask more proficient students to prove their solutions are correct using two different strategies.

4 Assess

See It, Do It, Say It, Write It

Step 1 Draw a model of a division sentence on the board. Ask students to write the sentence the model represents.

Step 2 Have students build or draw a different model that represents the same division sentence.

Step 3 Ask students to explain their models to a partner.

Step 4 Tell the pairs to write a brief word problem for the division sentence on the board. Have students share their word problems in small groups or with the class.

Looking Ahead: Pre-teach

Divide by 8 and 9 In the next lesson, students will learn about dividing by 8 and 9. As students become more comfortable with division, they will be able to do more math calculations in their heads. This is called *mental math.*

Example

Find 816 ÷ 8 using mental math.

You know that 800 ÷ 8 = 100 and 16 ÷ 8 = 2, so 816 ÷ 8 = 102.

Find each quotient using mental math.

1. 990 ÷ 9 110
2. 481 ÷ 8 60 R1
3. 369 ÷ 9 41

Write each quotient. Show the remainder if there is one.

23 42 ÷ 7 = 6
24 63 ÷ 7 = 9
25 60 ÷ 6 = 10
26 420 ÷ 7 = 60
27 7 ÷ 7 = 1
28 36 ÷ 6 6
29 77 ÷ 7 11
30 125 ÷ 6 20 R5
31 214 ÷ 7 30 R4

Solve.

32 FOOD There are blueberry and apple pies in the cafeteria. There are 42 pieces of each type of pie, but there is 1 more apple pie than blueberry pie. Each blueberry pie has 1 more piece than each apple pie. How many of each type of pie is there? How many pieces is each type of pie cut into?

There are 7 apple pies cut into 6 pieces each. There are 6 blueberry pies cut into 7 pieces each.

Vocabulary Check **Write the vocabulary word that completes each sentence.**

33 The remainder is the number that is left after one whole number is divided by another.

34 A(n) multiple of a number is the product of that number and any whole number.

35 Writing In Math How does the inverse operation of division help you when solving division problems?

Sample answer: You can ask: "What do I need to multiply the divisor by to get the dividend?" This is easier to do mentally than to use division. Also, multiplication is useful for checking answers.

Spiral Review

Write each quotient.

36 24 ÷ 3 = 8
37 24 ÷ 4 = 6
38 18 ÷ 3 = 6
39 36 ÷ 4 = 9

Ticket Out the Door

Word Problem

Write the following on the board.

Marita has 52 wooden beads and 48 plastic beads. She uses the same number of wooden beads as plastic beads per necklace. If she has only 4 total beads left over, determine how many necklaces she can make and how many of each bead will go on each necklace. 8 necklaces with 6 of each kind of bead or 6 necklaces with 8 of each kind of bead

Have students solve the word problem. Tell them to provide proof or support that their answers are correct. Students will hand in their papers as they exit the classroom.

Lesson 3-6

Divide by 8 and 9

KEY Concept

As you become more comfortable with multiplication and division, try to use **mental math** as much as possible. Solving division problems using mostly mental math is called **short division.**

Ask yourself: 8 times what number equals 48? $8 \times 6 = 48$

$8\overline{)489}$ = 61 R1

Ask yourself: 8 times what number equals 9 or a number very close to 9? $8 \times 1 = 8$

As you practice short division, you will find ways to mark differences and remainders so that you do not have to do long division.

VOCABULARY

mental math to add, subtract, multiply, and divide in your head without using manipulatives, fingers, or pencil and paper

multiple a multiple of a number is the *product* of that number and any whole number. Example: 30 is a multiple of 10 because $3 \times 10 = 30$.

short division division using mental math

Memorize the division facts for 8 and 9.

Example 1

Write the division problem represented by the model.

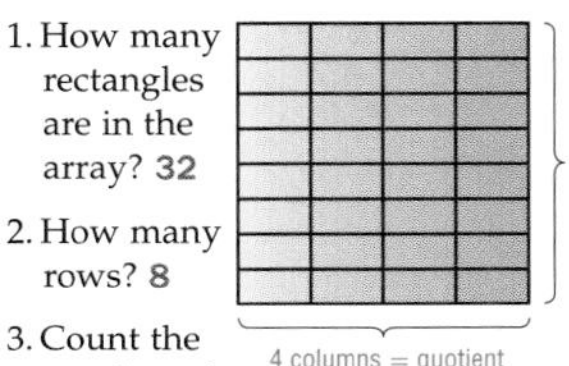

1. How many rectangles are in the array? 32
2. How many rows? 8
3. Count the number of columns. This is the quotient. 4
4. Write the division problem. $32 \div 8 = 4$
5. Check. $4 \times 8 = 32$

YOUR TURN!

Write the division problem represented by the model.

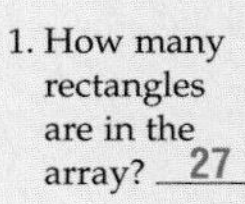

1. How many rectangles are in the array? 27
2. How many rows? 9
3. Count the number of columns. This is the quotient. 3
4. Write the division problem. 27 ÷ 9 = 3
5. Check. 3 × 9 = 27

GO ON

Lesson Notes

Lesson 3-6

Lesson Planner

Objective Divide when the divisor is 8 or 9.

Vocabulary **mental math, multiple, short division**

Materials/Manipulatives algebra tiles, grid paper, number line, two-color counters

Chapter Resource Masters

- CRM Vocabulary and English Language Development (p. A70)
- CRM Skills Practice (p. A71)
- CRM Problem-Solving Practice (p. A72)
- CRM Homework Practice (p. A73)

1 Introduce

Vocabulary

Mental Math Write several short division expressions with 8 or 9 as divisors on the board. Model how to find one of the quotients using *short division.* Ask volunteers to explain step by step how they can use short division to find the quotients of the other expressions.

2 Teach

Key Concept

Foundational Skills and Concepts After students have read through the Key Concept box, have them try these exercises.

1. How could you predict $8\overline{)489}$ would give you a remainder? Think $489 = 480 + 9$. Use mental math to see $8 \times 60 = 480$, and $9 \div 8$ will then have a remainder.
2. What is short division? doing the division using mostly mental math

Additional Example 1

Write the division problem represented by the model.

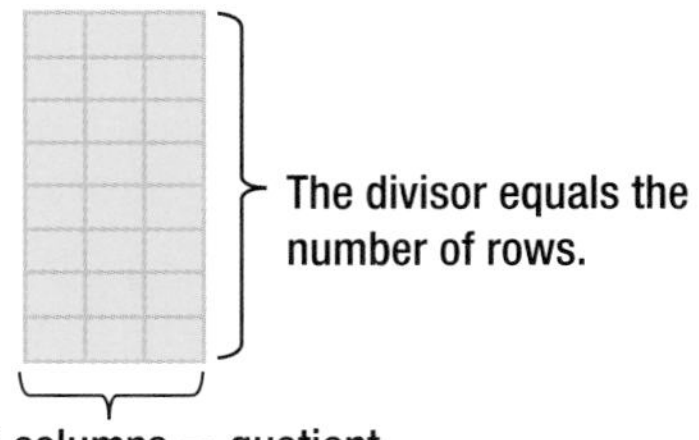

1. How many rectangles are in the array? 24
2. How many rows? 8
3. Count the number of columns. This is the quotient. 3
4. Write the division problem. $24 \div 8 = 3$
5. Check. $3 \times 8 = 24$

Additional **Example 2**

Find 465 ÷ 9. Show the remainder.

1. Rewrite the problem in vertical format. $9\overline{)465}$

2. Look at the first digit. The divisor is greater than the first two digits. What number multiplied by 9 is close to 46? 5

$$\begin{array}{r} 5 \\ 9\overline{)465} \\ -45 \\ \hline 1 \end{array}$$

Multiply. Write the product under the dividend. Now use mental math to subtract. $46 - 45 = 1$

3. Bring down the last digit. What is it? 5 What number multiplied by 9 is close to 15? 1

$$\begin{array}{r} 5 \\ 9\overline{)465} \\ -45\downarrow \\ \hline 15 \end{array}$$

4. Multiply. Write the product under the dividend. Then subtract.

$$\begin{array}{r} 51 \\ 9\overline{)465} \\ -45 \\ \hline 15 \\ -9 \\ \hline 6 \end{array}$$

5. There are no more digits. The answer is 51 with a remainder of 6. Write 51 R6.

Example 2

Find 289 ÷ 9. Show the remainder.

1. Rewrite the problem in vertical format. $9\overline{)289}$
2. Look at the first digit. The divisor is greater than the first digit, so look at the first two digits. What number multiplied by 9 is close to 28? 3 $\begin{array}{r} 3 \\ 9\overline{)289} \\ -27 \\ \hline 1 \end{array}$

   Multiply. Write the product under the dividend. Now use mental math to subtract. **28 − 27 = 1**
3. Bring down the last digit. What is it? 9 $\begin{array}{r} 32 \\ 9\overline{)289} \\ -27\downarrow \\ \hline 19 \end{array}$

   What number multiplied by 9 is close to 19? 2
4. Multiply. Write the product under the dividend. Then subtract. $\begin{array}{r} 32 \\ 9\overline{)289} \\ -27 \\ \hline 19 \\ -18 \\ \hline 1 \end{array}$
5. There are no more digits. The answer is 32 with a remainder of 1. Write 32 R1.

YOUR TURN!

Find 315 ÷ 8. Show the remainder.

1. Rewrite the problem in vertical format. $8\overline{)315}$
2. Look at the first digit. The divisor is greater than the first digit, so look at the first two digits. What number multiplied by 8 is close to 31? 3 $\begin{array}{r} 3 \\ 8\overline{)315} \\ -24 \\ \hline 7 \end{array}$

   Multiply. Write the product under the dividend. Now use mental math to subtract. 31 − 24 = 7
3. Bring down the last digit. $\begin{array}{r} 39 \\ 8\overline{)315} \\ -24\downarrow \\ \hline 75 \end{array}$

   What number multiplied by 8 is close to 75? 9
4. Multiply. Write the product under the dividend. Then subtract. $\begin{array}{r} 39 \\ 8\overline{)315} \\ -24 \\ \hline 75 \\ -72 \\ \hline 3 \end{array}$
5. There are no more digits. The answer is 39 with a remainder of 3. Write 39 R 3.

Who is Correct?

Find 117 ÷ 9.

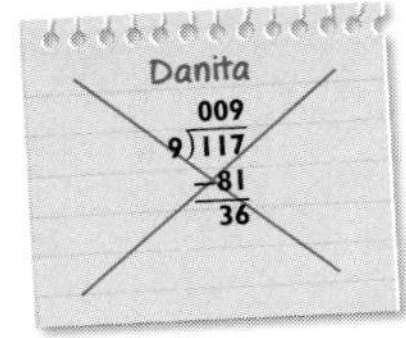

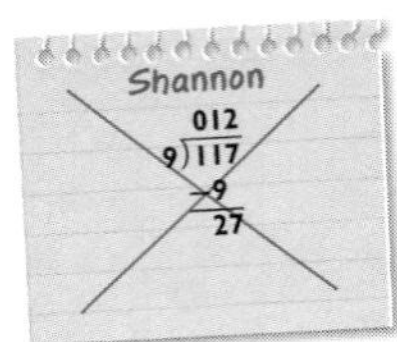

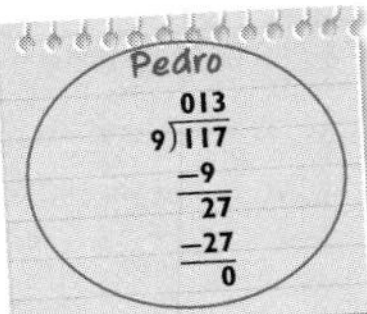

Circle correct answer(s). Cross out incorrect answer(s).

128 **Chapter 3** Division

Math Coach Notes

Multiples Emphasizing multiples while teaching division will help students grasp the concept of remainders. Focus on finding the closest multiple without exceeding the dividend so that students will be able to relate the difference of the closest multiple and the dividend as the amount leftover, or remainder.

Who *is Correct?*

Diagnostic Teaching

- Danita's work is incorrect. She did not divide the dividend one digit at a time.
- Shannon's work is incorrect. She made a calculation error in the ones place of the quotient.
- Pedro's work is correct. He divided and subtracted correctly.

Remind students that the 0 before 1 is not necessary.

Guided Practice

Write the division problem represented by the model.

1. 27 ÷ 9 = 3

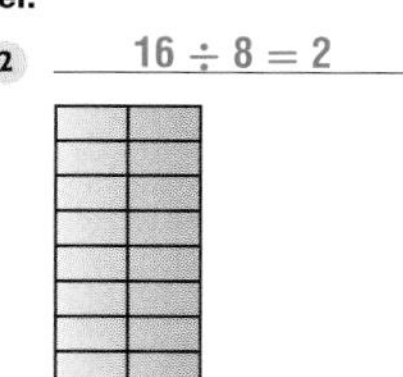

2. 16 ÷ 8 = 2

Step by Step Practice

3. Find 128 ÷ 8. Use short division.

Step 1 Look at the first digit in the dividend. Because the 8 is greater than the 1, look at the first two digits in the dividend.

Step 2 What number multiplied by 8 is close to 12 without going over? 1 Write the 1 in the tens place of the quotient.

Step 3 12 − 8 = 4. Write the difference next to the next digit in the dividend.

Step 4 What number will you divide now? 48

Step 5 What number multiplied by 8 is close to 48 without going over? 6 Write the 6 in the ones place of the quotient.

Step 6 The quotient is 16.

Check. 16 × 8 = 128

GO ON

Lesson 3-6 Divide by 8 and 9 129

Are They Getting It?

Check students' understanding of division operations by writing these problems on the board. Ask students to point out wrong answers and explain why they are wrong.

1. 382 ÷ 9 = 42 R4 means there are 42 multiples of 4 in 382. This is incorrect. There are 42 multiples of 9 in 382 with a remainder of 4.
2. This array represents 64 ÷ 8. This is correct.

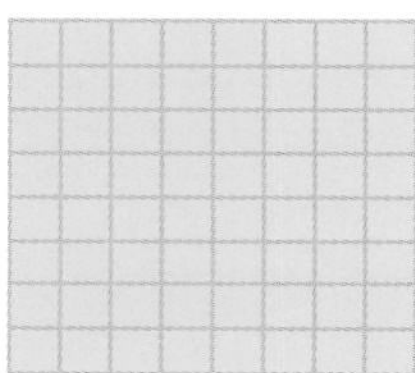

3. The quotient for 595 ÷ 8 is 75. This is incorrect. The quotient for 595 ÷ 8 is 74 R3.

Using Manipulatives

Algebra Tiles When presenting models of division sentences, use concrete materials such as algebra tiles to make arrays.

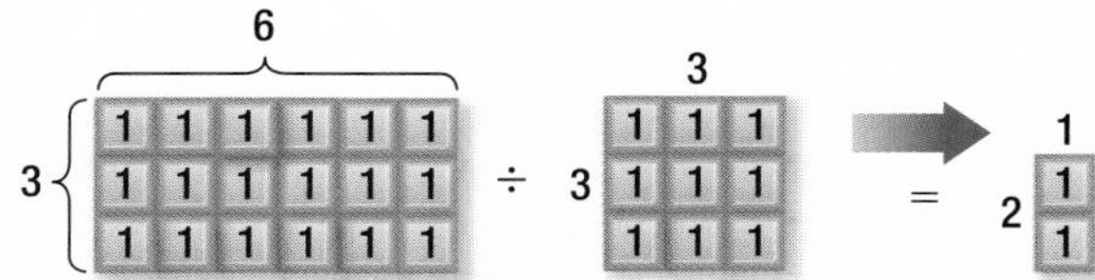

Two-Color Counters Use counters to move into groups or to form arrays to solve division problems.

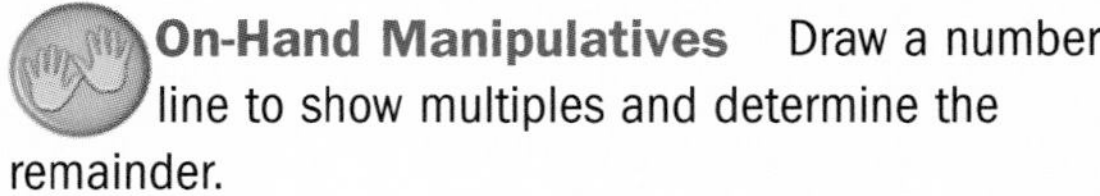

On-Hand Manipulatives Draw a number line to show multiples and determine the remainder.

Math Coach Notes

Strategies

1. Begin this lesson by using concrete materials. Use counters to model some division problems. Ask volunteers to find the quotient and prove it using inverse operations. Have volunteers create more models of division problems and ask their peers to find the quotients.
2. Draw arrays on grid paper to practice both multiplication and division. Have students write the sentence represented by each model, as well as the quotient.

Common Error *Alert*

Exercises 4–8 If students have difficulty with Exercises 4-8, they might be confused about the format of short division. Sometimes marking differences and remainders differently than they do during long division can lead to computational errors. Remind students to focus on one digit at a time and get the multiple as close as possible without exceeding the number they are dividing.

English Learner Strategy

Guiding Questions Write 27 ÷ 8 on a sheet of paper. Then ask students the following questions to ensure that they understand the concept.

- Read this expression aloud. Which kind of problem is this?
- How do you show this expression with pattern blocks?
- How do you explain the terms *dividend, divisor, quotient,* and *remainder* in this expression?
- Write this expression in vertical format. How do you find the quotient?
- How can you find the quotient using mental math? How can inverse operations prove your quotient is correct?

Math Coach Notes

Check For Reasonableness Tell students to monitor quotients for reasonableness by comparing them to the dividend. Quotients will always be less than the dividends. If the quotient is greater, ask students to check their work for errors. Another way to check for reasonableness is to use estimates. Round the divisor and the dividend and perform short division. If the actual quotient is very different from the estimate, check for computational mistakes.

Find each quotient. Show the remainder if there is one.

4. 108 ÷ 9 = $9\overline{)108}$ with quotient 12   12 × 9 = 108

5. 104 ÷ 8 = 13

6. 126 ÷ 9 = 14

7. 247 ÷ 8 = 30 R7

8. 145 ÷ 9 = 16 R1

Step by Step Problem-Solving Practice

Problem-Solving Strategies
- ☐ Draw a diagram.
- ☐ Use logical reasoning.
- ☑ Make a table.
- ☐ Solve a simpler problem.
- ☐ Work backward.

Solve.

9. COMMUNITY SERVICE The eleventh graders were repairing houses during spring break. For every 8 hours a student worked, he or she earned 1 class credit.

At the end of two weeks, the students worked a total of 720 hours. Each student worked an equal number of hours. If 10 students participated, how many credits did they earn in all?

Understand Read the problem. Write what you know.

There are 10 students. For every 8 hours worked, they received 1 credit. They worked 720 hours total.

Plan Pick a strategy. One strategy is to make a table.

Hours worked by each student	8	16	24	32	40	48	56	64	72
Total hours for 10 students	80	160	240	320	400	480	560	640	720
Credits earned	10	20	30	40	50	60	70	80	90

Solve Look at the table. Find when the total hours worked is 720. The students earned 90 credits in all.

Check Does the answer make sense? Look over your solution. Did you answer the question?

130 **Chapter 3** Division

Intervention Strategy — Linguistic/ Kinesthetic Learners

Division Stations Ask students to work in small groups to write division word problems for their classmates. Students should include a separate key of the answers to their word problems. Post groups' word problems in different areas of the room and ask students to rotate around to each station and solve the problems. Make concrete materials available at each station so students have choices in the kinds of models they create to solve the problems. Students should check their work against the groups' answer keys before moving to the next station. Collect students' work and discuss the exercises together as a class afterward.

10 CONSTRUCTION A builder buys lumber by the linear foot. For each 9-foot length she pays $5. How much does she pay for 81 linear feet of lumber? Check off each step.

✓ Understand: I circled key words.

✓ Plan: To solve the problem, I will make a table.

✓ Solve: The answer is $45.

✓ Check: I checked my answer by making sure it makes sense.

LANDSCAPING The flower beds are planted in rows and columns.

11 LANDSCAPING The flower beds in front of school are placed in rows and columns of equal length. If there are 64 flowers planted in all, how many rows and how many columns are there?

8 rows and 8 columns

12 **Reflect** Choose one fact family from the multiplication facts for 8 and another fact family for 9. Write all the facts for both families. Sample answers:

$4 \times 8 = 32$	$9 \times 6 = 54$
$8 \times 4 = 32$	$6 \times 9 = 54$
$32 \div 4 = 8$	$54 \div 9 = 6$
$32 \div 8 = 4$	$54 \div 6 = 9$

Skills, Concepts, and Problem Solving

Write the division problem represented by the model.

13 $32 \div 8 = 4$

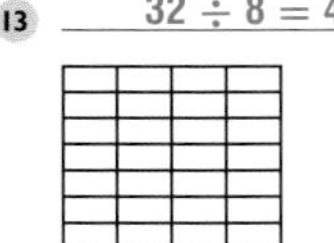

14 $36 \div 9 = 4$

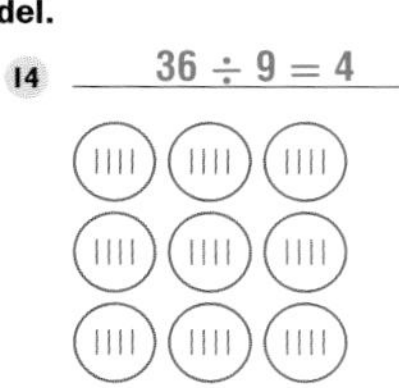

Intervention Strategy

Visual/ Logical Learners

Arrays for 48 Hand out grid paper to each student. Students can also use counters if they need them. Tell them to draw arrays for as many division problems as they can with a dividend of 48. Students should write the division sentence next to each corresponding array. Remind students to think of fact families to make sure they create all possible arrays.

Odd/Even Assignments

Exercises 13–35 are structured so that students practice the same concepts whether they are assigned the odd or even problems.

In-Class Assignment

Have students complete Exercises 17, 22, 30, 34, 35, and 38 to ensure that they understand the concept.

Multi-Step Problem If students have difficulty with Exercises 13 and 14, they might not understand which numbers to use for their calculations. Creating a diagram or chart can help keep the information separate. Have students work in cooperative pairs. Write a few word problems in the same style as these two examples. Ask students to practice breaking down the problems into small chunks, even working with concrete materials to create models if needed. When students think they have the correct solution, have them reread the problem to make sure their answer is reasonable and complete.

Intervention Strategy

Kinesthetic/ Interpersonal Learners

Grouping Students Ask students to practice dividing their classmates into groups. Write each student's name on a craft stick or index card. With the sticks or cards in a container, draw one name. This student will come to the front of the room and draw a card from a set of cards numbered from 1 to 10. The number card drawn indicates how many groups the student should divide the class into. The student will move classmates into groups that reflect the division sentence created by the number of students and the drawn card. This student should write the division sentence and quotient on the board when the grouping is complete. Then he or she can draw the name of the next student to do the division.

Math Coach Notes

Exercise Logic Encourage students to try activities that work their logic and math skills like building models, cooking, planning trips, and playing math games. If the activity is fun and can include friends or family members, the students are more likely to practice and gain fluency.

Find each quotient.

15 $81 \div 9 =$ 9

16 $24 \div 8 =$ 3

17 $72 \div 9 =$ 8

18 $64 \div 8 =$ 8

19 $54 \div 9 =$ 6

20 $16 \div 8 =$ 2

21 $27 \div 9 =$ 3

22 $40 \div 8 =$ 5

23 $9 \div 9 =$ 1

24 $42 \div 7 =$ 6

25 $18 \div 9 =$ 2

26 $80 \div 8 =$ 10

27 $198 \div 9 =$ 22

28 $168 \div 8 =$ 21

29 $171 \div 9 =$ 19

30 $136 \div 8 =$ 17

Solve. Show your work.

SHOPPING Bottled water costs $9 a case.

31 If Nalani has $80, how many cases of water can she buy?

$80 \div 9 = 8$ R8; Nalani can buy 8 cases.

32 How many dollars will Nalani have left?

$8 \times 9 = 72$; $80 - 72 = 8$; She will have $8 left.

SWIMMING There are 85 students in the swim class. The game they are playing needs teams with 9 students on each team.

33 How many complete teams will there be?

$85 \div 9 = 9$ R4; They will have 9 complete teams.

34 How many more students would be needed to make another team?

They would need 5 more students to make another team.

SWIMMING There are 85 students in the swim class.

132 Chapter 3 Division

Math Challenge

Missing Digits Challenge students to find the missing digits that make these division problems true. Ask more proficient students to create problems with missing numbers for classmates to solve.

```
      5 □              2 □
9 ) 4 □ 7        8 ) □ 1 □
  − 4 5            − 1 6
      3 □              5 9
    − 3 □            − 5 □
        1                3
```

$487 \div 9 = 54$ R1 $\quad$ $219 \div 8 = 27$ R3

35 GAMES During 9 months, Da Jon paid $135 to play an online video game. If he paid the same amount each month, how much did he pay for 1 month?

$15

Vocabulary Check **Write the vocabulary word that completes each sentence.**

36 When you calculate a problem without using any tools (like paper and a pencil, or a calculator), you are performing mental math.

37 Short division is finding out how many times one number goes into another number using mental math.

38 Writing in Math Write two different ways that you could find the answer to $90 \div 10$.

Sample answers: Count how many times 10 can be subtracted from 90; try multiplication: $10 \times 9 = 90$; add 10 repeatedly until arriving at 90.

Spiral Review

Find each quotient.

39 $35 \div 7 =$ 5

40 $18 \div 6 =$ 3

41 $42 \div 6 =$ 7

42 $63 \div 7 =$ 9

Solve. (Lesson 3-5, p. 121)

43 BUSINESS A store had sales of $1,750 in a 7-hour period. What were the sales per hour?

$250

44 FOOD Two cheese pizzas and two sausage pizzas were cut into 28 pieces. The cheese pizzas were cut into an equal number of pieces, and the sausage pizzas were cut into a different but equal number of pieces. How many pieces were in each pizza? Assume each pizza had over 5 pieces.

6 pieces for one type of pizza and 8 for the other type of pizza

See It, Do It, Say It, Write It

Step 1 Write several division problems in vertical format on the board. Ask student volunteers to find the quotients.

Step 2 Have students model the problems using manipulatives or drawings. Use inverse operations to prove the quotients are correct.

Step 3 Write two more division problems in vertical format on the board. This time show all of the steps to finding the quotients, but make a few errors in each problem. Have students work in pairs. Tell them to determine if each problem is solved correctly. If problems are incorrect, students should explain and correct the errors. Have students share their evaluations in small groups or with the class.

Step 4 Ask students to write a word problem using $7\overline{)28}$ as a part of the solution. Ask them to explain in words how to find the quotient.

Ticket Out the Door

Division Problems

Write the following on the board.

1. $9\overline{)702}$ 78

2. $8\overline{)339}$ 42 R3

Have students find each quotient. They will hand in their papers as they exit the classroom.

Chapter 3 Progress Check 3

Formative Assessment

Use the Progress Check to assess students' mastery of the previous lessons. Have students review the lesson indicated for the problems they answered incorrectly.

Odd/Even Assignments

Exercises are structured so that students practice the same concepts whether they are assigned the odd or even problems.

Common Error Alert

Use Models Tell students that when they have to create their own models, they should use the ones given in previous exercises as examples to follow. They should note that the number of rows in the array is represented by the divisor of the division expression, and the number of columns in the array is represented by the quotient of the division expression.

Exercise 17 This is a real-world situation that does not always come out to a whole number quotient.

Chapter 3 **Progress Check 3** (Lessons 3-5 and 3-6)

Write the division problem represented by each model.

1 $40 \div 8 = 5$

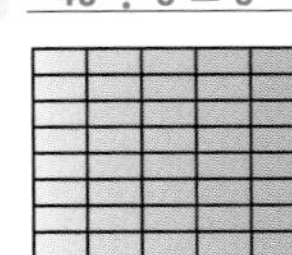

2 $36 \div 9 = 4$

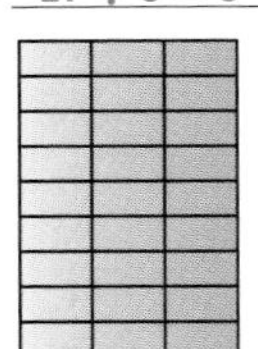

3 $27 \div 9 = 3$

4 $48 \div 8 = 6$

Find each quotient. Show a remainder if there is one.

5 $72 \div 8 =$ 9

6 $81 \div 9 =$ 9

7 $45 \div 9 =$ 5

8 $56 \div 8 =$ 7

9 $90 \div 8 =$ 11 R2

10 $50 \div 9 =$ 5 R5

11 $35 \div 9 =$ 3 R8

12 $61 \div 8 =$ 7 R5

13 $85 \div 8 =$ 10 R5

14 $20 \div 8 =$ 2 R4

15 $38 \div 9 =$ 4 R2

16 $40 \div 9 =$ 4 R4

Solve.

17 **SHOPPING** Paul is buying shirts. The shirts cost $8 each. If Paul has $43, how many shirts can he purchase? How much money will he have left?

He can buy 5 shirts. He will have $3 left.

134 **Chapter 3** Division

Data-Driven Decision Making

Students missing Exercises . . .	Have trouble with . . .	Should review and practice . . .
1-4	writing division problems represented by given models.	SSG Lessons 3-5 and 3-6, pp. 121 and 127 CRM Skills Practice, pp. A67 and A71
5-16	finding quotients with and without remainders.	SSG Lessons 3-5 and 3-6, pp. 121 and 127 CRM Skills Practice, pp. A67 and A71
17	solving word problems involving division problems (with and without remainders).	CRM Problem-Solving Practice, pp. A68 and A72

Study Guide

Vocabulary and Concept Check

divisor, *p. 92*
inverse operations, *p. 92*
multiple, *p. 113*
quotient, *p. 92*
remainder, *p. 113*

Write the vocabulary word that completes each sentence.

1. A(n) multiple of a number is the product of that number and any whole number.
2. Inverse operations are operations that undo each other.
3. The number that follows the division sign in a division sentence is the divisor.
4. A number that is left after one whole number is divided by another is a(n) remainder.

Label each diagram below. Write the correct vocabulary term in each blank.

5. dividend
$$\frac{24}{8} = 3$$

6. divisor
$$\frac{77}{11} = 7$$

7. quotient
$$8\overline{)56} \quad 7$$

Lesson Review

3-1 Model Division (pp. 92–98)

Draw an array to model each expression.

8. $12 \div 3$

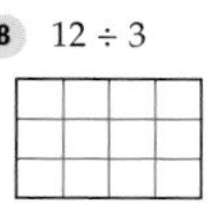

9. $16 \div 4$

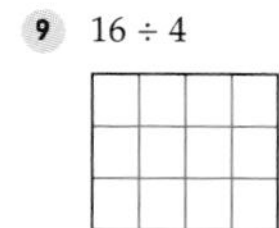

Write in two different formats.

10. $55 \div 5$ $\frac{55}{5}$ $5\overline{)55}$

11. $20 \div 2$ $\frac{20}{2}$ $2\overline{)20}$

Example 1

Draw an array to model the expression 9 ÷ 3.

1. Identify the dividend. 9
   This is the *total number of rectangles* in the array.
2. Identify the divisor. 3
   This is the number of *rows*.
3. Draw an array with 9 rectangles in 3 rows.
4. The number of columns in the array is the quotient. 3
5. Check by multiplying the quotient by the divisor. **3 × 3 = 9**

1	4	7
2	5	8
3	6	9

3 columns = quotient

Study Guide

Formative Assessment

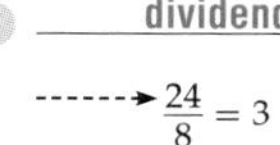

Chapter 3

Vocabulary and Concept Check

If students have difficulty answering Exercises 1–7, remind them that they can use the page references to refresh their memories about the vocabulary terms.

Vocabulary Review Strategies

Remember Vocabulary Divide the class into small groups. Have the groups work together to determine a method to teach their classmates how to remember the meanings of the vocabulary terms. The groups should then create guidelines or a visual to teach the method to their classmates. Students may choose any of the following (or come up with their own method):

- Place and rearrange the vocabulary words on a page to form patterns.
- Associate each word with a finger to remember it.
- Pair pictures with words to learn vocabulary.
- Visualize the word and its definition.

Lesson Review

Each example walks the students through the main concepts of this chapter. If the given examples are not sufficient to review the questions, remind students that the page references tell them where to review that topic in their textbooks.

Find **Extra Practice** for these concepts in the Practice Worksheets, pages A50–A73.

Classroom Management

Early Finishers Some students will not require as much time to complete their study guides. For those students who seem to have a solid understanding of the materials from the chapter, suggest they develop a small quiz from which you can pull additional review questions to be used at a later time. These could be presented to the remaining members of the class who could use the extra practice.

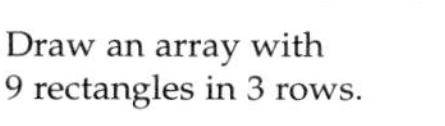

FOLDABLES® Study Organizer — Dinah Zike's Foldables®

Review Have students exchange their completed Foldables with a partner. They should each solve the division problems (without looking under the tabs for the answers). Students can grade each other's work. (For complete instructions, see Chapter Resource Masters, p. A47.)

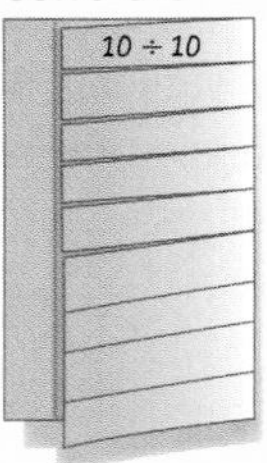

Math Coach Notes

Study Tables Help students create a study checklist. The checklist should include the following items:

- drawing models for division expressions.
- knowing more than one format for representing a division expression.
- knowing what is special about division by 0, 1, and 10.
- being able to divide by all remaining digits from 0–9 (other than 0, 1, and 10).
- performing long division.

Students should put a checkmark next to each topic when they feel they have a good grasp of the process.

If students do not understand any of the topics in the list above, try to get them additional help prior to a formal evaluation.

Intervention Strategy — Logical/Interpersonal Learners

Solve It! Write the following on the board:

A store has 489 pre-orders for a new music DVD. It can buy the album in cases of 8 for $50. How many cases should the store buy for the pre-orders? How much will this purchase cost the store? 62 cases; $3,100

Have students work in pairs or small groups. Ask students to read the problem out loud together and determine a strategy to solve for the answer. Tell students to record all of their computations on a sheet of paper. Encourage students to reread the problem to test their answer for reasonableness and completeness. Students can share their problem-solving processes in small groups or with the class.

3-2 Divide by 0, 1, and 10
(pp. 99–105)

Find each quotient.

12. 3 ÷ 1 = 3
13. 4 ÷ 0 = not possible
14. 0 ÷ 8 = 0
15. 6 ÷ 6 = 1
16. 80 ÷ 10 = 8
17. 100 ÷ 10 = 10

Example 2

Find 50 ÷ 10.

1. What number is the divisor? 10
2. What number times 10 equals 50? 5
3. Write the quotient. **50 ÷ 10 = 5**
4. Check. **5 × 10 = 50**

3-3 Divide by 2 and 5
(pp. 107–112)

Find each quotient.

18. 20 ÷ 2 = 10
19. 12 ÷ 2 = 6
20. 15 ÷ 5 = 3
21. 55 ÷ 5 = 11

Example 3

Find 25 ÷ 5.

1. Solve using related multiplication.
2. What number multiplied by 5 is 25? 5
3. Write the quotient. 25 ÷ 5 = 5
4. Check. 5 × 5 = 25

3-4 Divide by 3 and 4
(pp. 113–119)

Find each quotient. Show the remainder.

22. 18 ÷ 3 6
23. 26 ÷ 3 8 R2
24. 35 ÷ 4 8 R3
25. 36 ÷ 4 9

Example 4

Find 14 ÷ 4. Show the remainder.

1. Rewrite the problem in vertical format.
2. What number multiplied by 4 is equal to or less than 14? 3
   4 × 3 = 12
   This is close without going over.
   Multiply. Write the product under the dividend.

$$\begin{array}{r} 3 \\ 4\overline{)14} \\ -12 \\ \hline 2 \end{array}$$

3. Since there are no more digits to bring down, the answer is 3 R2.
4. Check. **(3 × 4) + 2 = 14**

Intervention Strategy — Logical Learners

Inverse Operations Stress the significance of division being the *inverse* or "backward" operation of multiplication. If students are feeling unsure of the operation or their answers, it is a good idea to have them check their solutions by multiplying the *quotients* by the *divisors* to see if they arrive at the *dividend.*

3-5 Divide by 6 and 7 (pp. 121–126)

Find each quotient. Show any remainders.

26 48 ÷ 6 = 8

27 578 ÷ 7 = 82 R4

28 522 ÷ 6 = 87

29 56 ÷ 7 = 8

Example 5

Find 288 ÷ 6.

1. Rewrite the pattern in vertical format.
2. Look at the first two digits. What number multiplied by 6 is close to 28? 4

   4 × 6 is 24. Put the 4 in the tens place in the quotient. Bring down next digit.
3. What number multiplied by 6 is 48? 8
   Complete the division.
4. The quotient is 48.

$$\begin{array}{r} 4 \\ 6\overline{)288} \\ -24 \\ \hline 48 \end{array} \qquad \begin{array}{r} 48 \\ 6\overline{)288} \\ -24 \\ \hline 48 \\ -48 \\ \hline 0 \end{array}$$

3-6 Divide by 8 and 9 (pp. 127–133)

Write the division problem represented by the model.

30 54 ÷ 9 = 6

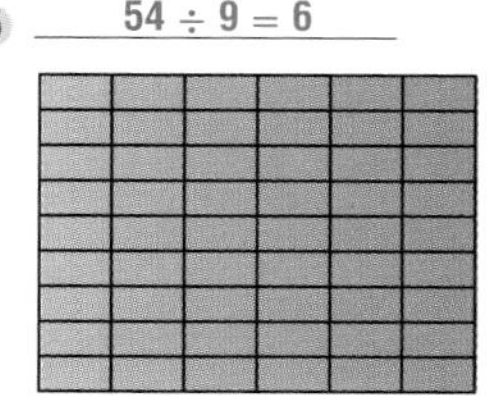

Find each quotient. Use short division.

31 80 ÷ 8 = 10

32 252 ÷ 9 = 28

33 376 ÷ 8 = 47

34 81 ÷ 9 = 9

Example 6

Write the division problem represented by the model.

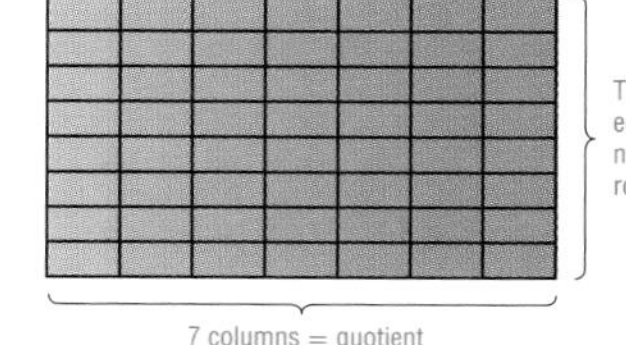

1. How many rectangles are in the array? 56
2. How many rows? 8
3. Count the number of columns. This is the quotient. 7
4. Write the division problem. 56 ÷ 8 = 7
5. Check. 8 × 7 = 56

Chapter 3 Study Guide 137

Ticket Out the Door

Write Problems Have each student develop two division problems with real-world applications. Require that at least one problem have a remainder. You could give them a list of some possible topics about which they could write their division problems, such as sports, transportation, money, cooking, shopping, hobbies, and so on. Suggest that students write their division problems about a topic that interests them.

The next day, present some of their problems to the class at the board.

Note This!

Show Work Encourage students to show their work as they find multiples while solving for quotients. Tell students to jot their work in the margins or on a piece of scrap paper. Sometimes similar multiples will pop up in later problems and if students show their work where they can access it later, those future problems will be easier because the work has already been done.

Math Coach Notes

Use More Models Help students by having them create additional models of division expressions. The extra visual aids may help to reinforce the concept of division with those students who may be struggling.

Models should be limited to the less-complicated division expressions.

Create models for:

- those with smaller divisors (0–12);
- those with dividends ≤ 100.

Fact Families When studying division facts, tell students to remember that each is part of a fact family. Practicing division facts with their multiplication family members will reinforce this relationship. Students can check their work using inverse operations and fact families.

Intervention Strategy — Intrapersonal/Naturalist Learners

Real-World Examples Challenge students to find examples of when they use division in their everyday lives. Encourage students to use their environment for inspiration. Have them write a list of examples collected from their daily routines, both at school and at home. Ask volunteers to share their examples with the class.

Chapter 3

Chapter Test

Chapter Resource Masters

Additional forms of the Chapter 3 Tests are available.

Test Format	Where to Find it
Chapter 3 Test	Math Online macmillanmh.com
Blackline Masters	Assessment Masters, p. 36

Customize and create multiple versions of your chapter tests and their answer keys. All of these questions from the chapter tests are available on ExamView® Assessment Suite.

Online Assessment and Reporting
macmillanmh.com

This online assessment tool allows teachers to track student progress with easily accessible comprehensive reports available for every student. Assess students using any internet-ready computer.

Alternative Assessment

Use Portfolios Ask students to write examples of each type of division problem presented in this chapter in their portfolios. Ask them to include a model or sketch with the examples, wherever they may be needed. Have students solve each problem in their portfolios, showing all the steps required.

Chapter 3 Chapter Test

Write each expression in two different formats.

1. 21 ÷ 7 $7\overline{)21}$ $\frac{21}{7}$
2. 72 ÷ 8 $8\overline{)72}$ $\frac{72}{8}$

Write the division problem represented by the model.

3. 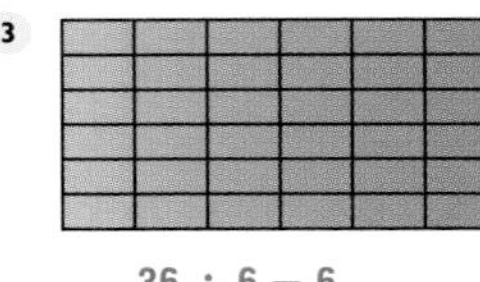
36 ÷ 6 = 6

4.  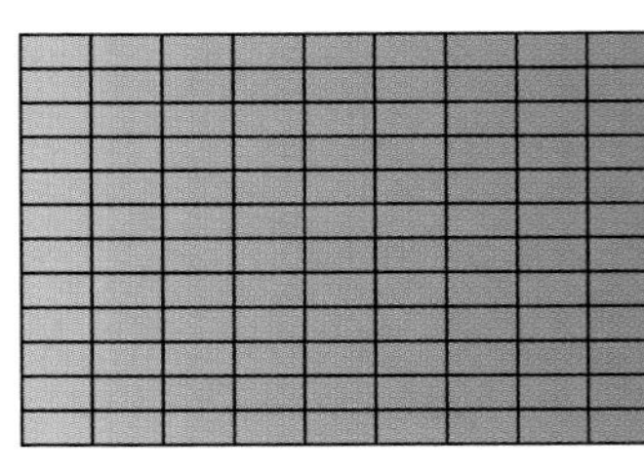
108 ÷ 12 = 9

5. 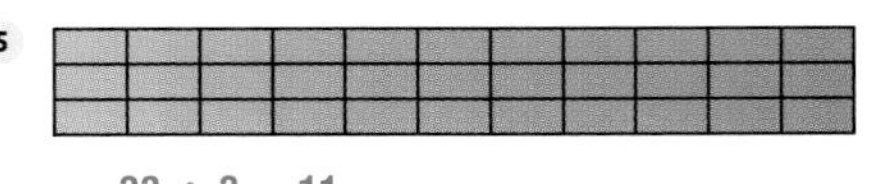
33 ÷ 3 = 11

Find each quotient. Show the remainder if there is one.

6. 20 ÷ 10 = 2
7. 11 ÷ 1 = 11
8. 0 ÷ 5 = 0
9. 60 ÷ 10 = 6
10. 9 ÷ 3 = 3
11. 8 ÷ 0 = not possible
12. 14 ÷ 7 = 2
13. 63 ÷ 9 = 7
14. 33 ÷ 3 = 11
15. 0 ÷ 2 = 0
16. 20 ÷ 10 = 2
17. 35 ÷ 5 = 7
18. 17 ÷ 5 = 3 R2
19. 51 ÷ 6 = 8 R3
20. 33 ÷ 4 = 8 R1

GO ON

138 **Chapter 3** Test

English Learner Strategy

Assessment Allow students time to look over the assessment. Have students take a close look at all the problem directions, as well as any terms in the word problems. Provide an opportunity for students to clarify any words they think they do not understand by conducting a brief question-and-answer period, or provide a dictionary or a translation manual for those who have a primary or native language other than English.

Find each quotient. Show the remainder if there is one.

21 $58 \div 8 =$ 7 R2 22 $57 \div 9 =$ 6 R3 23 $36 \div 2 =$ 18

24 $45 \div 5 =$ 9 25 $64 \div 8 =$ 8 26 $324 \div 6 =$ 54

27 $24 \div 3 =$ 8 28 $72 \div 4 =$ 18 29 $49 \div 7 =$ 7

Solve.

SCHOOL The principal wants to give a ribbon to every student who competes in the spelling bee. Ribbons are packaged 8 to a bundle.

30 If all 468 students compete, how many bundles of ribbons will the principal need?

59

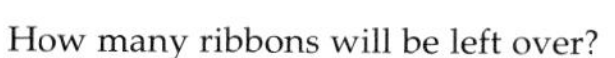

Award ribbon

31 How many ribbons will be left over?

4

32 LIBRARY The library has 672 books that need to be placed on 8 new shelves. If each shelf is to have the same number of books, how many books will be in each group?

84

FOOD The cafeteria needs a basket of 6 rolls per table for the banquet on Friday. They have baked 320 rolls.

33 How many baskets can be filled?

53

34 How many extra rolls will there be after the baskets are filled?

2

Correct the mistakes.

35 Orlando said that all fact families for multiplication and division have four equations. Give an example of a fact family with four equations. Give an example of a fact family with two equations that shows that Orlando's statement is false.

Sample answer: $5 \times 4 = 20$, $4 \times 5 = 20$, $20 \div 4 = 5$, $20 \div 5 = 4$; $6 \times 6 = 36$, $36 \div 6 = 6$

Learning From Mistakes

Missed Questions Review commonly missed questions as a small group or class. Ask students to share their methods of answering each question. Try to point out when any errors occur and take corrective measures.

Math Coach Notes

Test-Taking Tip Ensure students read each problem carefully. They should verify that their answers make sense in context. Have them ask themselves questions such as: Could 57×9 really be 63?

Data-Driven Decision Making

Students missing Exercises . . .	Have trouble with . . .	Should review and practice . . .
1–5	writing division expressions.	CRM Skills Practice, pp. A51, A55, A59, A63, A67, and A71
6–29	finding quotients and showing the remainders.	CRM Skills Practice, pp. A51, A55, A59, A63, A67, and A71
30–35	solving word problems involving division (both with and without remainders).	CRM Problem-Solving Practice, pp. A52, A56, A60, A64, A68, and A72

Chapter 3 Test Practice

Diagnose Student Errors

Survey student responses for each item. Class trends may indicate common errors and misconceptions.

1. A factors not in the same fact family
B factors not in the same fact family
C factors not in the same fact family
(D) correct

2. A guess
B calculation error
(C) correct
D guess

3. A guess
(B) correct
C division error, $\$54 \div 3 = \$18$
D misinterpreted required operation, multiplied instead of divided

4. A misinterpreted definition of quotient
B misinterpreted definition of dividend
(C) correct
D misinterpreted definition of multiple

5. A guess
B calculation error, $765 \div 9 = 85$
(C) correct
D guess

6. A multiplication error, $12 \times 8 = 96$
B misinterpreted concept of grouping
(C) correct
D multiplication error, $11 \times 10 = 110$

7. A guess
(B) correct
C division error, $3{,}840 \div 8 = 480$
D guess

8. A guess
B multiplication error
(C) correct
D multiplication error

9. A possible, $12 \div 1 = 12$
B possible, $0 \div 12 = 0$
(C) correct
D possible, $12 \div 12 = 1$

Chapter 3 Test Practice

Choose the best answer and fill in the corresponding circle on the sheet at right.

1 Which equation can be used to check $10 \times 4 = 40$?

A $40 \div 8 = 5$
B $10 \times 10 = 100$
C $4 \times 4 = 16$
(D) $40 \div 10 = 4$

2 Chandani wants to share her music CD collection with her sister. If Chandani has 24 CDs and gives her sister half of her collection, how many CDs will each sister have?

A 8 CDs
B 10 CDs
(C) 12 CDs
D 20 CDs

3 Jeans are on sale this week. How much would one pair of jeans cost during this sale?

SALE
Jeans
3 for $54

A $16
(B) $18
C $21
D $162

4 The number that is left after one whole number is divided by another is the ______.

A quotient
B dividend
(C) remainder
D multiple

5 Ms. Wantobi is dividing counters equally into 9 jars for a math project. If she has a total of 765 counters, how many will go in each jar?

A 73 counters
B 84 counters
(C) 85 counters
D 91 counters

6 The music teacher wants to divide the band students into 8 equal groups. If there are 128 total students in band, which grouping will work?

A 8 groups of 12 students
B 9 groups of 15 students
(C) 8 groups of 16 students
D 11 groups of 10 students

7 The Lorenz family traveled 3,840 miles on their summer vacation. If they traveled the same number of miles per day and finished the trip in 8 days, how many miles per day did they travel?

A 460 miles
(B) 480 miles
C 510 miles
D 530 miles

GO ON

140 Chapter 3 Test Practice

10. A misinterpreted how many quarters in a dollar
(B) correct
C misinterpreted how many quarters in a dollar
D miscalculation

11. A multiplication error, $14 \times 9 = 126$
B multiplication error, $15 \times 9 = 135$
C multiplication error, $16 \times 9 = 154$
(D) correct

8 Karlie reads about 40 pages per hour. If she finishes her book in 9 hours, about how many pages are in this book?

A 180 pages

B 270 pages

(C) 360 pages

D 540 pages

9 Which of the following is not possible?

A $12 \div 1$ (C) $12 \div 0$

B $0 \div 12$ D $12 \div 12$

10 If Shaun has 40 quarters, how many dollars does he have?

A $5

(B) $10

C $15

D $20

11 Enrique is baking cookies. He wants to make 153 large cookies to sell for a school fundraiser. If he can make 9 cookies per batch, how many batches will he need to bake?

A 14 batches

B 15 batches

C 16 batches

(D) 17 batches

ANSWER SHEET

Directions: Fill in the circle of each correct answer.

1	A	B	C	**D**
2	A	B	**C**	D
3	A	**B**	C	D
4	A	B	**C**	D
5	A	B	**C**	D
6	A	B	**C**	D
7	A	**B**	C	D
8	A	B	**C**	D
9	A	B	**C**	D
10	A	**B**	C	D
11	A	B	C	**D**

Success Strategy
Read the entire question before looking at the answer choices. Watch for words like *not* that change the whole question.

Chapter 3 Test Practice **141**

Diagnosing Student Errors and Misconceptions

Review Sharing the answer key could benefit students. Have students score their own Test Practice and revise their responses, as needed.

After doing so, take an informal class poll in order to determine the number of students missing particular questions. This can help indicate any misconceptions the class may have with the material.

For example, students may be confused with Exercise 4. They may confuse the different terms relating to division problems. If several students make this mistake, students may benefit from further explanation of this type of problem.

Eliminate Wrong Answers If students are not able to successfully eliminate wrong answer choices, point out the following:

Exercise 1 Remind students that multiplication and division are inverse operations. You can use one to check the other and vice versa.

Exercise 9 Be sure students understand that division by zero means having a divisor of zero. This is not possible because you cannot take a group of things and divide them into zero. Zero divided by a number is very different. In this case, zero is the dividend and represents zero items. Taking zero items and dividing them into groups of any number still gives you zero.

Chapter 4

Chapter Overview

Chapter-at-a-Glance

Lesson	Math Objective	State/Local Standards
4-1 Commutative Property (pp. 144–150)	Know and use the Commutative Properties of Addition and Multiplication.	
4-2 Associative Property (pp. 151–157)	Know and use the Associative Properties of Addition and Multiplication.	
Progress Check 1 (p. 158)		
4-3 Distributive Property (pp. 159–164)	Know and use the Distributive Property of Multiplication.	
4-4 Order of Operations (p. 165–170)	Use the order of operations to evaluate expressions.	
Progress Check 2 (p. 171)		

Content-at-a-Glance

The diagram below summarizes and unpacks Chapter 4 content.

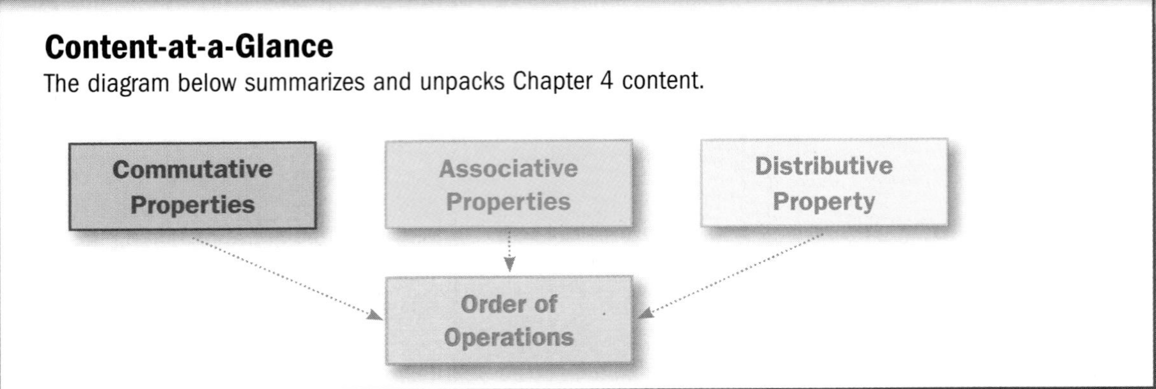

Online Assessment and Reporting
macmillanmh.com

Chapter Assessment Manager

Diagnostic

Diagnose students' readiness.

	Student Study Guide/ Teacher Edition	Assessment Masters	Technology
Course Placement Test		1	ExamView® Assessment Suite
Book 1 Pretest		8	ExamView® Assessment Suite
Chapter 4 Pretest		44	ExamView® Assessment Suite
Quiz/Preview	SSG 143		Math Online macmillanmh.com StudentWorks™ Plus

Formative

Identify students' misconceptions of content knowledge.

	Student Study Guide/ Teacher Edition	Assessment Masters	Technology
Progress Checks	SSG 158, 171		Math Online macmillanmh.com StudentWorks™ Plus
Vocabulary Review	SSG 172		Math Online macmillanmh.com
Lesson Assessments			ExamView® Assessment Suite
Are They Getting It?	TE 146, 153, 161, 167		

Summative

Determine student success in learning the concepts in the lesson, chapter, or book.

	Student Study Guide/ Teacher Edition	Assessment Masters	Technology
Chapter 4 Test	SSG 176	47	ExamView® Assessment Suite
Test Practice	SSG 178	50	ExamView® Assessment Suite
Alternative Assessment	TE 176	53	
See It, Do It, Say It, Write It	TE 150, 157, 164, 170		
Book 1 Test		55	ExamView® Assessment Suite

Back-mapping and Vertical Alignment **McGraw-Hill's *Math Triumphs*** intervention program was conceived and developed with the final result in mind: student success in grade-level mathematics, including Algebra 1 and beyond. The authors, using the **NCTM Focal Points and Focal Connections** as their guide, developed this brand-new series by backmapping from grade-level and Algebra 1 concepts, and vertically aligning the topics so that they build upon prior skills and concepts and serve as a foundation for future topics.

Chapter Resource Manager

	Lesson 4-1	Lesson 4-2	Lesson 4-3	Lesson 4-4
Concept	Commutative Property	Associative Property	Distributive Property	Order of Operations
Objective	Know and use the Commutative Properties of Addition and Multiplication.	Know and use the Associative Properties of Addition and Multiplication.	Know and use the Distributive Property of Multiplication.	Use the order of operations to evaluate expressions.
Math Vocabulary	Commutative Property of Addition Commutative Property of Multiplication product sum	addend Associative Property of Addition Associative Property of Multiplication factor	Distributive Property of Multiplication	order of operations
Lesson Resources	**Materials** • Construction paper • Grid paper • Index cards **Manipulatives** • Algebra tiles • Bucket balance **Other Resources** CRM Vocabulary and English Language Development CRM Skills Practice CRM Problem-Solving Practice CRM Homework Practice	**Materials** • Grid paper • Notebook paper **Manipulatives** • Algebra tiles • Base-ten rods • Geoboard • Unit cubes **Other Resources** CRM Vocabulary and English Language Development CRM Skills Practice CRM Problem-Solving Practice CRM Homework Practice	**Materials** • Objects as counters • Number cubes • Playing cards **Manipulatives** • Geoboard • Two-color counters **Other Resources** CRM Vocabulary and English Language Development CRM Skills Practice CRM Problem-Solving Practice CRM Homework Practice	**Materials** • Construction paper • Markers • Objects as counters **Manipulatives** • Algebra tiles • Bucket balance **Other Resources** CRM Vocabulary and English Language Development CRM Skills Practice CRM Problem-Solving Practice CRM Homework Practice
Technology	Math Online macmillanmh.com StudentWorks™ Plus ExamView® Assessment Suite	Math Online macmillanmh.com StudentWorks™ Plus ExamView® Assessment Suite	Math Online macmillanmh.com StudentWorks™ Plus ExamView® Assessment Suite	Math Online macmillanmh.com StudentWorks™ Plus ExamView® Assessment Suite

Intervention Strategy

Introduce the Distributive Property

Ask students what it means to distribute food or pamphlets. Offer them the dictionary definition of *distribute:* to spread out so as to cover something. When we use the Distributive Property, we spread out the multiplication over the addition. Students often forget to multiply the second set of numbers. Have students physically draw arrows to show the distribution.

Examples: $7(3 + 4) = (7 \times 3) + (7 \times 4)$
$= 21 + 28$
$= 49$

$5(20 - 9) = (5 \times 20) - (5 \times 9)$
$= 100 - 45$
$= 55$

$7(9 - 2) = (7 \times 9) - (7 \times 2)$
$= 63 - 14$
$= 49$

Have students draw arrows to represent the Distributive Property. Simplify.

1. 2(7 + 20)
14 + 40 = 54

2. 10(50 − 3)
500 − 30 = 470

3. 2(4 + 13)
8 + 26 = 34

4. 9(2 + 9)
18 + 81 = 99

5. 6(4 + 2)
24 + 12 = 36

6. 32(20 + 5)
640 + 160 = 800

7. 6(12 − 4)
72 − 24 = 48

8. 18(10 − 2)
180 − 36 = 144

Chapter 4 Chapter Notes

Real-World Applications

Properties Read each of the situations below. Relate the situations to number properties.

- The Kafburn Knights basketball team scored 6 points in the first quarter. They did not make any free throws. Did they score 2 three-pointers or 3 two-pointers? This situation shows an example of the Commutative Property. It illustrates that 2×3 and 3×2 both equal 6.
- The student council collected $43 in bills, $5.50 in quarters, and $3.25 in dimes and nickels at a bake sale. Melissa added the amount of bills and quarters, then added the amount of the dimes. Zach added the amount of quarters and dimes, then added the amount of the bills. Did the two arrive at the same total? This situation shows an example of the Associative Property; both addition problems total $51.75.

Intervention Strategy

Write Number Sentences

Step 1 Divide students into small groups. Give each group three number cubes.

Step 2 Students roll the cubes.

Step 3 Students write number sentences using the Commutative, Associative, and Distributive Properties.

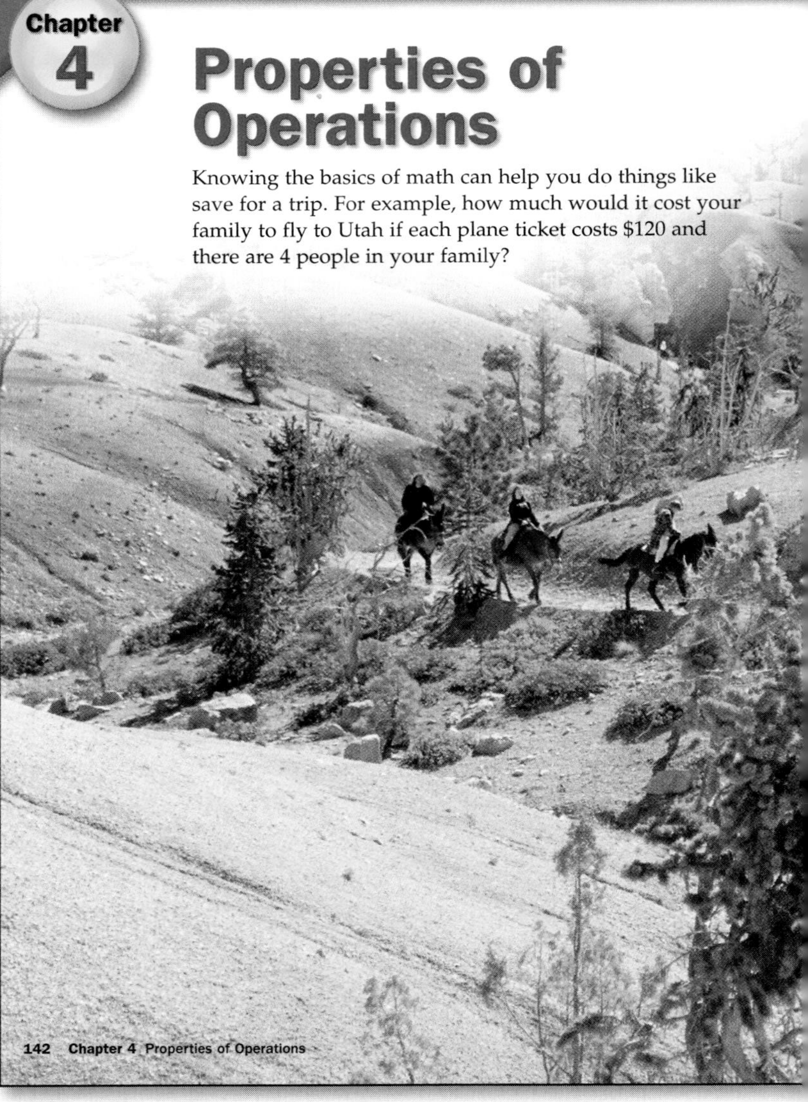

Chapter 4
Properties of Operations
Knowing the basics of math can help you do things like save for a trip. For example, how much would it cost your family to fly to Utah if each plane ticket costs $120 and there are 4 people in your family?
142 Chapter 4 Properties of Operations

Key Vocabulary

Find interactive definitions in 13 languages in the **eGlossary** at macmillanmh.com.

English **Español** *Introduce the most important vocabulary terms from Chapter 4.*

Commutative Property of Addition **propiedad conmutativa de la adición**
the order in which two numbers are added does not change the sum (p. 144)

Commutative Property of Multiplication **propiedad conmutativa de la multiplicación**
the order in which two numbers are multiplied does not change the product (p. 144)

Associative Property of Addition **propiedad asociativa de la adición**
the grouping of the addends does not change the sum (p. 151)

Associative Property of Multiplication **propiedad asociativa de la multiplicación**
the grouping of the factors does not change the product (p. 151)

Distributive Property of Multiplication **propiedad distributiva de la multiplicación**
to multiply a sum by a number, you can multiply each addend by the number and add the products (p. 159)

order of operations **orden de las operaciones**
rules that tell what order to use when evaluating expressions (p. 165)

STEP 1 Quiz Are you ready for Chapter 4? Take the Online Readiness Quiz at *macmillanmh.com* to find out.

STEP 2 Preview Get ready for Chapter 4. Review these skills and compare them with what you'll learn in this chapter.

What You Know	What You Will Learn
You know how to multiply. **Examples:** $7 \times 4 = 28$ $4 \times 7 = 28$ **TRY IT!** 1 $5 \times 5 =$ 25 2 $10 \times 10 =$ 100 3 $7 \times 12 =$ 84 4 $2 \times 24 =$ 48	*Lesson 4-1* The order in which you multiply numbers does not change the answer. This is called the **Commutative Property of Multiplication**. $7 \times 4 = 28$ $4 \times 7 = 28$ The answer is the same.
You know how to add. **Examples:** $4 + 3 + 2 = 9$ $2 + 3 + 4 = 9$ **TRY IT!** 5 $3 + 5 + 10 =$ 18 6 $10 + 5 + 3 =$ 18 7 $20 + 3 + 3 =$ 26 8 $3 + 20 + 3 =$ 26	*Lesson 4-2* Grouping numbers you are adding in different ways does not change the answer. This is called the **Associative Property of Addition**. $(4 + 3) + 2 = 9$ $7 + 2 = 9$ $4 + (3 + 2) = 9$ $4 + 5 = 9$
You know how to add and multiply. **Example:** $(2 \times 4) + (2 \times 5) = 18$ $8 + 10 = 18$ **TRY IT!** 9 $(5 \times 2) + (3 \times 3) =$ 19 10 $(10 \times 9) + (1 \times 4) =$ 94 11 $(6 \times 3) + (4 \times 1) =$ 22 12 $(6 \times 3) + (4 \times 2) =$ 26	*Lesson 4-3* Distribute a number by multiplying it with each member of a group. This is called the **Distributive Property**. $2(4 + 5) =$ $(2 \times 4) + (2 \times 5) =$ $8 + 10 = 18$

143

Vocabulary Preview

- As students complete the Chapter Preview, have them make a list of important terms throughout the chapter.
- Using graph paper, have students create a word search of at least 10 important terms throughout the chapter, including the key vocabulary terms.
- Instead of giving a list of the terms to search for, have students make a list of the definitions of the terms. The seeker will then have to search for the terms described by their definition.
- Once students have finished creating their word searches, have them trade with a partner to complete the challenge.

Step 1

Pretest/Prescribe Students can take the Online Readiness Quiz or the Diagnostic Pretest in the Assessment Masters.

Step 2 Preview

Use this pre-chapter activity to activate students' prior knowledge, build confidence, and help students preview the lessons.

Guide students through the directions on p. A74 in the Chapter Resource Masters to create their own Foldable graphic organizer for use with this chapter.

Home Connections

- Have students write a list of five daily events in which the order done does or does not matter. Example: The order in which you clean your body does not matter, as long as your entire body gets clean.

Professional Development

Targeted professional development has been articulated throughout **McGraw-Hill's *Math Triumphs*** intervention program. **The McGraw-Hill Professional Development Video Library** provides short videos that support the **NCTM Focal Points and Focal Connections.** For more information, visit macmillanmh.com.

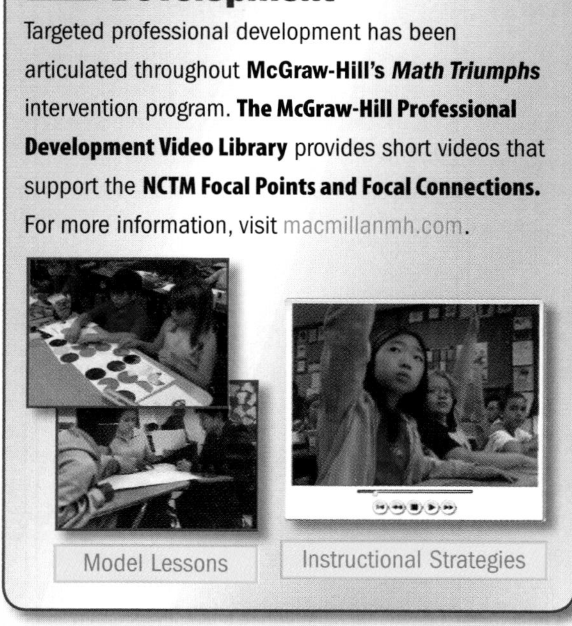

Lesson 4-1

Lesson Notes

Lesson Planner

Objective Know and use the Commutative Properties of Addition and Multiplication.

Vocabulary **Commutative Property of Addition**, **Commutative Property of Multiplication**, **product**, **sum**

Materials/Manipulatives algebra tiles, bucket balance, construction paper, grid paper, index cards

Chapter Resource Masters

- CRM Vocabulary and English Language Development (p. A77)
- CRM Skills Practice (p. A78)
- CRM Problem-Solving Practice (p. A79)
- CRM Homework Practice (p. A80)

1 Introduce

Vocabulary

Access Vocabulary Write an addition problem and a multiplication problem on the board. Ask for volunteers to go to the board and solve each problem. Ask students to identify which answer is the *sum* and which answer is the *product.* Also ask students to name the opposite operations of *addition* and *multiplication*.

2 Teach

Key Concept

Foundational Skills and Concepts After students have read through the Key Concept box, have them try these exercises.

1. Why is $3 + 5 = 5 + 3$ an example of the Commutative Property of Addition? $8 = 8$
2. Why is $4 \times 5 = 5 \times 4$ an example of the Commutative Property of Multiplication? $20 = 20$
3. What does the Commutative Property say? The order in which 2 numbers are added or multiplied does not matter.

Lesson 4-1 **Commutative Property**

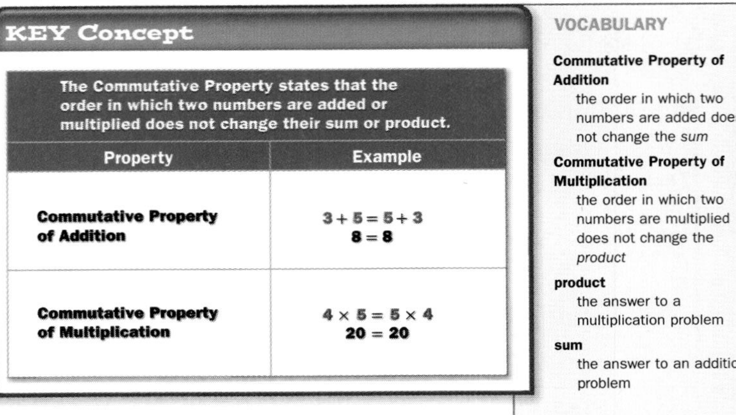

KEY Concept

The Commutative Property states that the order in which two numbers are added or multiplied does not change their sum or product.

Property	Example
Commutative Property of Addition	$3 + 5 = 5 + 3$ $8 = 8$
Commutative Property of Multiplication	$4 \times 5 = 5 \times 4$ $20 = 20$

VOCABULARY

Commutative Property of Addition the order in which two numbers are added does not change the *sum*

Commutative Property of Multiplication the order in which two numbers are multiplied does not change the *product*

product the answer to a multiplication problem

sum the answer to an addition problem

The Commutative Property tells you that order does not matter when you are adding or multiplying.

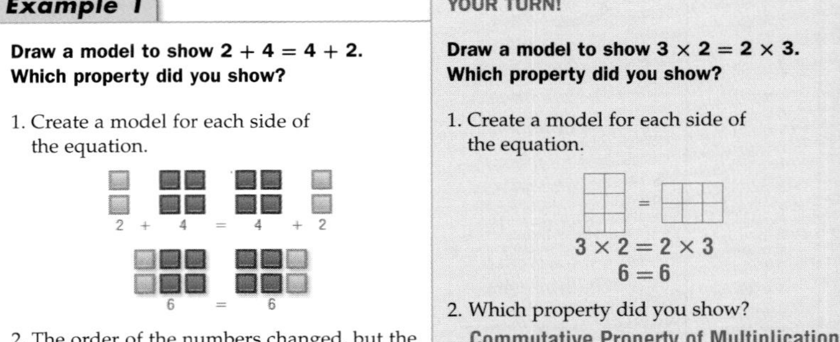

Example 1

Draw a model to show $2 + 4 = 4 + 2$. Which property did you show?

1. Create a model for each side of the equation.

2. The order of the numbers changed, but the sum did not. This is the Commutative Property of Addition.

YOUR TURN!

Draw a model to show $3 \times 2 = 2 \times 3$. Which property did you show?

1. Create a model for each side of the equation.

$3 \times 2 = 2 \times 3$
$6 = 6$

2. Which property did you show?
Commutative Property of Multiplication

144 **Chapter 4** Properties of Operations

Additional **Example 1**

Draw a model to show $3 + 5 = 5 + 3$. Which property did you show?

1. Create a model for each side of the equation.

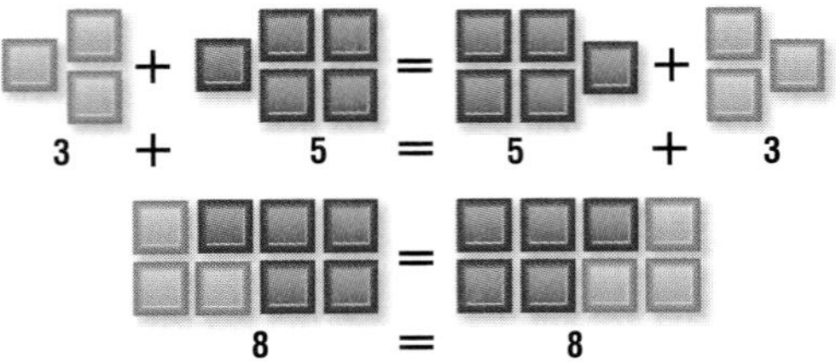

2. The order of the numbers changed, but the sum did not. This is the Commutative Property of Addition.

Example 2

Use the Commutative Property to fill in the blank. Check your answer.

$8 \times 6 =$ _____ $\times 8$

1. Use the Commutative Property of Multiplication.

   $8 \times 6 = 6 \times 8$

2. Check by multiplying the numbers on each side of the equation.

   $8 \times 6 = 6 \times 8$
   $48 = 48$

YOUR TURN!

Use the Commutative Property to fill in the blank. Check your answer.

$9 + 3 =$ _____ $+ 9$

1. Use the Commutative Property of Addition.

   $9 + 3 = \underline{\ 3\ } + 9$

2. Check by adding the numbers on each side of the equation.

   $9 + 3 = 3 + 9$
   $12 = 12$

Who is Correct?

Give an example of the Commutative Property of Multiplication.

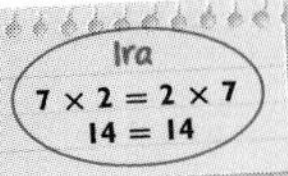

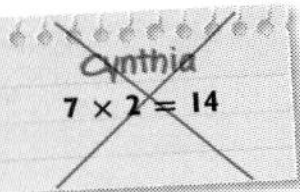

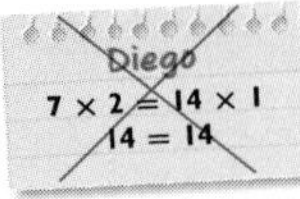

Circle correct answer(s). Cross out incorrect answer(s).

Guided Practice

Draw a model to show each equation.

1. $2 + 5 = 5 + 2$
   Which property did you show?
   Commutative Property of Addition

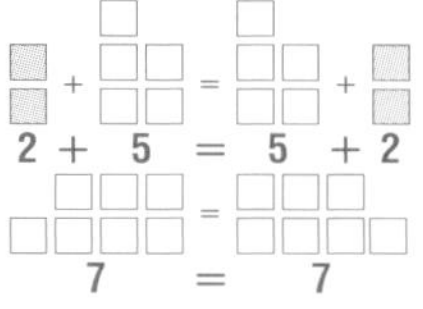

2. $3 \times 4 = 4 \times 3$
   Which property did you show?
   Commutative Property of Multiplication

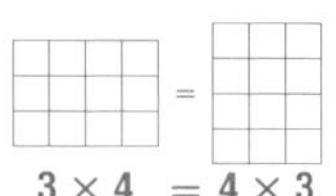

Additional *Example 2*

Use the Commutative Property to fill in the blank. Check your answer.
$3 \times 7 =$ _____ $\times 3$

1. Use the Commutative Property of Multiplication.

   $3 \times 7 = 7 \times 3$

2. Check by multiplying the numbers on each side of the equation.

   $3 \times 7 = 7 \times 3$
   $21 = 21$

Who *is Correct?*

Diagnostic Teaching

- Ira is correct. He showed the Commutative Property of Multiplication because the order of the numbers being multiplied changed, but the product did not.
- Cynthia is incorrect. She wrote an example of a multiplication equation and not an example of the Commutative Property of Multiplication.
- Diego is incorrect. The numbers being multiplied on the left side of the equation are not the same numbers as the numbers being multiplied on the right side of the equation, even though both products are the same. This is not an example of the Commutative Property of Multiplication.

3 Practice

Using Manipulatives

Bucket Balance When presenting Example 2, use a bucket balance to give students a visual concept of equality using the Commutative Properties of Addition and Multiplication. Show the buckets unbalanced before filling in the blank with the correct value. Show the buckets balanced after filling in the blank with the correct value.

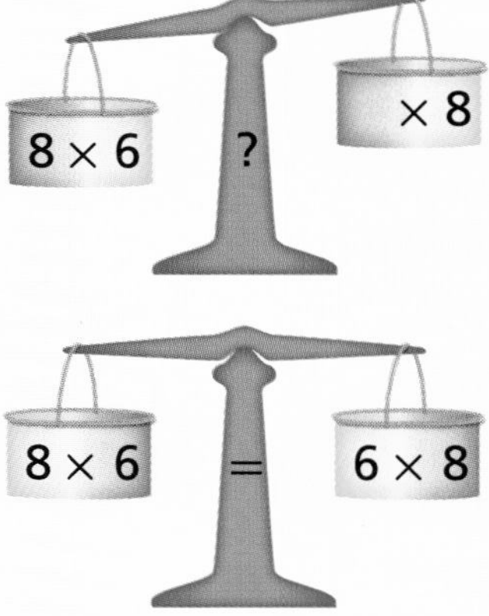

Grid Paper Use grid paper to demonstrate the Commutative Property of Multiplication. Make a grid that is 6 rows of 8 columns and a grid that is 8 rows of 6 columns. Both grids have a total of 48 squares, which verifies equality regardless of the order of the factors.

On-Hand Manipulatives Cut out small, different-colored squares of construction paper to place as arrays or as models for equations.

Math Coach Notes

Strategies

1. When using the Commutative Properties of Addition and Multiplication, there are patterns to follow.
   - first term + second term = second term + first term
   - first term × second term = second term × first term
2. Write these equations on the board to help students recognize and follow the patterns.

Intervention Strategy — Interpersonal Learners

Find Sums If students are having difficulty understanding the Commutative Property, give three different students three different numbers. Ask the students to find the sum of the numbers by adding the numbers in different order. Ask them to explain why they always get the same answer. Have students write a rule in their own words.

Step by Step Practice

Use the Commutative Property to fill in the blank. Check your answer.

3 $12 + 9 = 9 +$ ____

Step 1 The order in which two numbers are <u>added</u> does not change the sum. The property shown is the <u>Commutative</u> Property of <u>Addition</u>.

Step 2 Which number is not shown on the right side of the equation? Fill in the blank.

$12 + 9 = 9 + \underline{12}$

Step 3 Check. Add the numbers on each side of the equation.

$12 + 9 = 9 + \underline{12}$

$21 = \underline{21}$

Use the Commutative Property to fill in each blank. Check your answer.

4 $3 \times 9 = \underline{9} \times 3$

$27 = \underline{27}$

5 $\underline{18} + 5 = 5 + 18$

$\underline{23} = 23$

6 $8 + 11 = \underline{11} + \underline{8}$

$\underline{19} = \underline{19}$

7 $5 \times 6 = \underline{6} \times \underline{5}$

$\underline{30} = \underline{30}$

8 $4 + \underline{7} = 7 + \underline{4}$

$\underline{11} = \underline{11}$

9 $2 \times \underline{6} = 6 \times \underline{2}$

$\underline{12} = \underline{12}$

Draw a model to show each equation.

10 $2 \times 5 = 5 \times 2$

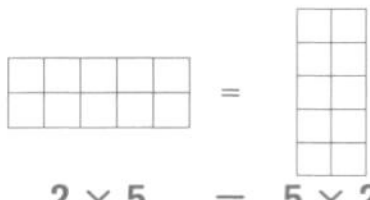

$2 \times 5 = 5 \times 2$

11 $7 + 3 = 3 + 7$

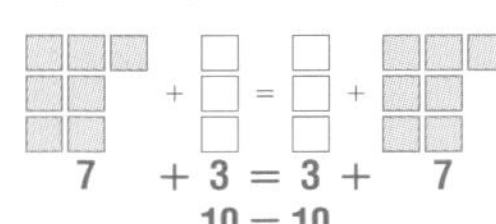

$7 + 3 = 3 + 7$

$10 = 10$

146 **Chapter 4** Properties of Operations

Are They Getting It?

Check students' understanding of the Commutative Properties by writing these problems on the board. Have students explain the incorrect information in each problem. Encourage students to use a diagram in their explanation.

1. $24 + 11 =$ ____ + ____

   $24 + 11 = 24 + 11$ This is incorrect; the order of the numbers did not change.

2. $5 \times 8 =$ ____ × ____

   $5 \times 8 = 8 \times 5$ This is correct.

3. $9 \times 9 =$ ____ × ____

   $9 \times 9 = 9 \times 9$ This is correct because the numbers are the same; you cannot tell if the order changed.

Step by Step Problem-Solving Practice

Problem-Solving Strategies
- ☐ Draw a diagram.
- ☐ Look for a pattern.
- ☐ Guess and check.
- ☑ Act it out.
- ☐ Solve a simpler problem.

Solve.

12 SHOPPING Jacob bought 3 boxes of pens with 5 pens in each box. Lydia bought 5 boxes of pens with 3 pens in each box. Compare the number of pens Jacob and Lydia bought. Justify your answer.

Understand Read the problem. Write what you know.

Jacob bought 3 boxes with 5 pens each.

Lydia bought 5 boxes with 3 pens each.

Plan Pick a strategy. One strategy is to act it out.

Arrange pens in rows and columns to show the pens that Jacob and Lydia bought. Then, write an expression to model each arrangement.

Solve Jacob's arrangement is 3 rows by 5 columns.

He has 15 pens.

The expression is 3×5.

Lydia's arrangement is 5 rows by 3 columns.

She has 15 pens.

The expression is 5×3.

The number of pens that Jacob bought is equal to the number of pens that Lydia bought.

Check Multiply the numbers on each side of the equation.

$3 \times 5 = 5 \times 3$

$15 = 15$

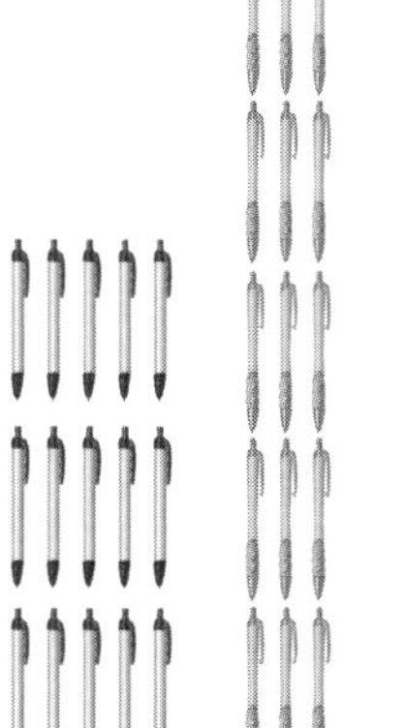

Jacob's pens Lydia's pens

Intervention Strategy — Auditory Learners

Songs Use songs as ways to help students learn the Commutative Properties of Addition and Multiplication. Arrange students into pairs and have each group create a song that uses the key concepts of the Commutative Properties. Each group can present their song to the rest of the class. Have the students pick the best two songs. Print the songs and give each student a copy for reference.

Note This!

Study Strategies As students encounter a new property, have them start an index-card file of properties. Cards should include the title of the property, a brief description of it, and an example. When they re-encounter the property, they can revisit their index cards to refresh their memories.

Math Coach Notes

Symbolic Expressions The Commutative Properties of Addition and Multiplication are written symbolically as follows: *For any numbers a and b,* it is true that:

$$a + b = b + a$$

$$a \times b = b \times a$$

When using symbolic expressions, students need to acquire symbolic manipulative skills to solve the equation.

Math Coach Notes

Directions Use a computer to make the following connection to the Commutative Property. Visit a map web site to get directions from one place to another. Have students do research to find the reverse directions. Ask them to compare the directions and relate this to the addition of numbers.

Odd/Even Assignments

Exercises 17–38 are structured so that students practice the same concepts whether they are assigned the odd or even problems.

In-Class Assignment

Have students complete Exercises 17, 20, 32, 34, and 43 to ensure that they understand the concept.

Intervention Strategy — Logical Learners

Work Backward Arrange students into pairs and have half of the groups start with a number that represents a *sum* and the other half start with a number that represents a *product.* Have one student create an addition problem or a multiplication problem that has the *sum* or *product* represented by the number. Have the other student verify the answer by using the Commutative Properties of Addition and Multiplication.

13 JEWELRY Missy has 7 boxes of necklaces with 3 necklaces in each box. Sari has 3 boxes of necklaces with 7 necklaces in each box. Compare the number of necklaces. Justify your answer.
Check off each step.

✔ Understand: I circled key words.

✔ Plan: To solve the problem, I will act it out.

✔ Solve: The answer is They each have 21 necklaces; $7 \times 3 = 3 \times 7$, $21 = 21$.

✔ Check: I checked my answer by multiplying the numbers on each side of the equation.

14 COIN COLLECTING Billy has 35 coins. His brother gave him 62 more coins. Roberto has 62 coins. His father gave him 35 more coins. Compare the number of coins. Justify your answer.

They have the same number of coins; $35 + 62 = 62 + 35$, $97 = 97$.

15 STORES The Corner Store had 15 sweaters on display. Ten more sweaters were delivered in the afternoon. The Sweater Store had 10 sweaters on display. In the afternoon delivery, 15 more sweaters arrived. Compare the number of sweaters. Justify your answer.

Both stores had the same number of sweaters; $15 + 10 = 10 + 15$, $25 = 25$.

16 **Reflect** How do you know that $65 + 98 = 98 + 65$ without adding?

Answers will vary. Sample answer: The Commutative Property of Addition states that the order in which two numbers are added does not change the sum. The numbers on either side of the equals sign are the same, but in different order.

Skills, Concepts, and Problem Solving

Draw a model to show each equation.

17 $6 \times 5 = 5 \times 6$
Which property did you show?
Commutative Property of Multiplication

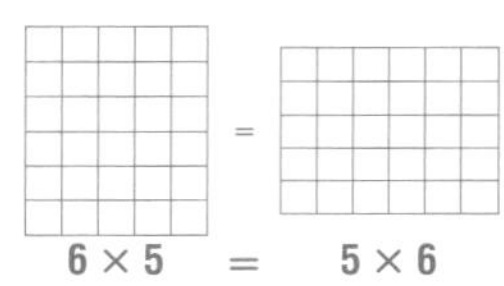

18 $4 + 5 = 5 + 4$
Which property did you show?
Commutative Property of Addition

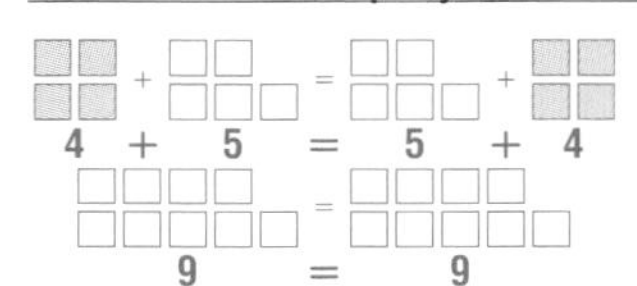

148 **Chapter 4** Properties of Operations

Intervention Strategy — Visual Learners

Model the Commutative Property

1. Have students write a two-digit addition problem on a sheet of paper.
2. Arrange students into pairs and pass out index cards to each pair.
3. Have students rewrite each addend of their addition problem on a separate index card.
4. Then have students write the plus sign and the equal sign on separate index cards.
5. Ask students to arrange their index cards to exactly represent their original addition problem.
6. Then ask students to rearrange their index cards to show the Commutative Property of Addition.

Use the Commutative Property to fill in each blank. Check your answer.

19 $7 + 6 =$ __6__ $+ 7$
__13__ $= 13$

20 $39 + 28 = 28 +$ __39__
$67 =$ __67__

21 $5 \times 9 = 9 \times$ __5__
$45 =$ __45__

22 $18 \times 5 =$ __5__ $\times 18$
__90__ $= 90$

23 $48 + 37 =$ __37__ $+$ __48__
__85__ $=$ __85__

24 __11__ $+$ __15__ $= 15 + 11$
__26__ $=$ __26__

25 __6__ $\times$ __7__ $= 7 \times 6$
__42__ $=$ __42__

26 $9 \times 8 =$ __8__ $\times$ __9__
__72__ $=$ __72__

27 $5 +$ __26__ $= 26 +$ __5__
$31 =$ __31__

28 __55__ $+ 44 =$ __44__ $+ 55$
__99__ $= 99$

29 $8 \times$ __4__ $=$ __4__ $\times 8$
$32 =$ __32__

30 $5 \times$ __9__ $= 9 \times$ __5__
$45 =$ __45__

31 $2 \times$ __27__ $=$ __27__ $\times 2$
__54__ $= 54$

32 __3__ $\times 18 =$ __18__ $\times 3$
__54__ $= 54$

Solve.

33 HOBBIES Sarah has 5 bags of marbles with 10 marbles in each bag. Noah has 10 bags of marbles with 5 marbles in each bag. Compare the number of marbles. Justify your answer.

They have the same number of marbles; $5 \times 10 = 10 \times 5$, $50 = 50$

34 SHAPES Elian has 27 triangles and 15 squares. Mykia has 15 triangles and 27 squares. Compare the number of shapes. Justify your answer.

They have the same number of shapes; $27 + 15 = 15 + 27$

Note This!

General Tips Emphasize to students that when they are taking notes they should:

1. Write down the title because it gives the big picture of the lesson.
2. Leave a few lines blank when moving from one point to the next for additional notes later.
3. Put a question mark beside homework problems that they do not understand. Have them seek help at a later time.

Use Borders Students can place a border around definitions and properties in their notes to make those sections of their notes stand out. Then, when they need to refer back to their notes or study for a test, the definitions and properties will be easier to locate.

Math Challenge

Memory Game Have students create a memory game with at least 20 cards. Ten cards will have an expression and 10 other cards will have the related fact for that expression. Students can play the memory game by finding matches of the related facts. The student with the most matches wins the round of play.

 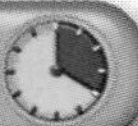

See It, Do It, Say It, Write It

Step 1 Write 5 single-digit addition problems and 5 single-digit multiplication problems on the board.

Step 2 Have students fill in the right side of each equation using the Commutative Property.

Step 3 Arrange students in pairs and have them explain to each other how they can rearrange the order of the numbers but still get the same answers for the problems.

Step 4 Have students write in their own words the definitions of each of the Commutative Properties in their math journals.

Looking Ahead: Pre-teach

Associative Property In the next lesson, students will learn how to use the Associative Property to simplify mental calculations and to check results.

Example

Fill in the blank with the correct value. Then check your answer.

$$(2 \times 3) \times 4 = 2 \times (\_\_\_ \times 4)$$
$$(2 \times 3) \times 4 = 2 \times (\underline{\ 3\ } \times 4)$$
$$(2 \times 3) \times 4 = 2 \times (3 \times 4)$$
$$6 \times 4 = 2 \times 12$$
$$24 = 24$$

Have students use the Associative Properties to mentally find each sum or product.

1. $4 \times 4 \times 1 =$ 16
2. $22 + 8 + 11 =$ 41
3. $5 \times 4 \times 2 =$ 40

35 GAMES Felipe had 14 game cards. He bought 12 more game cards. Wanda had 12 game cards. She bought 14. Compare the number of game cards. Justify your answer.

They have the same number of game cards; $14 + 12 = 12 + 14$, $26 = 26$.

36 MUSIC Nicolas saved 23 songs to one jump drive and 35 to another. Eliza saved 35 songs to one jump drive and 23 to another. Compare the number of songs they saved. Justify your answer.

They saved the same number of songs; $23 + 35 = 35 + 23$, $58 = 58$.

37 NUMBERS If you know that $195 + 126 = 321$, what is the sum of $126 + 195$? 321

38 NUMBERS If you know that $26 \times 11 = 286$, what is the product of 11×26? 286

Vocabulary Check **Write the vocabulary word that completes each sentence.**

39 The Commutative Property of Addition states that the order in which two numbers are added does not change the sum.

40 The product is the answer to a multiplication problem.

41 The Commutative Property of Multiplication states that the order in which two numbers are multiplied does not change the product.

42 The answer to an addition problem is the sum.

43 Writing in Math Use the Commutative Property of Multiplication to rewrite the expression 8×7. Does this change the product? Explain.

7×8; No, the Commutative Property of Multiplication states that the order in which two numbers are multiplied does not change the product.

150 Chapter 4 Properties of Operations

Ticket Out the Door

Oral Problems Have students line up at the door in single file. As each student approaches the door, instruct him or her to use the Commutative Property to answer a question, such as 4 plus 7 is equal to? 5 times 6 is equal to what number? Continue until all students have exited the classroom.

Lesson 4-2 Associative Property

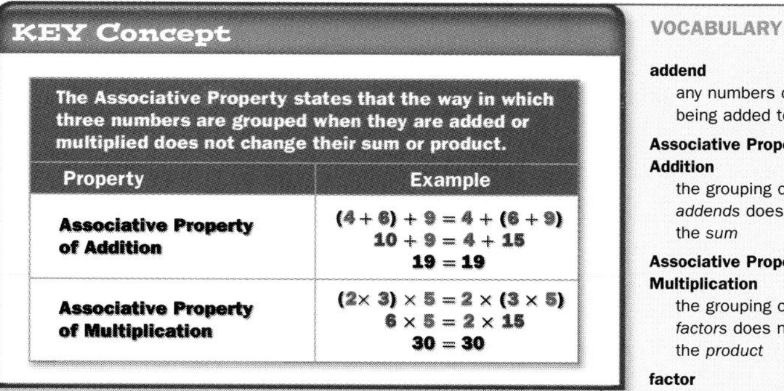

KEY Concept

The Associative Property states that the way in which three numbers are grouped when they are added or multiplied does not change their sum or product.

Property	Example
Associative Property of Addition	$(4 + 6) + 9 = 4 + (6 + 9)$ $10 + 9 = 4 + 15$ $19 = 19$
Associative Property of Multiplication	$(2 \times 3) \times 5 = 2 \times (3 \times 5)$ $6 \times 5 = 2 \times 15$ $30 = 30$

VOCABULARY

addend
any numbers or quantities being added together

Associative Property of Addition
the grouping of the *addends* does not change the *sum*

Associative Property of Multiplication
the grouping of the *factors* does not change the *product*

factor
a number that divides a whole number evenly

The **Associative Property** uses grouping with parentheses to make addition and multiplication easier.

Example 1

Draw a model to show $(2 + 3) + 4 = 2 + (3 + 4)$. Which property did you show?

1. Create a model for each side of the equation.

$(2 + 3) + 4 = 2 + (3 + 4)$

$5 + 4 = 2 + 7$

$9 = 9$

2. The grouping of the addends did not change the sum. This is the Associative Property of Addition.

YOUR TURN!

Draw a model to show $(1 \times 3) \times 2 = 1 \times (3 \times 2)$. Which property did you show?

1. Create a model for each side of the equation.

$1 \times 3 \quad 1 \times 3 = 3 \times 2$

$6 = 6$

2. Which property did you show?
Associative Property of Multiplication

GO ON

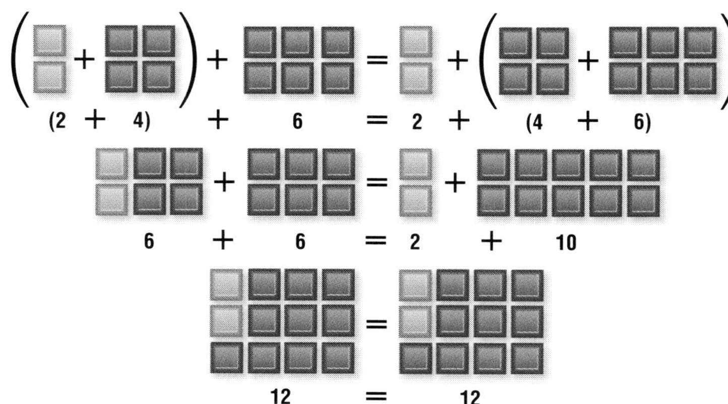

Additional Example 1

Draw a model to show $(2 + 4) + 6 = 2 + (4 + 6)$. Which property did you show?

1. Create a model for each side of the equation.

$(2 + 4) + 6 = 2 + (4 + 6)$

$6 + 6 = 2 + 10$

$12 = 12$

2. The grouping of the addends did not change the sum. This is the Associative Property of Addition.

Lesson Notes

Lesson 4-2

Lesson Planner

Objective Know and use the Associative Properties of Addition and Multiplication.

Vocabulary **addend, Associative Property of Addition, Associative Property of Multiplication, factor**

Materials/Manipulatives algebra tiles, base-ten rods, geoboard, grid paper, notebook paper, unit cubes

Chapter Resource Masters

- CRM Vocabulary and English Language Development (p. A81)
- CRM Skills Practice (p. A82)
- CRM Problem-Solving Practice (p. A83)
- CRM Homework Practice (p. A84)

1 Introduce

Vocabulary

Access Vocabulary Write a three-number addition problem and a three-number multiplication problem on the board. Ask volunteers to solve each problem. Ask students to identify which answer is the sum and which is the product. Then ask which set of numbers are the *addends* and which set are the *factors.*

Nonexamples Talk about what *addends* and *factors* are and which operations do not have addends and factors.

2 Teach

Key Concept

Foundational Skills and Concepts After students have read through the Key Concept box, have them try these exercises.

1. Show an example of the Associative Property of Addition. $(4 + 6) + 9 = 4 + (6 + 9)$
2. Show an example of the Associative Property of Multiplication. $(2 \times 3) \times 5 = 2 \times (3 \times 5)$

Additional **Example 2**

Use the Associative Property to fill in the blank. Check your answer.

$(2 \times 5) \times 3 = 2 \times (\_\_\_\_ \times 3)$

1. Use the Associative Property of Multiplication.

$(2 \times 5) \times 3 = 2 \times (5 \times 3)$

2. Check by multiplying the numbers on each side of the equation.

$(2 \times 5) \times 3 = 2 \times (5 \times 3)$

$10 \times 3 = 2 \times 15$

$30 = 30$

3 Practice

Using Manipulatives

Geoboards Use the geoboards to give students a visual concept of the equality using the Associative Property of Addition and Multiplication. First show the product of the numbers that are grouped within the parentheses using the geoboard. Next show the product of the two remaining numbers using the geoboard. The resulting geoboards should look identical to each other.

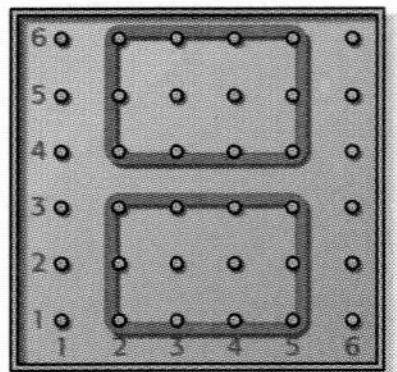

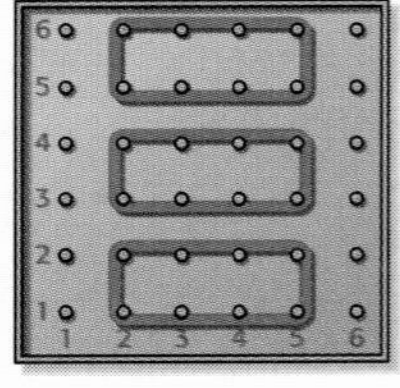

$(3 \times 4) \times 2 = 3 \times (4 \times 2)$

Grid Paper Demonstrate with grid paper. Make a grid that is 3 rows of 4 columns and a grid that is 2 rows of 4 columns. Multiply the first grid by 2 and the second grid by 3. Both grids should have a total of 24 squares, which verifies equality.

On-Hand Manipulatives Use notebook filler paper. Draw vertical lines and fill in the squares like grid paper or arrays.

Example 2

Use the Associative Property to fill in the blank. Check your answer.

$(7 \times 5) \times 2 = 7 \times (\_\_\_\_ \times 2)$

1. Use the Associative Property of Multiplication.
   $(7 \times 5) \times 2 = 7 \times (5 \times 2)$
2. Check by multiplying the numbers on each side of the equation.
   $(7 \times 5) \times 2 = 7 \times (5 \times 2)$
   $35 \times 2 = 7 \times 10$
   $70 = 70$

YOUR TURN!

Use the Associative Property to fill in the blank. Check your answer.

$(2 + 4) + 1 = 2 + (\_\_\_\_ + 1)$

1. Use the Associative Property of Addition.
   $(2 + 4) + 1 = 2 + (\underline{4} + 1)$
2. Check by adding the numbers on each side of the equation.
   $(2 + 4) + 1 = 2 + (4 + 1)$
   $6 + 1 = 2 + 5$
   $7 = 7$

Who is Correct?

Use the Associative and Commutative Properties to find the sum of 25 + 94 + 75 mentally.

Add the numbers first that give you a 0 in the ones place. This will make it easier to mentally add the third number.

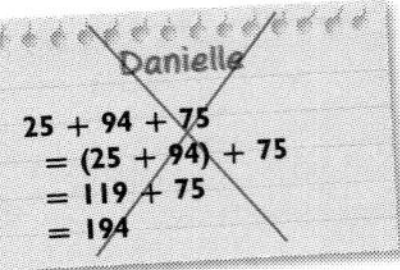

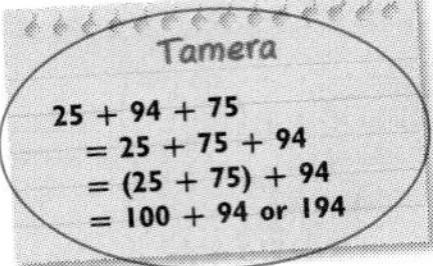

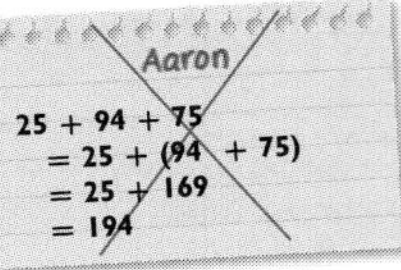

Circle correct answer(s). Cross out incorrect answer(s).

Guided Practice

Draw a model to show each equation.

1. $(1 + 2) + 3 = 1 + (2 + 3)$
   Which property did you show?
   Associative Property of Addition

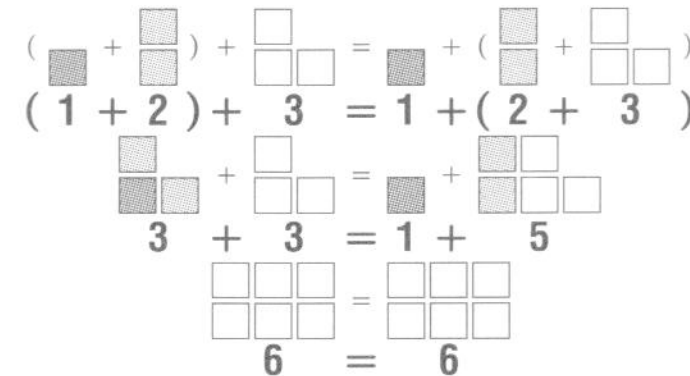

Who *is Correct?*

Diagnostic Teaching

- Danielle's answer is correct, but her grouping makes adding mentally difficult. Adding the grouped number may not be difficult mentally, but adding the third number will be.
- Tamera is correct and her grouping makes adding mentally easier. She grouped the two numbers together in a way that results in a number that is easier to add to a third number.
- Aaron's answer is correct, but like Danielle's, his grouping makes adding mentally difficult. Adding the grouped numbers may not be difficult to add mentally but adding the third number will be.

2 $(2 \times 3) \times 4 = 2 \times (3 \times 4)$
Which property did you show?
Associative Property of Multiplication

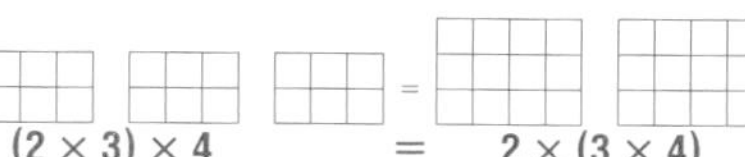

$(2 \times 3) \times 4 = 2 \times (3 \times 4)$

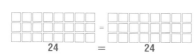

$24 = 24$

Step by Step Practice

Use the Associative Property to find the sum mentally.

3 $8 + 4 + 16$

Step 1 Look for two numbers whose sum is 10, 20, 30, or another multiple of 10. The sum of 4 and 16 is a multiple of 10: 20.

Step 2 Rewrite the expression using the Associative Property.
$8 + 4 + 16 = 8 + (4 + 16)$

Step 3 Find the sum.
$8 + (4 + 16) = 8 + 20$ or 28

Add the numbers first that make it easier to mentally add the third number.

Use the Associative Property to fill in each blank. Check your answer.

4 $(9 \times 5) \times 2 = 9 \times (5 \times 2)$
$45 \times 2 = 9 \times 10$
$90 = 90$

5 $7 + (3 + 8) = (7 + 3) + 8$
$7 + 11 = 10 + 8$
$18 = 18$

6 $5 \times 4 \times 3 = (5 \times 4) \times 3$
$= 20 \times 3$
$= 60$

7 $(14 + 19) + 1 = 14 + (19 + 1)$
$33 + 1 = 14 + 20$
$34 = 34$

Use the Commutative and Associative Properties to find each sum or product mentally.

8 $9 + 21 + 30 = (9 + 21) + 30$
$= 30 + 30$
$= 60$

9 $5 \times 21 \times 6 = 21 \times (5 \times 6)$
$= 21 \times 30$
$= 630$

GO ON

Are They Getting It?

Check students' understanding of the Associative Properties by writing these problems on the board. Have students explain the incorrect information in each problem. Encourage students to use a diagram in their explanation.

1. $32 + 8 + 16 = (\_\_\_\_ + \_\_\_\_) + \_\_\_\_$

   $(32 + 8) + 16 = 40 + 16 = 56$ This is correct.

2. $3 \times 4 \times 5 = (\_\_\_\_ \times \_\_\_\_) \times \_\_\_\_$

   $(3 \times 4) \times 5 = 12 \times 5 = 60$ This grouping is incorrect; mentally it is easier to multiply 20 times 3 than 12 times 5.

Math Coach Notes

Strategies

1. When using the Associative Properties of Addition and Multiplication, there is a pattern that can be followed. Unlike the Commutative Property that changes the order, the Associative Property changes the grouping.
2. Write these equations on the board to help students see the pattern.
   - (first + second) + third = first + (second + third)
   - (first × second) × third = first × (second × third)

Intervention Strategy

Verbal/ Linguistic Learners

Communicate Arrange students into pairs. Students alternate solving three-number addition and multiplication problems. Have one student solving the grouped numbers and the other student solving the remaining operation. Have students reverse roles to solve each problem. Students should discuss their methods of solving each problem. Was one problem-solving method easier using mental math?

English Learner Strategy

Vocabulary Use a highlighter or colored pencil to highlight, circle, or underline key words in word problems. Have students keep a list of these words with their definitions.

Common Error *Alert*

Associative Property Operations Students sometimes have difficulty understanding which operations are used when using the Associative Property. Ask them to solve the following.

$$(7 + 3) + 2 \stackrel{?}{=} 7 + (3 + 2)$$

$$(8 - 4) - 1 \stackrel{?}{=} 8 - (4 - 1)$$

$$(3 \times 6) \times 2 \stackrel{?}{=} 3 \times (6 \times 2)$$

$$(9 \div 3) \div 6 \stackrel{?}{=} 9 \div (3 \div 6)$$

If both sides are equal, then the Associative Property pertains to that operation. If both sides are not equal, then the property does not apply.

Math Coach Notes

Symbolic Expressions The Associative Properties of Addition and Multiplication can be symbolically written. *For any numbers a and b,* it is true that:

$$(a + b) + c = a + (b + c)$$

$$(a \times b) \times c = a \times (b \times c)$$

Every symbolic expression must be accompanied by a statement of what each symbol means. The statement *for any numbers a and b* should be explained to students because they will encounter the concept of generality. When the students are introduced to something that is true for all numbers, you are introducing the students to the heart of algebra.

Step by Step Problem-Solving Practice

Problem-Solving Strategies
- ☐ Look for a pattern.
- ☐ Guess and check.
- ☑ Solve a simpler problem.
- ☐ Work backward.

Solve.

10 SCHOOL DAYS Mr. Daniels sold 75 tickets to the school play on Monday, 52 tickets on Tuesday, and 48 tickets on Wednesday. How many tickets did Mr. Daniels sell in all? Explain your reasoning.

Understand Read the problem. Write what you know. The number of tickets sold was __75__, __52__, and __48__.

In this problem, the words "in all" mean to __add__.

Plan Pick a strategy. One strategy is to solve a simpler problem.

Look for two numbers that will have a sum with a 0 in the ones place. Add those numbers together first.

Solve Write an expression for how many tickets Mr. Daniels sold in all.

__48__ + __52__ + __75__

Use the Associative Property of Addition to rewrite the expression so that it is easier to simplify mentally. Then find the sum.

__48__ + __52__ + __75__ = (__48__ + __52__) + __75__
= __100__ + __75__ or __175__

Check Use a calculator to find the sum.

11 STAMP COLLECTING Uma has 44 stamps in her collection. Elena gave her 22 more stamps. Uma then bought 6 more stamps. How many stamps does Uma have in all? Explain your reasoning. Check off each step.

__✔__ Understand: I circled key words.

__✔__ Plan: To solve the problem, I will __solve a simpler problem__.

__✔__ Solve: The answer is __72 stamps; 44 + 22 + 6 = 50 + 22 = 72__.

__✔__ Check: I checked my answer by __using a calculator__.

Intervention Strategy

Logical Learners

Mental Computation Use grouping strategies to help students learn the Associative Properties of Addition and Multiplication. Give each student 10 addition problems and 10 multiplication problems. Have them rewrite the problems using the Associative Properties of Addition and Multiplication. Instruct them that they should do the computation mentally after they group the numbers. Review each problem to verify their groupings.

12 SPORTS Marty bought the boxes of whistles shown. Each whistle cost \$2. How much did Marty spend? Explain your reasoning.

$\$80; 8 \times 5 \times 2 = 8 \times (5 \times 2)$

$= 8 \times 10$ or 80

13 COOKING A casserole recipe calls for 2 packages of cheese. Marisela needs to make 3 casseroles. Each package of cheese costs \$1.50. Find the cost of the cheese for all 3 casseroles. Explain your reasoning.

$\$9; 2 \times 1.50 \times 3 = (2 \times 1.50) \times 3 = 3 \times 3$ or 9

14 **Reflect** Give an example of the Associative Property of Addition. Check your answer.

Answers will vary. Sample answer: $(9 + 5) + 2 =$

$9 + (5 + 2); 14 + 2 = 9 + 7; 16 = 16$

Skills, Concepts, and Problem Solving

Draw a model to show each equation.

15 $(3 + 4) + 1 = 3 + (4 + 1)$
Which property did you show?

Associative Property of Addition

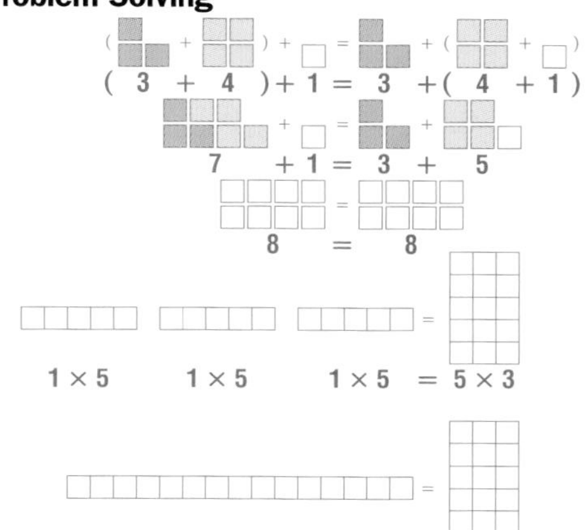

16 $(1 \times 5) \times 3 = 1 \times (5 \times 3)$
Which property did you show?

Associative Property of Multiplication

$1 \times 5 \quad 1 \times 5 \quad 1 \times 5 = 5 \times 3$

$15 = 15$

GO ON

Common Error *Alert*

Many Ways to Group If students are having difficulty understanding the Associative Property, have them review grouping addition and multiplication problems to solve mentally. Reassure them that there is more than one way to group to solve mentally depending on their individual number sense.

Odd/Even Assignments

Exercises 15–31 are structured so that students practice the same concepts whether they are assigned the odd or even problems.

In-Class Assignment

Have students complete Exercises 16, 19, 21, 26, 27, 31, and 34 to ensure that they understand the concept.

Intervention Strategy — Kinesthetic Learners

Use Unit Cubes and Base-Ten Rods

1. Have students use unit cubes and base-ten rods to represent a given three-number addition problem. Ask them to add two numbers together using the least number of unit cubes.
2. Have the students show their sums using the base-ten rods and unit cubes.
3. Ask: Did you group the correct two numbers together?
4. Arrange the students into pairs and have them explain why they grouped the way they did. Ask: Did your partner use the least number of unit cubes?

Note This!

Property Names When taking notes about properties, students should write the entire name of the property in the first reference followed by an abbreviation in parentheses. Each time the property is referenced thereafter, students should use the abbreviation. This will save writing time and will allow students time to process what they are writing, instead of just getting the words on the paper. For example, the Associative Property of Multiplication can be abbreviated APOM.

Common Error *Alert*

Group Addends If students are having difficulty understanding the Associative Property, then ask them to add the following numbers the easiest way possible:

$$17 + 99 + 1$$

Have them explain their choices and try other ways to verify their decisions. Have them write a rule in their own words.

Use the Associative Property to fill in each blank. Check your answer.

17 $36 + (14 + 19) = (\underline{36} + 14) + 19$
$36 + 33 = \underline{50} + 19$
$\underline{69} = \underline{69}$

18 $8 \times (5 \times 4) = (\underline{8} \times 5) \times 4$
$8 \times 20 = \underline{40} \times 4$
$\underline{160} = \underline{160}$

19 $6 \times (5 \times 3) = \underline{(6 \times 5) \times 3}$
$= \underline{30} \times \underline{3}$
$= \underline{90}$

20 $18 + (22 + 37) = \underline{(18 + 22) + 37}$
$= \underline{40} + \underline{37}$
$= \underline{77}$

21 $(36 + 14) + 16 = \underline{36 + (14 + 16)}$
$= \underline{36} + \underline{30}$
$= \underline{66}$

22 $(63 + 13) + 17 = \underline{63 + (13 + 17)}$
$= \underline{63} + \underline{30}$
$= \underline{93}$

Use the Commutative and Associative Properties to find each sum or product mentally.

23 $15 \times 7 \times 2 = (\underline{15} \times \underline{2}) \times \underline{7}$
$= \underline{30} \times \underline{7}$
$= \underline{210}$

24 $12 \times 3 \times 5 = (\underline{12} \times \underline{5}) \times \underline{3}$
$= \underline{60} \times \underline{3}$
$= \underline{180}$

25 $102 + 89 + 18 = (\underline{102} + \underline{18}) + \underline{89}$
$= \underline{120} + \underline{89}$
$= \underline{209}$

26 $15 + 77 + 85 = (\underline{15} + \underline{85}) + \underline{77}$
$= \underline{100} + \underline{77}$
$= \underline{177}$

Solve. Justify your answer.

27 SHOPPING Lana bought the packages of highlighters shown. Each highlighter cost $2. How much did Lana spend?

$120; $12 \times 5 \times 2 = 12 \times (5 \times 2)$
$= 12 \times 10$ or 120

28 CONSTRUCTION Tregg has 17 nails. Isabel gave him 13 more nails. Tregg then bought 18 more nails. How many nails does Tregg have in all?

48 nails; $17 + 13 + 18 = (17 + 13) + 18 = 30 + 18 = 48$

29 FOOD Diana bought 4 packs of gum. Each pack contained 12 sticks of gum. The next week, she bought 2 more packs of gum. How many sticks of gum did Diana have in all?

96 sticks of gum; $4 \times 12 \times 2 = (4 \times 2) \times 12 = 8 \times 12 = 96$

156 **Chapter 4** Properties of Operations

Math Challenge

Group Adding Arrange students into groups of four or five. Each student should write a two-digit number between 11 and 80 on a small sheet of paper. Place the papers with the numbers in the middle of the group so that all group members can see. Each student finds the total of the five numbers by grouping the numbers however he or she sees best. After the group agrees on the sum, have students share their strategies for how they associated the numbers to find the sum.

30 NUMBERS If you know that $3 + (5 + 4) = 12$, then what is the sum of $(3 + 5) + 4$?

12

31 NUMBERS If you know that $2 \times (6 \times 11) = 132$, what is the product of $(2 \times 6) \times 11$?

132

Vocabulary Check **Write the vocabulary word that completes each sentence.**

32 The Associative Property of Multiplication states that the grouping of the factors does not change the product.

33 The Associative Property of Addition states that the grouping of the addends does not change the sum.

34 Writing in Math Explain how you can use the Commutative and Associative Properties to help you find sums and products mentally.

Sample answer: The Commutative and Associative Properties state that the numbers that are added or multiplied can be rearranged. You can find sums and products mentally by grouping numbers whose sums and products are easily found.

Spiral Review

Solve. (Lesson 4-1, p. 144)

35 SAFETY Manuel has 5 boxes of safety glasses with 12 pairs of glasses in each box. Stephany has 12 boxes of safety glasses with 5 pairs of glasses in each box. Compare the number of glasses. Explain your reasoning.

They have the same number of glasses; $5 \times 12 = 12 \times 5$, $60 = 60$.

Solve.

36 $9 \times 3 =$ 3 $\times 9$

37 $8 \times 7 = 7 \times$ 8

38 $215 +$ 150 $= 150 + 215$

39 $14 + 23 =$ 23 $+ 14$

Ticket Out the Door

On-the-Spot Problem Have students line up at the door in single file. As each student approaches the door, instruct the student to use the Associative Property to find answers mentally by grouping values that are found easily. Examples: $4 + 2 + 6$, $12 + 8 + 7$, $34 + 3 + 7$. Continue until all students have exited the classroom.

See It, Do It, Say It, Write It

Step 1 Write 5 three-number addition problems and 5 three-number multiplication problems.

Step 2 Have students put parentheses around two of the numbers that can be computed mentally using the Associative Property. Students should do this for two of the addition and two of the multiplication problems.

Step 3 Arrange students into pairs and have them explain to each other how they rearranged the grouping of the numbers, and why they get the same answers no matter what the grouping.

Step 4 Have students write in their own words the definitions of each of the Associative Properties in their math journals.

Looking Ahead: Pre-teach

Distributive Property In the next lesson, students will learn how to use the Distributive Property in equations and expressions with variables.

Example

Use the Distributive Property and a model to find 3×11.

1. Draw an array to show 3×11.
2. Draw a line to separate the factor 11 into the tens and ones places.
3. Multiply to find the two products.
   $3 \times 10 = 30$
   $3 \times 1 = 3$
4. Add the products.
   $30 + 3 = 33$
   So, $3 \times 11 = 33$.

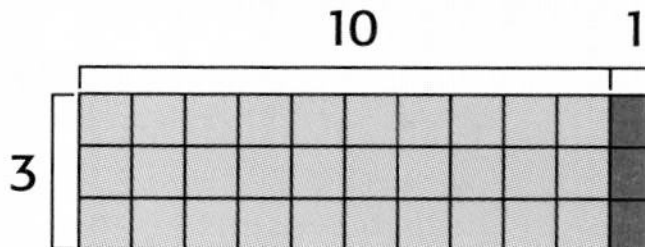

Use the Distributive Property to find each product.

1. $4 \times 13 = 52$
2. $2(6 + 3) = 18$
3. $6(2 + 7) = 54$

Chapter 4 Progress Check 1

Formative Assessment

Use the Progress Check to assess students' mastery of the previous lessons. Have students review the lesson indicated for the problems they answered incorrectly.

Odd/Even Assignments

Exercises are structured so that students practice the same concepts whether they are assigned the odd or even problems.

Common Error Alert

Properties If students are having difficulties with the Associative and Commutative Properties, have them make index cards like the following:

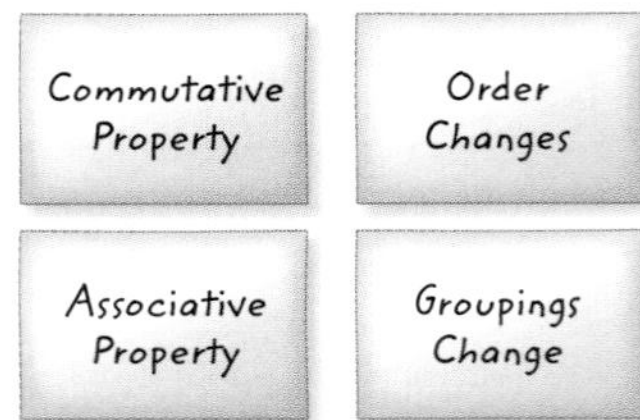

Exercise 2 Remind students that there are two Associative Properties, one for addition and one for multiplication. Answers need to indicate the operation in the problem.

Exercise 8 Did students read the problem carefully to find that they must count the number of packages, as well as read the packages for information to solve the problem?

Progress Check 1 (Lessons 4-1 and 4-2)

Draw a model to show $1 + 5 = 5 + 1$. Which property did you show?

1. Commutative Property of Addition

   $1 + 5 = 5 + 1$

   $6 = 6$

Draw a model to show $(1 \times 5) \times 3 = 1 \times (5 \times 3)$. Which property did you show?

2. Associative Property of Multiplication

   1×5 1×5 1×5 = 5×3

   $15 = 15$

Use the Commutative Property to fill in each blank with the correct value. Check your answer.

3. $21 + 36 = 36 + 21$; $57 = 57$
4. $9 \times 3 = 3 \times 9$; $27 = 27$

Use the Commutative and Associative Properties to find each sum or product mentally.

5. $3 + 16 + 7 = (3 + 7) + 16 = 10 + 16$ or 26
6. $5 \times 6 \times 3 = (5 \times 6) \times 3 = 30 \times 3$ or 90

Solve. Justify your answer.

7. **FITNESS** Brian does 30 minutes of aerobics on Tuesdays, 45 minutes on Thursdays, and 20 minutes on Saturdays. How many minutes of aerobics does Brian do altogether?

   95 min; $30 + 45 + 20 = (30 + 20) + 45 = 50 + 45 = 95$

8. **SHOPPING** Lela bought the packages of pens shown. Each pen cost \$2. How much did Lela spend?

   \$80; $8 \times 5 \times 2 = (8 \times 5) \times 2 = 40 \times 2 = 80$

158 Chapter 4 Properties of Operations

Data-Driven Decision Making

Students missing Exercises . . .	Have trouble with . . .	Should review and practice . . .
1-2	drawing a model to represent number properties.	SSG Lesson 4-1, p. 144 CRM Skills Practice, p. A78
3-6	using number properties to rewrite and simplify expressions.	SSG Lessons 4-1 and 4-2, pp. 144 and 151 CRM Skills Practice, pp. A78 and A82
7-8	solving word problems by using number properties.	CRM Problem-Solving Practice, pp. A79 and A83

Lesson 4-3 Distributive Property

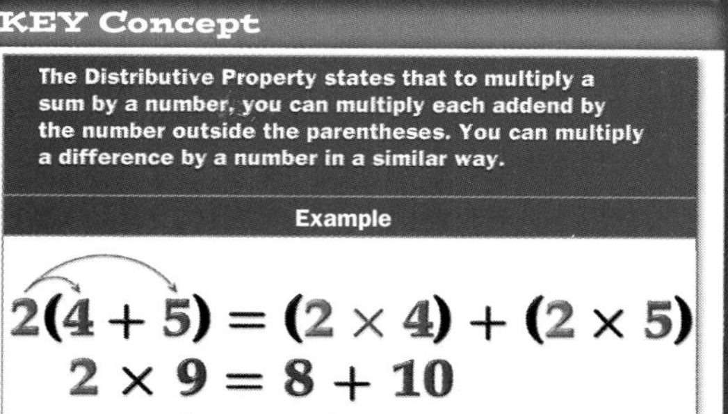

KEY Concept
The Distributive Property states that to multiply a sum by a number, you can multiply each addend by the number outside the parentheses. You can multiply a difference by a number in a similar way.
Example

$$2(4 + 5) = (2 \times 4) + (2 \times 5)$$
$$2 \times 9 = 8 + 10$$
$$18 = 18$$

VOCABULARY

Distributive Property of Multiplication to multiply a *sum* by a number, you can multiply each *addend* by the number and add the *products*

Example 1

Use the Distributive Property and a model to find 5 × 12.

1. Draw a model to show 5 × 12.

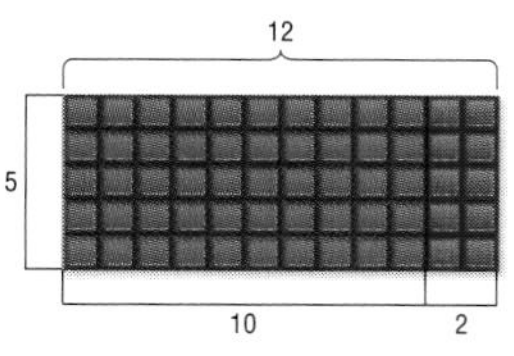

2. Draw a line to separate the factor 12 into tens and ones places.
   $5 \times 12 = 5 \times (10 + 2)$
3. Multiply to find the two products.
   $5 \times 10 = 50$
   $5 \times 2 = 10$
4. Add the products.
   $50 + 10 = 60$ So, $5 \times 12 = 60$.

YOUR TURN!

Use the Distributive Property and a model to find 3 × 13.

1. Draw a model to show 3 × 13.

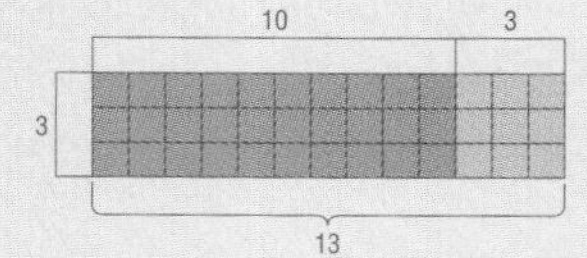

2. Draw a line to separate the factor 13 into tens and ones places.
   $3 \times 13 = 3 \times (10 + 3)$
3. Multiply to find the two products.
   $3 \times 10 = 30$ $3 \times 3 = 9$
4. Add the products.
   $30 + 9 = 39$
   So, $3 \times 13 = 39$.

GO ON

Additional Example 1

Use the Distributive Property and a model to find 4 × 13.

1. Draw a model to show 4 × 13.

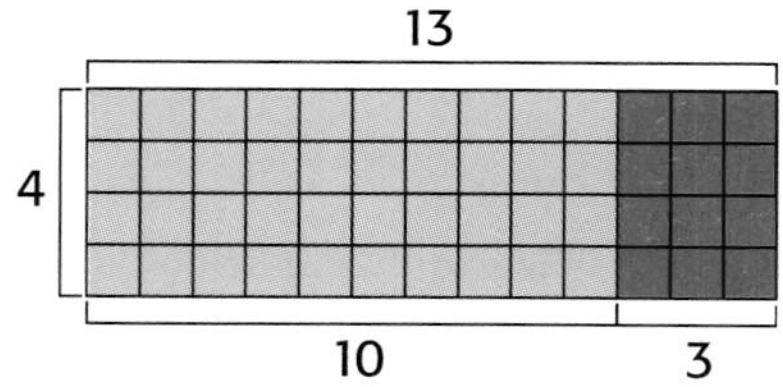

2. Draw a line to separate the factor 13 into tens and ones places.
   $4 \times 13 = 4 \times (10 + 3)$
3. Multiply to find the two products. $4 \times 10 = 40$ $4 \times 3 = 12$
4. Add the products. $40 + 12 = 52$
   So, $4 \times 13 = 52$.

Lesson Notes

Lesson 4-3

Lesson Planner

Objective Know and use the Distributive Property of Multiplication.

Vocabulary **Distributive Property of Multiplication**

Materials/Manipulatives geoboard, number cubes, objects as counters, playing cards, two-color counters

Chapter Resource Masters

- CRM Vocabulary and English Language Development (p. A85)
- CRM Skills Practice (p. A86)
- CRM Problem-Solving Practice (p. A87)
- CRM Homework Practice (p. A88)

1 Introduce

Vocabulary

Access Vocabulary Write a problem on the board that represents the Distributive Property. Ask for one volunteer to go to the board and solve the problem. Ask another volunteer to identify each part of the problem using the words *sum, addend,* and *product*.

Nonexamples Talk about other words that are not included when using the Distributive Property, such as quotient.

2 Teach

Key Concept

Foundational Skills and Concepts After students have read through the Key Concept box, have them try these exercises.

1. What operations are being used? addition and multiplication
2. Write the Distributive Property in your own words. Sample answer: You can multiply the sum by a number and get the same answer as multiplying each number by the number and then adding.

Additional Example 2

Use the Distributive Property to find 4(8 – 2).

1. Use the Distributive Property.
2. Simplify inside the parentheses.
3. Subtract.

$4(8 - 2) = (4 \times 8) - (4 \times 2)$

$= 32 - 8$

$= 24$

3 Practice

Using Manipulatives

Geoboards Use geoboards to give students a visual concept of the operations using the Distributive Property. First, use the Distributive Property to set up the problem. Next show the distribution and the operation using the geoboards.

$4(3 + 2) = (4 \times 3) + (4 \times 2) = 12 + 8$

$= 20$

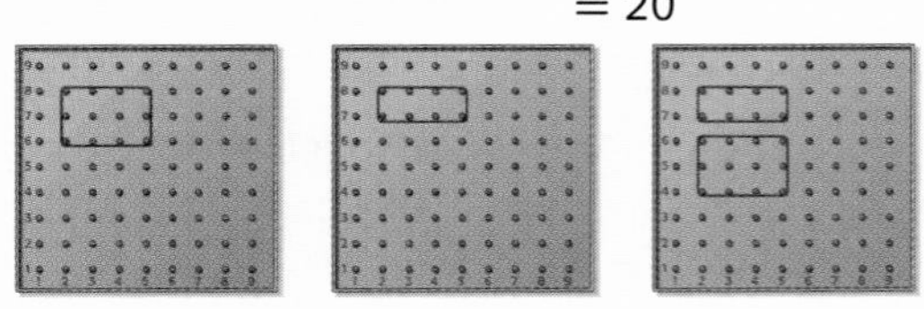

Two-Color Counters Demonstrate the Distributive Property using two-color counters. Use either color to represent the value being distributed to show that each value inside the parentheses is being multiplied by the distributed value.

On-Hand Manipulatives Use different types of beans or beans and corn to represent each value.

Example 2

Use the Distributive Property to find 3(10 – 2).

1. Use the Distributive Property. $3(10 - 2) = (3 \times 10) - (3 \times 2)$
2. Simplify inside the parentheses. $= 30 - 6$
3. Subtract. $= 24$

YOUR TURN!

Use the Distributive Property to find 5(7 + 1).

1. Use the Distributive Property. $5(7 + 1) = (5 \times 7) + (5 \times 1)$
2. Simplify inside the parentheses. $= 35 + 5$
3. Add. $= 40$

Who is Correct?

Use the Distributive Property to find 3(40 – 7).

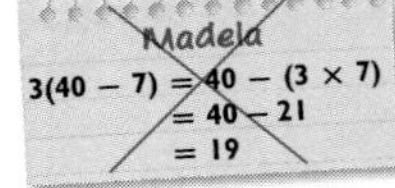

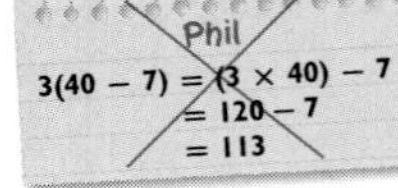

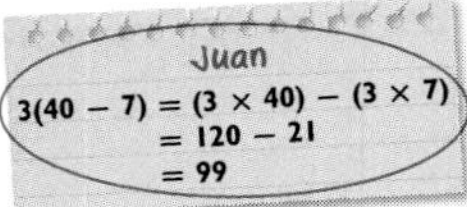

Circle correct answer(s). Cross out incorrect answer(s).

Guided Practice

1. Use the Distributive Property and a model to find 3×14.

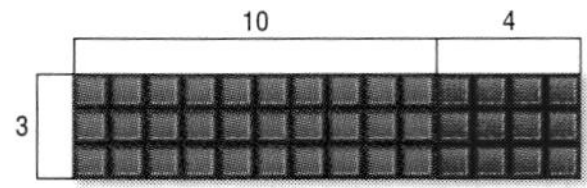

Multiply to find the two products.

$3 \times 10 = 30$; $3 \times 4 = 12$

Add the products.

$30 + 12 = 42$.

So, $3 \times 14 = 42$.

160 Chapter 4 Properties of Operations

Who is Correct?

Diagnostic Teaching

- Madela's answer is incorrect. She did not distribute the 3 properly. She did not multiply the 3 by 40.
- Phil's answer is incorrect. He did not distribute the 3 properly. He did not multiply the 3 by 7.
- Juan's answer is correct because he did distribute the 3 properly to the numbers inside the parentheses. Then he subtracted the products.

Step by Step Practice

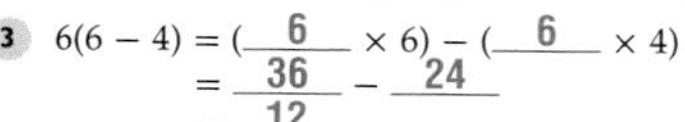

2 Use the Distributive Property to find 9(7 + 4).

Step 1 Use the Distributive Property.

9(7 + 4) = (9 × __7__) + (9 × __4__)

Step 2 Simplify inside the parentheses.

(9 × 7) + (9 × 4) = __63__ + __36__

Step 3 Add. 63 + 36 = __99__

Use the Distributive Property to find each product. Show your work.

3 6(6 − 4) = (__6__ × 6) − (__6__ × 4)
= __36__ − __24__
= __12__

4 7(9 + 5) = (__7__ × 9) + (__7__ × 5)
= __63__ + __35__
= __98__

5 8(5 + 6) = __8 × 5 + 8 × 6; 40 + 48__
= 88

6 4(8 − 2) = __(4 × 8) − (4 × 2) = 32 − 8__
= 24

Step by Step Problem-Solving Practice

Problem-Solving Strategies
- ☑ Use a model.
- ☐ Look for a pattern.
- ☐ Guess and check.
- ☐ Act it out.
- ☐ Solve a simpler problem.

Solve.

7 BASKETBALL Enrico made five 3-point baskets, and Derek made six 3-point baskets in their last basketball game. How many points did they score in all?

Understand Read the problem. Write what you know.
Enrico made __5__ 3-point baskets.
Derek made __6__ 3-point baskets.

Plan Pick a strategy. One strategy is to use a model. Draw a model to represent the number of baskets the boys scored.

5 baskets 6 baskets

Solve Show the number of points scored.

__3__ × 5 + __3__ × 6
= __15__ + __18__
= __33__

3 points each

3 × 5 3 × 6

Enrico and Derek scored __33__ points in all.

Check Does your answer make sense? How many *baskets* were made in all? __11__

GO ON

Are They Getting It?

Check students' understanding of the Distributive Property by writing these problems on the board. Have students explain the incorrect information in each problem. Encourage students to use a diagram in their explanation.

1. 5(8 − 5) = (__5__ × __8__) + (__5__ × __5__) = 40 + 25 = 75

   This is incorrect. The sign between the values within the parentheses in the original problem is subtraction, but in the answer it is written as addition.

2. 3(5 + 7) = (__3__ × __5__) + (__5__ × __7__) = 15 + 35 = 50

   This is incorrect. The second operation within the parentheses is multiplying the original values in the parentheses.

3. 2(8 − 6) = (__2__ × __8__) − (__2__ × __6__) = 16 − 12 = 4

   This is correct.

Math Coach Notes

Strategies

1. When using the Distributive Property, draw arrows from the value outside the parentheses to each value inside the parentheses.

   5(3 − 7) =

2. The arrows will show the students that they multiply each value inside the parentheses by 5.

   5(3 − 7) = (5 × 3) − (5 × 7)

3. Have students place the arrows to help them remember to multiply both terms using the Distributive Property.

English Learner Strategy

Vocabulary When using the Distributive Property, have students draw arrows from the value outside the parentheses to each value inside the parentheses. Instruct them to label the arrows with the word in their native language that means *to multiply.*

Odd/Even Assignments

Exercises 12–31 are structured so that students practice the same concepts whether they are assigned the odd or even problems.

In-Class Assignment

Have students complete Exercises 12, 16, 20, 26, 30, and 33 to ensure that they understand the concept.

Common Error *Alert*

Transfer Signs A common error that students make when using the Distributive Property is to overlook the sign between the numbers within the parentheses. Ask them to solve the following using arrows and the Distributive Property.

$$3(9 + 4) = (3 \times 9) + (3 \times 4)$$

Have students draw an additional arrow under the problem from the sign between the numbers within the parentheses to the sign between the distributed operations.

$$3(9 + 4) = (3 \times 9) + (3 \times 4)$$

8 SCHOOL Mateo answered 12 five-point questions and 12 two-point questions correctly on his last history test. What was Mateo's test score? Check off each step.

✓ Understand: I circled key words.

✓ Plan: To solve the problem, I will use a model.

✓ Solve: The answer is 84.

✓ Check: I checked my answer by making sure my answer makes sense.

9 MONEY Ahmed earned \$15 each week for 7 weeks. He spent \$6 each week for 7 weeks. How much money does Ahmed have left?

\$63

10 BASKETBALL Penelope made 15 two-point baskets and 15 three-point baskets during this basketball season. How many points did Penelope score during the season?

75 points

11  Reflect What do you *distribute* when you use the Distributive Property?

Answers will vary. Sample answer: When you multiply each addend by a number, that number is distributed to each addend.

Skills, Concepts, and Problem Solving

Use the Distributive Property and a model to find each product.

12 $4 \times 16 =$ 64

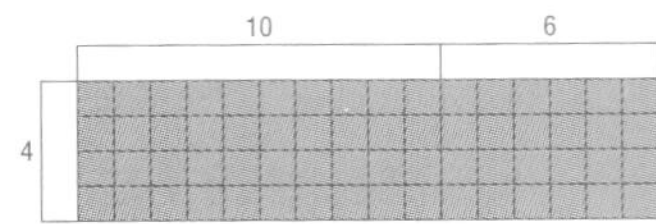

13 $5 \times 15 =$ 75

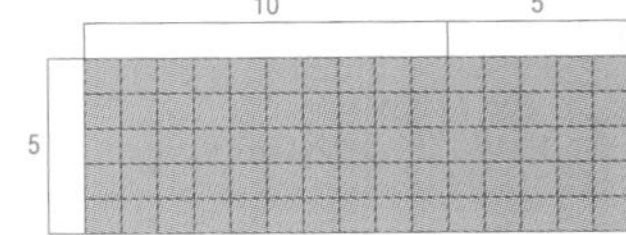

Write the value that makes each equation true.

14 $6 \times 27 = (6 \times 20) + (6 \times$ 7 $)$

15 $5(12 - 4) = (5 \times$ 12 $) - (5 \times 4)$

16 $15 \times 48 = (15 \times$ 40 $) + (15 \times 8)$

17 $28(8 - 5) = (28 \times$ 8 $) - (28 \times 5)$

162 Chapter 4 Properties of Operations

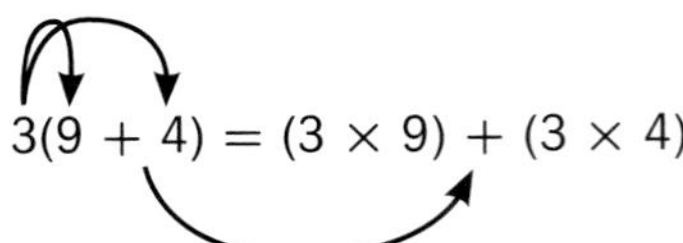

Intervention Strategy — Spatial/Visual Learners

Use Drawings Explain to students that if they learn best using colors, shapes, visual designs, charts, maps, or images, then they are likely a visual or spatial learner. Drawing the arrows to show which terms are multiplied and the arrow to verify the operation sign is a benefit for visual learners because they have a picture to associate with the work that needs to be done. When visual students are faced with a problem that they cannot remember how to do, they have a visual aid to help them. Encourage such students to draw the arrows. It is simply a way to show work. Using colors to draw the arrows may be an even greater benefit.

Use the Distributive Property to find each product. Show your work.

18 $14(5 + 3) = (14 \times 5) + (14 \times 3) = 70 + 42 = 112$

19 $12(9 - 2) = (12 \times 9) - (12 \times 2) = 108 - 24 = 84$

20 $5(11 - 4) = (5 \times 11) - (5 \times 4) = 55 - 20 = 35$

21 $8(6 - 3) = (8 \times 6) - (8 \times 3) = 48 - 24 = 24$

22 $2(5 + 18) = (2 \times 5) + (2 \times 18) = 10 + 36 = 46$

23 $4(8 + 15) = (4 \times 8) + (4 \times 15) = 32 + 60 = 92$

24 $18(2 + 3) = 36 + 54 = 90$

25 $3(8 + 13) = 24 + 39 = 63$

26 $11(7 - 2) = 77 - 22 = 55$

27 $4(12 - 5) = 48 - 20 = 28$

Use the Distributive Property to solve. Show your work.

28 FOOTBALL The Mustangs scored 3 touchdowns (each worth 6 points) and 3 field goals (each worth 3 points). How many points did the football team score?

27 points; $3(6 + 3) = (3 \times 6) + (3 \times 3) = 18 + 9 = 27$

29 MONEY Marisa earned \$18 each day for 8 days. She spent \$3 on lunch each day for 8 days. How much money does Marisa have left?

\$120; $8(18 - 3) = (8 \times 18) - (8 \times 3) = 144 - 24 = 120$

30 PARTIES Your parents are paying for a party at your favorite restaurant. There will be 20 people at the party. Use the menu. How much will your parents spend if everyone orders the hamburger/fries special with a large soda?

\$140; $20(6 + 1) = (20 \times 6) + (20 \times 1) = 120 + 20 = 140$

Tony's Corner Cafe
Lunch Menu
Hamburger/Fries Special $6.00
Meatloaf Special $7.00
Small Soda $.60
Large Soda $1.00

31 TRIPS You are part of a group of 7 friends planning a trip to the art museum. Admission to the museum costs \$6. A bus ticket to the museum costs \$3. What is the total cost of the trip?

\$63; $7(6 + 3) = (7 \times 6) + (7 \times 3) = 42 + 21 = 63$

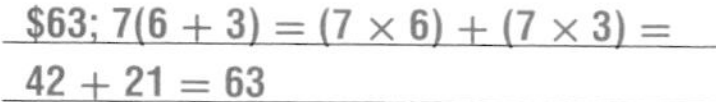

GO ON

Intervention Strategy — Logical Learners

Number Cubes Have students write three expressions—one with two terms, one with three terms, and one with four terms. Randomly select a single-digit number by rolling a number cube. Have students distribute that number to the expression with two terms. Roll the number cube again and have students distribute the number to the expression with three terms. Repeat for the four-term expression. Students can trade papers and check their partner's work.

Note This!

Note-Taking Strategies As students encounter new information, they need to know their personal limitations. Make sure that they *do not* rely upon their memories for important information. Instruct students to take thorough notes. Explain that even though the new information is fresh in their minds, a few minutes later the new information is replaced with newer information. Writing down new information ensures that students can refresh their memories quickly.

Math Challenge

Model Distribution Have students use a deck of playing cards. Assign one student as the dealer and have the rest of the students be players. Have one student roll a number cube. The number that appears on the number cube is how many cards the dealer gives to each player. In this activity the dealer represents the value being distributed, and the players represent the values inside the parentheses. Continue until all the students have been the dealer.

See It, Do It, Say It, Write It

Step 1 Write the following problem on the board:

7(9 − 5) = (____ × ____) − (____ × ____)

Step 2 Have students draw arrows to show the Distributive Property, including the sign, and then solve.

Step 3 Arrange students into pairs and have them explain to each other how they distributed each value to get the solution.

Step 4 Have students write the definition of the Distributive Property in their own words in their math journals.

Looking Ahead: Pre-teach

Order of Operations In the next lesson, students will learn how to use the correct order of operations to evaluate expressions.

Example

Find the value of 9 ÷ 3 + (3 + 2) + 8.

parentheses = 9 ÷ 3 + 5 + 8
multiply/divide = 3 + 5 + 8
add/subtract = 8 + 8
= 16

Find the value of each expression.

1. 10 + (3 × 5) ÷ 5 + 2 15
2. (2 × 7) − 9 ÷ 3 11
3. 10 − (3 + 1) ÷ 2 8

Vocabulary Check **Write the vocabulary word that completes the sentence.**

32 The Distributive Property states that to multiply a sum by a number, you can multiply each addend by the same number and add the products.

33 Writing in Math The Distributive Property can be used to write 5 × (4 + 4) = (5 × 4) + (5 × 4). Can the Distributive Property also be used to write 5 × (7 + 1) = (5 × 7) + (5 × 1)? Explain why or why not.

Yes; 5 × 8 = 5 × (4 + 4) = (5 × 4) + (5 × 4) = 20 + 20 = 40 and 5 × 8 = 5 × (7 + 1) = (5 × 7) + (5 × 1) = 35 + 5 = 40.

Spiral Review

Use the Commutative and Associative Properties to find each sum or product. (Lessons 4-1, p. 144 and 4-2, p. 151)

34 12 + 37 + 18 = (12 + 18) + 37
= 30 + 37
= 67

35 8 × 7 × 5 = 7 × (8 × 5)
= 7 × 40
= 280

SHOPPING **Elan and Fala spent the day shopping on Saturday. Their receipts are shown below.** (Lessons 4-1, p. 144 and 4-2, p. 151)

36 The expression (6 + 3) + 2 represents the amount of money Elan and Fala spent at SNACK Bag. Use the Associative Property to write a second expression that represents the amount they spent on snacks.

6 + (3 + 2)

37 The equation 20 + 7 = 27 represents the amount of money Elan and Fala spent at Sports 1. Use the Commutative Property to write a second equation that represents the amount they spent on clothing.

7 + 20 = 27

STOP

164 Chapter 4 Properties of Operations

Ticket Out the Door

Solve and Exit Write a problem on the board. Have students solve the problem using the Distributive Property. Have students show you their solutions as they exit the classroom.

Lesson 4-4

Order of Operations

KEY Concept

You must follow the **order of operations** to evaluate mathematical expressions correctly.

Order of Operations	Symbol
1. Calculate operations inside parentheses.	(parentheses) [brackets]
2. Multiply and divide in order from left to right.	× ÷
3. Add and subtract in order from left to right.	+ −

VOCABULARY

order of operations rules that tell what order to use when evaluating expressions
(1) Calculate operations inside parentheses.
(2) Multiply and divide in order from left to right.
(3) Add and subtract in order from left to right.

Sometimes parentheses are used to set a number apart from other operations.

Example 1

Find the value of 3 − 2 + 12 ÷ 4.

Use the order of operations. There are no grouping symbols.

$3 - 2 + 12 \div 4 = 3 - 2 + 3$ Multiply and divide from left to right.
$= 1 + 3$ Add and subtract from left to right.
$= 4$

From left to right, subtraction comes first in this problem.

YOUR TURN!

Find the value of 7 − 5 + 3 × 3.

Use the order of operations. There are no grouping symbols.

$7 - 5 + 3 \times 3 = 7 - 5 + \underline{9}$ Multiply and divide from left to right.
$= \underline{2} + \underline{9}$ Add and subtract from left to right.
$= \underline{11}$

GO ON

Additional Example 1

Find the value of 9 + 14 ÷ 7 × 4.

Use the order of operations.
There are no grouping symbols.

$9 + 14 \div 7 \times 4 = 9 + 2 \times 4$ Multiply and divide from left to right.
$= 9 + 8$
$9 + 8 = 17$ Add and subtract from left to right.

Lesson Notes

Lesson 4-4

Lesson Planner

Objective Use the order of operations to evaluate expressions.

Vocabulary **order of operations**

Materials/Manipulatives algebra tiles, bucket balance, construction paper, markers, objects as counters

Chapter Resource Masters

- CRM Vocabulary and English Language Development (p. A89)
- CRM Skills Practice (p. A90)
- CRM Problem-Solving Practice (p. A91)
- CRM Homework Practice (p. A92)

1 Introduce

Vocabulary

Access Vocabulary Write a problem on the board that has all the operations identified in this lesson. Ask for one volunteer to go to the board and solve the first step of the problem. Repeat this until all three steps are performed. After each step write the step number beside the operation. Ask another volunteer to identify each step of the problem using the definitions.

2 Teach

Key Concept

Foundational Skills and Concepts After students have read through the Key Concept box, have them try these exercises.

1. What operations are at the same level? multiplication and division; addition and subtraction
2. The operations below are scrambled. Write them in the correct order.
   Multiplication and Division
   Grouping Symbols
   Add and Subtract

   1. Grouping Symbols
   2. Multiply and Divide
   3. Add and Subtract

Additional **Example 2**

Find the value of $2 \times 3 + (9 - 5) \div 4 - 5$.

$2 \times 3 + (9 - 5) \div 4 - 5 =$
$2 \times 3 + 4 \div 4 - 5$
Calculate operations inside parenthesis.

$= 6 + 4 \div 4 - 5$ Multiply and divide.

$= 6 + 1 - 5$ Multiply and divide.

$= 7 - 5$ Add.

$= 2$ Subtract.

3 Practice

Using Manipulatives

Algebra Tiles Use unit blocks to give students a visual concept of the order of operations. First show the problem using unit cubes.

$3 + (4 - 2) \div 2$

$3 + (4 - 2) \div 2$

Next show the simplified answer after each operation until the expression is simplified.

Bucket Balance When presenting Example 2, use a bucket balance to give students another visual concept of equality after performing the order of operations. Show the buckets balanced after each operation to reflect the equality of the simplified value.

On-Hand Manipulatives Lay colored squares of paper or construction paper or different coins for unit blocks against white paper. Use markers to draw the operation symbols. Use a measuring scale for a bucket balance.

Example 2

Find the value of $58 - (16 \div 4) \times 3$.

$58 - (16 \div 4) \times 3$	$= 58 - 4 \times 3$	Calculate operations inside parentheses.
	$= 58 - 12$	Multiply.
	$= 46$	Subtract.

YOUR TURN!

Find the value of $20 \div 5 + (3 + 2) \times 12 - 6$.

$20 \div 5 + (3 + 2) \times 12 - 6$	$= 20 \div 5 +$ _5_ $\times 12 - 6$	Calculate operations inside parentheses.
	$=$ _4_ $+$ _60_ $- 6$	Multiply and divide from left to right.
	$=$ _64_ $- 6$	Add.
	$=$ _58_	Subtract.

Who is Correct?

Find the value of $10 \div 2 + (2 + 2) \times 2$.

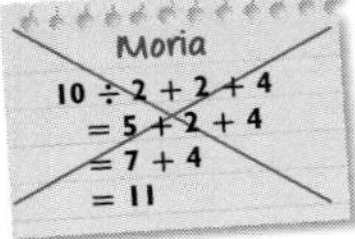

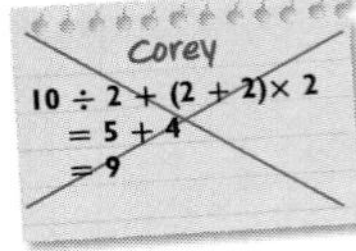

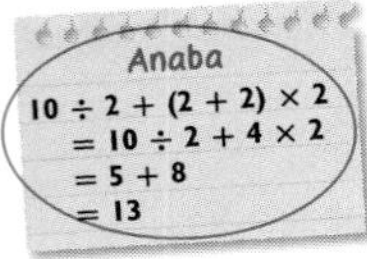

Circle correct answer(s). Cross out incorrect answer(s).

Guided Practice

Name the step that should be performed first.

1. $4 \times 6 + (30 - 3) \div 3$ _subtraction_
2. $26 \div 1 - (1 + 7) \times 2$ _addition_
3. $9 + 5 \div 5 + 2 \times 6$ _division_
4. $8 + 2 \div 2 \times 5 - 1$ _division_

166 Chapter 4 Properties of Operations

Who *is Correct?*

Diagnostic Teaching

- Moria's answer is incorrect. She did not follow the order of operations. She should have performed the operations in the parentheses first.
- Corey's answer is incorrect. He did the operations from left to right.
- Anaba's answer is correct. She followed the order of operations.

Step by Step Practice

5 Find the value of $70 - 6 \times (12 - 7) - 5 + 2$.

Step 1 Use the order of operations.
Calculate operations inside parentheses.
$70 - 6 \times (12 - 7) - 5 + 2 = 70 - 6 \times (\underline{5}) - 5 + 2$

Step 2 Multiply and divide.
$70 - 6 \times 5 - 5 + 2 = 70 - \underline{30} - 5 + 2$

Step 3 Add and subtract.
$70 - 30 - 5 + 2 = \underline{40} - 5 + 2$
$= \underline{35} + 2$
$= \underline{37}$

Find the value of each expression.

6 $9 - (1 + 8) + 3 = 9 - \underline{9} + 3$
$= \underline{0} + \underline{3}$
$= \underline{3}$

7 $8 \div 2 + (5 \times 2) - 7 = 8 \div 2 + \underline{10} - 7$
$= \underline{4} + \underline{10} - 7$
$= \underline{14} - 7$
$= \underline{7}$

8 $20 - 16 \div 4 \times 2 + (7 - 4) = \underline{15}$

9 $(4 \times 3) \times 5 \div 5 - (3 + 6) = \underline{3}$

10 $30 \div (2 + 3) + 2 \times 12 = \underline{30}$

11 $50 \div (7 + 3) \times 4 \div 2 = \underline{10}$

12 $(12 - 2) \div (4 + 1) - 0 = \underline{2}$

13 $15 - 3 + (2 \times 8) \div 4 = \underline{16}$

Are They Getting It?

Check students' understanding of the order of operations by writing these problems on the board. Have students point out wrong answers and explain why they are wrong. Encourage students to use a diagram in their explanations.

1. $9 + (27 \div 3) - (4 \times 3) = 9 + 9 - 12$
This is correct. The first operations performed were the operations in parentheses.

2. $2 \times 3 + (9 - 5) \div 4 - 5 = 6 + (9 - 5) \div 4 - 5$
This is incorrect. The operations were performed from left to right. The operation inside the parentheses should have been performed first.

3. $6 + 4 + 5 \div 5 \times 3 = 6 + 4 + 1 \times 3$
This is correct. There are no parentheses, so the division is performed first.

Math Coach Notes

Evaluate Expressions Every expression should be evaluated using the standard properties of number operations. To do this, students must have a good understanding of the properties. To emphasize the importance of the order of operations, illustrate how one problem could be solved several different ways to arrive at different answers. The reason for the order is so that there is one correct answer.

Note This!

Study Strategies Students often have trouble with the multiplication and division from left to right and the addition and subtraction from left to right. Explain that the phrase "from left to right" is what really defines the order for these steps.

Common Error *Alert*

Circle and Check If students are having difficulty with the order of operations, give the class the following problem. Ask them to solve it individually. Have students circle the operation and write the step number above the circle.

$$21 + 4 \times 5 - \overset{1}{(5 - 3)} + 18 \div 3$$

Have the students circle the next step and write the step number in the circle. After simplifying the expression, have another student check each step and verify the step number.

English Learner Strategy

Reference Material Provide students with 8.5" × 11" poster board. Turn the board to landscape orientation. On the right side of the board, students should write the order of operations in English. On the left side, students should write the order of operations in their native languages (aligned with the steps in English). In between the lists, include an expression that is simplified at each step in the order.

Step by Step Problem-Solving Practice

Problem-Solving Strategies
- ☐ Draw a diagram.
- ☐ Guess and check.
- ☐ Act it out.
- ☑ Solve a simpler problem.
- ☐ Work backward.

14 NUTRITION Marcos has 2 baskets that hold 12 oranges each. He has 6 more baskets of 10 oranges each. Write and simplify an expression to find how many oranges Marcos has in all.

Understand Read the problem. Write what you know.
There are baskets with __12__ oranges each and baskets with __10__ oranges each.

Plan Pick a strategy. One strategy is to solve a simpler problem. In this case, solving a simpler problem means to work on smaller parts of the expression, one at a time.

Solve Write an expression for the total number of oranges.

__2__ × 12 + __6__ × 10
2 baskets of 12   6 baskets of 10

Simplify the expression using the order of operations.
2 × 12 + 6 × 10
= __24__ + __60__ Multiply.
= __84__ Add.

Marcos has __84__ oranges.

Check You can use addition to check.
12 + 12 + 10 + 10 + 10 + 10 + 10 + 10 = __84__

Write and simplify an expression to solve each problem.

15 NATURE Brandy likes to watch birds. She saw 1 wren make 2 nests and 3 wrens each make 4 nests. Five nests were damaged during a storm. How many nests were left?
Check off each step.

__✔__ Understand: I circled key words.
__✔__ Plan: To solve the problem, I will __solve a simpler problem__.
__✔__ Solve: The answer is __9 nests; 2 + 3 × 4 − 5 = 2 + 12 − 5 = 14 − 5 = 9__.
__✔__ Check: I checked my answer by __using repeated addition__.

168 Chapter 4 Properties of Operations

Intervention Strategy — Naturalist Learners

Write an Acronym Ask students who love animals and nature to write an acronym for the first letters of the words in the order of operations. An example is:

Parading
Monkeys
Down
A
Street

16 COLLECTIONS Tyler bought 3 packs of comic books. Each pack had 5 comic books. He gave 7 comic books to his brother. Then he bought 2 more packs of comic books with 18 books in each. How many comic books does Tyler have now?

44 comic books; $3 \times 5 - 7 + 2 \times 18 = 15 - 7 + 36 = 8 + 36 = 44$

17 PHOTOGRAPHY Marlene was looking through her photo album. She looked at 6 pages with 4 photos each. She removed 2 photos. Then she looked at 10 pages with 8 photos each. She removed 6 photos. Finally she looked at 2 pages with 2 photos each. How many photos were left in the album?

100 photos; $6 \times 4 - 2 + 10 \times 8 - 6 + 2 \times 2 = 24 - 2 + 80 - 6 + 4 =$

$22 + 80 - 6 + 4 = 102 - 6 + 4 = 96 + 4 = 100$

18  Reflect Explain why $16 \div 2 + 6$ has a different value than $16 \div (2 + 6)$.

Answers will vary. Sample answer: They will have a different value because in $16 \div 2 + 6$ you will divide first. In $16 \div (2 + 6)$ you will add first.

Skills, Concepts, and Problem Solving

Name the step that should be performed first in each expression.

19 $3 \times 2 + 4 \div 2 - 2$ multiplication

20 $2 \times (3 - 6) + 9 \div 3$ subtraction

21 $(7 - 2 \times 4) - 8 \div 1$ multiplication

22 $4 + (6 - 2 \times 7) \div 2$ multiplication

23 $3(100 + 25) \times 2 - 25$ addition

24 $7 + 12 \div 15 \times 3$ division

Find the value of each expression.

25 $50 \div 5 + 3 \times 2 - (8 - 2) =$ 10

26 $13 + 8 \div 2 - (10 + 2) =$ 5

27 $16 - 4 \times 0 + 18 - 15 =$ 19

28 $(9 - 6) + 8 \div 4 + 5 \times 6 =$ 35

29 $7 + 12 \times 3 - (4 - 4) =$ 43

30 $2 \times (14 - 6) \div 2 =$ 8

31 $8 \times (10 - 2) - 12 =$ 52

32 $21 + 4 \times 5 - (5 - 3) =$ 39

GO ON

Math Challenge

Write Number and Word Problems Arrange students into pairs and have one student write a number sentence that has multiple operations. Have the other student write a word problem that represents the number sentence created by his or her partner. Share the word problem with the class to check for understanding and correctness.

Intervention Strategy — Auditory Learners

Say it Out Loud Auditory learners will need to state their acronym softly to themselves each time they use the order of operations. They benefit from hearing the steps as they work the problems. Explain the importance of whispering to themselves or mouthing the words without any voice.

Odd/Even Assignments

Exercises 19–34 are structured so that students practice the same concepts whether they are assigned the odd or even problems.

In-Class Assignment

Have students complete Exercises 20, 25, 30, 34, and 37 to ensure that they understand the concept.

Assess

See It, Do It, Say It, Write It

Step 1 Write the following problem on the board:

$2 + 10 \div 2 - (2 \times 3)$

Step 2 Have students circle each operation as they simplify and then write the step number in the circle.

Step 3 Arrange students in pairs and have them explain to each other how they used the order of operations to simplify.

Step 4 Have students write the meaning of the *order of operations* in their math journals using their own words.

Intervention Strategy

Linguistic/ Logical Learners

Write an Explanation Ask students to write a paragraph about the order of operations in their journals. They should explain what it is and why it is needed. Encourage students to include a few examples.

Write and simplify an expression to solve each problem.

33 BOOKS Ramona borrowed 2 stacks of books with 8 books each. She then returned 9 books. Then Ramona borrowed 2 stacks of 5 books each. How many books does Ramona have now?

17 books ; $2 \times 8 - 9 + 2 \times 5 = 16 - 9 + 10 = 7 + 10 = 17$

34 COLLECTIONS Don had 100 collector cards. He sold 5 packs of baseball cards with 10 cards each. He then bought 3 packs of football cards with 12 cards each. Then Don sold 25 hockey cards. How many cards does Don have left?

61 cards; $100 - 5 \times 10 + 3 \times 12 - 25 = 100 - 50 + 36 - 25 = 50 + 36 - 25 =$
$86 - 25 = 61$

Vocabulary Check **Write the vocabulary word that completes each sentence.**

35 Always calculate operations inside ___parentheses___ first.

36 The ___order of operations___ is a set of rules that tells what order to follow when evaluating an expression.

37 Writing in Math Does $30 - (10 - 5)$ equal $(30 - 10) - 5$? Explain.

No; $30 - (10 - 5) = 25$ and $(30 - 10) - 5 = 15$; the parentheses change the order in which the expressions are simplified.

Spiral Review

Solve. Explain your reasoning. (Lesson 4-2, p. 151)

38 SPORTS Amy bought the boxes of softballs shown. Each softball cost $4. How much did Amy spend?

$64; $8 \times 2 \times 4 = 8 \times (2 \times 4) = 8 \times 8$

Use the Commutative Property to fill in each blank. Check your answer. (Lesson 4-1, p. 144)

39 $68 + 16 =$ ___16___ + ___68___
___84___ = ___84___

40 ___17___ + ___12___ $= 12 + 17$
___29___ = ___29___

Ticket Out the Door

Say the Order Have students line up at the door in single file. As each student approaches the door, instruct them to say the next operation in the correct order. Continue through the order of operations (repeating them several times) until all students have exited the classroom.

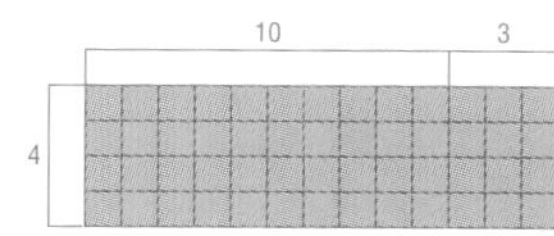

Progress Check 2 (Lessons 4-3 and 4-4)

Use the Distributive Property and a model to find each product.

1 $4 \times 13 =$ 52

2 $6 \times 16 =$ 96

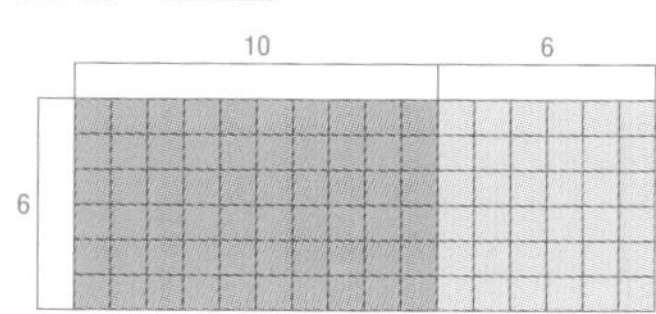

Name each operation that should be performed first.

3 $8 - 4 \times (7 + 4) \div 2$ addition

4 $3 \times 2 - (12 \div 4) + 6$ division

Use the Distributive Property to find each product. Show your work.

5 $7(3 + 2) =$ $21 + 14 = 35$

6 $6(8 - 2) =$ $48 - 12 = 36$

7 $3(9 + 5) =$ $(3 \times 9) + (3 \times 5) =$ $27 + 15 = 42$

8 $6(15 - 7) =$ $(6 \times 15) - (6 \times 7) =$ $90 - 42 = 48$

Find the value of each expression.

9 $18 + 12 \div 4 \times (5 - 2) + 7 =$ 34

10 $10 - (2 - 1) + 16 \div 2 \times (1 + 1) =$ 25

11 $28 \div 2 \times 8 + 4 \div 2 =$ 114

12 $64 \div 4 \times 5 - (30 - 18) \div 4 =$ 77

Solve. Explain your reasoning.

13 **BASKETBALL** Joan made six 2-point field goals and two 3-point field goals. How many points did Joan score?

18 points; $6 \times 2 + 2 \times 3 = 12 + 6 = 18$

14 **SHOPPING** Payton had 50 pencils. He sold 3 bags of pencils with 5 pencils each. He then bought 2 packs of pencils with 10 pencils each. Then Payton gave 20 pencils to his sister. How many pencils does Payton have left?

35 pencils; $50 - 3 \times 5 + 2 \times 10 - 20 = 50 - 15 + 20 - 20 = 35 + 20 - 20 = 55 - 20 = 35$

Chapter 4 Properties of Operations 171

Progress Check 2

Chapter 4

Formative Assessment

Use the Progress Check to assess students' mastery of the previous lessons. Have students review the lesson indicated for the problems they answered incorrectly.

Odd/Even Assignments

Exercises are structured so that students practice the same concepts whether they are assigned the odd or even problems.

Common Error *Alert*

One Step at a Time If students are having difficulties with the order of operations, insist that they show all steps. Each time a step is performed, they should rewrite the expression in its entirety with only the substituted value of the operation they performed in that step. They should re-analyze the next step that should be done according to the order of operations.

Exercise 9 If a student simplified the expression as 70, they added 18 to 3 instead of adding 18 to 9, which is the value of $12 \div 4 \times 3$.

Exercise 13 Some students may read the problem quickly when looking for numbers only. They may miss the written words that express numbers, such as six and two. Have them highlight key words in each problem.

Data-Driven Decision Making

Students missing Exercises . . .	Have trouble with . . .	Should review and practice . . .
1–2	drawing a model to represent the Distributive Property.	SSG Lesson 4-3, p. 159 CRM Skills Practice, p. A86
3–4	deciding what to do first using the order of operations.	SSG Lesson 4-4, p. 165 CRM Skills Practice, p. A90
5–8	using the Distributive Property to simplify an expression that contains variables.	CRM Skills Practice, p. A86
9–12	using the order of operations to evaluate expressions.	SSG Lesson 4-4, p. 165 CRM Skills Practice, p. A90
13–14	solving word problems in which the Distributive Property and order of operations are used.	CRM Problem-Solving Practice, pp. A87 and A91

Chapter 4

Study Guide
Formative Assessment

Vocabulary and Concept Check

If students have difficulty answering Exercises 1–7, remind them that they can use the page references to refresh their memories about the vocabulary terms.

Vocabulary Review Strategies

Graphic Organizers Have students fold a sheet of paper in half vertically. On the left side they should write the vocabulary terms. On the right side they should provide a summary of each term and include examples when appropriate. They should show two examples for each of the number properties listed.

Lesson Review

Each example walks the students through the main concepts of this chapter. If the given examples are not sufficient to review the questions, remind students that the page references tell them here to review that topic in their textbooks.

Find **Extra Practice** for these concepts in the Practice Worksheets, pages A77–A92.

Classroom Management

Pair and Share Pair a student who understands the material with another student who needs extra support. Have students take turns explaining the examples to each other. One student can do the odd problems, while the other does the even problems. Have students check each other's work.

Study Guide

Vocabulary and Concept Check

Associative Property of Addition, *p. 151*
Associative Property of Multiplication, *p. 151*
Commutative Property of Addition, *p. 144*
Commutative Property of Multiplication, *p. 144*
Distributive Property, *p. 159*
order of operations, *p. 165*

Write the vocabulary word that completes each sentence.

1. The property that states that the order in which two numbers are multiplied does not change the *product* is the Commutative Property of Multiplication.

2. The property that states that the grouping of the factors does not change the *product* is the Associative Property of Multiplication.

3. $(2 + 4) + 7 = 2 + (4 + 7)$ shows the Associative Property of Addition.

4. $3(2 + 5) = 3 \times 2 + 3 \times 5$ or $3(5 - 2) = 3 \times 5 - 3 \times 2$ is the Distributive Property of Multiplication.

5. $3 + 9 = 9 + 3$ shows the Commutative Property of Addition.

Write the correct vocabulary term in the blank.

6. Distributive Property

$$2(4 + 5) = (2 \times 4) + (2 \times 5)$$

7. order of operations

1) Calculate operations inside parentheses.

2) Multiply and divide from left to right.

3) Add and subtract from left to right.

Lesson Review

4-1 Commutative Property (pp. 144–150)

Use the Commutative Property to fill in each blank. Check your answer.

8. $2 \times 8 = \underline{8} \times 2$
   $16 = \underline{16}$

9. $\underline{15} + 7 = 7 + 15$
   $\underline{22} = \underline{22}$

10. $\underline{18} + 4 = \underline{4} + \underline{18}$
    $\underline{22} = 22$

Example 1

Draw a model to show 4 + 2 = 2 + 4. Which property did you show?

1. Create a model for each side of the equation.

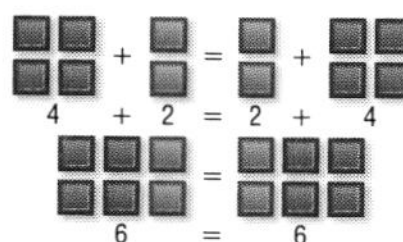

2. The order of the numbers changed, but the sum did not. This is the Commutative Property of Addition.

4-2 Associative Property (pp. 151–157)

Use the Associative Property to fill in each blank. Check your answer.

11. $8 \times (4 \times 3) = (8 \times \underline{4}) \times 3$
    $\underline{8 \times 12 = 32 \times 3}$
    $\underline{96 = 96}$

12. $(5 + 9) + 3 = 5 + (\underline{9} + 3)$
    $\underline{14 + 3 = 5 + 12}$
    $\underline{17 = 17}$

Example 2

Use the Associative Property to fill in each blank. Check your answer.

$(6 \times 3) \times 2 = 6 \times (\_\_\_\_ \times 2)$

Use the Associative Property of Multiplication.
$(6 \times 3) \times 2 = 6 \times (3 \times 2)$

Check by multiplying the numbers on each side of the equation.
$(6 \times 3) \times 2 = 6 \times (3 \times 2)$
$18 \times 2 = 6 \times 6$
$36 = 36$

13. $2 + (13 + 15) = (\underline{2} + \underline{13}) + \underline{15}$
    $2 + \underline{28} = 15 + \underline{15}$
    $\underline{30} = \underline{30}$

Dinah Zike's Foldables®

Review Remind students to refer to their Foldables as they progress through the Chapter 4 Study Guide. Instruct them to include additional notes and examples to clarify the notes they have already taken.

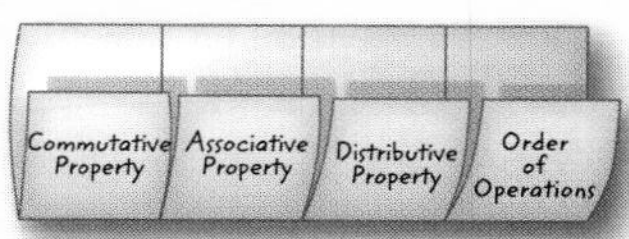

Have students work in small groups to use their Foldables to quiz each other on the major topics of the chapter. (For complete instructions, see Chapter Resource Masters, p. A74.)

Note This!

Create a Checklist Help students create a study checklist. The checklist should include all of the following items:

- Commutative Property
- Associative Property
- Distributive Property
- Order of operations

Students should put a checkmark next to each topic when they feel they have mastered the property or process.

Intervention Strategy — Interpersonal Learners

Write Distribution Expressions Divide the class into small groups. Have each member of the class write a distributive expression such as 3(2 + 5) on one index card. Students should place all the cards in one pile. Divide the cards evenly—one for each group. Students should work together in small groups to write the other half of the expressions, for example, $3 \times 2 + 3 \times 5$. Come back as a class to solve each expression.

Draw a model to show each equation.

14 $(2 \times 3) \times 5 = 2 \times (3 \times 5)$
Which property did you show?
Associative Property of Multiplication

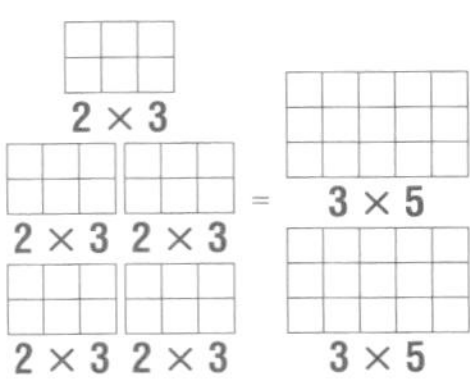

15 $(2 + 3) + 4 = 2 + (3 + 4)$
Which property did you show?
Associative Property of Addition

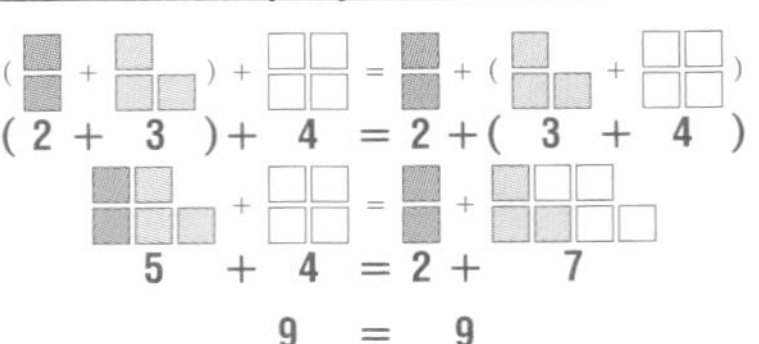

Example 3

Draw a model to show (1 × 3) × 4 = 1 × (3 × 4). Which property did you show?

1. Create a model for each side of the equation.

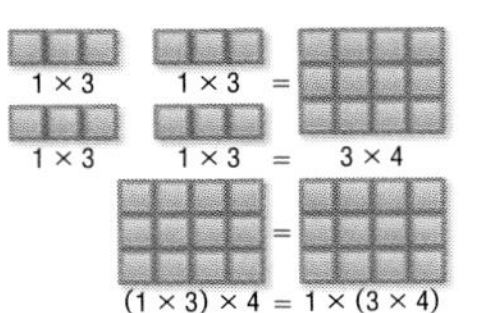

2. The grouping of the factors did not change the product.

Associative Property of Multiplication

Use the Commutative and Associative Properties to find each sum or product mentally.

16 $4 \times 7 \times 5 = 4 \times$ __5__ $\times 7$
$= ($__4__ $\times 5) \times 7$
$=$ __20__ $\times 7$
$=$ __140__

17 $11 + (9 + 4) = ($__11__ $+ 9) + 4$
$=$ __20__ $+ 4$
$=$ __24__

Example 4

Use the Commutative and Associative Properties to find the sum mentally.

$15 + 9 + 5$

Determine which grouping would help you find the sum using mental math.
Group 15 and 5. Then find the sum.

$15 + 9 + 5 = 15 + 5 + 9$
$= (15 + 5) + 9$
$= 20 + 9$
$= 29$

Intervention Strategy — Linguistic/Auditory Learners

Class Discussion Ask a student volunteer to describe the Commutative Property. Ask two more volunteers to describe the Associative Property and the Distributive Property. Then, as a class, discuss the differences between the three properties. Write examples on the board during the class discussion.

4-3 Distributive Property (pp. 159–164)

Use the Distributive Property to find each product.

18 $9(5 - 3) = (\underline{9} \times 5) - (\underline{9} \times 3)$
$= \underline{45} - \underline{27}$
$= \underline{18}$

19 $5(4 + 8) = (\underline{5} \times 4) + (\underline{5} \times 8)$
$= \underline{20} + \underline{40}$
$= \underline{60}$

Example 5

Use the Distributive Property to find 7(8 + 3).

$7(8 + 3) = (7 \times 8) + (7 \times 3)$

Solve within the parentheses. Then add.
$(7 \times 8) + (7 \times 3) = 56 + 21$
$= 77$

4-4 Order of Operations (pp. 165–170)

Find the value of each expression.

20 $10 + 8 \div 2 - 1 \times 3 = \underline{11}$

21 $11 - 7 + 3 \times 8 = \underline{28}$

22 $125 \div 5 \times 7 = \underline{175}$

23 $15 \div 3 + 4 \times 7 - 10 = \underline{23}$

Example 6

Find the value of 6 − 2 + 15 ÷ 3 × 4.

Use the order of operations.
There are no grouping symbols.
Multiply and divide.
$6 - 2 + 15 \div 3 \times 4 = 6 - 2 + 5 \times 4$
$= 6 - 2 + 20$

Add and subtract.
$6 - 2 + 20 = 4 + 20$
$= 24$

Find the value of each expression.

24 $3 \times 4 - (4 - 2) + 6 \div 2 = \underline{13}$

25 $23 - 4 + (9 \times 2) \div 9 = \underline{21}$

26 $6 + 4 \div (8 - 6) \times 2 = \underline{10}$

27 $7 + 3 \times 5 + (6 \times 2) = \underline{34}$

Example 7

Find the value of 18 ÷ 3 + (2 + 1) × 4 − 5.

Use the order of operations.
Calculate operations inside parentheses.
$18 \div 3 + (2 + 1) \times 4 - 5 = 18 \div 3 + 3 \times 4 - 5$

Multiply and divide.
$18 \div 3 + 3 \times 4 - 5 = 6 + 12 - 5$

Add and subtract.
$6 + 12 - 5 = 18 - 5$
$= 13$

Common Error Alert

Write Each Step If students are not simplifying the expressions in Exercises 20–27 correctly, ensure they are showing each step as they simplify each expression. Often students will cross off numbers and write new numbers above the operation they completed, or combine steps and try to solve too much mentally. Insist that students write the entire expression each and every time they perform a single operation.

Ticket Out the Door

Write Examples Have students write an example of the following five properties: Commutative Property of Addition, Commutative Property of Multiplication, Associative Property of Addition, Associative Property of Multiplication, and Distributive Property. They should hand their written properties as they exit the classroom.

Chapter 4 Chapter Test

Chapter Resource Masters

Additional forms of the Chapter 4 Tests are available.

Test Format	Where to Find it
Chapter 4 Test	Math Online macmillanmh.com
Blackline Masters	Assessment Masters, p. 47

Customize and create multiple versions of your chapter test and their answer keys. All of these questions from the chapter tests are available on ExamView® Assessment Suite.

Online Assessment and Reporting
macmillanmh.com

This online assessment tool allows teachers to track student progress with easily accessible, comprehensive reports available for every student. Assess students using any internet-ready computer.

Alternative Assessment

Use Portfolios Ask students to write an example of each property in their portfolios. They should write an equation that illustrates the property and then label the property. For assessing the order of operations, have students write two expressions with the same numbers in the same order, but with different operations that each simplify to a different answer. They can either alter the operations or use parentheses to generate a different answer.

Chapter 4 Chapter Test

Use the Commutative Property to fill in each blank. Check your answer.

1. $4 \times 6 = \underline{6} \times 4$; $24 = \underline{24}$
2. $\underline{11} + 9 = 9 + 11$; $\underline{20} = \underline{20}$
3. $7 + 9 = \underline{9} + \underline{7}$; $\underline{16} = \underline{16}$
4. $7 \times 12 = \underline{12} \times \underline{7}$; $\underline{84} = \underline{84}$
5. Give an example of the Commutative Property of Addition. Check your example.
   Answers will vary. Sample answer: $6 + 5 = 5 + 6$; $11 = 11$

Use the Associative Property to fill in each blank. Check your answer.

6. $3 \times (4 \times 10) = (\underline{3} \times 4) \times 10$; $= \underline{12} \times 10$; $= \underline{120}$
7. $9 + (1 + 15) = (\underline{9} + 1) + 15$; $= \underline{10} + 15$; $= \underline{25}$
8. $4 + (16 + 13) = (\underline{4} + \underline{16}) + \underline{13}$; $= \underline{20} + \underline{13}$; $= \underline{33}$
9. $(7 \times 2) \times 5 = \underline{7} \times (\underline{2} \times \underline{5})$; $= \underline{7} \times \underline{10}$; $= \underline{70}$
10. Give an example of the Associative Property of Multiplication. Check your answer.
   Answers will vary. Sample answer: $(3 \times 2) \times 5 = 3 \times (2 \times 5)$; $6 \times 5 = 3 \times 10$; $30 = 30$

Use the Distributive Property to find each product. Show your work.

11. $9(2 + 5) = \underline{18 + 45 = 63}$
12. $2(20 - 8) = \underline{40 - 16 = 24}$

Solve.

13. $16 + 8 \div 4 \times 5 - (16 - 10) = \underline{20}$
14. $(7 - 3) \times 3 \div 4 + (11 + 8) = \underline{22}$

GO ON

176 Chapter 4 Test

English Learner Strategy

Assessment Allow students to read the word problems in the assessment. Provide an opportunity for students to clarify and define any words they do not understand.

Solve. Explain your reasoning.

15 **COOKING** Winston needs 3 gallons of stew for a potluck dinner. Each gallon of stew requires 2 cans of beef gravy. Each can of beef gravy costs \$1.20. How much will the gravy for the stew cost?

\$7.20; $3 \times 2 \times 1.20 = (3 \times 1.20) \times 2 = 3.60 \times 2 = 7.20$

16 **SHOPPING** Devin bought 4 boxes of markers with 5 markers in each box. Katie purchased 5 boxes with 4 markers in each box. Compare the number of markers.

They bought the same number of markers; $4 \times 5 = 5 \times 4$.

17 **FITNESS** Sofia participated in two 50-minute aerobics sessions last week and three 50-minute aerobics sessions this week. How many minutes did she work out during both weeks?

250 min.; $2(50) + 3(50) = 100 + 150 = 250$

18 **POPULATION** An apartment complex has 3 units. Four people lived in each unit. Then 8 people moved away. The next month, 2 families of 5 moved into the complex. How many people live in the apartment complex now?

14 people; $3 \times 4 - 8 + 2 \times 5 = 12 - 8 + 10 = 4 + 10 = 14$

Correct the mistakes.

19 **ART** Terri purchased 3 boxes of paint tubes, each containing 8 tubes of paint. Raul purchased 8 boxes, each containing 3 paint tubes. Raul told Terri that he bought more tubes of paint than she did because he bought more boxes. What mistake did Raul make?

They bought the same number of paint tubes. Raul is only counting the boxes.

He needs to find the number of paint tubes in each box; $3 \times 8 = 8 \times 3$; $24 = 24$.

20 **FOOD** At the school cafeteria, the cook had 7 sandwiches. Two students purchased 1 each. The cook then sold two teachers 2 each. Her assistant made 11 more sandwiches. She dropped 1 of them on the floor, so it had to be thrown away. The assistant said, "Now you only have 10 sandwiches to sell." What mistake did she make?

They have 11 to sell. The correct answer is: $7 - 2 \times 1 - 2 \times 2 + 11 - 1 = 7 - 2 - 4 + 11 - 1 = 11$. She added instead of multiplying 2 and 1.

STOP

Learning from Mistakes

Missed Questions Review commonly missed questions as a small group or class. Ask students to share their methods of answering each question. Try to point out when any errors occur and take corrective measures.

Common Error *Alert*

Mark Word Problems If students are using the wrong operations for word problems, then have them underline key words in word problems. They should underline any words that indicate which operation to use and circle numbers used in the calculation. They can also cross out numbers and words that are not important to the problem.

Data-Driven Decision Making

Students missing Exercises . . .	Have trouble with . . .	Should review and practice . . .
1–5	using the Commutative Properties to simplify expressions.	SSG Lesson 4-1, p. 144 CRM Skills Practice, p. A78
6–10	using the Associative Properties to simplify expressions.	SSG Lesson 4-2, p. 151 CRM Skills Practice, p. A82
11–12	using the Distributive Property to simplify expressions.	SSG Lesson 4-3, p. 159 CRM Skills Practice, p. A86
13–14	using the order of operations to simplify expressions.	SSG Lesson 4-4, p. 165 CRM Skills Practice, p. A90
15–20	solving problems in which number properties and order of operations are used.	CRM Problem-Solving Practice, pp. A79, A83, A87, and A91

Chapter 4 Test Practice

Diagnose Student Errors

Survey student responses for each item. Class trends may indicate common errors and misconceptions.

1. A did not notice only order changed, numbers are the same
   Ⓑ correct
   C did not notice only order changed, numbers are the same
   D did not notice only order changed, numbers are the same
2. A 48 should be 49
   Ⓑ correct
   C 103 should be 130
   D 47 should be 49
3. Ⓐ correct
   B misinterpreted Distributive Property
   C incorrect sign, × should be +
   D misinterpreted Distributive Property
4. A didn't follow order of operations
   B didn't follow order of operations
   Ⓒ correct
   D didn't follow order of operations
5. A misinterpreted Distributive Property
   Ⓑ correct
   C misinterpreted Distributive Property
   D guess
6. Ⓐ correct
   B misinterpreted Associative Property
   C misinterpreted Associative Property
   D guess
7. A guess
   B misinterpreted Commutative Property
   Ⓒ correct
   D misinterpreted Commutative Property
8. A miscalculated
   B miscalculated
   Ⓒ correct
   D miscalculated
9. A miscalculated
   B miscalculated
   Ⓒ correct
   D miscalculated

Chapter 4 Test Practice

Choose the best answer and fill in the corresponding circle on the sheet at right.

1 If $9 \times 8 \times 7 = 504$, then what is $7 \times 9 \times 8$?

A 567   Ⓑ 504   C 448   D 343

2 $49 \times (130 \times 62) =$

A $(48 \times 130) \times 26$
Ⓑ $(49 \times 130) \times 62$
C $(49 \times 103) \times 62$
D $(47 \times 130) \times 62$

3 Olivia wants to paint the two opposite walls in her bedroom. If she knows the dimensions of one wall, which expression can help her figure out the square footage of both walls?

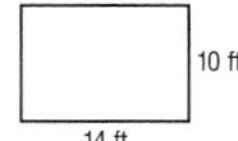

Ⓐ $2(10 \times 14)$ B $2(14) + 10$ C $2(14) \times 2(10)$ D $2 + (14 \times 10)$

4 $33 \div 3 \times 5 - (4 \times 3) =$

A 954   B 187   Ⓒ 43   D 6

5 Which property is shown in the sentence below?

$21 \times (8 + 5) = (21 \times 8) + (21 \times 5)$

A Associative Property of Addition
Ⓑ Distributive Property
C Commutative Property of Addition
D Identity Property of Multiplication

6 Which property is shown in the sentence below?

$(346 \times 751) \times 203 = 346 \times (751 \times 203)$

Ⓐ Associative Property of Multiplication
B Distributive Property
C Commutative Property of Multiplication
D Associative Property of Addition

7 Which property is shown in the sentence below?

$33 \times 1 = 1 \times 33$

A Associative Property of Addition
B Distributive Property
Ⓒ Commutative Property of Multiplication
D Associative Property of Multiplication

GO ON

178 Chapter 4 Test Practice

10. A 15 should be 13
    B 50 should be 52
    C 8 should be 6
    Ⓓ correct
11. A miscalculated
    B miscalculated
    Ⓒ correct
    D miscalculated
12. Ⓐ correct
    B wrong operation
    C wrong operation
    D wrong operation

8 Tyra has 24 minutes left in class. Before lunch, she has 2 more classes that are each 35 minutes and 1 that is 40 minutes. How many minutes does Tyra have before lunch?

A 94   (C) 134

B 114   D 84

---

9 What is the value of the number sentence?

$$25 \times (5 - 2) \div 5 - 12$$

A 285   (C) 3

B 363   D 15

---

10 $13 \times 52 \times 6 =$

A $52 \times 6 \times 15$ C $13 \times 8 \times 52$

B $6 \times 13 \times 50$ (D) $6 \times 52 \times 13$

---

11 Janet bought 5 packs of erasers with 10 erasers each. Jorge gave Janet 2 erasers. Then Janet gave 9 erasers to each of 3 friends. How many erasers does Janet have now?

A 15   (C) 25

B 30   D 47

12 Tamar sleeps 8 hours each night. Which expression represents how many hours he sleeps in a week?

(A) 8×7 C $8 \div 7$

B $8 + 7$ D $8 - 7$

ANSWER SHEET

Directions: Fill in the circle of each correct answer.

1	A	**B**	C	D
2	A	**B**	C	D
3	**A**	B	C	D
4	A	B	**C**	D
5	A	**B**	C	D
6	**A**	B	C	D
7	A	B	**C**	D
8	A	B	**C**	D
9	A	B	**C**	D
10	A	B	C	**D**
11	A	B	**C**	D
12	**A**	B	C	D

Success Strategy

If two answers seem correct, compare them for differences. Reread the problem to find the best answer between the two.

Diagnosing Student Errors and Misconceptions

Sight Recognition Students often have trouble remembering the differences between the properties. Help students to make connections between the names of the properties and their meanings, or between the root of the property name and its meaning. Associative contains the word *associate,* which means *to join as a partner.* Illustrate an Associative Property problem and use the words *to join or partner* when you group the numbers to simplify the expression.

Point out to students that the Distributive Property problems have parentheses and a number outside one parenthesis. This format indicates the Distributive Property.

Chapter 5

Chapter Overview

Chapter-at-a-Glance

Lesson	Math Objective	State/Local Standards
5-1 Parts of a Whole and Parts of a Set (pp. 182–188)	Interpret parts of a whole and parts of a set as fractions.	
5-2 Equivalent Fractions and Equivalent Forms of One (pp. 189–195)	Write equivalent fractions using equivalent forms of one.	
Progress Check 1 (p. 196)		
5-3 Mixed Numbers and Improper Fractions (pp. 197-204)	Write mixed numbers as improper fractions and improper fractions as mixed numbers.	
5-4 Least Common Denominator and Greatest Common Factors (pp. 205–212)	Find the GCF of two or more numbers and find the LCD of two or more fractions with unlike denominators.	
Progress Check 2 (p. 213)		
5-5 Compare and Order Fractions (pp. 214–222)	Compare and order fractions.	
5-6 Simplify Fractions (pp. 223-230)	Write fractions in simplest form.	
Progress Check 3 (p. 231)		

Content-at-a-Glance

The diagram below summarizes and unpacks Chapter 5 content.

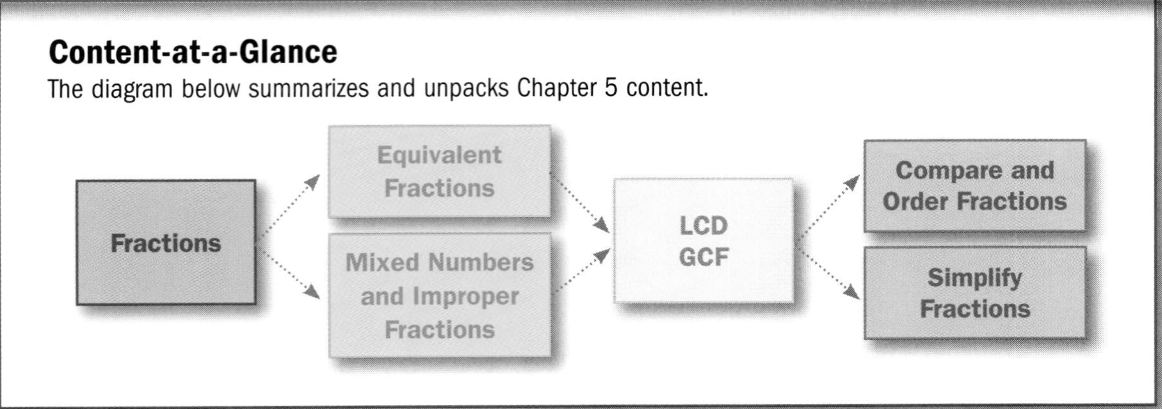

Online Assessment and Reporting
macmillanmh.com

Chapter Assessment Manager

Diagnostic

Diagnose students' readiness.

	Student Study Guide/ Teacher Edition	Assessment Masters	Technology
Course Placement Test		1	ExamView® Assessment Suite
Book 2 Pretest		58	ExamView® Assessment Suite
Chapter 5 Pretest		61	ExamView® Assessment Suite
Quiz/Preview	SSG 181		Math Online macmillanmh.com StudentWorks™ Plus

Formative

Identify students' misconceptions of content knowledge.

	Student Study Guide/ Teacher Edition	Assessment Masters	Technology
Progress Checks	SSG 196, 213, 231		Math Online macmillanmh.com StudentWorks™ Plus
Vocabulary Review	SSG 232		Math Online macmillanmh.com
Lesson Assessments			ExamView® Assessment Suite
Are They Getting It	TE 185, 192, 201, 209, 219, 227		

Summative

Determine student success in learning concepts in the lesson, chapter, or book.

	Student Study Guide/ Teacher Edition	Assessment Masters	Technology
Chapter 5 Test	SSG 236	64	ExamView® Assessment Suite
Test Practice	SSG 238	67	ExamView® Assessment Suite
Alternative Assessment	TE 236	70	
See It, Do It, Say It, Write It	TE 188, 195, 204, 212, 222, 230		
Book 2 Test		94	ExamView® Assessment Suite

Back-mapping and Vertical Alignment **McGraw-Hill's *Math Triumphs*** intervention program was conceived and developed with the final result in mind: student success in grade-level mathematics, including Algebra 1 and beyond. The authors, using the **NCTM Focal Points and Focal Connections** as their guide, developed this brand-new series by backmapping from grade-level and Algebra 1 concepts, and vertically aligning the topics so that they build upon prior skills and concepts and serve as a foundation for future topics.

Chapter Resource Manager

	Lesson 5-1	Lesson 5-2	Lesson 5-3	Lesson 5-4
Concept	Parts of a Whole and Parts of a Set	Equivalent Fractions and Equivalent Forms of One	Mixed Numbers and Improper Fractions	Least Common Denominator and Greatest Common Factors
Objective	Interpret parts of a whole and parts of a set as fractions.	Write equivalent fractions using equivalent forms of one.	Write mixed numbers as improper fractions and improper fractions as mixed numbers.	Find the GCF of two or more numbers, and find the LCD of two or more fractions with unlike denominators.
Math Vocabulary	denominator fraction numerator set whole	equivalent forms of one equivalent fractions Identity Property of Multiplication value	denominator improper fraction mixed number numerator	composite number greatest common factor (GCF) least common denominator (LCD) least common multiple (LCM) prime factorization prime number
Lesson Resources	**Materials** • Grid paper • Number line **Manipulatives** • Base-ten blocks • Fraction circles • Fraction tiles • Money **Other Resources** CRM Vocabulary and English Language Development CRM Skills Practice CRM Problem-Solving Practice CRM Homework Practice	**Materials** • Everyday objects • Fraction bar kit **Manipulatives** • Fraction circles • Fraction tiles • Two-Color counters **Other Resources** CRM Vocabulary and English Language Development CRM Skills Practice CRM Problem-Solving Practice CRM Homework Practice	**Materials** • Everyday objects • Index cards **Manipulatives** • Fraction circles • Fraction tiles **Other Resources** CRM Vocabulary and English Language Development CRM Skills Practice CRM Problem-Solving Practice CRM Homework Practice	**Materials** • Egg cartons • Index cards • Paper (factor trees) **Manipulatives** • Counters • Fraction strips • Number cubes **Other Resources** CRM Vocabulary and English Language Development CRM Skills Practice CRM Problem-Solving Practice CRM Homework Practice
Technology	Math Online macmillanmh.com StudentWorks™ Plus ExamView® Assessment Suite	Math Online macmillanmh.com StudentWorks™ Plus ExamView® Assessment Suite	Math Online macmillanmh.com StudentWorks™ Plus ExamView® Assessment Suite	Math Online macmillanmh.com StudentWorks™ Plus ExamView® Assessment Suite

SSG Student Study Guide
CRM Chapter Resource Masters

TE Teacher Edition
DVD

Lesson 5-5	Lesson 5-6	
Compare and Order Fractions	Simplify Fractions	**Concept**
Compare and order fractions.	Write fractions in simplest form.	**Objective**
common denominators equivalent forms of one least common denominator (LCD) least common multiple (LCM)	greatest common factor (GCF) simplest form	**Math Vocabulary**
Materials • Everyday objects **Manipulatives** • Fraction circles • Fraction tiles **Other Resources** CRM Vocabulary and English Language Development CRM Skills Practice CRM Problem-Solving Practice CRM Homework Practice	**Materials** • Everyday objects • Hundred table • Index cards **Manipulatives** • Fraction circles • Grid paper **Other Resources** CRM Vocabulary and English Language Development CRM Skills Practice CRM Problem-Solving Practice CRM Homework Practice	**Lesson Resources**
Math Online macmillanmh.com StudentWorks™ Plus ExamView® Assessment Suite	Math Online macmillanmh.com StudentWorks™ Plus ExamView® Assessment Suite	**Technology**

Intervention Strategy

Explanations

As a warm-up exercise for Lesson 5-5, ask students to write about how to order unit fractions such as $\frac{1}{4}$ and $\frac{1}{7}$. Their answers should consist of two to three sentences. Ask students to read their responses. If their answers are incomplete or incorrect, ask questions to help them form complete responses, or ask them to give examples to clarify their responses. Have them write revisions based upon your feedback and turn them in. You may read one or two responses that you feel are well done.

Next, ask students to write in their notes, how they think they will compare fractions that are not unit fractions, such as $\frac{2}{3}$ and $\frac{3}{4}$. Teach the lesson, and during the last five minutes of class, ask students to read what they had written at the beginning of class and respond to it.

Chapter 5 Chapter Notes

Real-World Applications

Grades Mrs. Kamstra has a class of 24 students. On the last test that she gave, the students' scores were as follows: $\frac{1}{8}$ of them received As, $\frac{1}{2}$ received Bs, $\frac{1}{4}$ received Cs, $\frac{1}{12}$ received Ds, and $\frac{1}{24}$ received Fs. Using a common denominator, decide how many students from the class received each letter grade. 3 students received As, 12 students received Bs, 6 students received Cs, 2 students received Ds, 1 student received an F.

Intervention Strategy

Fraction of Our Days

1. Ask students to break their days down into at least five categories, which could include, for example, sleeping, school, and getting ready.
2. For each activity, have students write the fraction of the day that is spent on that activity. Reduce each fraction to its lowest terms.
3. Order each activity from the most time to the least time spent on an activity.
4. Have students share their results with the class.

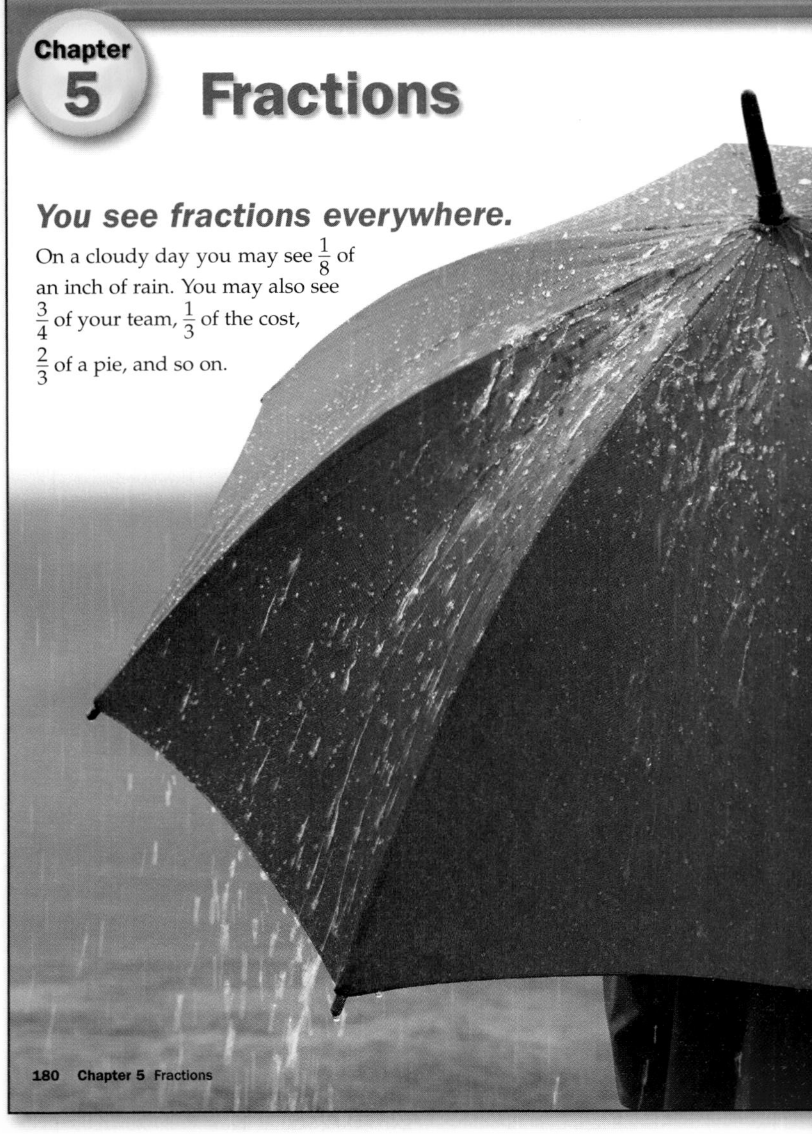

Chapter 5 Fractions
You see fractions everywhere.
On a cloudy day you may see $\frac{1}{8}$ of an inch of rain. You may also see $\frac{3}{4}$ of your team, $\frac{1}{3}$ of the cost, $\frac{2}{3}$ of a pie, and so on.
180 Chapter 5 Fractions

Key Vocabulary

Find interactive definitions in 13 languages in the **eGlossary** at macmillanmh.com.

English **Español** *Introduce the most important vocabulary terms from Chapter 5.*

equivalent fractions **fracciones equivalentes**

fractions that represent the same number (p. 189)

$\frac{3}{4} = \frac{6}{8}$

equivalent forms of one **formas equivalentes de la unidad**

different expressions that represent the same whole number 1 (p. 189)

least common denominator (LCD) **mínimo común denominador (MCD)**

the least common multiple of the denominators of two or more fractions, used as a denominator (p. 205)

The LCD of $\frac{1}{12}$ and $\frac{1}{8}$ is 24.

greatest common factor (GCF) **máximo común divisor (MCD)**

the greatest number that is a factor of two or more numbers (p. 205)

simplest form **forma reducida**

a fraction in which the numerator and the denominator have no common factor greater than 1 (p. 223)

$\frac{3}{5}$ is the simplest form of $\frac{6}{10}$.

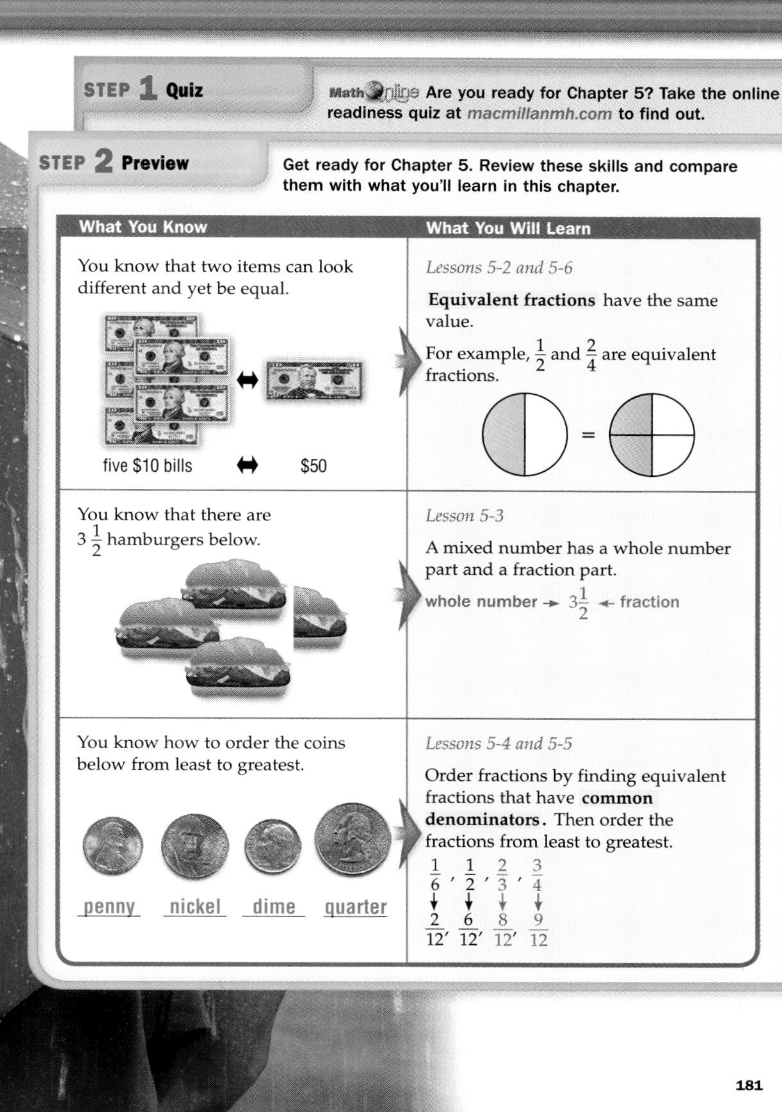
STEP 1 Quiz

Math Online Are you ready for Chapter 5? Take the online readiness quiz at macmillanmh.com to find out.

STEP 2 Preview

Get ready for Chapter 5. Review these skills and compare them with what you'll learn in this chapter.

What You Know	What You Will Learn
You know that two items can look different and yet be equal. five \$10 bills ↔ \$50	*Lessons 5-2 and 5-6* **Equivalent fractions** have the same value. For example, $\frac{1}{2}$ and $\frac{2}{4}$ are equivalent fractions.
You know that there are $3\frac{1}{2}$ hamburgers below.	*Lesson 5-3* A mixed number has a whole number part and a fraction part. whole number → $3\frac{1}{2}$ ← fraction
You know how to order the coins below from least to greatest. penny nickel dime quarter	*Lessons 5-4 and 5-5* Order fractions by finding equivalent fractions that have **common denominators**. Then order the fractions from least to greatest. $\frac{1}{6}, \frac{1}{2}, \frac{2}{3}, \frac{3}{4}$ → $\frac{2}{12}, \frac{6}{12}, \frac{8}{12}, \frac{9}{12}$

181

Step 1 Quiz

Pretest/Prescribe Students can take the Online Readiness Quiz or the Diagnostic Pretest in the Assessment Masters.

Step 2 Preview

Use this pre-chapter activity to activate students' prior knowledge, build confidence, and help students preview the lessons.

Dinah Zike's Foldables®

Guide students through the directions on p. A93 in the Chapter Resource Masters to create their own Foldable graphic organizer for use with this chapter.

Home Connections

- Give the fraction of your family that is male and the fraction of your family that is female. Name two equivalent fractions for each.
- Determine what fraction of your week is spent sleeping and what fraction of your week is spent in school. Then write both fractions in simplest form.

Vocabulary Preview

- As students complete the Chapter Preview, have them make a list of important terms throughout the chapter.
- Divide students into pairs. Have each pair choose two to four terms from the list.
- Each student pair will work together to create vocabulary boxes, following the model below.

Write the vocabulary word.	Draw a model, illustration, or example of the word.
Definition (in words)	Something that is *not* the word

Professional Development

Targeted professional development has been articulated throughout **McGraw-Hill's *Math Triumphs*** intervention program. **The McGraw-Hill Professional Development Video Library** provides short videos that support the **NCTM Focal Points and Focal Connections.** For more information, visit macmillanmh.com.

Lesson 5-1

Lesson Notes

Lesson Planner

Objective Interpret parts of a whole and parts of a set as fractions.

Vocabulary **denominator**, **fraction**, **numerator**, **set**, **whole**

Materials/Manipulatives base-ten blocks, fraction circles, fraction tiles, grid paper, money, number line

Chapter Resource Masters

- CRM Vocabulary and English Language Development (p. A96)
- CRM Skills Practice (p. A97)
- CRM Problem-Solving Practice (p. A98)
- CRM Homework Practice (p. A99)

Vocabulary

Fractions Distribute sheets for students to make and name fraction bars. Call on students to name the *numerator* and *denominator* in each fraction. Ask: What number represents the *whole?* the *part?*

2 Teach

Key Concept

Foundational Skills and Concepts After students have read through the Key Concept box, have them try these exercises.

1. In the fraction $\frac{12}{24}$, what is the numerator? 12 What is the denominator? 24
2. Draw the model below on the board. Ask students to state what fraction of the rectangle is shaded. Have them write the fraction and identify the numerator and denominator.

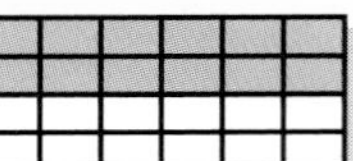

$\frac{12}{24}$; 12; 24

Lesson 5-1

Parts of a Whole and Parts of a Set

KEY Concept

In a **fraction**, the number above the fraction bar is called the **numerator**. The number below the fraction bar is called the **denominator**.

$$\frac{\textbf{numerator}}{\textbf{denominator}} = \frac{\textbf{number of parts being used}}{\textbf{number of parts that make a whole}}$$

A fraction can name part of a **whole**.

The flag of France is divided into three equal parts: red, white, and blue. Each color of the flag represents $\frac{1}{3}$ of the whole flag.

$$\frac{\text{number of red parts}}{\text{number of colors in flag}} = \frac{1}{3}$$

The area of the entire flag represents one whole. Each color represents an equal area, or $\frac{1}{3}$, of the flag.

A fraction can also name part of a **set**.

In a checkers set that contains 24 pieces, 12 of the pieces are red. Among all the checkers, $\frac{12}{24}$ are red.

$$\frac{12}{24} = \frac{\text{number of red checkers}}{\text{number of pieces in all}}$$

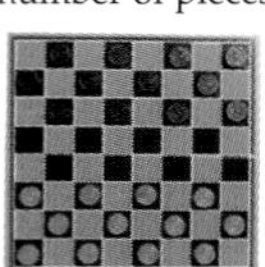

VOCABULARY

denominator
the number below the bar in a *fraction* that tells how many equal parts are in the whole or the set
$\frac{5}{6}$ ← denominator

fraction
a number that represents part of a whole or part of a set
Examples: $\frac{1}{2}, \frac{2}{3}, \frac{3}{4}, \frac{5}{6}$

numerator
the number above the bar in a *fraction* that tells how many equal parts are being used
$\frac{5}{6}$ ← numerator

set
a collection of objects

whole
the entire amount or object

When using a whole, parts are regions of equal size inside the whole. When using a set, parts are an equal number of items in the set.

182 Chapter 5 Fractions

Intervention Strategy

Kinesthetic Learners

Use Drawings If students are having difficulty with the parts of a whole, have them examine the drawing to determine how many red bricks there are in the wall of 20 bricks. Instruct them to have the red bricks as the numerator (part) and the 20 as the denominator (whole). $\frac{13}{20}$

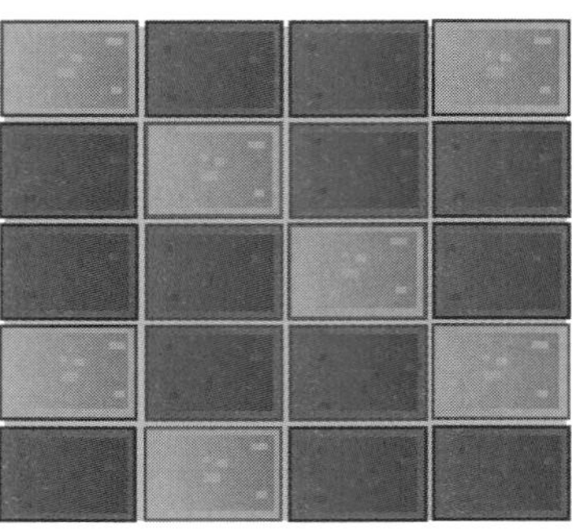

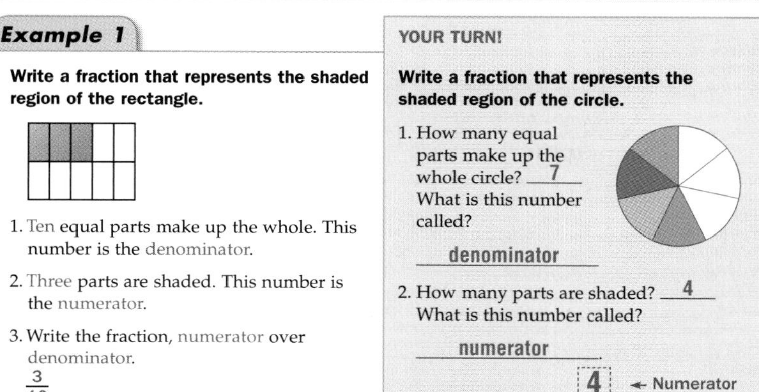

Example 1

Write a fraction that represents the shaded region of the rectangle.

1. Ten equal parts make up the whole. This number is the denominator.
2. Three parts are shaded. This number is the numerator.
3. Write the fraction, numerator over denominator.
$\frac{3}{10}$

YOUR TURN!

Write a fraction that represents the shaded region of the circle.

1. How many equal parts make up the whole circle? 7
What is this number called?
denominator
2. How many parts are shaded? 4
What is this number called?
numerator
3. Write the fraction. $\frac{4}{7}$ ← Numerator ← Denominator

Example 2

Write a fraction that represents the number of circles in the set.

1. There are 7 objects in the set.
7 is the denominator.
2. There are 2 circles in the set.
2 is the numerator.
3. Write the fraction.
$\frac{2}{7}$

YOUR TURN!

Write a fraction that represents the number of turtles in the set.

1. How many animals are in the set altogether? 5
What is this number called?
denominator
2. How many turtles are in the set? 2
What is this number called?
numerator
3. Write the fraction. $\frac{2}{5}$ ← Numerator ← Denominator

GO ON

Lesson 5-1 Parts of a Whole and Parts of a Set 183

Additional Example 1

Write a fraction that represents the shaded region of the rectangle.

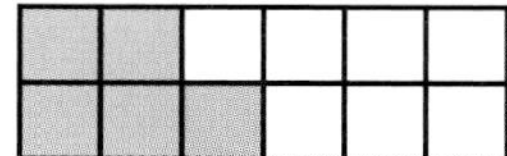

1. Twelve equal parts make up the whole. This number is the denominator.
2. Five parts are shaded. This number is the numerator.
3. Write the fraction, numerator over denominator. $\frac{5}{12}$

Additional Example 2

Write a fraction to represent the number of bananas in the set.

1. There are 5 pieces of fruit in the set. 5 is the denominator.
2. There are 2 bananas in the set.
2 is the numerator.
3. Write the fraction. $\frac{2}{5}$

Intervention Strategy — Naturalist Learners

Nature's Fractions

1. Have students work in small groups.
2. Walk around the school building. Tell students to find at least four representations of fractions. Examples may include types of trees, flowers or bushes, sizes of pebbles or leaves, and colors of birds.
3. Instruct each group to write their examples down. For instance, they might write "two of the five rose bushes have white roses." Tell them to include the fraction.
4. Have each group present one or two of their findings to the rest of the class. Discuss what is the whole or the set and what the part is.

Math Coach Notes

Money The optimal introductory fraction model is money. Introduce fractions as decomposition or partition, i.e., a collection of objects in equal groups. A dime decomposes to 10 pennies, a nickel to 5 pennies, a quarter into 5 nickels, and so on. In these examples, the importance of the *whole* and what the whole unit is in each case, the dime, the nickel, the quarter, and so on, is spotlighted.

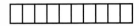

3 Practice

Using Manipulatives

Fraction Tiles When presenting Example 1, use fraction tiles. Using the tenths fraction tile, have students count off tenths until they arrive at three-tenths. Remind them that the entire bar is the whole, (the denominator), and the 3 shaded parts is the part (the numerator).

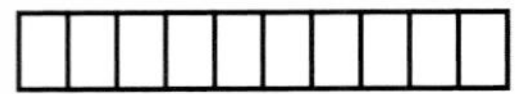

Base-Ten Blocks When using base-ten blocks, alternate between using units and rods so students will see that 3 rods out of 10 rods represents the same fraction as 3 units out of 10 units.

On-Hand Manipulatives When presenting fractions, use money. In Example 1, illustrate how one dollar can be divided or partitioned into 10 dimes, or one dime is equal to 10 pennies.

Math Coach Notes

Strategies

1. Have students begin the lesson making and naming fraction bars. Use the bars throughout the lesson as concrete examples. Have students write the fractions on the bars and say them aloud.
2. The optimum way for students to learn fractions is to use multiple concrete models, manipulatives, and pictorial representations. Have students use both parts of a set and parts of a whole to represent the same fraction. Drill students repeatedly by asking what is the whole, or the denominator, and what is the part, or the numerator.
3. Use real-world examples so students will connect fractions outside of math class. For instance, there are 24 students, 3 of whom have red hair; and there are 7 books, 2 that are hard back. Have students name fractions that represent these real-world examples.

Who is Correct?

Write a fraction to represent the number of Xs in the set.

T X X T X T X X T

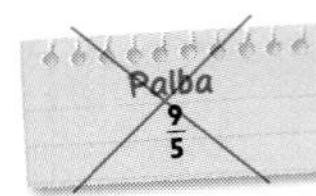

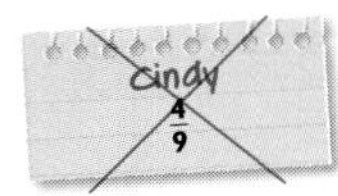

Circle correct answer(s). Cross out incorrect answer(s).

Guided Practice

Write a fraction to represent each situation.

1. the shaded region of the square

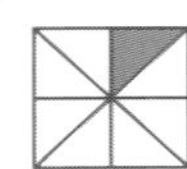

$\frac{\text{number of shaded parts}}{\text{number of equal parts}} = \frac{1}{8}$

2. the number of suns in the set

  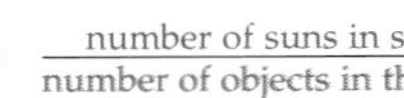 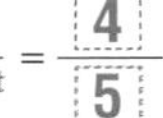

$\frac{\text{number of suns in set}}{\text{number of objects in the set}} = \frac{4}{5}$

3. Draw a picture to model the fraction $\frac{2}{3}$. Use equal parts of a whole.

Draw a figure. Divide it into 3 equal parts. Shade 2 parts.

$\frac{2}{3} = \frac{\text{number of shaded parts}}{\text{number of equal parts}}$

184 **Chapter 5** Fractions

Who *is Correct?*

Diagnostic Teaching

- Palba wrote $\frac{9}{5}$. This is incorrect. She switched the numerator and denominator.
- Cindy wrote $\frac{4}{9}$. This is incorrect because there are 5 Xs, not 4.
- Terrell wrote $\frac{5}{9}$. This is correct because there are 9 figures and 5 Xs.

Step by Step Practice

4 Write a fraction to represent the number of students in the group with their arms raised.

Step 1 Count to find the denominator.

5 people make up the whole group.

Step 2 Count to find the numerator.

4 people have their arms raised.

Step 3 Write the fraction. $\frac{\text{numerator}}{\text{denominator}} = \frac{4}{5}$

Draw a picture to model the fraction. Use equal parts of a whole.

5 $\frac{4}{7}$ 

Draw a whole with 7 equal parts.

Shade 4 parts.

Draw a picture to model the fraction. Use a set of objects.

6 $\frac{3}{4}$ 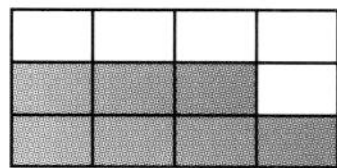

Write a fraction to represent each situation.

7 What fraction represents the shaded part of the rectangle? $\frac{7}{12}$

8 What fraction of the set of balls are the footballs? $\frac{3}{11}$

9 What fraction of the set of balls are neither baseballs nor footballs? $\frac{6}{11}$

Common Error Alert

Multi-Step Problem If a student is unable to draw a model for Exercise 5, he or she may not understand how a fraction represents part of a set. Begin with color counters and lay 7 on the table. Ask: How many counters are in the set of counters? Then turn one over to another color. How many are a different color in the set? Three out of seven is $\frac{3}{7}$. Continue until all the counters are the second color, naming, writing, and reading the fraction for each.

Note This!

Connections Instruct students to draw the diagrams and models in their notes, and clearly write the fraction the drawing represents. Sometimes students try to conserve paper by taking "abbreviated" notes, but then miss crucial information that would help them connect to the concept. If necessary, have a stack of note paper available in class at all times for student use.

Are They Getting It?

Check students' understanding of fractions by writing these problems on the board. Ask students to point out wrong answers. Tell them to use a number line or another visual aid to show why the answers are correct or incorrect.

1. The fraction $\frac{3}{8}$ represents the number of 1s in the set.
   1, 5, 3, 1, 4, 6, 1, 5 This is correct. There are 8 numbers and 3 numbers are ones.

2. The fraction $\frac{1}{5}$ represents the shaded part.
   This is incorrect. The bar is divided into sixths, not fifths.

3. There are 5 pencils and 6 pens. The fraction $\frac{5}{6}$ represents the number of pencils to the total number in the set. This is incorrect. The fraction $\frac{5}{11}$ represents the number of pencils in the set.

Common Error *Alert*

Identify Key Words If a student struggles with the word problems, he or she may have difficulty visualizing what fraction the words represent. Encourage these students to break the problem down, underline or highlight key words, and always draw a model or picture. For instance, in Exercise 11, ask the student to rephrase each sentence. Point out that the key words are "not blue." Have the student draw jackets, or just circles, and color 2 of them blue; 1, red; and 4, green.

Math Coach Notes

Graphic Organizers Most students benefit from visual or graphic organizers. One example is a sequence map. A sequence map for writing a fraction to represent a model might look like this.

1. The number in the set or the number of equal parts is the denominator.

↓

2. The part being considered or the part that is shaded is the numerator.

→

3. Write $\frac{\text{numerator}}{\text{denominator}}$

Step by Step Problem-Solving Practice

Problem-Solving Strategies
- ☑ Draw a picture.
- ☐ Look for a pattern.
- ☐ Guess and check.
- ☐ Act it out.
- ☐ Work backward.

Solve.

10 SNACKS Amber brought cookies to her after-school meeting. She gave 5 friends 1 cookie each. She had 2 cookies left. What fraction of the cookies were left?

Understand Read the problem. Write what you know.
Five friends received __1__ cookie each.
There are __2__ cookies left.

Plan Pick a strategy. One strategy is to draw a picture. Draw a circle to represent the cookie that each friend received. Draw 2 shaded circles to represent the cookies that were left.

Solve Count the total number of circles. This is the number for the whole. It is the __denominator__ of the fraction.

There are 2 cookies left. This is the number for the part. It is the __numerator__ of the fraction.

$$\frac{\text{part}}{\text{whole}} = \frac{\text{numerator}}{\text{denominator}} = \frac{2}{7}$$

Check Look at the numbers in the problem. Does the solution answer the question? Is it reasonable?

11 ONLINE SHOPPING Leon's family ordered jackets online. Two jackets were blue, one was red, and four were green. What fraction of the jackets ordered were not blue?
Check off each step.

- __✔__ Understand: I circled key words.
- __✔__ Plan: To solve the problem, I will __draw a picture__.
- __✔__ Solve: The answer is __$\frac{5}{7}$__.
- __✔__ Check: I checked my answer by __looking back to see if my answer was reasonable__.

12 SCHOOL For a school party, Mr. Gomez brought 24 fruit bars. His 19 students ate 1 bar each. What fraction of the fruit bars were eaten? __$\frac{19 \text{ fruit bars eaten}}{24}$__

186 Chapter 5 Fractions

Intervention Strategy

Visual/ Auditory Learners

Fraction Bar Kit

1. Hand out fraction bar sheets. Have students cut, fold, and label to twelfths.
2. Write a fraction on the board and then state it out loud. Tell students to represent the fraction by shading the correct fraction bar. Share results. Repeat several times.
3. Now write a word phrase, such as, "two of the five students are girls." Have students represent the fraction by shading. Share results. Repeat several times, saying the phrase out loud as you write it on the board.
4. Now hand out grid paper. Show students how to represent fractions using squares of the grid. Use this as an opportunity to have larger numbers or an odd number of squares to represent the whole.
5. After students have used the grid paper to represent fractions, have students form pairs. Tell them to pose fractions to one another. Then have them use the grid paper to represent the fraction.

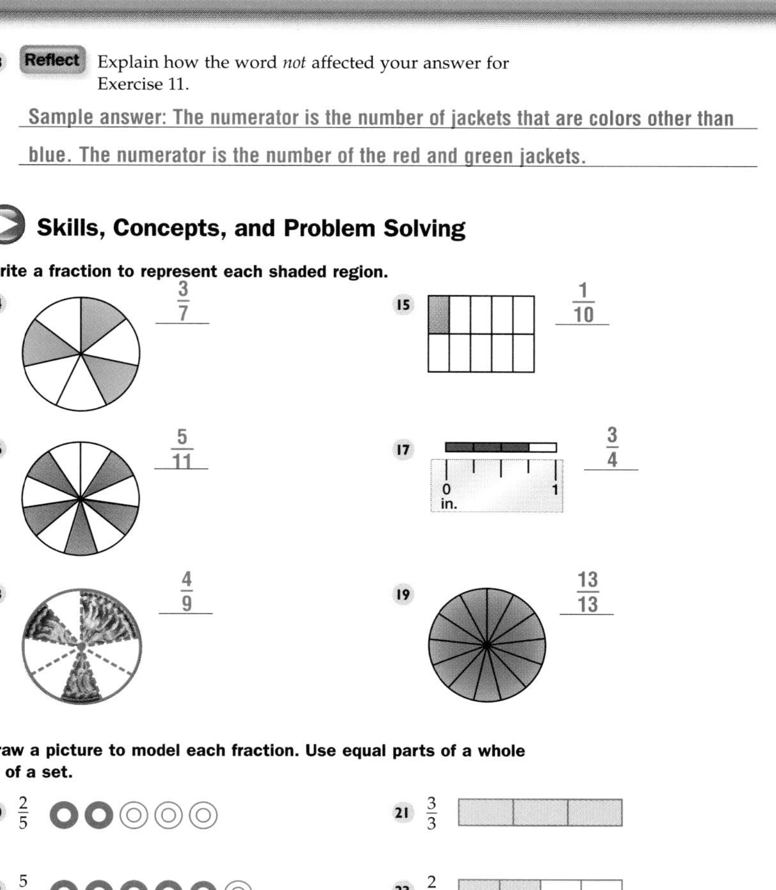

13 Reflect Explain how the word *not* affected your answer for Exercise 11.
Sample answer: The numerator is the number of jackets that are colors other than blue. The numerator is the number of the red and green jackets.
Skills, Concepts, and Problem Solving
Write a fraction to represent each shaded region.
14 3/7
15 1/10
16 5/11
17 3/4
0
in.
1
18 4/9
19 13/13
Draw a picture to model each fraction. Use equal parts of a whole or of a set.
20 2/5
21 3/3
22 5/6
23 2/4
24 Draw two pictures to model the fraction 4/5. Use equal parts of a whole for one picture and parts of a set for the other picture.
GO ON
Lesson 5-1 Parts of a Whole and Parts of a Set 187

Math Challenge

Model Random Fractions Give each student a set of fraction circles and two number cubes. One number cube is numbered from 0 to 5 and will represent the part. The other is numbered from 5 to 10 and will represent the whole.

Working in pairs, each student will roll a cube. Tell them to roll again if a 0 comes up. Whoever first represents the fraction correctly using the fraction circles gets the point.

Odd/Even Assignments

Exercises 14–28 are structured so that students practice the same concepts whether they are assigned the odd or even problems.

In-Class Assignment

Have students complete Exercises 18, 23, 25, and 31 to ensure that they understand the concept.

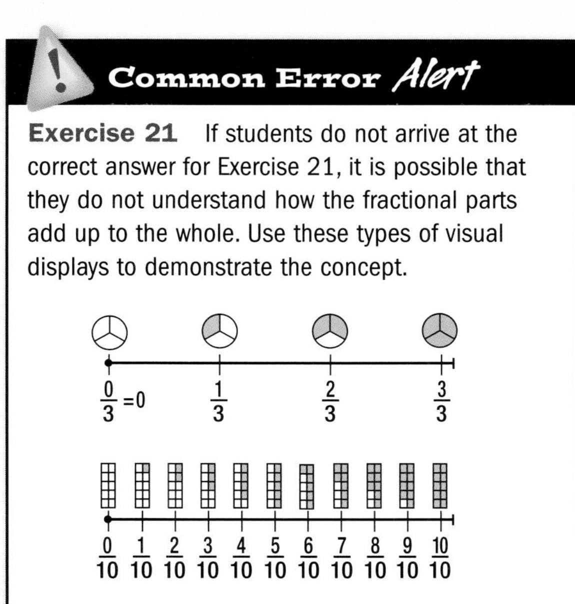

Common Error Alert
Exercise 21 If students do not arrive at the correct answer for Exercise 21, it is possible that they do not understand how the fractional parts add up to the whole. Use these types of visual displays to demonstrate the concept.
0/3 = 0
1/3
2/3
3/3
0/10 1/10 2/10 3/10 4/10 5/10 6/10 7/10 8/10 9/10 10/10

See It, Do It, Say It, Write It

Step 1 Write several fractions on the board. Model how to represent them with drawings or models.

Step 2 Ask students to draw a number line on paper. Give them a fraction to represent on the number line. Share solutions in a class discussion.

Step 3 Have students work in pairs. Write a fraction on the board. Tell students to write a word phrase to represent the fraction. Model first. For example, $\frac{13}{16}$ might be "thirteen out of sixteen students finished all their homework." Have students share their work with the class. Repeat several times.

Step 4 Have students work alone. Tell them to write what a fraction is. Tell them to include a picture or a model.

Looking Ahead:

Equivalent Fractions and Equivalent Forms of One In the next lesson, students will learn about equivalent fractions and equivalent forms of one.

Example

Fill in the model to represent the same fraction.

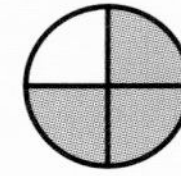 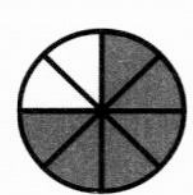

$\frac{3}{4} = \frac{?}{8}$ 6

What can you multiply the denominator 4 by to get 8? 2

Multiply 4 by 2 to get 8. So multiply the fraction by $\frac{2}{2}$, an equivalent form of one.

$\frac{3}{4} = \frac{3 \times 2}{4 \times 2} = \frac{6}{8}$ So, $\frac{3}{4} = \frac{6}{8}$

Find equivalent fractions. Use models if needed.

1. $\frac{1}{3}$ $\frac{3}{9}$ **2.** $\frac{4}{5}$ $\frac{8}{10}$ **3.** $\frac{7}{10}$ $\frac{14}{20}$

Solve.

25 SHOPPING Rafael had a $100 gift certificate. He spent $41 on shoes and $32 on pants. What fraction of the gift certificate did he use? $\frac{73}{100}$

26 WORDS What fraction of the letters in *Triumphs* are consonants? $\frac{6}{8}$

27 SCHOOL Lakesha's score on her math exam is shown at the right. What fraction of the questions did she answer incorrectly? $\frac{2}{25}$

23 out of 25 correct!

28 PETS My friend told me that of her dog's 5 puppies, $\frac{2}{5}$ are females. How many female puppies are there? 2
How many puppies are there altogether? 5

Vocabulary Check **Write the vocabulary word that completes each sentence.**

29 In a fraction, the top number is the numerator, and the bottom number is the denominator.

30 The whole is an entire amount or object.

31 Writing in Math In your own words, describe what the numerator and denominator of a fraction represent. Be sure to use the words *numerator* and *denominator*.

Answers will vary. Sample answer: The numerator is the top number in a fraction. It is part of a whole. The denominator is the bottom number in a fraction. It is the whole.

Draw a picture to model each fraction. Use equal parts of a whole or of a set.

32 $\frac{2}{5}$ **33** $\frac{4}{4}$ **34** $\frac{3}{8}$

STOP

188 Chapter 5 Fractions

Ticket Out the Door

Different Representations Hand out a fraction strip with some number of parts shaded to student pairs. Tell students to represent their fraction in four ways. First, they will write their fraction using a numerator and a denominator. Then they will write an example using only words. Next, they will use two types of models to represent the fraction. They will draw a picture of their models on their papers. Students cannot use a fraction strip as one of their models, and they must use parts of a set for one model.

Student volunteers can present their findings. Have them hand in their papers as they exit the classroom.

Lesson 5-2 Equivalent Fractions and Equivalent Forms of One

KEY Concept

Equivalent fractions are fractions that have the same **value**.

1 unit

$\frac{1}{2}$

$\frac{1}{2}$ is equivalent to $\frac{2}{4}$.

$\frac{1}{4}$

$\frac{2}{4}$ is equivalent to $\frac{3}{6}$.

$\frac{1}{6}$

$\frac{3}{6}$ is equivalent to $\frac{4}{8}$.

$\frac{1}{8}$

$\frac{4}{8}$ is equivalent to $\frac{6}{12}$.

$\frac{1}{12}$

So, $\frac{1}{2} = \frac{2}{4} = \frac{3}{6} = \frac{4}{8} = \frac{6}{12}$.

An **equivalent form of one** is any nonzero number divided by itself. Put another way, it is a fraction that equals 1.

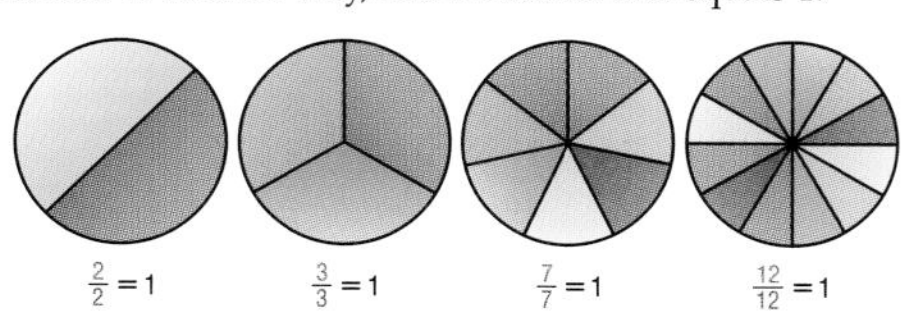

$\frac{2}{2} = 1$ $\frac{3}{3} = 1$ $\frac{7}{7} = 1$ $\frac{12}{12} = 1$

Remember that any number multiplied by 1 or divided by 1 is equal to itself. The Identity Property of Multiplication states $4 \times 1 = 4$. So, $\frac{3}{4} \times 1 = \frac{3}{4}$. You can replace 1 with a fraction that represents 1 such as $\frac{2}{2}$.

$$\frac{3}{4} \times 1 = \frac{3}{4} \rightarrow \frac{3}{4} \times \frac{2}{2} = \frac{6}{8}$$

So, $\frac{3}{4} = \frac{6}{8}$

VOCABULARY

equivalent forms of one
different expressions that represent the whole number 1
Example: $\frac{2}{2}, \frac{3}{3}, \frac{4}{4}$

equivalent fractions
fractions that represent the same number
Example: $\frac{3}{4} = \frac{6}{8}$

Identity Property of Multiplication
when multiplying a number by 1, the product is the same as the given number
Example: $8 \times 1 = 8 = 1 \times 8$

value
the amount of a number

You can name an endless number of fractions that are equivalent to any fraction.

Intervention Strategy

Kinesthetic/ Visual Learners

Fraction Circles If students are having difficulty with equivalents of 1, use fraction circles. Have students model fractions, such as $\frac{1}{6}$ and $\frac{4}{6}$. Then have them model $\frac{6}{6}$. How much does $\frac{6}{6}$ represent? one whole

Lesson Notes

Lesson 5-2

Lesson Planner

Objective Write equivalent fractions using equivalent forms of one.

Vocabulary **equivalent forms of one, equivalent fractions, Identity Property of Multiplication, value**

Materials/Manipulatives everyday objects, fraction bar kit, fraction circles, fraction tiles, two-color counters

Chapter Resource Masters

- CRM Vocabulary and English Language Development (p. A100)
- CRM Skills Practice (p. A101)
- CRM Problem-Solving Practice (p. A102)
- CRM Homework Practice (p. A103)

1 Introduce

Vocabulary

Fractions Vocabulary Hand out sheets for students to make and name fraction bars. Call on students to name *equivalent fractions* for each *fraction*.

2 Teach

Key Concept

Foundational Skills and Concepts After students have read through the Key Concept box, have them try these exercises.

1. What do $\frac{2}{2}, \frac{3}{3}, \frac{7}{7}$, and $\frac{12}{12}$ have in common? They all are equal to one.
2. Explain why a number over the same number in a fraction is equivalent to 1. A fraction is a division problem, and a number divided by the same number is 1.

Additional **Example 1**

Complete the models to name an equivalent fraction.

$\frac{3}{4} = \frac{\square}{8}$

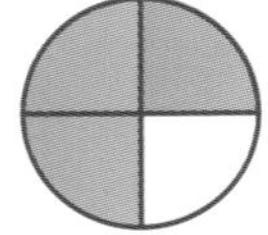

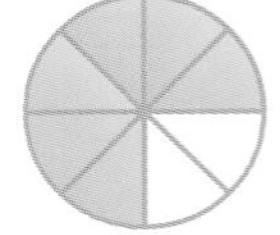

1. Use the denominator to find an equivalent fraction. $4 \times 2 = 8$

2. Multiply the fraction $\frac{3}{4}$ by an equivalent form of one.

$\frac{3}{4} = \frac{3 \times 2}{4 \times 2} = \frac{6}{8}$

So, $\frac{3}{4} = \frac{6}{8}$.

Additional **Example 2**

Name two fractions equivalent to $\frac{2}{5}$.

1. Multiply the original fraction by an equivalent form of one, such as $\frac{2}{2}$.

$\frac{2}{5} = \frac{2 \times 2}{5 \times 2} = \frac{4}{10}$

2. Multiply the original fraction by another equivalent form of one, such as $\frac{4}{4}$.

$\frac{2}{5} = \frac{2 \times 4}{5 \times 4} = \frac{8}{20}$

So, $\frac{2}{5} = \frac{4}{10}$ and $\frac{2}{5} = \frac{8}{20}$.

Example 1

Complete the models to name an equivalent fraction.

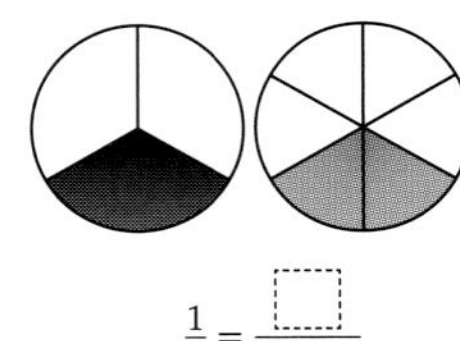

$\frac{1}{3} = \frac{\square}{6}$

1. Use the denominator to find an equivalent fraction. $3 \times 2 = 6$
2. Multiply the fraction $\frac{1}{3}$ by an equivalent form of one.

$\frac{1}{3} = \frac{1 \times 2}{3 \times 2} = \frac{2}{6}$ So, $\frac{1}{3} = \frac{2}{6}$.

YOUR TURN!

Complete the models to name an equivalent fraction.

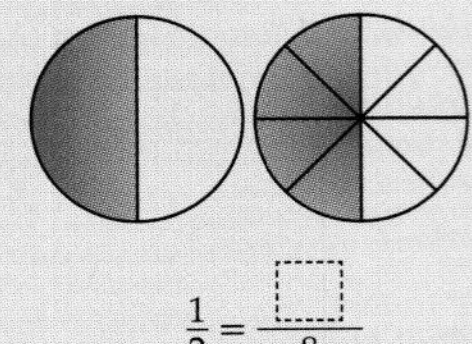

$\frac{1}{2} = \frac{\square}{8}$

1. Use the denominator to find an equivalent fraction. $2 \times \underline{4} = 8$
2. What fraction should you multiply $\frac{1}{2}$ by to get an equivalent fraction? $\underline{\frac{4}{4}}$

$\frac{1}{2} = \frac{1 \times 4}{2 \times 4} = \frac{4}{8}$ So, $\frac{1}{2} = \frac{4}{8}$.

Example 2

Name two fractions equivalent to $\frac{6}{8}$.

1. Multiply the original fraction by an equivalent form of one, such as $\frac{2}{2}$.

$\frac{6}{8} = \frac{6 \times 2}{8 \times 2} = \frac{12}{16}$

2. Multiply the original fraction by another equivalent form of one, such as $\frac{3}{3}$.

$\frac{6}{8} = \frac{6 \times 3}{8 \times 3} = \frac{18}{24}$

So, $\frac{6}{8} = \frac{12}{16}$ and $\frac{6}{8} = \frac{18}{24}$.

YOUR TURN!

Name two fractions equivalent to $\frac{8}{10}$.

1. Multiply the original fraction by an equivalent form of one.

$\frac{8}{10} = \frac{8 \times 2}{10 \times 2} = \frac{16}{20}$

2. Multiply the original fraction by another equivalent form of one.

$\frac{8}{10} = \frac{8 \times 3}{10 \times 3} = \frac{24}{30}$ Answers will vary.

So, $\frac{8}{10} = \frac{16}{20}$ and $\frac{8}{10} = \frac{24}{30}$.

GO ON

190 **Chapter 5** Fractions

Intervention Strategy Visual/Logical Learners

Build a Fraction Wall Have students work in small groups to create a fraction wall. Have them start by drawing one fraction bar and labeling it "One Whole." Then have them create bars underneath that are divided into halves, thirds, fourths, and so on. This will help them visualize the equivalent forms of one.

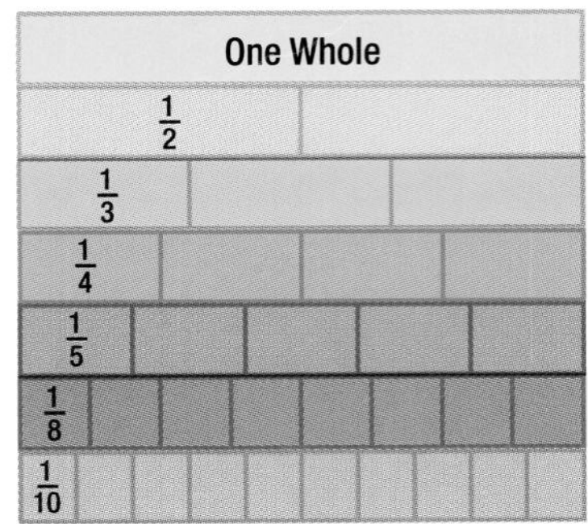

Who is Correct?

Write an equivalent fraction for $\frac{10}{15}$.

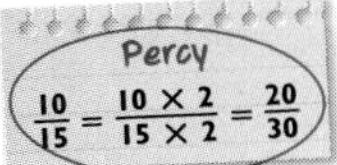

Percy
$\frac{10}{15} = \frac{10 \times 2}{15 \times 2} = \frac{20}{30}$

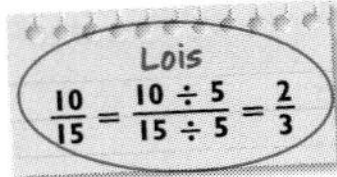

Felice
$\frac{10}{15} = \frac{10 \times 10}{15 \times 15} = \frac{100}{225}$

Circle correct answer(s). Cross out incorrect answer(s).

Guided Practice

1 Complete the models to name an equivalent fraction. $\frac{1}{4} = \frac{2}{8}$

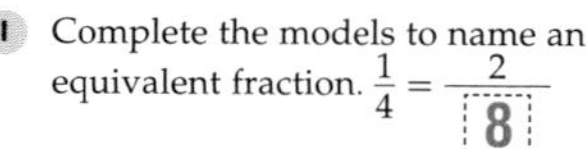

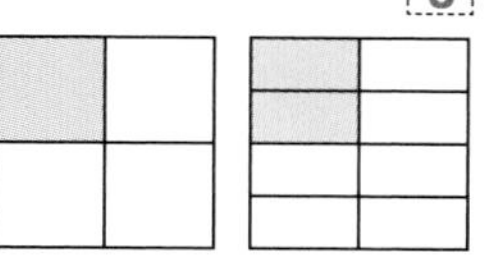

2 Complete the models to name two fractions equivalent to $\frac{4}{6}$. $\frac{2}{3}$ $\frac{8}{12}$

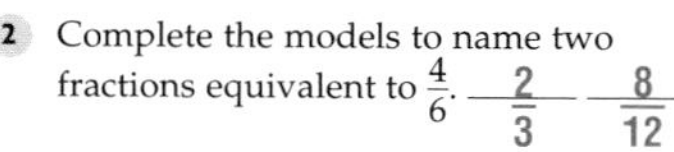

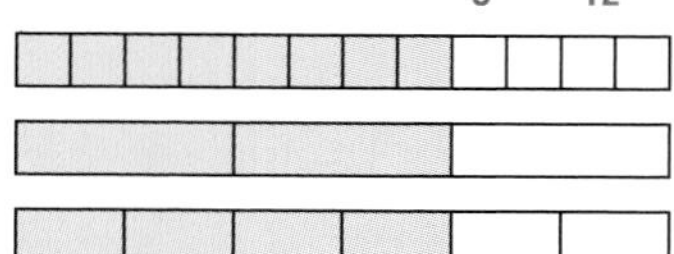

3 This circle shows $\frac{1}{4}$ shaded.

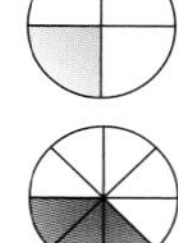

Which fractional part equals $\frac{1}{4}$? Circle Three

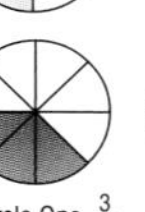

Circle One $\frac{3}{8}$ Circle Two $\frac{2}{6}$ Circle Three $\frac{2}{8}$

Step by Step Practice

4 Name a fraction equivalent to $\frac{8}{10}$.

Step 1 Choose an equivalent form of one by which to multiply.

Step 2 Multiply the numerators and denominators.

$$\frac{8}{10} = \frac{8 \times 3}{10 \times 3} = \frac{24}{30}$$

Who is Correct?

Diagnostic Teaching

- Percy is correct. He multiplied both the numerator and the denominator by 2.
- Lois is correct. She divided both the numerator and the denominator by 5.
- Felice is incorrect. She did not multiply by an equivalent form of one.

Remind students to use equivalent forms of one and either multiply or divide to find equivalent fractions.

3 Practice

Using Manipulatives

Models Use fraction circles, fraction tiles, and drawings to represent fractions. Ask: What is an *equivalent form of one?* Have students multiply the equivalent form of one with the fraction to find the *equivalent fraction.*

Nonexamples Use the manipulatives to model fractions that are not equivalent forms of one. Have students give examples of non-equivalent fractions.

On-Hand Manipulatives Use objects like paper circles or bars, granola bars, pizzas, or pancakes to show students how these objects can be divided into fractional parts that all together form a whole.

Note This!

Review for Questions Tell students to review their notes as soon as they can after a class. At the beginning of each class, ask students what questions they found when reviewing their notes. This will ensure that they are reviewing their notes regularly, as well as correcting any misconceptions or misunderstandings.

Common Error *Alert*

Multi-Step Problem If a student is unable to draw a model for Exercise 9, he or she may not understand how equivalent fractions equal the same amount. Begin with fraction circles and show examples of equivalent fractions. Ask: Are the fractions equivalent? Have the student place the equivalent fractions on top of each other. Ask: Are the diagrams exactly the same size? Continue with other equivalent fractions.

Math Coach Notes

Strategies

1. Have students begin the lesson by practicing simplifying fractions. Use fraction circles throughout the lesson as concrete examples. Have students write the fractions using the fraction circles and simplify.
2. The optimum way for students to learn fraction equivalents is to use multiple concrete models, manipulatives, and pictorial representations. Have students use two different fraction equivalents to represent the same fraction. Drill students repeatedly by asking whether the fractions are equivalent and in the simplest form.
3. Use real-world examples so students will connect fractions outside of math class. Have students name fractions that represent these examples.

Complete to name an equivalent fraction.

5 $\frac{2}{3} = \frac{6}{\square}$ $\frac{2}{3} \times \frac{3}{3} = \frac{6}{9}$

6 $\frac{4}{6} = \frac{12}{18}$

7 $\frac{1}{2} = \frac{8}{16}$

8 $\frac{2}{3} = \frac{12}{18}$

Step by Step Problem-Solving Practice

Problem-Solving Strategies
- ☑ Draw a diagram.
- ☐ Look for a pattern.
- ☐ Guess and check.
- ☐ Solve a simpler problem.
- ☐ Work backward.

Solve.

9 NUTRITION Taneesha and David each ate the same amount of their own pizzas. David ate $\frac{4}{6}$ of his pizza. If Taneesha's pizza is divided into 12 equal pieces, how much did Taneesha eat?

Understand Read the problem. Write what you know. David ate $\frac{4}{6}$ of his pizza. Taneesha ate an equal amount.

Plan Pick a strategy. One strategy is to draw a picture. Draw 6 equal parts. Shade 4 to show $\frac{4}{6}$.

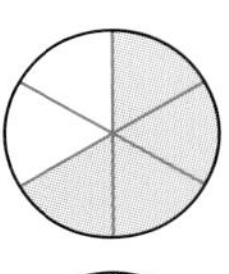

Draw another figure with twice as many parts. Shade to equal $\frac{4}{6}$.

Solve Count the total parts and the shaded parts of the second figure.

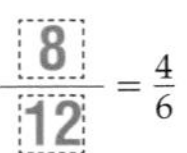

$\frac{8}{12} = \frac{4}{6}$

Taneesha ate $\frac{8}{12}$ of her pizza.

Check Does the answer make sense?

GO ON

Are They Getting It?

Check students' understanding of equivalent fractions by writing these problems on the board. Have students explain the incorrect information in each problem. Tell them to use a fraction circle or another visual aid to show why the answers are correct, or are not correct.

Name two equivalent fractions.

1. $\frac{18}{27}$ Sample answer: $\frac{6}{9}; \frac{2}{3}$ This is correct.
2. $\frac{9}{12}$ Sample answer: $\frac{6}{9}; \frac{3}{4}$ This is incorrect. The first fraction is not equivalent.
3. $\frac{10}{14}$ Sample answer: $\frac{20}{28}; \frac{5}{7}$ This is correct.

10 FOOD Sharon's dad baked two same-sized pans of brownies for Sharon's birthday party. One pan is cut into 12 equal pieces. The other pan is cut into 36 equal pieces. How many pieces from the 36 pieces pan equal one serving of the 12 pieces pan? Check off each step.

✓ Understand: I circled key words.

✓ Plan: To solve the problem, I will draw a diagram.

✓ Solve: The answer is 3 pieces.

✓ Check: I checked my answer by multiplying $\frac{1}{12}$ by $\frac{3}{3}$.

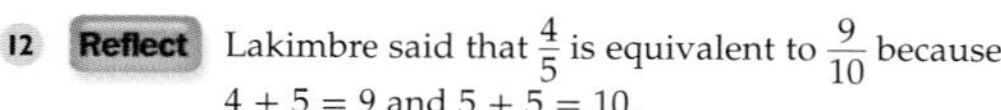

11 KITES Thomas receives $\frac{5}{9}$ of a 100-foot kite string. Jordan receives $\frac{2}{3}$ of a different 100-foot string. Did they receive the same amounts of string? Explain.

No, Jordan received more because when Jordan's fraction is rewritten with 9 in the denominator, the numerator is 6.

12 **Reflect** Lakimbre said that $\frac{4}{5}$ is equivalent to $\frac{9}{10}$ because $4 + 5 = 9$ and $5 + 5 = 10$.

Explain what was incorrect in Lakimbre's thinking. Be sure to use the terms *numerator* and *denominator* in your explanation.

See margin.

Skills, Concepts, and Problem Solving

Complete each model to name an equivalent fraction.

13 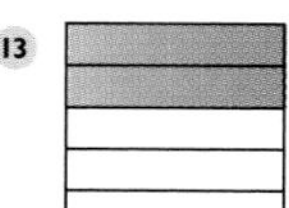 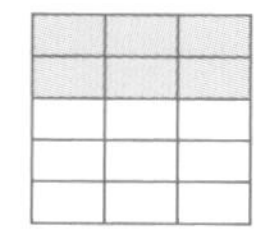 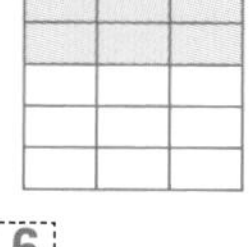 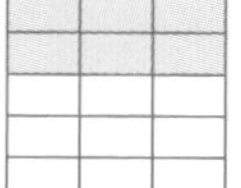

$\frac{2}{5} = \frac{6}{15}$

14  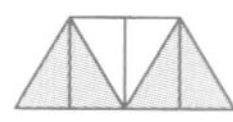

$\frac{2}{3} = \frac{4}{6}$

Intervention Strategy — Visual/Kinesthetic Learners

Materials: Fraction-Bar Kit

1. Hand out fraction-bar sheets. Have students cut, fold, and label the bars to twelfths.
2. Write a fraction on the board. Tell students to use their bars to find equivalent fractions. For instance, write $\frac{2}{3}$ on the board. Ask a student to model the fraction. Then have the student place other fraction bars on the model of $\frac{2}{3}$. What other fraction parts fit on the model exactly? Repeat with other fractions.
3. Equivalent fractions can also be visualized using grid paper. Ask students to make a 4×7 array. Tell them to shade in 14 of the squares. What is the fraction? Now write $\frac{14}{28} = \frac{\square}{4}$ on the board. Have students fill in the numerator. Repeat with other fractions.

Common Error *Alert*

Exercise 12 If students are having difficulty determining if two fractions are equivalent, have them cross multiply and compare the products.

$$\frac{4}{5} \times \frac{9}{10}$$

$$4 \times 10 = 5 \times 9$$

$$40 \neq 45$$

Additional Answer

Exercise 12 Answers will vary. Sample answer: To find an equivalent fraction, multiply by any fraction equal to one. Lakimbre added instead of multiplying, and his method of adding was also incorrect. In this case, Lakimbre should multiply both the numerator and the denominator by 5.

$$\frac{4}{5} \times \frac{5}{5} = \frac{20}{25}$$

The fraction $\frac{4}{5}$ is equivalent to $\frac{20}{25}$. Other equivalent fractions are $\frac{8}{10}, \frac{12}{15}, \frac{16}{20}, \frac{24}{30}, \frac{28}{35}, \frac{32}{40}, \frac{36}{45}$, and $\frac{40}{50}$.

Odd/Even Assignments

Exercises 13–25 are structured so that students practice the same concepts whether they are assigned the odd or even problems.

In-Class Assignment

Have students complete Exercises 14, 16, 21, 23, and 28 to ensure that they understand the concept.

Intervention Strategy

Interpersonal/ Visual Learners

Represent Fractions

1. Have students work in pairs or alone.
2. Each pair should have an ample supply of two-colored counters. Ask students to represent a fraction using the counters. This would be done by placing 3 counters of one color over 4 counters of another color.

3. Tell students to use this model to form equivalent fractions to $\frac{3}{4}$. To do this, they will make another fraction with the same number and color of counters and place it alongside their first model.

4. Have each pair write down the fractions they make. Discuss the results. Then repeat with other fractions.

Math Coach Notes

Study Tip Encourage visual learners to draw pictures of equivalent fractions in their notes. These students may also benefit from making fraction bars or fraction circles and using them at home when they study.

Complete to name an equivalent fraction.

15 $\frac{1}{11} = \frac{5}{55}$

16 $\frac{6}{7} = \frac{12}{14}$

Name two equivalent fractions for each fraction.

17 $\frac{1}{2}$ Sample answer: $\frac{6}{12}$; $\frac{18}{36}$

18 $\frac{2}{3}$ Sample answer: $\frac{4}{6}$; $\frac{6}{9}$

19 $\frac{3}{5}$ Sample answer: $\frac{6}{10}$; $\frac{9}{15}$

20 $\frac{5}{7}$ Sample answer: $\frac{10}{14}$; $\frac{15}{21}$

21 $\frac{3}{4}$ Sample answer: $\frac{6}{8}$; $\frac{9}{12}$

22 $\frac{1}{10}$ Sample answer: $\frac{2}{20}$; $\frac{3}{30}$

Solve.

23 CONSTRUCTION Pam had two pieces of wood the same length. She cut the first piece into 6 equal parts. She cut the second piece into 12 equal parts. Suppose Pam uses 3 parts from the first piece of wood. How many parts from the second piece could Pam use to make an equal length?

6 parts

24 HOBBIES Tonya and Robert sewed same-sized quilts. Robert's quilt is made of 4 yellow pieces and 10 pieces altogether. Tonya's quilt is made of 20 pieces altogether. How many yellow pieces are in Tonya's quilt?

8 pieces

25 WHEELS Two bicycle wheels are shown at the right. One has 4 spokes. The other has 16. Shade an area on the second tire that is equivalent to the shaded area of the first.

Complete to show equivalent fractions that represent both wheels.

$\frac{1}{4} = \frac{4}{16}$

GO ON

Math Challenge

Circles and Cubes Give each student a set of fraction circles and two number cubes. One number cube is numbered from 1 to 6 and will represent the numerator of the fraction. The other is numbered from 7 to 12 and will represent the denominator of the fraction.

Working in pairs, each student will roll a cube. Have each student show with his or her fraction circles an equivalent fraction of the one made from the number cubes.

Vocabulary Check **Write the vocabulary word that completes each sentence.**

26 A(n) equivalent form of one is any nonzero number divided by itself.

27 Equivalent fractions are fractions that have the same value.

28 **Writing in Math** Write a letter to your friend Pia describing equivalent forms of one.

Answers will vary. Students should describe that equivalent forms of one are expressions that represent one; example $\frac{2}{2}, \frac{4}{4}, \frac{5}{5}$.

Spiral Review

Write a fraction to represent each situation. (Lesson 5-1, p. 182)

29 the number of hands showing five fingers up

$\frac{5}{8}$

30 the number of open mailboxes

$\frac{1}{4}$

31 the number of blue jerseys

$\frac{2}{5}$

32 the number of triangles

$\frac{4}{7}$

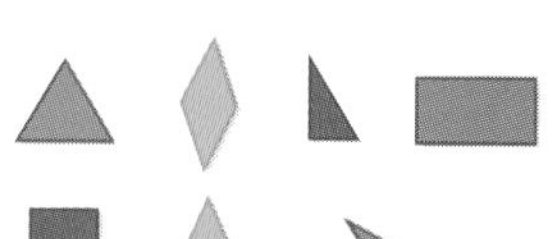

STOP

Ticket Out the Door

Equivalent Fractions Hand out a fraction written on an index card to each student. Each student should write four equivalent fractions. Students will hand in their papers as they exit the classroom.

See It, Do It, Say It, Write It

Step 1 Write a fraction on the board. Model how to represent an equivalent fraction with a drawing or model. Do this several times with different fractions.

Step 2 Ask students to draw a fraction circle on paper. Give them a fraction to represent. Repeat by having students draw other fractions. Share solutions in a class discussion.

Step 3 Have students work in pairs. Write a fraction on the board. Tell students to write an equivalent fraction to represent the fraction on the board. Have students share their work with the class. Repeat several times.

Step 4 Have students work alone. Tell them to write a definition of equivalent fraction, and tell them to include a picture or a model.

Looking Ahead: Pre-teach

Mixed Numbers and Improper Fractions In the next lesson, students will learn about mixed numbers and improper fractions.

Example

Write $2\frac{1}{3}$ as an improper fraction.

1. Find how many thirds are in 2. Multiply 2 by 3.

   $2 \times 3 = 6$

2. Add the number of thirds in the fraction. This is how many thirds are in the mixed fraction.

   $6 + 1 = 7$

3. Write the total number of thirds as an improper fraction.

   $2\frac{1}{3} = \frac{7}{3}$

Chapter 5 Progress Check 1

Formative Assessment

Use the Progress Check to assess students' mastery of the previous lessons. Have students review the lesson indicated for the problems they answered incorrectly.

Odd/Even Assignments

Exercises are structured so that students practice the same concepts whether they are assigned the odd or even problems.

Common Error *Alert*

Write-In Boxes If students are having difficulties identifying the fractions, provide them with a visual using boxes and have them fill in the missing numbers, such as:

$$\frac{\text{number of shaded parts}}{\text{number of total parts}} = \frac{\square}{\square}$$

Progress Check 1 (Lessons 5-1 and 5-2)

Write a fraction to represent each unshaded region.

1 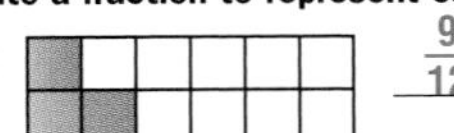 $\frac{9}{12}$

2 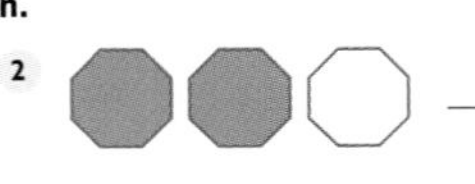 $\frac{1}{3}$

3 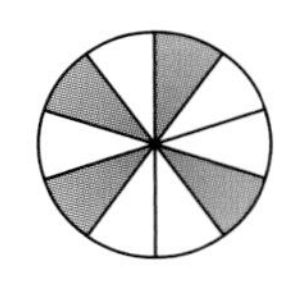 $\frac{6}{10}$

4 $\frac{5}{6}$

Draw a picture to model each fraction. Use equal parts of a whole or of a set.

5 $\frac{6}{7}$ Students should draw any whole divided into 7 equal parts with 6 shaded, or any set of 7 with 6 shaded.

6 $\frac{5}{5}$ Students should draw any whole divided into 5 equal parts with 5 shaded, or any set of 5 with 5 shaded.

Name two equivalent fractions.

7 $\frac{1}{3}$ Sample answer: $\frac{2}{6}$; $\frac{3}{9}$

8 $\frac{3}{4}$ Sample answer: $\frac{6}{8}$; $\frac{9}{12}$

9 $\frac{2}{5}$ Sample answer: $\frac{4}{10}$; $\frac{20}{50}$

10 $\frac{4}{11}$ Sample answer: $\frac{8}{22}$; $\frac{12}{33}$

11 Complete the model to name two fractions equivalent to $\frac{2}{3}$.
$\frac{4}{6}$, $\frac{6}{9}$

Solve.

12 **WORDS** What fraction of the letters in *Mississippi* are i's? $\frac{4}{11}$

13 **FITNESS** Nina swam the length of the pool 5 times. What fraction of her swim does one length represent?
$\frac{1}{5}$

196 Chapter 5 Fractions

Data-Driven Decision Making

Students missing Exercises . . .	Have trouble with . . .	Should review and practice . . .
1–4	writing a fraction from a model.	SSG Lesson 5-1, p. 182 CRM Skills Practice, p. A97
5–6	drawing a visual representation of a fraction.	SSG Lesson 5-1, p. 182 CRM Skills Practice, p. A97
7–10	naming equivalent fractions.	SSG Lesson 5-2, p. 189 CRM Skills Practice, p. A101
11	using a model to write equivalent fractions.	CRM Skills Practice, p. A101
12–13	writing a fraction from a word problem.	CRM Problem-Solving Practice, pp. A98 and A102

Mixed Numbers and Improper Fractions

KEY Concept

When the numerator of a fraction is greater than the denominator, it means you have more parts than the number of parts into which the whole was divided.

In other words, you have more parts than one whole.

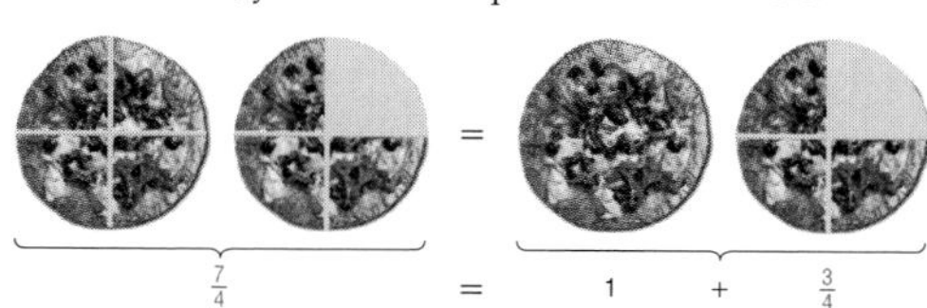

A fraction in which the numerator is greater than the denominator is called an **improper fraction.**

$\frac{7}{4}$ is an improper fraction.

You can see that $\frac{7}{4}$ of a pizza is the same as $1\frac{3}{4}$ pizzas. Both pizzas are divided into 4 parts. The denominator does not change. The number $1\frac{3}{4}$ is called a **mixed number.** It has a whole number part and a fraction part.

The values of the fractions to the right of 1 are greater than 1. These can be written as improper fractions or mixed numbers.

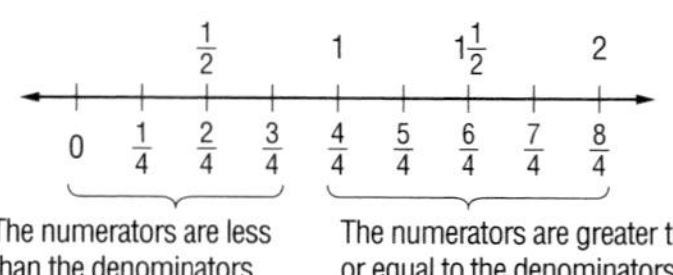

VOCABULARY

denominator
the number below the bar in a fraction that tells how many equal parts are in the whole or the set

improper fraction
a fraction with a numerator that is greater than or equal to the denominator
Examples: $\frac{17}{3}$, $\frac{5}{5}$

mixed number
a number that has a whole number part and a fraction part
Example:
$6\frac{1}{2}$ ← fraction
└ whole number

numerator
the number above the bar in a fraction that tells how many equal parts are being used

When solving a problem, you usually write your answer as a mixed number, not an improper fraction.

Intervention Strategy

Visual/ Kinesthetic Learners

Model Fractions If students are having difficulty with identifying improper fractions, tell them to draw fraction bar(s) to model the fractions. This will show them visually that the fraction is greater than 1.

Lesson Notes

Lesson 5-3

Lesson Planner

Objective Write mixed numbers as improper fractions and improper fractions as mixed numbers.

Vocabulary **denominator, improper fraction, mixed number, numerator**

Materials/Manipulatives everyday objects, fraction circles, fraction tiles, index cards

Chapter Resource Masters

- CRM Vocabulary and English Language Development (p. A104)
- CRM Skills Practice (p. A105)
- CRM Problem-Solving Practice (p. A106)
- CRM Homework Practice (p. A107)

Vocabulary

Examples Write an improper fraction and a mixed number that are equal on the board. Call on students to identify the *improper fraction* and the *mixed number.* Ask: What can you say about both values?

2 Teach

Key Concept

Foundational Skills and Concepts After students have read through the Key Concept box, have them try these exercises.

1. Can a mixed number and an improper fraction be equal? yes
2. What mixed number is equivalent to $\frac{7}{4}$? $1\frac{3}{4}$
3. How would you describe an improper fraction? a fraction with the numerator greater than the denominator

Additional **Example 1**

Change $2\frac{2}{3}$ to an improper fraction using drawings.

1. Model the mixed number using circles. The denominator tells how many parts in each whole.

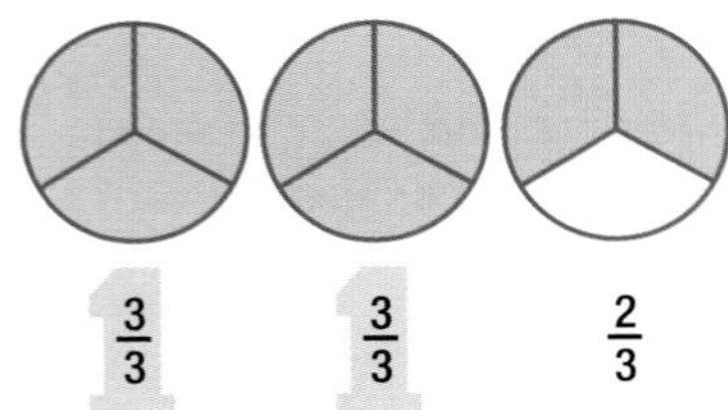

$$1 \quad \frac{3}{3} \qquad 1 \quad \frac{3}{3} \qquad \frac{2}{3}$$

2. Count the number of shaded thirds that make $2\frac{2}{3}$.
There are 8 shaded thirds in the model.
Write 8 thirds as $\frac{8}{3}$.

Additional **Example 2**

Change $\frac{9}{4}$ to a mixed number using fraction strips.

1. Model the improper fraction using strips. Mark four equal sections. Since the denominator is 4, each strip is divided into 4 parts.

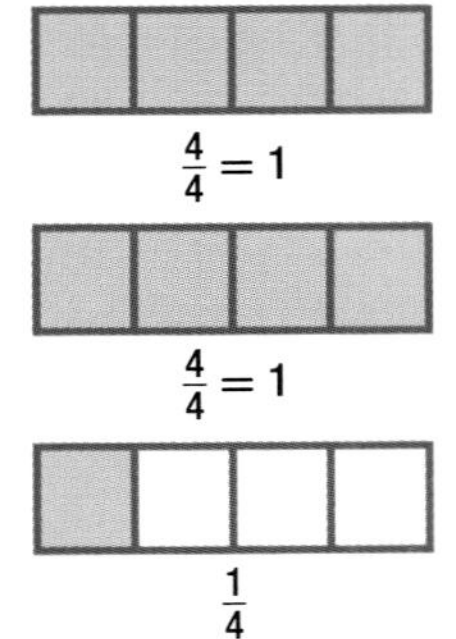

$\frac{4}{4} = 1$

$\frac{4}{4} = 1$

$\frac{1}{4}$

2. Write the whole number part of the mixed number. 2

3. Write the fraction part of the mixed number. $\frac{1}{4}$

4. Write the mixed number. $2\frac{1}{4}$

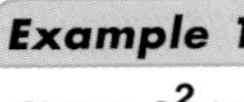

Example 1

Change $3\frac{2}{5}$ to an improper fraction using drawings.

1. Model the mixed number using circles. The denominator tells how many parts in each whole.

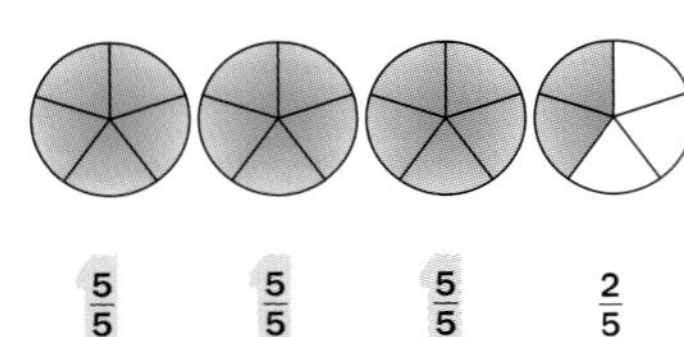

$$1 \ \frac{5}{5} \qquad 1 \ \frac{5}{5} \qquad 1 \ \frac{5}{5} \qquad \frac{2}{5}$$

2. Count the number of shaded fifths that make $3\frac{2}{5}$.
There are 17 shaded fifths in the model.
Write 17 fifths as $\frac{17}{5}$.

YOUR TURN!

Change $2\frac{3}{4}$ to an improper fraction using drawings.

1. Model the mixed number using circles.

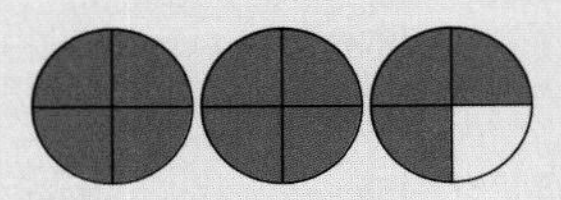

2. Count the number of fourths that make $2\frac{3}{4}$.
How many shaded fourths are in the model? $\frac{11}{4}$

Write $2\frac{3}{4}$ as an improper fraction. $\frac{11}{4}$

Example 2

Change $\frac{11}{3}$ to a mixed number using fraction strips.

1. Model the improper fraction using strips. Mark three equal sections. Since the denominator is 3, each strip is divided into 3 parts.

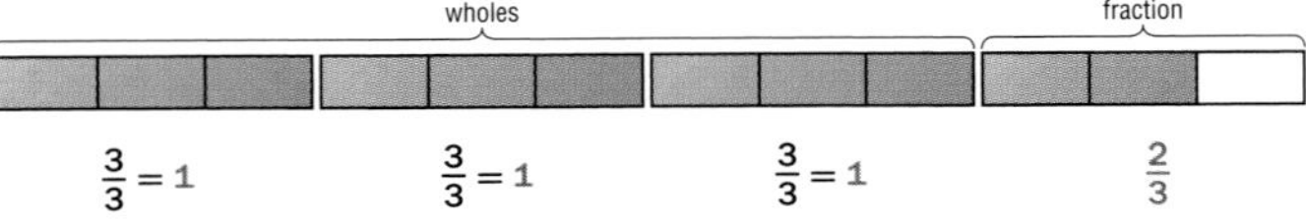

$\frac{3}{3} = 1 \qquad \frac{3}{3} = 1 \qquad \frac{3}{3} = 1 \qquad \frac{2}{3}$

2. Write the whole number part of the mixed number. 3
3. Write the fraction part of the mixed number. $\frac{2}{3}$
4. Write the mixed number. $3\frac{2}{3}$

198 **Chapter 5** Fractions

Intervention Strategy **Intrapersonal Learners**

Class Participation Advise students to take part in discussions, and to follow what everyone is saying. When something is said that a student feels should be noted or discussed more, write it down. Point out to students that one of the best ways to learn is to ask questions if they do not understand something or cannot follow the thread of the discussion. Hold a question-and-answer period to allow this open exchange.

YOUR TURN!

Change $\frac{17}{7}$ to a mixed number using fraction strips.

1. Model the improper fraction using strips. Mark equal sections. Shade each fraction strip.

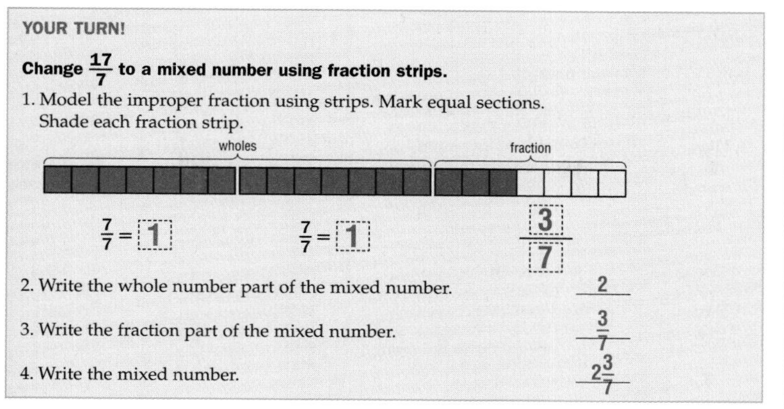

$\frac{7}{7} = 1$ $\frac{7}{7} = 1$ $\frac{3}{7}$

2. Write the whole number part of the mixed number. 2
3. Write the fraction part of the mixed number. $\frac{3}{7}$
4. Write the mixed number. $2\frac{3}{7}$

Example 3

Write $4\frac{2}{3}$ as an improper fraction.

1. Find how many thirds are in 4. Multiply 4 by 3. $4 \times 3 = 12$
2. Add the thirds to find the numerator of the improper fraction. $12 + 2 = 14$
3. Keep the denominator the same. Write the improper fraction. $4\frac{2}{3} = \frac{14}{3}$
4. Write Steps 1–3 as one process. $4\frac{2}{3} = \frac{4 \times 3 + 2}{3} = \frac{12 + 2}{3} = \frac{14}{3}$

YOUR TURN!

Write $4\frac{3}{5}$ as an improper fraction.

1. Find how many fifths are in 4. Multiply 4 by 5.

the whole number of the mixed number

$4 \times \underline{5} = \underline{20}$

the denominator of the mixed number

2. Add the fifths to find the numerator of the improper fraction.
$\underline{20} + 3 = \underline{23}$
3. Write the improper fraction. $\frac{23}{5}$
4. Write Steps 1–3 as one process. $\frac{4 \times 5 + 3}{5} = \frac{20 + 3}{5} = \frac{23}{5}$

Intervention Strategy Logical/Visual Learners

Example 3 Students who have difficulty with Example 3 may benefit from drawing a picture. Have them draw four circles to represent the four wholes. Each circle should be divided into 3 parts. Then have them draw a circle to model $\frac{2}{3}$. Count up the thirds.

Additional Example 3

Write $5\frac{3}{5}$ as an improper fraction.

1. Find how many fifths are in 5. Multiply 5 by 5.
$5 \times 5 = 25$
2. Add the fifths to find the numerator of the improper fraction.
$25 + 3 = 28$
3. Keep the denominator the same.
Write the improper fraction.
$5\frac{3}{5} = \frac{28}{5}$
4. Write Steps 1–3 as one process.
$5\frac{3}{5} = \frac{5 \times 5 + 3}{5} = \frac{25 + 3}{5} = \frac{28}{5}$

Math Coach Notes

Study Tips Tell students that when they study, they should begin with the concepts they find the most difficult. This way, they are doing the most challenging part of their studying when they are their freshest. Also, encourage students to think about the most productive time of the day for them to study and stick to it.

Common Error *Alert*

Discuss the Differences Students often get improper fractions and mixed numbers confused. Hold a classroom discussion about ways to remember the meaning of each vocabulary word. Tell students to remember that a "mixed" number has a mix of the kind of numbers, i.e., a whole number and a fraction. A proper fraction is the kind you normally see; an improper fraction is the alternative.

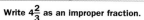

Additional **Example 4**

Write $\frac{45}{6}$ as a mixed number.

1. Divide the numerator by the denominator.

$$\begin{array}{r} 7 \\ 6\overline{)45} \\ -42 \\ \hline 3 \end{array}$$

2. The quotient is the whole number part of the mixed number. The fraction part is written as $\frac{\text{remainder}}{\text{divisor}}$.

$\frac{45}{6} = 7\frac{3}{6} = 7\frac{1}{2}$

Using Manipulatives

Fraction Circles and Fraction Tiles Models of improper fractions and mixed numbers using circles and tiles look the same. Every model has more than one circle or tile and at least one circle or tile is completely shaded. Ask: What is an *improper fraction?* Have students convert improper fractions to *mixed numbers.*

On-Hand Manipulatives Use objects like paper circles or bars, granola bars, pizzas, or pancakes to show students how these objects can be divided into fractional parts, which all together form a whole or a whole and a fractional part.

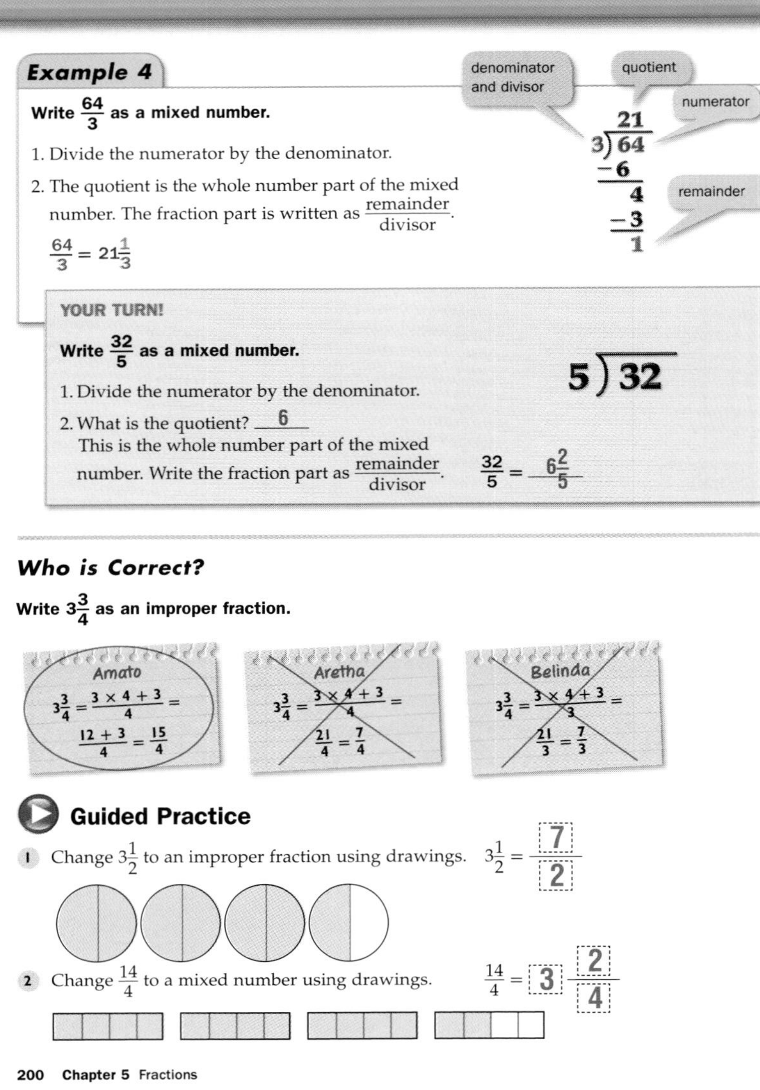

Example 4
Write $\frac{64}{3}$ as a mixed number.
1. Divide the numerator by the denominator.
2. The quotient is the whole number part of the mixed number. The fraction part is written as $\frac{\text{remainder}}{\text{divisor}}$.
$\frac{64}{3} = 21\frac{1}{3}$
denominator and divisor
quotient
numerator
remainder
YOUR TURN!
Write $\frac{32}{5}$ as a mixed number.
1. Divide the numerator by the denominator.
2. What is the quotient? 6
This is the whole number part of the mixed number. Write the fraction part as $\frac{\text{remainder}}{\text{divisor}}$.
$\frac{32}{5} = 6\frac{2}{5}$
Who is Correct?
Write $3\frac{3}{4}$ as an improper fraction.
Amato
Aretha
Belinda
Guided Practice
1 Change $3\frac{1}{2}$ to an improper fraction using drawings. $3\frac{1}{2} = \frac{7}{2}$
2 Change $\frac{14}{4}$ to a mixed number using drawings. $\frac{14}{4} = 3\frac{2}{4}$
200 Chapter 5 Fractions

Who *is Correct?*

Diagnostic Teaching

- Amato is correct.
- Aretha is incorrect. She did not compute the numerator correctly.
- Belinda is incorrect. She did not write the correct denominator. She also computed the numerator incorrectly.

Remind students to check their work.

Step by Step Practice

3 Write $9\frac{2}{3}$ as an improper fraction.

Step 1 Find how many thirds are in 9.

$9 \times 3 = 27$

Step 2 Add the number of thirds in the fraction.

$27 + 2 = 29$

Step 3 Write the total number of thirds as an improper fraction.

$\frac{29}{3}$

Step 4 Write Steps 1–3 as one process.

$9\frac{2}{3} = \frac{3 \times 9 + 2}{3} = \frac{29}{3}$

Write each mixed number as an improper fraction.

4 $1\frac{3}{7} = \frac{7 \times 1 + 3}{7} = \frac{10}{7}$

5 $2\frac{3}{8} = \frac{19}{8}$

6 $2\frac{8}{9} = \frac{26}{9}$

7 $7\frac{1}{2} = \frac{15}{2}$

8 $3\frac{2}{7} = \frac{23}{7}$

9 $5\frac{3}{4} = \frac{23}{4}$

10 $6\frac{1}{5} = \frac{31}{5}$

Write each improper fraction as a mixed number.

11 $\frac{7}{4} = 1\frac{3}{4}$

12 $\frac{14}{6} = 2\frac{2}{6}$

13 $\frac{31}{3} = 10\frac{1}{3}$

14 $\frac{21}{5} = 4\frac{1}{5}$

15 $\frac{41}{9} = 4\frac{5}{9}$

16 $\frac{42}{5} = 8\frac{2}{5}$

English Learner Strategy

Guiding Questions Draw a model of a mixed number on the board. Then ask students the following questions to ensure that they understand the concept.

- Which are the whole pieces?
- Which piece is not whole? How much of the piece is there?
- How would you write the mixed number?
- How would you write the improper fraction?
- How do you use multiplication and addition to rewrite the mixed number as an improper fraction? Use a model to reinforce the steps.

Math Coach Notes

Strategies

1. Have students begin the lesson by modeling mixed numbers. Use various models throughout the lesson as a concrete example for students. Have students write the fraction as a mixed number and as an improper fraction.
2. The most effective way for students to learn fractions is to work with fractions. The more hands-on practice the students have, the more they will retain the information. Use as many models as possible to capture students' various interests.
3. Use real-world examples so that students will connect with the practicality of the concept. Fractions are everywhere, and it is important for students to see how many places outside of the classroom use fractions.

Are They Getting It?

Check students' understanding of mixed numbers and improper fractions by writing these problems on the board. Have students explain any incorrect information. Tell them to use a fraction strip or another visual aid to show why the answers are correct or are incorrect.

Write each mixed number as an improper fraction.

1. $4\frac{3}{8}$ $\quad 4\frac{3}{8} = \frac{8 \times 4 + 3}{8} = \frac{15}{8}$ This is incorrect. The 8 and 4 were added instead of multiplied.
2. $2\frac{7}{11}$ $\quad 2\frac{7}{11} = \frac{11 \times 7 + 2}{11} = \frac{79}{11}$ This is incorrect. The numerator was multiplied by the denominator.
3. $7\frac{4}{5}$ $\quad 7\frac{4}{5} = \frac{5 \times 7 + 4}{5} = \frac{39}{5}$ This is correct.

Note This!

Record Page Number Instruct students that you often use the textbook to refer to ideas that are learned in class. Inform them that recording the page number of corresponding ideas and homework assignments can come in handy later on.

Intervention Strategy

Linguistic Learners

Vocabulary Tables When students are being presented with several new vocabulary words, it can be helpful for them to have a separate sheet of paper to keep track of the words and their meanings. Have students create a three-column table. Students should write the new vocabulary word in the left-hand column. In the middle column, have them write the definition. In the right column, they can place an example and include an illustration if possible.

Common Error *Alert*

Multi-Step Problem If a student is unable to work backward for Exercise 17, he or she may not understand how to convert an improper fraction to a mixed number. Have the student draw several fraction strips, each divided into thirds. Have students shade in sections of the fraction strips until they have shaded 22 sections. Ask: How many fraction strips are completely shaded? How many sections are not shaded, or left over? Have the students write their answers as a mixed number.

Step by Step Problem-Solving Practice

Problem-Solving Strategies
- ☐ Draw a diagram.
- ☐ Look for a pattern.
- ☐ Guess and check.
- ☐ Act it out.
- ☑ Work backward.

Solve.

17 NUMBER SENSE Isaac had friends over for quesadillas. The quesadillas were divided into thirds. The friends ate a total of 22 pieces. Write an improper fraction and a mixed number for the total amount of quesadillas the friends ate.

Understand Read the problem. Write what you know.

The quesadillas are cut into thirds.

The friends ate 22 pieces.

Plan Pick a strategy. One strategy is to work backward. Start by writing the improper fraction. Use the improper fraction to write the mixed number.

Solve Write the improper fraction representing the amount the friends ate.

$\frac{22}{3}$ ← number of pieces eaten ← number of pieces in each quesadilla

Divide the numerator by the denominator to write the mixed number.

$$\begin{array}{r} 7 \\ 3\overline{)22} \\ -21 \\ \hline 1 \end{array}$$

The friends ate $\frac{22}{3}$ or $7\frac{1}{3}$ quesadillas.

Check You can draw the quesadillas to verify your answer.

202 Chapter 5 Fractions

Math Challenge

Game of Converting Write mixed numbers and improper fractions on index cards. Students can work in pairs or in small groups. Each group should have a stack of cards. Shuffle the cards and place them facedown. One student will take a card, and then students will convert the mixed numbers to improper fractions and improper fractions to mixed numbers. Whoever converts the number correctly first gets a point. The student with the most points when the cards are all drawn wins.

18 CRAFTS Janice had ribbon for a craft project. She cut each ribbon into 8 equal parts. She used 23 of the parts. Write the number of ribbon parts she used as an improper fraction and a mixed number. Check off each step.

✔ Understand: I circled key words.

✔ Plan: To solve the problem, I will work backward.

✔ Solve: The answer is $\frac{23}{8}$; $2\frac{7}{8}$ ribbon parts.

✔ Check: I checked my answer by drawing the parts to verify.

19 MANUFACTURING FunForAll Games packages 3 number cubes in each game box. At the end of the day, one production line had 14 number cubes left. Write the number of game boxes that can be completed with the leftover number cubes as an improper fraction and a mixed number.

$\frac{14}{3}$; $4\frac{2}{3}$ game boxes

20 **Reflect** Draw a diagram showing $2\frac{3}{4} = \frac{11}{4}$. Explain your diagram using the words *improper fraction, mixed number, numerator,* and *denominator.*

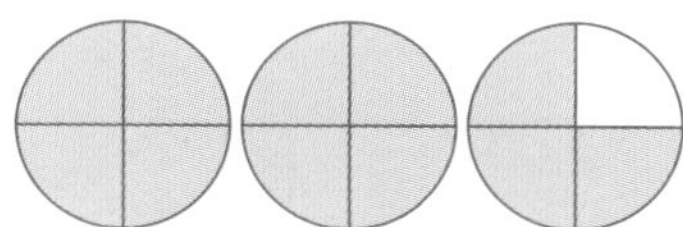

See margin.

Skills, Concepts, and Problem Solving

Change each mixed number to an improper fraction using drawings.

21 $2\frac{5}{6} = \frac{17}{6}$

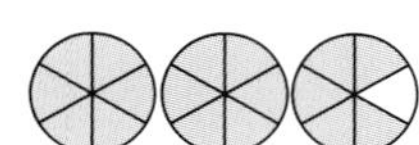

22 $3\frac{2}{3} = \frac{11}{3}$

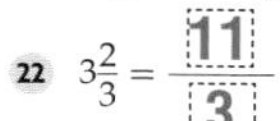

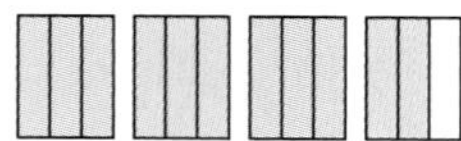

GO ON

Intervention Strategy Naturalist Learners

Model Improper Fractions

1. Have students work in pairs or individually.
2. Hand out index cards to each pair or individual. Tell students to shade in one card. Then tell them to divide another card into fourths and to shade in one-fourth.
3. Now have them fold the first shaded card into fourths. How many shaded fourths are there?
4. What fraction is equal to $1\frac{1}{4}$? Now ask them to use the same method to model $2\frac{2}{3}$.
5. If desired, reverse this activity. Have students divide three index cards into halves. Tell them to shade two of the cards completely and half of the last card. What improper fraction is modeled? What fraction is equivalent? Repeat.

Common Error *Alert*

Mixed Numbers to Improper Fractions

Students may have difficulty changing mixed numbers to improper fractions because they use the wrong operations.

Show the following example.

$4\frac{2}{3}$ should equal $\frac{14}{3}$ (numerator: $4 \times 3 + 2$)

Ask students to explain the error if someone converts $4\frac{2}{3}$ to $\frac{9}{3}$. The numerator was found by using only addition: $4 + 3 + 2$.

Odd/Even Assignments

Exercises 21–30 are structured so that students practice the same concepts whether they are assigned the odd or even problems.

In-Class Assignment

Have students complete Exercises 21, 25, 28, 29, and 33 to ensure that they understand the concept.

Additional Answer

Exercise 20 Sample answer: For the improper fraction, the numerator is the total number of shaded sections, and the denominator is the total number of sections in each fraction circle or bar. For the mixed fraction, the whole number part is 2 because there are two whole circles shaded. The fractional part is $\frac{3}{4}$ because three out of the four sections are shaded.

4 Assess

See It, Do It, Say It, Write It

Step 1 Write an improper fraction on the board. Model how to represent the improper fraction on a number line. Do this several times with different fractions.

Step 2 Have students work in pairs. Write an improper fraction on the board. Tell students to write an equivalent fraction as a mixed number.

Step 3 Have students share their work with the class. Repeat several times.

Step 4 Have students work alone. Tell them to describe an improper fraction and tell them to include a picture or a model.

Looking Ahead: Pre-teach

LCD and GCF In the next lesson, students will learn about least common denominators and greatest common factors.

Example

Find the GCF of 18 and 24 by making a list.

1. List the factors by pairs.

Factors of 18	Factors of 24
1 × 18	1 × 24
2 × 9	2 × 12
3 × 6	3 × 8
	4 × 6

18: 1, 2, 3, (6), 9, 18

24: 1, 2, 3, 4, (6), 8, 12, 24

2. The common factors are 1, 2, 3, and 6.

The greatest common factor of 18 and 24 is 6.

Find the GCF.

1. 12 and 20 4
2. 25 and 30 5
3. 22 and 44 22

Write each improper fraction as a mixed number.

23 $\frac{5}{2} = 2\frac{1}{2}$ 24 $\frac{11}{2} = 5\frac{1}{2}$ 25 $\frac{10}{3} = 3\frac{1}{3}$

Write each mixed number as an improper fraction.

26 $1\frac{1}{2} = \frac{3}{2}$ 27 $4\frac{2}{3} = \frac{14}{3}$ 28 $2\frac{3}{5} = \frac{13}{5}$

Solve.

29 CARPENTRY Jason had pieces of wood that were the same length. He cut each piece into 6 equal parts. He used 15 of the parts to make a birdhouse. Write the number of pieces of wood he used as an improper fraction and a mixed number.

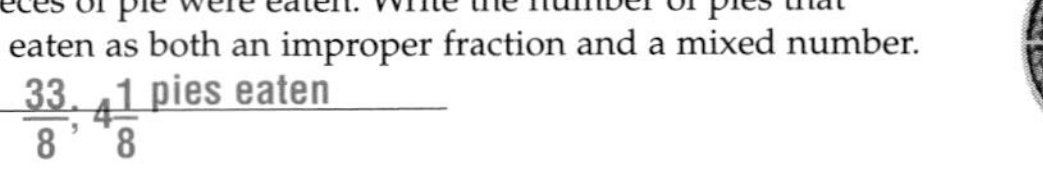

$\frac{15}{6}$, $2\frac{3}{6}$ pieces of wood

30 FOOD Each pie at a party was cut as shown. At the party, 33 pieces of pie were eaten. Write the number of pies that were eaten as both an improper fraction and a mixed number.

$\frac{33}{8}$, $4\frac{1}{8}$ pies eaten

Vocabulary Check **Write the vocabulary word that completes each sentence.**

31 A(n) improper fraction is a fraction with a numerator that is greater than or equal to the denominator.

32 The number $3\frac{3}{4}$ is called a(n) mixed number.

33 Writing in Math A coffee shop charges \$2 for $\frac{1}{4}$ pound of coffee. How much do they charge for $1\frac{3}{4}$ pounds of coffee? Explain.

The improper fraction is $\frac{7}{4}$. Multiply 7 by \$2 for a total price of \$14.00.

Spiral Review

Name two equivalent fractions. (Lesson 5-2, p. 189)

34 $\frac{1}{5}$ Sample answer: $\frac{2}{10}$; $\frac{3}{15}$ 35 $\frac{1}{3}$ Sample answer: $\frac{7}{21}$; $\frac{14}{42}$

204 Chapter 5 Fractions

Ticket Out the Door

Shade Models Hand out fraction circles with some number of parts shaded (representing an improper fraction) to student pairs. Tell students to represent their fractions as mixed numbers. First, they will write their fraction using a numerator and a denominator. Next, they will draw two types of models to represent the fraction.

Student volunteers can present their findings. Have them hand in their papers as they exit the classroom.

Lesson 5-4

Least Common Denominator and Greatest Common Factors

KEY Concept

A multiple of a number is the product of that number and any whole number. To find the **least common multiple (LCM)** of two or more numbers, list the multiples of each number. Then find the least multiple the numbers have in common.

Multiples of 8	Multiples of 6	Multiples of 12
$8 \times 1 = 8$	$6 \times 1 = 6$	$12 \times 1 = 12$
$8 \times 2 = 16$	$6 \times 2 = 12$	$12 \times 2 = 24$
$8 \times 3 = 24$	$6 \times 3 = 18$	$12 \times 3 = 36$
$8 \times 4 = 32$	$6 \times 4 = 24$	$12 \times 4 = 48$

The least common number in all three lists is 24.
The LCM is 24.

The **least common denominator (LCD)** of a set of fractions is the LCM of their denominators.

The LCD for the fractions $\frac{3}{8}$, $\frac{1}{6}$, and $\frac{5}{12}$ is 24.

The **greatest common factor (GCF)** of two whole numbers is the greatest number that is a factor of both numbers.

Factors of 42	Factors of 54
1×42	1×54
2×21	2×27
3×14	3×18
6×7	6×9

The greatest common number in both lists is 6.
The GCF of 42 and 54 is 6.

Every **composite number** can be written as a product of **prime numbers**. A prime number is a whole number greater than one whose only factors are one and itself.

VOCABULARY

composite number
a number greater than 1 with more than two factors
Example: 4 and 6

greatest common factor (GCF)
the greatest number that is a factor of two or more numbers
Example: The GCF of 30 and 75 is 15.

least common denominator (LCD)
the least common multiple of the denominators of two or more fractions, used as a denominator
Example: The LCD of $\frac{1}{12}$ and $\frac{1}{8}$ is 24.

least common multiple (LCM)
the least whole number greater than 0 that is a common multiple of two or more numbers
Example: The LCM of 2 and 3 is 6.

prime factorization
expressing a composite number as a product of its prime factors
Example:
$30 = 3 \times 2 \times 5$

prime number
any whole number greater than 1 with exactly two factors, 1 and itself
Examples: 7, 13, and 19

The first five prime numbers are 2, 3, 5, 7, and 11.

GO ON

Intervention Strategy

Linguistic Learners

LCM and GCF Students often confuse the least common multiple and the greatest common factor. Remind them of the meaning of *factor* and *multiple.* A factor is a number that is multiplied by another number to get a product. A multiple is a product. An LCM of a group of numbers cannot be less than any one of the numbers in the group. A GCF of a group of numbers cannot be greater than any one of the numbers in the group. Challenge students to explain the differences to a partner. Have the partners work together to write and present an example of an LCM and a GCF.

Lesson Notes

Lesson 5-4

Lesson Planner

Objective Find the GCF of two or more numbers, and find the LCD of two or more fractions with unlike denominators.

Vocabulary **composite number**, **greatest common factor (GCF)**, **least common denominator (LCD)**, **least common multiple (LCM)**, **prime factorization**, **prime number**

Materials/Manipulatives counters, egg cartons, fraction strips, index cards, number cubes, paper (factor trees)

Chapter Resource Masters

- CRM Vocabulary and English Language Development (p. A108)
- CRM Skills Practice (p. A109)
- CRM Problem-Solving Practice (p. A110)
- CRM Homework Practice (p. A111)

1 Introduce

Vocabulary

Review Names Ask students to state what each of the following stands for:

LCM Least Common Multiple
LCD Least Common Denominator
GCF Greatest Common Factor

2 Teach

Key Concept

Foundational Skills and Concepts After students have read through the Key Concept box, have them try these exercises.

1. What type of number has exactly two factors? prime
2. What kind of number is not a prime number? composite number
3. What is the LCD for fractions with denominators 6, 8, and 12? 24

Additional **Example 1**

Find the least common denominator (LCD) of $\frac{1}{3}, \frac{1}{7}$, and $\frac{1}{21}$.

Find the LCM of the denominators.

1. List the multiples of each denominator.

   3: 3, 6, 9, 12, 15, 18, 21, 24, 27, . . .

   7: 7, 14, 21, 28, 35, 42, 49, . . .

   21: 21, 42, 63, 84, 105, . . .

2. Circle the numbers that are common to all three lists. The least of these numbers is the LCM.

   3: 3, 6, 9, 12, 15, 18, (21) 24, 27, . . .

   7: 7, 14, (21) 28, 35, 42, 49, . . .

   21: (21) 42, 63, 84, 105, . . .

The LCM of 3, 7, and 21 is 21.

The LCD of $\frac{1}{3}, \frac{1}{7}$, and $\frac{1}{21}$ is 21.

The **prime factorization** of a number is the product of its prime factors.

One way to find the prime factorization is to use a factor tree.

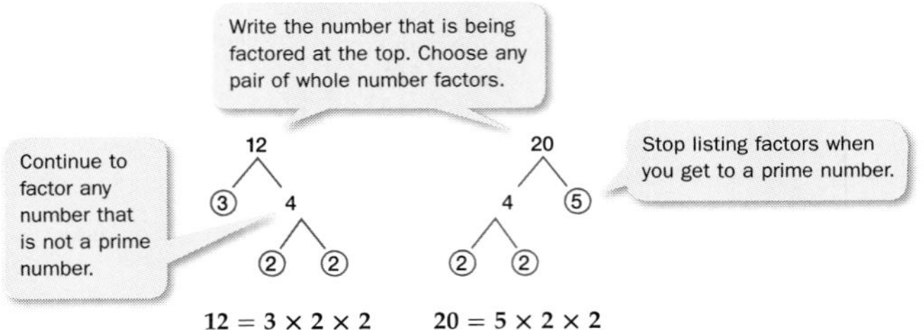

Write the number that is being factored at the top. Choose any pair of whole number factors.
Continue to factor any number that is not a prime number.
Stop listing factors when you get to a prime number.
12
3
4
2
2
20
4
5
2
2

$12 = 3 \times 2 \times 2$ $\quad 20 = 5 \times 2 \times 2$

List prime factors from greatest to least.

Example 1

Find the least common denominator (LCD) of $\frac{1}{3}, \frac{1}{4}$, and $\frac{1}{6}$.

Find the LCM of the denominators.

1. List the multiples of each denominator.

   3: 3, 6, 9, 12, 15, 18, 21, 24, 27, 30, …
   4: 4, 8, 12, 16, 20, 24, 28, 32, 36, 40, 44, …
   6: 6, 12, 18, 24, 30, …

2. Circle the numbers that are common to all three lists. The least of these numbers is the LCM.

   3: 3, 6, 9, (12), 15, 18, 21, (24), 27, 30, …
   4: 4, 8, (12), 16, 20, (24), 28, 32, 36, 40, 44, …
   6: 6, (12), 18, (24), 30, …

The LCM of 3, 4, and 6 is 12.

The LCD of $\frac{1}{3}, \frac{1}{4}$, and $\frac{1}{6}$ is 12.

YOUR TURN!

Find the least common denominator (LCD) of $\frac{1}{2}, \frac{1}{5}$, and $\frac{1}{10}$.

Find the LCM of the denominators.

1. List the multiples of each number.

   2: 2, 4, 6, 8, 10, 12, ...
   5: 5, 10, 15, 20, 25, 30, ...
   10: 10, 20, 30, 40, 50, 60, ...

2. Circle the numbers that are common to all three lists. The least of these numbers is the LCM.

   2: 2, 4, 6, 8, (10), 12, ...
   5: 5, (10), 15, 20, 25, 30, ...
   10: (10), 20, 30, 40, 50, 60, ...

What is the LCM of 2, 5, and 10? 10

What is the LCD of $\frac{1}{2}, \frac{1}{5}$, and $\frac{1}{10}$? 10

206 Chapter 5 Fractions

Note This!

Diagrams Instruct students to draw the diagrams and models in their notes using what suits their learning style. Some students are visual learners, so making a factor tree may be a better model than a list.

If the denominators have no common factors, or are prime numbers, instruct students that the denominators can be multiplied to find a common denominator.

$\frac{1}{2} + \frac{1}{3} = \frac{3}{6} + \frac{2}{6}$

English Learner Strategy

Create Posters Have students work in small groups or pairs to create posters that explain the similarities and differences between the GCF and the LCM. Tell students to include examples of the methods they use to find the GCF and LCM. Have groups present their posters.

Example 2

Find the GCF of 20 and 36 by using prime factors.

1. Write the prime factorization.

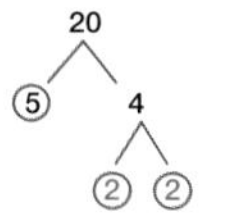

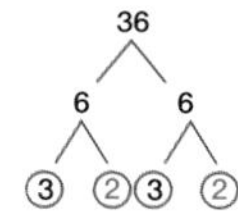

$20 = 5 \times 2 \times 2$ $\quad 36 = 3 \times 3 \times 2 \times 2$

2. The common prime factors are 2 and 2.

So, the GCF of 20 and 36 is 2×2 or 4.

YOUR TURN!

Find the GCF of 25 and 60 by using prime factors.

1. Write the prime factorization.

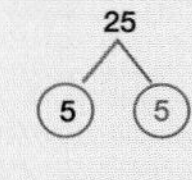

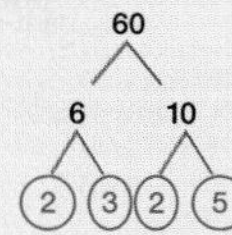

2. The common prime factor is 5.

So, the GCF of 25 and 60 is 5.

Example 3

Find the GCF of 42 and 56 by making a list.

1. List the factors by multiplied pairs.

Factors of 42	Factors of 56
1×42	1×56
2×21	2×28
3×14	4×14
6×7	7×8

42: 1, 2, 3, 6, 7, (14), 21, 42

56: 1, 2, 4, 7, 8, (14), 28, 56

2. The common factors are 1, 2, 7, and 14.

The GCF of 42 and 56 is 14.

YOUR TURN!

Find the GCF of 63 and 77 by making a list.

1. List the factors by multiplied pairs.

Factors of 63	Factors of 77
(1) × 63	(1) × 77
3 × 21	(7) × 11
(7) × 9	

2. The common factors are 1 and 7.

The GCF of 63 and 77 is 7.

Additional Example 2

Find the GCF of 18 and 45 by using prime factors.

1. Write the prime factorization.

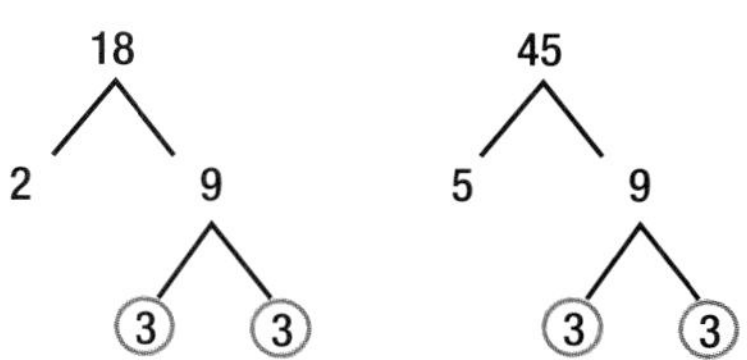

2. The common prime factors are 3 and 3.
   So, the GCF of 18 and 45 is 3×3 or 9.

Additional Example 3

Find the GCF of 32 and 56 by making a list.

1. List the factors by multiplied pairs.

Factors of 32	Factors of 56
1×32	1×56
2×16	2×28
4×8	4×14
	8×7

32: 1, 2, 4, (8), 16, 32

56: 1, 2, 4, 7, (8), 14, 28, 56

2. The common factors are 1, 2, 4, and 8.

The GCF of 32 and 56 is 8.

Intervention Strategy Interpersonal, Kinesthetic

Find the GCF Divide students into pairs and give each student a number cube. Both members of the pair roll their number cubes and use the numbers on the two cubes to write a two-digit number. Both students then write the factors of the two-digit number. The pairs roll their number cubes again to get another two-digit number and write the factors of the second two-digit number. Students should find the GCF of their numbers. Students can share their numbers and GCF with the class.

3 Practice

Using Manipulatives

On-Hand Manipulatives Have students draw a factor tree to find the prime factorizations of denominators. Ask: What is the LCM? Have students find the LCD of the fractions.

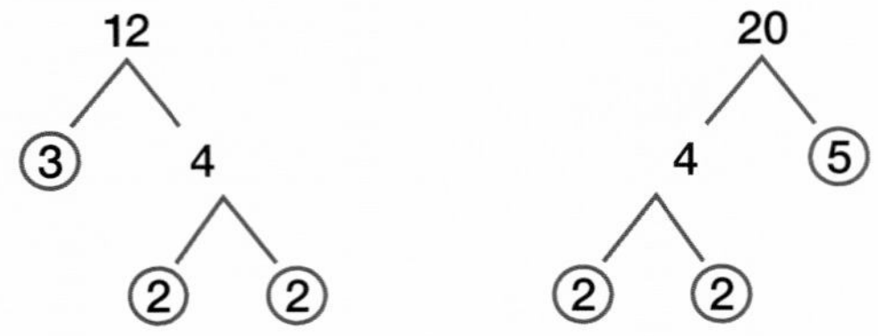

Math Coach Notes

Teach Each Other An effective way to remember mathematical concepts is to teach them to another person. Encourage students to work in pairs. Tell them to take turns teaching a concept to each other. Have students use the chalkboard or a dry-erase board, if available, for illustrations.

Who is Correct?

Find the LCD of $\frac{5}{6}$, $\frac{4}{9}$, and $\frac{11}{12}$.

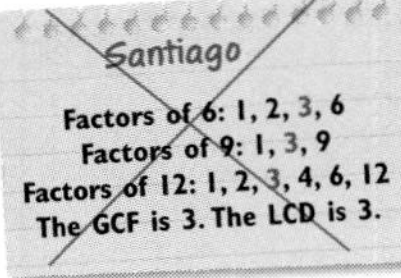

Santiago
Factors of 6: 1, 2, 3, 6
Factors of 9: 1, 3, 9
Factors of 12: 1, 2, 3, 4, 6, 12
The GCF is 3. The LCD is 3.

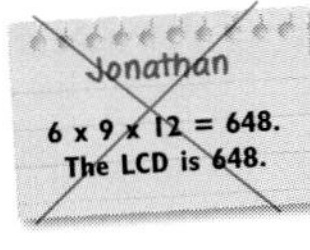

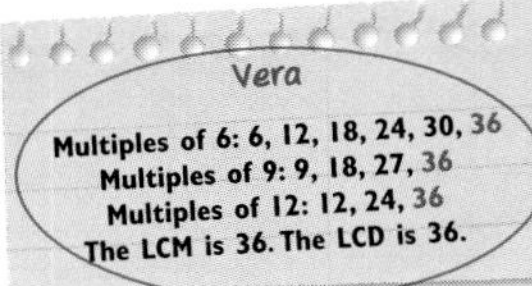

Vera
Multiples of 6: 6, 12, 18, 24, 30, 36
Multiples of 9: 9, 18, 27, 36
Multiples of 12: 12, 24, 36
The LCM is 36. The LCD is 36.

Circle correct answer(s). Cross out incorrect answer(s).

Guided Practice

1 Find the LCM of 3, 5, and 6. 30

Multiples of 3:
3, 6, 9, 12, 15, 18, 21, 24, 27, 30,...

Multiples of 5:
5, 10, 15, 20, 25, 30, 35, 40,...

Multiples of 6:
6, 12, 18, 24, 30, 36, 42, 48,...

2 Find the LCM of 10, 4, and 8. 40

Multiples of 10:
10, 20, 30, 40, 50,...

Multiples of 4:
4, 8, 12, 16, 20, 24, 28, 32, 36, 40,...

Multiples of 8:
8, 16, 24, 32, 40, 48,...

Step by Step Practice

3 Find the GCF of 3, 12, and 36 by using prime factors.

Step 1 Write the prime factorization.

Step 2 The common prime factor is 3.

So, the GCF of 3, 12, and 36 is 3.

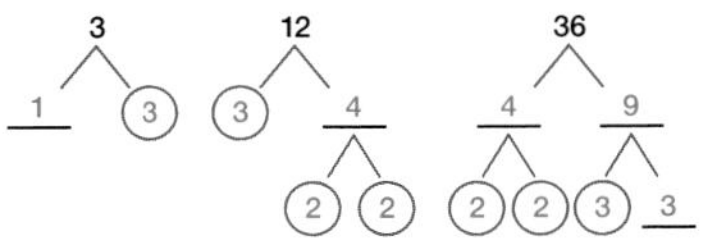

Who *is Correct?*

Diagnostic Teaching

- Santiago is incorrect; he found the GCF.
- Jonathan is incorrect; he multiplied the denominators. He found a common denominator, but not the **least** common denominator.
- Vera is correct.

Remind students that the LCD is the LCM of the numbers in the denominators.

Find the GCF of each set of numbers.

4 3 and 9 ___3___

Factors of 3: ___1, 3___

Factors of 9: ___1, 3, 9___

5 10 and 15 ___5___

6 48 and 60 ___12___

Find the LCM of each set of numbers.

7 2, 5, and 7 ___70___

8 3, 6, and 7 ___42___

Step by Step Problem-Solving Practice

Problem-Solving Strategies

- ☐ Look for a pattern.
- ☑ Use logical reasoning.
- ☐ Solve a simpler problem.
- ☐ Work backward.
- ☐ Act it out.

Solve.

9 MONEY The list shows the amounts of money that the club leader collected. Each member paid the same amount to attend a field trip. What is the most the trip could cost per member? Explain.

Money Collected from Members	
Monday	$42
Tuesday	$12
Wednesday	$60

Understand Read the problem. Write what you know. The club leader collected ___$42, $12, and $60 in all___. Each member paid the ___same___ amount.

Plan Pick a strategy. One strategy is to use logical reasoning. You need to know the amount each member paid. Logical reasoning tells you that you must find the greatest common factor of the amount of money collected each day.

Solve Write the factors of each amount.

Factors of 42	Factors of 12	Factors of 60
1 × 42	1 × 12	1 × 60
2 × 21	2 × (6)	2 × 30
3 × 14	3 × 4	3 × 20
(6) × 7	___	5 × 12
___	___	(6) × 10

The GCF of 42, 12, and 60 is ___6___.

Check Did you answer the question? If each member paid ___$6___, could the club leader collect the amounts listed?

GO ON

Are They Getting It?

Check students' understanding of LCM and GCF by writing these problems on the board. Have students explain the incorrect information in each problem. Tell them to use a fraction strip or another visual aid to show why the answers are correct or incorrect.

1. The LCM of 4 and 6 is 8. This is incorrect, the LCM is 12.
2. The LCM of 5 and 12 is 60. This is correct.
3. The LCD of $\frac{1}{3}$, $\frac{4}{7}$, and $\frac{3}{42}$ is 21. This is incorrect, the LCD is 42.
4. The GCF of 21, 49, and 56 is 7. This is correct.

Common Error *Alert*

Multi-Step Problem

Exercise 9 If a student is unable to use logical reasoning for Exercise 9, he or she may not understand how to write factors of each amount. Begin by listing factors or making a factor tree, and show the diagram of the factors.

Math Coach Notes

Strategies

1. Have students begin the lesson by practicing factoring numbers. Use a factor tree throughout the lesson as a concrete example. Have students write the factors using the factor tree and simplify.
2. The optimum way for students to learn how to factor is to use multiple concrete models, manipulatives, and pictorial representations. Drill students repeatedly by asking the GCF of numbers.
3. Use real-world examples so students will connect to factors outside of math class. Have students name factors that represent these real-world examples.

Odd/Even Assignments

Exercises 13–27 are structured so that students practice the same concepts whether they are assigned the odd or even problems.

In-Class Assignment

Have students complete Exercises 15, 17, 25, 27, and 30 to ensure that they understand the concept.

10 FOOD Frida wants to ship snacks to her cousin. She wants to ship 14 oatmeal squares, 12 granola bars, and 8 lemon bars. Frida can pack only one type of snack in each box. She must pack the same number of snacks in each box. What is the greatest number of snacks that Frida can pack in each box?
Check off each step.

✔ Understand: I circled key words.

✔ Plan: To solve the problem, I will use logical reasoning.

✔ Solve: The answer is 2 snacks.

✔ Check: I checked my answer by drawing a picture.

11 CARPENTRY Three boards have thicknesses of $\frac{1}{2}$, $\frac{1}{4}$, and $\frac{5}{8}$ inch. What is the least common denominator of the measures of the thickness of the boards?

8

12 **Reflect** Explain the relationship between the LCD and the LCM. Use an example.

Sample answer: The LCD is the LCM of the denominators in two or more fractions. The LCD of $\frac{1}{2}$ and $\frac{1}{10}$ is 10; the LCM of 2 and 10 is 10.

Skills, Concepts, and Problem Solving

Find the LCM of each set of numbers.

13 2, 3, 8 24

14 4, 5, 6 60

15 5, 6, 9, 10 90

16 3, 6, 18 18

210 **Chapter 5** Fractions

Math Challenge

Find the LCM Students make two sets of cards numbered from 1 to 10. The cards are shuffled and then all are dealt out and placed facedown in front of the students. Both students turn a card. Whoever names the LCM first gets 2 points. If a student calls a common multiple that is not the LCM, he or she gets 1 point. Each student only gets one chance. When the cards are gone, whoever has the most points wins.

Find the LCD of each set of fractions.

17 $\frac{3}{4}$ and $\frac{5}{6}$ 12

18 $\frac{1}{8}$ and $\frac{5}{12}$ 24

19 $\frac{1}{3}$, $\frac{3}{4}$, and $\frac{3}{5}$ 60

20 $\frac{3}{4}$, $\frac{1}{3}$, and $\frac{2}{9}$ 36

21 $\frac{3}{4}$, $\frac{2}{3}$, $\frac{7}{9}$, and $\frac{3}{12}$ 36

22 $\frac{3}{4}$, $\frac{1}{3}$, $\frac{5}{6}$, and $\frac{2}{9}$ 36

23 $\frac{2}{3}$, $\frac{3}{4}$, $\frac{3}{8}$, and $\frac{5}{12}$ 24

24 $\frac{3}{4}$, $\frac{3}{5}$, $\frac{7}{10}$, and $\frac{5}{12}$ 60

Solve.

25 FLOWERS Rayna is planting flowers. She has enough flowers to plant 6, 7, or 14 in each row. What is the least number of flowers she could have?
42 flowers

BASKETBALL **Use the table at the right for Exercises 26 and 27. The numerator is the number of free throws made. The denominator is the number of free throws attempted.**

26 If you were to rewrite the stats to be fractions with the least common denominator (LCD), what is the LCD of these fractions?
60

Last Night's Basketball Stats	
Player	Free Throws
Williams	$\frac{9}{12}$
Hawkins	$\frac{1}{5}$
Torres	$\frac{4}{6}$
Rollins	$\frac{8}{10}$

27 Rewrite each fraction with the LCD.

$\frac{9}{12} = \frac{45}{60}$ $\frac{1}{5} = \frac{12}{60}$

$\frac{4}{6} = \frac{40}{60}$ $\frac{8}{10} = \frac{48}{60}$

GO ON

Math Coach Notes

Analyze the Table Instruct students to analyze the table for Exercises 26–27 by reading the direction line and each column heading so they understand the information given. Even though the information in the table is clear and concise, it would be hard to determine who shot the best from the free-throw line. Rewriting each fraction with the LCD will allow the students to compare the numerators and the statistics.

Intervention Strategy Visual/Logical Learners

Egg Carton Math Write numbers on the bottom of egg cartons. Place two objects, such as counters or pennies, inside the carton. Shake the carton. When it opens, have students find the GCF of the numbers.

Factor Game Have students play the factor game to practice factors and learn more about prime and composite numbers. Students play in pairs. Tell them to make a 6 by 6 array. Beginning with the left, top square, students number the squares from 1 to 36 moving from left to right. One student circles a number, and the other student uses another color to circle all the factors of that number. When all the numbers are circled (and they can be circled only once), students find the sum of their circled numbers. The highest score wins.

4 Assess

See It, Do It, Say It, Write It

Step 1 Write three fractions on the board. Model how to find the factors of each fraction with a drawing or model. Do this several times with different fractions.

Step 2 Ask students to draw a factor tree on paper. Give them a few numbers to factor with their factor tree. Repeat with different numbers and students drawing factor trees. Share solutions in a class discussion.

Step 3 Have students work in pairs. Write two fractions on the board. Tell students to make a factor tree to represent each fraction on the board. Have students share their work with the class. Repeat several times.

Step 4 Have students work alone. Tell them to describe an LCD, and include a picture or a model.

Looking Ahead: Pre-teach

Compare and Order Fractions In the next lesson, students will learn how to compare and order fractions.

Example

Order the fractions $\frac{3}{4}$, $\frac{5}{6}$, and $\frac{4}{9}$ from least to greatest.

1. Find the LCM of 4, 6, and 9.
   The LCM is 36.
2. Write the equivalent fractions that have 36 in the denominator.

   $\frac{3}{4} = \frac{3 \times 9}{4 \times 9} = \frac{27}{36}$

   $\frac{5}{6} = \frac{5 \times 6}{6 \times 6} = \frac{30}{36}$

   $\frac{4}{9} = \frac{4 \times 4}{9 \times 4} = \frac{16}{36}$
3. Compare the numerators of the equivalent fractions. $16 < 27 < 30$
4. Order the fractions from least to greatest.
   $\frac{4}{9}, \frac{3}{4}, \frac{5}{6}$

Vocabulary Check **Write the vocabulary word that completes each sentence.**

28 ___Prime factorization___ is expressing a composite number as a product of its prime factors.

29 The ___least common denominator___ for two or more fractions is the least common multiple of denominators of the fractions.

30 **Writing in Math** Explain the difference between finding the LCM and the GCF of two numbers.

Sample answer: The LCM is the least common multiple of two or more numbers. For example, the LCM of 12 and 8 is 24. The GCF is the greatest common factor of two or more numbers. The GCF of 12 and 8 is 4.

Spiral Review

Write each improper fraction as a mixed number. (Lesson 5-3, p. 197)

31 $\frac{5}{2} = 2\frac{1}{2}$ 32 $\frac{11}{2} = 5\frac{1}{2}$ 33 $\frac{10}{3} = 3\frac{1}{3}$

Write each mixed number as an improper fraction. (Lesson 5-3, page 197)

34 $1\frac{1}{2} = \frac{3}{2}$ 35 $4\frac{2}{3} = \frac{14}{3}$ 36 $2\frac{3}{5} = \frac{13}{5}$

Draw a picture to model each fraction. Use equal parts of a whole or of a set. (Lesson 5-1, p. 182)

37 $\frac{1}{5}$ 

38 $\frac{3}{3}$  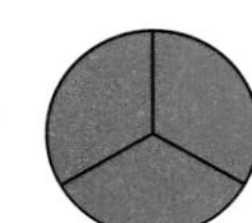

39 $\frac{4}{6}$ 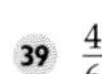 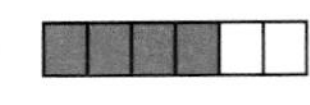

Solve.

40 **POPULATION** In Wallyville, $\frac{1}{6}$ of the students play a team sport. In Hoppsburg, $\frac{1}{4}$ of the students play a team sport. In Salston, $\frac{1}{8}$ of the students playing a team sport. Find the least common denominator of these three fractions. (Lesson 5-4, p. 205)

___24___

Ticket Out the Door

LCM or GCF Make cards with two whole numbers on one side. Write the LCM and GCF on the other side. Hold up cards with the two whole nmbers showing. Call on students to give the LCM and GCF for the two numbers. If they answer correctly, they can exit the classroom. Repeat until each student has exited the classroom.

Progress Check 2 (Lessons 5-3 and 5-4)

1 Write the prime factorization for 56. $2 \times 2 \times 2 \times 7$

Find the GCF of each set of numbers.

2 24 and 36 12

3 12, 20, and 32 4

Find the LCD of each set of fractions.

4 $\frac{1}{2}$ and $\frac{5}{6}$ 6

5 $\frac{5}{8}$ and $\frac{3}{20}$ 40

Write each improper fraction as a mixed number.

6 $\frac{9}{2} = 4\frac{1}{2}$

7 $\frac{13}{5} = 2\frac{3}{5}$

8 $\frac{15}{4} = 3\frac{3}{4}$

9 $\frac{12}{7} = 1\frac{5}{7}$

10 $\frac{33}{8} = 4\frac{1}{8}$

11 $\frac{40}{7} = 5\frac{5}{7}$

Write each mixed number as an improper fraction.

12 $6\frac{1}{2} = \frac{13}{2}$

13 $8\frac{2}{3} = \frac{26}{3}$

14 $2\frac{1}{7} = \frac{15}{7}$

15 $5\frac{3}{4} = \frac{23}{4}$

16 $1\frac{5}{8} = \frac{13}{8}$

17 $10\frac{3}{7} = \frac{73}{7}$

18 **ART** One art museum features four types of paintings. Modern art is $\frac{1}{2}$ of the collection. African art is $\frac{3}{16}$ of the collection. Asian art is $\frac{1}{4}$ of the collection and $\frac{2}{32}$ is early European. What is the least common denominator of these fractions?

32

19 **HOBBIES** Ruri swam $1\frac{2}{3}$ miles. Lola swam $\frac{6}{3}$ miles. Did they swim the same length?

No, Ruri swam $\frac{5}{3}$ of a mile, while Lola swam $\frac{6}{3}$ (or 2 miles).

Chapter 5 Fractions 213

Progress Check 2

Chapter 5

Formative Assessment

Use the Progress Check to assess students' mastery of the previous lessons. Have students review the lesson indicated for the problems they answered incorrectly.

Odd/Even Assignments

Exercises are structured so that students practice the same concepts whether they are assigned the odd or even problems.

Common Error *Alert*

Key Abbreviations

Exercises 2–5 Students need to remember that GCF stands for greatest common factor and that LCD stands for least common denominator. Remind them that the LCD is the same as the least common multiple (LCM) of the denominator.

Check Work If students have time, they should check their answers on many of these exercises (particularly Exercises 6–17) by going back and forth between mixed numbers and improper fractions.

Data-Driven Decision Making

Students missing Exercises . . .	Have trouble with . . .	Should review and practice . . .
1	writing the prime factorization of a number.	SSG Lesson 5-4, p. 205
2–5	finding GCF and LCD.	SSG Lesson 5-4, p. 205 CRM Skills Practice, p. A109
6–11	writing improper fractions as mixed numbers.	SSG Lesson 5-3, p. 197 CRM Skills Practice, p. A105
12–17	writing mixed numbers as improper fractions.	SSG Lesson 5-3, p. 197 CRM Skills Practice, p. A105
18–19	solving word problems with fractions.	CRM Problem-Solving Practice, pp. A106 and A110

Lesson 5-5 Lesson Notes

Lesson Planner

Objective Compare and order fractions.

Vocabulary **common denominators, equivalent forms of one, least common denominator (LCD), least common multiple (LCM)**

Materials/Manipulatives everyday objects, fraction circles, fraction tiles

Chapter Resource Masters

- CRM Vocabulary and English Language Development (p. A112)
- CRM Skills Practice (p. A113)
- CRM Problem-Solving Practice (p. A114)
- CRM Homework Practice (p. A115)

Vocabulary

Vocabulary Use Arrange students into groups of three and assign each student a fraction. Have each group *order the* fractions in ascending order.

2 Teach

Key Concept

Foundational Skills and Concepts After students have read through the Key Concept box, have them try these exercises.

1. What are two ways to compare fractions? Look at models of the fractions or find equivalent fractions to compare.
2. If the denominators are equal, what do you compare? the numerators

Lesson 5-5 Compare and Order Fractions

KEY Concept

One way to compare fractions is to look at models.

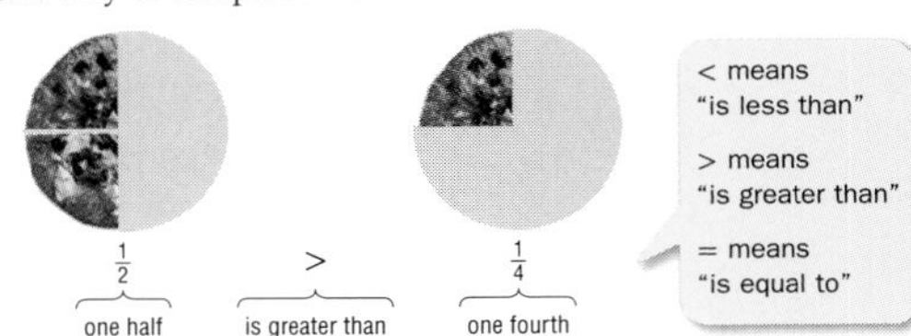

Another way to compare fractions is to find equivalent fractions that have the same denominators. Then compare the numerators. Fractions with **common denominators** are fractions that have the same denominator.

Look again at the pizza slices.

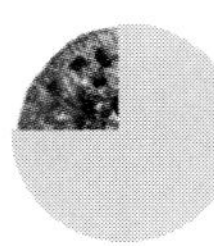

$\frac{1}{2} = \frac{1 \times 2}{2 \times 2} = \frac{2}{4}$

Because the denominators are equal, you can compare the numerators.

$\frac{2}{4} > \frac{1}{4}$

To order fractions, rename the fractions using their LCD. Then compare the numerators of the fractions.

VOCABULARY

common denominators the same denominator (bottom number) used in two or more fractions

equivalent forms of one different expressions that represent the same number Example: $\frac{3}{3}$

least common denominator (LCD) the least common multiple of the denominators of two or more fractions, used as a denominator Example: The LCD of $\frac{1}{12}$ and $\frac{1}{8}$ is 24.

least common multiple (LCM) the least whole number greater than one that is a common multiple of each of two or more numbers Example: The LCM of 3 and 5 is 15.

Recall that you can write equivalent fractions by multiplying by an **equivalent form of one.**

214 **Chapter 5** Fractions

Intervention Strategy — Visual/Logical Learners

Compare with Models Tell students to draw a model of $\frac{3}{4}$ as a rectangle that is divided into fourths. Ask them to shade 3 parts. Then ask them to make another model to represent $\frac{7}{10}$. Tell them that this rectangle should be the same size as their first rectangle, but divided into tenths. After they shade 7 parts, ask them to compare the models. Which shaded area is larger, that of the $\frac{3}{4}$ or $\frac{7}{10}$ model? Have students draw models to compare other fractions.

Fraction bars and fraction circles can also be used to compare the size of fractions. Remind students that the wholes must be of equal size.

Example 1

Use $<$, $=$, or $>$ to compare $\frac{3}{8}$ and $\frac{2}{3}$. Shade the models given.

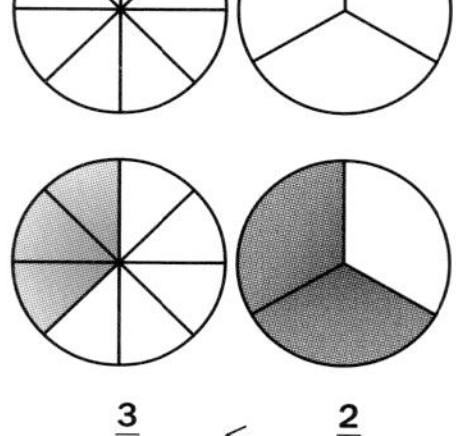

1. The circle on the left has 8 sections. Use it to model $\frac{3}{8}$. Shade 3 sections.
2. The circle on the right has 3 sections. Use it to model $\frac{2}{3}$. Shade 2 sections.
3. Compare the shaded areas. The symbol $<$ means "is less than."

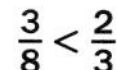

$\frac{3}{8} < \frac{2}{3}$

$\frac{3}{8} < \frac{2}{3}$

YOUR TURN!

Use $<$, $=$, or $>$ to compare $\frac{2}{5}$ and $\frac{4}{7}$. Shade the models given.

1. How many sections does the top fraction strip have? 5

   Use it to model $\frac{2}{5}$. How many sections should you shade? 2
2. How many sections does the bottom fraction strip have? 7

   Use it to model $\frac{4}{7}$. How many sections should you shade? 4
3. Compare the shaded areas.

   Use $<$, $=$, or $>$ to write a statement.

   $\frac{2}{5} < \frac{4}{7}$

Lesson 5-5 Compare and Order Fractions 215

Intervention Strategy

Interpersonal/ Visual Learners

Count Cars Students can sit outside or look through a window to count the number of cars that pass by. Tell them to use a tally chart to keep track of the color of each car. Then tell students to write a fraction for each color of car out of the total cars. Have them put the fractions for each color in order from greatest to least.

Additional Example 1

Use $<$, $=$, or $>$ to compare $\frac{3}{4}$ and $\frac{2}{3}$.

Shade the models given.

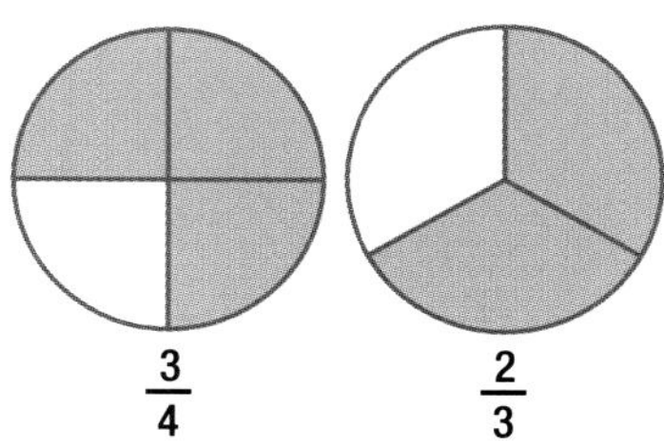

$\frac{3}{4}$ $\frac{2}{3}$

1. The circle on the left has 4 sections. Use it to model $\frac{3}{4}$. Shade 3 sections.
2. The circle on the right has 3 sections. Use it to model $\frac{2}{3}$. Shade 2 sections.
3. Compare the shaded areas. The symbol $>$ means "is greater than."

   $\frac{3}{4} > \frac{2}{3}$

Math Coach Notes

Erasing Instruct students to not erase anything unless they are convinced it is wrong. Point out that even if their eventual answer is incorrect, some part of their work could be worth partial credit.

Additional **Example 2**

Use <, =, or > to compare $\frac{3}{5}$ and $\frac{4}{7}$.

Rename the fractions using a common denominator.

1. Find the LCM of 5 and 7.

Multiples of 5	Multiples of 7
$5 \times 1 = 5$	$7 \times 1 = 7$
$5 \times 2 = 10$	$7 \times 2 = 14$
$5 \times 3 = 15$	$7 \times 3 = 21$
$5 \times 4 = 20$	$7 \times 4 = 28$
$5 \times 5 = 25$	$7 \times 5 = (35)$
$5 \times 6 = 30$	$7 \times 6 = 42$
$5 \times 7 = (35)$	$7 \times 7 = 49$

The LCD is 35.

2. Rename each fraction as an equivalent fraction with a denominator of 35.

$\frac{3}{5} = \frac{3 \times 7}{5 \times 7} = \frac{21}{35}$ $\qquad$ $\frac{4}{7} = \frac{4 \times 5}{7 \times 5} = \frac{20}{35}$

3. Compare the numerators of the equivalent fractions.

$21 > 20$

Write a statement using the equivalent fractions.

$\frac{21}{35} > \frac{20}{35}$

4. Replace the equivalent fractions with the original fractions.

$\frac{3}{5} > \frac{4}{7}$

Common Error *Alert*

Least Common Denominators When students are finding a common denominator, remind them that it is important to find the *least* common denominator and not just a common denominator.

Example 2

Use <, =, or > to compare $\frac{2}{3}$ and $\frac{4}{5}$.
Rename the fractions using a common denominator.

1. Find the LCM of 3 and 5.

Multiples of 3	Multiples of 5
$3 \times 1 = 3$	$5 \times 1 = 5$
$3 \times 2 = 6$	$5 \times 2 = 10$
$3 \times 3 = 9$	$5 \times 3 = (15)$
$3 \times 4 = 12$	$5 \times 4 = 20$
$3 \times 5 = (15)$	$5 \times 5 = 25$

The LCD is 15.

2. Rename each fraction as an equivalent fraction with a denominator of 15.

$\frac{2}{3} = \frac{2 \times 5}{3 \times 5} = \frac{10}{15}$

$\frac{4}{5} = \frac{4 \times 3}{5 \times 3} = \frac{12}{15}$

3. Compare the numerators of the equivalent fractions. $10 < 12$

Write a statement using the equivalent fractions. $\frac{10}{15} < \frac{12}{15}$

4. Replace the equivalent fractions with the original fractions. $\frac{2}{3} < \frac{4}{5}$

YOUR TURN!

Use <, =, or > to compare $\frac{5}{6}$ and $\frac{2}{3}$.
Rename the fractions using a common denominator.

1. Find the LCM of 6 and 3.

Multiples of 6	Multiples of 3
$6 \times 1 = 6$	$3 \times 1 = 3$
$6 \times 2 = 12$	$3 \times 2 = 6$

What common denominator should you use?
6

2. Rename each fraction as an equivalent fraction with the same denominators.

$\frac{5}{6} = \frac{5 \times 1}{6 \times 1} = \frac{5}{6}$

$\frac{2}{3} = \frac{2 \times 2}{3 \times 2} = \frac{4}{6}$

3. Compare the numerators of the equivalent fractions.

5 (>) 4

Write a statement using the equivalent fractions.

$\frac{5}{6} > \frac{4}{6}$

4. Replace the equivalent fractions with the original fractions.

$\frac{5}{6} > \frac{2}{3}$

216 Chapter 5 Fractions

Intervention Strategy Logical Learners

Compare Money Amounts Have students think about money. Ask: What fraction of one dollar is a quarter? $\frac{1}{4}$ What fraction of one dollar is a dime? $\frac{1}{10}$ Compare two dimes to one quarter using fractions. $\frac{2}{10} < \frac{1}{4}$ Ask student volunteers to pose other money-related fractions to compare.

Example 3

Order the fractions $\frac{5}{6}$, $\frac{3}{8}$, and $\frac{7}{12}$ from least to greatest.

1. Find the LCM of 6, 8, and 12.
   Multiples of 6: 6, 12, 18, 24, 30, …
   Multiples of 8: 8, 16, 24, 32, …
   Multiples of 12: 12, 24, 36, …

   The least common number in all three lists of multiples is 24. The LCM is 24.
2. Write equivalent fractions that have 24 as their denominators.

   $\frac{5}{6} = \frac{5 \times 4}{6 \times 4} = \frac{20}{24}$ $\frac{3}{8} = \frac{3 \times 3}{8 \times 3} = \frac{9}{24}$ $\frac{7}{12} = \frac{7 \times 2}{12 \times 2} = \frac{14}{24}$
3. Compare the numerators of the equivalent fractions. $9 < 14 < 20$
4. Order the fractions from least to greatest.

   $\frac{9}{24} < \frac{14}{24} < \frac{20}{24}$ means that $\frac{3}{8} < \frac{7}{12} < \frac{5}{6}$.

   So, from least to greatest, the fractions are $\frac{3}{8}, \frac{7}{12}, \frac{5}{6}$.

YOUR TURN!

Order the fractions $\frac{2}{3}$, $\frac{7}{9}$, and $\frac{4}{18}$ from least to greatest.

1. Find the LCM for the denominators.

   Multiples of 3: 3, 6, 9, 12, 15, 18, 21, 24, …
   Multiples of 9: 9, 18, 27, 36, 45, 54, …
   Multiples of 18: 18, 36, 54, …

   What is the least common number in all three lists of multiples?
   18 The LCM is 18.
2. Write equivalent fractions that have 18 in the denominators.

   $\frac{2}{3} = \frac{2 \times 6}{3 \times 6} = \frac{12}{18}$ $\frac{7}{9} = \frac{7 \times 2}{9 \times 2} = \frac{14}{18}$ $\frac{4}{18} = \frac{4 \times 1}{18 \times 1} = \frac{4}{18}$
3. Compare the numerators of the equivalent fractions.

   4 < 12 < 14
4. Order the fractions from least to greatest.

   $\frac{4}{18} < \frac{12}{18} < \frac{14}{18}$ means that $\frac{4}{18} < \frac{2}{3} < \frac{7}{9}$.

   So, from least to greatest, the fractions are $\frac{4}{18}, \frac{2}{3}, \frac{7}{9}$.

GO ON

English Learner Strategy

Compare to $\frac{1}{2}$ Ordering several fractions can be overwhelming for struggling students. One strategy is to first separate the fractions into two groups: those fractions greater than $\frac{1}{2}$ and those less than $\frac{1}{2}$. This helps students so that they have fewer fractions to compare at a time.

Additional *Example 3*

Order the fractions $\frac{2}{3}$, $\frac{3}{5}$, and $\frac{5}{9}$ from least to greatest.

1. Find the LCM of 3, 5, and 9.

   Multiples of 3: 3, 6, 9, 12, 15, 18, 21, 24, 27, 30, 33, 36, 39, 42, 45, . . .

   Multiples of 5: 5, 10, 15, 20, 25, 30, 35, 40, 45, . . .

   Multiples of 9: 9, 18, 27, 36, 45, . . .

   The least number in all three lists of mulitples is 45. The LCM is 45.
2. Write equivalent fractions that have 45 as their denominators.

   $$\frac{2}{3} = \frac{2 \times 15}{3 \times 15} = \frac{30}{45}$$

   $$\frac{3}{5} = \frac{3 \times 9}{5 \times 9} = \frac{27}{45}$$

   $$\frac{5}{9} = \frac{5 \times 5}{9 \times 5} = \frac{25}{45}$$
3. Compare the numerators of the equivalent fractions. $25 < 27 < 30$
4. Order the fractions from least to greatest.

   $\frac{25}{45} < \frac{27}{45} < \frac{30}{45}$ means that $\frac{5}{9} < \frac{3}{5} < \frac{2}{3}$.

   So, from least to greatest, the fractions are $\frac{5}{9}, \frac{3}{5}, \frac{2}{3}$.

Note This!

Big Picture To get the big picture of the lesson, tell students to write the name of the lesson on top of their notes for the day. Then tell them to highlight the lesson and the key words throughout the day's notes.

3 Practice

Using Manipulatives

Fraction Tiles Use fraction tiles as a model to compare fractions. Point out that the key part to using fraction tiles is that the tiles are the same length. Have students divide each tile into the same number of equal parts as the denominator and shade the numerator. Place the tiles side by side and compare the shaded parts. This will give students a visual model of comparing fractions.

Fraction Circles Have students use fraction circles as they would use fraction tiles.

On-Hand Manipulatives Use objects that can be divided into fractional parts, like paper circles or bars, granola bars, pizzas, or pancakes. Students can compare the fractional parts of these real-world items to compare fractions.

Who is Correct?

Use <, =, or > to compare $\frac{4}{5}$ and $\frac{4}{8}$.

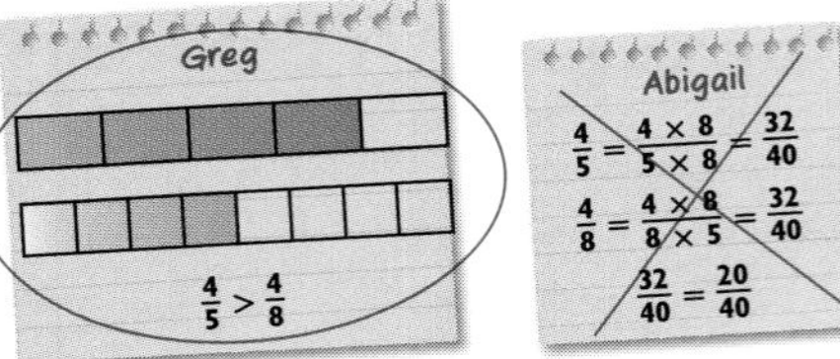

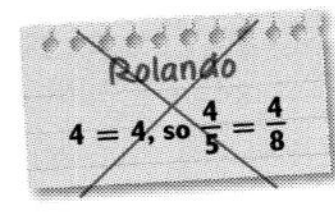

Circle correct answer(s). Cross out incorrect answer(s).

Guided Practice

Use <, =, or > to compare the fractions. Shade the models given.

1. $\frac{5}{6}$ (>) $\frac{3}{4}$

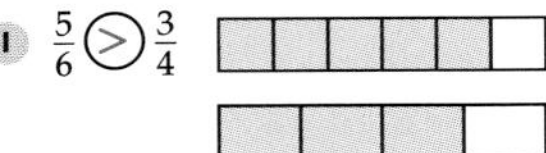

2. $\frac{3}{5}$ (>) $\frac{4}{10}$

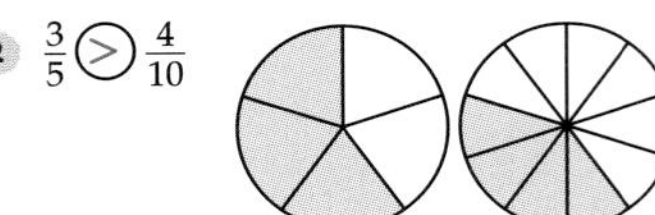

Step by Step Practice

3. Use <, =, or > to compare $\frac{2}{6}$ and $\frac{4}{9}$. Rename the fractions using a common denominator.

Step 1 Find the LCM of 6 and 9. 18

Step 2 Rename each fraction to an equivalent fraction.

$$\frac{2}{6} = \frac{2 \times 3}{6 \times 3} = \frac{6}{18} \qquad \frac{4}{9} = \frac{4 \times 2}{9 \times 2} = \frac{8}{18}$$

Step 3 Compare the numerators. Write a statement using the equivalent fractions. $\frac{6}{18}$ (<) $\frac{8}{18}$

Step 4 Replace the equivalent fractions with the original fractions. $\frac{2}{6}$ (<) $\frac{4}{9}$

Who *is Correct?*

Diagnostic Teaching

- Greg is correct. He used a model to find his answer.
- Abigail is incorrect. She did not multiply $\frac{4}{8}$ by an equivalent form of one.
- Rolando is incorrect. He compared only the numerators of the fractions.

Remind students that they can use models or rewrite the fractions with common denominators to compare them.

Order the fractions from least to greatest.

4. $\frac{5}{6}, \frac{3}{8}$, and $\frac{5}{12}$ ——— $\frac{3}{8}, \frac{5}{12}, \frac{5}{6}$

$\frac{5}{6} = \frac{5 \times 4}{6 \times 4} = \frac{20}{24}$

$\frac{3}{8} = \frac{3 \times 3}{8 \times 3} = \frac{9}{24}$

$\frac{5}{12} = \frac{5 \times 2}{12 \times 2} = \frac{10}{24}$

5. $\frac{1}{2}, \frac{2}{3}$, and $\frac{5}{9}$ ——— $\frac{1}{2}, \frac{5}{9}, \frac{2}{3}$

Step by Step Problem-Solving Practice

Problem-Solving Strategies
- ☑ Draw a diagram.
- ☐ Look for a pattern.
- ☐ Guess and check.
- ☐ Act it out.
- ☐ Solve a simpler problem.

Solve.

6. FITNESS Carissa and Laryssa are twins. They are very close in height. Carissa is 5 feet $2\frac{1}{4}$ inches tall, and Laryssa is 5 feet $2\frac{5}{8}$ inches tall. Who is taller?

Understand Read the problem. Write what you know.
Carissa is 5 feet $2\frac{1}{4}$ inches tall.
Laryssa is 5 feet $2\frac{5}{8}$ inches tall.

Plan Pick a strategy. One strategy is to draw a diagram.

Compare the two heights. Both heights are 5 feet and 2 inches. Only compare the fractional parts of each boy's height.

Draw a bar divided into 4 equal parts. Draw another bar of equal length. Divide it into 8 equal parts.

Solve Shade $\frac{1}{4}$ and $\frac{5}{8}$. Compare the shaded parts.

5 feet $2\frac{1}{4}$ (<) 5 feet $2\frac{5}{8}$

So, Laryssa is taller than Carissa.

Check Does the answer make sense?
Did you answer the question?

GO ON

English Learner Strategy

Make Connections Learning is primarily a process in which we make connections. Help students make more connections and construct meanings. Have students review the lessons in this chapter and the previous chapter and create an outline or graphic organizer that shows how the concepts of each lesson build on one another. Start students out by having them jot the phrase "Parts of a Whole" on a sheet of paper. Then have students review their text and complete the diagram with the other concepts that they have learned. Encourage them to add on to their outlines or organizers as they complete the study of the textbook. Show students examples of flowcharts, main-idea charts, tables, tree diagrams, and other graphic organizers to get them started.

Are They Getting It?

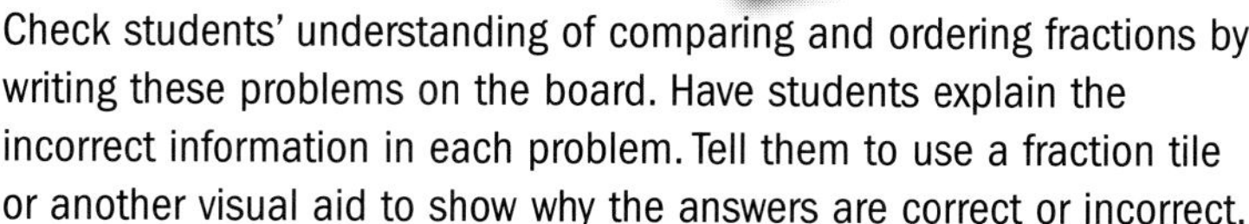

Check students' understanding of comparing and ordering fractions by writing these problems on the board. Have students explain the incorrect information in each problem. Tell them to use a fraction tile or another visual aid to show why the answers are correct or incorrect.

Order the fractions from least to greatest.

1. $\frac{2}{4}, \frac{3}{4}, \frac{4}{5}$ — $\frac{4}{5}, \frac{3}{4}, \frac{2}{4}$ — This is incorrect. The order is from greatest to least.
2. $\frac{5}{6}, \frac{6}{9}, \frac{7}{10}$ — $\frac{6}{9}, \frac{7}{10}, \frac{5}{6}$ — This is correct.
3. $\frac{6}{8}, \frac{8}{11}, \frac{10}{13}$ — $\frac{6}{8}, \frac{8}{11}, \frac{10}{13}$ — This is incorrect. The first two fractions should be switched.

Common Error *Alert*

Exercise 7 Encourage students to draw models of the baking pans in Exercise 7 to help them to compare the fractions.

Odd/Even Assignments

Exercises 10–26 are structured so that students practice the same concepts whether they are assigned the odd or even problems.

In-Class Assignment

Have students complete Exercises 11, 20, 25, and 29 to ensure that they understand the concept.

7 FOOD A taco casserole is cut into 36 equal pieces. In a same-sized pan, macaroni and cheese is cut into 24 equal pieces. At lunch, 24 pieces of the taco casserole are eaten, and 21 pieces of the macaroni are eaten. Which pan has more left in it?
Check off each step.

✓ Understand: I circled key words.

✓ Plan: To solve the problem, I will draw a diagram.

✓ Solve: The answer is more taco casserole is left.

✓ Check: I checked my answer by finding the LCD and simplifying the fraction.

8 WEATHER On Wednesday, it rained $\frac{6}{8}$ inch in Columbus and $\frac{5}{12}$ inch in Cleveland. Which city got more rain?

Columbus

9 **Reflect** Mindy said that $\frac{5}{8}$ is greater than $\frac{3}{4}$ because $5 > 3$ and $8 > 4$. Draw diagrams. Explain if Mindy is correct.

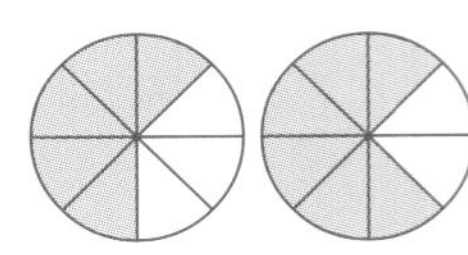

Sample answer: Mindy is incorrect. The equivalent form of $\frac{3}{4}$ is $\frac{6}{8}$, which is greater than $\frac{5}{8}$.

Skills, Concepts, and Problem Solving

Use <, =, or > to compare the fractions. Shade the models given.

10 $\frac{5}{10} = \frac{4}{8}$

11 $\frac{3}{8} < \frac{5}{6}$

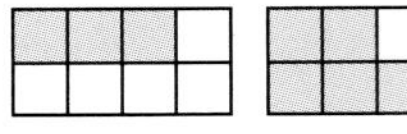

12 $\frac{6}{10} > \frac{3}{7}$

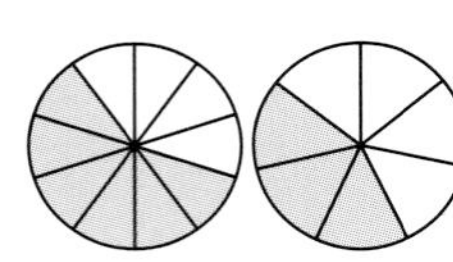

13 $\frac{7}{8} > \frac{5}{12}$

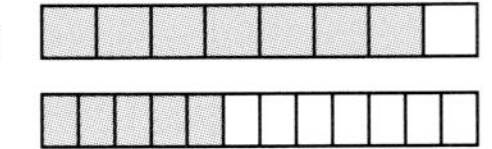

220 **Chapter 5** Fractions

English Learner Strategy

Guiding Questions If students continue to have difficulty renaming fractions to equivalent fractions before comparing them, ask the following questions.

- How can I find a fraction that is equivalent to $\frac{4}{12}$?
- How do you know if two fractions are equivalent?
- What makes the fractions $\frac{2}{3}$ and $\frac{8}{12}$ equivalent?
- What are two other fractions that are equivalent to $\frac{1}{4}$?

Use <, =, or > to compare the fractions. Shade the models given.

14 $\frac{1}{4}$ (<) $\frac{3}{8}$

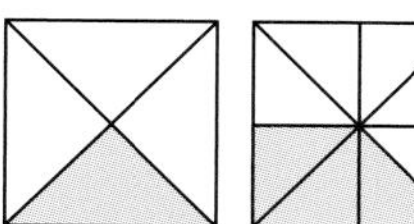

15 $\frac{1}{4}$ (<) $\frac{4}{7}$

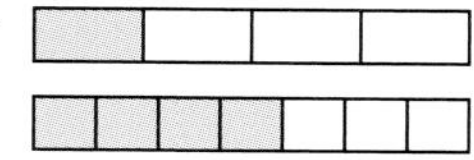

Order the fractions from least to greatest.

16 $\frac{1}{4}$ and $\frac{5}{6}$ $\frac{1}{4}, \frac{5}{6}$

17 $\frac{1}{8}$ and $\frac{5}{12}$ $\frac{1}{8}, \frac{5}{12}$

18 $\frac{1}{3}, \frac{1}{4},$ and $\frac{3}{5}$ $\frac{1}{4}, \frac{1}{3}, \frac{3}{5}$

19 $\frac{1}{2}, \frac{1}{3},$ and $\frac{2}{9}$ $\frac{2}{9}, \frac{1}{3}, \frac{1}{2}$

20 $\frac{1}{2}, \frac{2}{3}, \frac{7}{9},$ and $\frac{3}{12}$ $\frac{3}{12}, \frac{1}{2}, \frac{2}{3}, \frac{7}{9}$

21 $\frac{1}{2}, \frac{1}{3}, \frac{5}{6},$ and $\frac{2}{9}$ $\frac{2}{9}, \frac{1}{3}, \frac{1}{2}, \frac{5}{6}$

22 $\frac{2}{3}, \frac{3}{4}, \frac{3}{8},$ and $\frac{5}{12}$ $\frac{3}{8}, \frac{5}{12}, \frac{2}{3}, \frac{3}{4}$

23 $\frac{1}{2}, \frac{3}{5}, \frac{7}{10},$ and $\frac{5}{12}$ $\frac{5}{12}, \frac{1}{2}, \frac{3}{5}, \frac{7}{10}$

Solve.

24 BAKING Jodi needs $2\frac{3}{4}$ cups of flour to make a cake. She has $2\frac{5}{8}$ cups. Does she have enough? Explain.

No. She needs $2\frac{3}{4}$ cups, which equals $2\frac{6}{8}$. She has $2\frac{5}{8}$. She needs $\frac{1}{8}$ cup more flour.

25 ENTERTAINMENT Clara and Gwen went to the county fair. There was a pie-eating contest. The top three contestants ate $5\frac{5}{6}$ pies, $5\frac{11}{12}$ pies, and $5\frac{7}{8}$ pies, respectively. Which contestant ate the most pie? Who ate the least?

Contestant 2 ate the most at $5\frac{11}{12}$ pies, and Contestant 1 ate the least at $5\frac{5}{6}$.

26 SPORTS Ivan and Jamal each collected 6 soccer balls from the field. Divide the set of soccer balls to show that $\frac{1}{2} > \frac{1}{3}$.

Circle $\frac{1}{2}$ of the set of 6 soccer balls.

Circle $\frac{1}{3}$ of the set of 6 soccer balls.

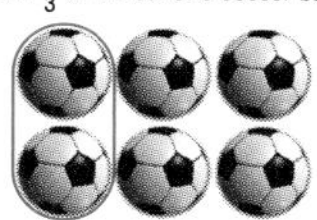

GO ON

Common Error *Alert*

Exercises 16–23 Remind students to write the original fractions in the answer, not the fractions with the common denominators.

Math Challenge

Greatest Fraction Make a set of 20 fraction cards. Students deal out all the cards evenly, keeping their cards facedown in front of them. Each student will flip his or her top card. The student who has the greatest fraction wins the cards. If the fractions are equivalent, students flip their next card. The student with the most cards at the end of the game wins.

4 Assess

See It, Do It, Say It, Write It

Step 1 Write three fractions on the board. Model how to compare and order each fraction with a drawing or model. Do this several times with different fractions.

Step 2 Give students a few fractions to compare and order. Repeat with students using models. Share solutions in a class discussion.

Step 3 Have students work in pairs. Write three fractions on the board. Tell students to make a model to represent each fraction on the board. Have students share their work with the class. Repeat several times.

Step 4 Have students work alone. Tell them to write how to compare and order fractions and tell them to include a picture or a model.

Looking Ahead: Pre-teach

Simplify Fractions In the next lesson, students will learn how to simplify fractions.

Example

Write $\frac{24}{42}$ in simplest form. Divide by the GCF.

1. List all the factors of the numerator and the denominator.

   The factors of 24 are: 1, 2, 3, 4, 6, 8, 12, 24

   The factors of 42 are: 1, 2, 3, 6, 7, 14, 21, 42

2. The greatest number in both lists is 6.
3. Divide the numerator and the denominator by the GCF.

   $\frac{24}{42} = \frac{24 \div 6}{42 \div 6} = \frac{4}{7}$

4. $\frac{24}{42}$ in simplest form is $\frac{4}{7}$.

Simply.

1. $\frac{15}{20}$ $\frac{3}{4}$
2. $\frac{26}{30}$ $\frac{13}{15}$

Vocabulary Check **Write the vocabulary word that completes each sentence.**

27 A(n) common denominator is the same denominator in two or more fractions.

28 The least common multiple or LCM is the least number greater than 1 that is a common multiple of each of two or more numbers.

29 **Writing in Math** Tim said that he ate more pizza than his younger brother. Tim ate $\frac{1}{2}$ of a pizza, and his younger brother ate $\frac{9}{10}$ of a pizza. Is Tim correct? Explain your reasoning.

No; Tim ate $\frac{1}{2}$ of a pizza. Using 10 as the LCD, $\frac{1}{2} = \frac{5}{10}$. Tim ate 5 out of 10 pieces of pizza, while his younger brother ate 9 out of 10 pieces of pizza.

Spiral Review

Solve. (Lesson 5-2, p. 189)

30 GROCERIES A 5-pound bag of medium-sized potatoes has 20 potatoes. A 2-pound bag of small potatoes has 16 potatoes. In each bag, how much does one potato weigh?

$\frac{1}{4}$ lb in the 5-lb bag; $\frac{1}{8}$ lb in the 2-lb bag

Draw a picture to model each fraction. Use equal parts of a whole or of a set. (Lesson 5-1, p. 182)

31 $\frac{2}{3}$

32 $\frac{7}{10}$

33 $\frac{6}{6}$

34 $\frac{1}{4}$

STOP

222 Chapter 5 Fractions

Ticket Out the Door

Order Students Have students work in groups of four. Assign each student a fraction. Have each group of students come to the head of the class. Students will place themselves in order from least to greatest and call out their fraction. You might want to write the equality sentence on the board with their presentation. Students will go back to their seats, exiting the classroom at the end of the presentations.

Lesson 5-6 Simplify Fractions

KEY Concept

A fraction is in **simplest form** or lowest terms when the numerator and the denominator of the fraction have no common factor other than 1.

How many fourths of this pizza are left to eat?

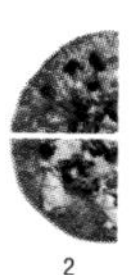

$\frac{2}{4}$

How much of this pizza is left to eat?

$\frac{1}{2}$ simplest form

The pizzas are equal in size. $\frac{1}{2}$ is written in simplest form because there is no number that will evenly divide into both the numerator and the denominator.

VOCABULARY

greatest common factor (GCF)
the greatest number that is a factor of two or more numbers
Example: The greatest common factor of 12, 18, and 30 is 6.

simplest form
a fraction in which the numerator and the denominator have no common factor greater than 1
Example: $\frac{3}{5}$ is the simplest form of $\frac{6}{10}$.

Any fraction can be written in simplest form by dividing the numerator and denominator by the GCF. You can also simplify using models and prime factorization.

Example 1

Write $\frac{8}{10}$ in simplest form. Use models. Shade an equivalent area and name the simplified fraction.

What factor divides evenly into 8 and 10?

1. Shade the circle segments so the shading in both circles covers the same amount of each circle.
2. Count the total number of parts and the shaded parts of the circle on the right. Write the equivalent fraction.

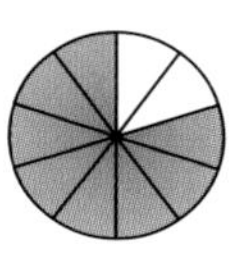

simplest form

$\frac{8}{10} = \frac{4}{5}$

Lesson Notes

Lesson 5-6

Lesson Planner

Objective Write fractions in simplest form.

Vocabulary **greatest common factor (GCF), simplest form**

Materials/Manipulatives everyday objects, fraction circles, grid paper, hundred table, index cards

Chapter Resource Masters

- CRM Vocabulary and English Language Development (p. A116)
- CRM Skills Practice (p. A117)
- CRM Problem-Solving Practice (p. A118)
- CRM Homework Practice (p. A119)

1 Introduce

Vocabulary

Vocabulary Use Write several fractions on the board, some in simplest form and some that need to be simplified. Call on students to determine whether each fraction is in *simplest form* or not.

2 Teach

Key Concept

Foundational Skills and Concepts After students have read through the Key Concept box, have them try these exercises.

1. How do you know when a fraction is in simplest form? There is no number that will evenly divide into both the numerator and denominator.
2. Write $\frac{2}{4}$ in simplest form. $\frac{1}{2}$

Additional *Example 1*

Write $\frac{3}{9}$ in simplest form. Use models. Shade an equivalent area and name the simplified fraction.

1. Shade the circle segments so the shading in both circles covers the same amount of each circle.
2. Count the total parts and the shaded parts of the circle below. Write the equivalent fraction.

What factor divides evenly into 3 and 9?

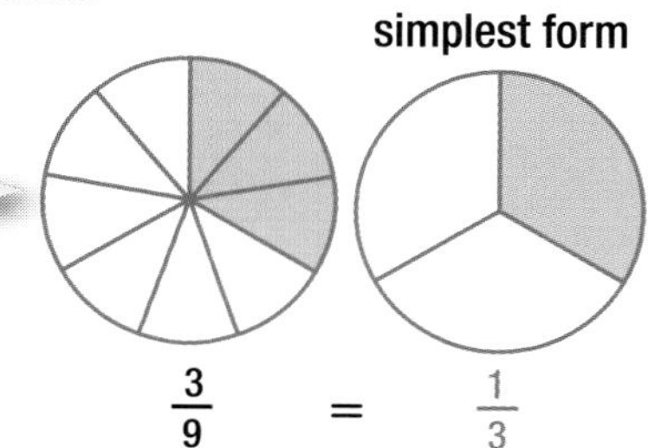

simplest form

$\frac{3}{9} = \frac{1}{3}$

Additional **Example 2**

Write $\frac{24}{40}$ in simplest form. Divide by the GCF.

1. List all the factors of the numerator and denominator.

   Factors of 24: 1, 2, 3, 4, 6, (8), 12, 24

   Factors of 40: 1, 2, 4, 5, (8), 10, 20, 40

2. The greatest common factor (GCF) is the greatest factor the numbers have in common. The greatest number in both lists is 8.

   Because 8 is the greatest number that will evenly divide both the numerator and the denominator, 8 is the GCF.

3. Divide the numerator and denominator by the GCF.

   $$\frac{24}{40} = \frac{24 \div 8}{40 \div 8} = \frac{3}{5}$$

4. So, $\frac{24}{40}$ in simplest form is $\frac{3}{5}$.

Common Error *Alert*

Simplify Fractions Students often encounter two major difficulties when simplifying fractions. First, they may have trouble finding a common factor when it is not obvious. The other common error is not simplifying a fraction to its lowest terms.

Remind students that a fraction is in simplest form when the numerator and denominator have no factors in common other than 1.

YOUR TURN!

Write $\frac{3}{15}$ in simplest form. Use models. Shade an equivalent area and name the simplified fraction.

1. Shade the circle segments so the shading in both circles covers the same amount of each circle.
2. Count the total number of parts and the shaded parts of the circle on the right. Write the equivalent fraction.

fraction = simplest form

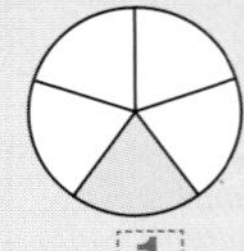

$\frac{3}{15} = \frac{1}{5}$

Example 2

Write $\frac{12}{20}$ in simplest form. Divide by the GCF.

Remember a factor is a number that is multiplied by another number to get a product. Example: 2 and 3 are factors of 6.

1. List all the factors of the numerator and the denominator.

   Factors of 12: 1, 2, 3, (4), 6, 12 Factors of 20: 1, 2, (4), 5, 10, 20

2. The **greatest common factor (GCF)** is the greatest factor the numbers have in common. The greatest number in both lists is 4. Because 4 is the greatest number that will evenly divide both the numerator and the denominator, 4 is the GCF.

   $\frac{12}{20}$ Both can be divided by 2 and 4.

3. Divide the numerator and denominator by the GCF. $\frac{12}{20} = \frac{12 \div 4}{20 \div 4} = \frac{3}{5}$

4. So, $\frac{12}{20}$ in simplest form is $\frac{3}{5}$.

YOUR TURN!

Write $\frac{15}{50}$ in simplest form. Divide by the GCF.

1. List all the factors of the numerator and the denominator.

   Factors of 15: 1, 3, 5, 15 Factors of 50: 1, 2, 5, 10, 25, 50

2. What is the greatest common number in both lists? 5

   The GCF of 15 and 50 is 5.

3. Divide the numerator and denominator by the GCF. $\frac{15}{50} = \frac{15 \div 5}{50 \div 5} = \frac{3}{10}$

4. What is the simplest form of $\frac{15}{50}$? $\frac{3}{10}$

224 Chapter 5 Fractions

Intervention Strategy Logical/Visual Learners

Tell students that they can simplify fractions by using prime factorization. To help them find the prime numbers from 1 to 100, have them make a chart of the numbers 1 to 100. Then follow the steps below.

1. Cross out 1. It is not a prime number.
2. Circle 2. It is the least positive prime number.
3. Cross out every multiple of 2.
4. Circle 3. It is another prime number.
5. Cross out all of the multiples of 3 (that are not already crossed out).
6. Circle 5, another prime number. Cross out all the multiples of 5.
7. Have students continue this process until all the numbers are circled or crossed out.

1	2	3	4	5	6	7	8	9	10
11	12	13	14	15	16	17	18	19	20
21	22	23	24	25	26	27	28	29	30
31	32	33	34	35	36	37	38	39	40
41	42	43	44	45	46	47	48	49	50
51	52	53	54	55	56	57	58	59	60
61	62	63	64	65	66	67	68	69	70
71	72	73	74	75	76	77	78	79	80
81	82	83	84	85	86	87	88	89	90
91	92	93	94	95	96	97	98	99	100

Example 3

Write $\frac{18}{30}$ in simplest form. Use prime factorization.

1. Use a factor tree to write the numerator as a product of prime numbers.
2. Use a factor tree to write the denominator as a product of prime numbers.
3. Replace the numerator with its prime factors. Replace the denominator with its prime factors. Find all equivalent forms of 1.

$\frac{18}{30} = \frac{3 \times 2 \times 3}{3 \times 2 \times 5}$

4. Eliminate all equivalent forms of 1.

$\frac{18}{30} = \frac{\cancel{3} \times \cancel{2} \times 3}{\cancel{3} \times \cancel{2} \times 5}$ $\frac{18}{30} = \frac{3}{5}$

Write the number that is to be factored at the top.

Choose any pair of whole number factors of 18 and 30.

Continue to factor each number that is not a prime number.

YOUR TURN!

Write $\frac{12}{42}$ in simplest form. Use prime factorization.

1. Use a factor tree to write the numerator as a product of prime numbers.
2. Use a factor tree to write the denominator as a product of prime numbers.
3. Replace the numerator with its prime factors. Replace the denominator with its prime factors. Find all equivalent forms of 1.

$\frac{12}{42} = \frac{2 \times 3 \times 2}{2 \times 3 \times 7}$

4. Eliminate all equivalent forms of 1. $\frac{12}{42} = \frac{\cancel{2} \times \cancel{3} \times 2}{\cancel{2} \times \cancel{3} \times 7}$

$\frac{12}{42} = \frac{2}{7}$

GO ON

Lesson 5-6 Simplify Fractions 225

Additional Example 3

Write $\frac{14}{42}$ in simplest form. Use prime factorization.

1. Use a factor tree to write the numerator as a product of prime numbers.

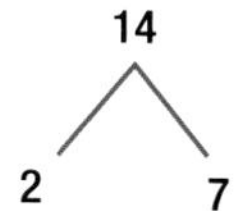

2. Use a factor tree to write the denominator as a product of prime numbers.

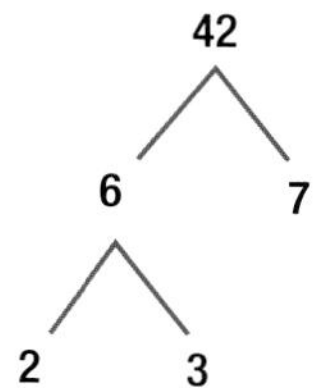

3. Replace the numerator with its prime factors. Replace the denominator with its prime factors. Find all equivalent forms of 1.

$\frac{14}{42} = \frac{2 \times 7 \times 1}{2 \times 7 \times 3}$

4. Eliminate all equivalent forms of 1.

$\frac{14}{42} = \frac{\cancel{2} \times \cancel{7} \times 1}{\cancel{2} \times \cancel{7} \times 3}$

$\frac{14}{42} = \frac{1}{3}$

Intervention Strategy Logical Learners

Practice Backward Have students work backward to check the prime factorization. Give students the following problem.

Which shows the prime factorization of 30?

A 3×10
B $2 \times 3 \times 5$
C 2×15
D $1 \times 5 \times 6$

Before students make their final choices, remind them that prime factorization fits two criteria:

1. It must include only prime numbers.
2. The factors must produce the correct product.

Give students similar exercises to practice.

Note This!

Describe Ask students to write a step-by-step description of how to simplify a fraction. Encourage them to include drawings and examples to support their descriptions.

3 Practice

Using Manipulatives

Grid Paper Suggest students use grid paper to model and find equivalent fractions.

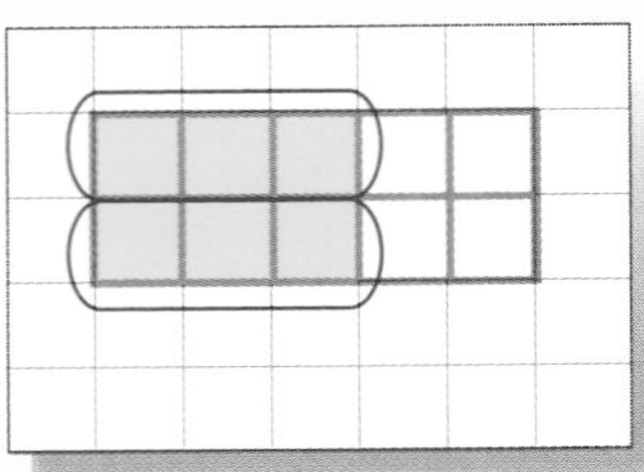

$\frac{6}{10} = \frac{3}{5}$

Fraction Circles Students can use fraction circles to write fractions in their simplest forms.
For Example 2:

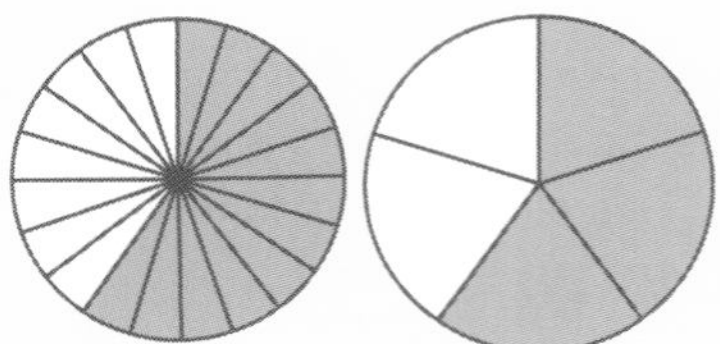

On-Hand Manipulatives Use objects that can be divided into fractional parts, like paper circles or bars, granola bars, pizzas, or pancakes. Students can compare the fractional parts of these real-world items to compare and simplify fractions.

Who is Correct?

Write $\frac{18}{45}$ in simplest form. Use any method.

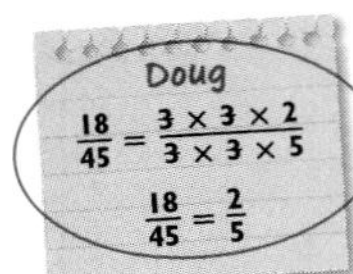

Doug
$\frac{18}{45} = \frac{3 \times 3 \times 2}{3 \times 3 \times 5}$
$\frac{18}{45} = \frac{2}{5}$

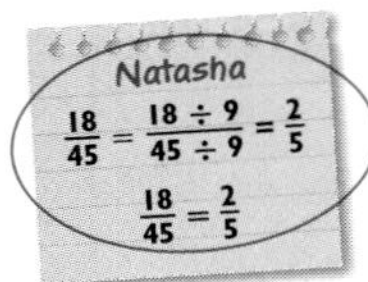

Natasha
$\frac{18}{45} = \frac{18 \div 9}{45 \div 9} = \frac{2}{5}$
$\frac{18}{45} = \frac{2}{5}$

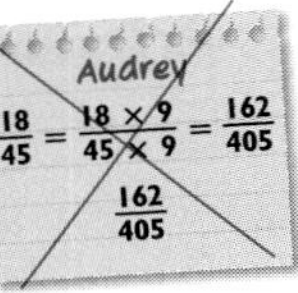

Audrey
$\frac{18}{45} = \frac{18 \times 9}{45 \times 9} = \frac{162}{405}$
$\frac{162}{405}$

Circle correct answer(s). Cross out incorrect answer(s).

Guided Practice

1. Write $\frac{6}{8}$ in simplest form. Use models. Shade an equivalent area and name the simplified fraction.

fraction = **simplest form**

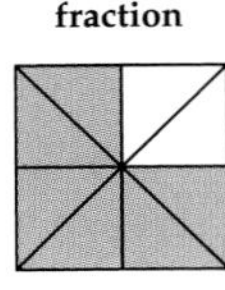

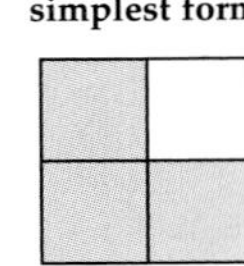

$\frac{6}{8}$ =

2. Write $\frac{4}{8}$ in simplest form. Divide by the GCF.

$\frac{4}{8} = \frac{4 \div 4}{8 \div 4} = \frac{1}{2}$

3. Write $\frac{8}{18}$ in simplest form. Divide by the GCF.

$\frac{8}{18} = \frac{8 \div 2}{18 \div 2} = \frac{4}{9}$

226 Chapter 5 Fractions

Who *is Correct?*

Diagnostic Teaching

- Doug is correct. He found the prime factors of the numerator and denominator and eliminated all equivalent forms of 1 to find the simplest form.
- Natasha is correct. She divided the numerator and denominator by 9 to find the simplest form.
- Audrey is incorrect. She multiplied by the GCF. The resulting fraction is not in simplest form.

Remind students that a fraction is in simplest form when the GCF of the numerator and denominator is 1.

Step by Step Practice

4 Write $\frac{12}{16}$ in simplest form. Use prime factorization.

Step 1 Write the numerator as a product of prime numbers.

Step 2 Write the denominator as a product of prime numbers.

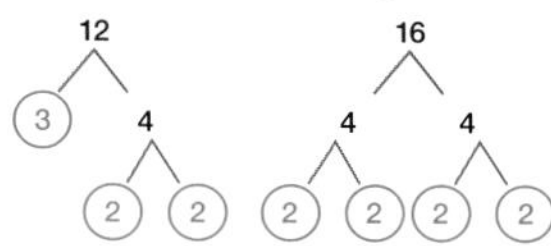

Step 3 Replace the numerator with its prime factors. Replace the denominator with its prime factors. Find and eliminate all equivalent forms of 1.

$$\frac{12}{16} = \frac{2 \times 2 \times 3}{2 \times 2 \times 2 \times 2} = \frac{3}{4}$$

Step 4 The simplest form of $\frac{12}{16}$ is $\frac{3}{4}$.

Write each fraction in simplest form. Use prime factorization.

5 $\frac{12}{30} = \frac{3 \times 2 \times 2}{3 \times 2 \times 5} = \frac{2}{5}$

6 $\frac{10}{15}$ $\frac{2}{3}$

7 $\frac{15}{18}$ $\frac{5}{6}$

8 $\frac{21}{28}$ $\frac{3}{4}$

Write each fraction in simplest form. Divide by the GCF.

9 $\frac{10}{25}$ $\frac{2}{5}$

10 $\frac{24}{32}$ $\frac{3}{4}$

11 $\frac{21}{49}$ $\frac{3}{7}$

Are They Getting It?

Check students' understanding of simplifying fractions by writing these problems on the board. Ask students to point out wrong answers and explain why they are wrong.

Write each fraction in simplest form.

1. $\frac{12}{36}$ $\quad \frac{12}{36} = \frac{12 \div 2}{36 \div 2} = \frac{6}{18}$ This is incorrect. It is not in simplest form.
2. $\frac{27}{33}$ $\quad \frac{27}{33} = \frac{3 \times 3 \times 3}{3 \times 11} = \frac{9}{11}$ This is correct.
3. $\frac{6}{7}$ $\quad \frac{6}{7} = \frac{12}{14}$ This is incorrect. It is not in simplest form.

Math Coach Notes

Use a Table Have students find equivalent and simplest fractions by thinking of the patterns on a multiplication table.

×	1	2	3	4	5	6	7	8	9	10
1	1	2	3	4	5	6	7	8	9	10
2	2	4	6	8	10	12	14	16	18	20
3	3	6	9	12	15	18	21	24	27	30
4	4	8	12	16	20	24	28	32	36	40
5	5	10	15	20	25	30	35	40	45	50
6	6	12	18	24	30	36	42	48	54	60
7	7	14	21	28	35	42	49	56	63	70
8	8	16	24	32	40	48	56	64	72	80
9	9	18	27	36	45	54	63	72	81	90
10	10	20	30	40	50	60	70	80	90	100

You can see the equivalent fractions for $\frac{3}{10}$ as you look across the table.

Common Error *Alert*

Factor Tree Students may have difficulty using a factor tree because they are not sure what to do next once they get to a prime number. Tell students that the branches end only at prime numbers. At that point, they are finished with that branch. Suggest they go back and multiply the prime numbers they find to make certain that their product is the original number.

Math Coach Notes

Study Tips Encourage students to list examples of real-world situations that involve simplifying fractions. For example, 3 out of 12, or $\frac{3}{12}$, of the songs on a CD have been played. This is $\frac{1}{4}$ of the songs. Or, there are 18 students in a group; 8 are boys. So, $\frac{4}{9}$ of the students are boys. Students are more likely to remember these examples because they are making connections to the material.

Step by Step Problem-Solving Practice

Problem-Solving Strategies
- ☐ Look for a pattern.
- ☑ Use logical reasoning.
- ☐ Solve a simpler problem.
- ☐ Work backward.
- ☐ Draw a diagram.

Solve.

12 LANDSCAPING Cody wants a border around his flower bed. He can choose brown or red bricks of the same size. If he uses brown bricks, he will use 54 of the 72 brown bricks he has. Write the fraction of the brown bricks he will use in simplest form.

Understand Read the problem. Write what you know.

He would use $\frac{54}{72}$ of the brown bricks.

Plan Pick a strategy. One strategy is to use logical reasoning.

Simplify the fraction that shows how many brown bricks he would use.

Solve Find the GCF of 54 and 72.

Divide the numerator and denominator by the GCF.

Factors of 54: 1, 2, 3, 6, 9, (18), 27, 54

Factors of 72: 1, 2, 3, 4, 6, 8, 9, 12, (18), 24, 36, 72

$$\frac{54}{72} = \frac{54 \div 18}{72 \div 18} = \frac{3}{4}$$

Check Use another method. Use prime factorization. Simplify the fraction.

Does your answer make sense? Did you answer the question?

Intervention Strategy Linguistic Learners

Write the Steps Encourage students to summarize and write the steps for simplifying fractions clearly and concisely in their notes. Have students work in small groups to present concise summaries to the class. Make sure students include the following points.

Simplify a Fraction

Method 1

1. Find a common factor of the numerator and denominator.
2. Divide both the numerator and denominator by the common factor.
3. Repeat this process until there are no more common factors.
4. The fraction is in simplest form when no more common factors exist.

Method 2

1. Find the GCF of the numerator and denominator.
2. Divide the numerator and the denominator by the GCF.

13 FITNESS James and Nat run on the track after school each day. James runs $\frac{16}{24}$ of a mile in 4 minutes. Nat runs $\frac{18}{27}$ of a mile in the same time. James says he ran faster. Is he correct? Explain.

Check off each step.

✓ Understand: I circled key words.

✓ Plan: To solve the problem, I will write each fraction in simplest form.

✓ Solve: The answer is no, they ran the same distance in same time.

✓ Check: I checked my answer by dividing each fraction by its GCF.

14 SCHOOL Doris correctly answered 54 out of 60 questions on her last test. What fraction of the questions did she answer correctly? $\frac{54}{60}$

Simplify your answer to its simplest form. $\frac{9}{10}$

What fraction of the questions did she answer incorrectly? $\frac{6}{60}$

Simplify your answer to its simplest form. $\frac{1}{10}$

15 **Reflect** Explain which method used for simplifying fractions you prefer and why.

Answers will vary. Students should select one of the following: using models, dividing by the GCF, or using prime factorization. Students should explain their answers.

Skills, Concepts, and Problem Solving

Write each fraction in simplest form. Use models. Shade an equivalent area and name the simplified fraction.

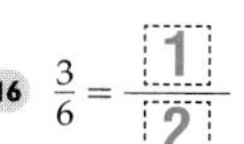

16 $\frac{3}{6} = \frac{1}{2}$

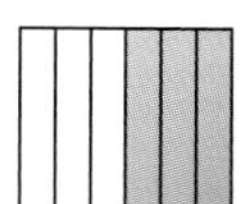

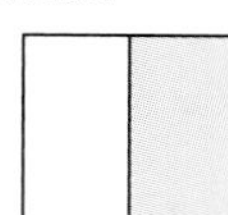

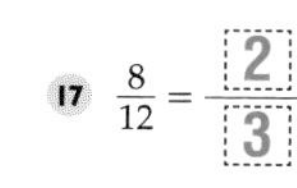

17 $\frac{8}{12} = \frac{2}{3}$

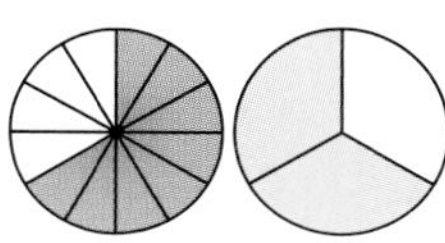

Write each fraction in simplest form. Use the GCF.

18 $\frac{36}{60} = \frac{3}{5}$ **19** $\frac{32}{40} = \frac{4}{5}$ **20** $\frac{60}{144} = \frac{5}{12}$ **21** $\frac{45}{90} = \frac{1}{2}$

GO ON

Math Challenge

Memory Game Have students write 10 pairs of fractions on index cards. Each pair will be a fraction and its equivalent in simplest form. Two students can shuffle their cards together and lay them facedown on the desk to play a memory game. One student chooses 2 cards. If they are equal, he or she wins the cards. If they are not equal, the cards are placed facedown where they were. The game is over when all the cards are gone. The student with the most cards wins.

Odd/Even Assignments

Exercises 16–27 are structured so that students practice the same concepts whether they are assigned the odd or even problems.

In-Class Assignment

Have students complete Exercises 16, 20, 25, 26, and 30 to ensure that they understand the concept.

English Learner Strategy

Guided Reading Sheets Place students into pairs. If possible, pair English Learners with native speakers of English. Have students work together to create guided reading sheets. Guided reading sheets consist of open-ended questions that ask for specific information given in the textbook. Students should include vocabulary and exercises in their guides. Have them create a separate answer sheet. Pairs should trade completed sheets with another pair to test their knowledge.

Intervention Strategy

Interpersonal/ Auditory Learners

Presentations Give student groups a fraction to simplify. Then assign each group either the method of shading in equivalent fractions, dividing by the GCF, or using prime factorization. Ask student groups to present their methods to the rest of the class. Encourage those sitting to ask questions and interact with the presenters.

4 Assess

See It, Do It, Say It, Write It

Step 1 Write a fraction on the board. Model how to write it in simplest form. Repeat with other fractions, using different methods.

Step 2 Give each student three fractions. Ask them to use the three methods taught in class to simply the fractions. They can work in pairs.

Step 3 Have students discuss their results with their partners. Have them check each other's work and give a new practice problem.

Step 4 Have students work alone. Tell students to write a paragraph about how they would simplify $\frac{12}{27}$. Ask them to include each step as well as the answer.

Math Coach Notes

Solve and Write Give students the following problem to solve. Thirty-six of 40 class members completed their homework last night. Express the fraction in simplest form. $\frac{9}{10}$

Then have students create their own word problems involving simplest form.

Write each fraction in simplest form. Use prime factorization.

22 $\frac{18}{27} = \frac{2}{3}$

23 $\frac{25}{30} = \frac{5}{6}$

24 $\frac{16}{48} = \frac{1}{3}$

25 $\frac{27}{39} = \frac{9}{13}$

Solve.

26 FOOD Rachel took 48 cookies to a picnic. She brought 8 cookies home. Write the fraction of cookies that were eaten in simplest form. $\frac{5 \text{ cookies eaten}}{6}$

The boys each made $\frac{4}{5}$ of the baskets attempted.

27 SPORTS Martin and Byron are playing a game where they each get 10 chances to throw a basketball into a hoop. After playing 6 games, they both make $\frac{4}{5}$ of the balls they throw. How many throws do they each make? 48 baskets

Vocabulary Check **Write the vocabulary word that completes each sentence.**

28 A fraction in simplest form is a fraction in which the numerator and the denominator have no common factor greater than 1.

29 The greatest common factor is the greatest number that divides evenly into two or more numbers.

30 Writing in Math Suppose that you had a fraction that had a symbol in it, such as $\frac{12x}{15x}$. What do you think this fraction is in simplest form? Explain your reasoning.

Answers will vary, but students should realize that an x divided by x is equivalent to one. The correct answer is $\frac{4}{5}$.

Spiral Review

Find the LCM of each set of numbers. (Lesson 5-5, p. 214)

31 2, 10, and 25 50

32 2, 3, and 7 42

Solve. (Lesson 5-4, p. 205)

33 COOKING A potato soup recipe needs $2\frac{3}{5}$ cups of milk. A broccoli soup recipe needs $2\frac{2}{3}$ cups of milk. Which recipe needs more milk? broccoli soup

Ticket Out the Door

Order Students Have students stand up in two single-file lines. The first student in one line should say a fraction. The first student in the second line should either state the fraction in simplest form or state that it is in simplest form. After you verify that the answer is correct, the next two students complete the activity. Students may exit after everyone has had a chance to either state or simplify a fraction.

Progress Check 3 (Lessons 5-5 and 5-6)

1 Write $\frac{4}{6}$ in simplest form. Solve by finding the GCF. $\frac{4}{6} = \frac{4}{6} \div \frac{2}{2} = \frac{2}{3}$

Write each fraction in simplest form.

2 $\frac{9}{12}$ $\frac{3}{4}$

3 $\frac{8}{32}$ $\frac{1}{4}$

4 $\frac{6}{14}$ $\frac{3}{7}$

5 $\frac{5}{25}$ $\frac{1}{5}$

Use <, =, or > to compare the fractions. Rename the fractions using a common denominator.

6 $\frac{2}{9} < \frac{7}{10}$

7 $\frac{3}{4} > \frac{1}{5}$

Order the fractions from least to greatest.

8 $\frac{1}{3}$ and $\frac{2}{5}$ $\frac{1}{3} < \frac{2}{5}$

9 $\frac{5}{9}$ and $\frac{7}{18}$ $\frac{7}{18} < \frac{5}{9}$

10 $\frac{2}{3}, \frac{2}{5}$, and $\frac{3}{4}$ $\frac{2}{5} < \frac{2}{3} < \frac{3}{4}$

11 $\frac{4}{9}, \frac{2}{3}$, and $\frac{3}{4}$ $\frac{4}{9} < \frac{2}{3} < \frac{3}{4}$

12 $\frac{3}{8}, \frac{1}{4}, \frac{3}{10}$, and $\frac{3}{5}$ $\frac{1}{4} < \frac{3}{10} < \frac{3}{8} < \frac{3}{5}$

13 $\frac{4}{5}, \frac{7}{20}, \frac{1}{2}$, and $\frac{9}{10}$ $\frac{7}{20} < \frac{1}{2} < \frac{4}{5} < \frac{9}{10}$

Solve.

14 **MONEY** Mrs. Hernandez's monthly budget is shown at the right. The most money is spent on food and health care. Which category has the next most money spent? housing

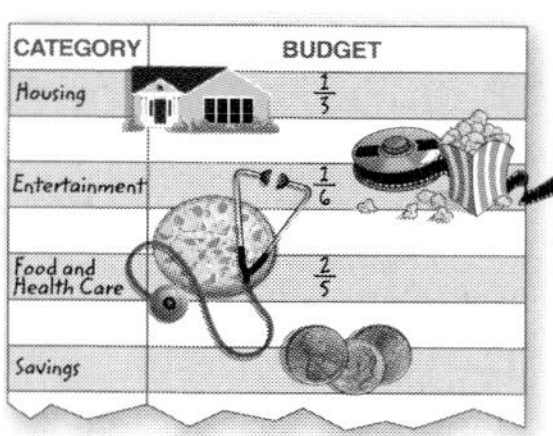

Chapter 5 Fractions 231

Progress Check 3

Chapter 5

Formative Assessment

Use the Progress Check to assess students' mastery of the previous lessons. Have students review the lesson indicated for the problems they answered incorrectly.

Odd/Even Assignments

Exercises are structured so that students practice the same concepts whether they are assigned the odd or even problems.

Common Error *Alert*

Key Abbreviations Students may need to be reminded of what GCF and LCD represent. The GCF is the greatest *factor* among a pair or set of numbers. The LCD is the least common denominator (or multiple) among given denominators.

EXERCISES 1–5 Students may find a simpler fraction, but not the simplest form of the fraction.

Data-Driven Decision Making

Students missing Exercises . . .	Have trouble with . . .	Should review and practice . . .
1–5	writing fractions in simplest form.	SSG Lesson 5-6, p. 223 CRM Skills Practice, p. A117
6–13	renaming fractions using a common denominator and using inequality signs to compare or order them.	SSG Lessons 5-5, p. 214 CRM Skills Practice, p. A113
14	solving word problems involving comparing fractions with different denominators.	CRM Problem-Solving Practice, pp. A114 and A118

Chapter 5 Study Guide
Formative Assessment

Vocabulary and Concept Check

If students have difficulty answering Exercises 1–6, remind them that they can use the page references to refresh their memories about the vocabulary terms.

Vocabulary Review Strategies

Vocabulary Flashcards Have students create their own sets of vocabulary flashcards by writing each vocabulary word on one side of index cards or half-sheets of paper. On the other side, they can either write the definition or an example that demonstrates the definition of the term.

The students can study the words by looking at the vocabulary term and stating its definition (flipping the card over to check and see if they got the definition correct), or they can read the side with the definition or study the example and state the corresponding vocabulary term (flipping the card over to see if they got the correct term).

Lesson Review

Each example walks the students through the main concepts of the chapter. If the given examples are not sufficient to review the questions, remind students that the page references tell them here to review that topic in their textbooks.

Find **Extra Practice** for these concepts in the Practice Worksheets, pages A96–A119.

Classroom Management

Pair and Share Pair a student who understands the material with another student who could use some support. Have students take turns explaining the examples to each other. In this case, they will both benefit, whether by doing the explaining or having it explained to them in a new way.

Chapter 5 Study Guide

Vocabulary and Concept Check

common denominators, *p. 214*
composite number, *p. 205*
equivalent forms of one, *p. 189*
equivalent fractions, *p. 189*
greatest common factor (GCF), *p. 205*
improper fraction, *p. 197*
least common denominator (LCD), *p. 205*
least common multiple (LCM), *p. 205*
mixed number, *p. 197*

Write the vocabulary word that completes each sentence.

1. The least common multiple of the denominators (bottom numbers) of two or more fractions is the least common denominator (LCD).
2. The least common multiple (LCM) is the least whole number greater than 0 that is a common multiple of two or more numbers.
3. A(n) mixed number is a number with a whole number part and fraction part.
4. $\left(\frac{3}{4} = \frac{6}{8}\right)$ is an example of equivalent fractions.

Label each diagram below. Write the correct vocabulary term in each blank.

5. numerator

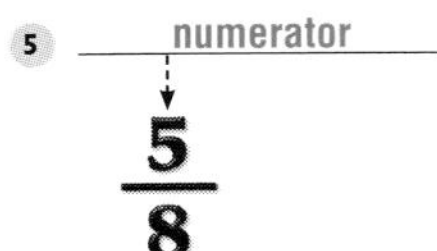

6. denominator

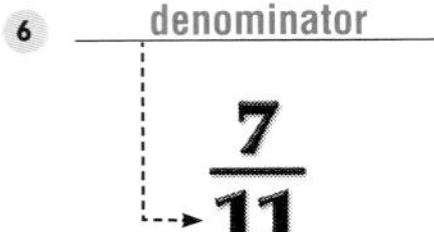

Lesson Review

5-1 Parts of a Whole and Parts of a Set (pp. 182–188)

Write a fraction to represent each situation.

7. the shaded region of the hexagon $\frac{1}{6}$

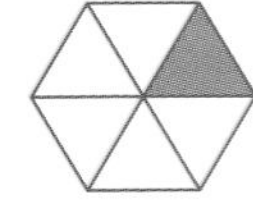

8. the number of hearts in the set $\frac{3}{6}$

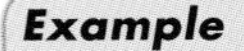

Example 1

Write a fraction to represent the shaded region of the rectangle.

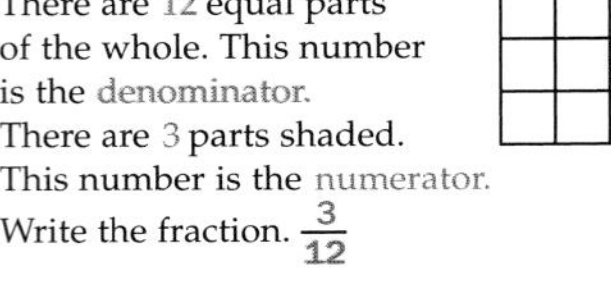

There are 12 equal parts of the whole. This number is the denominator.
There are 3 parts shaded. This number is the numerator.
Write the fraction. $\frac{3}{12}$

232 **Chapter 5** Study Guide

5-2 Equivalent Fractions and Equivalent Forms of One (pp. 189–195)

Complete to name an equivalent fraction.

9 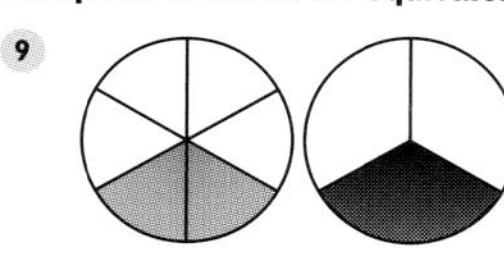

$\frac{2}{6} = \frac{1}{3}$

10 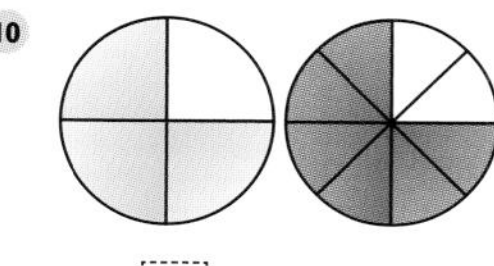

$\frac{3}{4} = \frac{6}{8}$

Example 1

Complete to name an equivalent fraction.

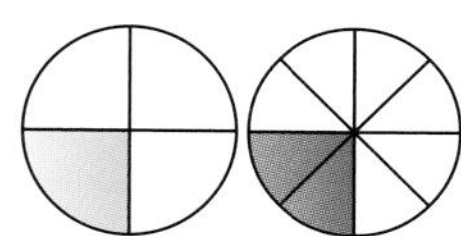

$\frac{1}{4} = \frac{2}{8}$

Ask yourself, "What can I multiply the denominator 4 by to get 8"?

Multiply 4 by 2 to get 8. Multiply the fraction by $\frac{2}{2}$.

$\frac{1}{4} = \frac{1 \times 2}{4 \times 2} = \frac{2}{8}$

So, $\frac{1}{4} = \frac{2}{8}$.

5-3 Mixed Numbers and Improper Fractions (pp. 197–204)

Name two equivalent fractions.

11 $\frac{1}{2}$ Sample answer: $\frac{2}{4}$; $\frac{3}{6}$

12 $\frac{1}{4}$ Sample answer: $\frac{2}{8}$; $\frac{3}{12}$

13 Write $4\frac{1}{5}$ as an improper fraction. $\frac{21}{5}$

14 Write $\frac{73}{4}$ as a mixed number. $18\frac{1}{4}$

Example 2

Write $3\frac{2}{4}$ as an improper fraction.

Multiply. 3×4
Add. $12 + 2$
Write the total number of fourths as an improper fraction.

$$\frac{3 \times 4 + 2}{4} = \frac{12 + 2}{4} = \frac{14}{4}$$

Dinah Zike's Foldables®

Review Remind students to complete and refer to their Foldables as they progress through the Chapter 5 Study Guide. Have students share their circular models. Then suggest that students share the examples they have written with a partner. Students should explain their examples to each other. (For complete instructions, see Chapter Resource Masters, p. A93.)

Math Coach Notes

Use Models Have students use models if they are in need of more visualization of equivalent fractions. For some students, actually seeing the same amounts of shading between graphs makes a significant difference from just following an algorithm.

Intervention Strategy — Kinesthetic Learners

Hands On! Create a BINGO game that is based upon changing back and forth between mixed numbers and improper fractions. For example, you could say, "G:$1\frac{2}{5}$." The students would have to look down their G columns on their BINGO cards for $\frac{7}{5}$.

Common Error *Alert*

Review more than one method for finding the LCMs and GCFs If students are having difficulty with Exercises 15–22, be sure that they know there is more than one method for arriving at the correct answer. One way is by listing factors and multiples; the other way is to use the prime factorization technique. Give them examples in addition to the ones in this study guide, if needed.

5-4 Least Common Denominator and Greatest Common Factors (pp. 205–212)

Find the least common multiple (LCM) of each set of numbers.

15 2, 4, and 7 28

16 2, 5, and 6 30

17 9, 8, and 36 72

18 4, 26, and 52 52

Find the greatest common factor (GCF) of each set of numbers.

19 14 and 70 14

20 20 and 75 5

21 48 and 80 16

22 45 and 120 15

Example 3

Find the least common multiple (LCM) of 3, 4, and 6.

List the multiples of each number. Find the numbers that are common in all three lists. The least of these numbers is the LCM.

Multiples of 3: 3, 6, 9, 12, 15, 18, 21, 24, 27, 30, …
Multiples of 4: 4, 8, 12, 16, 20, 24, 28, 32, …
Multiples of 6: 6, 12, 18, 24, …

The LCM of 3, 4, and 6 is 12.

Example 4

Find the greatest common factor (GCF) of 32 and 56 by using prime factors.

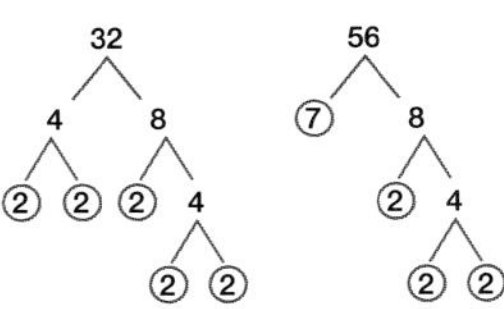

The common factors are 2, 2, and 2.
So, the GCF of 32 and 56 is $2 \times 2 \times 2$ or 8.

5-5 Compare and Order Fractions (pp. 214–222)

23 Use <, =, or > to compare $\frac{1}{6}$ and $\frac{2}{8}$. Shade the models given.

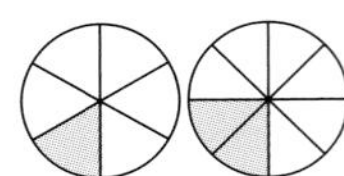

$\frac{1}{6} < \frac{2}{8}$

24 Use <, =, or > to compare $\frac{1}{3}$ and $\frac{2}{9}$. Rename the fractions using a common denominator.

$\frac{1}{3} > \frac{2}{9}$

Example 5

Use <, =, or > to compare $\frac{3}{4}$ and $\frac{4}{5}$. Shade the models given.

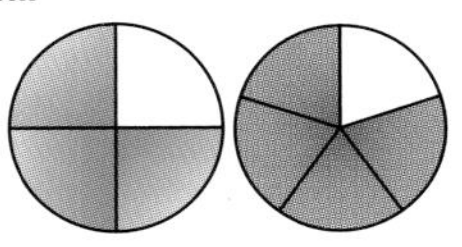

Compare the shaded areas.

Use <, =, or > to write a statement. $\frac{3}{4} < \frac{4}{5}$

234 Chapter 5 Study Guide

25 Order the fractions $\frac{3}{4}, \frac{5}{6}$, and $\frac{11}{12}$ from least to greatest.

$\frac{3}{4} < \frac{5}{6} < \frac{11}{12}$

26 $\frac{7}{8}, \frac{3}{4}, \frac{11}{14}$

$\frac{3}{4} < \frac{11}{14} < \frac{7}{8}$

27 $\frac{8}{30}, \frac{3}{15}, \frac{4}{45}$

$\frac{4}{45} < \frac{3}{15} < \frac{8}{30}$

Example 6

Order $\frac{5}{8}, \frac{4}{9}$, and $\frac{7}{12}$ from least to greatest.

Find the LCM of 8, 9, and 12.

Multiples of 8: 8, 16, 24, 32, 40, 48, 56, 64, 72, 80, ...
Multiples of 9: 9, 18, 27, 36, 45, 54, 63, 72, 81, ...
Multiples of 12: 12, 24, 36, 48, 60, 72, 84, ...

The LCD of the fractions is 72. Write equivalent fractions.

$\frac{5}{8} = \frac{5 \times 9}{8 \times 9} = \frac{45}{72}$ $\quad \frac{4}{9} = \frac{4 \times 8}{9 \times 8} = \frac{32}{72}$

$\frac{7}{12} = \frac{7 \times 6}{12 \times 6} = \frac{42}{72}$

$\frac{32}{72} < \frac{42}{72} < \frac{45}{72}$ means that $\frac{4}{9} < \frac{7}{12} < \frac{5}{8}$.

5-6 Simplify Fractions (pp. 223–230)

28 Write $\frac{6}{8}$ in simplest form. Shade an equivalent area and name the simplified fraction.

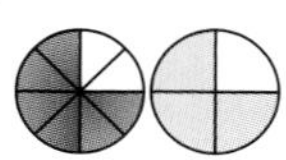

fraction = simplest form

$\frac{6}{8} = \frac{3}{4}$

Write each fraction in simplest form.

29 $\frac{20}{28} = \frac{5}{7}$

30 $\frac{14}{35} = \frac{2}{5}$

31 $\frac{18}{50} = \frac{9}{25}$

32 $\frac{9}{36} = \frac{1}{4}$

Example 7

Write $\frac{6}{10}$ in simplest form. Use models. Shade an equivalent area and name the simplified fraction.

Shade the segments so it covers same amount in each circle.

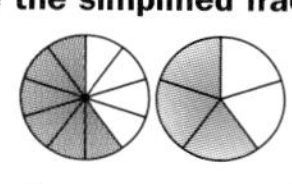

$\frac{6}{10} = \frac{3}{5}$

Example 8

Write $\frac{15}{18}$ in simplest form. Divide by the GCF.

List all the factors of the numerator and of the denominator.

Factors of 15: 1, (3), 5, 15
Factors of 18: 1, 2, (3), 6, 9, 18

The GCF of 15 and 18 is 3.

Divide the numerator and denominator by the GCF. $\frac{15}{18} = \frac{15 \div 3}{18 \div 3} = \frac{5}{6}$

Common Error Alert

Exercises 29–32 If students are having difficulty with Exercises 29-32, they may be attempting to simplify their fractions without performing all the steps listed in Example 8. Unless the numbers are extremely easy to work with, it is important to list all of the factors of both the numerator and denominator to help reduce the fraction to its simplest form. It is a common problem for a student to reduce a fraction but not with the greatest common factor. In other words, they are finding an equivalent fraction, but it is not in simplest form. Stress to students the importance of showing their work.

Intervention Strategy — Visual Learners

Use Models For some students, it may be very helpful if you provide them with a set of unshaded fraction circles that are divided into various numbers of sections. Then if students are having trouble making a comparison among fractions, the students could rely on their fraction circles.

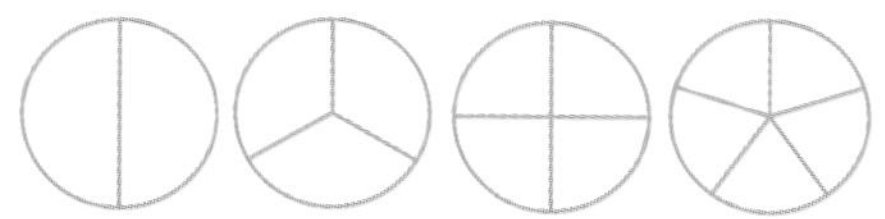

Ticket Out the Door

Do These Problems Have students answer seven problems of the following types: (1) writing equivalent fractions, (2) writing a mixed number as an improper fraction, (3) writing an improper fraction as a mixed number, (4) finding a least common denominator, (5) finding a greatest common factor, (6) comparing and ordering fractions, and (7) simplifying fractions. Ask them to write their answers and hand them to you as they exit the classroom.

Chapter 5 Chapter Test

Chapter Resource Masters

Additional forms of the Chapter 5 Tests are available.

Test Format	Where to Find it
Chapter 5 Test	Math Online macmillanmh.com
Blackline Masters	Assessment Masters, p. 64

Customize and create multiple versions of your chapter test and their answer keys. All of these questions from the chapter tests are also available on ExamView® Assessment Suite.

Online Assessment and Reporting
macmillanmh.com

This online assessment tool allows teachers to track student process with easily accessible, comprehensive reports available for every student. Assess students using any internet-ready computer.

Alternative Assessment

Use Portfolios Ask students to write examples of all the different types of problems from this chapter. This should include all of the following: naming equivalent fractions, changing a mixed number to an improper fraction, changing an improper fraction to a mixed number, finding the LCD, finding the GCF, comparing fractions, ordering fractions from least to greatest, and simplifying (reducing) fractions.

Chapter 5 Chapter Test

Write a fraction to represent each shaded region or part of a set.

1. 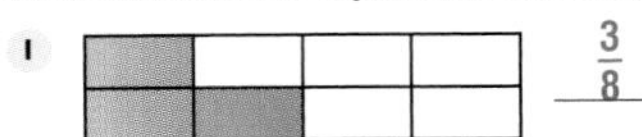 $\frac{3}{8}$

2.  $\frac{2}{7}$

Name two equivalent fractions.

3. $\frac{1}{6}$ Sample answer: $\frac{2}{12}, \frac{3}{18}$

4. $\frac{9}{12}$ Sample answer: $\frac{3}{4}, \frac{18}{24}$

Write each mixed number as an improper fraction.

5. $3\frac{2}{5} = \frac{17}{5}$

6. $2\frac{1}{5} = \frac{11}{5}$

7. $7\frac{4}{9} = \frac{67}{9}$

8. $4\frac{1}{4} = \frac{17}{4}$

Write each improper fraction as a mixed number.

9. $\frac{23}{4} = 5\frac{3}{4}$

10. $\frac{27}{12} = 2\frac{3}{12}$

Use <, =, or > to compare the pairs of fractions. Rename the fractions using a common denominator.

11. $\frac{1}{5} < \frac{2}{9}$

12. $\frac{3}{8} < \frac{5}{12}$

Find the least common multiple (LCM) of each set of numbers.

13. 3, 7, and 9 63

14. 2, 3, and 8 24

Order the fraction sets from least to greatest.

15. $\frac{4}{9}, \frac{3}{5}$, and $\frac{1}{2}$ $\frac{4}{9} < \frac{1}{2} < \frac{3}{5}$

16. $\frac{2}{3}, \frac{3}{5}$, and $\frac{6}{8}$ $\frac{3}{5} < \frac{2}{3} < \frac{6}{8}$

GO ON

236 Chapter 5 Test

English Learner Strategy

Assessment Allow students time to look over the assessment. Have students take a close look at all the words and symbols in the problem directives, as well as all of the terms in the word problems. Be sure students understand what is being asked of them in each problem. If there are some students struggling with terminology, try to offer further explanation of what is being asked.

17 Write $\frac{18}{20}$ in simplest form. Divide by the GCF.

The GCF is 2. The simplest form of $\frac{18}{20}$ is $\frac{9}{10}$.

Solve.

18 **ENTERTAINMENT** At a reception, two cakes were the same size. One cake was cut into 36 equal pieces. The other cake was cut into 48 equal pieces. At the end, there was exactly the same amount of each cake remaining. If 12 pieces of the 36-piece cake were left, then how many pieces of the 48-piece cake were left?

16 pieces

19 **CONSTRUCTION** A carpenter had a stack of boards. He cut each board into 4 equal pieces. He used 17 pieces. Write an improper fraction and a mixed number for the number of board pieces he used.

$\frac{17}{4}$, $4\frac{1}{4}$ boards

20 **CAFETERIA** On Wednesdays, $\frac{1}{4}$ of the students buy pizza. On Fridays, $\frac{1}{2}$ of the same number of students buy sandwiches. Which item is bought by more students?

sandwiches; $\frac{1}{2} > \frac{1}{4}$

Correct the mistakes.

21 Blake took 36 cupcakes to school. He brought one dozen cupcakes home. He said that $\frac{1}{3}$ of the cupcakes were eaten. What mistake did Blake make?

Actually, $\frac{1}{3}$ of the cupcakes were *not* eaten; $\frac{2}{3}$ of the cupcakes were eaten.

Learning from Mistakes

Missed Questions Review commonly missed questions as a small group or class. Ask students to share their methods of answering each question. Try to point out when any errors occur and take corrective measures.

Data-Driven Decision Making

Students missing Exercises . . .	Have trouble with . . .	Should review and practice . . .
1-2	writing fractions from a model.	SSG Lesson 5-1, p.182
3–10	naming two equivalent fractions; writing mixed numbers as improper fractions and vice versa.	SSG Lessons 5-2, 5-3, pp. 189 and 197 CRM Skills Practice, pp. A101 and A105
11–12	renaming and comparing fractions.	SSG Lessons 5-4, 5-5, pp. 205 and 214 CRM Skills Practice, p. A113
13–16	finding the LCM and ordering fractions from least to greatest.	SSG Lessons 5-4, 5-5, pp. 205 and 214 CRM Skills Practice, pp. A109 and A113
17	writing a fraction in simplest form.	SSG Lessons 5-6, p. 223 CRM Skills Practice, p. A117
18–21	solving word problems involving fractions.	CRM Problem-Solving Practice, pp. A102, A106, A110, and A114

Test Practice

Diagnose Student Errors

Survey student responses for each item. Class trends may indicate common errors and misconceptions.

1. (A) correct
B miscalculated equivalency
C misinterpreted how many pieces Yago ate
D set up fraction inverted

2. A miscalculated equivalency, $\frac{3}{9} = \frac{1}{3}$
(B) correct
C added 2 to numerator and denominator
D guess

3. A compared numerators or denominators and did not make equivalent denominators
B miscalculated equivalency
(C) correct
D misinterpreted concept of comparison

4. A guess
(B) correct
C misread number of shaded parts in fraction
D miscalculated equivalency of shaded parts in fraction

5. A ordered fractions from greatest to least
B guess
(C) correct
D guess

6. A guess
(B) correct
C changed the order of the fractions
D misinterpreted concept of comparison

7. A guess
(B) correct
C miscalculated denominator
D misinterpreted number of shaded parts in model

8. (A) correct
B guess
C miscalculated equivalency, $\frac{1}{2} = \frac{5}{10}$
D miscalculated equivalency, $\frac{2}{5} = \frac{4}{10}$

Test Practice

Choose the best answer and fill in the corresponding circle on the sheet at right.

1 Marnie and Yago shared a pizza. The pizza was cut into 8 equal pieces. If Yago ate 4 of the pieces, what fraction of the pizza did he eat?

(A) $\frac{1}{2}$ C $\frac{7}{8}$
B $\frac{3}{4}$ D 2

2 Which fraction is equal to $\frac{2}{3}$?

A $\frac{3}{9}$ C $\frac{4}{5}$
(B) $\frac{4}{6}$ D $\frac{7}{10}$

3 Which symbol makes the sentence true?

$\frac{7}{12} \square \frac{5}{6}$

A > (C) <
B = D +

4 Which mixed number does the model represent?

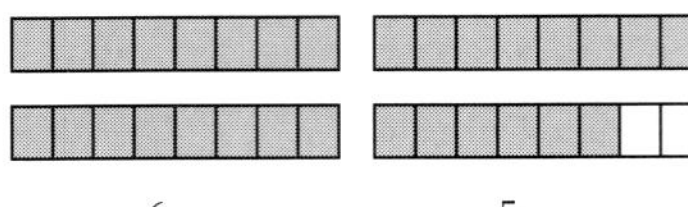

A $4\frac{6}{6}$ C $3\frac{5}{8}$
(B) $3\frac{3}{4}$ D $3\frac{1}{2}$

5 Order these fractions from least to greatest: $\frac{7}{8}, \frac{1}{2}, \frac{3}{4}$.

A $\frac{7}{8}, \frac{3}{4}, \frac{1}{2}$ (C) $\frac{1}{2}, \frac{3}{4}, \frac{7}{8}$
B $\frac{7}{8}, \frac{1}{2}, \frac{3}{4}$ D $\frac{3}{4}, \frac{7}{8}, \frac{1}{2}$

6 Salvador finished $\frac{4}{6}$ of his homework before dinner. His sister Sonia finished $\frac{6}{8}$ of her homework before dinner. Which math sentence is correct?

A $\frac{4}{6} > \frac{6}{8}$ C $\frac{6}{8} < \frac{4}{6}$
(B) $\frac{4}{6} < \frac{6}{8}$ D $\frac{4}{6} = \frac{6}{8}$

7 Which fraction does the shaded part of the model represent?

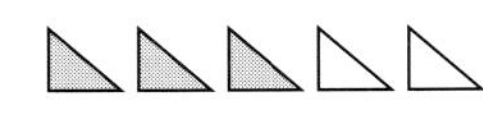

A $\frac{1}{4}$ C $\frac{3}{10}$
(B) $\frac{3}{5}$ D $\frac{2}{5}$

8 Write $\frac{8}{10}$ in simplest form.

(A) $\frac{4}{5}$ C $\frac{1}{2}$
B $\frac{2}{3}$ D $\frac{2}{5}$

GO ON

238 **Chapter 5** Test Practice

9. A misinterpreted number of parts in model
(B) correct
C guess
D misinterpreted number of shaded parts in model

10. A confused order of numerator and denominator
(B) correct
C misread denominator
D misread denominator

11. (A) correct
B misinterpreted relationship of fractions to one whole, $\frac{4}{5}$ not equal to 1
C guess
D misinterpreted relationship of fractions to one whole, $\frac{1}{2}$ not equal to 1 or point B

12. (A) correct
B only compared numerators
C only compared denominator
D misinterpreted concept of comparison

9 Which fraction does the model represent?

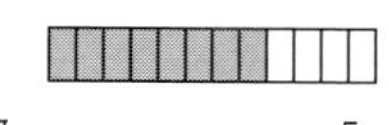

A $\frac{7}{9}$ C $\frac{5}{8}$

(B) $\frac{8}{12}$ D $\frac{7}{12}$

10 Which shows one-fifth written in fraction form?

A $\frac{5}{1}$ C $\frac{1}{15}$

(B) $\frac{1}{5}$ D $\frac{1}{50}$

11 Which fraction is equal to the number at point *C* on the number line?

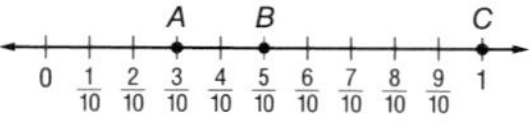

(A) $\frac{5}{5}$ C $\frac{8}{12}$

B $\frac{4}{5}$ D $\frac{1}{2}$

12 Which symbol makes the sentence true?

$\frac{1}{2} \square \frac{1}{12}$

(A) > C <

B = D +

ANSWER SHEET

Directions: Fill in the circle of each correct answer.

1	(A)	B	C	D
2	A	(B)	C	D
3	A	B	(C)	D
4	A	(B)	C	D
5	A	B	(C)	D
6	A	(B)	C	D
7	A	(B)	C	D
8	(A)	B	C	D
9	A	(B)	C	D
10	A	(B)	C	D
11	(A)	B	C	D
12	(A)	B	C	D

Success Strategy

If you do not know the answer to a question, go on to the next question. Come back to the problem, if you have time. You might find another question later in the test that will help you figure out the skipped problem.

Diagnosing Student Errors and Misconceptions

Review When working on the problems, have students show their work on a separate sheet of notebook paper that can be used later as a reference as needed. After the class has completed the Test Practice problems, go over all the correct responses and have the students score their own responses or trade and grade papers.

If it is found that the mistakes are not computational and students do not understand the question, further class instruction may be necessary. As another alternative, students could be strategically paired to help each other.

Common Error *Alert*

Reminders If students are not able to successfully eliminate wrong answer choices, they may need the reminders.

Exercise 4 Point out to students that when interpreting a model, any time one whole model is completely shaded, this represents 1. The other partially shaded model will give the fractional portion of the mixed number.

Exercise 11 Any time a fraction has the same number in its numerator and denominator, it represents 1.

Chapter 6

Chapter Overview

Chapter-at-a-Glance

Lesson	Math Objective	State/Local Standards
6-1 Add Fractions with Like Denominators (pp. 242–248)	Add simple fractions that have the same numbers in the denominators.	
6-2 Subtract Fractions with Like Denominators (pp. 249–255)	Subtract simple fractions that have the same numbers in the denominators.	
Progress Check 1 (p. 256)		
6-3 Add Fractions with Unlike Denominators (pp. 257–262)	Add simple fractions that have different numbers in the denominators.	
6-4 Subtract Fractions with Unlike Denominators (pp. 263–268)	Subtract simple fractions that have different numbers in the denominators.	
Progress Check 2 (p. 269)		

Content-at-a-Glance

The diagram below summarizes and unpacks Chapter 6 content.

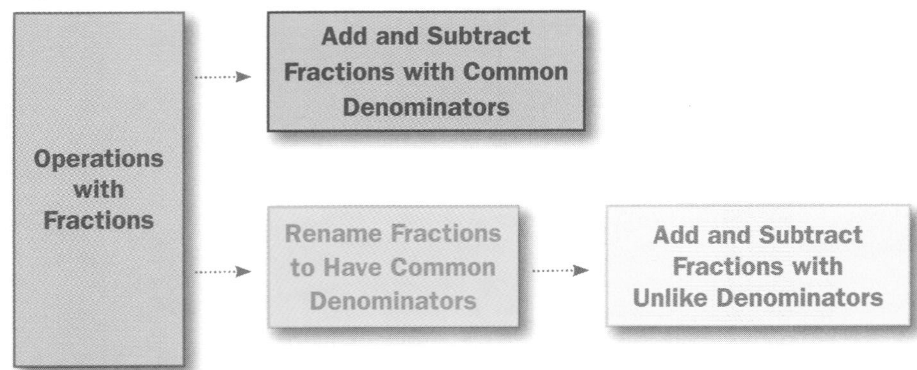

Online Assessment and Reporting
macmillanmh.com

Chapter Assessment Manager

Diagnostic — Diagnose students' readiness.

	Student Study Guide/ Teacher Edition	Assessment Masters	Technology
Course Placement Test		1	ExamView® Assessment Suite
Book 2 Pretest		58	ExamView® Assessment Suite
Chapter 6 Pretest		72	ExamView® Assessment Suite
Quiz/Preview	SSG 241		Math Online macmillanmh.com StudentWorks™ Plus

Formative — Identify students' misconceptions of content knowledge.

	Student Study Guide/ Teacher Edition	Assessment Masters	Technology
Progress Checks	SSG 256, 269		Math Online macmillanmh.com StudentWorks™ Plus
Vocabulary Review	SSG 270		Math Online macmillanmh.com
Lesson Assessments			ExamView® Assessment Suite
Are They Getting It?	TE 245, 251, 260, 266		

Summative — Determine student success in learning the concepts in the lesson, chapter, or book.

	Student Study Guide/ Teacher Edition	Assessment Masters	Technology
Chapter 6 Test	SSG 274	75	ExamView® Assessment Suite
Test Practice	SSG 276	78	ExamView® Assessment Suite
Alternative Assessment	TE 274	81	
See It, Do It, Say It, Write It	TE 248, 255, 262, 268		
Book 2 Test		94	ExamView® Assessment Suite

Back-mapping and Vertical Alignment **McGraw-Hill's *Math Triumphs*** intervention program was conceived and developed with the final result in mind: student success in grade-level mathematics, including Algebra 1 and beyond. The authors, using the **NCTM Focal Points and Focal Connections** as their guide, developed this brand-new series by backmapping from grade-level and Algebra 1 concepts, and vertically aligning the topics so that they build upon prior skills and concepts and serve as a foundation for future topics.

Chapter Resource Manager

	Lesson 6-1	Lesson 6-2	Lesson 6-3	Lesson 6-4
Concept	Add Fractions with Like Denominators	Subtract Fractions with Like Denominators	Add Fractions with Unlike Denominators	Subtract Fractions with Unlike Denominators
Objective	Add simple fractions that have the same numbers in the denominators.	Subtract simple fractions that have the same numbers in the denominators.	Add simple fractions that have different numbers in the denominators.	Subtract simple fractions that have different numbers in the denominators.
Math Vocabulary	common denominator like fractions simplest form	common denominator like fractions	least common denominator (LCD) prime factorization unlike fractions	least common denominator (LCD) prime factorization unlike fractions
Lesson Resources	**Materials** • Crayons • Graph paper • Measuring cup • Number line **Manipulatives** • Fraction tiles • Fraction circles **Other Resources** CRM Vocabulary and English Language Development CRM Skills Practice CRM Problem-Solving Practice CRM Homework Practice	**Materials** • Ruler • Measuring cup • Number line **Manipulatives** • Fraction tiles • Fraction circles **Other Resources** CRM Vocabulary and English Language Development CRM Skills Practice CRM Problem-Solving Practice CRM Homework Practice	**Materials** • Paper and pencil **Manipulatives** • Fraction circles • Fraction tiles **Other Resources** CRM Vocabulary and English Language Development CRM Skills Practice CRM Problem-Solving Practice CRM Homework Practice	**Materials** • Paper and pencil **Manipulatives** • Fraction circles • Fraction tiles **Other Resources** CRM Vocabulary and English Language Development CRM Skills Practice CRM Problem-Solving Practice CRM Homework Practice
Technology	Math Online macmillanmh.com StudentWorks™ Plus ExamView® Assessment Suite	Math Online macmillanmh.com StudentWorks™ Plus ExamView® Assessment Suite	Math Online macmillanmh.com StudentWorks™ Plus ExamView® Assessment Suite	Math Online macmillanmh.com StudentWorks™ Plus ExamView® Assessment Suite

Intervention Strategy

More on Least Common Denominators and Equivalent Fractions

In order to add or subtract fractions, you must have a common denominator. When the denominators are not the same, you need to find the LCD. Prime factorization is a method that can be used to find the LCD and the equivalent fractions with like denominators.

Find the least common denominator for $\frac{5}{12}$ and $\frac{1}{9}$ using prime factorization.

Step 1

Write each denominator as a product of prime factors.

$12 = 2 \times 2 \times 3$ $\qquad$ $9 = 3 \times 3$

Step 2

Determine which prime factors the numbers have in common.

$12 = 2 \times 2 \times \textcircled{3}$ $\qquad$ $9 = 3 \times \textcircled{3}$

Step 3

Multiply all of the factors together including the common factor only once. This gives you the least common denominator.

$2 \times 2 \times 3 \times 3 = 36$

There were 5 factors, but we only use 4 since 3 is a common factor to both denominators.

Step 4

Set up the fractions and multiply the denominators by the numbers that will make each denominator 36. The number you use for the denominator is also multiplied by the numerator.

$$\frac{5 \times 3}{12 \times 3} = \frac{15}{36}$$

$$\frac{1 \times 4}{9 \times 4} = \frac{4}{36}$$

Step 5

The equivalent fractions are $\frac{15}{36}$ and $\frac{4}{36}$.

You can now add or subtract them.

Have the students use prime factorization to find the LCD for each set of fractions.

1. $\frac{3}{8}$ and $\frac{2}{9}$

2. $\frac{1}{4}$ and $\frac{3}{15}$

3. $\frac{5}{6}$ and $\frac{1}{10}$

4. $\frac{7}{8}$ and $\frac{2}{3}$

Time Management Use this activity as a bellringer for Lesson 3 or as a quick class activity during the study of Lesson 3. Students will need to become familiar with LCDs when they learn to add or subtract fractions.

Chapter 6 Chapter Notes

Real-World Applications

Shopping Roberta is planning to make a quilt. She has $\frac{1}{8}$ of a yard of blue fabric and $\frac{1}{4}$ of a yard of red fabric. How much fabric does Roberta have? Roberta has $\frac{3}{8}$ yards of fabric.

Intervention Strategy

Write Directions

Step 1 Have students work in small groups.

Step 2 Each group will be responsible for writing four sets of step-by-step directions about each of the following:

- how to add fractions;
- how to subtract fractions.

Step 3 Along with each set of directions, the groups should provide an example that illustrates each process.

Step 4 Have groups share their directions with the class. The class should compare the sets to decide if any steps have been left out.

Chapter 6

Add and Subtract Fractions

You add and subtract fractions every day.

You do this mostly with money. How many quarters are in $3? What is a dollar and a half plus a dollar and a half? If movie tickets cost $5 each, how much will it cost you and a friend to go?

240 Chapter 6 Add and Subtract Fractions

Key Vocabulary

Find interactive definitions in 13 languages in the **eGlossary** at macmillanmh.com.

English **Español** *Introduce the most important vocabulary terms from Chapter 6.*

common denominator **denominadore comunes**
the same denominator (bottom number) used in two or more fractions (p. 242)

like fractions **fracciones semejantes**
fractions that have the same denominator (p. 242)
$\frac{1}{5}$ and $\frac{2}{5}$

simplest form **forma reducida**
a fraction in which the numerator and denominator have no common factor other than 1 (p. 242)

prime factorization **factorización prima**
a way of expressing a composite number as a product of its prime factors (p. 257)

unlike fractions **fracciones no semejantes**
fractions with different denominators (p. 257)
$\frac{1}{4}$ and $\frac{2}{3}$

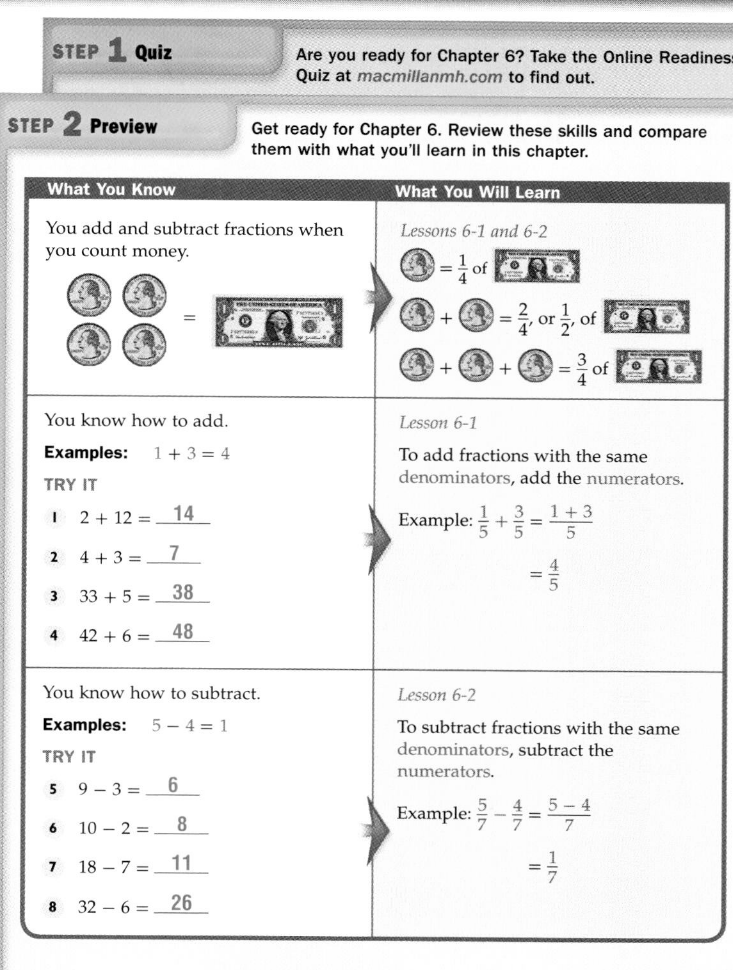

STEP 1 Quiz Are you ready for Chapter 6? Take the Online Readiness Quiz at macmillanmh.com to find out.

STEP 2 Preview Get ready for Chapter 6. Review these skills and compare them with what you'll learn in this chapter.

What You Know	What You Will Learn
You add and subtract fractions when you count money. (4 quarters) = (dollar bill)	*Lessons 6-1 and 6-2* (quarter) $= \frac{1}{4}$ of (dollar) (quarter) + (quarter) $= \frac{2}{4}$, or $\frac{1}{2}$, of (dollar) (quarter) + (quarter) + (quarter) $= \frac{3}{4}$ of (dollar)
You know how to add. **Examples:** $1 + 3 = 4$ **TRY IT** 1 $2 + 12 =$ 14 2 $4 + 3 =$ 7 3 $33 + 5 =$ 38 4 $42 + 6 =$ 48	*Lesson 6-1* To add fractions with the same denominators, add the numerators. Example: $\frac{1}{5} + \frac{3}{5} = \frac{1+3}{5}$ $= \frac{4}{5}$
You know how to subtract. **Examples:** $5 - 4 = 1$ **TRY IT** 5 $9 - 3 =$ 6 6 $10 - 2 =$ 8 7 $18 - 7 =$ 11 8 $32 - 6 =$ 26	*Lesson 6-2* To subtract fractions with the same denominators, subtract the numerators. Example: $\frac{5}{7} - \frac{4}{7} = \frac{5-4}{7}$ $= \frac{1}{7}$

241

Vocabulary Preview

- As students complete the Chapter Preview, have them make a list of important terms throughout the chapter.
- Have students make a word scramble of each term on the list, including Key Terms.
- Once the words are scrambled, put students into pairs.
- Pairs should then exchange papers. One student should read a definition that matches the first scrambled term on the paper. The partner will then need to unscramble the word. Then the partners switch roles. Partners should continue to switch roles until all of the words on both papers have been unscrambled.

Step 1 Quiz

Pretest/Prescribe Students can take the Online Readiness Quiz or the Diagnostic Pretest in the Assessment Masters.

Step 2 Preview

Use this pre-chapter activity to activate students' prior knowledge, build confidence, and help students preview the lessons.

Dinah Zike's Foldables®

Guide students through the directions on p. A120 in the Chapter Resource Masters to create their own Foldable graphic organizer to use with this chapter.

Home Connections

- Use a measuring cup to determine how many $\frac{1}{8}$ cups it takes to make 2 cups, $\frac{1}{4}$ cups it takes to make 2 cups, $\frac{1}{3}$ cups it takes to make 2 cups, and $\frac{1}{2}$ cups it takes to make 2 cups. After finding the answers, write each situation as an addition problem.

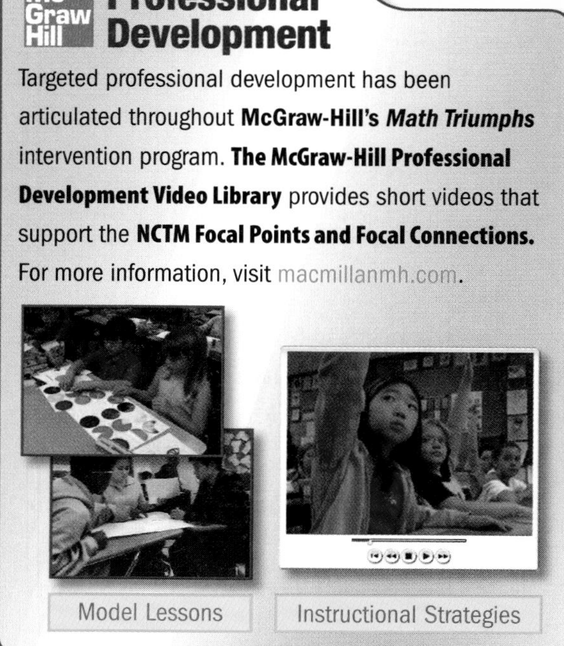

Professional Development

Targeted professional development has been articulated throughout **McGraw-Hill's *Math Triumphs*** intervention program. **The McGraw-Hill Professional Development Video Library** provides short videos that support the **NCTM Focal Points and Focal Connections.** For more information, visit macmillanmh.com.

Lesson 6-1

Lesson Notes

Lesson Planner

Objective Add simple fractions that have the same numbers in the denominators.

Vocabulary **common denominator**, **like fractions**, **simplest form**

Materials/Manipulatives crayons, fraction circles, fraction tiles, graph paper, measuring cup, number line

Chapter Resource Masters

- CRM Vocabulary and English Language Development (p. A123)
- CRM Skills Practice (p. A124)
- CRM Problem-Solving Practice (p. A125)
- CRM Homework Practice (p. A126)

Vocabulary

Fractions Hand out grid paper for students to make and name fraction bars to use for adding fractions. Call on students to name the *common denominator* in each *like fraction*. Ask: Are the fractions in *simplest form?*

Key Concept

Foundational Skills and Concepts After students have read through the Key Concept box, have them try these exercises.

1. In the equation $\frac{1}{5} + \frac{2}{5} + \frac{2}{5}$, are the fractions like fractions? If so, what is the common denominator? Yes; the common denominator is 5.
2. Ask students to explain how each of the fractions below connects to one dollar.

   $\frac{1}{4}$ A quarter is $\frac{1}{4}$ of a dollar.

   $\frac{1}{4} + \frac{1}{4}$ Two quarters are $\frac{1}{2}$ of a dollar.

   $\frac{1}{4} + \frac{1}{4} + \frac{1}{4}$ Three quarters are $\frac{3}{4}$ of a dollar.

Lesson 6-1

Add Fractions with Like Denominators

KEY Concept

To add fractions, the fractions must have **common denominators**.

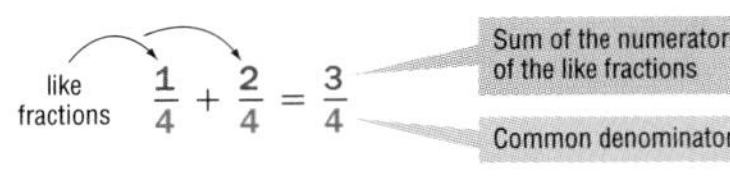

To add **like fractions**, add the numerators. The denominators stay the same. You can use money to help you understand this rule.

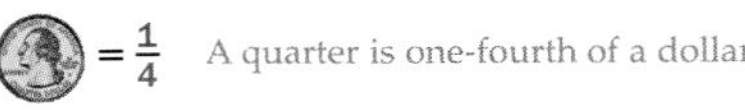

$= \frac{1}{4}$
A quarter is one-fourth of a dollar.

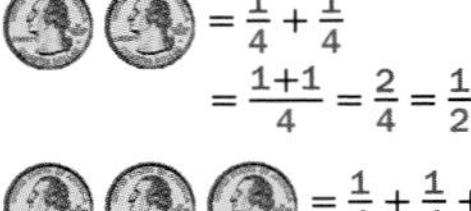

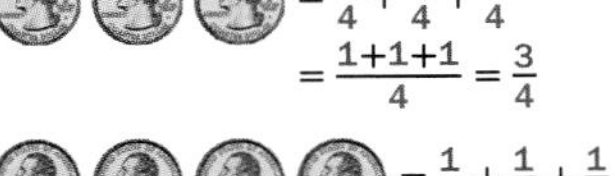

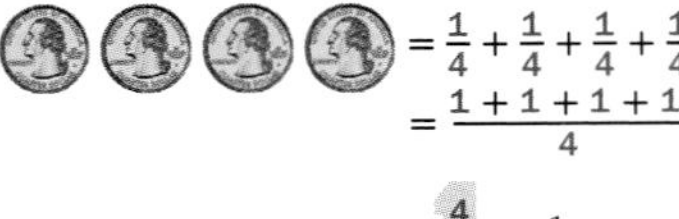

$= \frac{4}{4}$, or 1

Here is a different example.

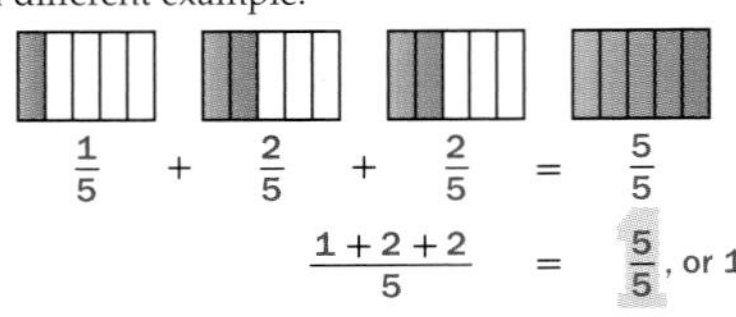

$\frac{1}{5} + \frac{2}{5} + \frac{2}{5} = \frac{5}{5}$
$\frac{1+2+2}{5} = \frac{5}{5}$, or 1

VOCABULARY

common denominator the same denominator (bottom number) used in two or more fractions

like fractions fractions that have the same denominator

simplest form a fraction in which the numerator and the denominator have no common factor other than 1

Example: $\frac{3}{5}$ is the simplest form of $\frac{6}{10}$.

Always write the sum of like fractions in simplest form. A fraction is in **simplest form**, or lowest terms, when the numerator and the denominator have no common factor other than 1.

Intervention Strategy — Kinesthetic Learners

Fraction Models

Add $\frac{1}{4} + \frac{1}{4}$.

Step 1 Group students in pairs. Have each partner model $\frac{1}{4}$.

$\frac{1}{4}$	$\frac{1}{4}$	$\frac{1}{4}$	$\frac{1}{4}$

Step 2 Combine the partners' models. Count how many fourths there are in all $\frac{1}{4} + \frac{1}{4} = \frac{2}{4}$

$\frac{1}{2}$

$\frac{1}{4}$	$\frac{1}{4}$	$\frac{1}{4}$	$\frac{1}{4}$

Step 3 Simplify. $\frac{2}{4} = \frac{1}{2}$

Step 4 Have pairs share how they solved the problem.

Example 1

Add $\frac{1}{8} + \frac{3}{8}$ using a drawing.

1. Draw a circle with 8 equal parts.
2. Color 1 part to show $\frac{1}{8}$ of the circle.
3. Color 3 parts to show $\frac{3}{8}$ of the circle.

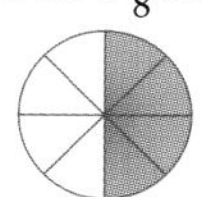

4. Count the total number of colored parts.
5. Write the sum.

$$\frac{1}{8} + \frac{3}{8} = \frac{1+3}{8} = \frac{4}{8}$$

YOUR TURN!

Add $\frac{1}{6} + \frac{2}{6}$ using a drawing.

1. Draw a circle with __6__ equal parts.
2. Color __1__ part.
3. Color __2__ parts.

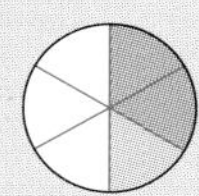

4. How many colored parts are there? __3__
5. Write the sum. $\frac{3}{6}$

Example 2

Add $\frac{3}{4} + \frac{3}{4}$. Write the sum in simplest form.

1. The common denominator is 4.
2. Add the numerators. $\frac{3+3}{4} = \frac{6}{4}$
3. Write in simplest form. $\frac{6}{4} = \frac{6 \div 2}{4 \div 2} = \frac{3}{2}$

The GCF of 6 and 4 is 2. Recall that the GCF is the largest number that divides evenly into two or more numbers.

YOUR TURN!

Add $\frac{5}{3} + \frac{2}{3}$. Write the sum in simplest form.

1. The common denominator is __3__.
2. Add the numerators. $\frac{5 + 2}{3} = \frac{7}{3}$
3. What is the sum in simplest form? $\frac{7}{3}$

GO ON

Additional Example 1

Add $\frac{1}{5} + \frac{2}{5}$ using a drawing.

1. Draw a circle with 5 equal parts.
2. Color 1 part.
3. Color 2 parts.
4. Count the total number of colored parts.
5. Write the sum.
   $\frac{1}{5} + \frac{2}{5} = \frac{1+2}{5} = \frac{3}{5}$

Additional Example 2

Add $\frac{4}{6} + \frac{4}{6}$. Write the sum in simplest form.

1. The common denominator is 6.
2. Add the numerators. $\frac{4+4}{6} = \frac{8}{6}$
3. Write in simplest form. $\frac{8}{6} = \frac{8 \div 2}{6 \div 2} = \frac{4}{3}$

Common Error *Alert*

Intermediate Steps If students are consistently trying to add the denominators, show students an intermediate step of writing the fractions as one fraction.

$\frac{1}{5} + \frac{3}{5} = \frac{1+3}{5} = \frac{4}{5}$

Intervention Strategy Visual Learners

Make Manipulatives

Materials: graph paper, crayons

1. Have pairs mark off any size on graph paper. Count the number of boxes in this area to use as the denominator of a fraction (whole).
2. Next, color and count any number of the boxes in the area for the numerator.
3. Have pairs write their fractions and share their models.
4. Quiz them by adding a fraction (with a like denominator) to their fraction.
5. Finally, have students order the fraction models in a class lineup.

Additional **Example 3**

Add $\frac{5}{9} + \frac{4}{9}$. Write the sum in simplest form.

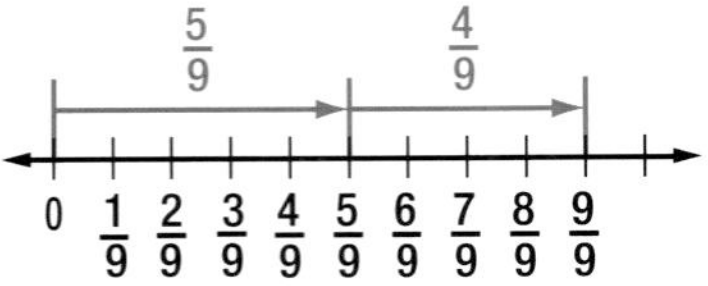

1. Mark off a segment length of $\frac{5}{9}$.
2. Add $\frac{4}{9}$ to the $\frac{5}{9}$ by extending your arrow.
3. Write the fraction in simplest form. $\frac{9}{9} \div$  $= 1$

3 Practice

Using Manipulatives

Fraction Tiles When presenting Example 2, use fraction tiles to represent each fraction. Using the fourths fraction bar, have students count off fourths until they arrive at three-fourths. Have them do the same for the other addend of three-fourths. Remind them that the entire bar is the whole, or denominator, and the three shaded sections represent the part, or numerator. Have them add the two fraction bars together.

Fraction Circles Model fractions frequently using fraction circles, as shown in Example 1.

On-Hand Manipulatives Have students draw number lines on the board or use rulers to count numbers when adding fractions.

Example 3

Add $\frac{1}{5} + \frac{4}{5}$. Write the sum in simplest form.

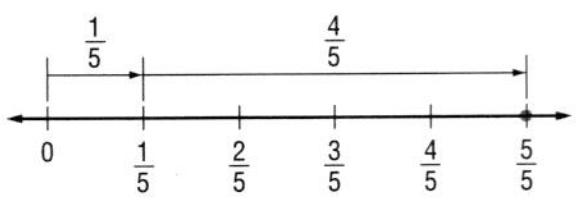

1. Mark off a segment length of $\frac{1}{5}$.
2. Add $\frac{4}{5}$ to the $\frac{1}{5}$ by extending your arrow.
3. Write the fraction in simplest form.

$\frac{5}{5} \div \frac{5}{5} = 1$

YOUR TURN!

Add $\frac{2}{6} + \frac{1}{6}$. Write the sum in simplest form.

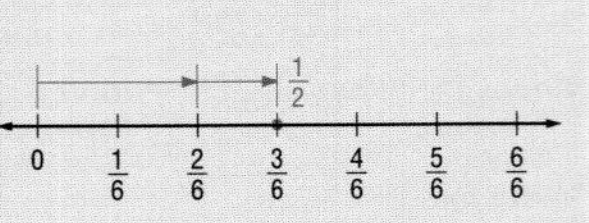

1. Mark off a segment length of $\frac{2}{6}$.
2. Add $\frac{1}{6}$ to the $\frac{2}{6}$ by extending your arrow.
3. Write the fraction in simplest form. $\frac{1}{2}$

Who is Correct?

Add $\frac{4}{5} + \frac{3}{5}$.

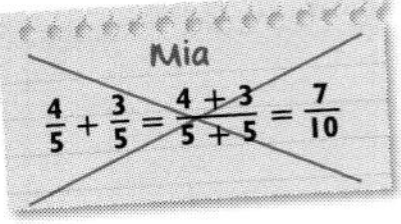

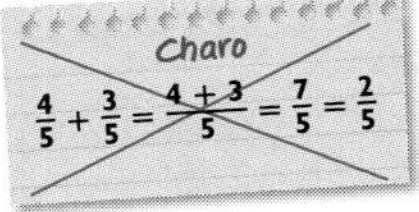

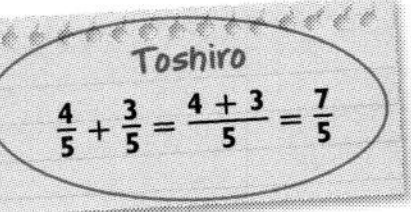

Circle correct answer(s). Cross out incorrect answer(s).

Guided Practice

Add using drawings.

1. $\frac{1}{6} + \frac{4}{6} = \frac{5}{6}$

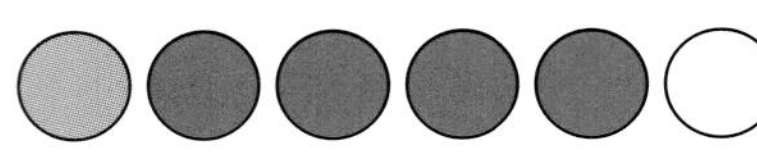

Who *is Correct?*

Diagnostic Teaching

- Mia is incorrect. She added the numerators and the denominators.
- Charo is incorrect. He did not show the whole number when he wrote the fraction in simplest form.
- Toshiro is correct.

Remind students to review their work for careless mistakes.

2 $\frac{3}{4} + \frac{2}{4} = \frac{5}{4}$

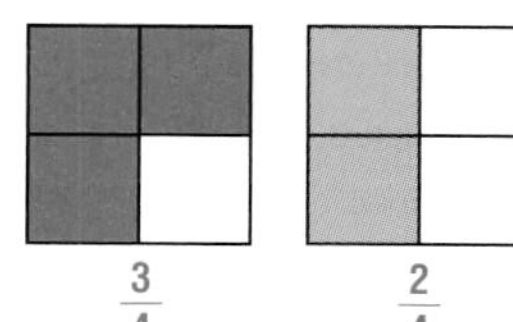

Step by Step Practice

3 Find $\frac{1}{12} + \frac{3}{12}$. Write the sum in simplest form.

Step 1 Check to see if the denominators are the same or different.

$\frac{1}{12} + \frac{3}{12}$ like denominators

Step 2 Add the numerators.

$\frac{1 + 3}{12}$

Step 3 Write the sum of the numerators over the like denominator.

$\frac{1 + 3}{12} = \frac{4}{12}$

Step 4 Write the fraction in simplest terms.

$\frac{4}{12} = \frac{4 \div 4}{12 \div 4} = \frac{1}{3}$

Add. Write each sum in simplest form.

4 $\frac{6}{9} + \frac{2}{9} = \frac{6 + 2}{9} = \frac{8}{9}$

5 $\frac{12}{18} + \frac{3}{18} = \frac{15}{18} = \frac{5}{6}$

6 $\frac{1}{2} + \frac{1}{2} = \frac{2}{2} = 1$

7 $\frac{2}{3} + \frac{2}{3} = \frac{4}{3}$

Are They Getting It?

Check students' understanding of adding fractions by writing these problems on the board. Have students explain the incorrect information in each problem. Tell them to use a number line or another visual aid to show why the answers are correct or are incorrect.

Add. Write each sum in simplest form.

1. $\frac{1}{3} + \frac{1}{3} = \frac{2}{6}$ This is incorrect. The denominators were added.
2. $\frac{2}{7} + \frac{3}{7} = \frac{5}{7}$ This is correct.
3. $\frac{2}{9} + \frac{1}{9} = \frac{3}{9}$ This is incorrect because the fraction is not in simplest form.

Math Coach Notes

Strategies

1. Have students begin the lesson by adding fractions using fraction bars. Use the bars throughout the lesson as concrete examples.
2. The ideal way for students to learn to add fractions is to use concrete models or manipulatives. When students are practicing, ask them repeatedly if the fractions are like fractions.
3. Write the following addition problem on the board. Then ask for the answer.

   3 fifths
   + 1 fifths
   4 fifths

Note This!

Own Words When students are taking notes, make sure that they state the facts and ideas using their own words so that they will think about what the statements really mean. Inform them that this procedure helps transfer the method to their long-term memory.

Common Error Alert

Multi-Step Problem If a student is unable to draw a diagram for Exercise 8, he or she may not understand how fractions need to have a common denominator. Show the students how to make a fraction bar for each fraction that has the same number of units as the denominator. Then they should shade the numerators and add them.

Note This!

Concept Map Most students benefit from visual or graphic organizers. One example is a concept map. A concept map for adding fractions might look like this:

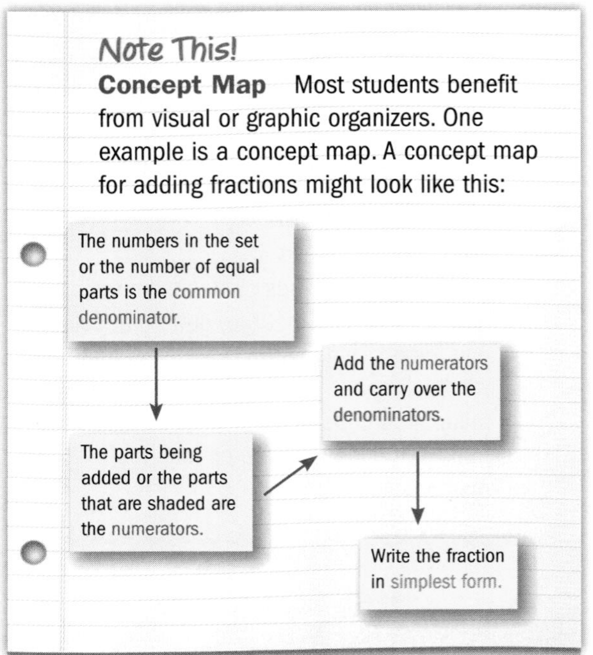

The numbers in the set or the number of equal parts is the common denominator.
The parts being added or the parts that are shaded are the numerators.
Add the numerators and carry over the denominators.
Write the fraction in simplest form.

Step by Step Problem-Solving Practice

Problem-Solving Strategies
- ☑ Draw a diagram.
- ☐ Look for a pattern.
- ☐ Guess and check.
- ☐ Solve a simpler problem.
- ☐ Work backward.

Solve. Write your answer in simplest form.

8 WEATHER Yesterday it rained $\frac{3}{10}$ of an inch. Today it rained $\frac{1}{10}$ of an inch. How much did it rain altogether?

Understand Read the problem. Write what you know.
It rained $\frac{3}{10}$ of an inch yesterday. It rained $\frac{1}{10}$ of an inch today.

Plan Pick a strategy. One strategy is to draw a diagram.
Draw 10 equal parts. Shade 3 to show the $\frac{3}{10}$ of an inch it rained yesterday.
Shade 1 part to show $\frac{1}{10}$ of an inch it rained today.

$\frac{10}{10}$ $\frac{1}{10}$ $\frac{3}{10}$

Solve Count the shaded parts. $\frac{3}{10} + \frac{1}{10} = \frac{4}{10}$

Write in simplest form. $= \frac{4 \div 2}{10 \div 2} = \frac{2}{5}$

Check Does the answer make sense? Review your drawing. Look at your drawing as two equal parts. Is one of those parts shaded?

9 FAMILY Logan ate $\frac{1}{6}$ of a pizza. Colin ate $\frac{1}{6}$ of the pizza, and Landon ate $\frac{2}{6}$ of the pizza. What fraction of the pizza was eaten? Write in simplest form.

Check off each step.

✔ Understand: I circled key words.
✔ Plan: To solve the problem, I will draw a diagram.
✔ Solve: The answer is $\frac{2}{3}$ of the pizza was eaten.
✔ Check: I checked my answer by adding the fractions.

246 Chapter 6 Add and Subtract Fractions

Intervention Strategy — Linguistic/Logical Learners

Riddles Give students this riddle to ponder during the lesson. Challenge them to solve all parts of it before the end of the lesson.

1. **Riddle 1:** I am a day of the week. I am only one day of the week. What is my fraction? $\frac{1}{7}$
2. **Riddle 2:** I am a fraction. My denominator is 7. However, I am not just a part of the whole thing. I am the whole thing. What is my numerator? 7
3. What do you get if you add the answer to **Riddle 1** to the answer to **Riddle 2?** $\frac{1}{7} + \frac{7}{7} = \frac{8}{7}$

10 BOOKS Shontelle has a bookcase. Science fiction takes up $\frac{7}{12}$ of the shelves. Mysteries take up $\frac{2}{12}$ of the shelves, and comic books take up $\frac{1}{12}$ of the shelves. What fraction of the bookcase is filled?

$\frac{7}{12} + \frac{2}{12} + \frac{1}{12} = \frac{10}{12} = \frac{5}{6}$ is filled

11 **Reflect** How is adding like fractions the same as adding whole numbers?

See TE margin.

Skills, Concepts, and Problem Solving

Add using drawings.

12 $\frac{3}{8} + \frac{1}{8} = \frac{4}{8} = \frac{1}{2}$

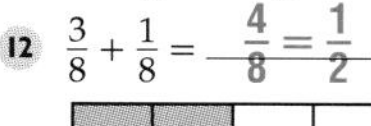

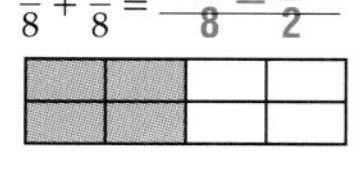

13 $\frac{2}{5} + \frac{1}{5} = \frac{3}{5}$

14 $\frac{4}{6} + \frac{3}{6} = \frac{7}{6}$

15 $\frac{4}{5} + \frac{4}{5} = \frac{8}{5}$

See TE margin for drawings.

Add. Write each sum in simplest form.

16 $\frac{3}{12} + \frac{7}{12} = \frac{5}{6}$

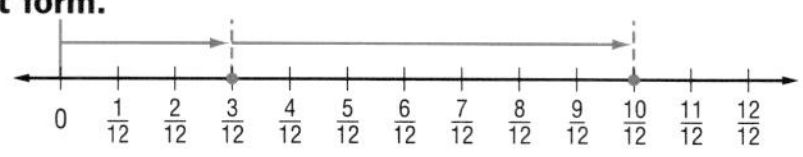

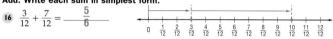

17 $\frac{2}{9} + \frac{1}{9} = \frac{1}{3}$

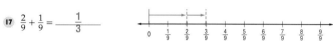

18 $\frac{1}{7} + \frac{3}{7} + \frac{1}{7} = \frac{5}{7}$

19 $\frac{5}{9} + \frac{1}{9} + \frac{2}{9} = \frac{8}{9}$

20 $\frac{1}{6} + \frac{5}{6} = 1$

21 $\frac{3}{7} + \frac{6}{7} = \frac{9}{7}$

Math Challenge

Bag of Fractions I Give each student a set of fraction circles and a paper bag. Working in pairs, one student puts the fraction circles in the bag. Then one student picks a fraction from the bag. The other student writes the fraction that will make the sum of the fractions a whole.

Additional Answers

Exercise 11 You add only the numerators, leaving the like denominators. Adding the numerators is an addition problem involving whole numbers.

Exercise 14

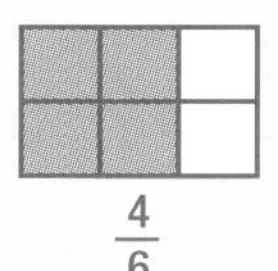

$\frac{4}{6}$

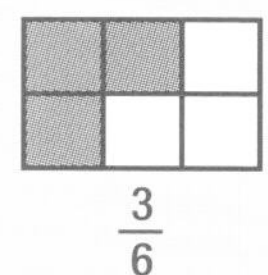

$\frac{3}{6}$

Exercise 15

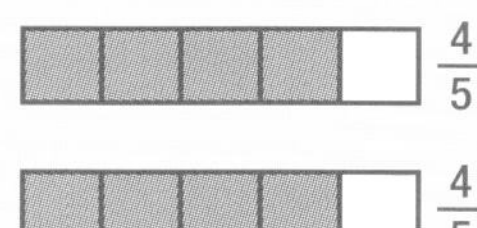

$\frac{4}{5}$

$\frac{4}{5}$

Odd/Even Assignments

Exercises 12–24 are structured so that students practice the same concepts whether they are assigned the odd or even problems.

In-Class Assignment

Have students complete Exercises 13, 17, 19, 23, and 27 to ensure that they understand the concept.

Common Error *Alert*

Demonstration If students are having difficulty adding like fractions, demonstrate using a small measuring cup ($\frac{1}{8}$ cup). Fill two cups with water. Add the two fractions as the two measuring cups are combined.

4 Assess

See It, Do It, Say It, Write It

Step 1 Write a fractional addition problem on the board. Model how to represent the fractions with a drawing or model. Do this several times with different addition problems.

Step 2 Ask students to draw a number line on paper. Give them fractions to add on the number line. Repeat the activity followed by a class discussion.

Step 3 Have students work in pairs. Write fractions on the board to add. Tell students to show the common denominator. Have students share their work with the class.

Step 4 Have students work alone. Tell them to write how to add fractions in their math journals. Tell them to include a picture or a model.

Additional Answer

Exercise 27 See students' work. Berta should add $\frac{3}{2}$ and $\frac{6}{2}$. She should add the numerators to get $\frac{9}{2}$.

Looking Ahead: Pre-teach

Subtract Fractions with Like Denominators

In the next lesson, students will learn how to subtract fractions with like denominators.

Example

Find $\frac{3}{5} - \frac{1}{5}$.

The common denominator is 5.

Subtract the numerators. $\frac{3-1}{5} = \frac{2}{5}$

Subtract.

1. $\frac{3}{8} - \frac{2}{8} = \frac{1}{8}$
2. $\frac{9}{10} - \frac{7}{10} = \frac{2}{10}$
3. $\frac{8}{9} - \frac{2}{9} = \frac{6}{9}$

Solve. Write your answer in simplest form.

22 FOOD Glenn sliced some cheese into 8 slices. He ate 3 slices. His sister ate 2 slices. What fraction of the cheese was eaten?
$\frac{5}{8}$ was eaten

23 HOBBIES Jade has 15 miniature tea sets. Last year she added 4 sets to her collection. This year she added 3 sets. What fraction of the sets did she collect in the past two years?
$\frac{7}{15}$ added

24 LUNCH The school cafeteria serves five different types of fruit at lunch. What fraction represents the sum of the top three favorite fruits? Explain how to solve this problem.
$\frac{8}{10}$; find the 3 largest fractions, then add the numerators and keep the denominator 10.

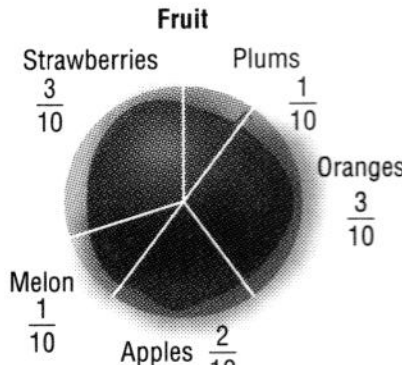

Vocabulary Check **Write the vocabulary word that completes each sentence.**

25 Fractions that have the same denominator are called like fractions.

26 Fractions that have the same denominators have common (or like) denominators.

27 **Writing in Math** Berta is mixing sand and water to make cement. She mixes 3 half-cups of water to 6 half-cups of sand. She wants to find the total number of cups she has mixed.

Write a note to Berta. Explain how to solve this problem. Do not forget to explain to her how to simplify her answer.

See TWE margin.

Ticket Out the Door

Fraction Strips Hand out fraction strips with a random number of equal units and shaded units to student pairs. Instruct groups to find another group to make like fractions. Have the groups add their fractions and write their findings on a sheet of paper. Student volunteers can present their findings. Have them hand in their papers as they exit the classroom.

Lesson 6-2

Subtract Fractions with Like Denominators

KEY Concept

To subtract fractions with **common denominators**, subtract the numerators. The denominator remains the same.

You started with 3 pieces. You ate 2 pieces. You have 1 piece left.

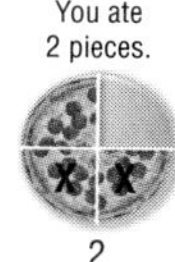

$\frac{3}{4} - \frac{2}{4} = \frac{1}{4}$

$\frac{3}{4} - \frac{2}{4} = \frac{3-2}{4}$

$= \frac{1}{4}$

VOCABULARY

common denominator
the same denominator (bottom number) used in two or more fractions, also called like denominator
Example: $\frac{1}{4}$ and $\frac{2}{4}$

common denominator

like fractions
fractions that have the same denominator
Example: $\frac{1}{5}$ and $\frac{2}{5}$

Write the difference of like fractions in simplest form. Remember that a fraction is in **simplest form** or lowest terms when the numerator and the denominator have no common factor other than 1.

Example 1

Subtract $\frac{5}{8} - \frac{3}{8}$ using a drawing.

1. Draw 8 equal parts.
2. Color 5 parts to show $\frac{5}{8}$.
3. Cross out 3 of the 5 colored parts.
4. Count the number of shaded parts that are not crossed out.
5. Write the fraction in simplest form.

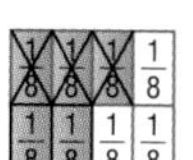

$\frac{5}{8} - \frac{3}{8} = \frac{5-3}{8}$

$= \frac{2}{8} = \frac{1}{4}$

GO ON

Additional Example 1

Subtract $\frac{3}{4} - \frac{1}{4}$ using a drawing.

1. Draw 4 equal parts.
2. Color 3 parts.
3. Cross out 1 of the 3 parts.
4. Count the number of shaded parts that are not crossed out. $\frac{3}{4} - \frac{1}{4} = \frac{3-1}{4}$
5. Write the fraction in simplest form. $= \frac{1}{2}$

Lesson Notes

Lesson 6-2

Lesson Planner

Objective Subtract simple fractions that have the same numbers in the denominators.

Vocabulary **common denominator, like fractions**

Materials/Manipulatives fraction circles, fraction tiles, measuring cup, number line, ruler

Chapter Resource Masters

- CRM Vocabulary and English Language Development (p. A127)
- CRM Skills Practice (p. A128)
- CRM Problem-Solving Practice (p. A129)
- CRM Homework Practice (p. A130)

1 Introduce

Vocabulary

Fractions Hand out a set of fraction tiles and a sheet of fraction subtraction problems to every student. Arrange students into pairs. Call on students to name the *common denominator* in each *like fraction*, then find the differences. Ask: Are the fractions in *simplest form?*

2 Teach

Key Concept

Foundational Skills and Concepts After students have read through the Key Concept box, have them try these exercises.

1. Consider: $\frac{3}{4} - \frac{2}{4}$. Are the fractions like fractions? If so, what is the common denominator? Yes; the common denominator is 4.
2. Is $\frac{1}{4}$ in simplest form? If not, simplify. Yes; it is in simplest form.

Additional **Example 2**

Subtract $\frac{11}{14} - \frac{4}{14}$. Write the difference in simplest form.

1. The common denominator is 14.
2. Subtract the numerators. $\frac{11 - 4}{14} = \frac{7}{14}$
3. Write the fraction in simplest form.
   $\frac{7}{14} = \frac{7 \div 7}{14 \div 7} = \frac{1}{2}$

YOUR TURN!

Subtract $\frac{5}{9} - \frac{4}{9}$ using a drawing.

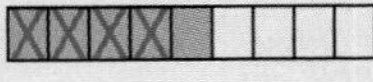

1. Draw 9 equal parts.
2. Color 5 parts.
3. Cross out 4 of the 5 colored parts.
4. How many shaded parts are not crossed out? 1
5. Write the fraction. $\frac{1}{9}$

Example 2

Subtract $\frac{13}{15} - \frac{4}{15}$. Write the difference in simplest form.

1. The common denominator is 15.
2. Subtract the numerators.
   $\frac{13 - 4}{15} = \frac{9}{15}$

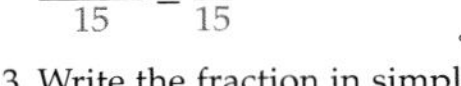

3. Write the fraction in simplest form.
   $\frac{9}{15} = \frac{9 \div 3}{15 \div 3} = \frac{3}{5}$

YOUR TURN!

Subtract $\frac{11}{16} - \frac{7}{16}$. Write the difference in simplest form.

1. The common denominator is 16.
2. Subtract the numerators.
   $\frac{11 - 7}{16} = \frac{4}{16}$
3. Write the fraction in simplest form.
   $\frac{4}{16} \div \frac{4}{4} = \frac{1}{4}$

Who is Correct?

Subtract $\frac{9}{10} - \frac{3}{10}$. Write the difference in simplest form.

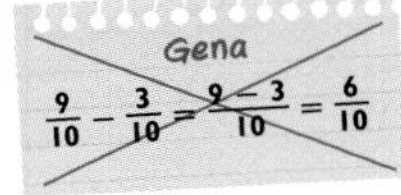

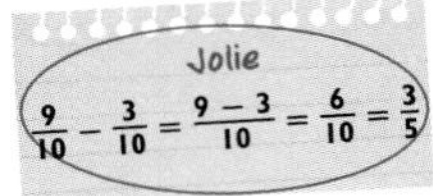

Jolie
$\frac{9}{10} - \frac{3}{10} = \frac{9-3}{10} = \frac{6}{10} = \frac{3}{5}$

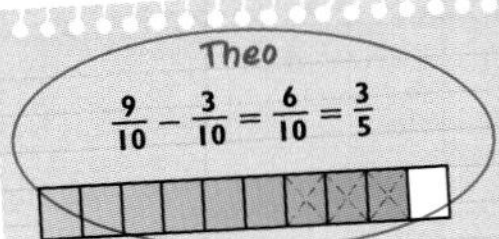

Circle correct answer(s). Cross out incorrect answer(s).

Who *is Correct?*

Diagnostic Teaching

- Gena is incorrect. She did not reduce the answer to simplest form.
- Jolie is correct.
- Theo is correct.

Remind students to write their answers in simplest form.

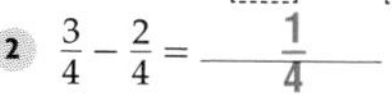

Guided Practice

Subtract using drawings. Write each difference in simplest form.

1 $\frac{5}{6} - \frac{3}{6} = \frac{2}{6} = \frac{1}{3}$

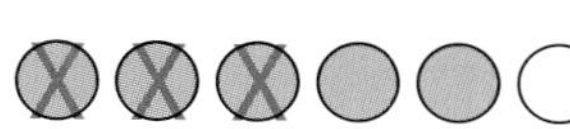

2 $\frac{3}{4} - \frac{2}{4} = \frac{1}{4}$

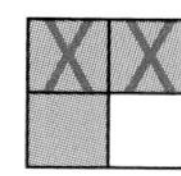

Step by Step Practice

3 Find $\frac{15}{20} - \frac{3}{20}$. Write the difference in simplest form.

Step 1 Are the denominators the same? yes

Step 2 Find the difference of the numerators. Use the like denominator. $\frac{15 - 3}{20} = \frac{12}{20}$

Step 3 Write the fraction in simplest form. $\frac{12}{20} = \frac{12 \div 4}{20 \div 4} = \frac{3}{5}$

Subtract. Write each difference in simplest form.

4 $\frac{5}{9} - \frac{2}{9} = \frac{5 - 2}{9} = \frac{3 \div 3}{9 \div 3} = \frac{1}{3}$

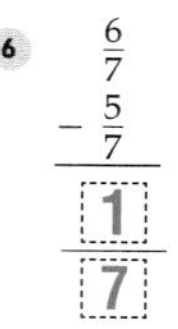

5 $\frac{12}{16} - \frac{9}{16} = \frac{3}{16}$

6 $\frac{6}{7} - \frac{5}{7} = \frac{1}{7}$

7 $\frac{17}{24} - \frac{11}{24} = \frac{6}{24} = \frac{1}{4}$

GO ON

Lesson 6-2 Subtract Fractions with Like Denominators 251

Are They Getting It?

Check students' understanding of subtracting fractions by writing these problems on the board. Have students explain the incorrect information in each problem. Tell them to use a number line or another visual aid to show why the answers are correct or are incorrect.

1. $\frac{7}{9} - \frac{4}{9} = \frac{3}{9}$ This is incorrect. The fraction is not in simplest form.

2. $\frac{15}{16} - \frac{3}{16} = \frac{12}{16}$ or $\frac{3}{4}$ This is correct.

3. $\frac{15}{21} - \frac{6}{21} = \frac{21}{21}$ or 1 This is incorrect. The numerators were added instead of subtracted.

3 Practice

Using Manipulatives

Fraction Tiles When presenting Example 2, use a model to represent the fraction that is the minuend. Using the thirteen-fifteenths model, have students cross out fifteenths until they have crossed out four. Have them count the number of shaded parts that are not crossed out. Remind them that the entire group of objects is the whole, or denominator, and the 9 shaded parts that are not crossed out represent the part, or numerator.

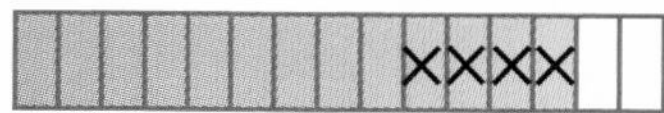

Fraction Circles Model fractions frequently using fraction circles.

On-Hand Manipulatives Have students draw number lines on the board or use rulers to count numbers when adding fractions.

Math Coach Notes

Strategies

1. Have students begin the lesson on subtracting fractions by reviewing the facts about adding fractions. Use the fraction strips throughout the lesson as concrete examples of subtracting fractions. Have students write the fractions in simplest form.

2. The ideal way for students to learn to subtract fractions is to use concrete models or manipulatives. As students practice, ask them repeatedly if the fractions are like fractions. Have them point out the common denominator.

Common Error *Alert*

Multi-Step Problem If a student is unable to draw a diagram for Exercise 8, show him or her how to make a fraction strip by shading the number of sections to match the minuend. Then cross out the number of sections that match the subtracted numerator. The remaining shaded parts are the numerator for the answer.

Note This!

Diagrams Encourage students to include diagrams in their notes for the examples discussed together.

Step by Step Problem-Solving Practice

Problem-Solving Strategies
- ☑ Draw a diagram.
- ☐ Look for a pattern.
- ☐ Guess and check.
- ☐ Work backward.

Solve. Write in simplest form.

8 HOBBIES Tory made 8 key chains. Four of the key chains were blue. She gave 2 of the blue key chains away. What fraction of the total number of key chains did she give away?

Understand Read the problem. Write what you know.

There are __8__ key chains. __4__ of the key chains are blue.

Tory gave __2__ of the blue key chains away.

Plan Pick a strategy. One strategy is to draw a diagram. Draw eight equal parts.

Solve Shade four to represent the 4 blue key chains. Cross out two of the shaded areas to show the 2 key chains that Tory gave away.

$\frac{4}{8} - \frac{2}{8} = \frac{2}{8}$ Count the unmarked shaded parts.

$= \frac{2 \div 2}{8 \div 2} = \frac{1}{4}$ Write in simplest form.

Check Does the answer make sense? Look over your solution. Did you answer the question?

9 GAMES Hakan designs computer games. Of the games he designed, $\frac{2}{6}$ are travel games and $\frac{3}{6}$ are racing games. What fraction shows the number of games that are not travel or racing games?

Check off each step.

✓ Understand: I circled key words.

✓ Plan: To solve the problem, I will __draw a diagram__.

✓ Solve: The answer is __$\frac{1}{6}$ are not travel or racing games__.

✓ Check: I checked my answer by __subtracting $\frac{3}{6} - \frac{2}{6}$__.

252 **Chapter 6** Add and Subtract Fractions

Intervention Strategy — Visual Learners

Model and Write Use a measuring cup with water to illustrate how to subtract like fractions. Allow students to empty the cup themselves and write problems based on their actions.

10 FITNESS Florence lives $\frac{9}{10}$ of a mile from school. On Tuesday she jogged $\frac{4}{10}$ of a mile toward school. How much farther did she have to go to get to school?

$\frac{5}{10} = \frac{1}{2}$ of a mile

11 Reflect How is subtracting like fractions the same as subtracting whole numbers?

See TWE margin.

Skills, Concepts, and Problem Solving

Subtract using drawings.

12 $\frac{7}{8} - \frac{5}{8} = \frac{2}{8}$

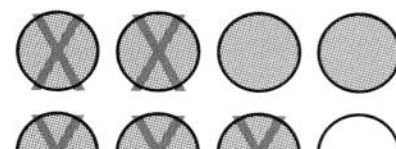

13 $\frac{6}{11} - \frac{2}{11} = \frac{4}{11}$

14 $\frac{5}{9} - \frac{3}{9} = \frac{2}{9}$

15 $\frac{7}{10} - \frac{1}{10} = \frac{6}{10}$

14, 15. See TWE margin for drawings.

Subtract. Write each difference in simplest form.

16 $\frac{4}{5} - \frac{2}{5} = \frac{2}{5}$

17 $\frac{7}{13} - \frac{2}{13} = \frac{5}{13}$

18 $\frac{7}{12} - \frac{5}{12} = \frac{2}{12} = \frac{1}{6}$

19 $\frac{9}{10} - \frac{4}{10} = \frac{5}{10} = \frac{1}{2}$

GO ON

Intervention Strategy Linguistic Learners

Solve and Write Write the following problems on the board: 3-sixths plus 1-sixth and 9-tenths minus 7-tenths. Ask students to solve the problems by reading each one out loud. Then have them model each problem using numbers.

3-sixths plus 1-sixth equals 4-sixths or $\frac{3}{6} + \frac{1}{6} = \frac{4}{6}$ or $\frac{2}{3}$.

9-tenths minus 7-tenths equals 2-tenths or $\frac{9}{10} - \frac{7}{10} = \frac{2}{10}$ or $\frac{1}{5}$.

Additional Answers

Exercise 11 See students' work. Sample answer: You subtract only the numerators, leaving the like denominators alone. This is just like subtracting whole numbers.

Exercise 14

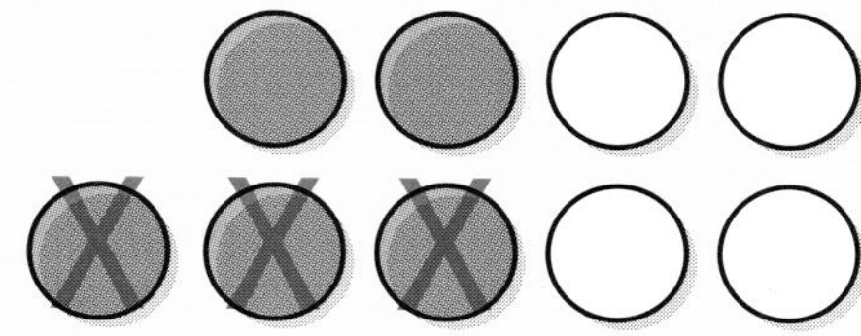

Exercise 15

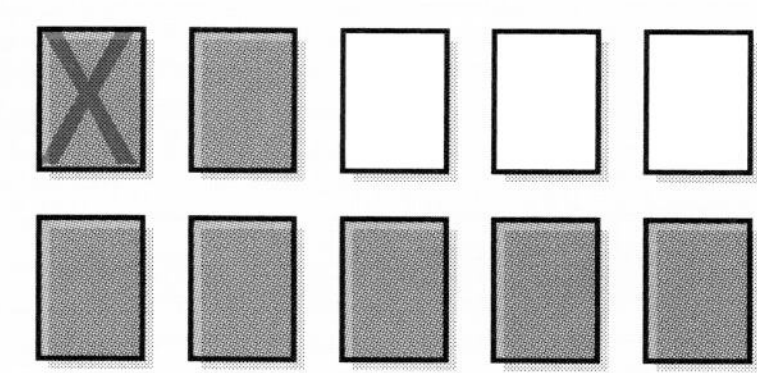

Common Error *Alert*

Exercises 18 and 19 Students may not have written their answers in simplest form. In each of these problems, the numerators and denominators have common factors.

Odd/Even Assignments

Exercises 12–24 are structured so that students practice the same concepts whether they are assigned the odd or even problems.

In-Class Assignment

Have students complete Exercises 13, 17, 21, 23, and 27 to ensure that they understand the concept.

Intervention Strategy Kinesthetic Learners

Shoe Length Have pairs of students measure each other's shoe length in fractions of an inch. Measuring should be to the nearest sixteenth of an inch or eighth of an inch. Have students compare each other's shoe length by finding the difference in lengths. Make sure that the fractions are like fractions prior to subtracting.

Subtract. Write each difference in simplest form.

20 $\frac{11}{16} - \frac{10}{16} = \frac{1}{16}$

21 $\frac{19}{36} - \frac{7}{36} = \frac{12}{36} = \frac{1}{3}$

Solve. Write in simplest form.

22 FOOD At a Thai restaurant, $\frac{3}{6}$ of the meals are very spicy, and $\frac{2}{6}$ of the meals are somewhat spicy. The rest of the meals served are mild. What fraction of the meals are mild? $\frac{1}{6}$ are mild.

23 SOFTBALL Pilar pitches $\frac{4}{9}$ of the game. Edna pitches $\frac{2}{9}$ of the game. What fraction of the game is left? $\frac{3}{9} = \frac{1}{3}$ is left.

24 MUSIC The school band's percussion section has $\frac{2}{12}$ bass drums, $\frac{5}{12}$ snare drums, and $\frac{1}{12}$ cymbals. What fraction of the percussion section plays an instrument other than these three instruments?
$\frac{4}{12} = \frac{1}{3}$ plays other instrument

Vocabulary Check **Write the vocabulary word that completes each sentence.**

25 When you subtract like fractions, you find the difference of the numerators and write it over the common denominator.

26 A fraction is in simplest form when its numerator and denominator have no common factor other than 1.

Math Challenge

Bag of Fractions II Give each student a set of fraction circles and a paper bag. Working in pairs, one student puts the fraction circles in the bag. Then one student picks a fraction from the bag. The other student writes the fraction that is the difference of the whole and their partner's fraction.

27 **Writing in Math** Miriam baked a pie that she cut into 8 equal slices. The next morning, $\frac{1}{4}$ of the pie was gone. Make a drawing to show how much pie is left. Then write an equation to represent this situation.

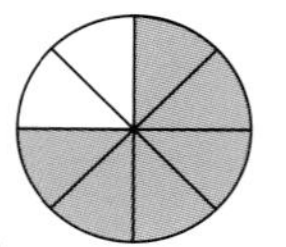

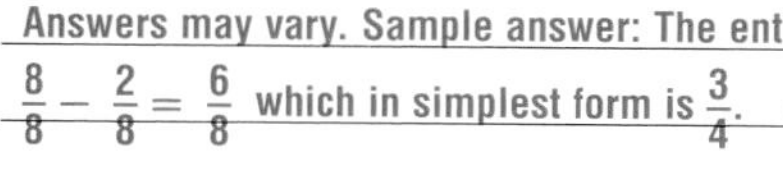

Answers may vary. Sample answer: The entire pie was $\frac{8}{8}$ or $\frac{4}{4}$. $\frac{8}{8} - \frac{2}{8} = \frac{6}{8}$ which in simplest form is $\frac{3}{4}$. $\frac{4}{4} - \frac{1}{4} = \frac{3}{4}$.

Spiral Review

Add. Write each sum in simplest form. (Lesson 6-1, p. 242)

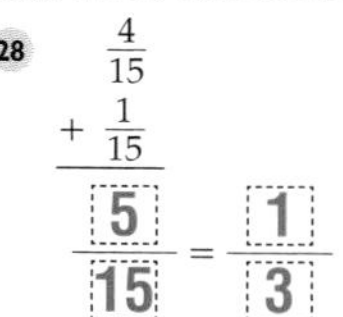

28 $\frac{4}{15} + \frac{1}{15} = \frac{5}{15} = \frac{1}{3}$

29 $\frac{3}{8} + \frac{1}{8} = \frac{4}{8} = \frac{1}{2}$

30 $\frac{2}{11} + \frac{3}{11} = \frac{5}{11}$

31 $\frac{1}{10} + \frac{3}{10} = \frac{4}{10} = \frac{2}{5}$

32 $\frac{3}{4} + \frac{1}{4} = \frac{4}{4} = 1$

33 $\frac{1}{8} + \frac{5}{8} = \frac{6}{8} = \frac{3}{4}$

Solve. Write the answer in simplest form. (Lesson 6-1, p. 242)

34 **GRAPES** Dan bought $\frac{1}{4}$ pound of red grapes and $\frac{3}{4}$ pound of green grapes.

How many pounds of grapes did Dan buy? 1 pound

35 **FLOWERS** Mr. Thompson's class planted $\frac{2}{7}$ of the flowers on Tuesday and $\frac{3}{7}$ of the flowers on Wednesday. What fraction of the flowers has Mr. Thompson's class planted? $\frac{5}{7}$

Ticket Out the Door

Pick From the Bag I Place random fraction tiles into a bag. Instruct students to select a tile from the bag. Have students subtract the fraction from a whole. Student volunteers can present their findings. Have them hand in their papers as they exit the classroom.

4 Assess

See It, Do It, Say It, Write It

Step 1 Write a fractional subtraction problem on the board. Model how to represent the fractions with a drawing or model. Do this several times with different subtraction problems.

Step 2 Ask students to draw a number line on paper. Give them fractions to subtract on the number line. Repeat the activity followed by a class discussion.

Step 3 Have students work in pairs. Write fractions on the board to subtract. Tell students to show the common denominator. Have students share their work with the class.

Step 4 Have students work alone. Tell them to write how to subtract fractions in their math journals. Tell them to include a picture or a model.

Looking Ahead: Pre-teach

Add Fractions with Unlike Denominators In the next lesson, students will learn how to add fractions with unlike denominators.

Example

Find $\frac{3}{4} + \frac{2}{3}$. Use prime factorization to find the LCD.

1. Write the prime factorization of each denominator.
   $4 = 2 \times 2 \quad 3 = 1 \times 3$

2. The LCM of the numbers contains only the factors in each number. If there are common factors, include them only one time. The denominators 4 and 3 have no factors in common.
   $LCD = 2 \times 2 \times 1 \times 3 = 12$

3. Rename each fraction using 12 as the denominator.
   $$\left(\frac{3 \times 3}{4 \times 3}\right) + \left(\frac{2 \times 4}{3 \times 4}\right) = \frac{9}{12} + \frac{8}{12}$$

4. Add the like fractions.
   $$\frac{9}{12} + \frac{8}{12} = \frac{17}{12}, \text{ or } 1\frac{5}{12}$$

Chapter 6 Progress Check 1

Formative Assessment

Use the Progress Check to assess students' mastery of the previous lessons. Have students review the lesson indicated for the problems they answered incorrectly.

Odd/Even Assignments

Exercises are structured so that students practice the same concepts whether they are assigned the odd or even problems.

Common Error *Alert*

Simplest Form Students may not necessarily reduce their fractions completely, or they may not convert improper fractions to mixed numbers.

Exercises 1–12 These exercises deal with like denominators; however, once the numerators are added or subtracted, the fractions may need to be reduced.

Exercises 13–16 In some cases the word problems require addition, and in other cases they require subtraction. Look for key words such as *how much more than* to indicate subtraction.

Chapter 6 Progress Check 1 (Lessons 6-1 and 6-2)

Add. Write each sum in simplest form.

1. $\frac{3}{5} + \frac{4}{5} = \frac{7}{5}$
2. $\frac{1}{3} + \frac{4}{3} = \frac{5}{3}$
3. $\frac{6}{7} + \frac{8}{7} = \frac{14}{7} = 2$
4. $\frac{4}{5} + \frac{6}{5} = \frac{10}{5} = 2$
5. $\frac{7}{9} + \frac{1}{9} = \frac{8}{9}$
6. $\frac{2}{11} + \frac{5}{11} = \frac{7}{11}$

Subtract. Write each difference in simplest form.

7. $\frac{8}{11} - \frac{3}{11} = \frac{5}{11}$
8. $\frac{4}{15} - \frac{2}{15} = \frac{2}{15}$
9. $\frac{6}{8} - \frac{2}{8} = \frac{4}{8} = \frac{1}{2}$
10. $\frac{5}{12} - \frac{1}{12} = \frac{4}{12} = \frac{1}{3}$
11. $\frac{9}{20} - \frac{5}{20} = \frac{4}{20} = \frac{1}{5}$
12. $\frac{12}{15} - \frac{7}{15} = \frac{5}{15} = \frac{1}{3}$

Solve.

13. **HOBBIES** Last week Ken added 3 stamps to his collection. This week he added 5 stamps to his collection. Now Ken has 25 collector stamps. What fraction of the stamps did he collect in the past two weeks?
$\frac{8}{25}$ stamps collected

14. **ART** Amado is creating a painting. He has the tubes of paint shown at the right. How much more red paint does he have than purple paint?
$\frac{1}{4}$ of a tube

$\frac{5}{8}$ full

$\frac{3}{8}$ full

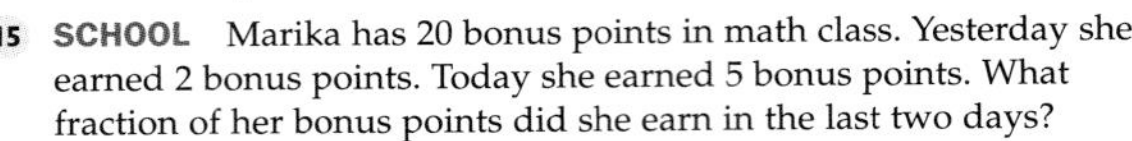

15. **SCHOOL** Marika has 20 bonus points in math class. Yesterday she earned 2 bonus points. Today she earned 5 bonus points. What fraction of her bonus points did she earn in the last two days?
$\frac{7}{20}$ earned in two days

16. **WORK** I have 10 projects that I must complete this week. If I complete 4 projects by Wednesday, what fraction must I complete before the end of the week?
$\frac{6}{10} = \frac{3}{5}$ projects to complete

256 Chapter 6 Add and Subtract Fractions

Data-Driven Decision Making

Students missing Exercises . . .	Have trouble with . . .	Should review and practice . . .
1–6	adding fractions with like denominators and writing the sums in simplest form.	SSG Lesson 6-1, p. 242 CRM Skills Practice, p. A124
7–12	subtracting fractions with like denominators and writing the differences in simplest form.	SSG Lesson 6-2, p. 249 CRM Skills Practice, p. A128
13–16	solving word problems involving adding and subtracting fractions with like denominators.	CRM Problem-Solving Practice, pp. A125 and A129

Lesson 6-3

Add Fractions with Unlike Denominators

KEY Concept

To add **unlike fractions,** you have to rename the fractions so they have like denominators. Use equivalent forms of 1 to write the fractions so each fraction has the same **least common denominator (LCD).**

Ways to Find the LCD for $\frac{4}{6} + \frac{1}{8}$

1. Find a common multiple of both denominators.

$$\frac{4}{6} + \frac{1}{8} = \frac{4 \times 4}{6 \times 4} + \frac{1 \times 3}{8 \times 3}$$
$$= \frac{16}{24} + \frac{3}{24}$$
$$= \frac{19}{24}$$

A common multiple of 6 and 8 is 24.

2. Use the prime factorization of each denominator.

$$\frac{4}{6} + \frac{1}{8} = \frac{4}{2 \times 3} + \frac{1}{2 \times 2 \times 2}$$
$$= \frac{4 \times 2 \times 2}{2 \times 2 \times 2 \times 3} + \frac{1 \times 3}{2 \times 2 \times 2 \times 3}$$
$$= \frac{16}{24} + \frac{3}{24} = \frac{19}{24}$$

VOCABULARY

least common denominator (LCD) the least common multiple of the denominators of two or more fractions, used as a denominator

prime factorization a way of expressing a composite number as a product of its prime factors

unlike fractions fractions with different denominators

Sometimes you must rename fractions in a problem. Only rename one fraction if one of the denominators is the LCD.

Example 1

Find $\frac{2}{3} + \frac{1}{6}$ using a model.

1. Model each fraction.

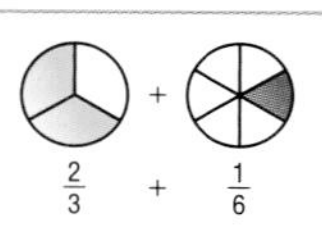

$\frac{2}{3}$ + $\frac{1}{6}$

2. Divide the circle with the thirds into sixths to create like denominators.

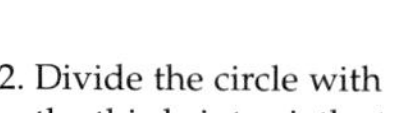

$\frac{4}{6}$ + $\frac{1}{6}$

3. Add the like fractions.

$\frac{4}{6} + \frac{1}{6} = \frac{5}{6}$

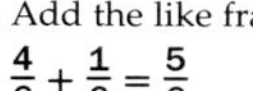

YOUR TURN!

Find $\frac{1}{2} + \frac{2}{5}$ using a model.

1. Model each fraction.

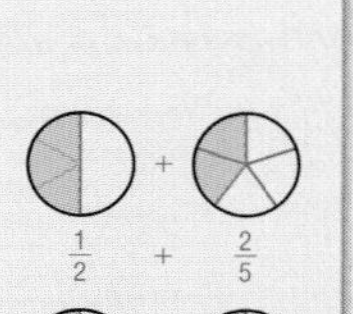

$\frac{1}{2}$ + $\frac{2}{5}$

2. Divide each circle into tenths to create like denominators.

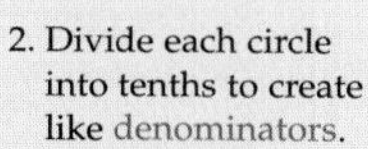

$\frac{5}{10}$ + $\frac{4}{10}$

3. Add the like fractions.

$\frac{5}{10} + \frac{4}{10} = \frac{9}{10}$

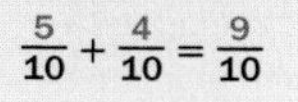

GO ON

Lesson Notes

Lesson 6-3

Lesson Planner

Objective Add simple fractions that have different numbers in the denominators.

Vocabulary **least common denominator (LCD)**, **prime factorization**, **unlike fractions**

Materials/Manipulatives fraction circles, fraction tiles, paper and pencil

Chapter Resource Masters

- CRM Vocabulary and English Language Development (p. A131)
- CRM Skills Practice (p. A132)
- CRM Problem-Solving Practice (p. A133)
- CRM Homework Practice (p. A134)

1 Introduce

Vocabulary

Vocabulary Use Hand out scrap paper and fraction circles for students to use to add fractions. Call on students to find like denominators using *prime factorization.* Have them name their *LCD* in each *unlike fraction.*

Additional Example 1

Find $\frac{1}{3} + \frac{4}{9}$ using a model.

1. Model each fraction.

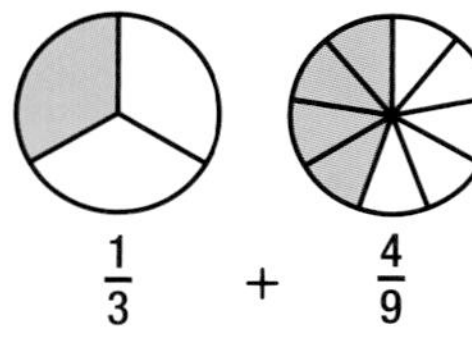

$\frac{1}{3}$ + $\frac{4}{9}$

2. Divide the circle with the thirds into ninths to create like denominators.

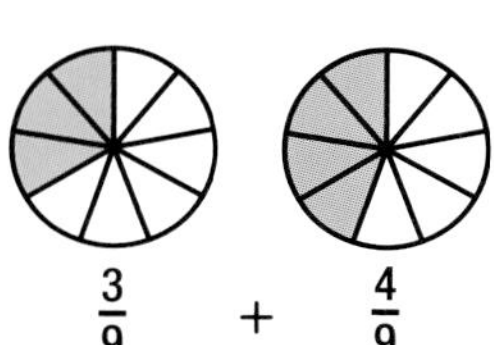

$\frac{3}{9}$ + $\frac{4}{9}$

3. Add the fractions.

$\frac{3}{9} + \frac{4}{9} = \frac{7}{9}$

2 Teach

Key Concept

Foundational Skills and Concepts

After students have read through the Key Concept box, have them try these exercises.

1. Are $\frac{4}{6}$ and $\frac{1}{8}$ like fractions? What is the common denominator? No; the common denominator is 24.
2. How is an equivalent form of 1 used to rewrite the fractions? It is used to find a common multiple of both denominators.

Additional **Example 2**

Find $\frac{1}{4} + \frac{5}{12}$. Use prime factorization to find the LCD.

1. Write the prime factorization of each denominator.

$4 = 2 \times 2 \qquad 12 = 2 \times 2 \times 3$

2. The LCM of the numbers contains only the factors in each number. If there are common factors, include them only one time. The denominators 4 and 12 have the factors 2 and 2 in common.

$\text{LCD} = 2 \times 2 \times 3 = 12$

3. Rename each fraction using 12 as the denominator.

$\frac{1 \times 3}{4 \times 3} + \frac{5}{12} = \frac{3}{12} + \frac{5}{12}$

4. Add the like fractions.

$\frac{3}{12} + \frac{5}{12} = \frac{8}{12} = \frac{2}{3}$

Example 2

Find $\frac{1}{6} + \frac{1}{8}$. Use prime factorization to find the LCD.

1. Write the prime factorization of each denominator. $6 = 2 \times 3 \quad 8 = 2 \times 2 \times 2$
2. The LCM of the numbers contains only the factors in each number. If there are common factors, include them only one time. The denominators 6 and 8 have one factor in common, 2.

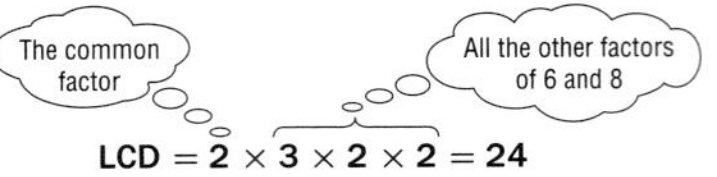

$\text{LCD} = 2 \times 3 \times 2 \times 2 = 24$

3. Rename each fraction using 24 as the denominator.

$\left(\frac{1 \times 4}{6 \times 4}\right) + \left(\frac{1 \times 3}{8 \times 3}\right)$

$= \frac{4}{24} + \frac{3}{24}$

4. Add the like fractions.

$\frac{4}{24} + \frac{3}{24} = \frac{7}{24}$

YOUR TURN!

Find $\frac{2}{9} + \frac{1}{15}$. Use prime factorization to find the LCD.

1. Write the prime factorization of each denominator.
   $9 = \underline{3 \times 3} \qquad 15 = \underline{3 \times 5}$
2. The LCD for these fractions is $\underline{45}$.
3. Rename each fraction so they have the LCD as their denominator.

$\left(\frac{2 \times 5}{9 \times 5}\right) + \left(\frac{1 \times 3}{15 \times 3}\right)$

$= \frac{10}{45} + \frac{3}{45}$

4. Add the like fractions.

$\frac{10}{45} + \frac{3}{45} = \frac{13}{45}$

Who is Correct?

Find the LCD for the fractions $\frac{5}{12}$, $\frac{3}{16}$, and $\frac{1}{2}$.

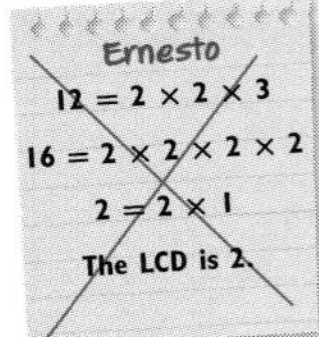

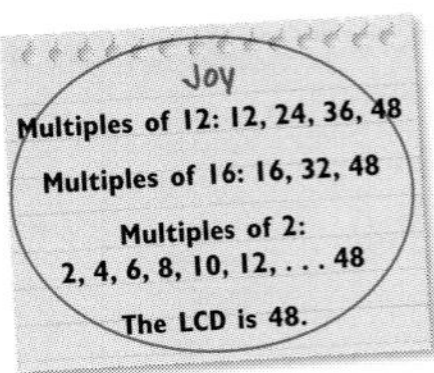

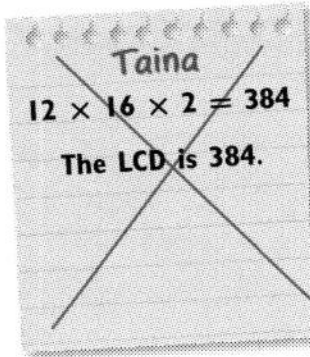

Circle correct answer(s). Cross out incorrect answer(s).

Math Coach Notes

Study Tips Remind students to set goals as they are studying; the goals will serve as roadmaps to get them where they want to be. Tell them that it is important to remain flexible with long-range goals in case circumstances change. Encourage students to congratulate themselves when they achieve a goal and mark it off their lists.

Who *is Correct?*

Diagnostic Teaching

- Ernesto is incorrect. His answer is the GCF.
- Joy is correct. She found the LCD.
- Taina is incorrect. She multiplied the denominators together. This does not always result in the LCD.

Tell students that in this problem, the LCD must be at least 16 or greater.

Guided Practice

Add using models.

1 $\frac{1}{2} + \frac{1}{8} = \frac{5}{8}$

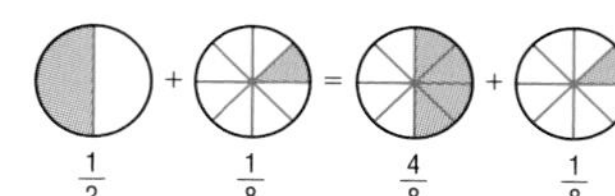

2 $\frac{3}{4} + \frac{11}{12} = \frac{20}{12}$

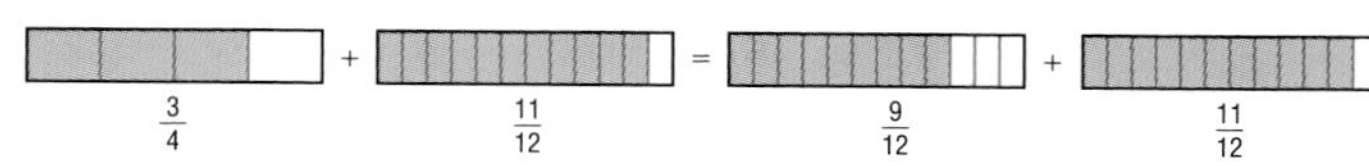

Name the LCD for each pair of fractions.

3 $\frac{4}{5}, \frac{1}{3}$ 15   4 $\frac{1}{2}, \frac{2}{7}$ 14   5 $\frac{2}{3}, \frac{5}{18}$ 18   6 $\frac{5}{6}, \frac{3}{8}$ 24

Step by Step Practice

7 Find $\frac{2}{3} + \frac{1}{4}$. Write the sum in simplest form.

Step 1 Determine the LCD. The LCD of 3 and 4 is 12. $3 = 3 \times 1$ $4 = 2 \times 2$

Step 2 Rename each fraction as an equivalent fraction.

$$\frac{2}{3} + \frac{1}{4}$$

$$= \left(\frac{2}{3} \times \frac{4}{4}\right) + \left(\frac{1}{4} \times \frac{3}{3}\right) = \frac{8}{12} + \frac{3}{12}$$

Step 3 Add the fractions with common denominators. $= \frac{8}{12} + \frac{3}{12} = \frac{11}{12}$

Add. Write each sum in simplest form.

8 $\frac{2}{6} + \frac{1}{3} = \left(\frac{2}{6} \times \frac{1}{1}\right) + \left(\frac{1}{3} \times \frac{2}{2}\right) = \frac{2 + 2}{6} = \frac{4}{6} = \frac{2}{3}$

9 $\frac{1}{2} + \frac{3}{4}$ $\frac{5}{4}$ 10 $\frac{3}{5} + \frac{1}{10}$ $\frac{7}{10}$ 11 $\frac{2}{4} + \frac{5}{6}$ $\frac{16}{12} = \frac{4}{3}$

GO ON

English Learner Strategy

Teach the Concept Students retain more about how to solve a problem when they have the opportunity to teach others. Students may need an opportunity to teach in their native languages. Encourage students to teach someone in their home how to add fractions with unlike denominators, even if that person already knows how to add unlike fractions.

3 Practice

Using Manipulatives

On-Hand Manipulatives When presenting Example 2, draw factor trees to represent the prime factorization of each of the denominators. Using the factor tree, have students write the prime factorization of 6 and 8. Have them cross out any repeated factors and multiply the other factors together. Remind them that the product of the prime numbers is the LCD.

Fraction Circles and Fraction Tiles

After students have found the LCD, have them use fraction circles and tiles to model the problems and check their answers. The original fraction should be the same size as the renamed fraction.

Math Coach Notes

Strategies

1. Have students begin the lesson by factoring numbers using a factor tree. Use the factor tree to find the common factors of numbers. Have students find the least common multiples.
2. An ideal way for students to use prime factorization to find the LCD is to use concrete models or manipulatives. When students are practicing, drill students repeatedly by asking if the fractions are like fractions. Have them point out the common denominator.

Note This!

Study Chunks Point out to students that good note-taking requires extra time and organization. Instruct them that it may help if they think of the time they spend reviewing notes as an investment. Remind them that this will save time later when it comes to studying for the test.

Step by Step Problem-Solving Practice

Problem-Solving Strategies

- ☐ Draw a diagram.
- ☑ Look for a pattern.
- ☐ Guess and check.
- ☐ Work backward.
- ☐ Solve a simpler problem.

Solve. Write your answer in simplest form.

12 SPORTS Alano increases his soccer training sessions by the same amount every 3 days. His first training lasts $\frac{1}{2}$ hour. He trains $\frac{5}{6}$ of an hour the second day and $\frac{7}{6}$ hours the third day. How much time will he spend training during the fourth session?

Understand Read the problem. Write what you know.

Alano began training $\frac{1}{2}$ hour the first day.

Later training sessions lasted $\frac{5}{6}$ of an hour and $\frac{7}{6}$ hours.

Plan Since he will increase his sessions by the same amount, one strategy is to look for a pattern. Find out how much time he increases each training session. Then add that amount to his last time.

Solve What number added to $\frac{1}{2}$ will give you $\frac{5}{6}$?

Find the LCD of $\frac{1}{2}$ and $\frac{5}{6}$. Rename $\frac{1}{2}$.

Multiples of 2 = 2, 4, (6)

Multiples of 6 = (6), 12, 18

LCD = 6

$\frac{1}{2} = \frac{3}{6}$

Subtract to find the time increase from the first to the second trainings.

$\frac{5}{6} - \frac{3}{6} = \frac{2}{6}$

Add $\frac{2}{6}$ to his last training.

third training + time increase = fourth session

$\frac{7}{6} + \frac{2}{6} = \frac{9}{6}$

Write in simplest form.

$\frac{9 \div 3}{6 \div 3} = \frac{3}{2}$

So, Alano spent $\frac{3}{2}$ hours during his fourth session.

Check Because you are adding positive numbers, the sum needs to be greater than each addend.

Are They Getting It?

Check students' understanding of adding unlike fractions by writing these problems on the board. Ask students to point out wrong answers and explain why they are wrong.

1. $\frac{2}{3} + \frac{5}{15} = \frac{15}{15}$, or 1 — This is correct.
2. $\frac{3}{8} + \frac{1}{6} = \frac{4}{14}$ — This is incorrect. The numerators and denominators were added.
3. $\frac{3}{4} + \frac{7}{10} = \frac{29}{20} = 1\frac{9}{20}$ — This is correct.

13 GARDENS The Joneses and the Smiths plant same-sized gardens. The Jones family plants $\frac{1}{5}$ of their garden in corn. The Smith family plants $\frac{3}{10}$ of their garden in corn. Write a fraction that shows how much of the total garden space is planted in corn.

Check off each step.

✓ Understand: I circled key words.

✓ Plan: To solve the problem, I will rename the fractions and add.

✓ Solve: The answer is $\frac{1}{2}$ planted in corn.

✓ Check: I checked my answer by add using models.

14 FITNESS Sumatra walks east $\frac{4}{9}$ of a mile to school every morning. On Saturday she walked to a friend's house, which is $\frac{1}{3}$ of a mile farther east from her school. How far did Sumatra walk to and from her friend's house on Saturday? $\frac{14}{9}$ mi

15 **Reflect** How is adding unlike fractions the same as adding like fractions?

See TWE margin.

Skills, Concepts, and Problem Solving

Name the LCD for each pair of fractions.

16 $\frac{2}{11}, \frac{1}{2}$ 22

17 $\frac{1}{4}, \frac{3}{16}$ 16

18 $\frac{3}{10}, \frac{1}{8}$ 40

Add using models. Write each sum in simplest form.

19 $\frac{1}{2} + \frac{2}{3} = \frac{7}{6}$

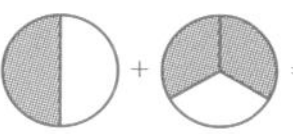
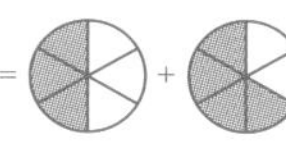

20 $\frac{3}{4} + \frac{5}{12}$ $\frac{7}{6}$

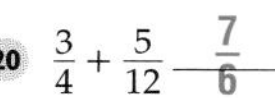
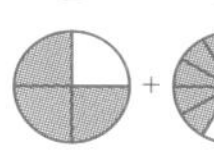
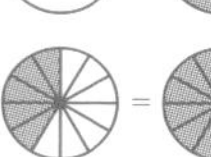

21 $\frac{3}{8} + \frac{2}{4}$ $\frac{7}{8}$

Math Challenge

More Than Two Addends Have students write a problem with three addends that are unlike fractions. Have students write another problem with four addends that are unlike fractions. Students should find the sums to both problems, but write the answers on separate sheets of paper. Students then trade problems with another student. Students should find the sums and then compare their answers with the author of the problems.

Additional Answer

Exercise 15 See students' work. Sample answer: After you rename the fractions to have common denominators, then it is the same. You add the numerators and simplify your answer.

Odd/Even Assignments

Exercises 16–30 are structured so that students practice the same concepts whether they are assigned the odd or even problems.

In-Class Assignment

Have students complete Exercises 17, 20, 24, 29, and 33 to ensure that they understand the concept.

Common Error Alert

Add Fractions When students are adding fractions with unlike denominators, they may add the numerators and the denominators without finding the LCD. Remind students how to find the LCD.

4 Assess

See It, Do It, Say It, Write It

Step 1 Write a fractional addition problem on the board with unlike denominators. Model how to find the LCD by using a factor tree. Do this several times with different addition problems.

Step 2 Ask students to draw a fractional model on paper. Give them fractions to add using their model. Repeat the activity followed by a class discussion.

Step 3 Have students work in pairs. Write unlike fractions on the board to add. Tell students to show the common denominator. Have students share their work with the class.

Step 4 Have students work alone. Tell them to write how to add unlike fractions in their math journals. Tell them to include a picture or a model.

Additional Answer

Exercise 33 See students' work. Sample answer: Students should realize that $\frac{2}{8}$ is not equal to $\frac{2}{12}$. The top and bottom of the fraction must be multiplied by the same number. The equation and answer are $\frac{6}{24} + \frac{6}{24} = \frac{12}{24} = \frac{1}{2}$.

Looking Ahead: Pre-teach

Subtract Fractions with Unlike Denominators
In the next lesson, students will learn how to subtract fractions with unlike denominators.

Example

Subtract. Write the difference in simplest form.

$\frac{3}{5} - \frac{1}{3}$

1. Find the LCD.
   The LCD of 5 and 3 is 15.
2. Rename each of the fractions to equivalent fractions with the denominator of 15.
   $\frac{3}{5} - \frac{1}{3} = \left(\frac{3}{5} \times \frac{3}{3}\right) - \left(\frac{1}{3} \times \frac{5}{5}\right) = \frac{9}{15} - \frac{5}{15}$
3. Subtract the fractions with common denominators.
   $\frac{9}{15} - \frac{5}{15} = \frac{4}{15}$

Add. Write each sum in simplest form.

22 $\frac{2}{3} + \frac{9}{12} = \frac{17}{12}$
23 $\frac{2}{3} + \frac{12}{15} = \frac{22}{15}$
24 $\frac{3}{10} + \frac{9}{100} = \frac{39}{100}$
25 $\frac{8}{12} + \frac{3}{8} = \frac{25}{24}$
26 $\frac{1}{2} + \frac{3}{5} = \frac{11}{10}$
27 $\frac{7}{11} + \frac{2}{3} = \frac{43}{33}$

Solve. Write the answer in simplest form.

28 PAINTING Lina and Marina were painting a house. On Monday they painted $\frac{3}{8}$ of the house. On Tuesday they painted another $\frac{1}{4}$ of the house. What fraction of the house did they have left to paint? $\frac{3}{8}$ left to paint

29 TRAVEL At a gas station Kurt asked for directions to the nearest town. The attendant told him to go $\frac{5}{8}$ of a mile south and then $\frac{1}{16}$ of a mile east. How far does Kurt have to drive to get to the town? $\frac{11}{16}$ of a mile

30 MUSIC Fiona practiced the piano $\frac{3}{15}$ of an hour Monday, $\frac{7}{10}$ of an hour Wednesday, and $\frac{3}{5}$ of an hour Friday. How many hours did Fiona practice this week? $\frac{3}{2}$ hours

Vocabulary Check **Write the vocabulary word that completes each sentence.**

31 Unlike fractions have different denominators.

32 The least common multiple of the denominators of two or more fractions is the least common denominator.

33 Writing in Math Correct Coty's mistake. $\frac{3}{12} + \frac{2}{8} = \frac{3}{12} + \frac{2}{12} = \frac{5}{12}$
Explain how to find the correct answer.

See TWE margin.

Spiral Review

Subtract. Write each difference in simplest form. (Lesson 6-2, p. 249)

34 $\frac{7}{9} - \frac{2}{9} = \frac{5}{9}$
35 $\frac{8}{9} - \frac{2}{9} = \frac{2}{3}$
36 $\frac{11}{10} - \frac{7}{10} = \frac{2}{5}$

Ticket Out the Door

Show What You Know Write an addition problem in which the addends are unlike fractions. Show each step of rewriting the fractions to have common denominators. Circle the sum and turn in your problem as you exit the classroom.

262 Chapter 6 Add and Subtract Fractions

Subtract Fractions with Unlike Denominators

KEY Concept

When you subtract fractions that are **unlike fractions**, you have to rename the fractions so that they have like denominators. Use equivalent forms of 1 to write the fractions so that each fraction has the **least common denominator (LCD).**

Ways to Find the LCD for $\frac{7}{6} - \frac{3}{15}$

1. Find a common multiple of both denominators.
   Multiples of 6: 6, 12, 18, 24, (30)
   Multiples of 15: 15, (30), 45

$$\frac{7}{6} - \frac{3}{15} = \frac{7 \times 5}{6 \times 5} - \frac{3 \times 2}{15 \times 2}$$

A common multiple of 6 and 15 is 30.

$$= \frac{35}{30} - \frac{6}{30}$$
$$= \frac{29}{30}$$

2. Use the prime factorization of each denominator.

$$\frac{7}{6} - \frac{3}{15} = \frac{7}{2 \times 3} - \frac{3}{3 \times 5}$$
$$= \frac{7 \times 5}{2 \times 3 \times 5} - \frac{3 \times 2}{2 \times 3 \times 5}$$
$$= \frac{35}{30} - \frac{6}{30}$$
$$= \frac{29}{30}$$

VOCABULARY

least common denominator (LCD)
the least common multiple of the denominators of two or more fractions, used as a denominator

prime factorization
a way of expressing a composite number as a product of its prime factors

unlike fractions
fractions with different denominators

In some problems, fractions have to be renamed. Only rename one fraction if one of the denominators is the LCD.

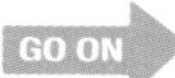

Intervention Strategy — Linguistic Learners

Build Knowledge Have students write a brief paragraph of how the previous lessons on adding and subtracting fractions with like denominators is helping them to understand this lesson. Have student volunteers read their paragraphs to the class.

Lesson Notes

Lesson 6-4

Lesson Planner

Objective Subtract simple fractions that have different numbers in the denominators.

Vocabulary **least common denominator (LCD)**, **prime factorization**, **unlike fractions**

Materials/Manipulatives fraction circles, fraction tiles, paper and pencil

Chapter Resource Masters

- CRM Vocabulary and English Language Development (p. A135)
- CRM Skills Practice (p. A136)
- CRM Problem-Solving Practice (p. A137)
- CRM Homework Practice (p. A138)

1 Introduce

Vocabulary

Use Vocabulary Hand out scrap paper and fraction circles for students to use for subtracting unlike fractions. Call on students to find like denominators using *prime factorization.* Have them name the *LCD* in each *unlike fraction.*

2 Teach

Key Concept

Foundational Skills and Concepts After students have read through the Key Concept box, have them try these exercises.

1. Are $\frac{7}{6}$ and $\frac{3}{15}$ like fractions? What is the common denominator? No; the common denominator is 30.
2. How is prime factorization used to subtract fractions with unlike denominators? to find the LCD

Additional **Example 1**

Find $\frac{3}{4} - \frac{5}{12}$ using a model.

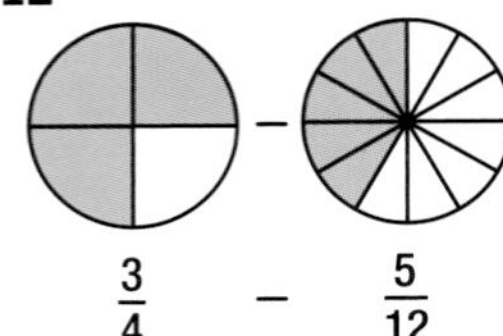

$\frac{3}{4} - \frac{5}{12}$

1. Divide the circle with the fourths into twelfths to create like denominators.

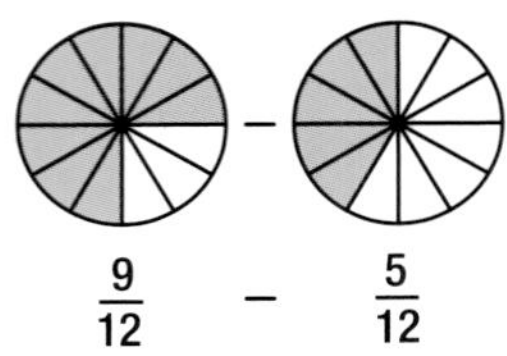

$\frac{9}{12} - \frac{5}{12}$

2. Subtract the like fractions.

$\frac{9}{12} - \frac{5}{12} = \frac{4}{12} = \frac{1}{3}$

Note This!

Show the Steps Explain to students how important it is to show all the steps when finding the difference. This makes it easier to locate mistakes when answers are incorrect.

Example 1

Find $\frac{1}{3} - \frac{1}{6}$ using a model.

1. Divide the circle with the thirds into sixths to create like denominators.
2. Subtract the like fractions.

$\frac{1}{3} - \frac{1}{6} = \frac{2}{6} - \frac{1}{6} = \frac{1}{6}$

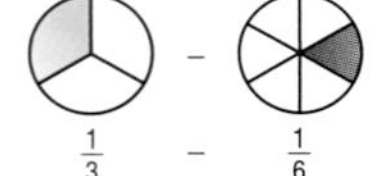

$\frac{1}{3} - \frac{1}{6}$

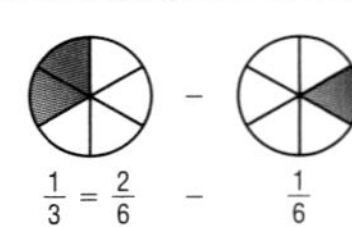

$\frac{1}{3} = \frac{2}{6} - \frac{1}{6}$

YOUR TURN!

Find $\frac{1}{3} - \frac{2}{9}$ using a model.

1. Model each fraction as a circle.
2. Divide each circle into ninths to create like denominators.
3. Subtract the like fractions. $\frac{3}{9} - \frac{2}{9} = \frac{1}{9}$

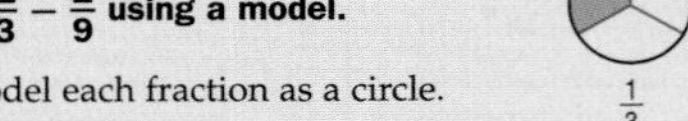

$\frac{1}{3} - \frac{2}{9}$

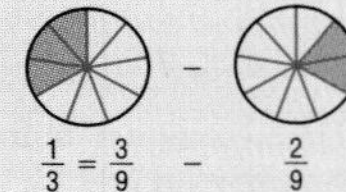

$\frac{1}{3} = \frac{3}{9} - \frac{2}{9}$

Example 2

Find $\frac{1}{12} - \frac{1}{15}$. Use prime factorization to find the LCD.

1. Write the prime factorization of each denominator. $12 = 2 \times 2 \times 3$; $15 = 3 \times 5$
2. The LCM of the numbers contains only the factors in each number. If there are common factors, include them only one time. The denominators 12 and 15 have one factor in common, 3. $\text{LCD} = 2 \times 2 \times 3 \times 5 = 60$
3. Rename each fraction using 60 as the denominator. $\frac{1 \times 5}{12 \times 5} - \frac{1 \times 4}{15 \times 4} = \frac{5}{60} - \frac{4}{60}$
4. Subtract the like fractions. $\frac{5}{60} - \frac{4}{60} = \frac{1}{60}$

YOUR TURN!

Find $\frac{7}{8} - \frac{5}{12}$. Use prime factorization to find the LCD.

1. Write the prime factorization of each denominator. $8 = \underline{2 \times 2 \times 2}$; $12 = \underline{2 \times 2 \times 3}$
2. The LCD for these fractions is $\underline{24}$.
3. Rename each fraction so they have common denominators.
4. Subtract the like fractions. $\underline{\frac{11}{24}}$

$\frac{7}{8} - \frac{5}{12} = \frac{7 \times 3}{8 \times 3} - \frac{5 \times 2}{12 \times 2} = \frac{21}{24} - \frac{10}{24}$

Additional **Example 2**

Find $\frac{13}{18} - \frac{5}{12}$. Use prime factorization to find the LCD.

1. Write the prime factorization of each denominator.

$18 = 2 \times 3 \times 3 \qquad 12 = 2 \times 2 \times 3$

2. The LCM of the numbers contains only the factors in each number. If there are common factors, include them only one time. The denominators 18 and 12 have 2 and 3 in common.

$\text{LCD} = 2 \times 3 \times 2 \times 3 = 36$

3. Rename each fraction using 36 as the denominator.

$\frac{13 \times 2}{18 \times 2} - \frac{5 \times 3}{12 \times 3} = \frac{26}{36} - \frac{15}{36}$

4. Subtract the like fractions.

$\frac{26}{36} - \frac{15}{36} = \frac{11}{36}$

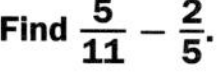

Who is Correct?

Find $\frac{5}{11} - \frac{2}{5}$.

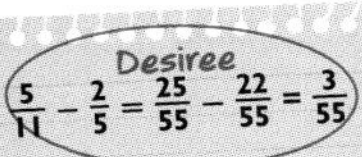

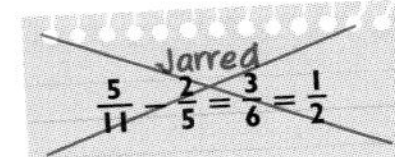

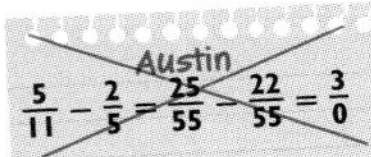

Circle correct answer(s). Cross out incorrect answer(s).

Guided Practice

Subtract using models.

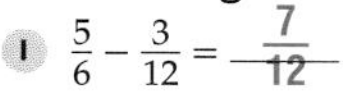

1. $\frac{5}{6} - \frac{3}{12} = \frac{7}{12}$

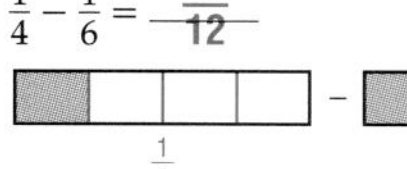

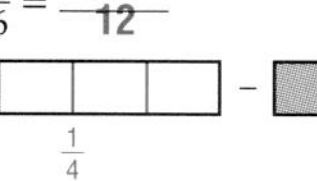

2. $\frac{1}{4} - \frac{1}{6} = \frac{1}{12}$

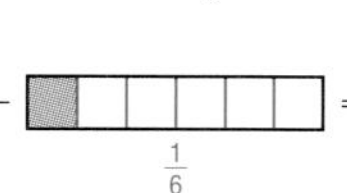

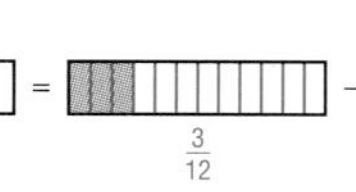

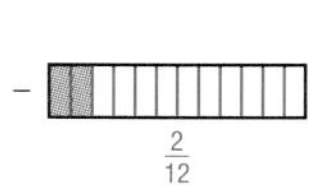

$\frac{5}{6} - \frac{3}{12} = \frac{10}{12} - \frac{3}{12}$

$\frac{1}{4} - \frac{1}{6} = \frac{3}{12} - \frac{2}{12}$

Step by Step Practice

3. Find $\frac{1}{2} - \frac{2}{5}$. Write the difference in simplest form.

Step 1 Determine the LCD.

$2 = 2 \times 1$
$5 = 5 \times 1$
The LCD of 2 and 5 is 10.

Step 2 Rename each fraction as an equivalent fraction with a denominator of 10.

$$\frac{1}{2} - \frac{2}{5}$$

$$= \left(\frac{1}{2} \times \frac{5}{5}\right) - \left(\frac{2}{5} \times \frac{2}{2}\right) = \frac{5}{10} - \frac{4}{10}$$

Step 3 Subtract the fractions with common denominators.

$$= \frac{5}{10} - \frac{4}{10}$$

$$= \frac{5 - 4}{10} = \frac{1}{10}$$

GO ON

3 Practice

Using Manipulatives

On-Hand Manipulatives When presenting Example 2, have students draw a factor tree to represent each prime factorization of the denominators. Using the factor tree, have students write the prime factorization of 12 and 15. Have them cross out any repeated factors and multiply the other factors together. Remind them that the product of the prime numbers is the LCD.

Fraction Circles and Fraction Tiles After students have found the LCD, have them use fraction circles or tiles to model the problem and check their answers. The original fraction should be the same size as the renamed fraction.

Who *is Correct?*

Diagnostic Teaching

- Desiree is correct.
- Jarred is incorrect. He did not find an LCD. He subtracted the numerators and the denominators.
- Austin is incorrect. He subtracted the denominators as well as the numerators.

Remind students to check their answers using the inverse operation, addition.

Common Error *Alert*

Multi-Step Problem If a student is unable to use logical reasoning for Exercise 11, he or she may not understand how fractions need to have a common denominator before you subtract them. Show students that they first need to see if the lesser denominator is a factor of the greater denominator. If this step does not work, then factor both denominators to find the LCD. In this case 10 is a factor of 50.

Use LCD If students are having difficulty subtracting fractions with unlike denominators, remind them that they must convert each fraction to like denominators using the LCD. If they do not choose the LCD, they may have to reduce the fraction to lowest terms.

Note This!

Listening Inform students that listening is a critical note-taking skill. Many students feel that because they can hear, they are listening. To really listen, they must understand what they are hearing. Advise them to listen first, then write their notes using their own words.

4. $\frac{6}{14} - \frac{2}{7} = \left(\frac{6}{14} \times \frac{1}{1}\right) - \left(\frac{2}{7} \times \frac{2}{2}\right) = \frac{6 - 4}{14} = \frac{2}{14} = \frac{1}{7}$

5. $\frac{11}{12} - \frac{3}{5} = \frac{19}{60}$

6. $\frac{8}{15} - \frac{1}{5} = \frac{5}{15} = \frac{1}{3}$

7. $\frac{3}{4} - \frac{2}{9} = \frac{19}{36}$

8. $\frac{5}{8} - \frac{1}{3} = \frac{7}{24}$

9. $\frac{3}{10} - \frac{27}{100} = \frac{3}{100}$

10. $\frac{10}{11} - \frac{1}{2} = \frac{9}{22}$

Step by Step Problem-Solving Practice

Problem-Solving Strategies
- ☐ Draw a diagram.
- ☐ Look for a pattern.
- ☑ Use logical reasoning.
- ☐ Guess and check.
- ☐ Work backward.

Solve. Write the answer in simplest form.

11. COMMUNITY SERVICE Kathy and Paloma collected $\frac{13}{50}$ ton of canned goods for a food bank. Their goal was to collect $\frac{1}{10}$ ton. Write a fraction that shows the difference between their goal and their collection.

Understand Read the problem. Write what you know.
The girls collected $\frac{13}{50}$ ton of canned goods.
Their goal was to collect $\frac{1}{10}$ ton.

Plan Pick a strategy. One strategy is to use logical reasoning. Compare the denominators. What relationship do you see?

Solve 50 is a multiple of 10. $10 \times 5 = 50$
Write $\frac{1}{10}$ as a fraction with a denominator of 50.
Subtract the like fractions.
$\frac{1}{10} = \frac{1 \times 5}{10 \times 5} = \frac{5}{50}$
So, the difference between their goal and the amount they collected is $\frac{4}{25}$ ton.

Check Because you are subtracting from $\frac{13}{50}$, the difference needs to be less than $\frac{13}{50}$. Is your answer less than $\frac{13}{50}$?
$\frac{13}{50} - \frac{5}{50} = \frac{8}{50} = \frac{4}{25}$

Are They Getting It?

Check students' understanding of subtracting unlike fractions by writing these problems on the board. Ask students to point out wrong answers and explain why they are wrong.

1. $\frac{4}{5} - \frac{1}{2} = \frac{8}{10} - \frac{5}{10} = \frac{3}{10}$ This is correct.
2. $\frac{10}{13} - \frac{7}{10} = \frac{3}{3}$ or 1 This is incorrect. The numerators and denominators were both subtracted.
3. $\frac{5}{7} - \frac{2}{3} = \frac{15}{21} - \frac{14}{21} = \frac{1}{21}$ This is correct.

12 CLEANING Pooja and Alise were washing the walls of a room. At the end of an hour, Pooja had washed $\frac{7}{8}$ of one wall, while Alise had washed $\frac{2}{3}$ of a different wall of the same size. Write a fraction that shows how much more Pooja had washed than Alisa. Check off each step.

✔ Understand: I circled key words.

✔ Plan: To solve the problem, I will find the LCD and subtract.

✔ Solve: The answer is $\frac{5}{24}$ more walls washed.

✔ Check: I checked my answer by drawing a diagram.

13 FOOD Dylan baked a meatloaf. He ate $\frac{1}{5}$, froze another $\frac{2}{5}$, and left the remaining meatloaf in the refrigerator. His sister ate $\frac{2}{15}$ of the meatloaf in the refrigerator. What fraction of the meatloaf in the refrigerator was left? $\frac{4}{15}$ left

14 **Reflect** Explain the first step to subtracting unlike fractions.

See TWE margin.

Skills, Concepts, and Problem Solving

Subtract using drawings. Write each difference in simplest form.

15 $\frac{1}{2} - \frac{1}{3} = \frac{1}{6}$

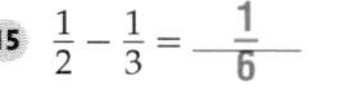

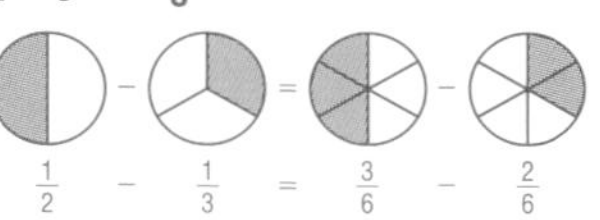

$\frac{1}{2} - \frac{1}{3} = \frac{3}{6} - \frac{2}{6}$

16 $\frac{11}{12} - \frac{1}{4} = \frac{8}{12} = \frac{2}{3}$

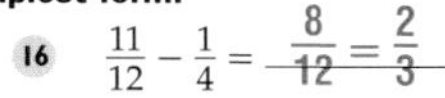

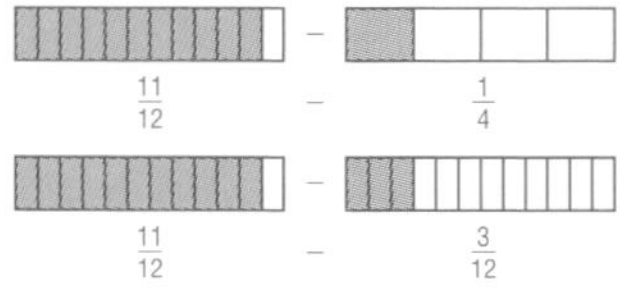

$\frac{11}{12} - \frac{1}{4}$

$\frac{11}{12} - \frac{3}{12}$

Subtract. Write each difference in simplest form.

17 $\frac{2}{3} - \frac{1}{4} = \frac{5}{12}$

18 $\frac{3}{10} - \frac{9}{100} = \frac{21}{100}$

19 $\frac{4}{7} - \frac{1}{3} = \frac{5}{21}$

20 $\frac{2}{3} - \frac{1}{12} = \frac{7}{12}$

21 $\frac{2}{3} - \frac{7}{15} = \frac{3}{15} = \frac{1}{5}$

22 $\frac{9}{10} - \frac{29}{100} = \frac{61}{100}$

GO ON

Lesson 6-4 Subtract Fractions with Unlike Denominators 267

Additional Answer

Exercise 14 See students' work. Sample answer: Use the denominators to find a least common denominator.

Odd/Even Assignments

Exercises 15–24 are structured so that students practice the same concepts whether they are assigned the odd or even problems.

In-Class Assignment

Have students complete Exercises 16, 17, 21, 24, and 28 to ensure that they understand the concept.

Math Challenge

Partner Differences Group students into pairs. Students should find $\frac{4}{5} - \frac{2}{7}$ by taking turns solving the problem. Without talking, one student writes the first step to completing the subtraction problem. Then the other student takes over and writes the next step, again without talking. Students should trade back and forth, each writing the next step until they have found the difference. The difference is $\frac{18}{35}$.

See It, Do It, Say It, Write It

Step 1 Write a fractional subtraction problem on the board with unlike denominators. Model how to find the LCD by using a factor tree. Do this several times with different subtraction problems.

Step 2 Ask students to draw a model of the fractions. Give them fractions to subtract using their model. Repeat the activity followed by a class discussion.

Step 3 Have students work in pairs. Write unlike fractions on the board to subtract. Tell students to show the common denominator. Have students share their work with the class.

Step 4 Have students work alone. Tell them to write how to subtract unlike fractions in their math journals. Tell them to include a picture or a model.

Additional Answer

Exercise 28 See students' work. Sample answer: If $\frac{2}{3}$ of the circle is blue and $\frac{1}{9}$ is yellow, then $\frac{2}{3} + \frac{1}{9} = \frac{6}{9} + \frac{1}{9} = \frac{7}{9}$ of the circle is blue and yellow. Subtract this fraction from the whole to find the fraction of the circle that is red. $\frac{9}{9} - \frac{7}{9} = \frac{2}{9}$; $\frac{2}{9}$ of the circle is red.

Solve. Write the answer in simplest form.

23 NATURE On Monday, Juanita's sunflower was $\frac{15}{16}$ inches tall. It had grown $\frac{3}{8}$ inch since Friday. How tall was Juanita's sunflower on Friday? $\frac{9}{16}$ inches tall

24 HOBBIES Trey has a project to complete. He decides to do $\frac{1}{8}$ of it on Monday, $\frac{3}{16}$ of it on Tuesday, and to finish the project on Friday. Write a fraction to represent how much of the project Trey will do on Friday. $\frac{11}{16}$ needed to finish

Vocabulary Check **Write the vocabulary word that completes each sentence.**

25 Unlike fractions have different denominators.

26 The least common multiple of the denominators of two or more fractions is the least common denominator (LCD).

27 To subtract unlike fractions, you have to first change them into like fractions.

28 Writing in Math $\frac{2}{3}$ of the circle is blue. $\frac{1}{9}$ of the circle is yellow. What fraction of the circle is red? Explain how to solve this problem. Set up an equation that shows your work.

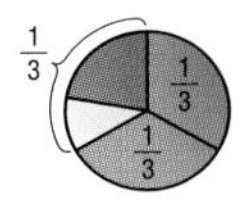

See TWE margin.

Spiral Review

Add. Write each sum in simplest form. (Lesson 6-3, p. 257)

29 $\frac{1}{4} + \frac{3}{7} = \frac{19}{28}$

30 $\frac{5}{3} + \frac{1}{9} = \frac{16}{9}$

31 $\frac{1}{6} + \frac{3}{7} = \frac{25}{42}$

Solve. (Lesson 6-1, p. 244)

32 SCHOOL In the school chorus, $\frac{2}{8}$ of the singers are sopranos, $\frac{3}{8}$ are altos, and $\frac{1}{8}$ are tenors. The others are baritone or bass. What fraction of the chorus is baritone or bass? $\frac{2}{8} = \frac{1}{4}$ is baritone or bass

268 Chapter 6 Add and Subtract Fractions

Ticket Out the Door

Write About It Have students write a description of the steps for finding the difference of two fractions that do not have common denominators. Students should hand in their descriptions as they exit the classroom.

Chapter 6 Progress Check 2 (Lessons 6-3 and 6-4)

Name the LCD for each pair of fractions.

1 $\frac{1}{9}, \frac{5}{27}$ 27

2 $\frac{1}{8}, \frac{7}{32}$ 32

3 $\frac{2}{5}, \frac{4}{9}$ 45

4 $\frac{5}{7}, \frac{1}{8}$ 56

Add. Write each sum in simplest form.

5 $\frac{1}{2} + \frac{3}{13} = \frac{19}{26}$

6 $\frac{5}{8} + \frac{5}{11} = \frac{95}{88}$

7 $\frac{3}{4} + \frac{1}{6} = \frac{11}{12}$

8 $\frac{3}{10} + \frac{1}{2} = \frac{8}{10} = \frac{4}{5}$

9 $\frac{1}{3} + \frac{4}{9} = \frac{7}{9}$

10 $\frac{9}{16} + \frac{3}{4} = \frac{21}{16}$

Subtract. Write each difference in simplest form.

11 $\frac{10}{15} - \frac{1}{3} = \frac{1}{3}$

12 $\frac{7}{40} - \frac{1}{8} = \frac{1}{20}$

13 $\frac{3}{5} - \frac{1}{4} = \frac{7}{20}$

14 $\frac{7}{9} - \frac{1}{7} = \frac{40}{63}$

Solve.

15 **FITNESS** Elias rode his bike to his grandmother's house, which was $\frac{2}{5}$ mile west from his house. He then rode to the park, which was $\frac{3}{8}$ mile farther west from his grandmother's house. How far did Elias ride if he rode from his house to the park and back home again?
$\frac{31}{20}$ or $1\frac{11}{20}$ miles

16 **NATURE** Jasmine measured her pet snake today. It had grown $\frac{1}{3}$ of an inch since the last measurement. How long was Jasmine's snake when she measured it last?
$\frac{29}{6}$ or $4\frac{5}{6}$ inches

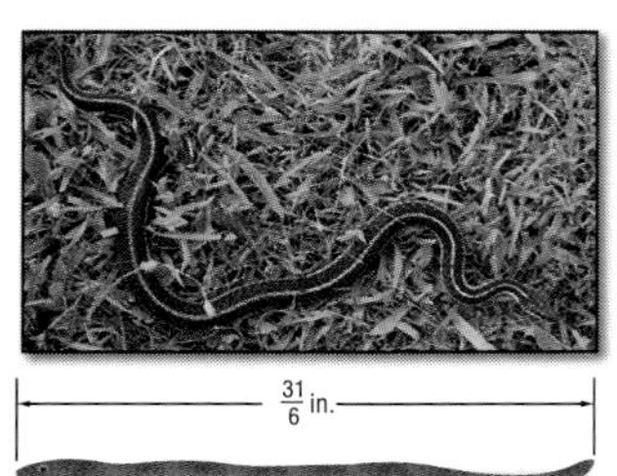

$\frac{31}{6}$ in.

Chapter 6 Add and Subtract Fractions 269

Progress Check 2

Chapter 6

Formative Assessment

Use the Progress Check to assess students' mastery of the previous lessons. Have students review the lesson indicated for the problems they answered incorrectly.

Odd/Even Assignments

Exercises are structured so that students practice the same concepts whether they are assigned the odd or even problems.

Common Error Alert

Finding LCDs Remind students of the two methods for finding an LCD: listing multiples and prime factorization.

Exercise 15 Suggest that students draw a sketch or map of the places referred to in this word problem. Students should label the distances between them to help them find the solution.

Data-Driven Decision Making

Students missing Exercises . . .	Have trouble with . . .	Should review and practice . . .
1-4	naming the LCD for pairs of fractions.	SSG Lesson 6-3, p. 257 CRM Skills Practice, p. A132
5-10	adding unlike fractions.	SSG Lesson 6-3, p. 257 CRM Skills Practice, p. A132
11-14	subtracting unlike fractions and writing the difference in simplest form.	SSG Lesson 6-4, p. 263 CRM Skills Practice, p. A136
15-16	solving word problems involving adding and/or subtracting unlike fractions.	CRM Problem-Solving Practice, pp. A133 and A137

Chapter 6 Study Guide
Formative Assessment

Vocabulary and Concept Check

If students have difficulty answering Exercises 1–8, remind them that they can use the page references to refresh their memories about the vocabulary terms.

Vocabulary Review Strategies

Vocabulary Flashcards Have students create their own set of vocabulary flashcards for each vocabulary word on index cards or half sheets of paper. On the set of cards, state either the definition or have an example on one side, and on the other side have the vocabulary term. Encourage students to quiz each other as they review for the test.

Lesson Review

Each example walks the students through the main concepts of this chapter. If the given examples are not sufficient to review the questions, remind students that the page references tell them where to review that topic in their textbooks.

Find **Extra Practice** for these concepts in the Practice Worksheets, pages A123–A138.

Classroom Management

Early Finishers Some students will not require as much time to study and review. Be sure to have a role for students who have a solid understanding of the content. For example, suggest that students write another example for each lesson. They can present these examples to their partners or to the class to help review the content.

Chapter 6 Study Guide

Vocabulary and Concept Check

common denominator, *p. 242*
least common denominator (LCD), *p. 257*
like fractions, *p. 242*
prime factorization, *p. 257*
simplest form, *p. 242*
unlike fractions, *p. 257*

Write the vocabulary word that completes each sentence. Some words may be used more than once.

1. Fractions that have the same denominator are called ___like fractions___.
2. $\frac{1}{2}$ is the ___simplest form___ of $\frac{3}{6}$.
3. The ___least common denominator (LCD)___ for $\frac{3}{15}$ and $\frac{1}{6}$ is 30.
4. $\frac{1}{6}$ and $\frac{2}{7}$ are examples of ___unlike fractions___.
5. The fractions $\frac{3}{8}$ and $\frac{7}{8}$ have a ___common denominator___.
6. $2 \times 3 \times 3$ is the ___prime factorization___ of 18.

Label each diagram below. Write the correct vocabulary term in each blank.

$\frac{2}{3}, \frac{4}{5}, \frac{1}{8}$

7. ___unlike fractions___

$$\frac{8}{9} - \frac{5}{6} = \frac{16}{18} - \frac{15}{18} = \frac{1}{18}$$

8. ___least common denominators (LCD) or like denominators___

Lesson Review

6-1 Add Fractions with Like Denominators (pp. 242–248)

Add. Write each sum in simplest form.

9. $\frac{2}{7} + \frac{3}{7} = \frac{5}{7}$
10. $\frac{5}{9} + \frac{3}{9} = \frac{8}{9}$
11. $\frac{3}{4} + \frac{1}{4} = \frac{4}{4} = 1$
12. $\frac{5}{11} + \frac{10}{11} = \frac{15}{11}$
13. $\frac{1}{12} + \frac{7}{12} = \frac{2}{3}$

Example 1

Find $\frac{1}{6} + \frac{2}{6}$. Write the sum in simplest form.

1. The common denominator is 6.
2. Add the numerators. $\frac{1}{6} + \frac{2}{6} = \frac{1+2}{6}$
3. Write in simplest form. $= \frac{3}{6} = \frac{3 \div 3}{6 \div 3} = \frac{1}{2}$

6-2 Subtract Fractions with Like Denominators (pp. 249–255)

Subtract. Write each difference in simplest form.

14. $\frac{8}{12} - \frac{4}{12} = \frac{4}{12} = \frac{1}{3}$
15. $\frac{9}{15} - \frac{3}{15} = \frac{6}{15} = \frac{2}{5}$
16. $\frac{7}{9} - \frac{4}{9} = \frac{3}{9} = \frac{1}{3}$
17. $\frac{7}{15} - \frac{2}{15} = \frac{5}{15} = \frac{1}{3}$
18. $\frac{14}{9} - \frac{8}{9} = \frac{6}{9} = \frac{2}{3}$

Example 2

Find $\frac{6}{10} - \frac{4}{10}$. Write the difference in simplest form.

1. The common denominator is 10.
2. Subtract the numerators. $\frac{6-4}{10} = \frac{2}{10}$
3. Simplify. $\frac{2}{10} = \frac{2 \div 2}{10 \div 2} = \frac{1}{5}$

FOLDABLES® Study Organizer Dinah Zike's Foldables®

Review Remind students to complete and refer to their Foldables as they progress through the Chapter 6 Study Guide. Have students choose one of the tabs, or topics, on their Foldables to "teach" to another student. Pair up students to teach each other their concepts. For complete instructions, see Chapter Resource Masters, p. A120.

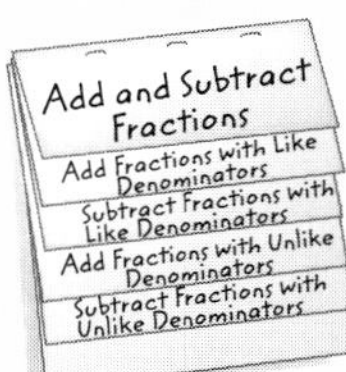

Note This!

Create a Checklist Help students create a study checklist. The checklist should include all of the following:

- Notes from class.
- Drawings from class.
- Foldable.
- Vocabulary terms and concepts.
- Lesson examples.
- All assignments and quizzes.
- Chapter 6 Study Guide.

Intervention Strategy

Using Key Words

Step 1

Write, or have students write, several fractions on index cards. Advise students to write equivalent fractions, unit fractions, and other fractions.

Step 2

Create a large number line on the board, on the floor using masking tape, or on poster board. Follow the model shown.

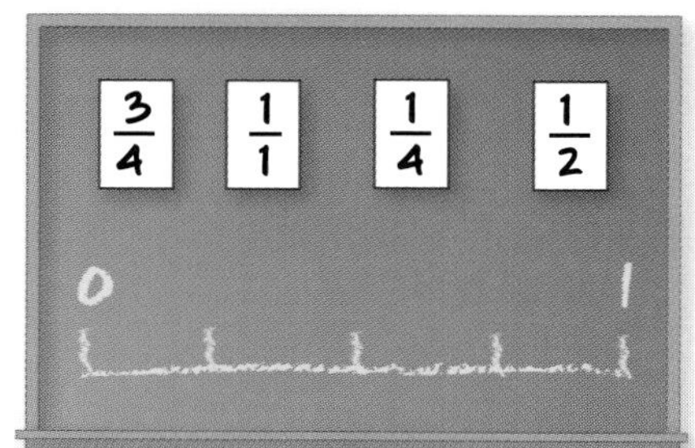

Step 3

Collect the fraction cards.

Step 4

Have a student pair or a small group of students draw four cards.

Step 5

Have the rest of the class work with the students to place the index cards with fractions correctly on the number line. Note that students may add intervals to correctly place fractions.

Math Coach Notes

Review GCF Help students by reviewing how to find the greatest common factor between numbers. This is an important step in simplifying their answers.

6-3 Add Fractions with Unlike Denominators (pp. 257–262)

Add using diagrams.

19 $\frac{1}{4} + \frac{3}{8}$ $\frac{5}{8}$

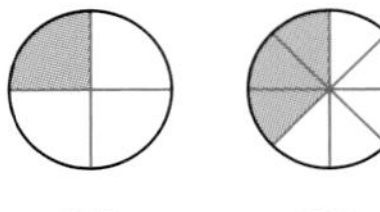

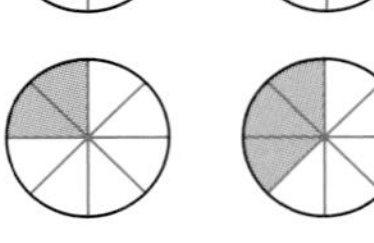

20 $\frac{1}{2} + \frac{1}{4}$ $\frac{3}{4}$

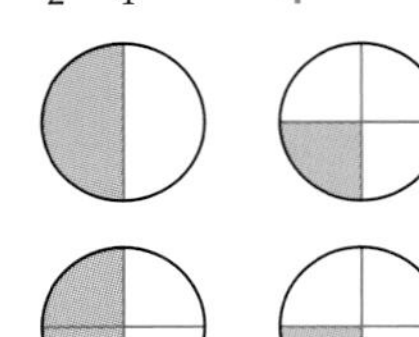

Add. Write each sum in simplest form.

21 $\frac{1}{12} + \frac{1}{8}$

$\frac{2}{24} + \frac{3}{24} = \frac{5}{24}$

22 $\frac{2}{15} + \frac{1}{9}$

$\frac{6}{45} + \frac{5}{45} = \frac{11}{45}$

23 $\frac{7}{10} + \frac{2}{15}$

$\frac{5}{6}$

Example 3

Find $\frac{3}{4} + \frac{1}{8}$ using diagrams.

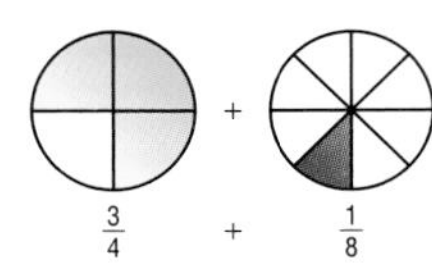

Divide the circle with the fourths into eighths to create like denominators.

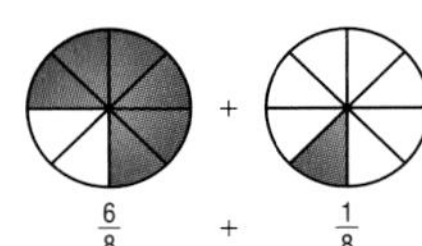

Add the fractions.

$\frac{3}{4} + \frac{1}{8} = \frac{6}{8} + \frac{1}{8} = \frac{7}{8}$

Example 4

Find $\frac{1}{8} + \frac{1}{6}$. Use prime factorization to find the LCD.

Write the prime factorization of each denominator.

$8 = 2 \times 2 \times 2$
$6 = 2 \times 3$

LCD $= 2 \times 2 \times 2 \times 3 = 24$

Rename each fraction using 24 as the denominator. $\left(\frac{1 \times 3}{8 \times 3}\right) + \left(\frac{1 \times 4}{6 \times 4}\right) = \frac{3}{24} + \frac{4}{24}$

Add the like fractions.

$\frac{3}{24} + \frac{4}{24} = \frac{7}{24}$

272 Chapter 6 Study Guide

Intervention Strategy Visual Learners

Use Drawings Have students use drawings if they are in need of models for adding and subtracting fractions. For some students, actually seeing the pieces reinforces the steps in the process, especially if the fractions contain unlike denominators.

Find $\frac{3}{4} + \frac{1}{6}$. $\frac{11}{12}$

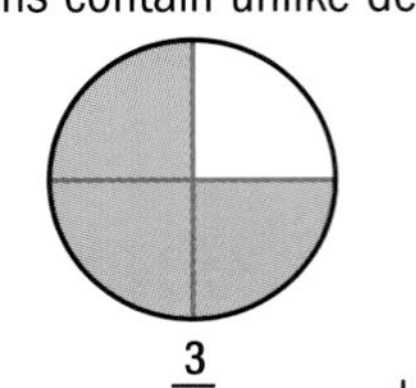

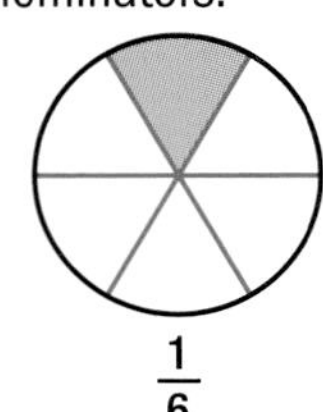

$\frac{3}{4}$ + $\frac{1}{6}$

6-4 Subtract Fractions with Unlike Denominators (pp. 263-268)

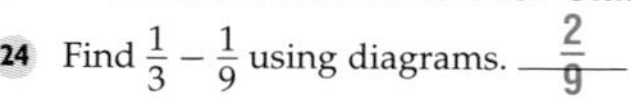

24 Find $\frac{1}{3} - \frac{1}{9}$ using diagrams. $\frac{2}{9}$

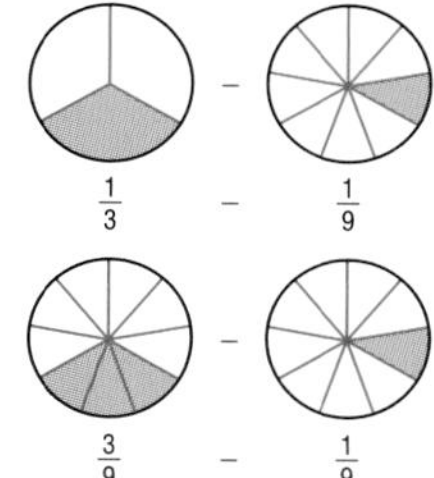

$\frac{1}{3} - \frac{1}{9}$

$\frac{3}{9} - \frac{1}{9}$

Example 5

Find $\frac{1}{4} - \frac{1}{8}$ using diagrams.

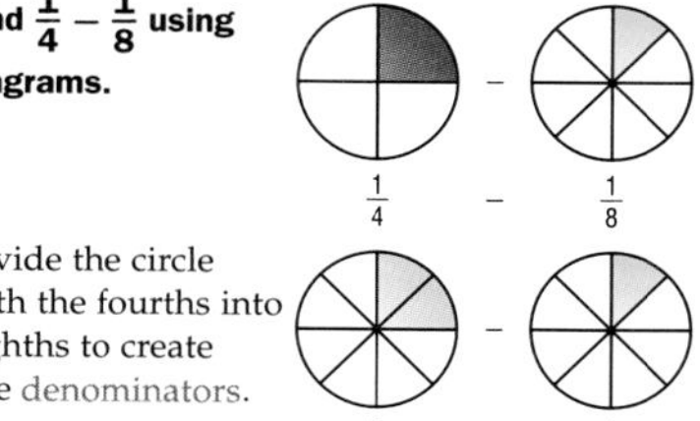

$\frac{1}{4} - \frac{1}{8}$

Divide the circle with the fourths into eighths to create like denominators.

$\frac{2}{8} - \frac{1}{8}$

Subtract the like fractions.

$\frac{1}{4} - \frac{1}{8} = \frac{2}{8} - \frac{1}{8} = \frac{1}{8}$

Subtract. Write each difference in simplest form.

25 $\frac{1}{7} - \frac{1}{28} = \frac{3}{28}$

$\frac{1}{7} - \frac{1}{28} = \frac{4}{28} - \frac{1}{28} = \frac{3}{28}$

26 $\frac{2}{5} - \frac{1}{10} = \frac{3}{10}$

$\frac{2}{5} - \frac{1}{10} = \frac{4}{10} - \frac{1}{10} = \frac{3}{10}$

27 $\frac{3}{4} - \frac{5}{12} = \frac{1}{3}$

$\frac{3}{4} - \frac{5}{12} = \frac{9}{12} - \frac{5}{12} = \frac{4}{12} = \frac{1}{3}$

28 $\frac{7}{9} - \frac{2}{27} = \frac{19}{27}$

$\frac{7}{9} - \frac{2}{27} = \frac{21}{27} - \frac{2}{27} = \frac{19}{27}$

Example 6

Find $\frac{1}{9} - \frac{1}{16}$. Use prime factorization to find the LCD.

Write the prime factorization of each denominator.

$9 = 3 \times 3$
$16 = 2 \times 2 \times 2 \times 2$

$\text{LCD} = 2 \times 2 \times 2 \times 2 \times 3 \times 3 = 144$

Rename each fraction using 144 as the denominator.

$$\left(\frac{1 \times 16}{9 \times 16}\right) - \left(\frac{1 \times 9}{16 \times 9}\right)$$

$$= \frac{16}{144} - \frac{9}{144}$$

Subtract the like fractions.

$\frac{16}{144} - \frac{9}{144} = \frac{7}{144}$

Ticket Out the Door

Do These Problems Have students answer four problems of the following types: (1) adding fractions with like denominators, (2) subtracting fractions with like denominators, (3) adding fractions with unlike denominators, and (4) subtracting fractions with unlike denominators. Have them give you their papers as they exit the classroom.

Common Error *Alert*

Carelessness It is possible that some students may be careless or forgetful. They might get accustomed to the *like* denominators from the earlier lessons of the chapter. When they get to the last sections (6-3 and 6-4) of the chapter, they may add or subtract the numerators without first converting to fractions with like denominators.

Chapter 6 Chapter Test

Chapter Resource Masters

Additional forms of the Chapter 6 Tests are available.

Test Format	Where to Find it
Chapter 6 Test	Math Online macmillanmh.com
Blackline Masters	Assessment Masters, p. 75

Customize and create multiple versions of your chapter tests and their answer keys. All of these questions from the chapter tests are available on ExamView® Assessment Suite.

Online Assessment and Reporting
macmillanmh.com

This online assessment tool allows teachers to track student progress with easily accessible comprehensive reports available for every student. Assess students using any internet-ready computer.

Alternative Assessment

Use Portfolios Ask students to write examples of all the different types of problems from this chapter. These include all of the following: adding fractions with like denominators, subtracting fractions with like denominators, adding fractions with unlike denominators, and subtracting fractions with unlike denominators.

Chapter 6 Chapter Test

Add. Write each sum in simplest form.

1. $\frac{3}{8} + \frac{1}{8} =$ $\frac{1}{2}$
2. $\frac{1}{12} + \frac{2}{12} =$ $\frac{1}{4}$
3. $\frac{1}{6} + \frac{2}{6} =$ $\frac{1}{2}$

Subtract. Write each difference in simplest form.

4. $\frac{5}{6} - \frac{1}{6} =$ $\frac{2}{3}$
5. $\frac{7}{9} - \frac{4}{9} =$ $\frac{1}{3}$
6. $\frac{3}{5} - \frac{1}{5} =$ $\frac{2}{5}$

Add. Write each sum in simplest form.

7. $\frac{2}{3} + \frac{9}{10} =$ $\frac{47}{30}$
8. $\frac{3}{7} + \frac{1}{4} =$ $\frac{19}{28}$
9. $\frac{7}{6} + \frac{4}{9} =$ $\frac{29}{18}$

Subtract. Write each difference in simplest form.

10. $\frac{4}{6} - \frac{1}{2} =$ $\frac{1}{6}$
11. $\frac{3}{10} - \frac{1}{5} =$ $\frac{1}{10}$
12. $\frac{2}{3} - \frac{2}{5} =$ $\frac{4}{15}$

Solve.

13. **BAKING** Marta has a cookie recipe that calls for $\frac{1}{4}$ cup sugar, and Dontonio has a cookie recipe that calls for $\frac{2}{4}$ cup sugar. How much sugar is needed altogether for their recipes?

$\frac{3}{4}$ cup

14. **TRAVEL** Tavio rode his bike to LeBron's house from his house. Then he rode his bike to school. How many miles did he ride in all? Use the map shown at the right.

$\frac{5}{4}$ or $1\frac{1}{4}$ mile

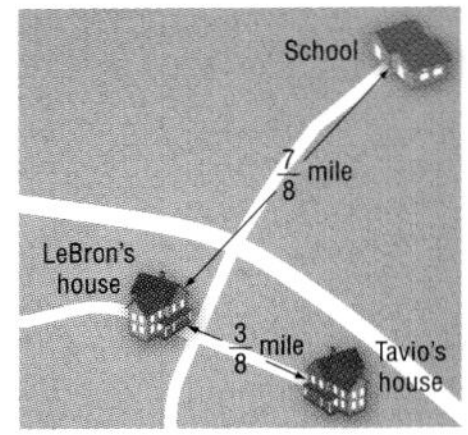

GO ON

274 Chapter 6 Test

English Learner Strategy

Assessment Allow students time to look over the assessment. Have the students read the problem directions and word problems for any words that need clarification prior to beginning the chapter test. Provide the students with an opportunity to define any words they think they do not understand.

15 **CONSTRUCTION** Mr. Ring needs a $\frac{3}{4}$ foot long board to finish a book case. He has a piece of lumber that is $\frac{7}{8}$ foot long. How much of the lumber does he need to cut? $\frac{1}{8}$-foot

16 **CRAFTS** Kelsey is buying fabric for a craft project. She buys $\frac{1}{4}$ yard of red fabric and $\frac{2}{3}$ yard of blue fabric. How much fabric did she buy altogether? $\frac{11}{12}$ of a yard

17 **FOOD** At the school cafeteria, the fifth graders ate $\frac{1}{9}$ of the chicken nuggets, and the sixth graders ate $\frac{3}{8}$ of the chicken nuggets. What fraction of the chicken nuggets were eaten by the fifth and sixth graders? $\frac{35}{72}$ chicken nuggets eaten

18 **LANDSCAPING** The Green Meadows landscaping company had a project at the swim club. Their goal was to work Monday, Tuesday, and Wednesday, and finish on Thursday. On Monday they completed $\frac{1}{4}$ of the job. On Tuesday they completed $\frac{1}{5}$ of the job. On Wednesday they completed $\frac{3}{8}$ of the job. How much was left for them to finish on Thursday? $\frac{7}{40}$ of the work left

Correct the mistakes.

19 **FITNESS** Fabio jogged $\frac{1}{10}$ mile before school and $\frac{3}{10}$ mile after school. He said to his friend, "I jogged a half mile today." What is wrong with Fabio's statement?

See TWE margin.

20 **TRIPS** A group of students went on a summer digging trip. While digging they found two ancient bone fragments. The first fragment measured $\frac{5}{12}$ inch. The second fragment measured $\frac{1}{8}$ inch. One of the students reported to their professor that the first fragment was $\frac{1}{4}$ inch longer than the second. By what amount was the student incorrect?

See TWE margin.

Learning From Mistakes

Missed Questions Review commonly missed questions as a small group or class. Ask students to share their methods of answering each question. Try to point out when any errors occur and take corrective measures.

Math Coach Notes

Word Problems Have students underline any key words in the word problems that might indicate which operation to use and circle any numbers that will be used in the calculation. They can also cross out any words that are not significant to solving the problem.

Additional Answer

Exercise 19 He jogged only $\frac{4}{10}$ mile, which is $\frac{1}{10}$ mile short of the $\frac{5}{10}$ or $\frac{1}{2}$ mile he claimed to jog.

Exercise 20 The student was incorrect by $\frac{1}{24}$ inch. The difference in the measures of the fragments is $\frac{7}{24}$, not the $\frac{6}{24}$ that the student probably calculated to get the reduced value of $\frac{1}{4}$.

Data-Driven Decision Making

Students missing Exercises . . .	Have trouble with . . .	Should review and practice . . .
1–3, 7–9	adding fractions and writing their sums in simplest form.	SSG Lesson 6-1 and 6-3, pp. 242 and 257 CRM Skills Practice, pp. A124 and A132
4–6, 10–12	subtracting fractions and writing their differences in simplest form.	SSG Lesson 6-2 and 6-4, pp. 249 and 263 CRM Skills Practice, pp. A128 and A136
13–20	solving word problems involving adding and subtracting fractions.	CRM Problem-Solving Practice, pp. A125, A129, A133, and A137

Chapter 6 Test Practice

Diagnose Student Errors

Survey student responses for each item. Class trends may indicate common errors and misconceptions.

1. A added both numerators and denominators
   B subtracted instead of added
   C guess
   Ⓓ correct
2. A subtracted both numerators and denominators
   Ⓑ correct
   C added numerators and have wrong denominator
   D added numerator and kept denominator same
3. A added all three fractions together
   B guess
   C subtracted the wrong two friends
   Ⓓ correct
4. Ⓐ correct
   B added the denominators
   C guess
   D guess
5. Ⓐ correct
   B subtracted the equivalent fractions
   C didn't subtract total from 1
   D wrong denominator
6. A miscalculated
   B miscalculated
   Ⓒ correct
   D added equivalent fractions
7. A added both numerators and denominators
   B reduced incorrectly
   Ⓒ correct
   D wrong denominator
8. A subtracted half from wrong trail
   Ⓑ correct
   C subtracted half from wrong trail
   D guess
9. A switched numerator and denominator of answer
   B guess
   Ⓒ correct
   D misinterpreted concept of comparison

Chapter 6 Test Practice

Choose the best answer and fill in the corresponding circle on the sheet at right.

1 Francine used $\frac{1}{8}$ gallon of milk for one recipe and $\frac{4}{8}$ gallon of milk for another recipe. How much milk did she use for both recipes?

A $\frac{5}{16}$ gallon C $\frac{1}{2}$ gallon
B $\frac{3}{8}$ gallon Ⓓ $\frac{5}{8}$ gallon

2 Which fraction has a value equal to $\frac{5}{6} - \frac{2}{6}$?

A $\frac{3}{0}$ C $\frac{7}{13}$
Ⓑ $\frac{1}{2}$ D $\frac{7}{6}$

3 Three friends split a large pizza. The table shows how much of the pizza each friend ate. How much more pizza did Jaden eat than Seth?

Dominic	$\frac{2}{12}$
Jaden	$\frac{6}{12}$
Seth	$\frac{4}{12}$

A $\frac{12}{12}$ or 1 whole C $\frac{4}{12}$ or $\frac{1}{3}$
B $\frac{5}{12}$ Ⓓ $\frac{2}{12}$ or $\frac{1}{6}$

4 $\frac{2}{9} + \frac{1}{3} =$ ____

Ⓐ $\frac{5}{9}$ C $\frac{2}{9}$
B $\frac{2}{12}$ D $\frac{6}{9}$

5 Gracie read $\frac{1}{4}$ of a book on Monday and $\frac{2}{3}$ of the book on Tuesday. How much more does she have to read?

Ⓐ $\frac{1}{12}$ C $\frac{11}{12}$
B $\frac{5}{12}$ D $\frac{11}{24}$

6 $\frac{3}{5} - \frac{1}{3} =$ ____

A $\frac{4}{5}$ Ⓒ $\frac{4}{15}$
B $\frac{15}{4}$ D $\frac{14}{15}$

7 Write the sum in simplest form: $\frac{1}{12} + \frac{2}{3}$.

A $\frac{3}{15}$
B $\frac{1}{4}$
Ⓒ $\frac{3}{4}$
D $\frac{9}{10}$

GO ON

276 Chapter 6 Test Practice

10. A miscounted number of shaded parts in model
    B miscounted number of shaded parts in model
    C miscounted number of parts in model
    Ⓓ correct
11. A guess
    Ⓑ correct
    C ordered from greatest to least
    D guess
12. Ⓐ correct
    B guess
    C reduced incorrectly
    D reduced only numerator

8 Oliver is hiking through a state park. He walks $\frac{1}{2}$ mile on Pike's Lake Trail. How much more does he need to hike to complete this trail?

Trail	Length
Eagle's Bluff	$\frac{5}{6}$ mile
Pike's Lake	$\frac{7}{8}$ mile
Riverside	$\frac{7}{10}$ mile

A $\frac{2}{6}$ mile C $\frac{1}{5}$ mile

(B) $\frac{3}{8}$ mile D $\frac{6}{8}$ mile

9 Solve. Write in simplest form.

$\frac{7}{10} + \frac{4}{5} =$ ______

A $\frac{2}{3}$ (C) $\frac{3}{2}$

B $\frac{11}{15}$ D $\frac{3}{5}$

10 Which fraction does the model represent?

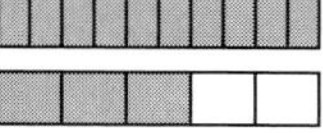

A $\frac{14}{10}$ C $\frac{14}{9}$

B $\frac{3}{2}$ (D) $\frac{8}{5}$

11 Order these fractions from least to greatest: $\frac{5}{6}, \frac{3}{4}, \frac{7}{12}$.

A $\frac{3}{4}, \frac{5}{6}, \frac{7}{12}$ C $\frac{5}{6}, \frac{3}{4}, \frac{7}{12}$

(B) $\frac{7}{12}, \frac{3}{4}, \frac{5}{6}$ D $\frac{3}{4}, \frac{7}{12}, \frac{5}{6}$

12 Write $\frac{6}{8}$ in simplest form.

(A) $\frac{3}{4}$ C $\frac{2}{3}$

B $\frac{1}{2}$ D $\frac{3}{8}$

1	A	B	C	**D**
2	A	**B**	C	D
3	A	B	C	**D**
4	**A**	B	C	D
5	**A**	B	C	D
6	A	B	**C**	D
7	A	B	**C**	D
8	A	**B**	C	D
9	A	B	**C**	D
10	A	B	C	**D**
11	A	**B**	C	D
12	**A**	B	C	D

Success Strategy
After answering all the questions, go back and check signs and operations, making sure you worked each problem correctly.

Diagnosing Student Errors and Misconceptions

Polls Take a poll to see how many students missed each question. Have a student volunteer come to the board and walk through finding the solutions for each of the most frequently missed questions.

Common Error *Alert*

Find Mistakes If students missed several problems due to computational errors, be sure that students have their work that they can review. Explain that without work shown, the point at which the mistake was made cannot be determined. Have students try to locate their mistakes; however, if they cannot find their mistakes, offer assistance for these problems.

Chapter 7

Chapter Overview

Chapter-at-a-Glance

Lesson	Math Objective	Local/State Standards
7-1 Introduction to Decimals (pp. 280–286)	Understand and model decimals.	
7-2 Equivalent Decimals (pp. 287–293)	Recognize and use equivalent decimals.	
Progress Check (p. 294)		
7-3 Compare and Order Decimals (pp. 295–302)	Compare and order decimals.	
7-4 Estimate Decimal Sums and Differences (pp. 303–309)	Estimate the sum or difference of two decimals.	
Progress Check (p. 310)		
7-5 Add Decimals (pp. 311–316)	Add decimals.	
7-6 Subtract Decimals (pp. 317–323)	Subtract decimals.	
Progress Check (p. 324)		

Content-at-a-Glance

The diagram below summarizes and unpacks Chapter 7 content.

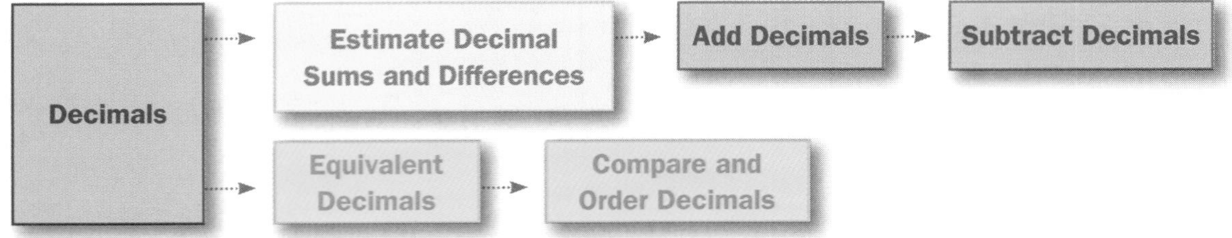

Online Assessment and Reporting
macmillanmh.com

Chapter Assessment Manager

Diagnostic

Diagnose students' readiness.

	Student Study Guide/ Teacher Edition	Assessment Masters	Technology
Course Placement Test		1	ExamView® Assessment Suite
Book 2 Pretest		58	ExamView® Assessment Suite
Chapter 7 Pretest		83	ExamView® Assessment Suite
Quiz/Preview	SSG 279		Math Online macmillanmh.com StudentWorks™ Plus

Formative

Identify students' misconceptions of content knowledge.

	Student Study Guide/ Teacher Edition	Assessment Masters	Technology
Progress Checks	SSG 294, 310, 324		Math Online macmillanmh.com StudentWorks™ Plus
Vocabulary Review	SSG 325		Math Online macmillanmh.com StudentWorks™ Plus
Lesson Assessments			ExamView® Assessment Suite
Are They Getting It	TE 283, 290, 298, 306, 314, 320		

Summative

Determine student success in learning concepts in the lesson, chapter, or book.

	Student Study Guide/ Teacher Edition	Assessment Masters	Technology
Chapter 7 Test	SSG 328	86	ExamView® Assessment Suite
Test Practice	SSG 330	89	ExamView® Assessment Suite
Alternative Assessment	TE 328	92	
See It, Do It, Say It, Write It	TE 286, 293, 302, 309, 316, 323		
Book 2 Test		94	ExamView® Assessment Suite

Back-mapping and Vertical Alignment **McGraw-Hill's *Math Triumphs*** intervention program was conceived and developed with the final result in mind: student success in grade-level mathematics, including Algebra 1 and beyond. The authors, using the **NCTM Focal Points and Focal Connections** as their guide, developed this brand-new series by backmapping from grade-level and Algebra 1 concepts, and vertically aligning the topics so that they build upon prior skills and concepts and serve as a foundation for future topics.

Chapter Resource Manager

	Lesson 7-1	Lesson 7-2	Lesson 7-3	Lesson 7-4
Concept	Introduction to Decimals	Equivalent Decimals	Compare and Order Decimals	Estimate Decimal sums and Differences
Objective	Understand and model decimals.	Recognize and use equivalent decimals.	Compare and order decimals.	Estimate the sum or difference of two decimals.
Math Vocabulary	decimal hundredths tenths thousandths	equivalent decimals hundredths tenths thousandths value	decimal	difference estimate round sum
Lesson Resources	**Materials** • Index cards **Manipulatives** • Money • Base-ten blocks **Other Resources** CRM Vocabulary and English Language Development CRM Skills Practice CRM Problem-Solving Practice CRM Homework Practice	**Materials** • Construction paper • Place-value charts **Manipulatives** • Money • Base-ten blocks **Other Resources** CRM Vocabulary and English Language Development CRM Skills Practice CRM Problem-Solving Practice CRM Homework Practice	**Materials** • Meter sticks • Number line • Place-value chart **Manipulatives** • Money • Base-ten blocks • Fraction tiles **Other Resources** CRM Vocabulary and English Language Development CRM Skills Practice CRM Problem-Solving Practice CRM Homework Practice	**Materials** • Index cards • Number line • Ruler **Manipulatives** • Money **Other Resources** CRM Vocabulary and English Language Development CRM Skills Practice CRM Problem-Solving Practice CRM Homework Practice
Technology	Math Online macmillanmh.com StudentWorks™ Plus ExamView® Assessment Suite	Math Online macmillanmh.com StudentWorks™ Plus ExamView® Assessment Suite	Math Online macmillanmh.com StudentWorks™ Plus ExamView® Assessment Suite	Math Online macmillanmh.com StudentWorks™ Plus ExamView® Assessment Suite

SSG Student Study Guide
CRM Chapter Resource Masters
TE Teacher Edition
DVD

	Lesson 7-5	Lesson 7-6
Concept	Add decimals	Subtract Decimals
Objective	Add decimals.	Subtract decimals.
Math Vocabulary	regroup rename sum	difference regroup rename
Lesson Resources	**Materials** • Grid paper **Manipulatives** • Money • Base-ten blocks • Fraction tiles **Other Resources** CRM Vocabulary and English Language Development CRM Skills Practice CRM Problem-Solving Practice CRM Homework Practice	**Materials** • Grid paper • Place-value chart **Manipulatives** • Money • Base-ten blocks • Fraction tiles **Other Resources** CRM Vocabulary and English Language Development CRM Skills Practice CRM Problem-Solving Practice CRM Homework Practice
Technology	Math Online macmillanmh.com StudentWorks™ Plus ExamView® Assessment Suite	Math Online macmillanmh.com StudentWorks™ Plus ExamView® Assessment Suite

Intervention Strategy

Reinforce Decimals Show students a hundreds flat.

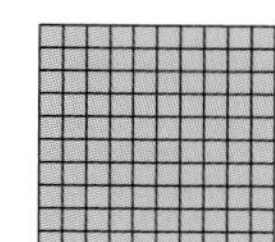

Then ask: What number does this represent? 100

Now show students the grid broken into 10 parts.

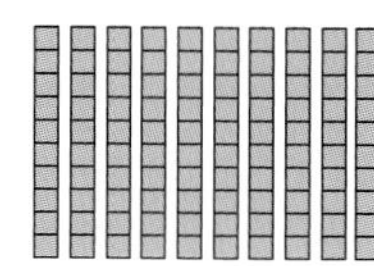

Take one rod away.
Ask: What number does this represent? 10

Break the rod into 10 equal parts.

Show one unit.
Ask: What number does this represent? 1

Discuss how each part would represent a decimal if you break the one-unit block into equal parts.

Chapter Notes

Real-World Applications

Costs Ernesto is running for student council class representative. He wants to buy everyone in his class a "Vote for Ernesto" badge. The badges will cost $30.94. He also wants to purchase campaign posters that will cost $12.36. How much money will Ernesto spend? $43.30

Intervention Strategy

Operations with Decimals

Step 1 Have students work in pairs.

Step 2 Using the decimals 46.2805 and 3.013, complete the following two problems.
- Add the two decimals. 49.2935
- Subtract the two decimals. 43.2675

Step 3 After completing the two problems, record two similarities that you noticed between problems and two differences you noticed between problems.

Step 4 Have pairs share their solutions, similarities, and differences with the class.

Decimals

We use money every day.

Before buying lunch, you count your money. Our money system is based on decimals.

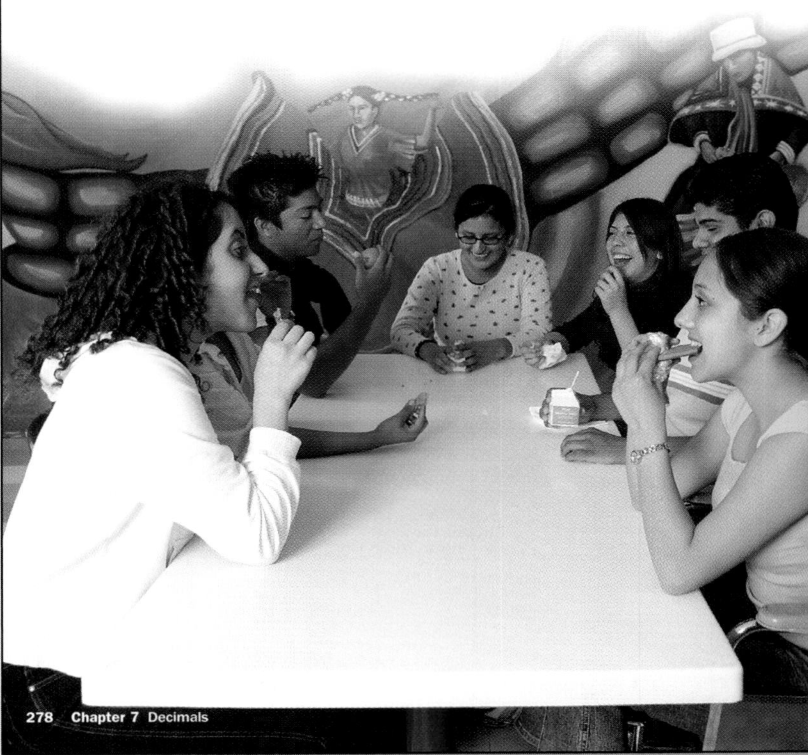

278 Chapter 7 Decimals

Key Vocabulary

Find interactive definitions in 13 languages in the **eGlossary** at macmillanmh.com.

English **Español** *Introduce the most important vocabulary terms from Chapter 7.*

decimal **decimal**
a number that can represent a whole number and a fraction (p. 280)

hundredths **centésimas**
the second decimal place to the right of the decimal point; one of one hundred equal parts (p. 280)

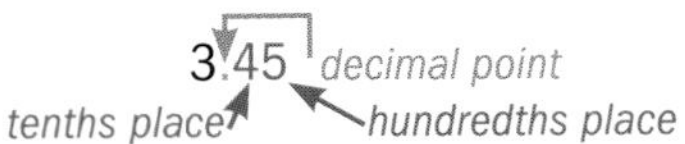

tenths **décimas**
the first decimal place to the right of the decimal point; one of ten equal parts or $\frac{1}{10}$ (p. 280)

thousandths **milésimas**
the third decimal place to the right of the decimal point (p. 280)

difference **diferencia**
the answer or result of a subtraction problem (p. 303)

regroup **reagrupar**
to use place value to exchange equal amounts when renaming a number (p. 311)

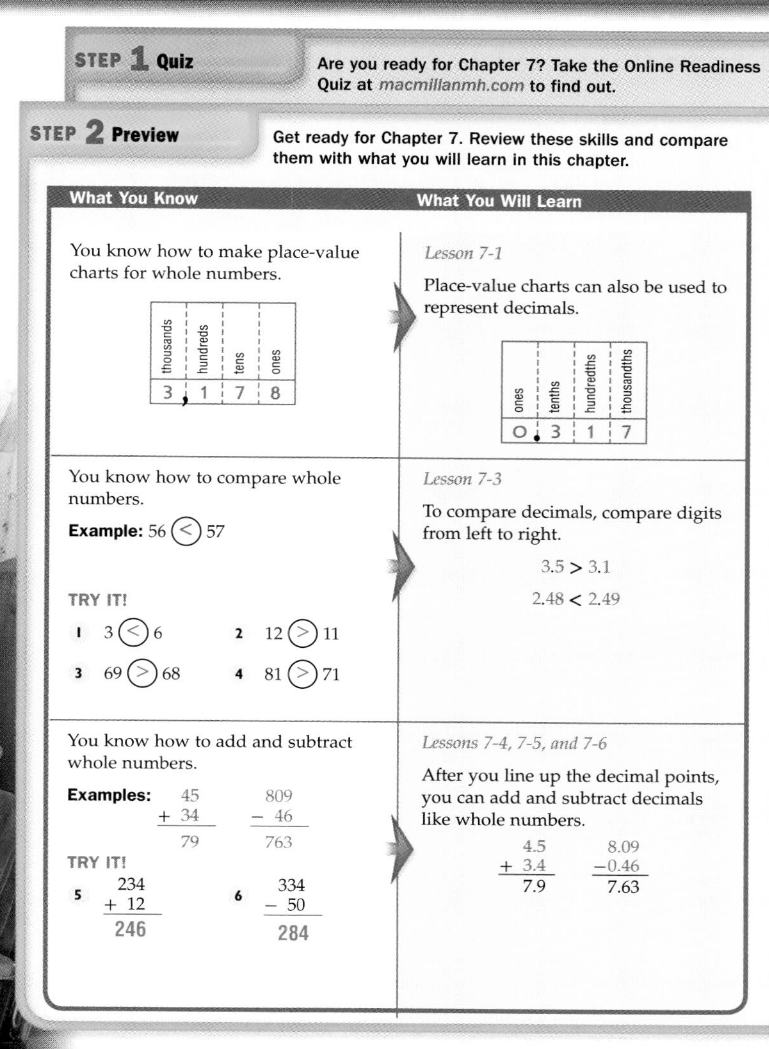

STEP 1 Quiz Are you ready for Chapter 7? Take the Online Readiness Quiz at *macmillanmh.com* to find out.

STEP 2 Preview Get ready for Chapter 7. Review these skills and compare them with what you will learn in this chapter.

What You Know	What You Will Learn
You know how to make place-value charts for whole numbers. thousands | hundreds | tens | ones 3 , 1 | 7 | 8	*Lesson 7-1* Place-value charts can also be used to represent decimals. ones | tenths | hundredths | thousandths 0 . 3 | 1 | 7
You know how to compare whole numbers. **Example:** 56 (<) 57 **TRY IT!** 1 3 (<) 6 2 12 (>) 11 3 69 (>) 68 4 81 (>) 71	*Lesson 7-3* To compare decimals, compare digits from left to right. 3.5 > 3.1 2.48 < 2.49
You know how to add and subtract whole numbers. **Examples:** 45 + 34 = 79 809 − 46 = 763 **TRY IT!** 5 234 + 12 = 246 6 334 − 50 = 284	*Lessons 7-4, 7-5, and 7-6* After you line up the decimal points, you can add and subtract decimals like whole numbers. 4.5 + 3.4 = 7.9 8.09 − 0.46 = 7.63

279

Vocabulary Preview

- Write several key vocabulary terms on the board.
- Call on student volunteers to predict what each term means.
- Start with the first word written on the board. Have students skim the chapter to find the definition of the term. Call on a student volunteer to read the definition out loud.
- Then have students skim the chapter to find an example of the term. Call on a student volunteer to write the example on the board.

Step 1 Quiz

Pretest/Prescribe Students can take the Online Readiness Quiz or the Diagnostic Pretest in the Assessment Masters.

Step 2 Preview

Use this pre-chapter activity to activate students' prior knowledge, build confidence, and help students preview the lessons.

Dinah Zike's Foldables®

Guide students through the directions on p. A139 in the Chapter Resource Masters to create their own Foldable graphic organizer to use with this chapter.

Home Connections

- Using a stopwatch, time five people running a predetermined distance one at a time. Record the times then put them in order from least to greatest to find the winner.
- Look in your refrigerator and find the price on the egg carton. Based on the price, determine how much it would cost to buy just one egg.

Mc Graw Hill Professional Development

Targeted professional development has been articulated throughout **McGraw-Hill's *Math Triumphs*** intervention program. **The McGraw-Hill Professional Development Video Library** provides short videos that support the **NCTM Focal Points and Focal Connections.** For more information, visit macmillanmh.com.

Lesson 7-1 Lesson Notes

Lesson Planner

Objective Understand and model decimals.

Vocabulary **decimal**, **hundredths**, **tenths**, **thousandths**

Materials/Manipulatives base-ten blocks, index cards, money

Chapter Resource Masters

- CRM Vocabulary and English Language Development (p. A141)
- CRM Skills Practice (p. A142)
- CRM Problem-Solving Practice (p. A143)
- CRM Homework Practice (p. A144)

1 Introduce

Vocabulary

Vocabulary Usage Model a whole with a dollar. What fraction of a dollar is a dime? one-tenth How is that written? $0.10 What fraction is a penny? one-hundredth How is that written? $0.01 Model a whole with 10 base-ten rods. What is one rod? one-tenth Show students how one-tenth can be written with a *decimal*. Now model a whole with a base-ten flat. How many units make up one flat? one hundred How can we write one unit using a *decimal?* 0.01

2 Teach

Key Concept

Foundational Skills and Concepts After students have read through the Key Concept box, have them try these exercises.

1. What is the name of the digit two places to the right of the decimal point? hundredth
2. What is the name of the digit to the left of the decimal point? whole number
3. What do the digits to the right of the decimal point represent? a fraction

Lesson 7-1 Introduction to Decimals

KEY Concept

Decimals and fractions represent both whole numbers and numbers between whole numbers. A decimal is another way to show a fraction with a denominator of 10, 100, 1,000, and so on.

In a decimal, the digit(s) to the left of the decimal point represent a whole number. The digit(s) to the right of a decimal point represent a fraction.

A digit one place to the right of the decimal point is a **tenth**.

A digit two places to the right of the decimal point is a **hundredth**.

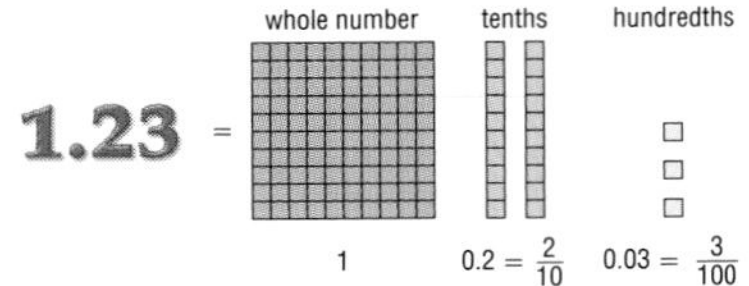

A digit three places to the right of the decimal point is a **thousandth**.

The number 840.672 is shown in the place-value chart below.

100	10	1	$0.1 = \frac{1}{10}$	$0.01 = \frac{1}{100}$	$0.001 = \frac{1}{1,000}$
hundreds	tens	ones	tenths	hundredths	thousandths
8	4	0 .	6	7	2

Read a decimal from left to right.

VOCABULARY

decimal
a number that can represent a whole number and a fraction; a decimal point separates the whole number from the fraction

hundredths
the second decimal place to the right of the decimal point; one of one hundred equal parts
Example: In 4.57, 7 is in the hundredths place.

tenths
the first decimal place to the right of the decimal point; one of ten equal parts or $\frac{1}{10}$
Example: In 3.6, 6 is in the tenths place.

thousandths
the third decimal place to the right of the decimal point; one of one thousand equal parts
Example: In 6.314, 4 is in the thousandths place.

Place values are based on powers of ten. From left to right, the value of each place is divided by 10.

280 Chapter 7 Decimals

English Learner Strategy

Visual Cues Make visual cues for students to distinguish when you are saying tenths or tens, hundreds or hundredths. You can use a flashcard that has the word and an associated color, or point to a place-value chart which also has the same colors. For example, the flashcard might be blue to represent tenths, and the column in the chart would also be blue.

Example 1

Write two and sixty-four hundredths as a decimal.

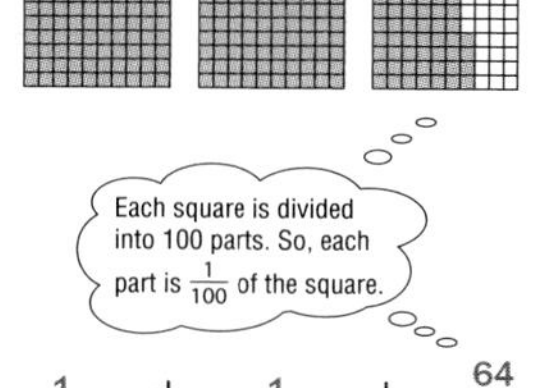

Each square is divided into 100 parts. So, each part is $\frac{1}{100}$ of the square.

$1 + 1 + \frac{64}{100}$

1. Use whole numbers and a fraction to write a sum for the model.

   $2 + \frac{64}{100}$

2. Rewrite the sum using the word *and*.

   2 and $\frac{64}{100}$

3. Write the expression as a decimal.

   2.64

YOUR TURN!

Write one and eighty-two hundredths as a decimal.

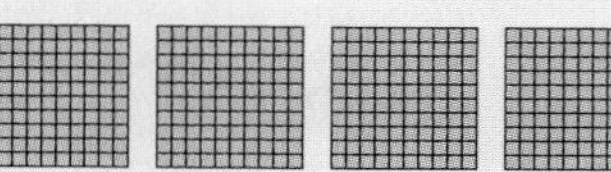

1. Use whole numbers and a fraction to write a sum for the model.

   $1 + 1 + 1 + \frac{82}{100}$

   Add the whole number parts to rewrite the sum.

   $3 + \frac{82}{100}$

2. Rewrite the sum using the word *and*.

   3 and $\frac{82}{100}$

3. Write the expression as a decimal.

   3.82

Example 2

Write 4.38 in words.

1. Name the decimal by the place value of the last digit to the right of the decimal point.

   4.38 ⟵ hundredths

2. There is a 4 to the left of the decimal point. At the decimal point, write *and*.

   So, 4.38 is four and thirty-eight hundredths.

YOUR TURN!

Write 6.4 in words.

1. What place value is the last digit to the right of the decimal point?

   tenths.

2. There is a 6 to the left of the decimal point. At the decimal point, write *and*.

   So, 6.4 is six and four tenths.

Intervention Strategy

Kinesthetic/ Visual Learners

Model Decimals Place students into groups of 4 or 5. Give students within each group index cards with different digits. Each student is assigned one number, while one student will receive a card with a decimal point. Tell students to arrange the cards in as many different ways as possible. Tell them to write the decimal in word form for each number they create. Then have groups come up and present their numbers to the class with each student holding a number card. Have students take turns saying the number they are representing.

Additional Example 1

Write three and thirty-two hundredths as a decimal.

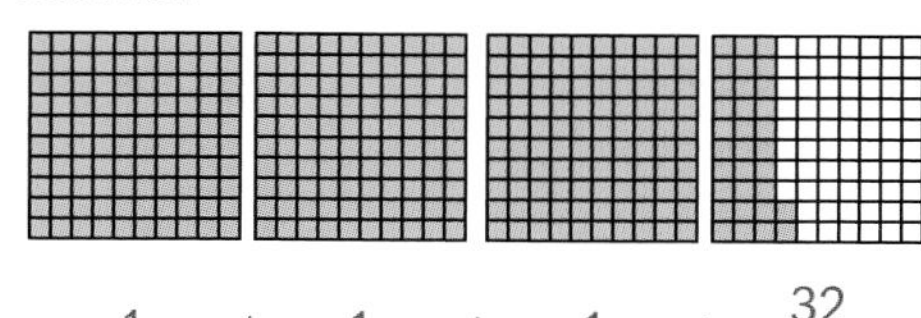

$1 + 1 + 1 + \frac{32}{100}$

1. Use whole numbers and a fraction to write a sum for the model.

   $3 + \frac{32}{100}$

2. Rewrite the sum using the word *and.*

   3 and $\frac{32}{100}$

3. Write the expression as a decimal. 3.32

Additional Example 2

Write 9.18 in words.

1. Name the decimal by the place value of the last digit to the right of the decimal point.

   9.18 ⟵hundredths

2. There is a 9 to the left of the decimal point. At the decimal point, write *and.*

   So, 9.18 is nine and eighteen hundredths.

Additional **Example 3**

Write thirteen and seven hundred eighty-nine thousandths as a number.

1. Write the number thirteen to represent the whole number part. 13
2. Use a decimal point to connect the whole number and fraction parts 13.
3. Write 789 to the right of the decimal point to represent seven hundred eighty-nine thousandths. 13.789
4. So thirteen and seven hundred eighty-nine thousandths is 13.789.

Using Manipulatives

On-Hand Manipulatives As an introduction to decimals, it may be helpful for students to understand that they already know something about decimals. Ask them to discuss money and the decimal representation of a penny, nickel, dime, and quarter. In Example 1, the decimal modeled with money would be:

2.64

Base-Ten Blocks Use base-ten blocks to model decimals. To represent $\frac{1}{10}$ you can use a whole made up of 100 units, shading 10, or a whole made up of 10 rods, shading 1.

Example 3

Write ten and three hundred fourteen thousandths as a number.

1. Write the number ten to represent the whole number part.

   10

2. Use a decimal point to connect the whole number and fraction parts.

   10.

3. Write 314 to the right of the decimal point to represent three hundred and fourteen thousandths.

   10.314

So, ten and three hundred fourteen thousandths is 10.314.

YOUR TURN!

Write twenty-seven and six thousandths as a number.

1. Write the number that represents twenty-seven.

   27

2. Use a decimal point to connect the whole number and fraction parts.

   27.

3. To the right of the decimal point, write the digits that represent six thousandths.

   27.006

So, twenty -seven and six thousandths is 27.006.

Who is Correct?

Write 12.07 in words.

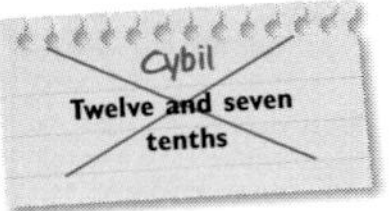

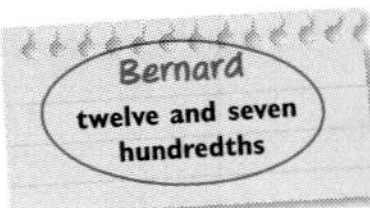

Circle correct answer(s). Cross out incorrect answer(s).

Guided Practice

Write a decimal for each model.

1 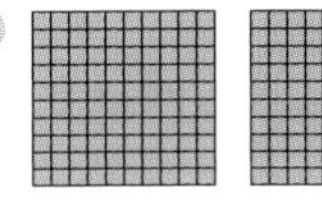

1.74

2 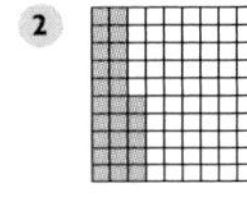

0.25

282 **Chapter 7** Decimals

Who *is Correct?*

Diagnostic Teaching

- Cybil is incorrect because the 7 is in the hundredths place, not the tenths place.
- Nuna is incorrect because in word form the decimal is an "and."
- Bernard wrote twelve and seven hundredths. This is correct.

Remind students that they should read the decimal out loud. Those are the words that they should write down.

Step by Step Practice

3 Write four and twenty-six thousandths as a decimal.

Step 1 Identify the whole number. Write it first.

four and twenty-six thousandths 4

Step 2 Place the decimal point. 4.

Step 3 Identify the digits for the fractional part of the decimal. 4.026 ← thousandths

four and twenty-six thousandths

Write each number as a decimal.

4 five and eighty-four hundredths

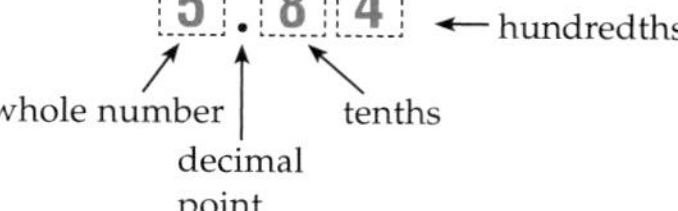

5 eleven and seven tenths
11.7

6 sixteen and thirty hundredths
16.30

7 four tenths
0.4

Write each number in words.

8 11.67
eleven and sixty-seven hundredths

9 8.03
eight and three hundredths

10 89.4
eighty-nine and four tenths

11 55.16
fifty-five and sixteen hundredths

Write each number as a decimal.

12 forty-two and eight tenths
42.8

13 ninety-one and sixty-three hundredths
91.63

14 six and ninety-seven hundredths
6.97

15 two hundred fifteen thousandths
0.215

Math Coach Notes

Strategies

1. Have students begin the lesson modeling tenths and hundredths using base-ten blocks. Use the blocks throughout the lesson, reminding students that each unit that makes up a whole flat is $\frac{1}{100}$. Each unit that makes up a whole of 10 rods is $\frac{1}{10}$.

2. The optimum way for students to learn decimals is to use multiple concrete models, manipulatives, and pictorial representations. Have students write a decimal in a place-value chart, represent the decimal on a number line, and use base-ten blocks or money to model the decimal.

Common Error *Alert*

Multi-Step Problem If a student is unable to write a decimal as a number as in Exercises 8 through 11, he or she may not understand how to translate the numbers to verbal phrases. Begin by having the student represent the number concretely. This ensures that he or she understands that a decimal number can represent the combination of a whole and parts of a whole. Then, have the student practice by writing numbers into a place-value chart. Remind students that the last word will be the place-value of the digit farthest to the right.

Are They Getting It?

Check students' understanding of decimals by writing these problems on the board. Ask students to point out wrong answers and explain why they are wrong.

1. The value of the red digit in 0.83 is $\frac{3}{10}$. This is incorrect. The value is $\frac{3}{100}$.
2. In word form, 9.99 is "nine and ninety-nine hundreds." This is incorrect. It is "nine and ninety-nine hundr*edths*."
3. The model shows 2.05. This is correct.

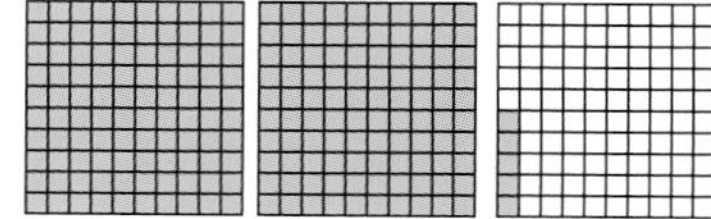

4. Seven thousandths written as a decimal is 0.007. This is correct.

Math Coach Notes

Make a Table Tell students to make a two-column table. Title the columns "Decimal" and "Standard Form." Tell students to go through their notes and write all the examples of decimals in numeric form they can find in the "Decimal column." Then have them write the word form. Review their work. They can use this as a study guide for the lesson.

Step by Step Problem-Solving Practice

Problem-Solving Strategies

- ☐ Draw a diagram.
- ☑ Use a model.
- ☐ Solve a simpler problem.
- ☐ Act it out.
- ☐ Work backward.

Solve.

16 BAKING Jessica's brother ate twenty-five hundredths of the cake Jessica baked. Write a decimal to show the amount of cake not eaten.

Understand — Read the problem. Write what you know.
Jessica's brother ate twenty-five hundredths of the cake.

Plan — Pick a strategy. One strategy is to use a model.

Solve — Draw a model to represent the whole cake. Shade the amount eaten.

Use a grid of 100 squares to represent the entire cake. Shade 25 squares to represent twenty-five hundredths of the cake.

How many squares are not shaded? 75 squares

This represents the amount of cake not eaten. How much cake is not eaten? seventy-five hundredths

Write the decimal. 0.75

Check — Use a place-value chart to check the value.

17 PLANTS Dwaine uses 1 gallon of water on his plant each week. Refer to the photo caption at the right. Write a decimal to show how much water Dwaine has left for the rest of the week.
Check off each step.

✔ Understand: I circled key words.

✔ Plan: To solve the problem, I will use a model.

✔ Solve: The answer is seven-tenths gallon.

✔ Check: I checked my answer by using a place-value chart to check the value.

PLANTS Dwaine used three-tenths gallon of water on Monday.

Intervention Strategy — Linguistic Learners

Real-World Examples Have students go through written material to find examples of decimals. Encourage them to find examples that are not just limited to money. Ask them to cut out the examples and glue them to paper or poster board. Each example must be labeled in context so the class will know what the decimal represents. Students can share their work with the class.

18 TRAVEL Solidad rode her bike seven tenths of a mile to school. Her friend Keri walked 0.07 of a mile to school. Did the two girls travel the same distance? Explain.

No; Solidad traveled 0.7, and Keri traveled 0.07. $0.7 \neq 0.07$

19 Reflect Annie says that seventy-five hundredths is equal to 0.75. Is Annie correct? Show work to explain your answer.

Yes, Annie is correct. The hundredths place has two decimal places, and 0.75 has two decimal places.

Skills, Concepts, and Problem Solving

Write a decimal for each model.

20 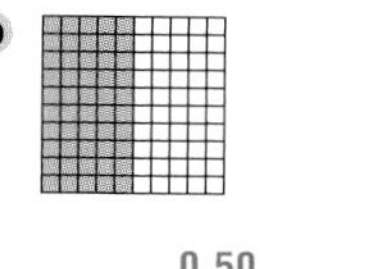

0.50

21 

0.34

Write each number in words.

22 0.9
nine tenths

23 18.03
eighteen and three hundredths

24 7.17
seven and seventeen hundredths

25 3.78
three and seventy-eight hundredths

Write each number as a decimal.

26 forty-forty and nineteen hundredths
44.19

27 ten and six hundredths
10.06

28 eight and seven tenths
8.7

29 nineteen and thirteen hundredths
19.13

30 seven hundred thirty-nine thousandths
0.739

31 six and ninety-one thousandths
6.091

GO ON

Odd/Even Assignments

Exercises 20–34 are structured so that students practice the same concepts whether they are assigned the odd or even problems.

In-Class Assignment

Have students complete Exercises 20, 24, 26, 31, 33, and 38 to ensure that they understand the concept.

Common Error *Alert*

Exercise 18 If students do not arrive at the correct answer for Exercise 18, it is possible that they did not differentiate the digits to the right of the decimal point. Use blocks to have them model 0.7 or $\frac{7}{10}$. Then have them model 0.07 or $\frac{7}{100}$. Discuss the differences between the two amounts. Write the number in a place-value chart to show how the numbers connect with the position.

Math Challenge

Memory Game Divide students into pairs. Have each student pair make a set of 20 cards to use for a memory game. Have them write a different decimal number on 10 of the cards. Then have them write the word forms of the ten decimals on the other 10 cards. Tell them to take the 20 cards and shuffle them, keeping them facedown. Have them place the cards in uniform rows and columns on their desks. One student will turn 2 cards looking for a match. If he or she gets a match, he or she may keep the cards; but if a match is not made, the cards are turned back over. The student with the most cards at the end of the game wins.

See It, Do It, Say It, Write It

Step 1 Write a decimal on the board. Model how to represent the decimal with a drawing or model. Do this several times with different models.

Step 2 Ask students to draw a number line on paper. Give them a decimal to represent on the number line. Repeat with students drawing decimals. Share solutions in a class discussion.

Step 3 Have students work in pairs. Write a decimal on the board. Tell students to write the word form of the decimal. Model first. Have students share their work with the class. Repeat several times.

Step 4 Tell students to write a definition for *decimal* using their own words. Ask them to include how decimals are related to fractions. Have them include a picture or a model.

Looking Ahead: Pre-teach

Equivalent Decimals In the next lesson, students will study equivalent decimals.

Example

Write a decimal for the model shown.

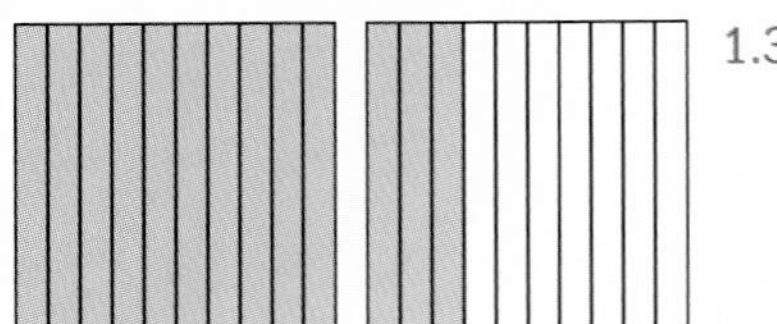

1.3

Write a decimal for each amount shown using hundredths.

1. 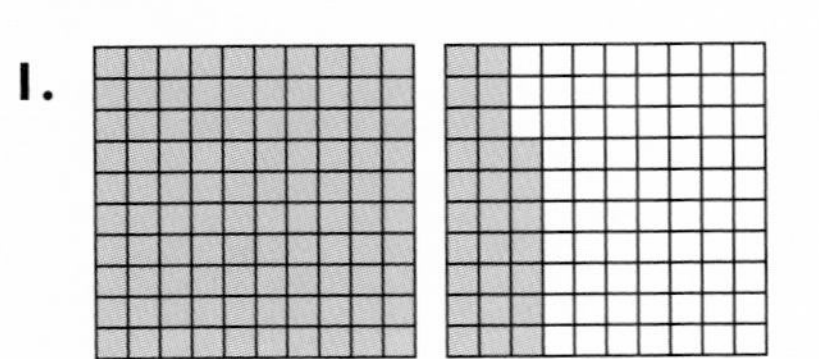 1.27

2. 0.74

Solve.

32 TIME It takes Monya fifteen minutes or twenty-five hundredths of an hour to get home from school. Write the time as a decimal.

0.25 hour

33 HOBBIES Adam collects trading cards. In Adam's collection, he has 63 out of 100 baseball cards he wants to collect. Write the number of baseball cards as a decimal.

0.63

HOBBIES Adam collects trading cards.

34 MONEY Paulina promises to give her little brother one and twenty-five hundreds of a dollar each week for cleaning her room. Write the amount as a decimal.

$1.25

Vocabulary Check **Write the vocabulary word that completes each sentence.**

35 The first digit to the right of the decimal point is the tenths place.

36 The second digit to the right of the decimal point is the hundredths place.

37 A(n) decimal is a number that can represent a whole number and a fraction.

38 Writing in Math Write the amount shown in the hundred block at the right in decimal form and in word form.

0.25; twenty-five hundredths

Describe different ways to represent this amount with real-life objects.

Sample answer: a quarter; twenty-five cents

STOP

286 Chapter 7 Decimals

Ticket Out the Door

Write and Sketch Write "forty-four and nineteen hundredths" on the board. Tell students to write the decimal form. Then write 16.05 on the board. Tell students to write the word form of the number and to draw a sketch to model the number. Student volunteers can present their findings. Have them hand in their papers as they exit the classroom.

Lesson 7-2 Equivalent Decimals

KEY Concept

Equivalent decimals are decimals that have the same **value**.

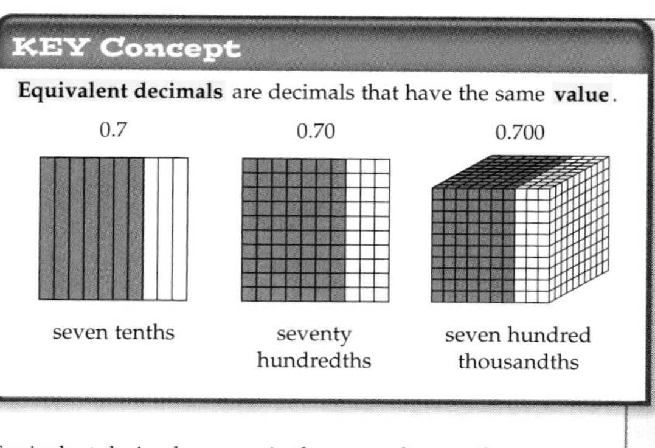

Equivalent decimals appear in the same place on the number line.

VOCABULARY

equivalent decimals decimals that represent the same number Example: 0.5 = 0.50

hundredths the second decimal place to the right of the decimal point; one of one hundred equal parts Example: In 4.57, 7 is in the hundredths place.

tenths the first decimal place to the right of the decimal point; one of ten equal parts Example: In 3.6, 6 is in the tenths place.

thousandths the third decimal place to the right of the decimal point; one of one thousand equal parts Example: In 8.231, 1 is in the thousandths place.

value the amount of a number

Example 1

Use a place-value chart to show that 3.45 is equivalent to 3.450.

1. Write 3.45 and 3.450 inside the place-value chart.

ones	tenths	hundredths
3.	4	5

2. Use the charts to compare one place value at a time.

   Both charts show:

   a ones value of 3

   a tenths value of 0.4

   a hundredths value of 0.05

   a thousandths value of 0.000

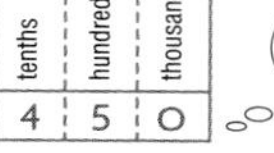

ones	tenths	hundredths	thousandths
3.	4	5	0

You can add zeros to the right of any decimal without changing its value.

3. So, 3.45 is equivalent to 3.450.

GO ON

Additional Example 1

Use a place-value chart to show that 6.7 is equivalent to 6.70.

1. Write 6.7 and 6.70 inside the place-value chart.

ones	tenths
6.	7

2. Use the charts to compare one place value at a time.

ones	tenths	hundredths
6.	7	0

   Both charts show: a ones value of 6

   a tenths value of 0.7

   a hundredths value of 0.00

3. So, 6.7 is equivalent to 6.70.

Lesson Notes

Lesson 7-2

Lesson Planner

Objective Recognize and use equivalent decimals.

Vocabulary **equivalent decimals, hundredths, tenths, thousandths, value**

Materials/Manipulatives base-ten blocks, construction paper, money, place-value chart

Chapter Resource Masters

- CRM Vocabulary and English Language Development (p. A145)
- CRM Skills Practice (p. A146)
- CRM Problem-Solving Practice (p. A147)
- CRM Homework Practice (p. A148)

1 Introduce

Vocabulary

Review Vocabulary Ask students to name the position of each digit in the number 273.019. How do you know if the digit is to the left or the right of the decimal point? Now ask the students to give you a number that is greater than and less than 273.019. Discuss how they know how to compare the sizes of the numbers. Prepare them to discover equivalent decimals.

2 Teach

Key Concept

Foundational Skills and Concepts After students have read through the Key Concept box, have them try these exercises.

1. What are equivalent decimals? decimals that have the same value
2. What are two decimals equivalent to 0.7? 0.70, 0.700

Additional *Example* 2

Use a model to find an equivalent decimal to 3.9 using hundredths.

1. Draw a model for 3.9.

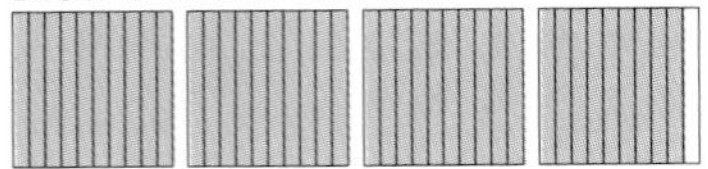

2. Draw an equivalent model using hundredths.

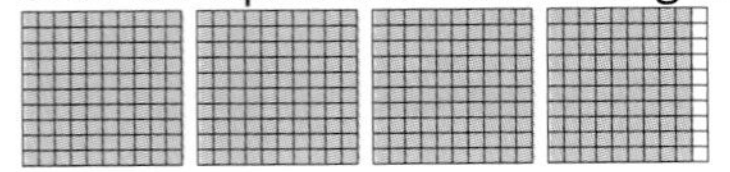

3. The same amount is shaded on the frames. So, 3.9 = 3.90.

Math Coach Notes

Connect Concepts

1. Show students how to connect to what they already know about place value to the tenths and hundredths places. Begin the lesson using base-ten blocks to show how parts of 100 are written.

2. Use a mix of representations, such as number lines, money, base-ten blocks, and drawings to provide students with visual displays of equivalent decimals.

Note This!

Write in the Same Format To help learn a concept, tell students to write a summary sheet. On the left side have them write the main idea, such as "decimals." On the right side have them write the details. For instance, they can write the names of the place values, the definition of decimal point, and so on. This summary sheet can help them make their notes more compact when it is time to study.

Common Error *Alert*

Thousandths Place Remind students that any zero to the right of the last digit in the decimal does not change the value of the number. This is important when using the thousandths place to write an equivalent decimal.

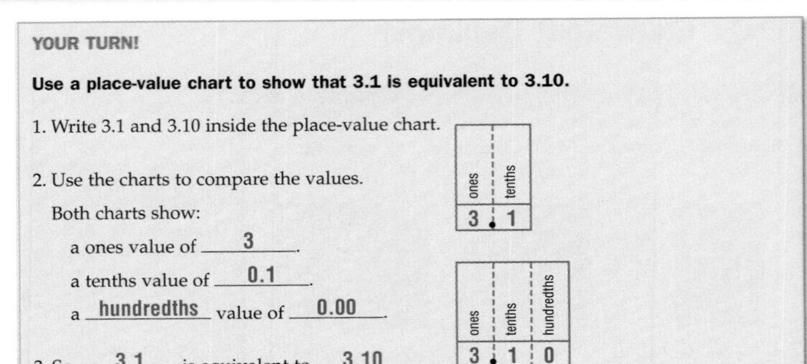

YOUR TURN!

Use a place-value chart to show that 3.1 is equivalent to 3.10.

1. Write 3.1 and 3.10 inside the place-value chart.

ones	tenths
3 .	1

2. Use the charts to compare the values.

Both charts show:

a ones value of 3.

a tenths value of 0.1.

a hundredths value of 0.00.

ones	tenths	hundredths
3 .	1	0

3. So, 3.1 is equivalent to 3.10.

Example 2

Use a model to find an equivalent decimal to 1.7 using hundredths.

1. Draw a model for 1.7.

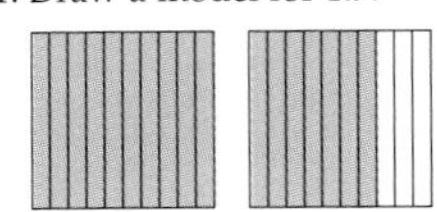

2. Draw an equivalent model using hundredths.

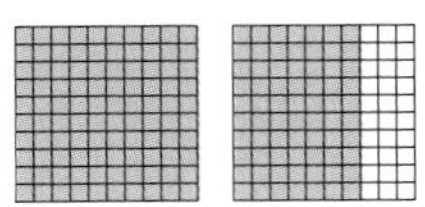

3. The same amount is shaded on the frames.

So, 1.7 = 1.70

YOUR TURN!

Use a model to find an equivalent decimal to 2.5 using hundredths.

1. Draw a model for 2.5.

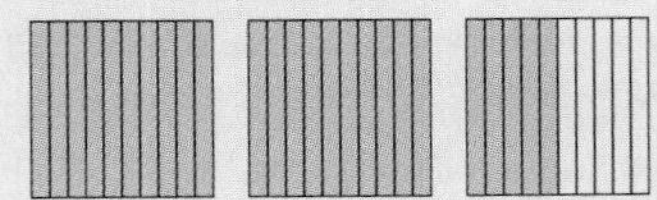

2. Draw an equivalent model using hundredths.

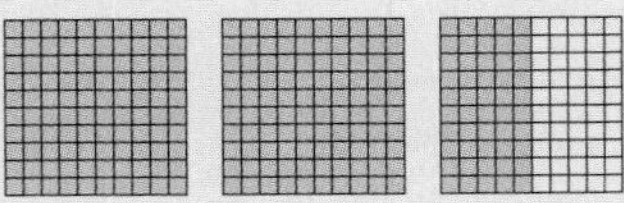

3. The same amount is shaded on the frames.

So, 2.5 = 2.50.

Intervention Strategy

Kinesthetic/ Visual Learners

Thousandths Place Students may have trouble visualizing models for the thousandths position. Assist students in creating a cube from paper that they have drawn 10 × 10 squares on each side. Explain that since there is length, width, and height to the cube there are a total of 10 × 10 × 10 or 1,000 squares in the cube. If they are still having difficulty, start building a model with connecting cubes to assist in the visualization process.

Who is Correct?

Write a decimal equivalent to 1.73 using thousandths.

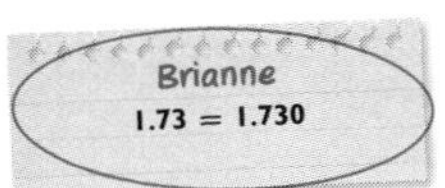

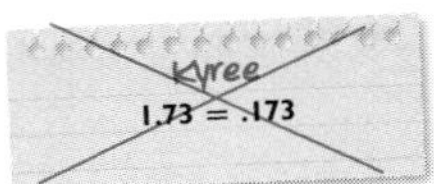

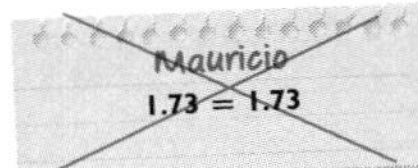

Circle correct answer(s). Cross out incorrect answer(s).

Guided Practice

Use a model to find each equivalent decimal.

1 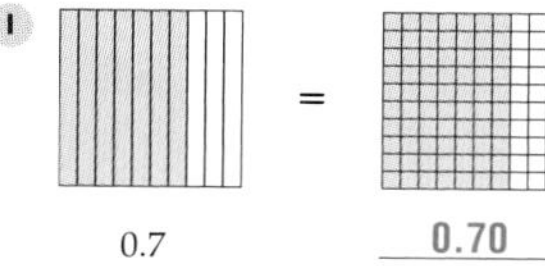

0.7 = 0.70

2 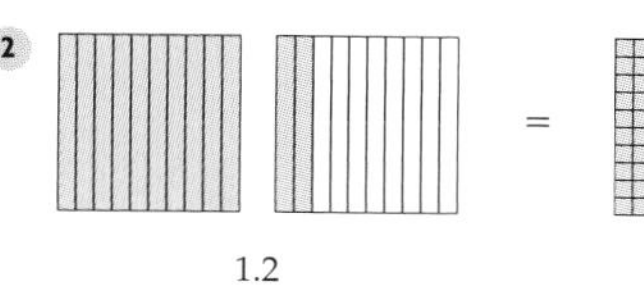 = 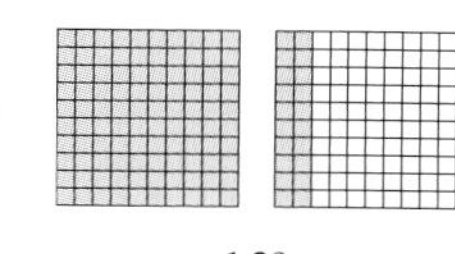

1.2 = 1.20

Step by Step Practice

3 Write a decimal equivalent to 8.13 using thousandths.

Step 1 To show 8.13, use a place-value chart through hundredths.

Step 2 To write an equivalent decimal through the thousandths place, make a place-value chart through thousandths.

Step 3 Use the charts to compare the values.

Step 4 8.13 is equivalent to 8.130.

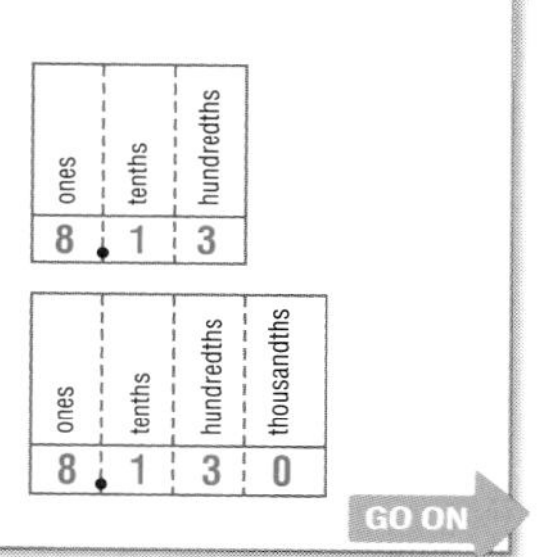

GO ON

Who *is Correct?*

Diagnostic Teaching

- Brianne is correct. She correctly used thousandths to write an equivalent statement that 1.73 = 1.730.
- Kyree is incorrect. She did not write decimals that are equivalent. .173 does use thousandths, but is not equivalent to 1.73.
- Mauricio is incorrect. He wrote equivalent decimals, but he did not use thousandths.

Remind students that they can use place-value charts to help them compare equivalent decimals.

Intervention Strategy

Kinesthetic/ Visual Learners

Modeling Have the students work in pairs. Have each student draw a model that represents a decimal. Trade papers and have the partner determine the decimal and draw an equivalent model. Make sure students spend time doing models of tenths, hundredths, and thousandths.

Math Coach Notes

Rewrite Notes Tell students that if they have taken their notes while in a hurry, the notes might be difficult to read. Encourage students to copy their notes when they get home. This will help them learn the concepts because they are revisiting them. It will also make it easier to study when their notes are legible.

Using Manipulatives

Base-Ten Blocks

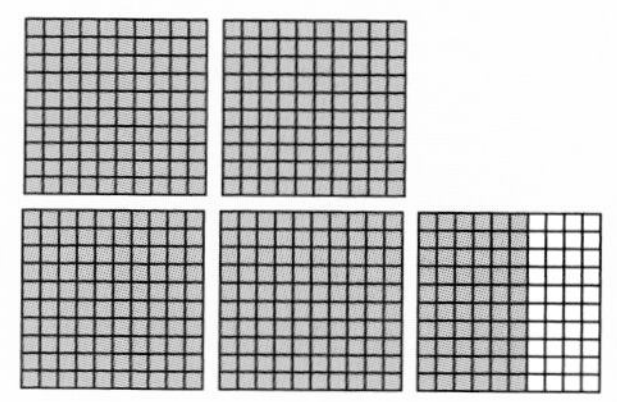

4.6

Money

$3.67

On-Hand Manipulatives Have students create place-value holders out of construction paper. For example, one red square equals hundredths.

Common Error *Alert*

Place-Value Charts Students may confuse whether or not decimals are equal when using a place-value chart. The students may not realize that just because one chart has 4 columns and another has 3, the decimals represented can still be equal. Tell students to look at the numbers, not the size of the chart.

English Learner Strategy

Currency Have students bring in currency from their native countries. Have them make a table to name and represent each amount. Use the dollars and coins in the same way as our money, making connections between the currencies. Give students an opportunity to present their currencies and tables to the class and "teach" about currency in their native country.

Math Coach Notes

Models When students compare models of tenths versus hundredths, make them realize that the models are the same as long as the same area is shaded. It may be helpful for students to take a tenths model and draw in the lines to make a hundredths model for comparison and vice versa.

SQ3R Method When students read their text, they can make the most of their time by using the SQ3R method. This acronym means to first survey by reading the introduction, the highlights, and the boldface lettering. Next, purposefully pose questions about the survey. Then, read the text, looking for answers to the questions that were created from the survey. Recite the answers to the questions, covering up the text to help memorize the answers. Finally, review the highlights, the questions, and the answers to aid in reading comprehension and concept retention.

For each decimal, write an equivalent decimal using thousandths.

4. 4.2 __4.200__

ones	tenths
4.	2

ones	tenths	hundredths	thousandths
4.	2	0	0

5. 7.9 __7.900__

ones	tenths
7.	9

ones	tenths	hundredths	thousandths
7.	9	0	0

Step by Step Problem-Solving Practice

Problem-Solving Strategies
- ☑ Draw a model.
- ☐ Use logical reasoning.
- ☐ Make an organized list.
- ☐ Solve a simpler problem.
- ☐ Work backward.

Solve.

6. Alfonso shaded three and five tenths using tenths models. How can Sheila shade the same value using hundredths models?

Understand Read the problem. Write what you know.
Alfonso shaded __3__ wholes, and __5__ tenths.
Sheila will shade the same value using __hundredths__.

Plan Pick a strategy. One strategy is to draw a model.

Solve Draw a model for 3.5.

Draw a model using hundredths. Shade the model to match the tenths model.

The equivalent decimal for 3.5 is __3.50__.

Check Use place-value charts to check.

290 **Chapter 7** Decimals

Are They Getting It?

Check students' understanding of equivalent decimals by writing these proble
on the board. Have students explain the incorrect information in each proble

1. These place-value charts represent the same decimal. This is correct.

tens	ones	tenths	hundredths
5	2.	4	7

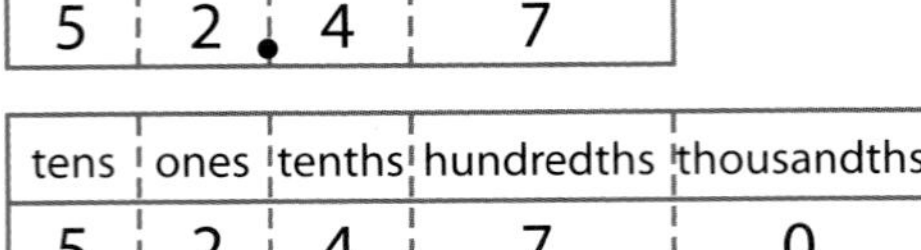

tens	ones	tenths	hundredths	thousandths
5	2.	4	7	0

2. The models represent the same decimal.
This is incorrect. The model on the left represents 0.4, and the model on the right represents 0.3.

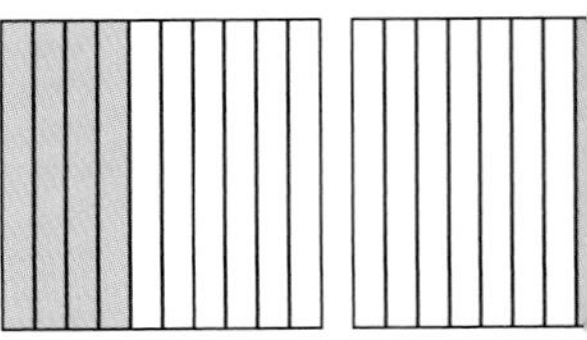

7 NUMBER SENSE Emily shaded two and nine tenths using tenths models. How can Cadeo shade the same value using hundredths models? Check off each step.

✔ Understand: I circled key words.

✔ Plan: To solve this problem, I will draw a model.

✔ Solve: The answer is shade 2 whole models and 90 squares of a third model.

✔ Check: I checked my answer by making place-value charts.

8 Jay shaded four and seven tenths using tenths models. How can Maria shade the same value using thousandths models?

Maria can shade 4 whole models and 700 squares of a thousandths model.

9 **Reflect** Explain why you can add zeros to the right of a decimal without changing its value.

Sample answer: Zeros have no value, so adding zeros to the right of a decimal amount will not change the place value of any number in the decimal.

Skills, Concepts, and Problem Solving

Use place-value charts to show equivalent decimals for each pair of numbers.

10 7.63 and 7.630

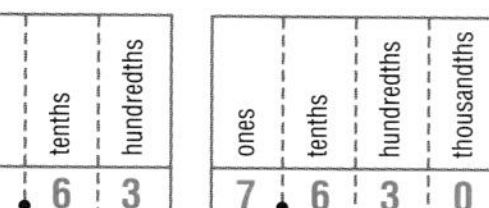

ones	tenths	hundredths
7.	6	3

ones	tenths	hundredths	thousandths
7.	6	3	0

11 8.9 and 8.90

ones	tenths
8.	9

ones	tenths	hundredths
8.	9	0

For each decimal, write an equivalent decimal using thousandths.

12 3.5 3.500

13 21.4 21.400

14 1.49 1.490

15 6.52 6.520

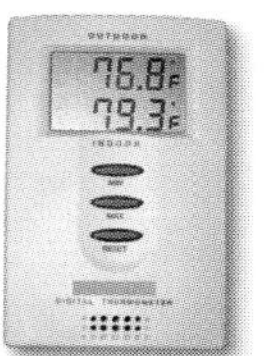

TEMPERATURE
A digital thermometer uses decimals to show temperature.

GO ON

Odd/Even Assignments

Exercises 10–27 are structured so that students practice the same concepts whether they are assigned the odd or even problems.

In-Class Assignment

Have students complete Exercises 10, 13, 16, 18, 23, 26, and 30 to ensure that they understand the concept.

Note This!

Monitor Pace Tell students not to be afraid to ask questions if they have missed something during class. Encourage them to tell you if you are moving too quickly. Tell students that often their classmates may have missed the same information or do not understand, so speaking up will benefit the entire class.

Common Error *Alert*

Exercise 8 If students are having difficulty with Exercise 8, encourage them to make the models representing the problem. Often times, when students see a model, they do not struggle as much as they do when trying to decipher the words.

English Learner Strategy

Note Differences English learners might get confused between the words *tens* and *tenths*, *hundreds* and *hundredths*, and *thousands* and *thousandths* because of the subtle differences between the words. Have these students write the six words on cards. Model a number such as 182.35 using base-ten blocks. Place the cards in the appropriate places so that these students can see that the decimal represents a part of the whole, and not the whole. Have them model a number and place the vocabulary words in the proper places. Use these cards as cues to show students as you teach.

Intervention Strategy

Linguistic/ Interpersonal Learners

Write instructions Have students write a paragraph about how to use models to determine if two decimals are equivalent. Once the students have completed their paragraph, have them write another paragraph explaining how to use a place-value chart to determine if two decimals are equivalent. Ask for volunteers to read their paragraphs out loud. As a class discuss how they think it is to hear the processes presented in different ways.

Note This!

Leave Room Instruct students to leave room on the page when taking notes. Inform them that this is like pausing before you begin a new sentence. Their notes will be much easier to read, and they will have space to add information later on, if needed. Point out that they should not try to fit everything onto one sheet of paper.

English Learner Strategy

Dry-Erase Boards To help English learners understand place-value equivalents, provide them with dry-erase boards. Ask them to write a decimal on their dry-erase boards. Then have students write a decimal equivalent for the number. Have students show you their solutions when they have finished. This is a quick way to check progress with concepts and vocabulary.

Math Coach Notes

Creativity Students who like to be creative should be encouraged. If this means doing their assignments in colored pencil or drawing complicated drawings for their notes and assignments, let them have this outlet. This may help creative students focus more directly on the task at hand, which may help them master the given topic.

Common Error *Alert*

Zero Placeholder Students may be confused as to what constitutes a zero placeholder. Explain to students that adding a zero to the end of a decimal does not change the value of the number, because zero adds no value.

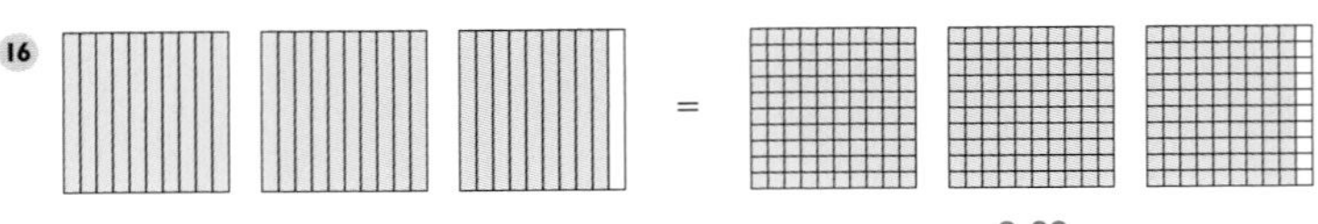

Use a model to find each equivalent decimal.

16 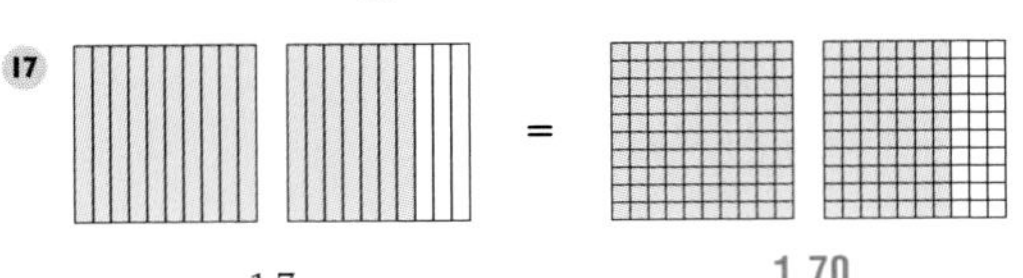

2.9 = 2.90

17 1.7 = 1.70

For each decimal, write an equivalent decimal using hundredths.

18 6.3 6.30

19 2.1 2.10

20 4.5 4.50

21 7.2 7.20

For each decimal, write an equivalent decimal using thousandths.

22 9.19 9.190

23 7.44 7.440

24 1.02 1.020

25 3.89 3.890

Solve.

26 SCHOOL Nadya's math homework says to write the decimal 2.5 as a dollar amount. Nadya knows that dollar amounts use decimals in the hundredths place. How can Nadya write 2.5 as a dollar amount using hundredths?

$2.50

27 WEATHER Jing Mei was helping her father take measurements from their weather station. Jing Mei's father read the rain gauge and told her to write down one and twenty-two hundredths for the amount of rainfall. How should Jing Mei write the number?

1.22

292 Chapter 7 Decimals

Intervention Strategy

Linguistic/ Visual Learners

Make a poster Have students create a poster that explains how to write equivalent fractions. They should include step-by-step directions that can be applied to any problem. Encourage students to use models and examples to illustrate the explanation. Have students display the poster in the classroom so that they can easily refer to it as they work on the rest of the unit.

Vocabulary Check **Write the vocabulary word or words that complete each sentence.**

28 Decimals that represent the same number are called equivalent decimals.

29 Value means the amount of a number.

30 **Writing in Math** Cierra and her brother Mark are doing their math homework. One problem says to write the fraction $\frac{9}{10}$ in decimal form. Cierra writes 0.90, and Mark writes 0.9. Who has the correct answer? Explain.

Ava and Mark both have the correct answer. 0.90 and 0.9 are equivalent decimals. You can add zeros to the right of any decimal without changing its value.

Spiral Review

Write each number as a decimal. (Lesson 7-1, p. 280)

31 nine and seven tenths 9.7

32 eighteen and thirty-two hundredths 18.32

33 twelve and four hundred and ninety-three thousandths 12.493

Write each number in words. (Lesson 7-1, p. 280)

34 5.9 five and nine tenths

35 4.25 four and twenty-five hundredths

36 81.07 eighty-one and seven hundredths

Solve. (Lesson 7-1, p. 280)

37 **SPORTS** Brianna is trying out for the school basketball team. Seven tenths of the positions have already been filled. Circle the decimal that correctly shows the number of positions that have been filled.

7.10 7.1 (0.7) 0.07

STOP

Ticket Out the Door

Quick Quiz Hand the students a half-sheet of paper that has the following two problems on it. The students will turn in their papers as they exit the classroom.

1. Find a decimal equivalent to 3.12 using thousandths. 3.120
2. Shade a thousandths model to represent this decimal.

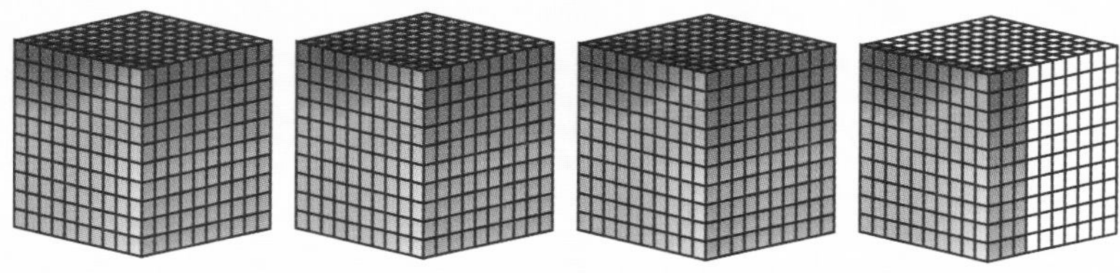

See It, Do It, Say It, Write It

Step 1 Write a tenths place decimal on the board. Show how to create a model to represent this decimal. Next show the students how to draw an equivalent model in the hundredths place and write the corresponding decimal.

Step 2 Give the class a tenths place decimal. Repeat the activity followed by a class discussion on finding equivalent decimals.

Step 3 Have students work in pairs generating decimals and constructing their models. Ask students to share their work with the class.

Step 4 Have students work alone. Tell them to write instructions on how to write equivalent decimals in their math journals. Tell them to include a model.

Looking Ahead: Pre-teach

Compare and Order Decimals In the next lesson, students will learn about comparing and ordering decimals.

Example

Two decimals are graphed on the number line. Which is greater? 0.80 > 0.65

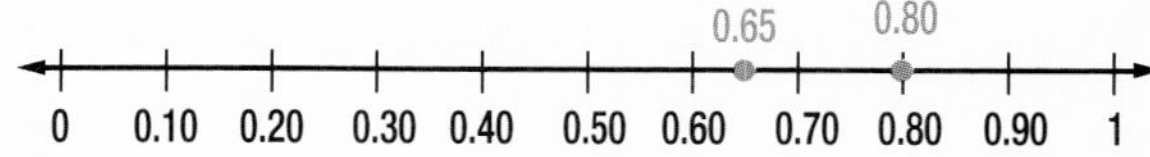

Which decimal is greater?

1. 4.35 > 4.05

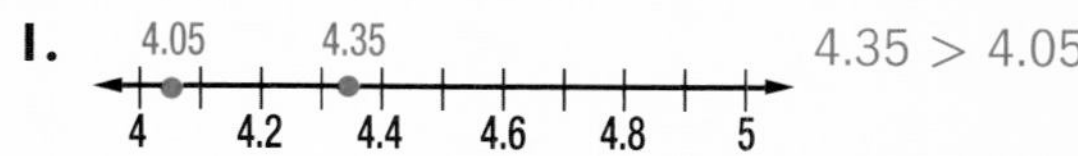

2. 10.45 > 10.30

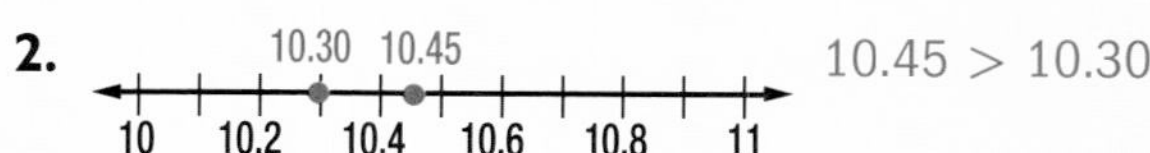

Chapter 7 Progress Check 1

Formative Assessment

Use the Progress Check to assess students' mastery of the previous lessons. Have students review the lesson indicated for the problems they answered incorrectly.

Odd/Even Assignments

Exercises are structured so that students practice the same concepts whether they are assigned the odd or even problems.

Common Error *Alert*

Decimals It is important that students are comfortable with the vocabulary of decimals. Make sure the students look for the "ths" at the ends of the words that tell you the value represents a decimal position.

Exercises 1–4 Make sure that students read the numbers carefully. This will ensure that they put the decimal point in the proper place.

Exercises 5–8 When writing equivalent decimals, remind students that ending zeros after the decimal point do not change the value of the number. They act only as place holders.

Chapter 7 Progress Check 1 (Lessons 7-1 and 7-2)

Write each decimal in words.

1. 5.8 five and eight tenths
2. 30.219 thirty and two hundred nineteen thousandths
3. 45.71 forty-five and seventy-one hundredths
4. 9.88 nine and eighty-eight hundredths

Write each number as a decimal.

5. seven and forty-one hundredths 7.41
6. nine and thirty-five hundredths 9.35
7. fourteen and five tenths 14.5
8. sixty and twenty-seven hundredths 60.27
9. Use a place-value chart to show equivalent decimals for 7.92 and 7.920.

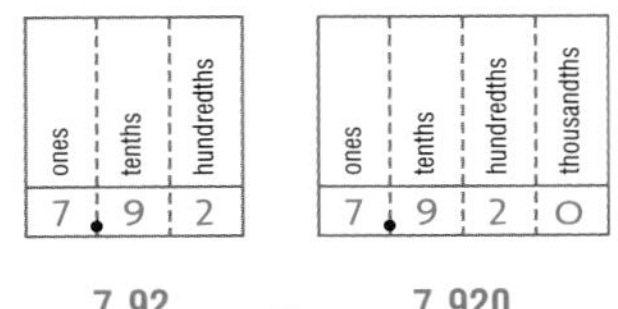

7.92 = 7.920

For each decimal, write an equivalent decimal using thousandths.

10. 5.64 5.640
11. 3.8 3.800
12. 8.7 8.700
13. 5.46 5.460
14. FITNESS Before lunch, Nikki walks 0.31 mile. After lunch, she walks another 0.310 mile. Does Nikki walk the same amount before and after lunch? Explain.

Yes. Sample answer: adding zeros to the right of digits in a decimal does not change the value of the decimal.

Data-Driven Decision Making

Students missing Exercises . . .	Have trouble with . . .	Should review and practice . . .
1-8	writing decimals as words and words as decimals.	SSG Lesson 7-1, p. 280 CRM Skills Practice, p. A142
9	using place-value charts to determine if decimals are equivalent.	SSG Lesson 7-2, p. 287 CRM Skills Practice, p. A146
10-13	writing decimal equivalents to the thousandths place.	SSG Lesson 7-2, p. 287 CRM Skills Practice, p. A146
14	solving word problems involving decimal equivalents.	SSG Lesson 7-2, p. 287 CRM Problem-Solving Practice, p. A147

Compare and Order Decimals

KEY Concept

To compare and order **decimals**, you can use a number line, decimal models, or place value.

Compare 2.19 and 2.1 using a number line.
Numbers to the right are greater than numbers to the left. 2.19 is to the right of 2.1, so 2.19 > 2.1.

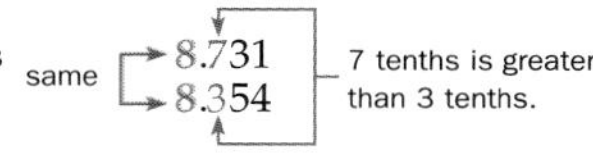

Compare 0.5 and 0.34 using models.

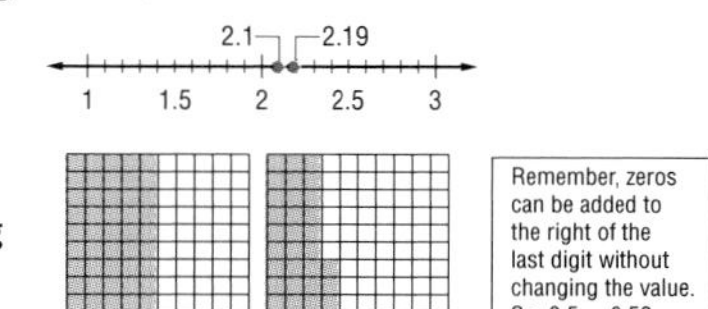

More of the first grid is shaded, so 0.5 > 0.34.

Compare 8.731 and 8.354 using place value.
Line up the decimal points. Compare digits from left to right. So, 8.731 > 8.354.

same — 8.731 / 8.354 — 7 tenths is greater than 3 tenths.

VOCABULARY

decimal
a number that can represent a whole number and a fraction; a decimal point separates the whole number from the fraction

Example 1

Write 2.11, 2.21, and 1.13 in order from least to greatest. Check your answer by graphing the decimals on a number line.

1. Compare the numbers two at a time.
   Compare the ones digits. 0.13 is the least of the three numbers. — **1.13 < 2.11 1.13 < 2.21**
   Compare the tenths digits of 2.11 and 2.21. 2.21 is the greatest number. — **2.21 > 2.11**
2. Write the numbers from least to greatest. — **1.13, 2.11, 2.21**
3. Check by graphing the decimals on a number line.

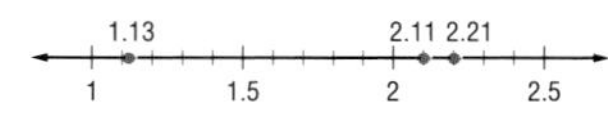

GO ON

Additional Example 1

Write 2.54, 3.45, and 2.84 in order from least to greatest. Check your answer by graphing the decimals on a number line.

1. Compare the numbers two at a time.
   Compare the ones digits. 3.45 > 2.54 3.45 > 2.84
   3.45 is the greatest of the three numbers.
   Compare the tenths digits of 2.54 and 2.84.
   2.54 is the least number.
2. Write the numbers from least to greatest. 2.54, 2.84, 3.45
3. Check by graphing the decimals on a number line.

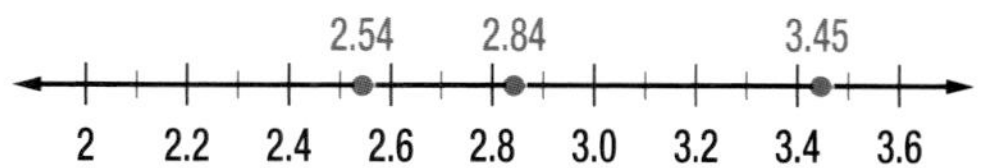

Lesson Notes

Lesson 7-3

Lesson Planner

Objective Compare and order decimals.

Vocabulary **decimal**

Materials/Manipulatives base-ten blocks, fraction tiles, metersticks, money, number line, place-value chart

Chapter Resource Masters

- CRM Vocabulary and English Language Development (p. A149)
- CRM Skills Practice (p. A150)
- CRM Problem-Solving Practice (p. A151)
- CRM Homework Practice (p. A152)

1 Introduce

Vocabulary

Decimal Vocabulary The vocabulary in this lesson has been covered, so connect with the previous lessons. Ask students which *decimal* is greater, 0.01 or 0.10. Discuss strategies. Guide students to realize that the position of the 1, whether in the *hundredths* or *tenths* position, determines the size of the *decimal.*

2 Teach

Key Concept

Foundational Skills and Concepts After students have read through the Key Concept box, have them try these exercises.

1. Which number is greater, 2.19, or 2.1? Describe two ways you know this is true. 2.19; 2.19 is to the right of 2.1 on the number line; the model for 2.19 is shaded more.
2. How are the numbers 8.731 and 8.354 compared? The decimal point is lined up and then the corresponding digits are compared.

Additional **Example 2**

Compare 1.75 and 1.5 using decimal models. Write a statement using the symbols <, =, or >.

1. Model each decimal.

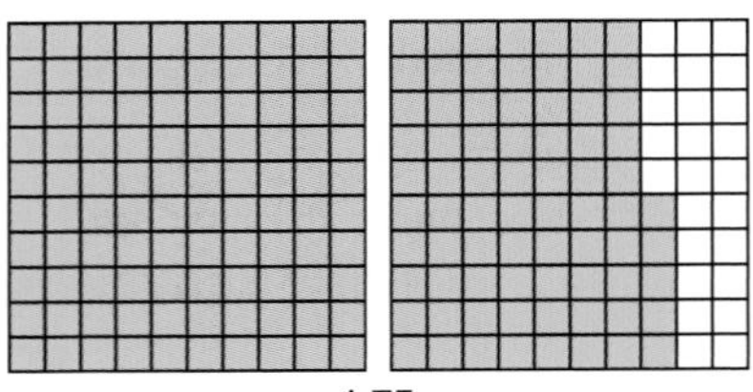

1.75

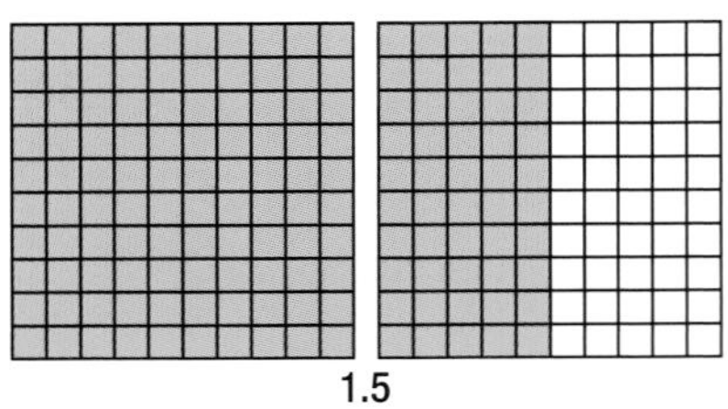

1.5

2. Compare the shaded regions.
1.75 > 1.5

YOUR TURN!

Write 4.55, 4.15, and 5.14 in order from least to greatest. Check your answer by graphing the decimals on a number line.

1. Compare the numbers two at a time.

   Compare the **ones** digits. 5.14 > **4.15** 5.14 > **4.55**

   5.14 is the greatest of the three numbers.

   Compare the **tenths** digits of 4.15 and 4.55. **4.15** < **4.55**

   4.15 is the least number.

2. Write the numbers from least to greatest.

   4.15, 4.55, 5.14

3. Check by graphing the decimals on a number line.

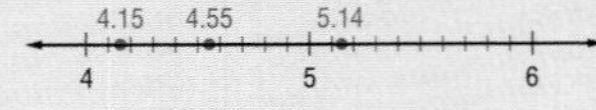

Example 2

Compare 0.12 and 0.2 using decimal models. Write a statement using the symbols <, =, or >.

1. Model each decimal.

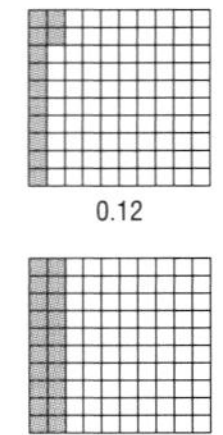

0.12

0.2

2. Compare the shaded regions.

   0.12 < 0.2

YOUR TURN!

Compare 0.5 and 0.45 using decimal models. Write a statement using the symbols <, =, or >.

1. Model each decimal.

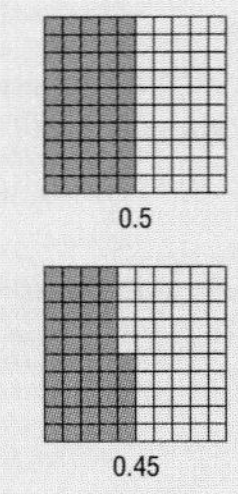

0.5

0.45

2. Compare the shaded regions.

   0.5 (>) 0.45

Intervention Strategy

Kinesthetic/ Interpersonal Learners

Graph Heights Have students work in pairs or small groups. Students can work together and measure each other's heights with metersticks. Tell them to use a decimal to show centimeters and millimeters; for example, a student who measures 1 meter, 60 centimeters, and 3 millimeters is 1.63 meters. Draw a number line on the board that will include the least and greatest measures in the classroom. Have students come and plot their heights on the number line, making certain to label the measure. Discuss the results in terms of *greater than* and *less than.*

Example 3

Compare 23.475 and 23.476 using place value. Write a statement using the symbols <, =, or >.

1. Line up the decimal points. Start at the left. Compare digit to digit until you find the place where the numbers are different.
2. 23.475 / 23.476 — 5 < 6 — 5 thousandths is less than 6 thousandths.
3. Write a statement using an inequality symbol. 23.475 < 23.476

YOUR TURN!

Compare 14.85 and 14.78 using place value. Write a statement using the symbols <, =, or >.

1. Line up the decimal points. Start at the left. Compare digit to digit until you find the place where the numbers are different.
2. tens place: 1 = 1
   ones place: 4 = 4
   tenths place: 8 > 7
3. Write a statement using an inequality symbol. 14.85 > 14.78

Who is Correct?

Write 3.04, 0.6, and 3.4 in order from greatest to least.

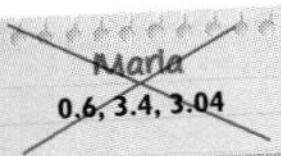

Circle correct answer(s). Cross out incorrect answer(s).

Guided Practice

Write the numbers in order from least to greatest. Check your answer by graphing the decimals on a number line.

1. 7.6, 8.5, 7.06 7.06, 7.6, 8.5

(Number line from 7 to 9 with points 7.06, 7.6, 8.5)

2. 0.6, 1.6, 0.60 0.06, 0.6, 1.6

(Number line from 0 to 1.5 with points 0.06, 0.6, 1.6)

Who *is Correct?*
Diagnostic Teaching

- Maria is incorrect. She wrote the numbers in no order.
- Luis is incorrect because 3.4 > 3.04.
- Kenesha wrote 3.4, 3.04, 0.6. This is correct.

Remind students to compare place value to place value until they find where the digits are different.

Additional *Example 3*

Compare 13.215 and 13.216 using place value. Write a statement using the symbols <, =, or >.

1. Line up the decimal points. Start at the left. Compare digit to digit until you find the place where the numbers are different.
2. 13.215 / 13.216 — 5 < 6 — 5 thousandths is less than 6 thousandths.
3. Write a statement using an inequality symbol.

   13.215 < 13.216

3 Practice

Using Manipulatives

Base-Ten Blocks Use base-ten blocks to model decimals.

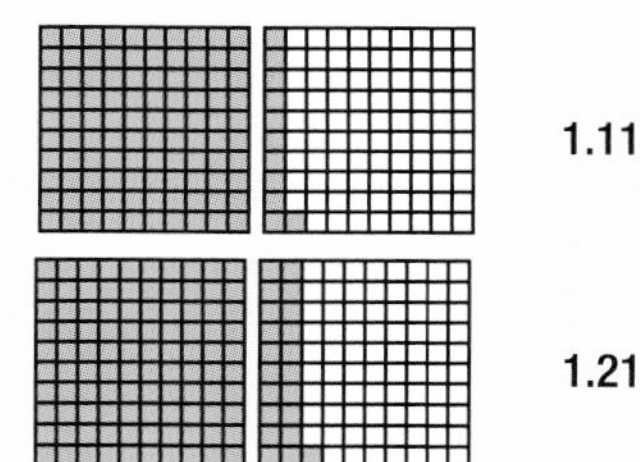

Fraction Tiles Represent tenths with fraction bars in 10 equal parts.

On-Hand Manipulatives Money can be used to represent decimals. Since this manipulative is well known and relevant, the concept may be easier for students to understand.

Math Coach Notes

Strategies

1. Begin this lesson with a hands-on activity to anchor the concepts. Show students a base-ten flat and model a decimal. Then have them work alone or in pairs to model two decimals and then determine the greater or lesser one. Check and discuss their results.
2. The best way for students to learn decimals is to use multiple concrete models, manipulatives, and pictorial representations. Have students compare decimals in a place-value chart, plot the numbers on a number line, and use base-ten blocks or money as models.

Compare each pair of decimals using models. Write <, =, or > in each circle to make a true statement.

3 0.32 and 0.64

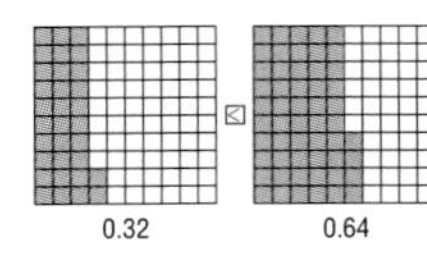

0.32 (<) 0.64

4 0.77 and 0.7

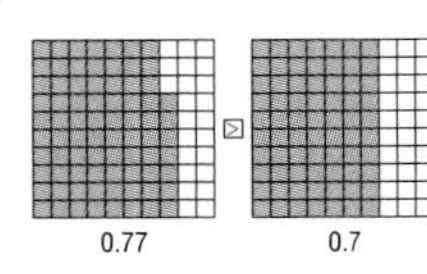

0.77 (>) 0.7

Step by Step Practice

5 Compare 75.430 and 75.45. Write <, =, or > in the circle to make a true statement.

Step 1 Line up the decimal points. Start at the left. Compare digit to digit.

tens place: 7 = 7

ones place: 5 = 5

tenths place: 4 = 4

hundredths place: 3 < 5

34.430

34.45

Remember: 34.45 = 34.450.

Step 2 Which place is different? hundredths place

Step 3 Write a statement using an inequality symbol.

75.430 (<) 75.45

Write <, =, or > in each circle to make a true statement.

6 34.16 and 35.15

Which place is different? ones place

34.16 (<) 35.15

7 8.925 and 8.725

Which place is different? tens place

8.925 (>) 8.725

8 7.03 (<) 7.13

9 0.88 (>) 0.8

10 12.340 (<) 12.430

11 17.80 (>) 17.180

Are They Getting It?

Check students' understanding of comparing and ordering decimals by writing these problems on the board. Ask students to point out wrong answers and explain why they are wrong.

1. The models represent 0.55 and 0.58.

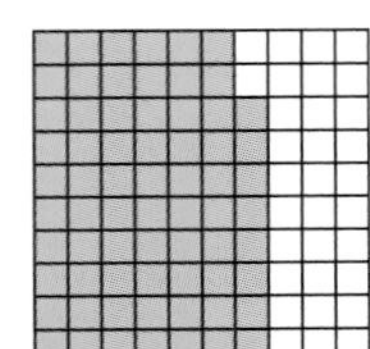

This is incorrect. The models show 0.65 and 0.68.

2. According to the number line, 11.85 < 11.8.

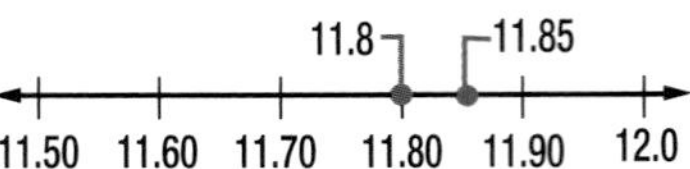

This is incorrect. The number line shows 11.85 to the right, which means it is the greater number.

3. The decimal 68.9 has a greater number in the hundredths place than 68.94. This is incorrect. 68.9 has a 0 in the hundredths place and 0 < 4.
4. On a number line, lesser numbers are to the left and greater numbers are to the right. This is correct.

Step by Step Problem-Solving Practice

Problem-Solving Strategies
- ☑ Use a graph.
- ☐ Use logical reasoning.
- ☐ Guess and check.
- ☐ Solve a simpler problem.
- ☐ Work backward.

Solve.

12 GROWTH Tania and Tevin keep record of their changes in growth. Last year they were the same height. After a year, Tania grew 2.53 centimeters, and Tevin grew 1.95 centimeters. Who is taller?

Understand Read the problem. Write what you know.

Tania grew 2.35 centimeters.

Tevin grew 1.95 centimeters.

Plan Pick a strategy. One strategy is to use a graph. Use a number line from 1 to 3. Divide the number line from 1 to 2 into equal parts. Do the same between 2 and 3.

1.95 2.35

1 1.1 1.2 1.3 1.4 1.5 1.6 1.7 1.8 1.9 2 2.1 2.2 2.3 2.4 2.5 2.6 2.7 2.8 2.9 3

Solve Graph 2.35 and 1.95 on the number line.

Tania is taller than Tevin.

Check Compare digits from left to right to compare.

13 INTEREST The First Federal Bank has an interest rate of 6.25 on savings accounts. National Savings Bank has an interest rate of 6.14 on savings accounts. Which bank offers the best interest rate?

Check off each step.

✔ Understand: I circled key words.

✔ Plan: To solve this problem, I will use a graph.

✔ Solve: The answer is First Federal Bank.

✔ Check: I checked my answer by Sample answer: comparing digits from left to right.

GO ON

Intervention Strategy

Kinesthetic/ Visual Learners

Shop Online Divide the class into groups of three. Have Group 1 find items online (or in print catalogs). The members of Group 1 should create a visual document of these items and their prices. Have Group 2 members compare the prices of the items two at a time. Example: $4.35 < $23.99. Finally, have Group 3 list all of the items in order from least to greatest.

English Learner Strategy

Guiding Questions Use base-ten blocks to represent 0.75 and 0.70. Then ask students the following questions.

- Which model represents the greatest decimal?
- What digit is in the hundredths place in the number 51.48?
- How do you use place value to compare and order 14.05 and 14.30?
- How do you use a number line to compare decimals?

Common Error *Alert*

Exercise 14 If a student has difficulty with Exercise 14, have him or her create a model to show what is happening. Have the student make a number line and plot 10.32 and 10.3 on the number line. Which number is to the left of the other? This number is less than the other.

Odd/Even Assignments

Exercises 16–32 are structured so that students practice the same concepts whether they are assigned the odd or even problems.

In-Class Assignment

Have students complete Exercises 16, 18, 20, 26, 30, and 35 to ensure that they understand the concept.

14 SPORTS In a track meet, Nicholas ran the 100-meter dash in 10.32 seconds. Tanya ran the race in 10.3 seconds. Who won the race?

Tanya; she ran the race in less time since $10.3 < 10.32$.

15 **Reflect** Is 4.04 greater or less than 4.004? Explain your answer.

Sample answer: 4.04 is greater than 4.004. The last digit in 4.04 is in the hundredths place, which is greater than the place value of the last digit in 4.004.

Skills, Concepts, and Problem Solving

Write <, =, or > in each circle to make a true statement. Check your answer by graphing the decimals on a number line.

16 $12.06 < 12.16$

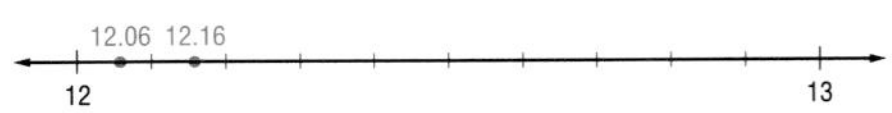

17 $0.17 > 0.09$

Write the numbers in order from least to greatest. Check your answers by graphing the decimals on a number line.

18 25.02, 25.20, 24.20

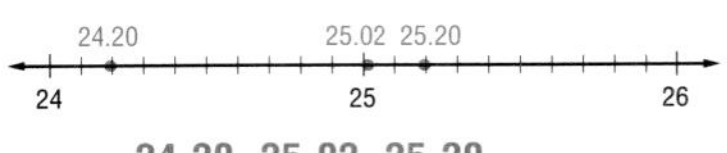

24.20, 25.02, 25.20

19 38.99, 40, 38.10

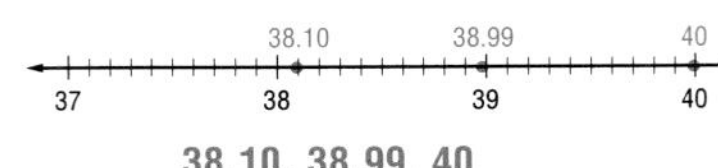

38.10, 38.99, 40

Intervention Strategy

Kinesthetic/ Visual Learners

Place-Value Chart Make a large place-value chart. Have students place it into a plastic page cover. They can write directly on the place-value chart to compare decimals by place value, and then erase and use it again.

10	1	.	0.1	0.01
tens	ones	.	tenths	hundredths

Compare each set of decimals using models. Write <, =, or > in each circle to make a true statement.

20 0.52 (<) 0.96

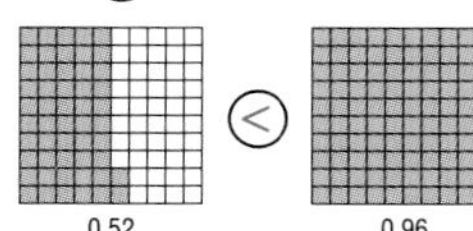

21 0.07 (<) 0.45

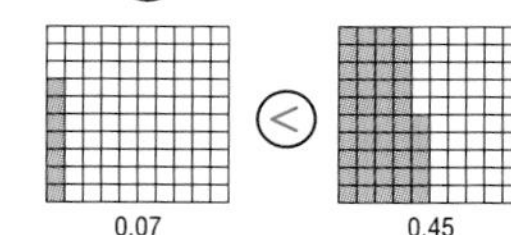

Write <, =, or > in each circle to make a true statement.

22 15.38 (<) 15.89

23 2.04 (<) 2.1

24 2.62 (>) 2.26

25 5.13 (<) 6.513

26 34.958 (<) 34.99

27 890.74 (>) 890.6

28 0.28 (<) 0.82

29 0.71 (<) 0.89

Solve.

30 AFTER SCHOOL After school, Craig spends 0.65 hour studying, 0.25 hour eating dinner, and 1.5 hour watching TV. Order the times Craig spends on these activities from least to greatest.

0.25, 0.65, 1.5

31 TRANSPORTATION The chart shown at the right shows the costs of train, bus, and taxi trips from Rahul's apartment to the county library. Order the costs from greatest to least.

Transportation	Cost
train	$1.60
bus	$1.25
taxi	$6.20

$6.20, $1.60, $1.25

Which choice is the most expensive?

taxi

32 GYMNASTICS Three girls are in a gymnastics competition. Rita scored 9.7, Mary 9.4, and Sujey 9.3. Order the scores from least to greatest.

9.3, 9.4, 9.7

Common Error Alert

Exercise 31 If students put the decimals in order for Exercise 31 but failed to answer which choice is most expensive, it may be due to a careless mistake. Encourage students to read the problem slowly and then ask themselves what they are being asked to do. Tell them to always check to see if they answered the question that was asked.

Math Challenge

Rolling for Digits Two or more students can complete this activity together. Each student rolls a number cube. This number is the digit in the tenths place of a decimal. Then they roll again. This number represents the digit in the hundredths place of the same decimal. After students write their two-digit decimal down, they repeat the process to write another two-digit decimal. Then they compare the two decimals. Students continue rolling and writing two-digit decimals until they have written and compared ten pairs of decimals.

See It, Do It, Say It, Write It

Step 1 Write two decimals on the board. Model how to graph and order the numbers on a number line. Repeat using other models and visual representations. Student volunteers can assist in solving.

Step 2 Have students work in pairs. Give each set a short list of decimals; these numbers can be made up or, to make them more relevant, use times from races, the lengths of songs on CDs, money amounts, measurements, and so on. Tell students to use a concrete and a pictorial representation to order the decimals.

Step 3 Have students share and discuss their results.

Step 4 Tell students to write a paragraph explaining how to order and compare decimals. Tell them to include examples.

Looking Ahead

Estimate Decimal Sums and Differences

In the next lesson, students will learn how to estimate decimal sums and differences. To estimate the sum or difference of a decimal, round each decimal to its nearest whole number and then perform the addition or subtraction.

Example

What is the sum of 3.16 and 7.91?

1. Round each addend to its nearest whole number.

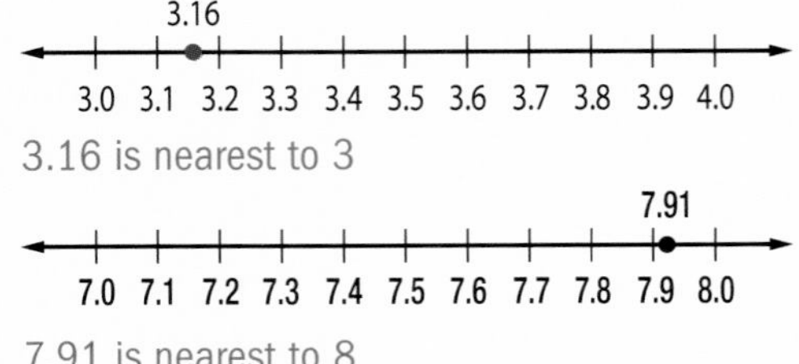

2. Find the sum of the rounded addends.
$3 + 8 = 11$

Vocabulary Check **Write the vocabulary word that completes each sentence.**

33 A(n) ___decimal point___ separates the whole number from the fraction.

34 A number that can represent a whole number and fraction is a ___decimal___.

35 **Writing in Math** Explain why a tenth is greater than a hundredth. Draw a model to decribe.

Sample answer: A tenth is only divided into 10 parts; a hundredth is divided into 100 parts; $\frac{1}{100}$ of a whole is smaller than 1/10 of a whole.

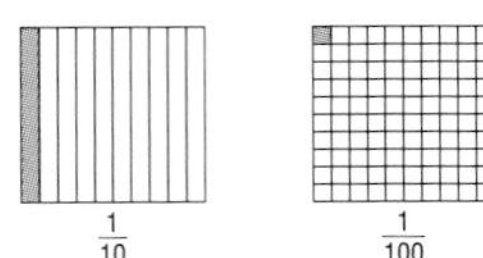

Spiral Review

Write each decimal in words. (Lesson 7-1, p. 280)

36 5.78 ___five and seventy-eight hundredths___.

37 13.2 ___thirteen and two tenths___.

38 62.41 ___sixty-two and forty-one hundredths___.

39 0.095 ___ninety-five thousandths___.

Solve. (Lesson 7-2, p. 287)

40 **DISTANCE** Chloe wanted to know the distance between his house and his friend Dina's house. Dina told him the distance was 0.30 mile. What other ways could Chloe write the distance between the two houses?

___0.3 mi; 0.300 mi___

STOP

Ticket Out the Door

Students in Order Give each student an index card with a decimal written on it. Then have students count off so the class is divided into groups of three. Each group of students should then put themselves in order from least decimal to greatest. Each group will then come to the board and present themselves as the decimals they represent, standing in order from least to greatest. Each group can explain their reasoning. Have them hand in their three cards in the proper order as they exit the classroom.

Lesson 7-4 Estimate Decimal Sums and Differences

KEY Concept

To **estimate** the **sum** of two or more decimals, **round** each decimal to the nearest whole number. Then add.

$$\begin{array}{r} 3.2 \\ +4.9 \end{array} \rightarrow \begin{array}{r} 3 \\ +5 \\ \hline 8 \end{array}$$

To estimate the **difference** of two decimals, round each decimal to the nearest whole number. Then subtract.

$$\begin{array}{r} 8.1 \\ -4.9 \end{array} \rightarrow \begin{array}{r} 8 \\ -5 \\ \hline 3 \end{array}$$

VOCABULARY

difference
the answer to or result of a subtraction problem

estimate
a number close to an exact value; an estimate indicates about how much
Example: 47 + 22 = 50 + 20 = 70

round
to find the nearest number based on a given place value

sum
the answer to or result of an addition problem

An estimate can help you determine whether the actual answer is reasonable.

Example 1

Estimate the sum of 3.92 and 8.14.

1. The greatest place value of 3.92 and 8.14 is the ones place.
2. Round the numbers to the greatest place value.

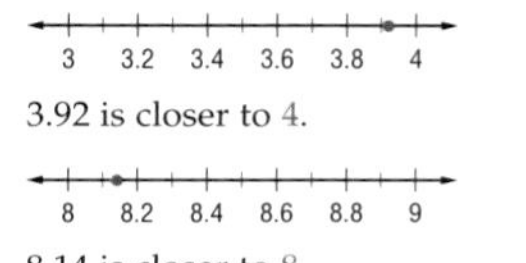

3.92 is closer to 4.

8.14 is closer to 8.

3. Add the rounded numbers.
8 + 4 = 12

YOUR TURN!

Estimate the sum of 4.89 and 9.07.

1. What is the greatest place value of the numbers?
ones
2. Round the value to the greatest place.

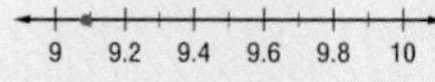

4.89 is closer to 5.

9 9.2 9.4 9.6 9.8 10

9.07 is closer to 9.

3. Add the rounded addends.
9 + 5 = 14

Additional Example 1

Estimate the sum of 3.59 and 1.34.

1. The greatest place value of 3.59 and 1.34 is the ones place.
2. Round the numbers to the greatest place value.

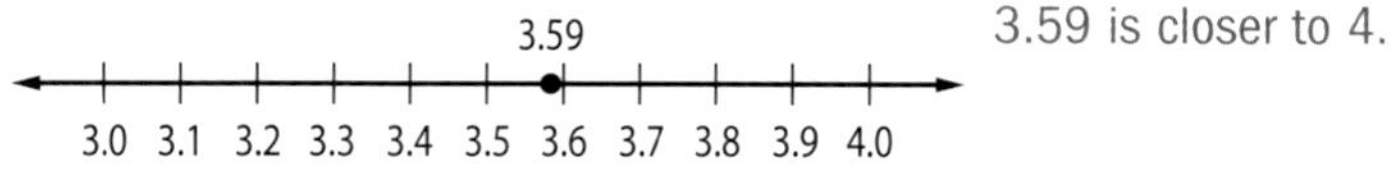

3.59 is closer to 4.

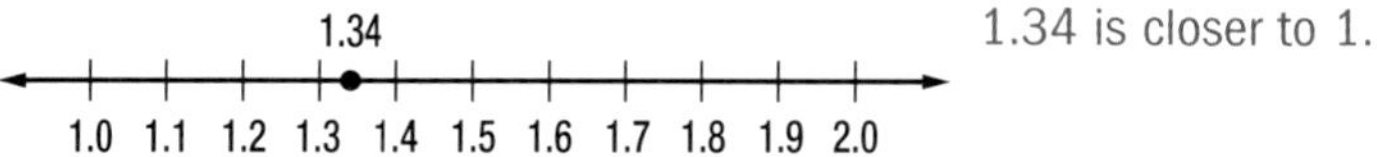

1.34 is closer to 1.

3. Add the rounded numbers. 4 + 1 = 5

Lesson Notes

Lesson 7-4

Lesson Planner

Objective Estimate the sum or the difference of two decimals.

Vocabulary **difference**, **estimate**, **round**, **sum**

Materials/Manipulatives index cards, money, number line, ruler

Chapter Resource Masters

- CRM Vocabulary and English Language Development (p. A153)
- CRM Skills Practice (p. A154)
- CRM Problem-Solving Practice (p. A155)
- CRM Homework Practice (p. A156)

1 Introduce

Vocabulary

Assess Vocabulary Use a number line to demonstrate the concept of rounding. Guide students to see that a number is rounded down if it is less than halfway between whole numbers. Show students that a number is rounded up to the next whole number if it is equal to or greater than halfway between whole numbers.

2 Teach

Key Concept

Foundational Skills and Concepts After students have read through the Key Concept box, have them try these exercises.

1. How do you estimate the sum of two or more decimals? Round each decimal to the nearest whole number and add.
2. How do you estimate the difference of two or more decimals? Round each decimal to the nearest whole number and subtract.

Additional **Example 2**

Estimate the difference of 21.9 and 13.41.

1. The greatest place of 21.9 and 13.41 is the tens place.
2. Round the numbers to the greatest place.

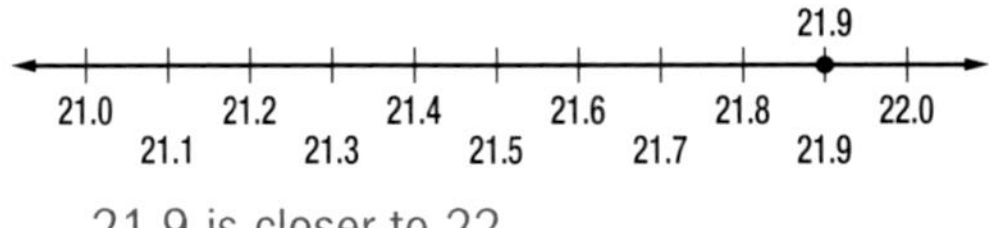

21.9 is closer to 22

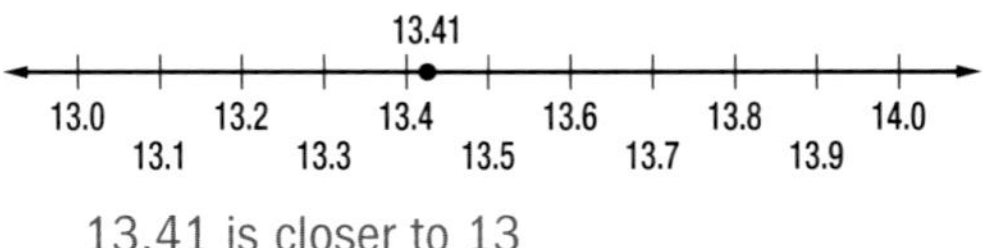

13.41 is closer to 13

3. Subtract the rounded numbers. $22 - 13 = 9$

Additional **Example 3**

Estimate the sum of $14.72, $18.31, and $21.86.

1. Round each amount to the nearest dollar. $15, $18, $22
2. Add the rounded numbers.

$$\begin{array}{r} 15 \\ 18 \\ +22 \\ \hline 55 \end{array}$$

3. The estimated sum is $55.

Example 2

Estimate the difference of 45.17 and 34.7.

1. The greatest place value of 45.17 and 34.7 is the tens place.
2. Round the numbers to the greatest place.

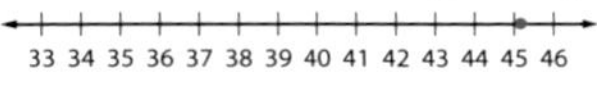

45.17 is closer to 45.

33 34 35 36 37 38 39 40 41 42 43 44 45 46

34.7 is closer to 35.

3. Subtract the rounded numbers. $45 - 35 = 10$

YOUR TURN!

Estimate the difference of 88.7 and 80.06.

1. What is the greatest place value of the numbers? tens
2. Graph the numbers. Round the numbers to the greatest place.

80 82 84 86 88 90

88.7 is closer to 89.

80 82 84 86 88 90

80.06 is closer to 80.

3. Subtract the rounded numbers. 89 − 80 = 9

Example 3

Estimate the sum of $26.83, $19.40, and $31.99.

1. Round each amount to the nearest dollar. $27; $19; $32
2. Add the rounded numbers.
3. The estimated sum is $78.

$$\begin{array}{r} \$27 \\ 19 \\ +\ 32 \\ \hline \$78 \end{array}$$

YOUR TURN!

Estimate the sum of $15.84, $83.20, and $20.95.

1. Round each amount to the nearest dollar. $16 $83 $21
2. Add the rounded numbers.
3. The estimated sum is $120.

$$\begin{array}{r} \$16 \\ 83 \\ +\ 21 \\ \hline \$120 \end{array}$$

304 **Chapter 7** Decimals

Intervention Strategy

Auditory/Kinesthetic Learners

Rounding Numbers

Materials: index cards

Give each student an index card. Have the students draw a large arrow on the index card. Say a decimal that goes up to the thousandths place. Ask the students to show you an “up arrow” if the number would get rounded up to the next whole number or show the “down arrow” if the value gets rounded down.

Who is Correct?

Estimate the difference of 7.81 and 5.12.

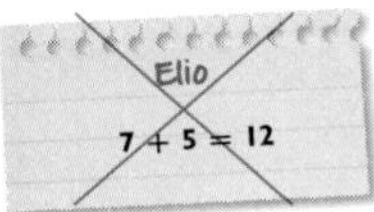

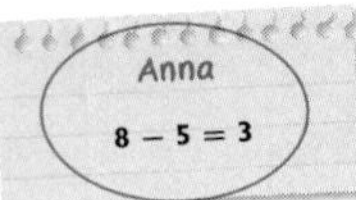

Circle correct answer(s). Cross out incorrect answer(s).

Guided Practice

Estimate the sum or difference for each set of numbers.

1. Estimate the difference of 49.9 and 21.08.

   Round each decimal to the tens place. 50 ; 21

   Subtract the rounded numbers. 50 − 21 = 29

2. Estimate the sum of $19.95, $34.10, and $44.98.

   Round each amount to the nearest dollar. $20 ; $34 ; $45

   Add the rounded numbers. $20 + $34 + $45 = $99

Step by Step Practice

3. Estimate the difference of 8.03 and 2.97.

   Step 1 Find the greatest place value of the numbers.

   ones

   Step 2 Round the decimals to the nearest whole numbers.

   8 ; 3

   Step 3 Estimate the difference.

   8 − 3 = 5

GO ON

3 Practice

Using Manipulatives

Number Line When teaching estimation, use a number line to show how you determine to round up or down. This visual aid will assist students in comprehending the topic. It also acts as a model for students who have difficulty with the concept.

Example: Round 4.75.

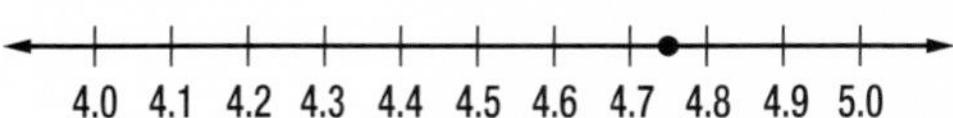

Answer: 5

Money When rounding with money, use money as a manipulative. The students will see that they need to add up the whole dollars; and if there are additional cents, they increase the number of dollars by 1 when the total is 50 cents or greater.

On-Hand Manipulatives Have students use rulers in place of number lines.

Common Error *Alert*

Estimation Students may have trouble understanding why they should estimate. Remind students that this process will help them know that their answer is close to correct. The process takes some time in the beginning, but with practice, it will become second nature.

Who *is Correct?*

Diagnostic Teaching

- Elio is incorrect. He rounded 7.81 to 7, but 7.81 is closer to 8. He also misinterpreted the word difference to mean addition instead of subtraction.
- Laurie is incorrect. She rounded 7.81 to 7, but 7.81 is closer to 8.
- Anna is correct.

Note This!

Paraphrase While taking notes, encourage students to use their own words. Sometimes students copy notes without thinking about what the concepts mean. When writing in their own words, students will discover that if it is difficult to rephrase a concept, it may mean they do not understand it. Encourage students to ask questions in class so that ideas are clear.

English Learner Strategy

Relate Terms Find the terms for *greater than, less than, right, and left* in the student's native language.

- Use these key words to demonstrate with groups of classroom items whose numbers are greater than or less than other groups of items.
- Move to a classroom number line. Use the key words to demonstrate how numbers to the right are larger and numbers to the left are smaller.
- Have students write notes along with diagrams or drawings. Tell them to write the key words in their native languages as well as English.

Math Coach Notes

Strategies

1. Focus on ensuring that students understand that estimation tells us if the answer we get is reasonable or not. Students may choose to skip this step because they think that it is not useful. Encourage students to use estimation as a means for determining that their work is correct.
2. Beginning with Example 3, model the money problems with money manipulatives. The students will connect with the concept much easier because they can see the direct correlation in their lives. Stress how estimation when shopping will help students to determine whether or not they have enough money to buy the items they want.

Estimate the sum of each set of numbers.

4 $10.93, $6.30, and $47.09
Amounts rounded to the nearest dollar: $11 ; $6 ; $47

Estimate: $11 + $6 + $47 = $64

5 $17.35, $67.94, and $10.01
Amounts rounded to the nearest dollar: $17 ; $68 ; $10

Estimate: $17 + $68 + $10 = $95

Estimate the difference of each pair of numbers.

6 7.11 and 3.01: amounts rounded to the nearest ones: 7 ; 3

Estimate: 7 − 3 = 4

7 24.77 and 13.92: amounts rounded to the nearest tens: 25 ; 14

Estimate: 25 − 14 = 11

Step by Step Problem-Solving Practice

Problem-Solving Strategies
- ☐ Draw a model.
- ☐ Use logical reasoning.
- ☐ Make a table.
- ☑ Solve a simpler problem.
- ☐ Work backward.

Solve.

8 COST Heidi said, "Mom! I saved $31.12 on a portable television at the Midnight Madness Sale!" Mom asked, "How much did you pay for it?" Heidi responded, "$83.89." About how much was the original price of the television?

Understand Read the problem. Write what you know.
Heidi saved $31.12 on a television.
She paid $83.89 for it.

Plan Pick a strategy. One strategy is to solve a simpler problem. Estimate the sum.

Solve Round the savings and Heidi's cost to the nearest dollar.
$31 ; $84
The original cost is the savings added to the amount paid. Find the estimated sum.
$31 + $84 = $115
The original cost of the television was about $115.

Check Use a number line to check your estimation.

Note This!

Stars and Highlights Tell students that they should star or highlight any problems that are difficult for them. When it is time to prepare for a test, they can focus on the concepts in these problems.

Are They Getting It?

Check students' understanding of estimating decimal sums and differences by writing these problems on the board. Ask students to identify the incorrect answers and to explain why they are wrong.

1. Estimate the sum of 4.21 and 8.77.

   4 + 8 = 12 This is incorrect. The rounded value for 8.77 should be 9.

2. 21.94 − 8.23 = 14 This is incorrect. The answer given is the estimate. The estimate gives us a way to determine whether the answer is reasonable; it does not give the answer to a problem.
3. Estimate the sum of $14.80, $7.25, and $9.85.

   15 + 7 + 10 = 32 This is correct.

Solve.

9 GAMES Cameron and his best friend, Max, are saving their money to buy a new game. Cameron has $11.89 and Max has $16.14. About how much money will the boys have if they add both amounts together? Check off each step.

✓ Understand: I circled key words.

✓ Plan: To solve this problem, I will solve a simpler problem.

✓ Solve: The answer is $28.

✓ Check: I checked my answer by by using a number line.

10 SPORTS Taryn and Crystal were racing to see who could run 100 yards in the shortest amount of time. When they finished, Taryn's time was 15.08 seconds and Crystal's time was 15.94 seconds. Estimate the difference to compare Taryn's time to Crystal's time.

Taryn's time was about 1 second faster than Crystal's.

11 **Reflect** Explain why estimating is an important skill.

Sample answer: because there are many situations when it is useful to estimate, such as when counting large numbers of people or objects, figuring out money amounts, planning travel times, and so on

Skills, Concepts, and Problem Solving

Round each pair of numbers. Estimate the sum.

12 3.99 + 1.14

4 + 1 = 5

13 69.11 + 69.99

69 + 70 = 139

14 9.17 + 20.12

9 + 20 = 29

15 1.99 + 15.99

2 + 16 = 18

GO ON

Math Challenge

Estimation Games Have students work in groups of four. Give each group a set of index cards and have them write the digits 0 through 9 on the cards. Have one additional card with a decimal point on it. Each student needs paper for their responses. One student will take the pile of cards and create a decimal number. The other students need to round the decimal. Write the number. Now rotate the cards to the next person. At the end of the allotted time, ask the students to add up all of their numbers. The person with the largest sum wins.

Math Coach Notes

Study Tip When it is time for a quiz or test, tell students to work with a partner or in small groups to discuss the concepts. Students are more likely to recall information that they talk about, and not just see or read.

Common Error *Alert*

Exercise 10 If students are having difficulty with Exercise 10, have the class act it out. Ask for five volunteers: assign two to be the runners, one for the time of 15.08 seconds and the other for the time of 15.94 seconds. Assign two students to be the timers and one to be the starter. Try to use stopwatches. In front of the classroom, have the runners stand next to each other. When the starter says "go", the timers should start timing and the runners should start running in place. When each timer gets to their designated time, they should hold up one hand so their runner will stop. Ask the class to describe what they see. You may need to do this more than once so that the class can see that one runner stops in about 15 seconds and the other stops in about 16 seconds.

Odd/Even Assignments

Exercises 12–29 are structured so that students practice the same concepts whether they are assigned the odd or even problems.

In-Class Assignment

Have students complete Exercises 14, 17, 22, 27, 28, and 32 to ensure that they understand the concept.

Math Coach Notes

Work by Example For Exercises 12–19, make sure that the students understand the directions. Assist students by demonstrating how you would work the problem. Have the class mimic your example as they do their work.

Common Error *Alert*

Exercise 28 If students are having difficulty with Exercise 28, have the students re-enact the problem. Give each pair of students a ruler or meterstick. Ask students to measure out each other's heights. Now look at the measurements and compare them. Ask probing questions like, "Who is taller?", "Who is shorter?", "Can you use your ruler to approximate the difference?".

English Learner Strategy

Guiding Questions Have two number lines available. Then ask students the following questions to ensure that they understand the concept.

- Place 1.32 on the number line. Is 1.32 closer to 1 or to 2? 1
- Place 4.85 on the number line. Is 4.85 closer to 4 or to 5? 5
- What is an estimate of the sum of 1.32 and 4.85? $1 + 5 = 6$
- What is the actual sum of 1.32 and 4.85? $1.32 + 4.85 = 6.17$
- Does this answer seem reasonable? Yes, 6.17 is close to 6.

Math Coach Notes

Vocabulary Review Make sure students remember which operations correlate to the terms *sum* and *difference*. If students are having difficulty with the word problems, this little reminder will help students be more successful with their work.

Study Tips When it comes to studying for a test, many students are not sure what to do. Set some time aside to demonstrate how to prepare for a test. Show students how to review notes, make sure they understand the vocabulary, and work out some practice problems. Make sure to tell students why they should study each item. Point out that it is helpful to keep track of spots where they had difficulty so that they can pay extra attention to these areas.

Round each pair of numbers. Estimate the sum.

16 41.98 + 38.03
42 + 38 = 80

17 57.06 + 29.82
57 + 30 = 87

18 \$72.30 + \$10.85
\$72 + \$11 = \$83

19 \$4.75 + \$12.36
\$5 + \$12 = \$17

Round each pair of numbers. Estimate each difference.

20 9.09 − 2.87
9 − 3 = 6

21 99.99 − 90.09
100 − 90 = 10

22 15.02 − 5.01
15 − 5 = 10

23 53.18 − 12.79
53 − 13 = 40

24 37.89 − 22.15
38 − 22 = 16

25 88.08 − 67.19
88 − 67 = 21

26 \$42.57 − \$11.03
\$43 − \$11 = \$32

27 \$75.88 − \$5.31
\$76 − \$5 = \$71

Solve.

28 MEASUREMENT Ari and his older brother Justin are measuring their heights to see who is taller. Ari is 48.9 inches tall, and Justin is 56.2 inches tall. Estimate the difference in inches between the two brothers' heights.

about 7 inches

29 GIFTS Maya is trying to estimate the amount of money she will need to buy 3 birthday gifts for her family. The video game for her brother costs \$49.95. The cookbook for her father costs \$38.79. The DVD for her mother costs \$25.15. About how much money will Maya need to buy all 3 gifts?

about \$114.00

Intervention Strategy

Linguistic/ Interpersonal Learners

Find Numbers Have students go through printed material, such as newspapers, to find decimal values. Examples of decimals are prices for music and prices for groceries. Tell students to work together to list each number and then group them by category.

Vocabulary Check **Write the vocabulary word that completes each sentence.**

30 A(n) estimate is a number close to an exact value.

31 Round means to find the nearest number based on a given place value.

32 **Writing in Math** Have you ever had to estimate an amount, such as an amount of money, time, number of people, or distance? Explain what you estimated and how you did it.

Sample answer: Yes; I had to estimate how much lunch money I would need for one week. I need between $1.00 and $1.35 per day. I multiplied both amounts by 5, then estimated an amount in between the two to get $6.00.

Spiral Review (Lesson 7-3, p. 295)

Solve.

33 Write 5.37, 5.82, and 4.96 in order from least to greatest.

4.96, 5.37, 5.82

34 Write 13.29, 13.74, and 13.21 in order from greatest to least.

13.74, 13.29, 13.21

Write $<$, $>$, or $=$ in each circle to make a true statement.

35 $21.29 > 21$

36 $26.04 = 26.040$

37 $4.91 > 4.8$

38 $378.1 < 378.15$

Solve.

39 **SHOPPING** Maxine, Ricardo, and Apurna went shopping at a pet supply store. Maxine spent $21.34; Ricardo spent $23.56; and Apurna spent $23.46. Write their spending in order from least to greatest.

$21.34, $23.46, $23.56

Who spent the most money?

Ricardo

STOP

Ticket Out the Door

Quick Quiz Have students number their papers from 1 to 2. Then give students the following exercises. The students will turn in their papers as they exit the classroom.

1. Estimate the sum of 13.41 and 9.83. $13 + 10 = 23$
2. Estimate the difference of 21.75 and 16.23. $22 - 16 = 6$

4 Assess

See It, Do It, Say It, Write It

Step 1 Write two decimals on the board.

Step 2 Have students place the numbers on a number line and determine if the number rounds up or down. Then have students find the estimated sum and difference of the numbers.

Step 3 As partners, have the students find the actual sum and difference. Discuss whether they think the answer is reasonable.

Step 4 Have volunteers come to the board to write the steps they took to find the sum and difference.

Looking Ahead: Pre-teach

Add Decimals In the next lesson, students will learn how to add decimals. To add decimals, they will learn to line up the addends by decimal point and then bring the decimal point straight down to the sum.

Example

$2.5 + 0.35 = ?$ 2.85

Add the decimals below.

1. $5.06 + 0.13$ 5.19
2. $1.18 + 0.06$ 1.24
3. $0.81 + 0.5$ 1.31

Chapter 7 Progress Check 2

Formative Assessment

Use the Progress Check to assess students' mastery of the previous lessons. Have students review the lesson indicated for the problems they answered incorrectly.

Odd/Even Assignments

Exercises are structured so that students practice the same concepts whether they are assigned the odd or even problems.

Common Error *Alert*

Inequality Signs This worksheet relies heavily upon the use of inequality signs. Be sure the students recall how to read $<$ and $>$.

Make Comparisons When comparing values of decimals and fractions or when adding decimals and fractions, tell students to convert all numbers to decimals. Then when they write their answers, they can go back to the fractional forms stated in the original problem.

Chapter 7 Progress Check 2 (Lessons 7-3 and 7-4)

Compare each pair of decimals using models. Write $<$, $=$, or $>$ in each circle to make a true statement.

1. 0.23 $<$ 0.32

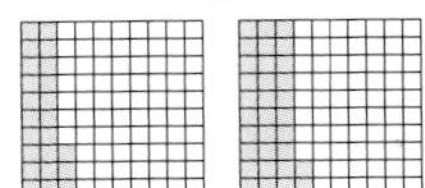

2. 0.86 $>$ 0.74

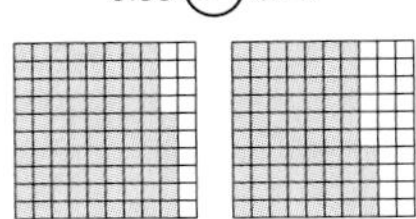

Compare each pair of decimals. Write $<$, $=$, or $>$ in each circle to make a true statement.

3. 3.33 $<$ 3.67
4. 41.5 $>$ 41.05
5. 98.09 $>$ 98.01

Order the numbers from least to greatest.

6. 6.19, 5.34, 6.7 ___5.34, 6.19, 6.7___
7. 3.29, 3.41, 3.25 ___3.25, 3.29, 3.41___

Round each pair of numbers. Estimate the sum or difference.

8. 4.95 + 56.03 =
   5 + 56 = 61
9. 13.07 − 0.29 =
   13 − 0 = 13
10. 26.92 − 11.08 =
   27 − 11 = 16
11. 24.85 + 4.76 =
   25 + 5 = 30

Solve.

12. **ART** A fifth-grade class is making a mural. Two groups of students are making different parts. The two parts will be combined to make the mural. One group makes a piece 3.80 yards long. The other group makes a piece 4.22 yards long. About how long will the mural be?
   ___about 8 yards___

310 **Chapter 7** Decimals

Data-Driven Decision Making

Students missing Exercises . . .	Have trouble with . . .	Should review and practice . . .
1-2	comparing decimals using models and using inequality symbols.	SSG Lesson 7-3, p. 295 CRM Skills Practice, p. A150
3-5	comparing decimals using place value, then using inequality symbols.	SSG Lesson 7-3, p. 295 CRM Skills Practice, p. A150
6-7	ordering numbers from least to greatest.	SSG Lesson 7-3, p. 295 CRM Skills Practice, p. A150
8-11	estimating the sum or difference of two decimals.	SSG Lesson 7-4, p. 303 CRM Skills Practice, p. A154
12	solving word problems that involve estimating decimal sums.	CRM Problem-Solving Practice, p. A155

Lesson 7-5 Add Decimals

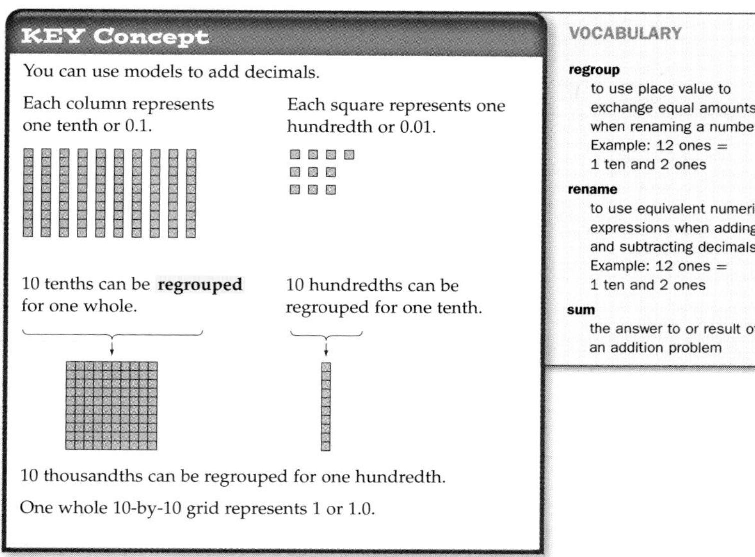

KEY Concept

You can use models to add decimals.

Each column represents one tenth or 0.1.

Each square represents one hundredth or 0.01.

10 tenths can be **regrouped** for one whole.

10 hundredths can be regrouped for one tenth.

10 thousandths can be regrouped for one hundredth.

One whole 10-by-10 grid represents 1 or 1.0.

VOCABULARY

regroup
to use place value to exchange equal amounts when renaming a number
Example: 12 ones = 1 ten and 2 ones

rename
to use equivalent numeric expressions when adding and subtracting decimals
Example: 12 ones = 1 ten and 2 ones

sum
the answer to or result of an addition problem

Another way to add decimals is to write the numbers vertically. Line up the decimal points. Then add as with whole numbers. Be sure to include the decimal point in the **sum**.

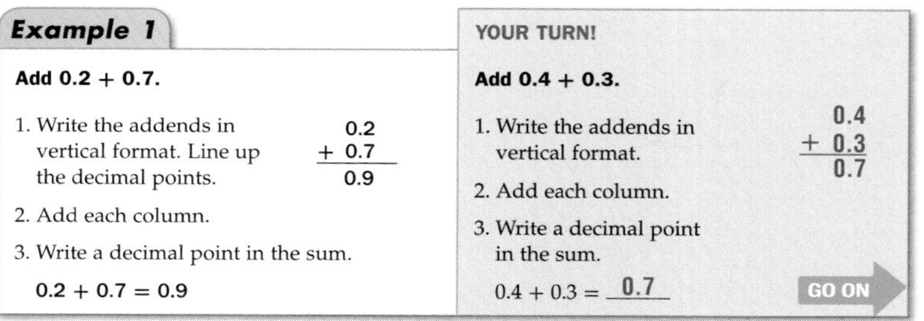

Example 1

Add 0.2 + 0.7.

1. Write the addends in vertical format. Line up the decimal points.
2. Add each column.
3. Write a decimal point in the sum.

$$\begin{array}{r} 0.2 \\ +\ 0.7 \\ \hline 0.9 \end{array}$$

0.2 + 0.7 = 0.9

YOUR TURN!

Add 0.4 + 0.3.

1. Write the addends in vertical format.
2. Add each column.
3. Write a decimal point in the sum.

$$\begin{array}{r} 0.4 \\ +\ 0.3 \\ \hline 0.7 \end{array}$$

0.4 + 0.3 = 0.7

GO ON

Additional Example 1

Add 0.3 + 0.5.

1. Write the addends in vertical format. Line up the decimal points.

$$\begin{array}{r} 0.3 \\ +0.5 \\ \hline 0.8 \end{array}$$

2. Add each column.
3. Write a decimal point in the sum.
   0.3 + 0.5 = 0.8

Lesson Notes

Lesson 7-5

Lesson Planner

Objective Add decimals.

Vocabulary **regroup**, **rename**, **sum**

Materials/Manipulatives base-ten blocks, fraction tiles, grid paper, money

Chapter Resource Masters

- CRM Vocabulary and English Language Development (p. A157)
- CRM Skills Practice (p. A158)
- CRM Problem-Solving Practice (p. A159)
- CRM Homework Practice (p. A160)

1 Introduce

Vocabulary

Decimal Vocabulary Review place value. Show students a base-ten model. Demonstrate how adding *decimals* is just like adding whole numbers.

2 Teach

Key Concept

Foundational Skills and Concepts After students have read through the Key Concept box, have them try these exercises.

1. When you regroup, what does the number one-tenth replace? ten hundredths
2. When you regroup, what does the number ten-tenths replace? one whole
3. When you regroup, what does the number ten-hundredths replace? one tenth

Additional **Example 2**

Find the sum of 21.73 and 8.125.

1. Write the addends vertically. Line up the decimal points.

	2	1.	7	3	0
+		8.	1	2	5
	2	9.	8	5	5

2. Include the decimal point in the sum.

3. Add columns from right to left. Rename as needed.
21.73 + 8.125 = 29.855

4. Check your answer by estimating the sum.

Math Coach Notes

Study Tip Suggest students write a number in the middle of a page. This is the sum. Then tell them to make two-term number sentences that have a sum of the inside number. For example, if students write a 3 on the inside, their number sentences might look like this:

1.80 + 1.20 ← 3 → 2.73 + 0.27
0.17 + 2.83 ↙ ↘ 0.75 + 2.25

Example 2

Find the sum of 14.17 and 8.302.

1. Write the addends vertically. Line up the decimal points.

Rename ten 1s as one 10.

	1				
	1	4.	1	7	0
+		8.	3	0	2
	2	2.	4	7	2

Add a zero here so the place values line up.

2. Include the decimal point in the sum.
3. Add columns from right to left. Rename as needed.
14.17 + 8.302 = 22.472
4. Check your answer by estimating the sum.

YOUR TURN!

Find the sum of 36.8 and 9.52.

1. Write the addends vertically. Line up the decimal points.

	3	6.	8	0
+		9.	5	2
	4	6.	3	2

2. Include the decimal point in the sum.
3. Add from right to left. Rename as needed.
36.83 + 9.52 = 46.32
4. Check your answer by estimating the sum.

Who is Correct?

Find the sum of 54.68 and 13.7.

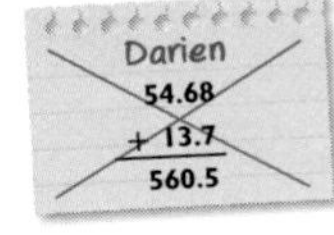

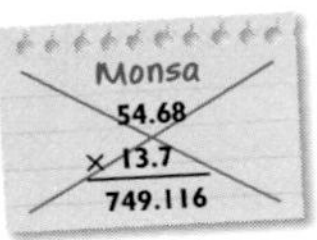

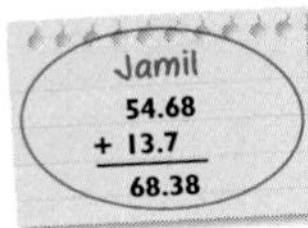

Circle correct answer(s). Cross out incorrect answer(s).

Who *is Correct?*

Diagnostic Teaching

- Darien is incorrect. He added the decimals like two whole numbers without lining up the decimal points.
- Monsa is incorrect. She multiplied the numbers.
- Jamil wrote 68.38. This is correct.

Remind students to line up the decimal points even though not every place-value column will have a digit for each addend. Have students add a 0 in the columns without a digit to help them keep the decimal points lined up.

Guided Practice

Add using decimal models.

1. 1.45 + 0.75 = 2.20

2. 0.03 + 0.51 = 0.54

Step by Step Practice

3. Find the sum of 8.664 and 2.053.

Step 1 Write the addends vertically. Line up the decimal points.

Step 2 Include the decimal point in the sum.

Step 3 Add. Check your answer by estimating the sum.

$$\begin{array}{r} 8.664 \\ +\ 2.053 \\ \hline 10.717 \end{array}$$

Place the decimal here.

74.01 + 2.5 =

74.01

+ 2.5

Find each sum.

4. 1.1 + 0.17 = 1.27

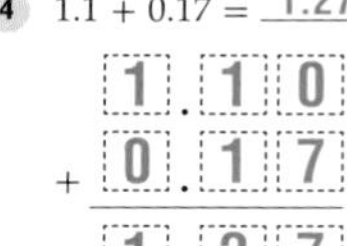

$$\begin{array}{r} 1.10 \\ +\ 0.17 \\ \hline 1.27 \end{array}$$

Write a zero as a placeholder.

5. 22.03 + 0.54 = 22.57	6. 3.20 + 9.11 = 12.31	7. 78.3 + 67.18 = 145.48
8. 44.4 + 3.53 = 47.93	9. 23.026 + 79.342 = 102.368	10. 5.927 + 58.24 = 64.167

GO ON

Lesson 7-5 Add Decimals 313

Intervention Strategy

Logical/ Visual Learners

Hundred-Square Grid Use a decimal model on the overhead to show students how 0.10 can be represented as 10 squares in a 100-square grid. Model how to add the decimals 0.45 + 0.13. Use two different colors so students can see the different addends. Now model 0.68 + 0.15. After finding the sum using the model, write a number sentence vertically on the grid. Model another addition problem, having students help find the answer. Then, assign addition sentences for students to work on using grid paper. Have volunteers come to the projector and demonstrate how to find the sum.

3 Practice

Using Manipulatives

Base-Ten Blocks Use base-ten blocks to model decimals. For Exercise 4:

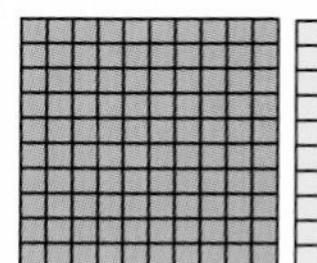

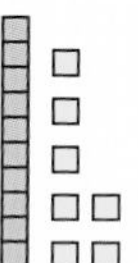

On-Hand Manipulatives Money is a manipulative that is well known and relevant. Use it as a model for decimal operations.

Fraction Tiles Represent tenths with fraction bars in 10 equal parts.

Math Coach Notes

Decimals Have students think of decimals as fractions. Point out to students that decimals are a special type of fraction. Ensure that this concept is understood by students. Do not teach them to add decimals just by lining up the decimals points; instead teach them to add decimals by adding parts of a whole, just as they did when adding fractions.

Explain to students that we line up decimal points before adding to combine like terms. For example, we combine tenths and tenths, hundredths and hundredths, and so on. Show students this example:

74.01 + 2.5 =

74.01

+ 2.5

Note This!

Lining Up Decimals When adding decimals, it is not uncommon for students to incorrectly line up the place values and decimal points. Tell students to use grid paper or draw a place-value chart.

English Learner Strategy

Guiding Questions Have base-ten blocks and grid paper available. Then ask students the following questions.

- Model 0.75 using blocks. Now model 0.13. What is the sum of the two decimals? Use grid paper to draw the models.
- How can you add decimals without using the blocks or grid paper?
- Why do you line up the decimal point when adding decimals?
- How do you use a number line to add decimals?

Math Coach Notes

Strategies

1. Begin this lesson with a hands-on activity. Have students begin the lesson by modeling decimals with base-ten blocks. Then have them model two decimals and find the sum. Use grid paper to pictorially represent the models. Then write the problems using number symbols. Students will see that only by aligning decimal points will the sum be correct.
2. Continue to emphasize to students that decimals are another way to represent fractions, or part of a whole.
3. Students should be guided to always estimate their answers before adding them. If they have lined up their decimal points incorrectly, it will become evident when their sum is not approximately the same as their estimate.
4. The best way for students to learn decimals is to use multiple concrete models, manipulatives, and pictorial representations. Have students add decimals in a place-value chart, plot and add the numbers on a number line, and use base-ten blocks or money as models to add decimals.

Step by Step Problem-Solving Practice

Problem-Solving Strategies
- ☐ Draw a diagram.
- ☐ Act it out.
- ☐ Guess and check.
- ☐ Use logical reasoning.
- ☑ Solve a simpler problem.

Solve.

11 BANKING Jenelle is saving for college. She had \$101.82 in her savings account. She earned \$55.15 one week and \$43.89 the next. Jenelle put all the money that she earned into her savings account. How much does she have now?

Understand Read the problem. Write what you know.

Jenelle had <u>\$101.82</u> in her account. She deposited <u>\$55.15</u> and <u>\$43.89</u> into the account.

Plan Pick a strategy. One strategy is to solve a simpler problem.

Add the numbers two at time.

Solve Add the amounts she earned in two weeks:

<u>\$55.15</u> + <u>\$43.89</u> = <u>\$99.04</u>

Add the amount she earned to the amount already in the bank to find the total amount.

<u>\$99.04</u> + <u>\$101.82</u> = <u>\$200.86</u>

Check Did you answer the question? You can check your answer by adding the three numbers in a different order.

12 BUSINESS Rodrigo has a business mowing lawns in the summer. He mowed four lawns last week. He earned \$25, \$15.50, \$21.75 and \$18.75 for the lawns. What were his weekly total earnings? Check off each step.

✔ Understand: I circled key words.

✔ Plan: To solve this problem, I will <u>solve a simpler problem</u>.

✔ Solve: The answer is <u>\$200.86</u>.

✔ Check: I checked my answer by <u>adding the numbers in a different order</u>.

314 Chapter 7 Decimals

Are They Getting It?

Check students' understanding of adding decimals by writing these problems on the board. Ask students to point out wrong answers and explain why they are wrong.

1. The models represent the sum of 0.68 and 0.09. This is incorrect. The models show 0.68 and 0.90.

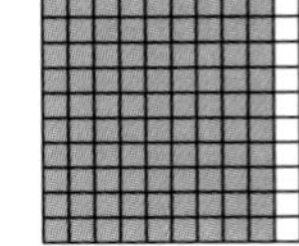

2. The number line shows 2.45 plus 0.70. This is correct.

3. 18.052 + 0.05 = 18.01 This is incorrect. 18.052 + 0.05 = 18.102.
4. The sum of 2.78 + 3.26 = 6.04. This is correct.

13 TRAVEL Esteban rode his bike 1.17 miles to school. After school, he rode 0.68 mile to a friend's house and 2.23 miles to the library. He then rode 0.43 mile home. How far did he ride altogether?

4.51 miles

14 Reflect How is adding decimals like adding whole numbers? How is adding decimals different from adding whole numbers?

Sample answer: It is the same in that after you line up the place values, you add the columns from right to left just as you would add whole numbers. The difference is that the decimal point is placed in the sum.

Skills, Concepts, and Problem Solving

Add using decimal models.

15 1.2 + 0.03 = 1.23

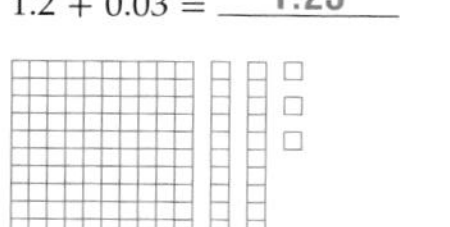

16 3.64 + 1.07 = 4.71

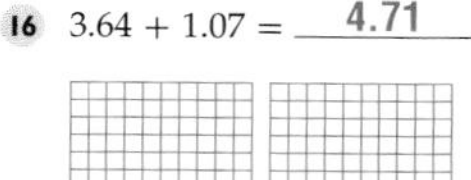

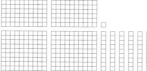

Find each sum.

17
```
  44.18
+ 89.13
 133.31
```

18
```
  11.92
+ 0.294
 12.214
```

19
```
  92.96
+ 55.1
 148.06
```

20
```
  10.19
  55.78
+ 13.44
  79.41
```

GO ON

Common Error *Alert*

Exercise 12 If students have difficulty with Exercise 12, they might not be writing 0s in the tenths and hundredths place for $25. Encourage students to write zeros in decimals, such as in $25.00. This will help them line up the place values when adding and subtracting decimals.

Odd/Even Assignments

Exercises 15–20 are structured so that students practice the same concepts whether they are assigned the odd or even problems.

In-Class Assignment

Have students complete Exercises 16, 19, 20, and 23 to ensure that they understand the concept.

Intervention Strategy — Logical/Linguistic Learners

Place-Value Chart Make a place-value chart students can place into a plastic page cover. They can use a wipe-off marker to write directly on the place-value chart to add decimals and then erase and use it again.

10	1	.	0.1	0.01	0.001
tens	ones	.	tenths	hundredths	thousandths
		.			
		.			

See It, Do It, Say It, Write It

Step 1 Write 1.53 and 0.92 on the board. Show students how to use base-ten blocks or grid paper to find the sum. Repeat with student volunteers to guide you to the answer. Model how to add using a number line or other models. Demonstrate how the sum is the same as if the numbers are lined up by their decimal points and added.

Step 2 Have students work in pairs. Give each pair two decimals; these numbers can be made up or can be more relevant decimals, such as times from races, the lengths of songs on CDs, money amounts, measurements, and so on. Have students use concrete or pictorial representations to add the decimals. Also have them add the numbers by writing the numbers vertically.

Step 3 Have students share and discuss their results.

Step 4 Tell students to write a paragraph explaining how to add decimals.

Looking Ahead: Pre-teach

Subtract Decimals In the next lesson, students will learn how to subtract decimals.

Example

Find 2.88 − 2.63. 0.25

Subtract the following numbers.

1. 8.93 − 6.71 2.22
2. 0.15 − 0.07 0.08
3. 1.01 − 0.99 0.02

Vocabulary Check **Write the vocabulary word that completes each sentence.**

21 A(n) ___decimal___ is a number that can represent whole numbers and fractions.

22 When you add decimals, the first thing you do is line up the ___decimal points___.

23 Writing in Math Pablo wrote the equation 8.9 + 14.03 = 23.2. How would you correct his mistake?

The answer should be 22.93. Pablo did not line up the place values correctly for 14.03. He mistakenly used 14.3.

Spiral Review

Write <, =, or > in each circle to make a true statement. Check your answer by placing the decimals on a number line. (Lesson 7-3, p. 295)

24 12.06 (<) 12.16

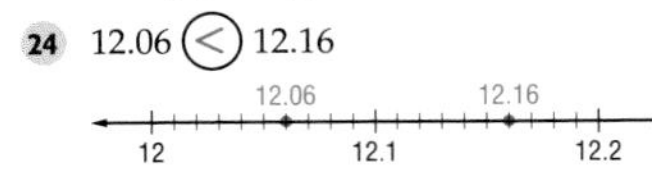

25 0.08 (<) 0.80

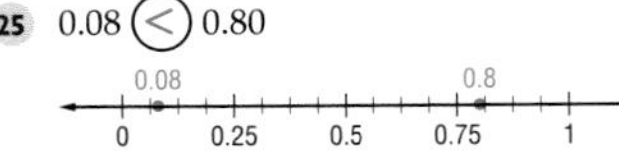

Write the numbers in order from least to greatest. (Lesson 7-3, p. 295)

26 3.6, 3.29, and 3.24
3.24, 3.29, 3.6

27 1.94, 1.97, and 1.09
1.09, 1.94, 1.97

Solve. (Lesson 7-3, p. 295)

28 FOOD At a sandwich shop, tuna salad sandwiches account for 0.3 of all sold sandwiches. Turkey sandwiches account for 0.20 of all sold sandwiches. Which type of sandwich accounts for more sales? Explain.

Sample answer: tuna salad;
0.3 = 0.30 and 0.3 > 0.20

316 Chapter 7 Decimals

Ticket Out the Door

Sum of Sets Write three sets of decimals on the board. Tell students to find the sum of each set. Ask them to draw a pictorial model for one of the sets. Students can hand in their papers as they exit the classroom.

1. Estimate the sum of 13.41 and 9.83. 13 + 10 = 23
2. 13.41 + 9.83 = 23.24
   Does the estimated sum seem reasonable? yes

Lesson 7-6 Subtract Decimals

KEY Concept

You can use models to subtract decimals.

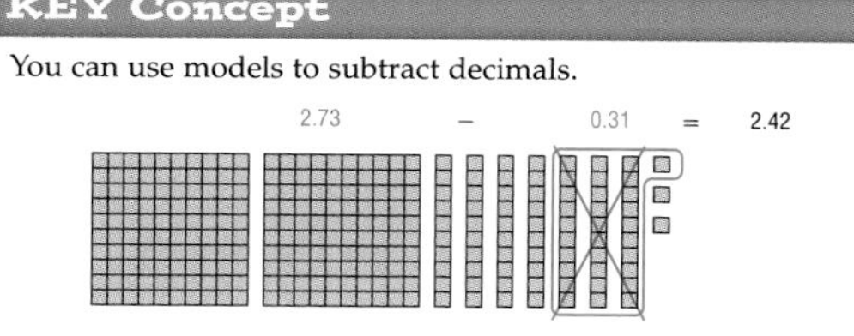

Another way to subtract decimals is to write the numbers vertically and line up the decimal points. Subtract the numbers as you would with whole numbers. Be sure to include the decimal point in the difference.

$7.29 - 2.65 = \square$

$7.29 - 2.65 = 4.64$

```
   6  12
   7. 2  9
 − 2. 6  5
   4. 6  4
```

You cannot subtract 6 tenths from 2 tenths. Rename 1 as 10 tenths. Take 1 from the ones place. Add 10 to the tenths place.

VOCABULARY

difference
the answer or result of a subtraction problem

regroup
to use place value to exchange equal amounts when renaming a number
Example: 12 ones = 1 ten 2 ones

rename
to use equivalent numeric representations when adding and subtracting decimals
Example: 12 ones = 1 ten and 2 ones

When subtracting decimals, remember to add zeros to the right of the last digit as needed so that both numbers have the same place value.

Example 1

Subtract 0.7 – 0.2.

1. Write the addends in vertial format. Line up the decimal points.

```
  0.7
− 0.2
  0.5
```

2. Subtract each column.
3. Write a decimal point in the difference.

0.7 – 0.2 = 0.5

YOUR TURN!

Subtract 0.4 – 0.3.

1. Write the addends in vertical format. Line up the decimal points.

```
  0.4
− 0.3
  0.1
```

2. Subtract each column.
3. Write a decimal point in the difference.

0.4 – 0.3 = 0.1

GO ON

Additional Example 1

Subtract 0.9 – 0.3.

```
  0.9
− 0.3
  0.6
```

1. Write the addends in vertical format. Line up the decimal points.
2. Subtract each column.
3. Write a decimal point in the difference.

0.9 – 0.3 = 0.6

Lesson Notes

Lesson 7-6

Lesson Planner

Objective Subtract decimals.

Vocabulary **difference**, **regroup**, **rename**

Materials/Manipulatives base-ten blocks, fraction tiles, grid paper, money, place-value chart

Chapter Resource Masters

- CRM Vocabulary and English Language Development (p. A161)
- CRM Skills Practice (p. A162)
- CRM Problem-Solving Practice (p. A163)
- CRM Homework Practice (p. A164)

1 Introduce

Vocabulary

Vocabulary Remind students that when subtracting, it is necessary to *regroup* if the top digit is less than the bottom digit.

2 Teach

Key Concept

Foundational Skills and Concepts After students have read through the Key Concept box, have them try these exercises.

1. What is 7.29 – 2.65? 4.64
2. What are some ways you can subtract two decimals? use a model; write the numbers vertically while lining up the decimal points

Additional **Example 2**

Find 1.26 – 0.36 using decimal models.

1. Model 1.26.

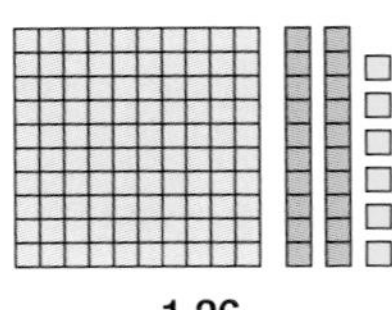

1.26

2. You need to take away 36 hundredths, but there are not enough rods in the model. Regroup. Separate the one whole into ten tenths.
3. Subtract 0.36 or 36 hundredths. The remaining blocks represent the difference.

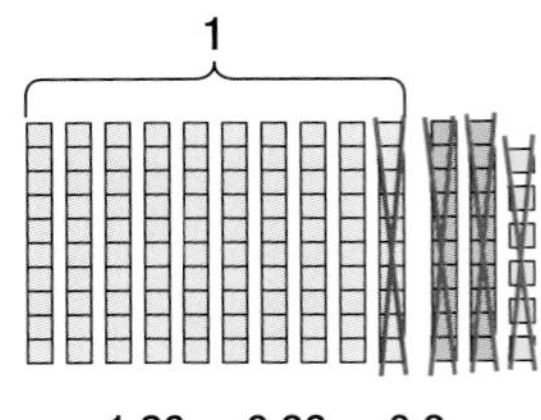

1.26 − 0.36 = 0.9

4. The model of the difference has 9 tenths rods.

   1.26 − 0.36 = 0.9

Example 2

Find 1.77 − 0.9 using decimal models.

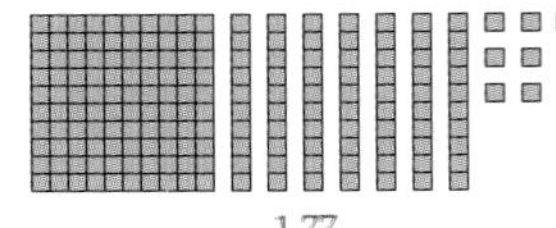

1.77

1. Model 1.77.
2. You need to take away nine tenths, but there are not nine rods in the model. Regroup. Separate the one whole into ten tenths.
3. Subtract 0.9 or nine tenths. The remaining blocks represent the difference.
4. The model of the difference has eight tenths rods and seven hundredths blocks. **1.77 − 0.9 = 0.87**

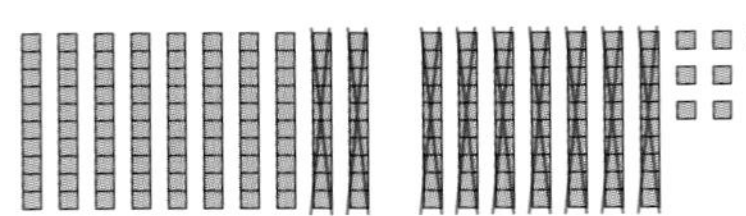

1.77 − 0.9 = 0.87

YOUR TURN!

Find 1.43 − 0.28 using decimal models.

1. Model 1.43.

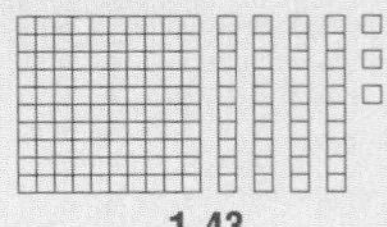

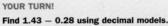

1.43

2. You need to take away 8 hundredths units. Regroup. Replace 1 tenths rod with 10 hundredths units.
3. Subtract 0.28. The remaining blocks represent the difference.

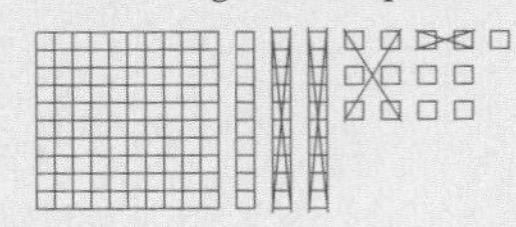

4. 1.43 − 0.28 = 1.15

Math Coach Notes

Sequence Maps Tell students that sequence maps can give them a visual way to organize the steps in mathematical problem solving. This sequence map shows the procedures in finding the difference between two decimals.

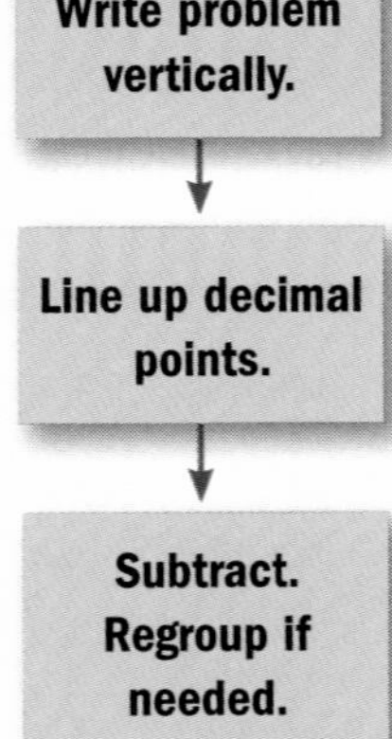

Intervention Strategy

Kinesthetic/Interpersonal Learners

Check Register To reinforce adding and subtracting decimals, show students how to keep track of saving and spending money as if they have a checking account. Give each student play money totaling \$100. Have them go through advertisements and choose at least five items they can purchase. You can even create blank "checks" that students can use to write the purchase amounts in word and decimal form, and then record and subtract how much they spend in their accounts.

Example 3

Find 4.136 − 2.71.

1. Write the numbers vertically. Line up the decimal points.
2. Write the decimal point in the difference.
3. Subtract the thousandths column.
4. Subtract the hundredths column.
5. You need to regroup to subtract the tenths column. Take 1 one and replace it with 10 tenths.
6. Subtract the ones column.
4.136 − 2.71 = 1.426

	3	11		
	4.	1	3	6
−	2.	7	1	0
	1.	4	2	6

Add a zero so that the number of place values is the same.

YOUR TURN!

Find 7.89 − 5.365.

1. Write the numbers vertically. Line up the decimal points.
2. Write the decimal point in the difference.
3. Subtract the thousandths column.
4. Subtract the hundredths column.
5. Subtract the tenths column.
6. Subtract the ones column.
7.89 − 5.365 = 2.525

			8	10
	7.	8	9	0
−	5.	3	6	5
	2.	5	2	5

Who is Correct?

Find 20.57 − 16.98.

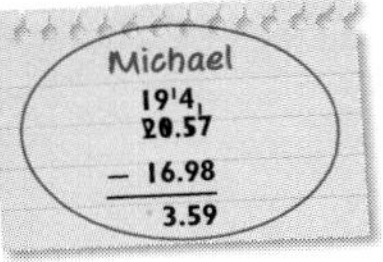

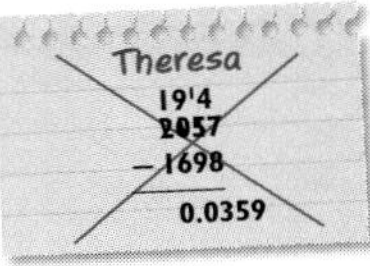

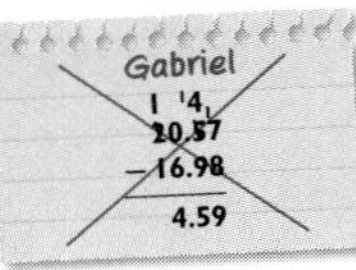

Circle correct answer(s). Cross out incorrect answer(s).

Guided Practice

Subtract using decimal models.

1. 0.71 − 0.56 = 0.15

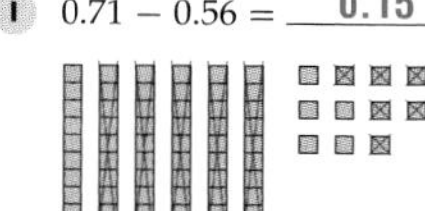

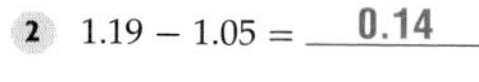

2. 1.19 − 1.05 = 0.14

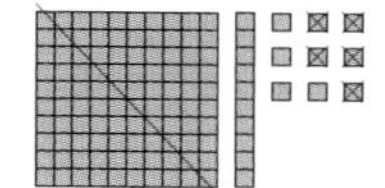

GO ON

Who *is Correct?*

Diagnostic Teaching

- Michael wrote 3.59. This is correct.
- Theresa is incorrect because she ignored the decimal points.
- Gabriel is incorrect. He did not regroup properly.

Remind students that when subtracting, it is necessary to regroup if the top digit is less than the bottom digit.

Additional *Example 3*

Find 36.942 − 23.19.

1. Write the numbers vertically. Line up the decimal points.

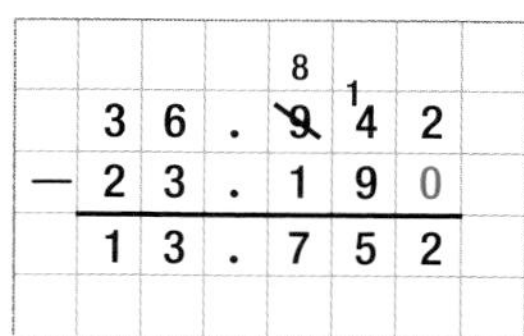

				8	1	
	3	6	.	9	4	2
−	2	3	.	1	9	0
	1	3	.	7	5	2

2. Write the decimal point in the difference.
3. Subtract the thousandths column. Rename. Take 4 hundredths and replace them with 14 hundredths. Take 9 tenths and replace them with 8 tenths.
4. Subtract the hundredths column.
5. Subtract the tenths column.
6. Subtract the ones column.
7. Subtract the tens column.

36.942 − 23.19 = 13.752

Using Manipulatives

Base-Ten Blocks Use base-ten blocks to model subtracting decimals.

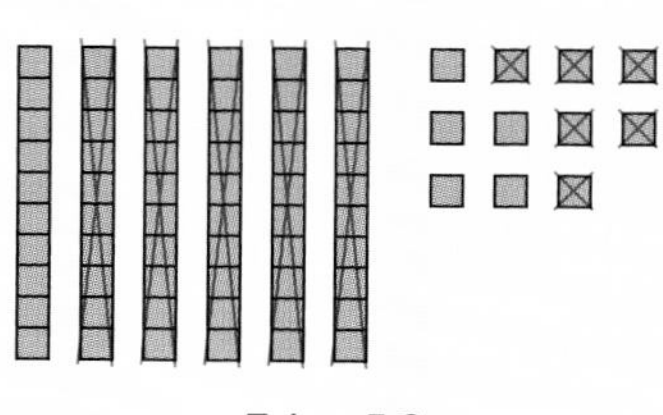

7.1 − 5.6

On-Hand Manipulatives Money is a manipulative that is familiar and relevant. Use it as a model for decimal operations.

Fraction Tiles Represent tenths with fraction bars.

Math Coach Notes

Strategies

1. Begin this lesson with a hands-on activity. Have students model decimals with base-ten blocks. Then have them model two decimals and find the difference. Make certain to show how to regroup using the concrete models. Now use grid paper to pictorially represent the models. Then write the problems using number symbols. Have students compare the difference they found using the models with the difference calculated on paper. Point out to students that only by aligning decimal points in the problem will the difference be correct.

2. Students should always estimate their answers before subtracting them. If they have lined up their decimal points incorrectly, it will become evident when their difference is not approximately the same as their estimate.

Step by Step Practice

3 Find 121.09 − 85.6.

Step 1 Write the numbers vertically. Line up the decimal points. Add any zeros to line up place values.

Step 2 Write the decimal point in the difference.

Step 3 Subtract the hundredths column.
Do you need to rename? no

Step 4 Subtract the tenths column.
Do you need to rename? yes

Step 5 Subtract the ones column.
Do you need to rename? yes

Step 6 Subtract the tens column.
Do you need to rename? yes

$$\begin{array}{r} 121.09 \\ -\ 85.60 \\ \hline 35.49 \end{array}$$

121.09 − 85.6 = 35.49
Check your answer by estimating the difference.

Subtract.

4 $\begin{array}{r} 0.331 \\ -\ 0.09 \\ \hline \end{array}$ 0.241

$$\begin{array}{r} \scriptsize{2\ 13} \\ 0.331 \\ -\ 0.090 \\ \hline 0.241 \end{array}$$

5 $\begin{array}{r} 1.9 \\ -0.7 \\ \hline \end{array}$ 1.2

6 $\begin{array}{r} 14 \\ -\ 3.78 \\ \hline \end{array}$ 10.22

7 $\begin{array}{r} 56.75 \\ -\ 9.08 \\ \hline \end{array}$ 47.67

8 $\begin{array}{r} 18 \\ -12.036 \\ \hline \end{array}$ 5.964

9 $\begin{array}{r} 7.5 \\ -\ 0.43 \\ \hline \end{array}$ 7.07

Are They Getting It?

Check students' understanding of subtracting decimals by writing these problems on the board. Have students explain the incorrect information in each problem. Tell them to use a drawing or another visual aid to show why the answers are correct or are incorrect.

1. The models represent the difference of 1.19 and 0.42.
This is incorrect. The model shows the sum, not the difference.

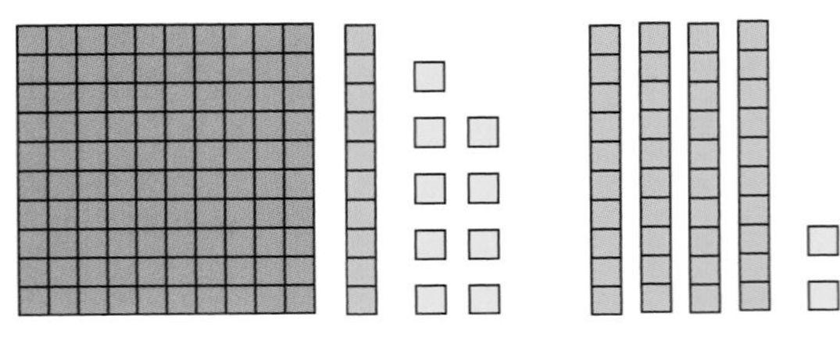

2. The number line shows 5.90 − 0.45. This is correct.

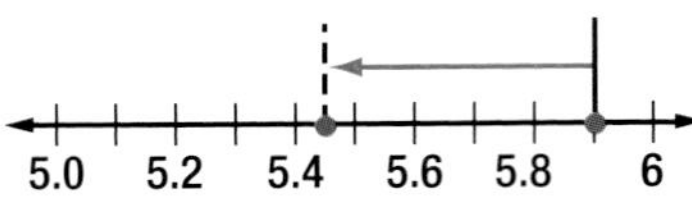

3. 5.03 − 4.16 = 0.87 This is correct.

4. 89.16 − 9.37 = 1.546
This is incorrect. 89.16 − 9.37 = 79.79

Step by Step Problem-Solving Practice

Problem-Solving Strategies
- ☐ Draw a diagram.
- ☐ Use logical reasoning.
- ☐ Act it out.
- ☐ Solve a simpler problem.
- ☑ Work backward.

Solve.

10 GIFTS Hector received $20.00 from his grandmother for his birthday. He spent $5.13 on trading cards and $2.98 on a book. He then gave $5.00 to his brother for helping him clean the garage and put the rest of the money into his savings account. How much of the $20.00 did Hector save?

Understand Read the problem. Write what you know.

Hector has $20.00. He spent $5.13, $2.98, and $5.00, and then saved the rest.

Plan Pick a strategy. One strategy is to work backward.

You can begin with $20.00. Subtract each of the three amounts he spent. The final difference is the amount he saves.

$20.00 (birthday money) − $5.13 (trading cards) = $14.87 (money left)

$14.87 (money left) − $2.98 (book) = $11.89 (money left)

$11.89 (money left) − $5.00 (money to brother) = $6.89 (savings)

Solve Fill in the blanks to find the amount he saved.

Hector saved $6.89.

Check Check your answer by adding the amount he spent to the amount saved. The total should be $20.00. You can also check your answer by estimating the difference.

11 GARDENING Owen grows tomatoes. He cans them in the summer to use during the winter. He started with 10.25 pounds of tomatoes. On three different days, he canned 1.75 pounds, 2.13 pounds, and 1.98 pounds. How many pounds of tomatoes did he not can? Check off each step.

✔ Understand: I circled key words.

✔ Plan: To solve this problem, I will work backward.

✔ Solve: The answer is 4.39 pounds.

✔ Check: I checked my answer by adding the amount of canned tomatoes to the amount not canned. The total should be 10.25 pounds.

GO ON

Common Error *Alert*

Use Manipulatives If students continue to have difficulty subtracting decimals, begin with subtracting whole numbers. Have students model subtraction using counters or algebra tiles to subtract whole numbers. Make certain that students know how to subtract 19 from 23 with regrouping, before scaffolding them to subtract 1.9 from 2.3 with regrouping.

Intervention Strategy — Logical Learners

Shading Use a decimal model on the overhead to show students to shade in the minuend. Then cross out the subtrahend to find the difference. Repeat with another example, getting help from student volunteers. Than have students use grid paper to subtract decimals independently.

Math Challenge

Subtraction by the Cards Students play in pairs. Students make four sets of cards numbered from 0 to 9. Shuffle the cards and place them facedown. Each student takes a turn choosing a card. The students will place each card they turn up to the right of the first, like this, until they have four cards in a row.

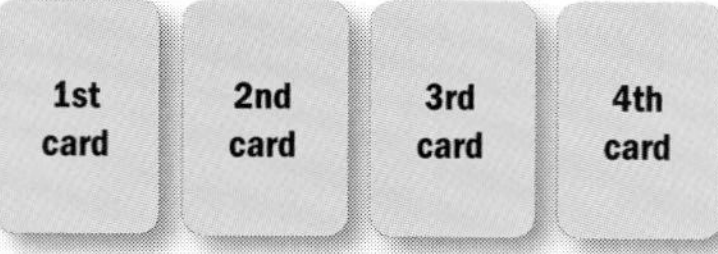

The four cards represent a four-digit number; cards 1 and 2 are the tens and ones places of a whole number, and cards 3 and 4 are the tenths and hundredths places of the fraction. Have students do this twice to result in 2 four-digit numbers. Students will take turns finding the difference of the two numbers. Whoever has the highest score after five rounds wins.

Odd/Even Assignments

Exercises 14–31 are structured so that students practice the same concepts whether they are assigned the odd or even problems.

In-Class Assignment

Have students complete Exercises 14, 17, 20, 26, 30, and 34 to ensure that they understand the concept.

Intervention Strategy — Kinesthetic Learners

Money Models Use money to model decimal subtraction. Give students \$1.00 in coins. Ask them to give you a dime. Then write the number problem on the board, \$1.00 − \$0.10 = \$0.90. Repeat with a similar exercise, each time writing the numbers to show the transaction. Write \$1.00 − \$0.36 on the board. Ask students to model the problem and find the difference. Repeat several times, with students writing the number sentence on paper each time.

12 COMMUNITY SERVICE Chris and Tito participated in a walk-a-thon to raise money for charity. Together, they walked 33.08 miles. Their goal was 20.5 miles. How much farther than their goal did they walk?

12.58 miles

13 **Reflect** Write a few sentences for a student who was absent from class explaining how to decide whether you have to regroup when subtracting decimals.

Sample answer: After the numbers are written vertically, look at each column of numbers. If the bottom number in the column is greater than the top number, then you have to regroup.

Skills, Concepts, and Problem Solving

Subtract using decimal models.

14 1.11 − .99 = .12

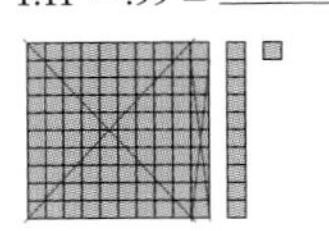

15 2.13 − 0.03 = 2.10

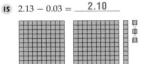

Subtract.

16 2.4 − 1.1 = 1.3

17 0.7 − 0.3 = 0.4

18 6.5 − 4.3 = 2.2

19 0.90 − 0.75 = 0.15

20 1.0 − 0.73 = 0.27

21 14.89 − 0.7 = 14.19

22 88.06 − 1.75 = 86.31

23 20.96 − 11.21 = 9.75

24 0.17 − 0.06 = 0.11

25 11.03 − 4.5 = 6.53

26 1.18 − 0.91 = 0.27

27 4.42 − 3.21 = 1.21

28 53.06 − 37.14 = 15.92

29 17.99 − 5.8 = 12.19

Solve.

30 CIVICS In a local election, one candidate received 24.85 percent of the vote. Another candidate received 33.13 percent. What percent more votes did the second candidate receive than the first?

8.28 percent

31 FOOD A chef had 36 cups of flour at the beginning of the week. On Monday, 10.33 cups of flour were used, and 5.25 cups were used on Tuesday. On Wednesday, the chef used 16.75 cups of flour. How much flour was left at the end of the day on Wednesday?

3.67 cups

Vocabulary Check **Write the vocabulary word that completes each sentence.**

32 When you regroup, you exchange equal amounts to rename a number.

33 The answer to a subtraction problem is called the difference.

34 Writing in Math Write about a real-life situation in which you would subtract decimals.

Sample answer: making a withdrawal from a bank account

Spiral Review

Find each sum. (Lesson 7-5, p. 311)

35 $\begin{array}{r} 0.31 \\ +\ 1.46 \\ \hline 1.77 \end{array}$

36 $\begin{array}{r} 1.49 \\ +\ 8.3 \\ \hline 9.79 \end{array}$

37 $\begin{array}{r} 22.462 \\ +\ 9.231 \\ \hline 31.693 \end{array}$

Solve. (Lesson 7-4, p. 303)

38 SCIENCE A compound contains 0.08 liter of acid, 1.16 liters of water, and 0.78 liter of base. Estimate how many total liters are in the compound.

about 2 L

STOP

Ticket Out the Door

Birth Dates Have students find a partner. Tell them to write their birth dates as decimals: the month is the whole number and the day is the decimal. So, a student whose birthday is June 12th is 6.12. A student whose birthday is July 4th is 7.04. Tell students to find the difference between their birth dates and their partners' birth dates. Make sure they subtract the smaller number from the larger number. Tell them to write the number sentences and differences on paper. They can hand in their papers as they exit the classroom.

4 Assess

See It, Do It, Say It, Write It

Step 1 Write 11.17 - 7.83 on the board. Have students guide you to find the answer. Use different manipulatives and pictorials to find the difference of several decimals.

Step 2 Give each student a sheet of grid paper. Ask them to model and solve 2.07 − 0.11 using the paper.

Step 3 Discuss the results. Repeat with a different problem.

Step 4 Tell students to write about four different methods to find the difference of decimals. These methods can be aligning decimal points or using base-ten models, grid paper, money, number lines, and place-value charts. Emphasize the words *different methods.* Ask them to write a few sentences about each and describe how they would use the various methods to find the difference of 3.24 and 1.89.

Common Error *Alert*

Writing in Math If students are having difficulty finding a topic to write about, give students some concrete examples that use estimation. Ask them to write a word problem describing how to estimate the cost of buying 3 CDs.

Chapter 7 Progress Check 3

Formative Assessment

Use the Progress Check to assess students' mastery of the previous lessons. Have students review the lesson indicated for the problems they answered incorrectly.

Odd/Even Assignments

Exercises are structured so that students practice the same concepts whether they are assigned the odd or even problems.

Common Error Alert

Line Up Decimal Points Remind students to keep their decimal points lined up when adding and subtracting decimals.

Exercise 13 The key words *how much more,* indicate subtraction is required.

Chapter 7 **Progress Check 3** (Lessons 7-5 and 7-6)

Add.

1. $0.20 + 0.19 =$ **0.39**
2. $1.35 + 1.07 =$ **2.42**
3. $10.4 + 8.7$ = **19.1**
4. $201.86 + 35.2$ = **237.06**
5. $27.1 + 15.9$ = **43.0**
6. $71.925 + 49.83$ = **121.755**

Subtract.

7. $0.17 - 0.10 =$ **0.07**
8. $1.03 - 0.2 =$ **0.83**
9. $48.09 - 10.7$ = **37.39**
10. $8.11 - 0.73$ = **7.38**
11. $78.03 - 19.5$ = **58.53**
12. $34.13 - 6.89$ = **27.24**

Solve.

13. **MONEY** Sharika and her friend set up lemonade stands at opposite sides of the neighborhood. Sharika made $43.12. Her friend made $36.83. How much more did Sharika make?
$6.29

14. **ART** Mr. Morales made three deposits in her bank account. She deposited amounts of $41.80, $64.25, and $125.50. How much did Mr. Morales deposit in all?
$231.55

324 Chapter 7 Decimals

Data-Driven Decision Making

Students missing Exercises . . .	Have trouble with . . .	Should review and practice . . .
1–6	adding decimals.	SSG Lesson 7-5, p.311 CRM Skills Practice, p. A158
7–12	subtracting decimals.	SSG Lesson 7-6, p.317 CRM Skills Practice, p. A162
13–14	solving word problems involving adding and subtracting decimals.	SSG Lessons 7-5 and 7-6, pp. 311 and 317 CRM Problem-Solving Practice, pp. A159 and A163

Study Guide

Vocabulary and Concept Check

decimal, *p. 280*
difference, *p. 303*
equivalent decimals, *p. 287*
estimate, *p. 303*
hundredths, *p. 280*
regroup, *p. 311*
rename, *p. 311*
round, *p. 303*
sum, *p. 303*
tenths, *p. 280*
thousandths, *p. 280*
value, *p. 287*

Write the vocabulary word that completes each sentence. Some words may be used more than once.

1. A(n) ___difference___ is an answer to a subtraction problem.
2. In 3.67, the 7 is in the ___hundredths___ place.
3. To ___regroup___ is to use place value to exchange equal amounts when renaming a number.
4. To find a(n) ___estimate___ of 39.8 plus 20.4, round the numbers to 40 and 20.
5. A(n) ___decimal___ is a number that can represent a whole number and a fraction.

Label each diagram below. Write the correct vocabulary term in each blank.

6. ___tenths___ → 28.75
7. ___equivalent decimals___ → 2.16 and 2.160
8. ___hundredths___ → 3.67

Lesson Review

7-1 Introduction to Decimals
(pp. 280–286)

9. Write a decimal for the model.

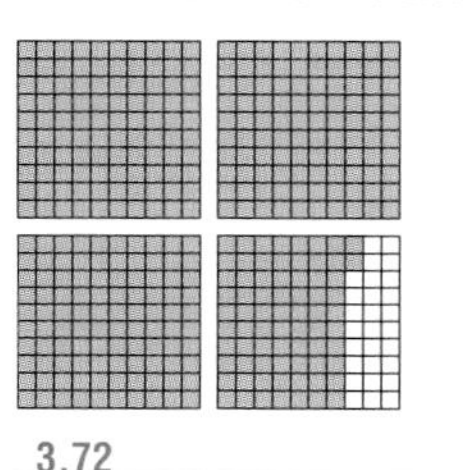

___3.72___

Example 1

Write one and fifty-six hundredths as a decimal.

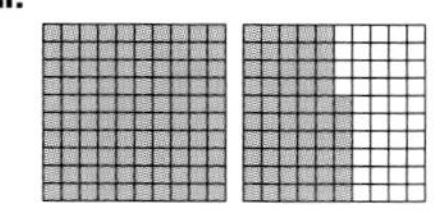

1. Use the whole numbers and a fraction to write a sum for the model.
   $1 + \frac{56}{100}$
2. Rewrite the sum using the word *and*.
   $1 \text{ and } \frac{56}{100}$
3. Write the expression as a decimal.
   1.56

Study Guide
Formative Assessment

Chapter 7

Vocabulary and Concept Check

If students have difficulty answering Exercises 1–8, remind them that they can use the page references to refresh their memories about the vocabulary terms.

Vocabulary Review Strategies

Group Review Divide students into groups of four. Students will sit in a circle. The first student states a definition. The next student to the right states the term and then recites the definition of another vocabulary term. This continues until students have a good grasp of the vocabulary.

Lesson Review

Each example walks the students through the main concepts of this chapter. If the given examples are not sufficient to review the questions, remind students that the page references tell them where to review that topic in their textbooks.

Find **Extra Practice** for these concepts in the Practice Worksheets, pages A141–A164.

Classroom Management

Early Finishers Some students will not require as much time to complete their study guides. For those students who seem to have a solid understanding of the materials from the chapter, suggest they write another example for each lesson. They can present these examples to other members of the class who could use the additional practice.

Dinah Zike's Foldables®

Review Divide students into pairs. Have students trade Foldables. One student will say a word. The other student recites the definition. Then one student says a definition, and the other students states the term. Call on pairs to write examples from their Foldables on the board. (For complete instructions, see Chapter Resource Masters, p. A139.)

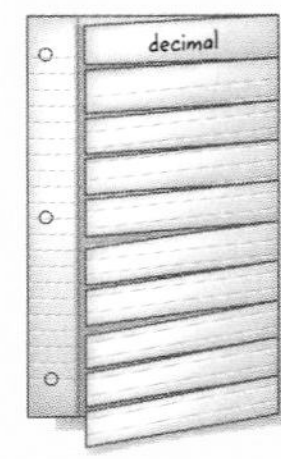

Note This!

Create a Checklist Help students create a study checklist. The checklist should include the following items:

- writing a decimal for a given model;
- writing a decimal in word form;
- finding equivalent decimals;
- comparing and ordering decimals;
- estimating decimal sums and differences;
- adding decimals;
- subtracting decimals.

Students should put a checkmark next to each topic when they feel they have a good grasp of the process.

7-2 Equivalent Decimals (pp. 287–293)

For each decimal, write an equivalent decimal using hundredths.

10 1.5 1.50

11 32.7 32.70

12 19.8 19.80

13 156.4 156.40

Example 2

Write a decimal equivalent to 17.3 using hundredths.

Write the decimal 17.3.

Add a zero to the right of the decimal point.

17.30 ← hundredths

7-3 Compare and Order Decimals (pp. 295–302)

Write <, =, or > in each circle to make a true statement.

14 7.35 (<) 8.35

15 98.47 (<) 98.67

16 243.69 (>) 243.68

17 3.50 (=) 3.5

Example 3

Compare 37.08 and 37.10 using place value. Write a statement using <, =, or >.

Start at the left. Compare digit to digit.

37.08
37.10

$0 < 1$ **0 tenths is less than 1 tenth.**

Write an inequality. 37.08 < 37.10

7-4 Estimate Decimal Sums and Differences (pp. 303–309)

18 Estimate the sum of 29.2 and 34.7.

Round the numbers to the ones place.

29 ; 35

Estimate the sum.

29 + 35 = 64

Find the actual sum.

$$\begin{array}{r} \overset{1}{2}9.2 \\ +\ 34.7 \\ \hline 63.9 \end{array}$$

Example 4

Estimate the difference of 47.3 and 42.8.

Use a number line to round each number to the ones place.

40 41 42 43 44 45 46 47 48 49 50

47.3 rounds to 47.

42.8 rounds to 43.

Subtract the rounded numbers.

47 − 43 = 4

326 Chapter 7 Study Guide

Estimate the sum or difference of each set of numbers.

19 29.2 + 34.7

30 + 35 = 65

20 15.78 + 4.09

16 + 4 = 20

21 38.19 − 12.47

38 − 12 = 26

22 51.91 − 47.83

52 − 48 = 4

7-5 Add Decimals (pp. 311-316)

Add.

23 20.1 + 19.6 = 39.7

24 3.72 + 10.83 = 14.55

25 15.34 + 32.60 = 47.94

26 42.860 + 100.215 = 143.075

Example 5

Find 25.3 + 19.6.

Write the numbers vertically. Line up the decimal points.

Rename 14 ones as 1 ten and 4 ones.

```
  1
  25.3
+ 19.6
  44.9
```

7-6 Subtract Decimals (pp. 317-323)

Subtract.

27 45.06 − 23.19 = 21.87

28 89.50 − 34.75 = 54.75

29 4.56 − 4.35 = 0.21

30 99.99 − 86.98 = 13.01

Example 6

Find 25.3 − 19.72.

Write the numbers vertically. Line up the decimal points.

```
  1 14 12 10
  2  5. 3  0
− 1  9. 7  2
     5. 5  8
```

Add a zero so that the number of place values is the same.

Common Error Alert

Add and Subtract Decimals Students often make careless mistakes when adding and subtracting decimals because they do not properly line up the decimal points. Remind students of this and give them some practice sheets with vertical lines supplied.

The other common error with subtracting decimals is understanding the concept of regrouping. It is important when introducing this topic that you demonstrate regrouping through the use of manipulatives.

Ticket Out the Door

Have students answer a total of four questions that you give them on a half-sheet of paper. For example, you could have one question from each of the following categories: (1) estimating a decimal sum or difference, (2) comparing and ordering decimals, (3) adding decimals (with or without a dollar symbol), and (4) subtracting decimals (with or without a dollar symbol). Students hand in their papers as they exit the classroom.

Chapter 7 Chapter Test

Chapter Resource Masters

Additional forms of the Chapter 7 Tests are available.

Test Format	Where to Find it
Chapter 7 Test	Math Online macmillanmh.com
Blackline Masters	Assessment Masters, p. 86

Customize and create multiple versions of your chapter tests and their answer keys. All of these questions from the chapter tests are available on ExamView® Assessment Suite.

Online Assessment and Reporting
macmillanmh.com

This online assessment tool allows teachers to track student progress with easily accessible comprehensive reports available for every student. Assess students using any internet-ready computer.

Alternative Assessment

Use Portfolios Ask students to write examples of each type of problem from this chapter in their portfolios. Ask them to include a diagram, model, sketch, or number line with the examples, wherever appropriate. Have students find the answer to each example in their portfolio and describe the steps taken in their own words to solve or simplify each one.

Chapter 7 Chapter Test

Write each decimal in words.

1. 4.7 four and seven-tenths
2. 3.15 three and fifteen hundredths
3. 14.165 fourteen and one hundred sixty-five thousandths
4. 200.08 two hundred and eight hundredths

Write the decimal.

5. 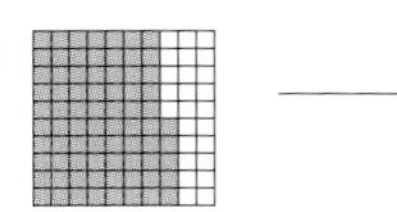 0.75

6. Thirteen and fifty-three hundredths 13.53

Compare 0.25 and 0.17 using models. Write <, =, or > in each circle to make a true statement.

7.  0.25 (>) 0.17

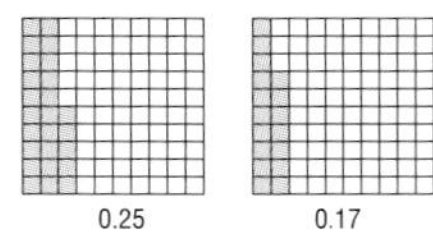

Compare each pair of decimals using place value. Write <, =, or > in each circle to make a true statement.

8. 28.9 (=) 28.90

9.  7.10 (>) 7.01

Write <, =, or > in the circle to make a true statement. Check your answer by placing the decimals on a number line.

10.  0.45 (<) 0.7

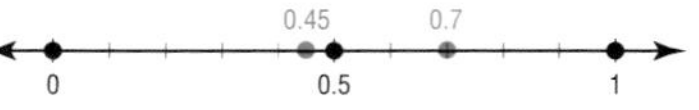

GO ON

328 Chapter 7 Test

English Learner Strategy

Assessment Allow students time to look over the assessment. Have the students take a close look at all the problem directions, as well as any terms in the word problems. Provide an opportunity for students to clarify any words they think they do not understand by conducting a brief question-and-answer period, or provide a dictionary or a translation manual for those who have a primary or native language other than English.

Order the numbers from least to greatest.

11 10.35, 10.50, 10.05 ___10.05, 10.35, 10.50___

Round each pair of numbers. Estimate each sum or difference.

12 48.2 + 30.9
Rounded numbers: ___48; 31___
Estimate: ___48 + 31 = 79___

13 48.2 − 30.9
Rounded numbers: ___48; 31___
Estimate: ___48 − 31 = 17___

Add.

14 7.83 + 48.95 = ___56.78___

15 28.11 + 0.95 = ___29.06___

Subtract.

16 63.19 − 13.8 = ___49.39___

17 277.18 − 69.41 = ___207.77___

Solve.

18 On Monday, the high temperature was 89.5°. On Tuesday, the high temperature was 89.2° Which day had the higher temperature? By how many degrees?

___Monday; 0.3°___

19 **FOOD** How much more were the café's dinner sales than its lunch sales?

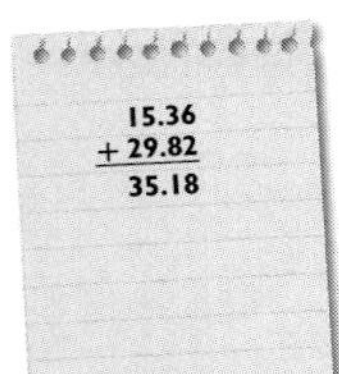

___$297.04___

Correct the mistakes.

20 Dion thinks that her sum is wrong. What mistake did Dion make?

___Dion did not rename the sum___

___of 1 + 5 + 9 as 1 ten and 5 ones.___

15.36
+ 29.82
35.18

STOP

Learning from Mistakes

Review Review commonly missed questions as a small group or class. Ask students to share their methods of answering each question. Try to point out when any errors occur and take corrective measures.

Intervention Strategy — Visual Learners

Compare Decimals When teaching comparison of decimals, use a circular coding for each number. For example, if you were comparing 237.95 and 237.81, you would have the students circle the 9 from 237.95 and the 8 from 237.81, indicating that the tenths digit is the first digit where the numbers differ and that these are the digits to compare.

Data-Driven Decision Making

Students missing Exercises . . .	Have trouble with . . .	Should review and practice . . .
1–6	writing the decimal represented by a diagram or words.	SSG Lesson 7–1, p. 280 CRM Skills Practice, p. A142
7–11	comparing and ordering decimals.	SSG Lesson 7–3, p. 295 CRM Skills Practice, p. A150
12–13	estimating decimal sums and differences.	SSG Lesson 7–4, p. 303 CRM Skills Practice, p. A154
14–17	adding and subtracting decimals.	SSG Lessons 7–5 and 7–6, pp. 311 and 317 CRM Skills Practice, pp. A158 and A162
18–20	solving word problems involving decimals and money.	CRM Problem-Solving Practice, pp. A155, A159, and A163

Chapter 7 Test Practice

Diagnose Student Errors

Survey student responses for each item. Class trends may indicate common errors and misconceptions.

1. A guess
B guess
Ⓒ correct
D guess

2. A rounded to nearest tens
Ⓑ correct
C rounded incorrectly to nearest tenths
D rounds to nearest ones

3. A guess
B regrouping error
C regrouping error
Ⓓ correct

4. Ⓐ correct
B regrouping error
C regrouping error
D subtracted in wrong direction

5. A subtracted instead of added
B did not regroup 1 to tenths column
C did not regroup 1 to ones column
Ⓓ correct

6. Ⓐ correct
B regrouping error
C added instead of subtracted and regrouping error
D added instead of subtracted

7. A guess
B guess
C guess
Ⓓ correct

8. A guess
B guess
C guess
Ⓓ correct

9. A miscalculation
Ⓑ correct
C miscalculation
D miscalculation

Chapter 7 Test Practice

Choose the best answer and fill in the corresponding circle on the sheet at right.

1 Which numbers are greater than 1.25?

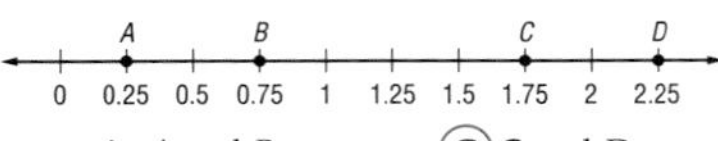

A *A* and *B*
Ⓒ *C* and *D*
B *B* only
D *D* only

2 Round 43.61 to the nearest tenth.

A 40
C 43.7
Ⓑ 43.6
D 44

3 Joaquin drove 186.37 miles to his grandmother's house. Then he drove another 132.85 miles before he needed to stop for gas. How many miles did he drive before he stopped for gas?

A 218.12 miles
C 319.12 miles
B 318.22 miles
Ⓓ 319.22 miles

4 Delmar finished his first race in 34.07 seconds. He finished his second race in 33.89 seconds. How much faster did he run the second race?

Ⓐ 0.18 seconds
C 0.22 seconds
B 0.42 seconds
D 1.82 seconds

5 72.64 + 8.5 =

A 64.14
C 71.14
B 70.14
Ⓓ 81.14

6 Mr. Marcero's class raised money for two animal shelters. Students raised $51.60 for a dog shelter and $42.75 for a cat shelter. How much more money did the dog shelter receive?

Ⓐ $8.85
C $93.35
B $9.85
D $94.35

7 Order the decimals from least to greatest 0.21, 0.35, 0.8, 0.7

A 0.7, 0.21, 0.35, 0.8
B 0.8, 0.21, 0.7, 0.35
C 0.35, 0.7, 0.21, 0.8
Ⓓ 0.21, 0.35, 0.7, 0.8

8 At the bookstore, Ashlynn spent $71.25. Matt spent $73.50. Tomás spent $73.65. Jada spent $72.40. Who spent the most money?

A Ashlynn
C Mark
B Jada
Ⓓ Tomás

GO ON

330 **Chapter 7** Test Practice

10. A rounded incorrectly
B rounded incorrectly
Ⓒ correct
D rounded incorrectly

11. Ⓐ correct; ending zeros do not change value
B $2.040 < 2.4$
C $2.44 > 2.4$
D $2.4 < 4.2$

12. A comparison error
Ⓑ correct
C comparison error
D misinterpreted concept of comparison

9 Which decimal represents the model shown below?

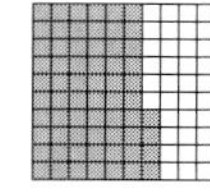

A 0.064
(B) 0.64
C 6.4
D 6.40

10 Which number is the closest estimate of the sum of 49.72 and 38.9?

A 87
B 88
(C) 89
D 90

11 Which number is equivalent to 2.4?

(A) 2.40
B 2.040
C 2.44
D 4.2

12 Which symbol makes the sentence true?

3.26 ◯ 3.260

A >
(B) =
C <
D +

ANSWER SHEET

Directions: Fill in the circle of each correct answer.

1	A	B	● C	D
2	A	● B	C	D
3	A	B	C	● D
4	● A	B	C	D
5	A	B	C	● D
6	● A	B	C	D
7	A	B	C	● D
8	A	B	C	● D
9	A	● B	C	D
10	A	B	● C	D
11	● A	B	C	D
12	A	● B	C	D

Success Strategy

Use estimates to check your answers. Substitute estimate figures for the numbers in each problem. Calculate and compare with the answers you chose. If your estimated answers are very different, recheck your work.

Diagnosing Student Errors and Misconceptions

Review Review the correct answers as a class. As student volunteers work through each problem on the board, have students try to find and correct their mistakes. If they are still having trouble, try to determine whether or not the mistake was due to a basic computational error, carelessness, or lack of understanding of the concept or algorithm needed to answer the question. Based upon what you discover, some review of the exercises may be required.

Chapter 8

Chapter Overview

Chapter-at-a-Glance

Lesson	Math Objective	State/Local Standards
8-1 Quadrilaterals (p.334-340)	Classify quadrilaterals.	
8-2 Triangles (p.341-347)	Classify triangles.	
Progress Check (p. 348)		
8-3 Circles (p.349-352)	Find the radius and diameter of a circle.	
8-4 Three Dimensional Figures (p.353-357)	Classify three-dimensional figures.	
Progress Check (p.358)		

Content-at-a-Glance

The diagram below summarizes and unpacks Chapter 8 content.

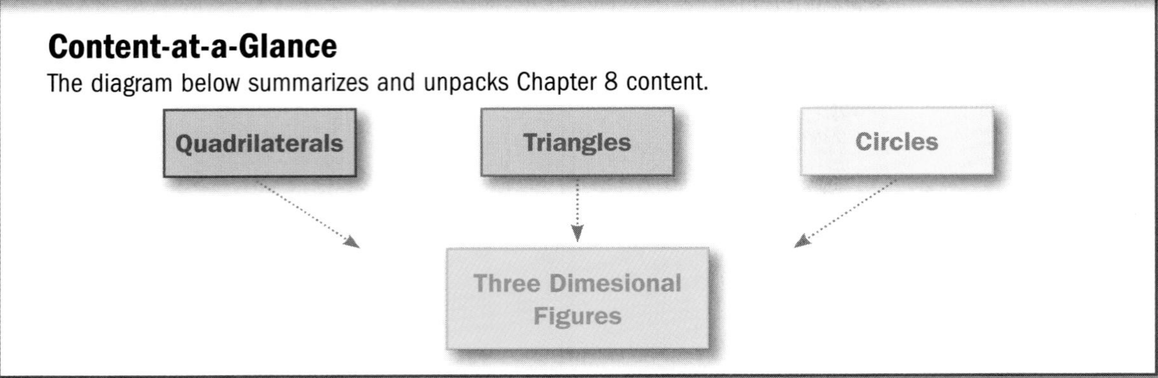

Online Assessment and Reporting
macmillanmh.com

Chapter Assessment Manager

Diagnostic

Diagnose students' readiness.

	Student Study Guide/ Teacher Edition	Assessment Masters	Technology
Course Placement Test		1	ExamView® Assessment Suite
Book 3 Pretest		97	ExamView® Assessment Suite
Chapter 8 Pretest		100	ExamView® Assessment Suite
Quiz/Preview	SSG 333		Math Online macmillanmh.com StudentWorks™ Plus

Formative

Identify students' misconceptions of content knowledge.

	Student Study Guide/ Teacher Edition	Assessment Masters	Technology
Progress Checks	SSG 348, 358		Math Online macmillanmh.com StudentWorks™ Plus
Vocabulary Review	SSG 359		Math Online macmillanmh.com
Lesson Assessments			ExamView® Assessment Suite
Are They Getting It?	TE 337, 344, 351, 355		

Summative

Determine student success in learning the concepts in the lesson, chapter, or book.

	Student Study Guide/ Teacher Edition	Assessment Masters	Technology
Chapter 8 Test	SSG 362	103	ExamView® Assessment Suite
Test Practice	SSG 364	106	ExamView® Assessment Suite
Alternative Assessment	TE 362	109	
See It, Do It, Say It, Write It	TE 340, 347, 352, 357		
Book 3 Test		133	ExamView® Assessment Suite

Back-mapping and Vertical Alignment **McGraw-Hill's *Math Triumphs*** intervention program was conceived and developed with the final result in mind: student success in grade-level mathematics, including Algebra 1 and beyond. The authors, using the **NCTM Focal Points and Focal Connections** as their guide, developed this brand-new series by backmapping from grade-level and Algebra 1 concepts, and vertically aligning the topics so that they build upon prior skills and concepts and serve as a foundation for future topics.

Chapter Resource Manager

	Lesson 8-1	Lesson 8-2	Lesson 8-3	Lesson 8-4
Concept	Quadrilaterals	Triangles	Circles	Three-Dimensional Figures
Objective	Classify quadrilaterals.	Classify triangles.	Find the radius and diameter of a circle.	Classify three-dimensional figures.
Math Vocabulary	parallel lines quadrilateral	acute angle congruent obtuse angle	circle diameter radius	edge face three-dimensional figure vertex
Lesson Resources	**Materials** • Grid paper • Ruler **Manipulatives** • Geoboard • Pattern blocks **Other Resources** CRM Vocabulary and English Language Development CRM Skills Practice CRM Problem-Solving Practice CRM Homework Practice	**Materials** • Index cards • Ruler **Other Resources** CRM Vocabulary and English Language Development CRM Skills Practice CRM Problem-Solving Practice CRM Homework Practice	**Materials** • String • Construction paper **Manipulatives** • Fraction circles **Other Resources** CRM Vocabulary and English Language Development CRM Skills Practice CRM Problem-Solving Practice CRM Homework Practice	**Materials** • Circle compass • Construction paper • Ruler • Scissors • Tape **Manipulatives** • Connecting cubes • Geometric Solids • Unit cubes **Other Resources** CRM Vocabulary and English Language Development CRM Skills Practice CRM Problem-Solving Practice CRM Homework Practice
Technology	**Math Online** macmillanmh.com StudentWorks™ Plus ExamView® Assessment Suite	**Math Online** macmillanmh.com StudentWorks™ Plus ExamView® Assessment Suite	**Math Online** macmillanmh.com StudentWorks™ Plus ExamView® Assessment Suite	**Math Online** macmillanmh.com StudentWorks™ Plus ExamView® Assessment Suite

Intervention Strategy

Geometry Picture Dictionary

Arrange students in pairs or small groups. Give each group a copy of the items that they need to have in their dictionary.

In order to review and master the vocabulary in the chapter, have the students create a picture dictionary.

The goal is to have a picture dictionary to use as a reference.

quadrilateral	acute triangle	circle	vertex
parallelogram	obtuse triangle	sphere	rectangular prism
rectangle	right triangle	cylinder	edge
square	scalene triangle	cone	face
rhombus	isosceles triangle	diameter	
trapezoid	equilateral triangle	radius	
parallel lines	congruent	triangular prism	

Each term must have a definition and a picture or drawing, labeled.

The dictionary can be presented in any form—digital, paper, video, and so on. The only requirement is that it is appropriate for all audiences. It utilizes specific pieces of information related to geometry and a sketch, cut out photo, or picture of something to do with the term. Ask each group to share their book with the class. If possible, find a class of younger students who are working on figures and share the books with them.

Chapter 8 Chapter Notes

Real-World Applications

Gardening Gabriella is planning a garden for her backyard. She cannot decide what figure her garden should be. Give Gabriella advice as if you were a landscape architect. Justify your responses using what you know about figures.

Intervention Strategy

Shapely Gardens

Step 1 Divide the class into small groups or pairs. Assign each group a figure that will be covered in this chapter. Tell that group to draw a garden that represents their figure.

Step 2 Place the drawings around the room. Have students look at the designs and write down at least two comments regarding each figure that are related to a geometric property of the figure.

Step 3 Have a class discussion regarding the comments each group made. This can be a nice lead-in activity when discussing the attributes of each figure.

Chapter 8 Geometry

There are triangles, circles, and figures all around us.

You see figures every day. Everywhere you go there are different figures. Some may be flat, or solid. Many windows and buildings form basic figures.

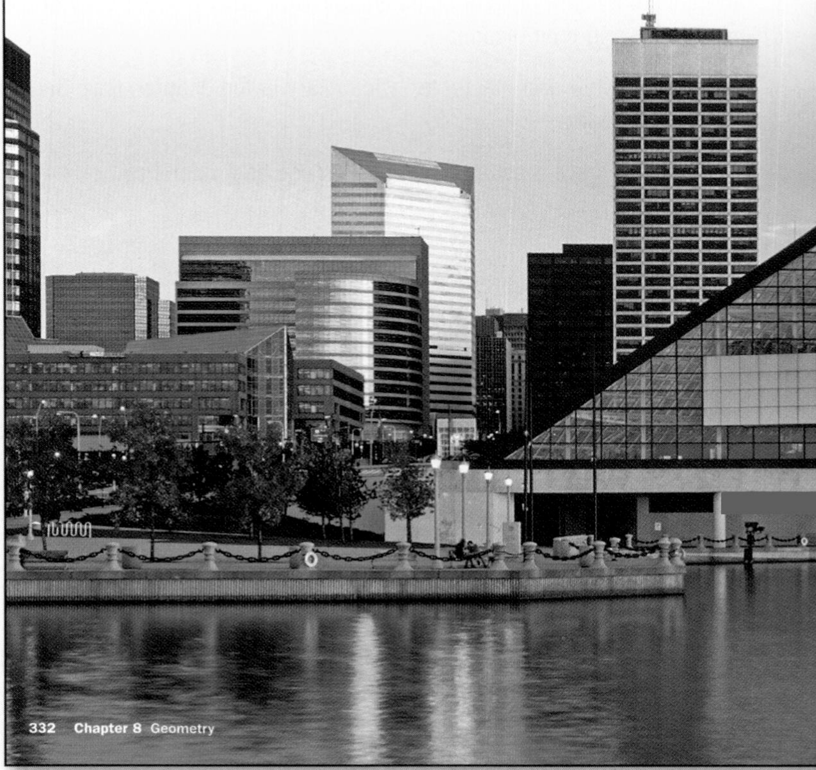

332 Chapter 8 Geometry

Key Vocabulary

Find interactive definitions in 13 languages in the **eGlossary** at macmillanmh.com.

English **Español** *Introduce the most important vocabulary terms from Chapter 8.*

parallel lines **rectus paralelas**
lines that are the same distance apart (p. 334)

acute angle **ángulo agudo**
an angle with a measure greater than 0° and less than 90° (p. 341)

face **cara**
the flat part of a three-dimensional figure (p. 353)

quadrilateral **cuadrilátero**
a shape that has four sides and four angles (p. 334)

congruent **congruente**
having the same size, shape, or measure (p. 341)

vertex **vértice**
a point on a three-dimensional figure where three or more edges meet (p. 353)

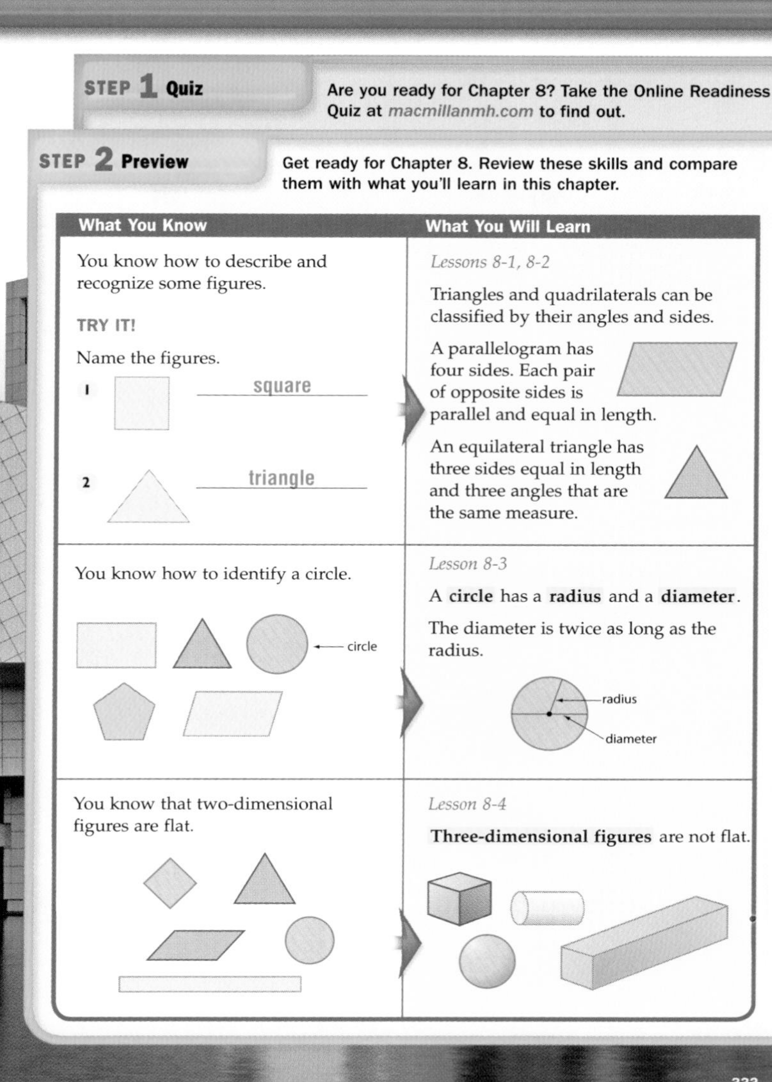
STEP 1 Quiz Are you ready for Chapter 8? Take the Online Readiness Quiz at macmillanmh.com to find out.

STEP 2 Preview Get ready for Chapter 8. Review these skills and compare them with what you'll learn in this chapter.

What You Know	What You Will Learn
You know how to describe and recognize some figures. **TRY IT!** Name the figures. 1 square 2 triangle	*Lessons 8-1, 8-2* Triangles and quadrilaterals can be classified by their angles and sides. A parallelogram has four sides. Each pair of opposite sides is parallel and equal in length. An equilateral triangle has three sides equal in length and three angles that are the same measure.
You know how to identify a circle. circle	*Lesson 8-3* A **circle** has a **radius** and a **diameter**. The diameter is twice as long as the radius. radius diameter
You know that two-dimensional figures are flat.	*Lesson 8-4* **Three-dimensional figures** are not flat.

333

Step 1 Quiz

Pretest/Prescribe Students can take the Online Readiness Quiz or the Diagnostic Pretest in the Assessment Masters.

Step 2 Preview

Use this pre-chapter activity to activate students' prior knowledge, build confidence, and help students preview the lessons.

Guide students through the directions on p. A165 in the Chapter Resource Masters to create their own Foldable graphic organizer for use with this chapter.

Home Connections

Ask students to look around their homes and write down at least five different items that represent figures that they see or use regularly.

Have students talk to their parents and/or caregivers to write down one example of how figures play a part in their everyday lives. Have students share their examples with the class.

Vocabulary Preview

- As students complete the Chapter Preview, have them make a list of important terms throughout the chapter. Include a sketch of the terms if appropriate.
- Using index cards, have students write terms on one side of the cards and definitions and sketches of terms on the other side. Ask them to also include any other information that will help them identify the figures.
- Once students are finished, have them trade their cards with other students to challenge their knowledge of the vocabulary in this chapter.

Mc Graw Hill
Professional Development
Targeted professional development has been articulated throughout McGraw-Hill's Math Triumphs intervention program. The McGraw-Hill Professional Development Video Library provides short videos that support the NCTM Focal Points and Focal Connections. For more information, visit macmillanmh.com.
Model Lessons
Instructional Strategies

Lesson 8-1

Lesson Notes

Lesson Planner

Objective Classify quadrilaterals.

Vocabulary **parallel lines, quadrilateral**

Materials/Manipulatives geoboard, grid paper, pattern blocks, ruler

Chapter Resource Masters

- CRM Vocabulary and English Language Development (p. A167)
- CRM Skills Practice (p. A168)
- CRM Problem-Solving Practice (p. A169)
- CRM Homework Practice (p. A170)

Vocabulary

Explore Vocabulary Using one of each type of pattern block, have students group the blocks by their attributes. Once students have grouped the *quadrilaterals*, have students write down reasons using the vocabulary to justify the groups that they made.

2 Teach

Key Concept

Foundational Skills and Concepts After students have read through the Key Concept box, have them try these exercises.

1. What is the name of the figure?

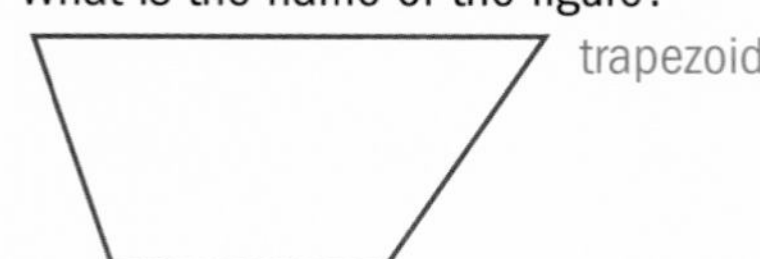

trapezoid

2. Name a figure that has four sides that has four right angles and four sides all the same length.
square

Lesson 8-1

Quadrilaterals

KEY Concept

Quadrilaterals have four sides and four angles. Some quadrilaterals have special names.

Type	Example	Description
rectangle		A rectangle has four right angles, with two pairs of equal sides.
square		A square has four right angles. All sides are equal.
parallelogram		The opposite sides of a parallelogram are parallel and equal in length.
rhombus These marks show equal sides.		All four sides of a rhombus are equal. Opposite sides are parallel.
trapezoid		A trapezoid has only one pair of opposite sides parallel.

VOCABULARY

parallel lines
lines that are the same distance apart; parallel lines do not meet or cross

quadrilateral
a figure that has four sides and four angles

Quadrilaterals can be classified by the size of their angles and the length of their sides.

Intervention Strategy

Visual Learners

Visual Organizer Many students will get the attributes for different figures confused. Assist them in creating a visual organizer that connects figures that share attributes.

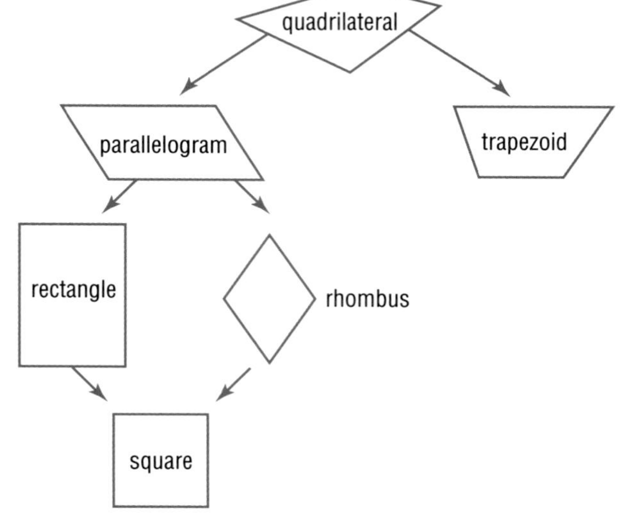

Example 1

Classify the figure in as many ways as possible.

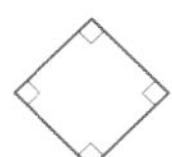

1. Look at the figure.
2. Are opposite sides equal?
   Yes
3. Are any of the opposite sides parallel?
   Yes
4. Does the figure have exactly one pair of parallel sides?
   No
5. The figure can be classified as a parallelogram, rectangle, square, and rhombus.

YOUR TURN!

Classify the figure in as many ways as possible.

1. Look at the figure.
2. Are opposite sides equal?
   Yes
3. Are any of the opposite sides parallel?
   Yes
4. Does the figure have exactly one pair of parallel sides?
   No
5. The figure can be classified as a parallelogram and rectangle.

Example 2

Identify the figure.

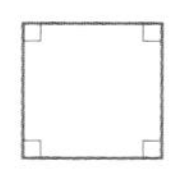

1. The figure has four sides.
   The figure is a quadrilateral.
2. All sides are equal in length.
   The figure is a rhombus or a square.
3. All angles are right angles.
   The figure is a square.

YOUR TURN!

Identify the figure.

1. The figure has four sides.
   The figure is a(n) quadrilateral.
2. There is one pair of parallel sides.
3. There are zero right angles.
   The figure is a(n) trapezoid.

Math Coach Notes

Strategies

1. Start this lesson by dividing the students into small groups and asking them to write down everything that they know about quadrilaterals. Encourage students to identify even slight differences in each of the quadrilaterals.
2. Next have the group exchange papers with another group. Have them look over the list and add anything that they know that is not on the list. Do this a few times until the lists seem complete.
3. Ask each group to share their list. Make a class list of information about quadrilaterals. Use this as a lead-in to the vocabulary and facts for the lesson.

Additional *Example 1*

Classify the figure in as many ways as possible.

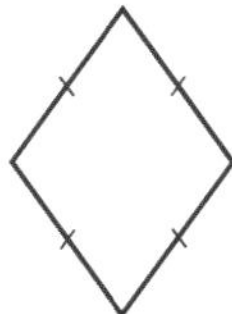

1. Look at the figure.
2. Are the opposite sides equal? Yes
3. Are any of the opposite sides parallel? Yes
4. Does the figure have exactly one pair of parallel sides? No
5. The figure can be classified as a parallelogram and rhombus.

Additional *Example 2*

Identify the figure.

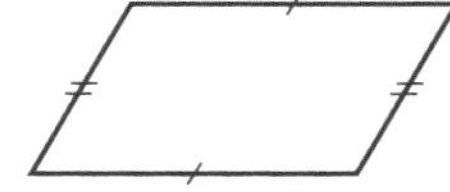

1. The figure has four sides.
   The figure is a quadrilateral.
2. There are 0 right angles.
   The figure is a parallelogram or rhombus.
3. All sides are not equal in length.
   The figure is a parallelogram.

Intervention Strategy

Visual/ Interpersonal Learners

Quadrilaterals Everywhere Have students write down as many examples of quadrilaterals that they see in the world around them, i.e., a parking sign, a label on a water bottle, and so on. Have students get into small groups and share their lists. Have the members of the group compile a group list. Then, as a class, create a list and see how many places quadrilaterals appear.

Note This!

Margin Notes Show students how to write notes within the body of their notebook paper and leave wide margins to add notes in the future. Tell students that as they study, they can write important points, concepts they need to review, or items that were stressed in class in the margins. When it is time for a quick review, they only need to focus on the margins, instead of all of their notes.

Using Manipulatives

Pattern Blocks Use pattern blocks as references for students.

Geoboards Students can use geoboards to explore the slight differences in the figures. It is a handy way to make small modifications for exploration.

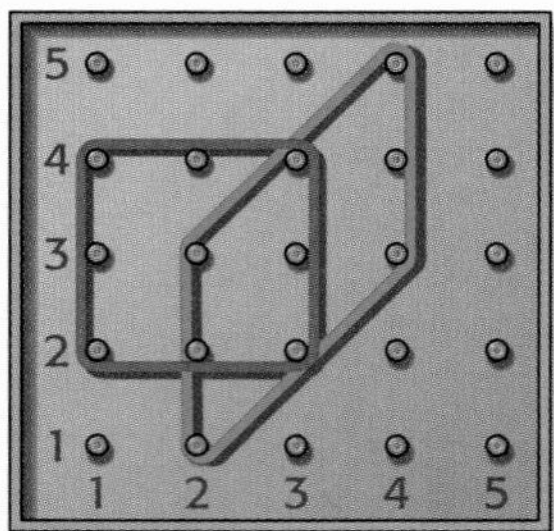

On-Hand Manipulatives Emphasize that grid paper and rulers are great tools to draw figures. The student can use them to draw figures and tape them into their notes.

Math Coach Notes

Exercise 2 Students may forget to list a rectangle in the classification of the quadrilateral. Remind students that a square is a special type of rectangle. A square fits the definition of a rectangle because it has four right angles and its opposite sides are congruent. The definition of a square also states that all four sides must be equal. So every square is a rectangle.

Who is Correct?

Draw a parallelogram.

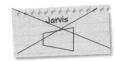

Jarvis Grady Alisa

Circle correct answer(s). Cross out incorrect answer(s).

Guided Practice

Classify each quadrilateral in as many ways as possible.

1

1. Are opposite sides equal? No
2. Are any of the opposite sides parallel? Yes
3. Does the figure have exactly one pair of parallel sides? Yes
4. The shape is a trapezoid.

2

1. Are opposite sides equal? Yes
2. Are any of the opposite sides parallel? Yes
3. Does the figure have exactly one pair of parallel sides? No
4. The shape is a parallelogram, rectangle, square, rhombus.

336 Chapter 8 Geometry

Who *is Correct?*

Diagnostic Teaching

- Jarvis is incorrect. He drew a trapezoid; a parallelogram needs two sets of equal parallel sides.
- Grady is incorrect. He drew a trapezoid; a parallelogram needs two sets of equal parallel sides.
- Alisa is correct.

Remind students that quadrilaterals can be classified by the size of their angles and the length of their sides.

Step by Step Practice

3 Identify the figure.

Step 1 The figure has <u>four</u> sides.

The figure is a(n) <u>quadrilateral</u>.

Step 2 Are any of the sides parallel? <u>yes</u>

Step 3 There are <u>two</u> pairs of parallel sides.

The figure is a(n) <u>parallelogram</u>.

Identify the figure.

4 The figure has <u>four</u> sides.

The figure is a(n) <u>quadrilateral</u>.

Are any of the sides parallel and equal? <u>yes</u>

There are <u>two</u> pairs of equal and parallel sides.

The figure is a(n) <u>rhombus</u>.

5 The figure has <u>four</u> sides.

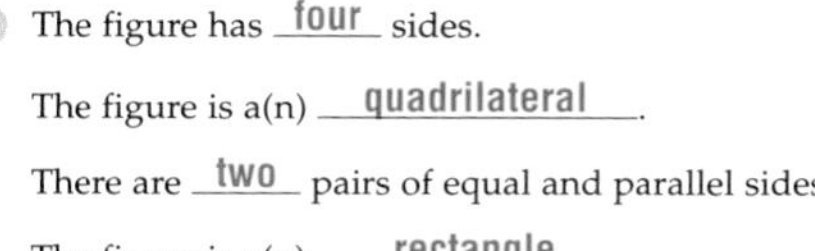

The figure is a(n) <u>quadrilateral</u>.

There are <u>two</u> pairs of equal and parallel sides.

The figure is a(n) <u>rectangle</u>.

English Learner Strategy

Connect Terms with Images Arrange students into groups with at least one English Learner in every group. Have each student identify the properties of a figure by pointing to them in a diagram. Have students take turns defining the figures in their own words.

Note This!

Daily Notes Encourage students to start their notes each day on a new page, and to date and number each page. Because the sequence of material is important, write on only one side of the paper. Students can tear out the pages or place them side by side for easier reviewing when studying for an exam.

Common Error *Alert*

Parallelogram When classifying quadrilaterals such as rectangles and squares, students will often forget the most basic form—a parallelogram. Remind them to start their classification or identification process with the most basic figure and work to the more specific.

Are They Getting It?

Check students' understanding of quadrilaterals by writing these problems on the board. Have students explain the incorrect information in each problem. Tell them to use the properties of the specific quadrilateral to justify their responses.

1. Are opposite sides equal? no
2. Are opposite sides parallel? no
3. Does the figure have exactly one pair of parallel sides? yes; This is a trapezoid.

   This is correct.

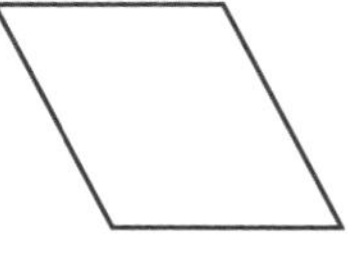

1. The figure has four sides. The figure is a quadrilateral.
2. Are any of the sides in the figure parallel? yes
3. There are 2 pairs of parallel sides. The figure is a square.

   This is incorrect. The figure is a parallelogram. There are no right angles, so the shape cannot be a square.

Intervention Strategy — Spatial Learners

Create Figures Arrange students into pairs and give each group a geoboard. Have one student select a figure from the Key Concept box. The other student makes the figure on the geoboard. Point out that right angles do not always look like right angles on a geoboard. Try to give hints regarding right angles if needed.

Note This!

Cornell Method Tell students that one researched method of notetaking is the Cornell Method. Draw the diagram below on the board and describe it to students.

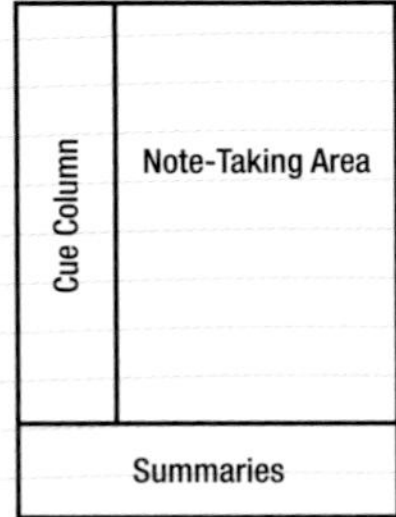

- Use the note-taking area to record your notes from class.
- Use the cue column to jot phrases, sketches, or other clues to understanding the concepts.
- After class, summarize the main idea of that day's lesson in the summaries area.

English Learner Strategy

Flashcards Have English Learners create flashcards for each type of quadrilateral. Have them draw a picture on one side of the card with the name of the figure in their native language. On the other side of the card have the name of the figure in English and the key features for the figure. Encourage students to go through the cards daily to help them to study.

Step by Step Problem-Solving Practice

Problem-Solving Strategies
- ☑ Use a diagram.
- ☐ Look for a pattern.
- ☐ Guess and check.
- ☐ Act it out.
- ☐ Work backward.

Solve.

6 TILES Pete is placing new tile on his kitchen floor. What quadrilateral figure describes the dark blue part of the tile Pete is using?

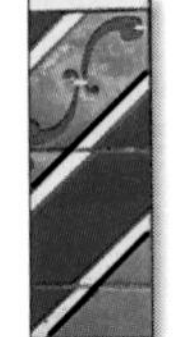

Understand — Read the problem. Write what you know. The figure of the pattern on the tile is a __quadrilateral__.

Plan — Pick a strategy. One strategy is to use a diagram.

Solve — Trace the outline of the figure. There are __four__ sides. There are __two__ pairs of parallel sides. The figure is a(n) __parallelogram__.

Check — Review the definition of the figure you named.

7 SKETCHING Anya is sketching a figure in art class. Anya's figure has four sides and four right angles. There are two sets of lines equal in length. Opposite sides are parallel. What is the name of the figure Anya is sketching? Check off each step.

__✓__ Understand: I circled key words.

__✓__ Plan: To solve the problem, I will __use a diagram__.

__✓__ Solve: The answer is a(n) __rectangle__.

__✓__ Check: I checked my answer by __reviewing the definition__.

8 **Reflect** The word *quadrilateral* has two parts. *Quad* means "four" and *lateral* means "side or relating to the side." In your own words, explain the meaning of the word quadrilateral.

Sample answer: Quadrilateral means a figure that has four sides.

Intervention Strategy — Logical Learners

Check Figures When students are identifying figures, they can use logic to help them. For example if they are trying to find out whether the sides of a figure are equal, then they do not need a ruler. Have students pick a side and place a piece of paper along the side so they can see the line. Then have students put a mark on the paper that will represent the length of the side. Compare the marks with another side of the figure to see if they are equal.

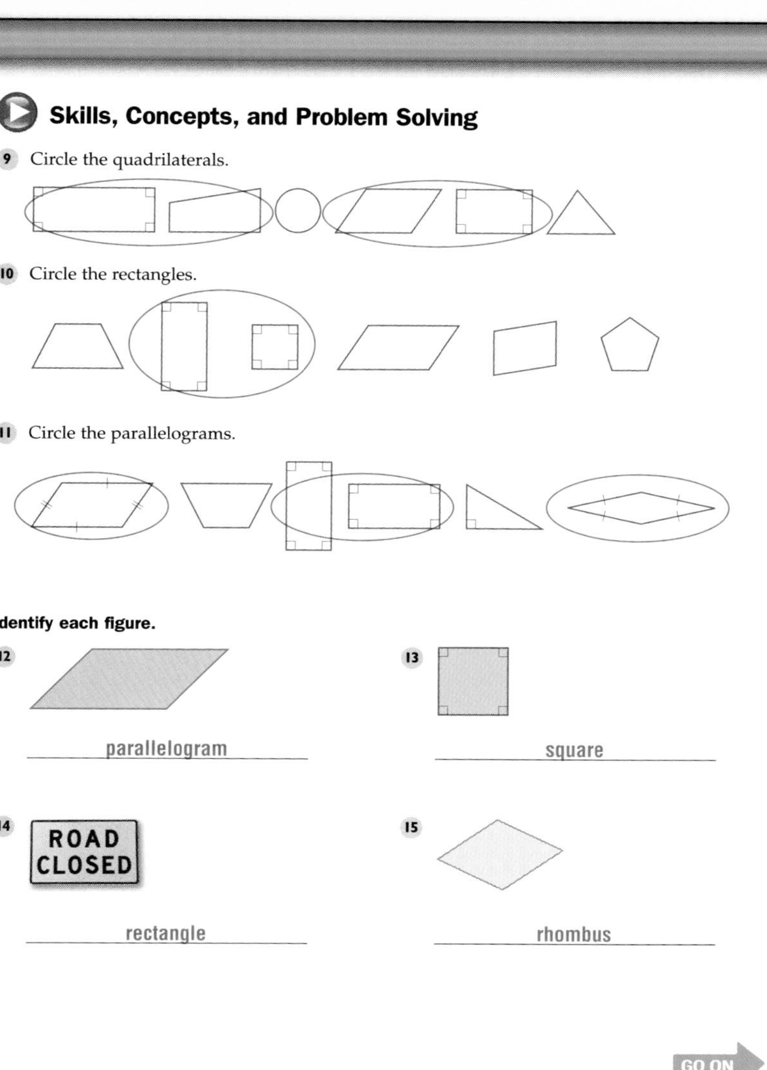

Skills, Concepts, and Problem Solving
9 Circle the quadrilaterals.
10 Circle the rectangles.
11 Circle the parallelograms.
Identify each figure.
12
parallelogram
13
square
14
ROAD
CLOSED
rectangle
15
rhombus
GO ON
Lesson 8-1 Quadrilaterals 339

Odd/Even Assignments

Exercises 9–19 are structured so that students practice the same concepts whether they are assigned the odd or even problems.

In-Class Assignment

Have students complete Exercises 10, 12, 16, 19, and 23 to ensure that they understand the concept.

Math Coach Notes

Classify Quadrilaterals Provide a table that helps students classify and name quadrilaterals.

Quadrilateral	Sides	Angles
trapezoid	one pair of parallel sides	
parallelogram	two pairs of parallel sides	
rhombus	two pairs of parallel sides; four congruent sides	
rectangle	two pairs of parallel sides	four right angles
square	two pairs of parallel sides; four congruent sides	four right angles

Math Challenge

Draw and Identify Have students create a sketch of a quadrilateral, a parallelogram, a rectangle, a square, a rhombus, and a trapezoid. Then have the students name each figure with as many names as they can. For example, a square meets the classifications of a quadrilateral, parallelogram, rhombus, and square.

Intervention Strategy

Visual Learners

Check Parallels When students are checking to see if the oppisite sides of a figure are parallel, they can use the lines on a sheet of notebook paper or the parallel sides of a ruler to help them. Remind them that using sight only is not acceptable in formal geometry or in real life.

4 Assess

See It, Do It, Say It, Write It

Step 1 Draw this figure on the board.

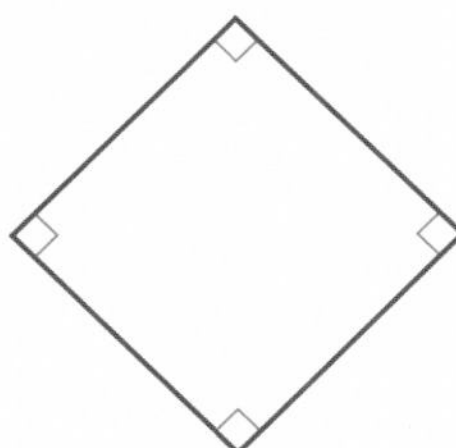

Step 2 Have students write down all the possible names for this figure.

Step 3 Arrange the students into pairs and have them justify each name using the properties of the figure.

Step 4 Have students write the definitions of each figure in their own words.

Looking Ahead: Pre-teach

Triangles In the next lesson, students will learn about triangles.

Example

Name the triangle by its angles and sides.

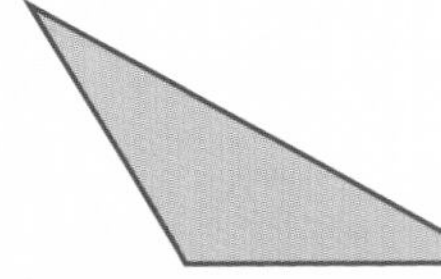

1. The figure has 3 sides and 3 angles. The figure is a triangle.
2. The triangle has three sides that are different lengths. The figure is a scalene triangle.
3. The triangle has one angle larger than 90°. The figure is an obtuse triangle.

Identify each figure.

16 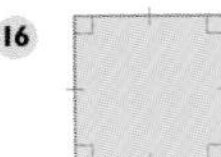

square

17 

rhombus

18 DESIGN Phillip is making a paper design. He cuts a shape that has four sides and four angles. Each side is a different length. None of the sides are parallel. What is the name of this figure?

quadrilateral

19 HOMEWORK Kim's math homework says to explain the differences between squares and rectangles. Kim writes, "All four sides on squares are equal. Only the opposite sides on rectangles are equal. Both kinds of shapes have four right angles." Is Kim completely correct? Explain.

No; a square is also a rectangle, so its sides can also be all the same length.

Vocabulary Check **Write the vocabulary word that completes each sentence.**

20 A(n) quadrilateral has four sides and four angles.

21 Parallel lines are lines that are the same distance apart; parallel lines do not meet or cross.

22 A rectangle with four equal sides and four equal angles is a(n) square.

23 Writing in Math Describe a rectangle in words.

Sample answer: A rectangle has four sides and four angles. Its opposite sides are equal and parallel. The angles are all right angles. Some rectangles have two longer sides and two shorter sides.

Ticket Out the Door

Ask students to draw a picture of each type of figure from the lesson. Next, have students pick one of the figures and write down everything that they know about the figure. Make sure to include the defining characteristics of the figure. Students will turn in their work as they exit the classroom.

Lesson 8-2 **Triangles**

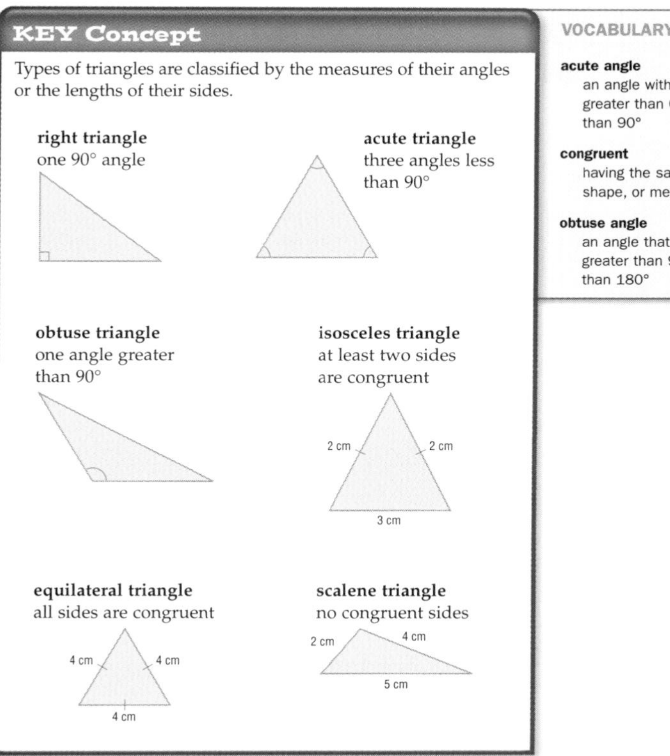
KEY Concept

Types of triangles are classified by the measures of their angles or the lengths of their sides.

right triangle
one 90° angle

acute triangle
three angles less than 90°

obtuse triangle
one angle greater than 90°

isosceles triangle
at least two sides are congruent

equilateral triangle
all sides are congruent

scalene triangle
no congruent sides

VOCABULARY

acute angle
an angle with a measure greater than 0° and less than 90°

congruent
having the same size, shape, or measure

obtuse angle
an angle that measures greater than 90° but less than 180°

Triangles can be named by their angles and sides. For example, a triangle with one right angle and two congruent sides is called an isosceles right triangle.

GO ON

Intervention Strategy

Visual/ Spatial Learners

Concept Map List the different types of triangles. Have students create a concept map listing the different types of triangles. Then have students describe the process they used in creating them.

Lesson Notes

Lesson 8-2

Lesson Planner

Objective Classify triangles.

Vocabulary **acute angle**, **congruent**, **obtuse angle**

Materials/Manipulatives index cards, ruler

Chapter Resource Masters

- CRM Vocabulary and English Language Development (p. A171)
- CRM Skills Practice (p. A172)
- CRM Problem-Solving Practice (p. A173)
- CRM Homework Practice (p. A174)

Vocabulary

Explore Vocabulary Draw a triangle on the board. Have a student volunteer tell you as much as he or she knows about the triangle. Try to give the triangle a name. Ask another student volunteer to draw another triangle with different features. Keep taking volunteers until all of the triangle classifications have been drawn. Use probing questions as hints to cover all types of triangles.

Key Concept

Foundational Skills and Concepts After students have read through the Key Concept box, have them try these exercises.

1. How do you classify an obtuse triangle? one angle is greater than 90°
2. How would you identify an acute triangle? three angles less than 90°
3. What types of triangles can be identified by their side lengths? scalene, isosceles, equilateral

Additional *Example 1*

Name the triangle by its sides.

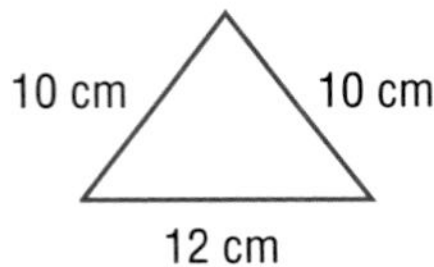

1. The triangle has 2 congruent sides.

2. The triangle is an isosceles triangle.

Additional *Example 2*

Name the triangle by its angles.

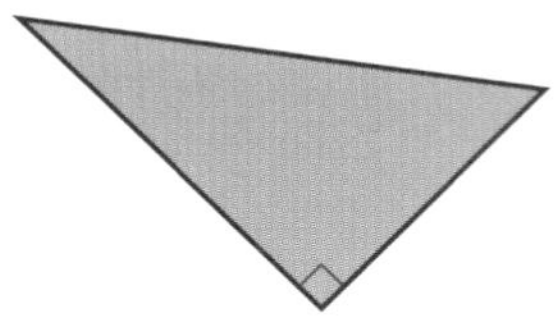

1. Use a right angle to show 90°. Compare the right angle to the angles of the triangle.

greater than 90°

less than 90°

2. There are two angles less than 90°.

3. There are no angles greater than 90°.

4. There is one right angle.

5. The triangle is a right triangle.

Note This!

Review Materials Suggest that students refer to their notes within 24 hours after taking them. Have students edit their notes for words and phrases that are illegible or do not make sense. Instruct them to edit the notes with a different colored pen to distinguish what they wrote in class from what they filled in later.

Example 1

Name the triangle by its sides.

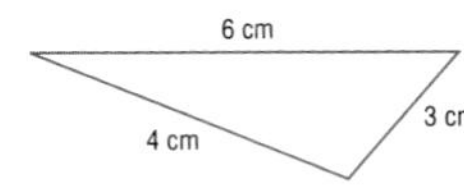

1. The triangle has no congruent sides.
2. The triangle is a scalene triangle.

YOUR TURN!

Name the triangle by its sides.

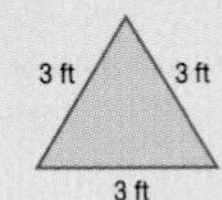

1. The triangle has 3 congruent sides.
2. The triangle is a(n) equilateral triangle.

Example 2

Name the triangle by its angles.

1. Use a right angle to show 90°. Compare the right angle to the angles of the triangle.
2. There are three angles less than 90°.
3. There are no angles greater than 90°.
4. There are no right angles.
5. The triangle is an acute triangle.

greater than 90°

less than 90°

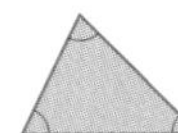

YOUR TURN!

Name the triangle by its angles.

1. Use a right angle to show 90°. Compare the right angle to the angles of the triangle.
2. There are two angles less than 90°.
3. There is one angle greater than 90°.
4. There are no right angles.
5. The triangle is a(n) obtuse triangle.

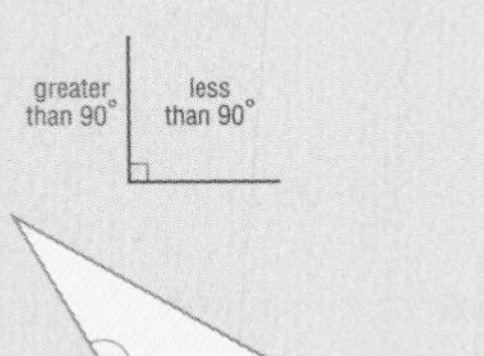

English Learner Strategy

Reference Cards Have English Learners use definitions in their native languages of angles to help them classify triangles. Allow them to write the classification on one side of an index card. They should draw the triangle and label it in English on the other side of the card for reference.

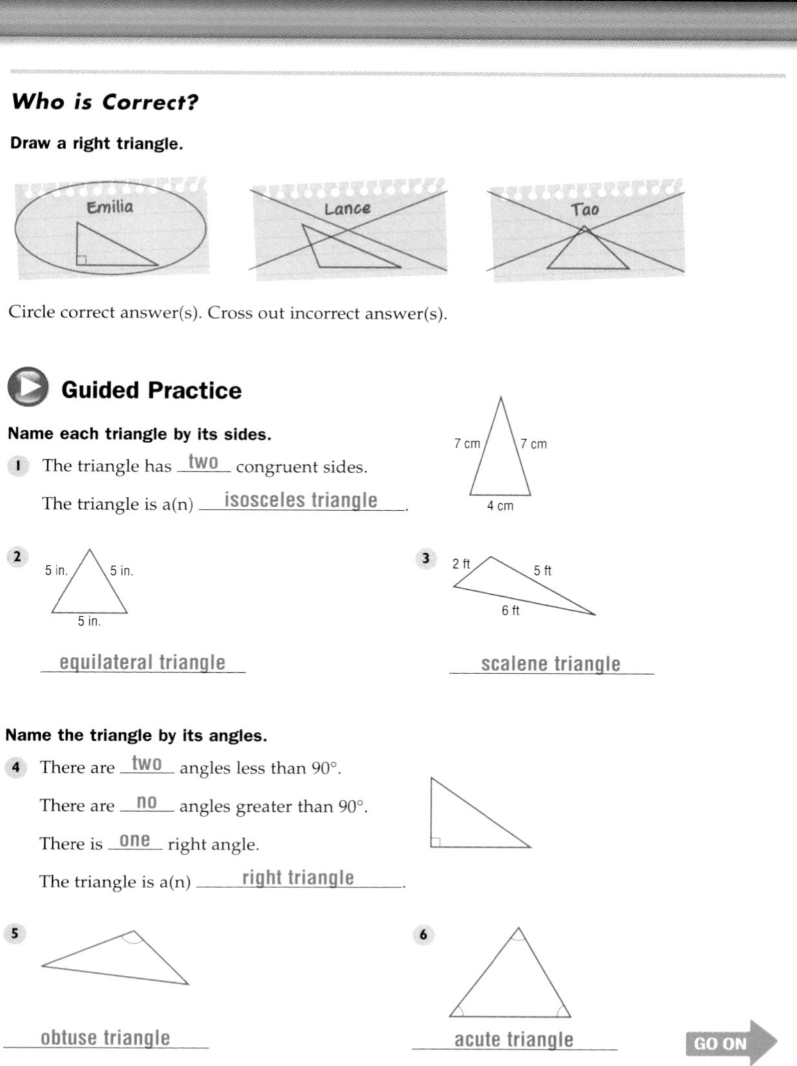

Who is Correct?

Draw a right triangle.

Circle correct answer(s). Cross out incorrect answer(s).

Guided Practice

Name each triangle by its sides.

1 The triangle has two congruent sides.

The triangle is a(n) isosceles triangle.

2 equilateral triangle

3 scalene triangle

Name the triangle by its angles.

4 There are two angles less than 90°.

There are no angles greater than 90°.

There is one right angle.

The triangle is a(n) right triangle.

5 obtuse triangle

6 acute triangle

GO ON

Lesson 8-2 Triangles 343

Who *is Correct?*

Diagnostic Teaching

- Emilia is correct. The triangle drawn is a right isosceles triangle.
- Lance is incorrect. The triangle he drew is scalene.
- Tao is incorrect. The triangle she drew is isosceles, but not right.

Remind students that a right triangle has exactly one right angle and that if two sides are congruent, the triangle is also isosceles.

Math Coach Notes

Practice Tip Exercises may require students to classify triangles by their sides and/or angles. Encourage students to study exercises carefully to avoid incorrectly classifying triangles.

3 Practice

Using Manipulatives

Ruler When presenting Example 1, have students use a ruler to draw the figure accurately in their notes. Point out that when drawing a model, students should make sure that they accurately meet the classifications.

On-Hand Manipulatives Show students that there are many real-world applications of triangles and quadrilaterals. Have students use pen and paper to draw all the types of triangles in the lesson to help them classify and remember the figures.

Math Coach Notes

Strategies

1. Start this lesson by explaining that triangles can be classified by either their side lengths, angle measures, or both.
2. Arrange students in pairs. Give each pair of students a ruler and briefly review how to use it. Ask students to use the corner of an index card as a reference for 90°. Have each pair use their tools to draw as many different triangles as possible. Have the students classify and label their triangles.
3. As a class, compare the classifications and discuss any common mistakes.

Common Error *Alert*

Directions Students often get frustrated when they get answers wrong and are not sure why. In this lesson, it is very common for students to use the wrong type of classification. Stress the importance of reading directions carefully.

Intervention Strategy

Real-World Triangles Provide students with pictures of architecture from around the world. Have students find examples of triangles in the buildings. Students should trace the triangles onto a sheet of paper. Prompt students to classify the triangles by their sides and angles.

Math Coach Notes

Mnemonic Device A mnemonic device is a phrase or rhyme that assists in memorizing information. Have students create a mnemonic device to help them remember the names for classification of sides and angles. For example, to classify a triangle by sides, you could have an equilateral triangle, a scalene triangle, or an isosceles triangle. If you take the letters S - S - I - E, you can get "Sing Songs in Elevators."

Common Error *Alert*

Exercises 8–10 Students may be confused by the directions for Exercises 8–10. The questions ask for two names for each triangle: one with respect to the angles and the other with respect to the sides. For example, an equilateral triangle is also an acute triangle, so its name using these directions would be "acute equilateral triangle."

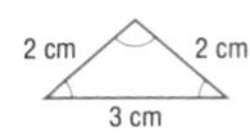

Step by Step Practice

7 Name the triangle by its angles and sides.

2 cm 2 cm 3 cm

Step 1 There are two congruent sides.

Step 2 There are three acute angles.

Step 3 There are no right angles.

Step 4 There are no obtuse angles.

Step 5 The triangle is a(n) isosceles acute triangle.

Name each triangle by its angles and sides.

8 number of congruent sides 2

number of acute angles 2

number of right angles 1

number of obtuse angles 0

The triangle is a(n) isosceles right triangle.

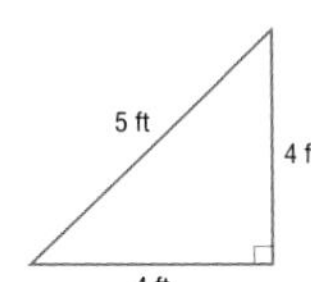

9 3 in. 4 in. 6 in.

obtuse scalene triangle

10

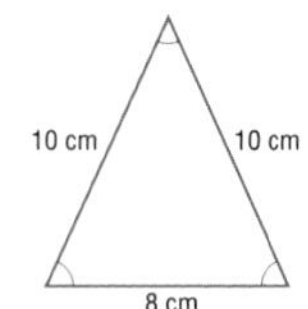

acute isosceles triangle

Are They Getting It?

Check students' understanding of triangle classification by writing these problems on the board. Have students explain any incorrect information in each problem. Tell them to use the corner of an index card or ruler to show why the answers are correct or incorrect.

1. Identify the triangle by its angles. isosceles
   This is incorrect. Isosceles is a classification based on side lengths not angles. This is an obtuse triangle.
   (120° 30° 30°)
2. Classify the triangle by its sides. scalene
   This is correct.
   (5 in. 3 in. 6 in.)

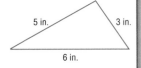

Step by Step Problem-Solving Practice

Problem-Solving Strategies
- ☑ Use a diagram.
- ☐ Look for a pattern.
- ☐ Guess and check.
- ☐ Act it out.
- ☐ Work backward.

Solve.

11 SAFETY Reginald saw a street sign that looked like the one at the right. Classify the shape of the sign.

Understand Read the problem. Write what you know.
Reginald saw a street sign.

Plan Pick a strategy. One strategy is to use a diagram.

Solve The street sign has 3 sides and 3 angles.
The figure is a(n) triangle.

The sides appear to be equal in length.
The figure is a(n) equilateral triangle.

Check Review the definition of the figure you named.

12 MATH Madison's math teacher drew a triangle on the board and asked her to name the shape. Madison saw that each side of the triangle was a different length. What kind of triangle did the math teacher draw? Check off each step.

✓ Understand: I circled key words.
✓ Plan: To solve the problem, I will use a diagram.
✓ Solve: The answer is a scalene triangle.
✓ Check: I checked my answer by reviewing the definition.

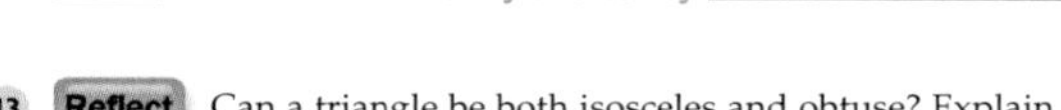

13 Reflect Can a triangle be both isosceles and obtuse? Explain.

Sample answer: Yes; an obtuse triangle can have two equal sides connecting at the obtuse angle, making it obtuse and isosceles.

Math Challenge

Triangle Identification Have students get into small groups. Give each group six index cards. Have the students label a card with each of the classifications of a triangle by either sides or angles, but not both. Assign one person the job of flipping over a card. Once the card is revealed, each student should draw a triangle that fits the description on the card. Rotate the dealer every turn.

Math Coach Notes

Exercise 11 Invite students to name other road signs and identify the figures that they model. Ask students to identify road signs that cannot be identified as figures in this lesson. This nonexample will help reinforce the concepts of the lesson.

Exercise 13 If students are struggling to identify whether this situation is possible, suggest that they draw a picture. Have them continue drawing pictures until they are sure of their answer.

Useful Tool When trying to determine if an angle is larger than 90°, smaller than 90°, or equal to 90°, you can use a protractor. Angle measures from 0° to 180° are labeled. Use this useful tool to assist you in determining how to classify a triangle by its angle measures.

Intervention Strategy

Share-Pair Divide students into pairs. Using small chalkboards or dry-erase boards, have one member of the pair draw a triangle and label enough information for his or her partner to identify the triangle by its sides or angles. The other member should classify the triangle. Once the problem is complete, the students should reverse roles.

English Learner Strategy

Guiding Questions Draw or reference a triangle. Label the sides. Then ask the students the following questions.

- What is labeled in the triangles? How do you know?
- What are the possible names for this triangle?
- How did you decide what type it is?

Now repeat with a triangle that has the angles labeled. Make sure the students look for key words, such as *angles* or *sides*.

Intervention Strategy

Naturalist/ Linguistic Learners

Create Models and Problems Take students on a walking field trip through the school. Ask students to bring their math journals and record any situations or objects where a triangle is present. Stop frequently for students to observe their environment and to make drawings or take notes. Visit places like the library, office, cafeteria, or gymnasium. When they return to the classroom, allow time for students to write, draw, and create a word problem that relies on classifying a triangle. Ask volunteers to present their work to the class.

Note This!

Daily Notes Encourage students to add notes every day from their daily lessons in their math journals. Include pictures or drawings, terms, and explanations in their own words. Ask students to write a few examples of the kinds of problems or concepts they have difficulty with, so that they can review them regularly. Emphasize that writing notes while the information is fresh will help students later as they work on their homework or study for tests.

Odd/Even Assignments

Exercises 14–24 are structured so that students practice the same concepts whether they are assigned the odd or even problems.

In-Class Assignment

Have students complete Exercises 14, 18, 22, 24, and 28 to ensure that they understand the concept.

Skills, Concepts, and Problem Solving

Name each triangle by its sides.

14 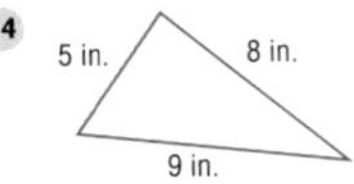

scalene triangle

15 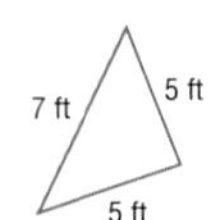

isosceles triangle

16 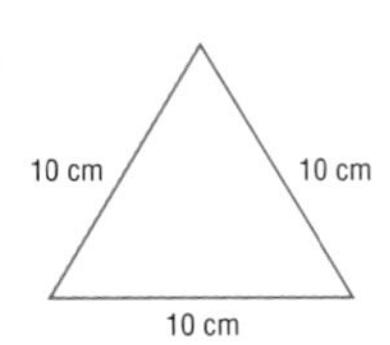

equilateral triangle

17 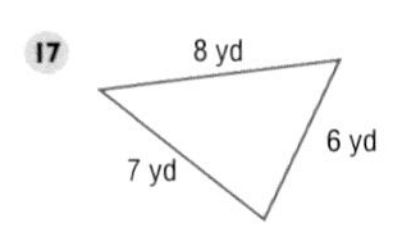

scalene triangle

Name each triangle by its angles.

18 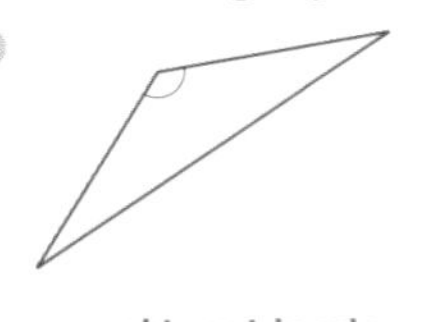

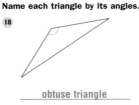

obtuse triangle

19

acute triangle

20 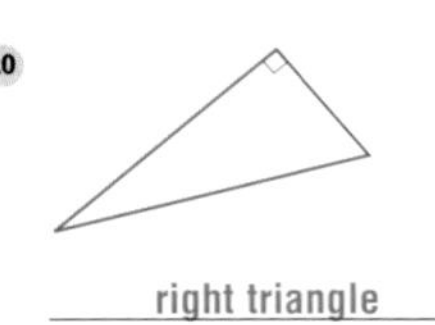

right triangle

21 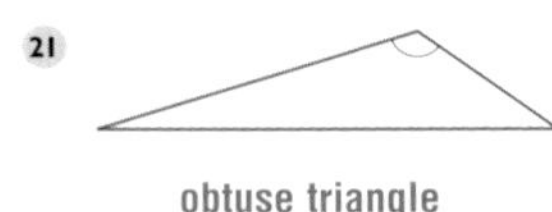

obtuse triangle

346 **Chapter 8** Geometry

English Learner Strategy

Vocabulary Sentences Have students write a one-sentence summary that explains the definition of a term used in this lesson or how to classify a triangle by angles or sides. Have students read their sentences out loud and explain them to you as needed, so that you can ensure that they understand the concepts accurately.

Name the triangle by its angles and sides.

22 (triangle with sides 11 cm, 9 cm, 3 cm)

scalene obtuse triangle

23 DRAWING Violeta draws an equilateral triangle with two sides that each measure 6 inches. What is the length of the third side?
6 inches

24 LUNCH Peyton shares a sandwich with his sister for lunch. He cuts the sandwich into two triangles. Look at the picture at the right. What type of triangles is the sandwich cut into?
right triangles

Vocabulary Check **Write the vocabulary word that completes each sentence.**

25 A(n) equilateral triangle has three equal sides.

26 Congruent means having the same size, shape, or measure.

27 A triangle with a right angle is a(n) right triangle.

28 Writing in Math Can a triangle be both a right triangle and an acute triangle?
Sample Answer: No; a right triangle has one angle that measures 90°. An acute triangle has three angles that all measure less than 90°.

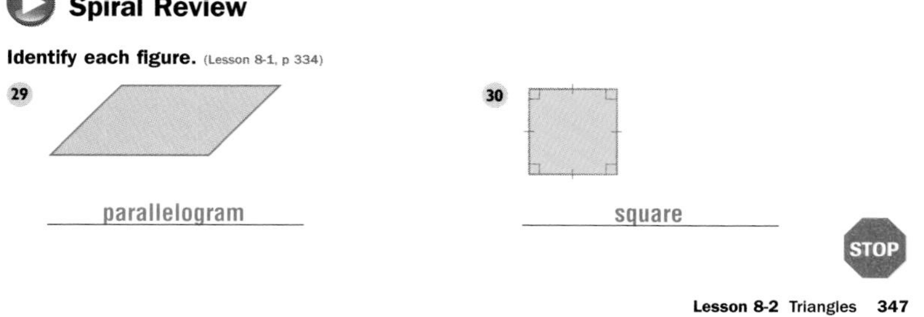

Spiral Review

Identify each figure. (Lesson 8-1, p 334)

29 parallelogram

30 square

STOP

Ticket Out the Door

Pair Classifications Have students get into pairs. Each student should draw a triangle and label enough parts so that it can be classified. Switch papers and classify the triangle. Have the students turn in their papers as they exit the classroom.

Note This!

Vocabulary Check When students are asked to answer a Vocabulary Check section, they should try to answer each problem from memory. The vocabulary words that they could not answer should be highlighted in their notes from the beginning of the lesson and referred to when doing homework and studying for tests.

4 Assess

See It, Do It, Say It, Write It

Step 1 Draw the following figure on the board.

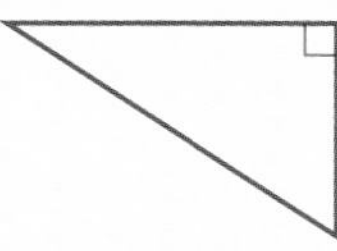

Step 2 Have students classify the figure by its angles and sides. scalene right triangle

Step 3 Arrange students into pairs and have them explain to each other how they classified the figure.

Step 4 Have students write how to classify triangles in their own words.

Looking Ahead: Pre-teach

Circles In the next lesson, students will learn about circles.

Example

6 cm

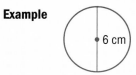

A circle has a radius that is half the measure of the diameter. What is the radius of the circle? 3 cm

Find the radius of each circle.

1. 9 mm

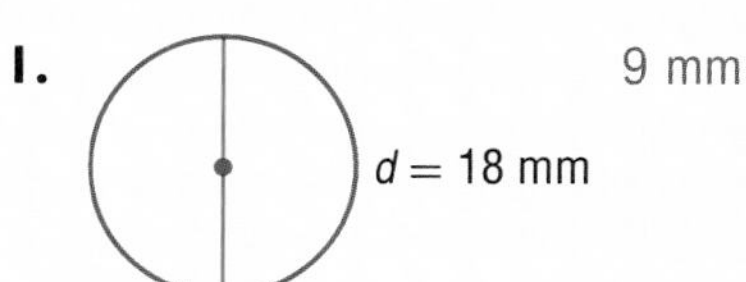

$d = 18$ mm

2. 11 in.

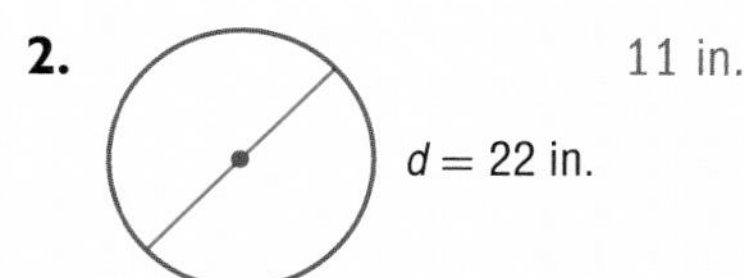

$d = 22$ in.

Chapter 8

Progress Check 1

Formative Assessment

Use the Progress Check to assess students' mastery of the previous lessons. Have students review the lesson indicated for the problems they answered incorrectly.

Odd/Even Assignments

Exercises are structured so that students practice the same concepts whether they are assigned the odd or even problems.

Common Error *Alert*

Identify Shapes Students need to be careful when identifying the characteristics of quadrilaterals and triangles. Remind students to look for the small differences between each type.

Exercises 9–10 Students may need to be reminded of the properties of quadrilaterals and triangles. Direct students to the charts made in their notes for assistance.

Progress Check 1 (Lessons 8-1 and 8-2)

Write the name of each figure.

1 rectangle

2 rhombus (parallelogram)

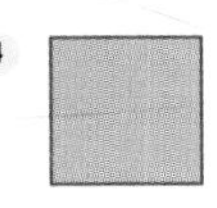

3 parallelogram

4 square

Name each triangle by its sides or angles.

5 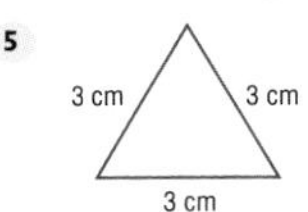

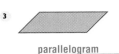

equilateral triangle

6 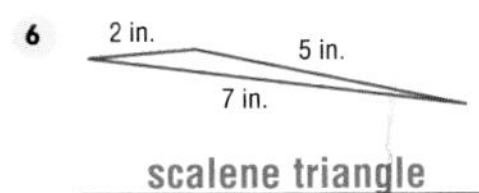

scalene triangle

7 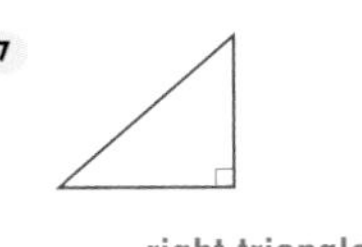

right triangle

8 

acute triangle

Solve.

9 **FIGURES** Jamie is drawing a quadrilateral figure. The top and bottom are not equal in length. There is one pair of parallel sides. What name would you give to the figure Jamie draws?

trapezoid

10 Can a right triangle also be equilateral? Explain.

Sample answer: No; a right triangle has an angle that measures exactly 90°, so the other two angles must be smaller than 90°. Equilateral triangles have all sides the same length and all angles the same size.

348 **Chapter 8** Geometry

Data-Driven Decision Making

Students missing Exercises . . .	Have trouble with . . .	Should review and practice . . .
1–4	classifying quadrilaterals.	SSG Lesson 8-1, p. 334 CRM Skills Practice, p. A168
5–8	classifying triangles by sides or angles.	SSG Lesson 8-2, p. 341 CRM Skills Practice, p. A172
9–10	solving word problems involving classifying quadrilaterals or triangles.	CRM Problem-Solving Practice, pp. A169 and A173

Lesson 8-3 Circles

KEY Concept

A **circle** is the set of all points in a plane that are the same distance from a point called the center.

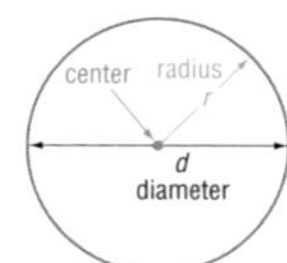

The letter d is used to represent the **diameter**.
The letter r is used to represent the **radius**.

VOCABULARY

circle
a closed figure in which all points are the same distance from a fixed point called the center

diameter
the distance across a circle through its center

radius
the distance from the center to any point on a circle

A diameter is 2 times as long as the radius.
The radius is $\frac{1}{2}$ as long as the diameter.

Example 1

Find the radius of the circle.

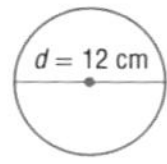

1. The radius is $\frac{1}{2}$ as long as the diameter.
2. One-half of 12 cm is 6 cm.
   $12 \text{ cm} \div 2 = 6 \text{ cm}$
3. The radius of the circle is 6 cm.

YOUR TURN!

Find the radius of the circle.

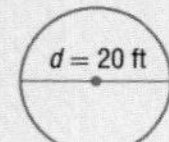

1. The radius is $\frac{1}{2}$ as long as the diameter.
2. One-half of 20 ft is 10 ft.
   20 ft ÷ 2 = 10 ft
3. The radius of the circle is 10 ft.

Additional Example 1

Find the radius of the circle.

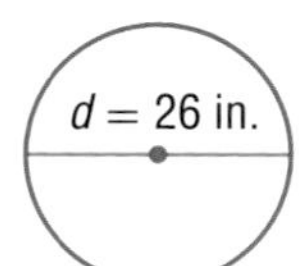

1. The radius is $\frac{1}{2}$ as long as the diameter.
2. One half of 26 in. is 13 in.
   26 in. ÷ 2 = 13 in.
3. The radius of the circle is 13 in.

Lesson Notes

Lesson 8-3

Lesson Planner

Objective Find the radius and diameter of a circle.

Vocabulary **circle**, **diameter**, **radius**

Materials/Manipulatives fraction circles, construction paper, string

Chapter Resource Masters

- CRM Vocabulary and English Language Development (p. A175)
- CRM Skills Practice (p. A176)
- CRM Problem-Solving Practice (p. A177)
- CRM Homework Practice (p. A178)

1 Introduce

Vocabulary

Explore Vocabulary Draw a circle on the board and ask a volunteer to come to the board. Have the student identify the *diameter* of the circle with arrows and blue chalk. Have another student identify the *radius* of the circle with arrows and red chalk.

2 Teach

Key Concept

Foundational Skills and Concepts After students have read through the Key Concept box, have them try these exercises.

1. Label the radius and diameter of the circle.

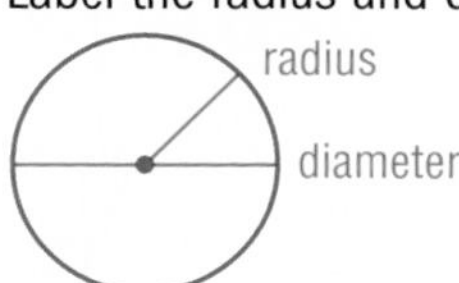

2. What conjecture can you make about the relationship between the radius and the diameter of a circle? The radius is half the diameter.

Math Coach Notes

Real-World Connections Have students find three circular items in their home. Trace the circles onto a sheet of paper. Label and measure the radius, center, and diameter of the circle.

Using Manipulatives

Fraction Circles When presenting this lesson, have students outline a fraction circle to help them draw the circle accurately. Point out that when drawing circles, students should make sure they know whether they are using the radius or the diameter.

On-Hand Manipulatives A string attached to a pencil is a good way students can learn to draw circles.

Note This!

Draw a Diagram Several terms used with circles are introduced in this lesson. Tell students to draw a circle in their notes and label the parts of the circle introduced in this lesson.

Intervention Strategy

Visual/ Logical Learners

Circles for Partners Arrange students into pairs and give each pair a large circle (whose diameter is larger than a ruler). Instruct the pair to find the center of the circle and measure the diameter and radius. Advise students that you will be collecting their results, so tell them make sure they write down everything they do. When all pairs are done and the work is collected, ask for volunteers to share their work. Ask students how they know that their results are correct.

Who is Correct?

A circle has a diameter of 6 inches. What is the radius of the circle?

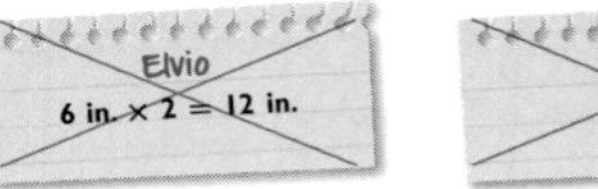

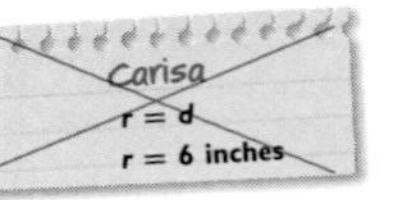

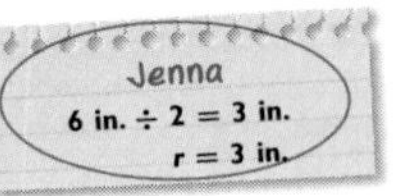

Circle correct answer(s). Cross out incorrect answer(s).

Guided Practice

Find the radius of each circle.

1. 10 in. ÷ 2 = 5 in.

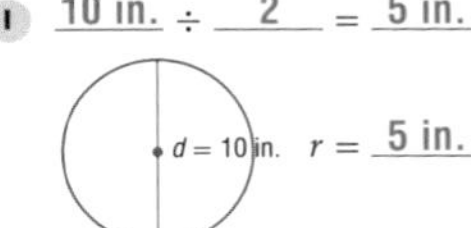

r = 5 in.

2. 4 cm ÷ 2 = 2 cm

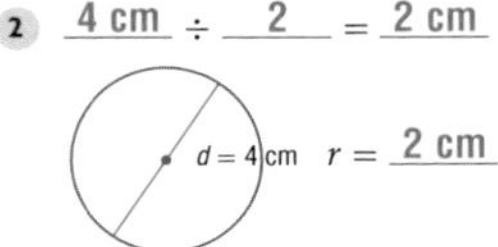

r = 2 cm

Step by Step Practice

3. Find the diameter of the circle.

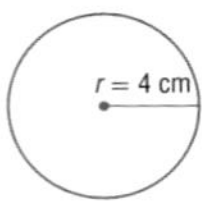

Step 1 The diameter is 2 times as long as the radius.

Step 2 Two times 4 cm is 8 cm.
2 × 4 cm = 8 cm

Step 3 The diameter of the circle is 8 cm.

Find the diameter of each circle.

4. 2 × 7 cm = 14 cm

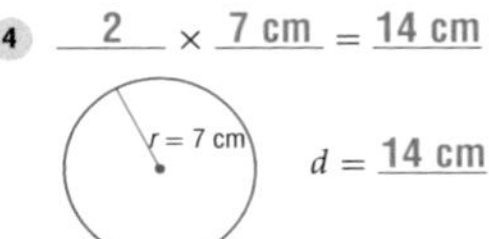

d = 14 cm

5. 2 × 9 in. = 18 in.

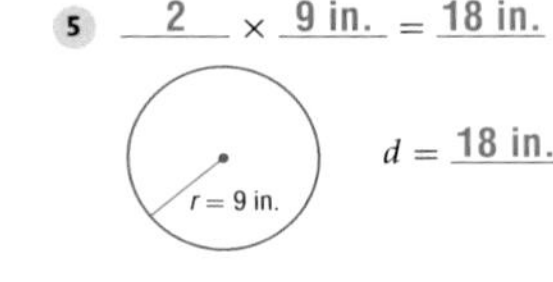

d = 18 in.

350 **Chapter 8** Geometry

Who *is Correct?*

Diagnostic Teaching

- Elvio is incorrect. The radius is half of the diameter.
- Carisa is incorrect. The radius does not equal the diameter; it is half as long as the diameter.
- Jenna is correct.

Remind students that the radius is always half the diameter.

Step by Step Problem-Solving Practice

Solve

Problem-Solving Strategies
- ☐ Use a diagram.
- ☐ Look for a pattern.
- ☐ Guess and check.
- ☐ Solve a simpler problem.
- ☑ Work backward.

6 PLAYGROUND Tionna wants to find the radius of the center circle on a basketball court. The line through the center of the circle measures 12 feet. What is the radius?

Understand Read the problem. Write what you know.

Tionna wants to find the radius of a circle.

Plan Pick a strategy. One strategy is to work backward.

Solve The diameter is 2 times the radius.

The radius is $\frac{1}{2}$ the diameter.

12 feet ÷ 2 = 6 feet

The radius of the circle is 6 feet.

Check Use multiplication to check. 2×6 feet $= 12$ feet

7 PAINTING Hassan is painting a large circle with a radius of 3 ft. What is the diameter of Hassan's painting? Check off each step.

✓ Understand: I circled key words.

✓ Plan: To solve the problem, I will work backward.

✓ Solve: The answer is 6 ft.

✓ Check: I checked my answer by using division.

8 **Reflect** Explain the difference between the radius and the diameter of a circle.

Sample answer: The radius is the distance from the center to any point on the edge of a circle. The diameter is the distance across through the center.

Skills, Concepts, and Problem Solving

Find the radius and diameter of each circle.

9 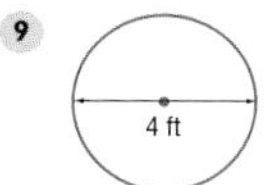

radius: 2 ft
diameter: 4 ft

10 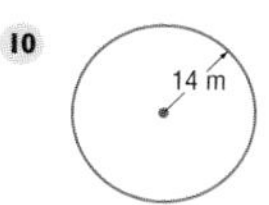

radius: 14 m
diameter: 28 m

GO ON

Are They Getting It?

Check students' understanding of circles by writing these problems on the board. Ask students to point out wrong answers and explain why they are wrong.

1. What is the radius of the circle? 15 mm This is incorrect, the radius is half of the diameter, or 4 mm.

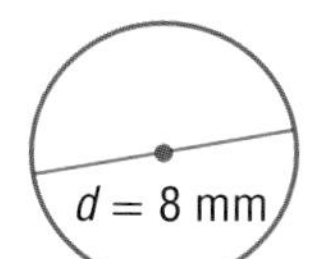

2. What is the diameter of the circle? 16 in. This is correct.

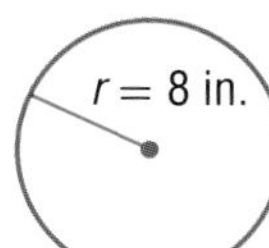

3. Draw a circle with diameter 10 ft. What is the radius of the circle? 20 ft This is incorrect. The drawing is correct, but the radius of the circle Is 5 ft.

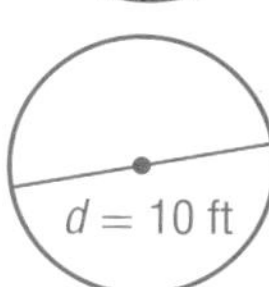

Common Error Alert

Finding the Radius Students may get confused when they need to determine the radius of a circle given the diameter. Since the radius is half of the diameter, students often forget which one is smaller, or which value needs to be cut in half. One way to help students remember is to point out that the word diameter is longer than the word radius, so diameter is the longer distance.

Math Coach Notes

Finding Diameter Finding the diameter does not seem as difficult for students to grasp. Remind students that diameter is larger, so multiply the radius by two to find the answer.

Odd/Even Assignments

Exercises 9–18 are structured so that students practice the same concepts whether they are assigned the odd or even problems.

In-Class Assignment

Have students complete Exercises 9, 13, 17, and 20 to ensure that they understand the concept.

Intervention Strategy

Visual/Logical Learners

Sketch and Solve Have students create a circle on a piece of construction paper. Have students label a radius, diameter, and center of the circle. Write down the steps used to find the radius if given the diameter.

Assess

See It, Do It, Say It, Write It

Step 1 Draw the following figure on the board.

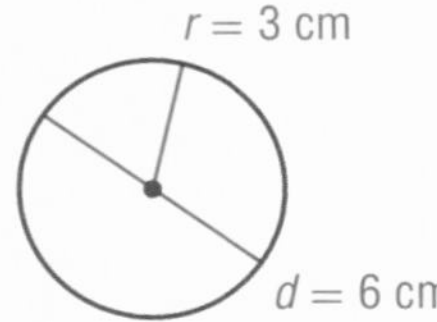

Step 2 Have the students label a radius and a diameter. What is the radius if the diameter is 6 centimeters? 3 cm

Step 3 Arrange the students in pairs and have them explain to each other how they know what the radius and diameter are and how they find their values.

Step 4 Have students write in their own words how they find the diameter if they are given the radius, and how they find the radius given the diameter.

Looking Ahead: Pre-teach

Three-Dimensional Figures In the next lesson, students will learn about three-dimensional figures.

Example

Identify the three-dimensional figure.

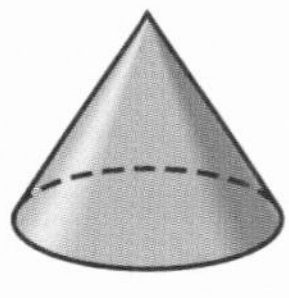

The figure is a cone.

Name each three-dimensional figure.

1. 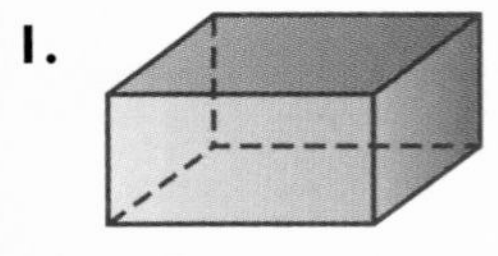 a rectangular prism

2. 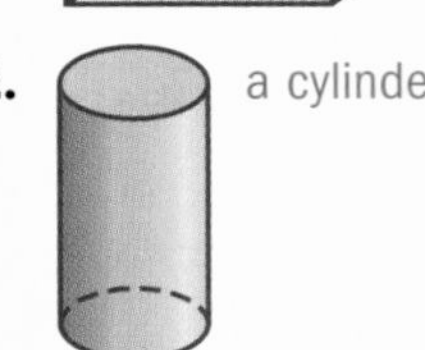 a cylinder

Find the radius or diameter.

11 $d = 10$ cm, $r =$ 5 cm

12 $d = 22$ yd, $r =$ 11 yd

13 $r = 8$ cm, $d =$ 16 cm

14 $r = 4$ in, $d =$ 8 in.

15 $r = 3$ yd, $d =$ 6 yd

16 $d = 40$ ft, $r =$ 20 ft

17 HOBBIES Dario collects circular clocks. The face of his largest clock has a radius of 23 inches. What is the diameter of the clock? 46 inches

18 SIZE Circle A has a radius of 10 cm. Circle B has a diameter of 24 cm. Which circle is larger? Circle B

Vocabulary Check **Write the vocabulary word that completes each sentence.**

19 The distance across a circle through its center is called the diameter.

20 Writing in Math Name some objects that have a diameter or a radius.

Sample answers: CD, cookie, coin, clock, tire/wheel, pizza

Spiral Review

Solve. (Lesson 8-1, p. 334)

21 DRAWING Eva draws a quadrilateral. All four sides have the same length. Its opposite sides are parallel. What quadrilateral did she draw?

rhombus or square or rectangle

Name each triangle by its angles. (Lesson 8-2, p. 341)

22 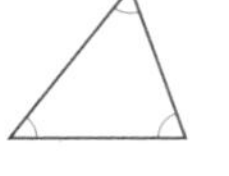 acute triangle

23 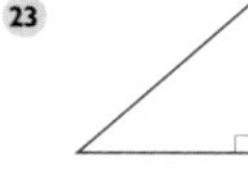 right triangle

352 **Chapter 8** Geometry

Ticket Out the Door

Vocabulary Modeled in the Classroom Instruct each student to give an example of an item found in the classroom that represents a vocabulary word from this lesson. Have students explain their examples as they exit the classroom.

Lesson 8-4 Three-Dimensional Figures

KEY Concept

Three-dimensional figures are named by the types of surfaces they have. Their surfaces can be curved, flat, or both.

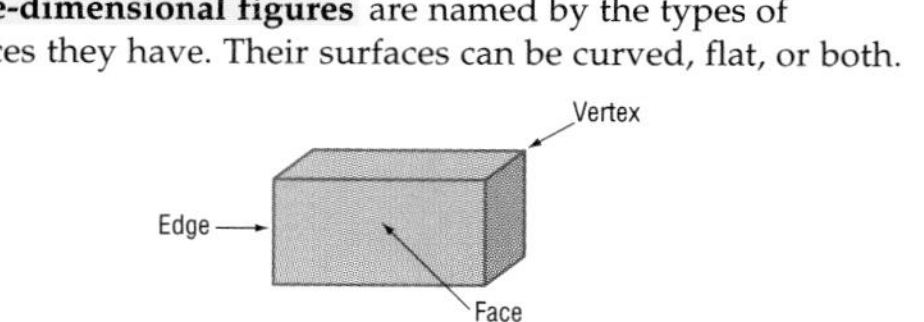

The base is an "end" face. The bases are shaded below.

Figure	Example	Description
rectangular prism		a prism with six rectangular faces
cube		a prism with six faces that are congruent squares
triangular prism		a prism that has triangular bases
cone		a solid that has a circular base and one curved surface from the base to a vertex
cylinder		a solid with two parallel, congruent, circular bases; a curved surface connects the bases
sphere		a solid figure that is a set of all points that are the same distance from the center

VOCABULARY

edge
the line segment where two faces of a three-dimensional figure meet

face
the flat part of a three-dimensional figure

three-dimensional figure
figure that has length, width, and height

vertex
the point on a three-dimensional figure where three or more edges meet

GO ON

Intervention Strategy — Kinesthetic Learners

Make Figures Encourage students to create a prism, a cone, and a cylinder using a circle compass, a ruler, scissors, and construction paper. Prior to cutting out the figures, have the students identify the figure and why they know it is that figure.

Lesson Notes — Lesson 8-4

Lesson Planner

Objective Classify three-dimensional figures.

Vocabulary **edge**, **face**, **three-dimensional figure**, **vertex**

Materials/Manipulatives circle compass, connecting cubes, construction paper, geometric solids, ruler, scissors, tape, unit cubes

Chapter Resource Masters

- CRM Vocabulary and English Language Development (p. A179)
- CRM Skills Practice (p. A180)
- CRM Problem-Solving Practice (p. A181)
- CRM Homework Practice (p. A182)

1 Introduce

Vocabulary

Explore Vocabulary Discuss the attributes of the various three-dimensional figures. Use models to prompt students with questions regarding faces, edges, and vertices. Have students compile a list or chart showing the characteristics that correspond with each figure.

2 Teach

Key Concept

Foundational Skills and Concepts After students have read through the Key Concept box, have them try these exercises.

1. What two-dimensional figures represent the bases of a cylinder? circles
2. How many faces are there in a rectangular prism? 6
3. How many faces are on a triangular prism? 5

Additional **Example 1**

Find the number of edges.

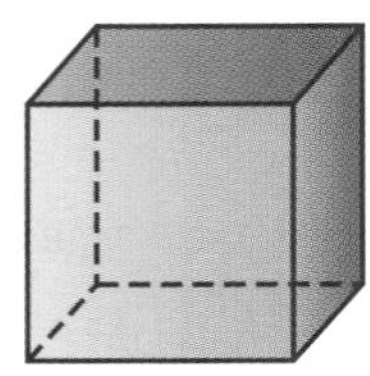

1. Does the shape have faces? yes

2. Do the faces meet? yes

3. Count the edges. There are 12 edges.

Additional **Example 2**

Identify the three-dimensional figure.

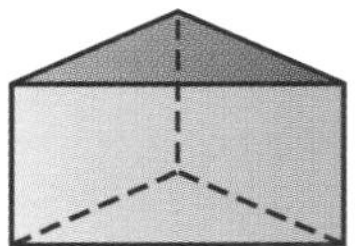

1. Is the figure flat, curved, or both? flat

2. Describe the bases. two triangular bases

3. The figure is a triangular prism.

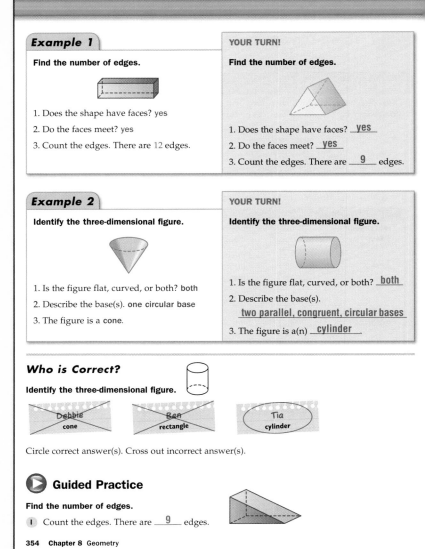

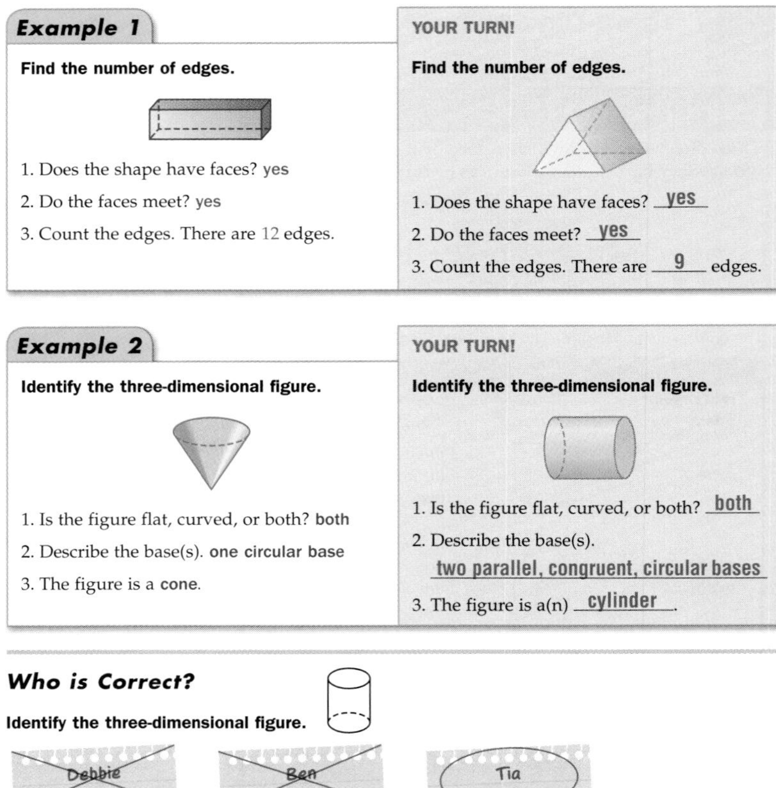

Example 1

Find the number of edges.

1. Does the shape have faces? yes
2. Do the faces meet? yes
3. Count the edges. There are 12 edges.

YOUR TURN!

Find the number of edges.

1. Does the shape have faces? yes
2. Do the faces meet? yes
3. Count the edges. There are 9 edges.

Example 2

Identify the three-dimensional figure.

1. Is the figure flat, curved, or both? both
2. Describe the base(s). one circular base
3. The figure is a cone.

YOUR TURN!

Identify the three-dimensional figure.

1. Is the figure flat, curved, or both? both
2. Describe the base(s). two parallel, congruent, circular bases
3. The figure is a(n) cylinder.

Who is Correct?

Identify the three-dimensional figure.

Circle correct answer(s). Cross out incorrect answer(s).

Guided Practice

Find the number of edges.

1 Count the edges. There are 9 edges.

354 **Chapter 8** Geometry

3 Practice

Using Manipulatives

Geometric Solids Use geometric models to show students three-dimensional views of a cube, rectangular prism, sphere, cone, square prism, and cylinder. Make sure to point out the bases on the models as well as the faces, edges, and vertices.

Unit Cubes/Connecting Cubes Allow students to experiment with rectangular prisms using unit cubes. Students can see how the shape may change, but the number of faces, edges, and vertices remain the same as long as the shape of the base is the same.

On-Hand Manipulatives Have students practice constructing their own geometric solids by creating the faces and bases on grid paper and then assembling the solids. The models will also help students study for tests and quizzes.

Who ***is Correct?***

Diagnostic Teaching

- Debbie is incorrect. A cone has a vertex and the given figure does not have a vertex.
- Ben is incorrect. A rectangle is a two-dimensional figure and the given figure is three-dimensional.
- Tia is correct.

Remind students that any figure with a curved surface is not a prism.

Step by Step Practice

2. Identify the three-dimensional figure.

Step 1 Is the figure flat, curved, or both? flat

Step 2 Describe the base(s). rectangular

Step 3 The figure is a(n) rectangular prism.

Identify each three-dimensional figure.

3. 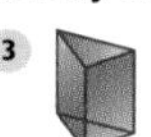

The figure is flat.

Describe the base(s). triangular

The figure is a(n) triangular prism.

4. 

The figure is curved and flat.

Describe the base(s). circular

The figure is a(n) cone.

Step by Step Problem-Solving Practice

Problem-Solving Strategies

- ☑ Use a diagram.
- ☐ Look for a pattern.
- ☐ Guess and check.
- ☐ Solve a simpler problem.
- ☐ Work backward.

Solve.

5. MUSEUM Isabel was looking at a structure at a museum. The structure was a large three-dimensional figure. What is the name of the figure?

Understand Read the problem. Write what you know.
Isabel was looking at a three-dimensional figure.

Plan Pick a strategy. One strategy is to use a diagram.

Solve Look at the photo. Describe the shape.
The shape has a circular base and one curved surface from the base to a vertex.

The three-dimensional figure is a cone.

Check Compare the figure to other figures in the lesson.

GO ON

Common Error *Alert*

Drawing Three-Dimensional Figures Many students will get frustrated because their figures never look like yours or the ones in the text. Take time to show students how to draw three-dimensional figures. They may enjoy drawing them and therefore be more motivated in class.

Math Coach Notes

New Vocabulary The concept of an edge or a face of a figure is new to students, as are many concepts in this chapter. Stress the importance of learning the vocabulary. Assist students by periodically quizzing them on the vocabulary.

Note This!

Draw and Label Several terms used with three-dimensional figures are introduced in this lesson. Encourage students to draw each figure and label the edges, faces, vertices, bases and any additional information that helps them distinguish the shapes.

Intervention Strategy

Naturalistic/ Interpersonal Learners

Real-World Figures Figures appear in the world around us in many different ways. Columns on porches are cylinders or prisms. Assign students to small groups. Give each group a location, such as the zoo or airport. Ask students to brainstorm where they would find one of the figures in this lesson in their location. Write down steps that would assist them in identifying the figures.

Are They Getting It?

Check students' understanding of three-dimensional figures by writing these problems on the board. Have students explain the incorrect information in each problem.

1. Find the number of edges.
   1. Does the figure have faces? yes
   2. Do the faces meet? yes
   3. Count the edges.
   4. There are 9 edges. This is correct
2. Identify the three-dimensional figure. The figure is a rectangular prism. This is incorrect. The two identical bases are triangles, so this is a triangular prism.

Math Coach Notes

Self-Check The concepts introduced in this lesson and chapter are often difficult ones for students. If students are having difficulty, perform a self-check to see what other strategies might help them. Ask yourself some of the following questions:

- Do I clearly establish the purpose for learning these concepts?
- What is the area in which my students struggle consistently?
- What am I doing to address this?
- What types of assessments do I give students?
- What information do these assessments give me?
- How am I using that information to improve students' comprehension?
- Am I modeling concepts and assignments?
- Am I providing examples to show students how to do the problems?

Odd/Even Assignments

Exercises 9–16 are structured so that students practice the same concepts whether they are assigned the odd or even problems.

In-Class Assignment

Have students complete Exercises 9, 12, 16, and 19 to ensure that they understand the concept.

Note This!

Teach with Notes Have students review their notes in class with a partner. One student can teach the other directly from his or her notes. Then students can trade positions. This technique will not only help students synthesize materials, but will also draw out any errors or misconceptions.

6 ART Rose's art teacher set a soup can on the table. She asked students to draw the shape of the can. What figure did Rose draw? Check off each step.

✓ Understand: I circled key words.

✓ Plan: To solve the problem, I will use a diagram.

✓ Solve: The answer is a cylinder.

✓ Check: I will check my answer by comparing figures in the lesson.

7 DINNER Benito's family had spaghetti and meatballs for dinner. He wanted to identify the shape of the meatballs. What figure are the meatballs?

sphere

8 **Reflect** What is the difference between three-dimensional figures and two-dimensional figures? Explain. Give an example of each.

Sample answer: Three-dimensional figures have width, length, and height, and can be solid. Two-dimensional figures have only two of three dimensions and are flat. A ball is a three-dimensional figure. A circle is a two-dimensional figure.

Skills, Concepts, and Problem Solving

Identify each three-dimensional figure.

9 sphere

10 cube

11 cone

12 cube

13 cylinder

14 triangular prism

English Learner Strategy

Guiding Questions Draw a prism and a cone. Then ask the students the following questions.

- Which figure is a prism?
- What figure has only one vertex?
- How many faces does the prism have?
- How do you identify the base of a prism or cylinder?
- How do you identify an edge?

Read each description. Identify the three-dimensional figure.

15 This figure has a curved surface, a circular top, and a circular shaped base.

cylinder

16 This figure has six rectangular faces. rectangular prism

Vocabulary Check **Write the vocabulary word that completes each sentence.**

17 A figure that has length, width, and height is a(n) three-dimensional figure.

18 A(n) edge is the line segment where two faces of a three-dimensional figure meet.

19 Writing in Math Explain why figures with curved surfaces cannot be prisms.

Sample answer: Prisms have flat surfaces called faces. Curved surfaces cannot be used to make faces, so figures with curved surfaces cannot be prisms.

Spiral Review

Find the radius or diameter. (Lesson 8-3, p. 349)

20 $r = 8$ cm

$d =$ 16 cm

21 $d = 24$ yd

$r =$ 12 yd

22 $d = 10$ ft

$r =$ 5 ft

Identify each figure. (Lesson 8-1, p. 334)

23 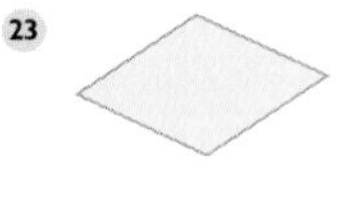

rhombus

24

rectangle

PLAYGROUND This playground structure is composed of three-dimensional figures.

Ticket Out the Door

As the students are leaving the classroom, ask them to tell you the number of faces, edges, and vertices of a three-dimensional figure that is covered in this lesson. Make sure to vary the choices as students exit.

Math Coach Notes

Reference Cards On one side of an index card draw a three-dimensional figure. On the other side of the card, list the distinguishing attributes. List any other important facts relating to the figure. To study, take turns with each side of the card to make sure that you are comfortable with the information.

See It, Do It, Say It, Write It

Step 1 Draw a cylinder on the board. Ask the students to identify as many parts of the cylinder as they can.

Step 2 Ask the students to draw a prism. Have the students justify why the figure they have drawn is a prism.

Step 3 In pairs ask students to take turns choosing a figure and then reciting the most common attributes.

Step 4 In their math journals, have students write down the important information about each figure that distinguishes it from the other. Also list similarities in figures that will help students classify them.

Lesson 8-4 Three-Dimensional Figures 357

Chapter 8 Progress Check 2

Formative Assessment

Use the Progress Check to assess students' mastery of the previous lessons. Have students review the lesson indicated for the problems they answered incorrectly.

Odd/Even Assignments

Exercises are structured so that students practice the same concepts whether they are assigned the odd or even problems.

Common Error Alert

Identify Figures In preparation for the chapter test, have students create a table that includes information about all of the figures that were covered in this chapter. This will help the students answer these review questions.

Exercises 3–8 When converting from diameter to radius, students often forget when to multiply and when to divide. Remind students that diameter is the larger dimension since it measures the whole width of the circle. Since diameter is a longer word, diameter is also the longer distance.

Chapter 8 Progress Check 2 (Lessons 8-3 and 8-4)

Find the radius and diameter of each circle.

1 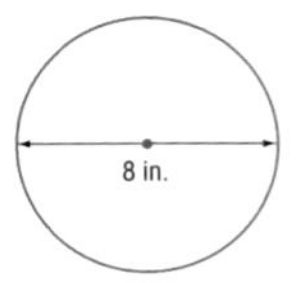

radius: 4 in.
diameter: 8 in.

2 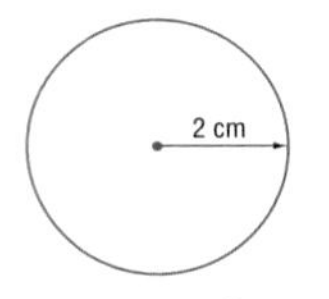

radius: 2 cm
diameter: 4 cm

Find the radius or diameter.

3 $d = 12$ cm
$r =$ 6 cm

4 $d = 20$ yd
$r =$ 10 yd

5 $r = 8$ cm
$d =$ 16 cm

6 $r = 11$ in.
$d =$ 22 in.

7 $r = 3$ yd
$d =$ 6 yd

8 $d = 30$ ft
$r =$ 15 ft

Identify each three-dimensional figure.

9 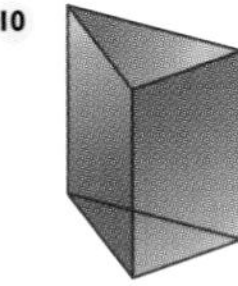

cylinder

10

triangular prism

11 **BASEBALL** According to baseball regulations, the pitcher's mound, which is circular, must have a diameter of 18 feet. What is the radius of a pitcher's mound?
9 feet

12 Ms. Jackson asked her students to draw three-dimensional figures. She told students to use objects as models for their figures. Maurice decided to draw a cereal box. What three-dimensional figure did Maurice draw?
rectangular prism

358 Chapter 8 Geometry

Data-Driven Decision Making

Students missing Exercises . . .	Have trouble with . . .	Should review and practice . . .
1–8	finding the radius and/or diameter of a circle.	SSG Lesson 8-3, p. 349 CRM Skills Practice, p. A176
9–10	identifying a three-dimensional figure.	SSG Lesson 8-4, p. 353 CRM Skills Practice, p. A180
11–12	solving word problems that require identifying three-dimensional figures.	CRM Problem-Solving Practice, pp. A177 and A181

Study Guide

Vocabulary and Concept Check

acute angle, *p. 341*
circle, *p. 349*
congruent, *p.341*
diameter, *p. 349*
edge, *p. 353*
face, *p. 353*
obtuse angle, *p. 341*
parallel lines, *p.334*
quadrilateral, *p. 334*
radius, *p. 349*
three-dimensional figure, *p. 353*
vertex, *p. 353*

Write the vocabulary word that completes each sentence.

1. A(n) ___edge___ is the line segment where two faces of a three-dimensional figure meet.
2. The distance across a circle through its center is called a(n) ___diameter___.
3. ___Congruent___ means having the same size, shape, or measure.
4. A(n) ___quadrilateral___ is a figure that has four sides and four angles.
5. An angle that measures greater than 90° but less than 180° is called a(n) ___obtuse angle___.

Label each diagram below. Write the correct vocabulary term in each blank.

6. ___radius___

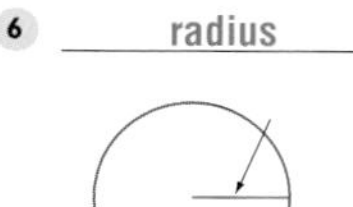

7. ___quadrilateral___

8. ___three-dimensional figure___

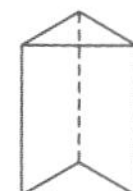

Intervention Strategy — Auditory Learners

Review Game Play a game with students during the last few minutes of class to reinforce some of the topics in the chapter. For example, ask the class, "I have four sides with opposite sides parallel and congruent. What figure am I?" Elicit the correct student response, "You are a parallelogram."

Study Guide
Formative Assessment

Chapter 8

Vocabulary and Concept Check

If students have difficulty answering Exercises 1–8, remind them that they can use the page references to refresh their memories about the vocabulary terms.

Vocabulary Review Strategies

Vocabulary Table Have students fold a sheet of notebook paper vertically. On the left side, they should list the vocabulary terms. On the right side, they should provide a definition or summary for each of the terms, including examples or summaries when appropriate. For example, when listing *acute angle,* students should draw an acute triangle and label it so that the acute angle is noted, and then write a definition.

Lesson Review

Each example walks the students through the main concepts of this chapter. If the given examples are not sufficient to review the questions, remind students that the page references tell them here to review that topic in their textbooks.

Find **Extra Practice** for these concepts in the Practice Worksheets, pages A167–A182.

Classroom Management

Pair and Share Pair a student who has a good grasp of the material with another student who needs extra support. Have the pairs take turns giving each other questions that they answer on paper (based upon the examples in the Study Guide). After answering the questions, if necessary, have the author of the questions explain the strategy and answer to the other student.

Dinah Zike's Foldables®

Review Prepare for the Chapter Test as a class. Ask students to use their Foldable to write review questions that they can go over in groups. (For complete instructions see, Chapter Resource Masters p. A165.)

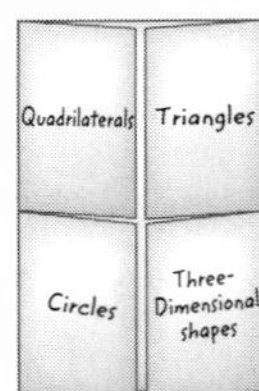

Note This!

Create a Checklist Help students create a study checklist. The checklist should include the following items:

- identifying and classifying different types of quadrilaterals;
- identifying and classifying different types of triangles;
- determining the radius and diameter of a circle;
- identifying various three-dimensional figures;
- naming and identifying faces, edges, and vertices in three-dimensional figures.

Students should put a check mark next to each topic when they feel they have a good grasp of the process.

Common Error Alert

Exercises 11 and 12 One of the common difficulties with questions like Exercises 11 and 12 is that students forget which names refer to triangles by angles and sides. Remind students to use the mnemonic devices that they created when studying Lesson 8-2. They can recite them quietly during studying to help them during the chapter test.

Lesson Review

8-1 Quadrilaterals (pp. 334-340)

Identify each figure.

9 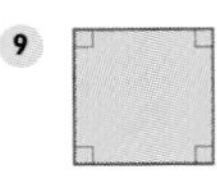

square

10 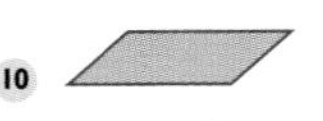

parallelogram

Example 1

Identify the figure.

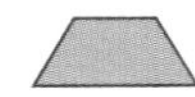

1. The figure has four sides.
   The figure is a(n) quadrilateral.
2. There is one pair of parallel sides.
3. There are no right angles.
   The figure is a(n) trapezoid.

8-2 Triangles (pp. 341-347)

Name each triangle by its sides or angles.

11 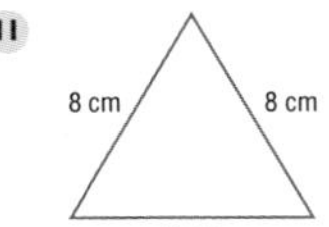

equilateral triangle

12 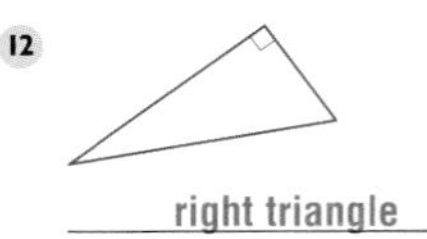

right triangle

Example 2

Name the triangle by its sides.

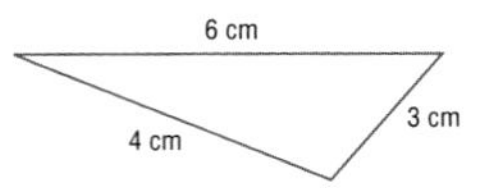

1. The triangle has no congruent sides.
2. The triangle is a scalene triangle.

360 Chapter 8 Study Guide

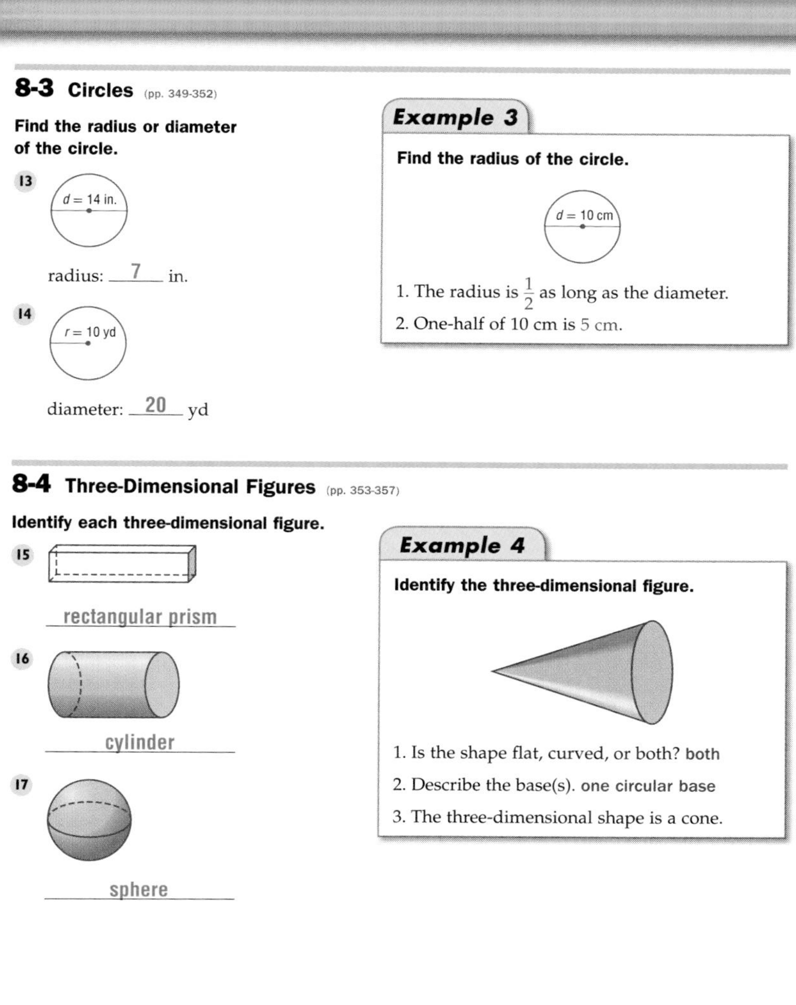

8-3 Circles (pp. 349-352)

Find the radius or diameter of the circle.

13 $d = 14$ in.

radius: 7 in.

14 $r = 10$ yd

diameter: 20 yd

Example 3

Find the radius of the circle.

$d = 10$ cm

1. The radius is $\frac{1}{2}$ as long as the diameter.
2. One-half of 10 cm is 5 cm.

8-4 Three-Dimensional Figures (pp. 353-357)

Identify each three-dimensional figure.

15 rectangular prism

16 cylinder

17 sphere

Example 4

Identify the three-dimensional figure.

1. Is the shape flat, curved, or both? both
2. Describe the base(s). one circular base
3. The three-dimensional shape is a cone.

Chapter 8 Study Guide 361

Math Coach Notes

Study Tips Encourage students to study out loud. As they read over their notes, have them talk through the notes, describe examples and sketches, and create their own examples. Students can "teach" their notes to themselves. This will help them remember the facts.

Intervention Strategy — Kinesthetic Learners

Use of Models For those students who seem to benefit from "hands-on" mathematical techniques, provide them with the opportunity to use three-dimensional models when working on those exercises.

Ticket Out the Door

Review Problems Divide the class into two small groups. Have each student in the first group create a problem that demonstrates his or her understanding of quadrilaterals or triangles. Similarly, have each student in the second group create a problem that demonstrates understanding of circles or three-dimensional figures. Have the groups exchange the problems and solve them before handing them in as they exit the classroom.

Chapter 8 Chapter Test

Chapter Resource Masters

Additional forms of the Chapter 8 Tests are available.

Test Format	Where to Find it
Chapter 8 Test	Math Online macmillanmh.com
Blackline Masters	Assessment Masters, p. 103

Customize and create multiple versions of your chapter test and their answer keys. All of these questions from the chapter tests are available on ExamView™ Assessment Suite.

Online Assessment and Reporting
macmillanmh.com

This online assessment tool allows teachers to track student progress with easily accessible comprehensive reports available for every student. Assess students using any internet-ready computer.

Alternative Assessment

Use Portfolios Ask students to write examples of each type of problem from this chapter in their portfolios. Ask the students to include a picture or model with each example and include all of the key features. As students write examples, have them write all of the steps needed to arrive at their answer in their own words.

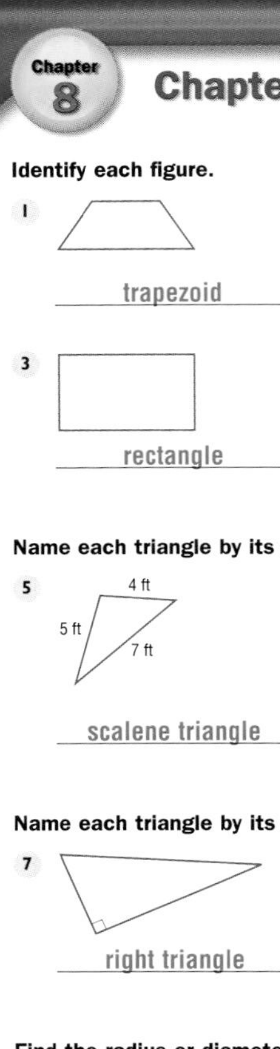
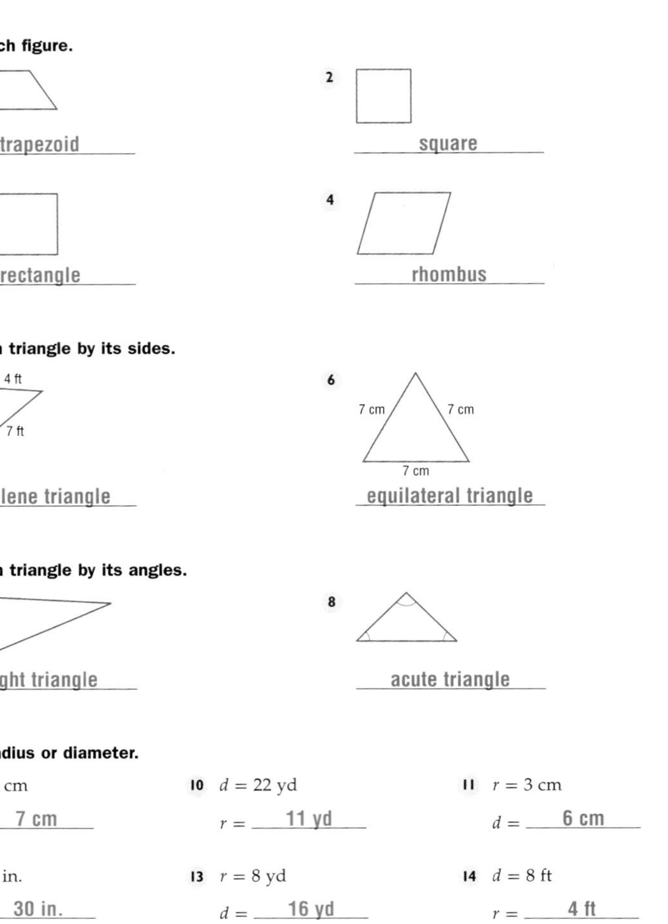

Chapter 8 Chapter Test

Identify each figure.

1 trapezoid

2 square

3 rectangle

4 rhombus

Name each triangle by its sides.

5 (4 ft, 5 ft, 7 ft) scalene triangle

6 (7 cm, 7 cm, 7 cm) equilateral triangle

Name each triangle by its angles.

7 right triangle

8 acute triangle

Find the radius or diameter.

9 $d = 14$ cm $r =$ 7 cm

10 $d = 22$ yd $r =$ 11 yd

11 $r = 3$ cm $d =$ 6 cm

12 $r = 15$ in. $d =$ 30 in.

13 $r = 8$ yd $d =$ 16 yd

14 $d = 8$ ft $r =$ 4 ft

GO ON

362 Chapter 8 Test

English Learner Strategy

Assessment Allow students time to look over the assessment. Have them take a close look at all of the problem directions, as well as any terms in the word problem. Provide an opportunity for students to clarify any words they think they do not understand by conducting a brief question-and-answer period, or provide a dictionary or translation manual for those who have a primary or native language other than English.

Identify each three-dimensional figure.

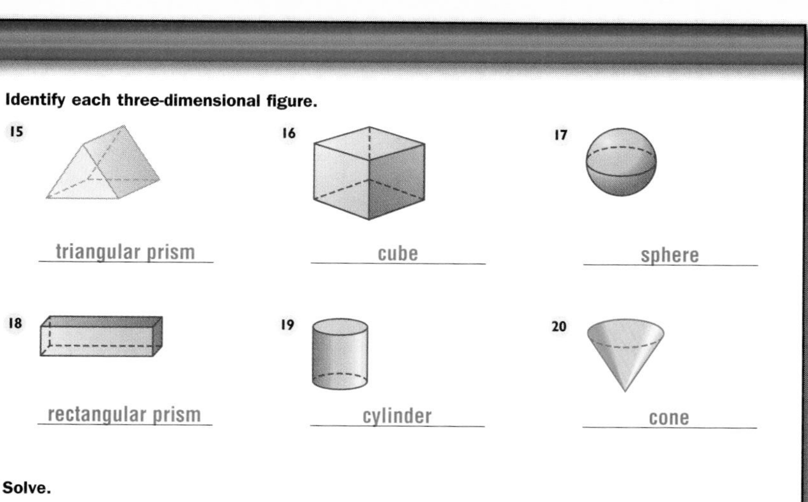

Solve.

21 **DRAWING** Mitchell is drawing a triangle. He makes each side of the triangle a different length. What kind of triangle did Mitchell draw?

scalene triangle

22 **COMPASS** Naomi is using a compass to draw a circle. When she is finished, Naomi uses a ruler to measure the diameter of her circle. The diameter is 18 inches. What is the radius of Naomi's circle?

9 inches

Correct the mistakes.

23 Mrs. Reyes asked students in her math class to draw three-dimensional figures. She set some objects on a table. She told students to use the objects as models for their figures. Paquito decided to use the roll of paper towels as a model. Look at Paquito's drawing. What did he do wrong?

Sample answer: He drew a cone, not a cylinder.

A cylinder should be a curved figure with two flat ends.

Learning from Mistakes

Missed Questions Review commonly missed questions as a small group or class. Ask students to share their methods of answering each question. Try to point out when any errors occur and take corrective measures.

Data-Driven Decision Making

Students missing Exercises . . .	Have trouble with . . .	Should review and practice . . .
1–4	identifying quadrilaterals.	SSG Lesson 8-1, p. 334 CRM Skills Practice, p. A168
5–8	naming triangles using the measures of their sides or angles.	SSG Lesson 8-2, p. 341 CRM Skills Practice, p. A172
9–14	finding the radius or diameter of a circle.	SSG Lesson 8-3, p. 349 CRM Skills Practice, p. A176
15–20	identifying three-dimensional figures.	SSG Lesson 8-4, p. 353 CRM Skills Practice, p. A180
21–23	solving word problems involving triangles, circles, and three-dimensional figures.	CRM Problem-Solving Practice, pp. A169, A173, A177, and A181

Chapter 8 Test Practice

Diagnose Student Errors

Survey student responses for each item. Class trends may indicate common errors and misconceptions.

1. A not a closed figure
Ⓑ correct
C circle
D triangle

2. A all sides are not equal, and no right angles
B figure has more than three sides
C angles are not right angles
Ⓓ correct

3. A all sides are not equal
B two sides are not equal
Ⓒ correct
D guess

4. A did not see right angle symbol
Ⓑ correct
C no angle is greater than 90°
D guess

5. Ⓐ correct
B no right angle, assumed two side lengths are equal
C no right angle, all sides are different lengths
D not a triangle

6. A did not read question carefully
Ⓑ correct
C multiplied radius by 3 instead of 2
D multiplied radius by 4 instead of 2

7. Ⓐ correct
B multiplied diameter by 2
C guess
D did not read question carefully

8. A did not understand attributes of a sphere
B guess
Ⓒ correct
D guess

9. A not a three-dimensional figure
Ⓑ correct
C not a three-dimensional shape
D not a specific name of a three-dimensional figure

Chapter 8 Test Practice

Choose the best answer and fill in the corresponding circle on the sheet at right.

1 Look at these figures. Which figure is a quadrilateral?

A  C ○
Ⓑ ◇ D △

2 Choose the correct name of the figure.

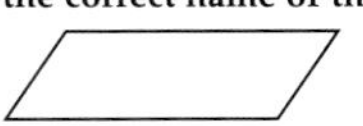

A square
B triangle
C rectangle
Ⓓ parallelogram

3 Choose the correct name of the triangle by the measure of its sides.

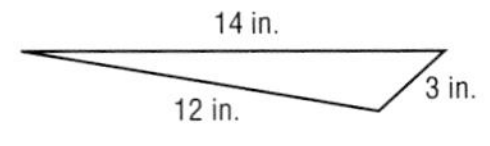

A equilateral triangle
B isosceles triangle
Ⓒ scalene triangle
D none of the above

4 Choose the correct name of the triangle by the measure of its angles.

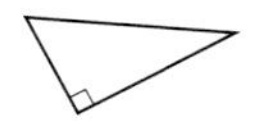

A acute triangle
Ⓑ right triangle
C obtuse triangle
D none of the above

5 Which of the following shows an isosceles right triangle?

Ⓐ 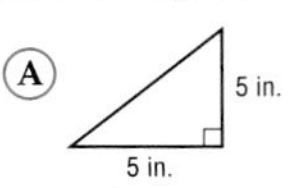

B 

C 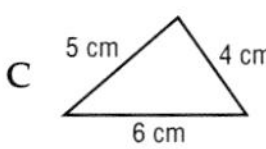

D ⏢

6 Choose the correct diameter.

$r = 3$

$d = ?$

A 3 C 9
Ⓑ 6 D 12

GO ON

364 Chapter 8 Test Practice

10. A has two circular bases
B guess
C has more than one vertex
Ⓓ correct

11. Ⓐ correct
B guess
C a cube does not involve triangles
D a rectangular prism does not involve triangles

7 Choose the correct radius.

$d = 18$

$r = ?$

(A) 9 C 18

B 27 D 36

8 Which of the following best describes the shape of a soccer ball?

A cone

B rectangular prism

(C) sphere

D vertex

9 Choose the correct name of the three-dimensional figure.

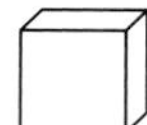

A square C rectangle

(B) cube D box

10 Which of the following figures shows a cone?

A  C 

B (D)

11 Which of the following describes the object below?

(A) triangular prism

B sphere

C cube

D rectangular prism

1	A	**B**	C	D
2	A	B	C	**D**
3	A	B	**C**	D
4	A	**B**	C	D
5	**A**	B	C	D
6	A	**B**	C	D
7	**A**	B	C	D
8	A	B	**C**	D
9	A	**B**	C	D
10	A	B	C	**D**
11	**A**	B	C	D

Success Strategy

After answering all the questions, go back and check your work. Make sure you circled the correct answer to each problem.

Diagnosing Student Errors and Misconceptions

Scoring When working on the Test Practice problems, have students show their work on a separate sheet of notebook paper that can be used later as a reference as needed. After the class has completed the Test Practice problems, go over all the correct responses and have the students score their own responses.

Have students try to find and correct their mistakes. If they are still having trouble, try to determine whether the mistake was due to a basic computational error or whether there is a misunderstanding of the concept. Try to resolve as many of these errors as time permits.

Chapter 9

Chapter Overview

Chapter-at-a-Glance

Lesson	Math Objective	State/Local Standards
9-1 Introduction to Area (pp. 368–372)	Estimate the area of a figure using a grid.	
9-2 Area of a Rectangle (pp. 373–378)	Find the area of a rectangle.	
Progress Check 1 (p. 379)		
9-3 Area of a Parallelogram (pp. 380–386)	Find the area of a parallelogram and derive a formula.	
9-4 Area of a Triangle (pp. 387–394)	Find the area of a triangle.	
Progress Check 2 (p. 395)		

Content-at-a-Glance

The diagram below summarizes and unpacks Chapter 9 content.

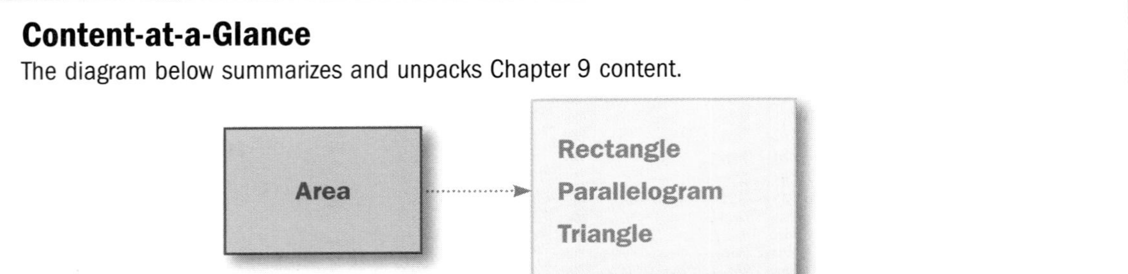

Online Assessment and Reporting
macmillanmh.com

Chapter Assessment Manager

Diagnostic

Diagnose students' readiness.

	Student Study Guide/ Teacher Edition	Assessment Masters	Technology
Course Placement Test		1	ExamView® Assessment Suite
Book 3 Pretest		97	ExamView® Assessment Suite
Chapter 9 Pretest		111	ExamView® Assessment Suite
Quiz/Preview	SSG 367		Math Online macmillanmh.com StudentWorks™ Plus

Formative

Identify students' misconceptions of content knowledge.

	Student Study Guide/ Teacher Edition	Assessment Masters	Technology
Progress Checks	SSG 379,395		Math Online macmillanmh.com StudentWorks™ Plus
Vocabulary Review	SSG 396		Math Online macmillanmh.com
Lesson Assessments			ExamView® Assessment Suite
Are They Getting It?	TE 371, 375, 383, 390		

Summative

Determine student success in learning the concepts in the lesson, chapter, or book.

	Student Study Guide/ Teacher Edition	Assessment Masters	Technology
Chapter 9 Test	SSG 400	114	ExamView® Assessment Suite
Test Practice	SSG 402	117	ExamView® Assessment Suite
Alternative Assessment	TE 400	120	
See It, Do It, Say It, Write It	TE 372, 378, 386, 394		
Book 3 Test		133	ExamView® Assessment Suite

Back-mapping and Vertical Alignment **McGraw-Hill's *Math Triumphs*** intervention program was conceived and developed with the final result in mind: student success in grade-level mathematics, including Algebra 1 and beyond. The authors, using the **NCTM Focal Points and Focal Connections** as their guide, developed this brand-new series by backmapping from grade-level and Algebra 1 concepts, and vertically aligning the topics so that they build upon prior skills and concepts and serve as a foundation for future topics.

Chapter Resource Manager

	Lesson 9-1	Lesson 9-2	Lesson 9-3	Lesson 9-4
Concept	Introduction to Area	Area of a Rectangle	Area of a Parallelogram	Area of a Triangle
Objective	Estimate the area of a figure using a grid.	Find the area of a rectangle.	Find the area of a parallelogram and derive a formula.	Find the area of a triangle.
Math Vocabulary	area square unit	area rectangle square square unit	area parallelogram rectangle square unit	area parallelogram rectangle square unit triangle
Lesson Resources	**Materials** • Ruler **Manipulatives** • Coordinate plane • Geoboard • Grid paper **Other Resources** CRM Vocabulary and English Language Development CRM Skills Practice CRM Problem-Solving Practice CRM Homework Practice	**Materials** • Construction paper • Grid paper • Index cards • Toy blocks **Manipulatives** • Base-ten blocks • Connecting cubes • Geoboard **Other Resources** CRM Vocabulary and English Language Development CRM Skills Practice CRM Problem-Solving Practice CRM Homework Practice	**Materials** • Cardstock • Grid paper • Paper **Manipulatives** • Geoboard • Tangram **Other Resources** CRM Vocabulary and English Language Development CRM Skills Practice CRM Problem-Solving Practice CRM Homework Practice	**Materials** • Grid paper • Index cards • Ruler **Manipulatives** • Geoboard • Tangram **Other Resources** CRM Vocabulary and English Language Development CRM Skills Practice CRM Problem-Solving Practice CRM Homework Practice
Technology	Math Online macmillanmh.com StudentWorks™ Plus ExamView® Assessment Suite	Math Online macmillanmh.com StudentWorks™ Plus ExamView® Assessment Suite	Math Online macmillanmh.com StudentWorks™ Plus ExamView® Assessment Suite	Math Online macmillanmh.com StudentWorks™ Plus ExamView® Assessment Suite

Intervention Strategy

Area Grid Art

Step 1

Give each student a piece of grid paper and a ruler.

Step 2

Instruct students to create a drawing using parallelograms, rectangles, and triangles. The drawings must include at least one of each shape. The drawing must represent a real-life object such as a house, a dog, a flower, or a person. Give each student an identification number to write on the back of his or her drawing.

Example: "Two Tulips"

Step 3

Collect the drawings. Pass them back to the class in a random fashion, making sure that each student receives someone else's drawing.

Step 4

Have students find the area of each figure in the drawing and the total area of the object(s) drawn. Staple the work to the drawing.

Step 5

Display the drawings and calculations. Have each student take his or her drawing and check the calculations.

Time Management Use this activity either prior to the end of the chapter as a way to review or during the study of Lesson 9-4. It will help students review how to find the areas of various shapes.

Chapter 9 Chapter Notes

Real-World Applications

New Tile Julio is putting new tile in his kitchen. If the kitchen is 12.5 feet wide and 17 feet long, how much tile will Julio need to purchase? Should he get the exact amount that the room requires?

Intervention Strategy

Area

Step 1 Separate students into pairs. Assign each pair a figure. Vary the shapes between triangles, rectangles, squares, and parallelograms. Give the students the dimensions of the figure. Make sure that all of the dimensions will have the same area.

Step 2 Using grid paper, have each pair draw their figure based on their dimensions.

Step 3 Have the pairs calculate the area.

Step 4 Have each pair present their work to the class.

Step 5 As a class discuss similarities and differences between the work that is presented. Make sure to note that all of the areas are the same, but the figure and dimensions varied.

Chapter 9 Area

Why is area important?

What if you compare your volleyball team's record with your cousin's, but the two of you play on different-sized courts? It would be an unfair comparison. Most school club teams play on volleyball courts that are of regulation size.

366 Chapter 9 Area

Key Vocabulary

Find interactive definitions in 13 languages in the **eGlossary** at macmillanmh.com.

English **Español** *Introduce the most important vocabulary terms from Chapter 9.*

area **área**
the number of square units needed to cover a region or plane figure (p. 368)

square unit **unidad cuadrada**
a unit for measuring area (p. 368)

rectangle **rectángulo**
a quadrilateral with four right angles; opposite sides are parallel and equal in length (p. 373)

square **cuadro**
a rectangle with four congruent sides (p. 373)

parallelogram **paralelogramo**
a quadrilateral in which each pair of opposite sides is parallel and equal in length (p. 380)

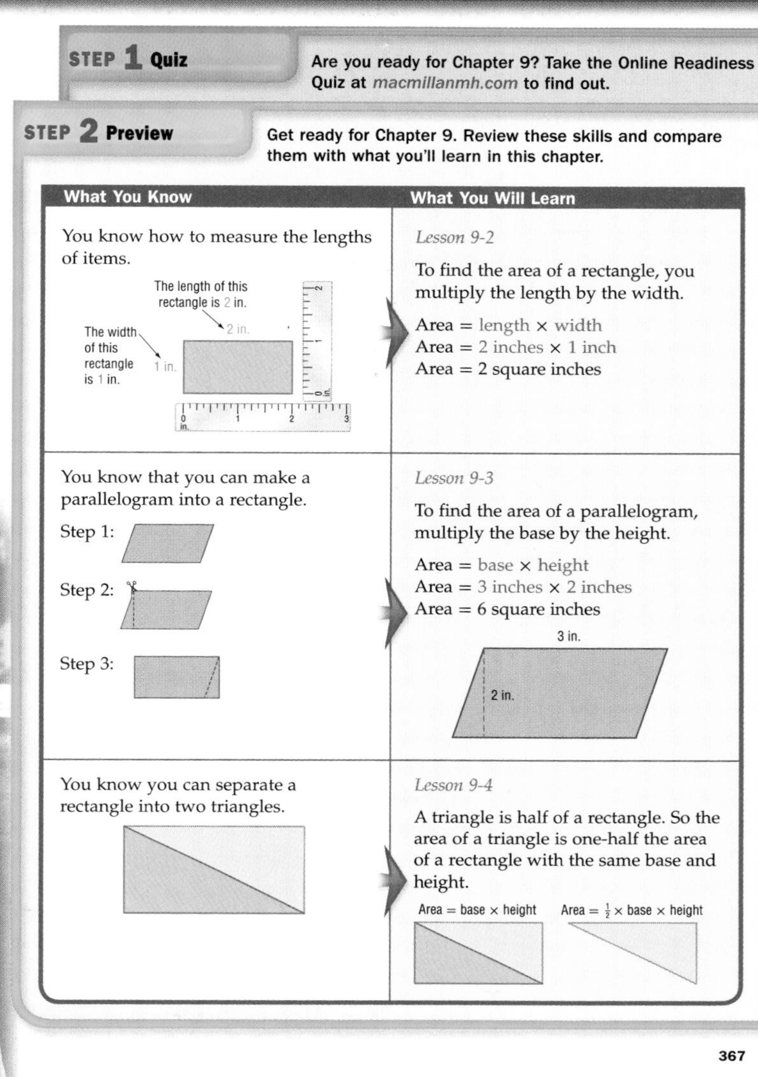

STEP 1 Quiz Are you ready for Chapter 9? Take the Online Readiness Quiz at *macmillanmh.com* to find out.

STEP 2 Preview Get ready for Chapter 9. Review these skills and compare them with what you'll learn in this chapter.

What You Know	What You Will Learn
You know how to measure the lengths of items. The length of this rectangle is 2 in. The width of this rectangle is 1 in.	*Lesson 9-2* To find the area of a rectangle, you multiply the length by the width. Area = length × width; Area = 2 inches × 1 inch; Area = 2 square inches
You know that you can make a parallelogram into a rectangle. Step 1: Step 2: Step 3:	*Lesson 9-3* To find the area of a parallelogram, multiply the base by the height. Area = base × height; Area = 3 inches × 2 inches; Area = 6 square inches (3 in., 2 in.)
You know you can separate a rectangle into two triangles.	*Lesson 9-4* A triangle is half of a rectangle. So the area of a triangle is one-half the area of a rectangle with the same base and height. Area = base × height; Area = $\frac{1}{2}$ × base × height

367

Step 1 Quiz

Pretest/Prescribe Students can take the Online Readiness Quiz or the Diagnostic Pretest in the Assessment Masters.

Step 2 Preview

Use this pre-chapter activity to activate students' prior knowledge, build confidence, and help students preview the lessons.

Dinah Zike's Foldables®

Guide students through the directions on p. A183 in the Chapter Resource Masters to create their own Foldable graphic organizer to use with this chapter.

Home Connections

- Find two rectangles that you think may have the same or close-to-the-same area but different dimensions. (No calculations should be done.)

Vocabulary Preview

- As students complete the Chapter Preview, have them make a list of important terms throughout the chapter.
- Divide students into pairs. Have the pairs compare their lists of terms to make one list.
- Then have students take turns defining the terms aloud to each other.
- Finally, have students take turns looking up the terms in the Glossary and reading the definitions out loud.

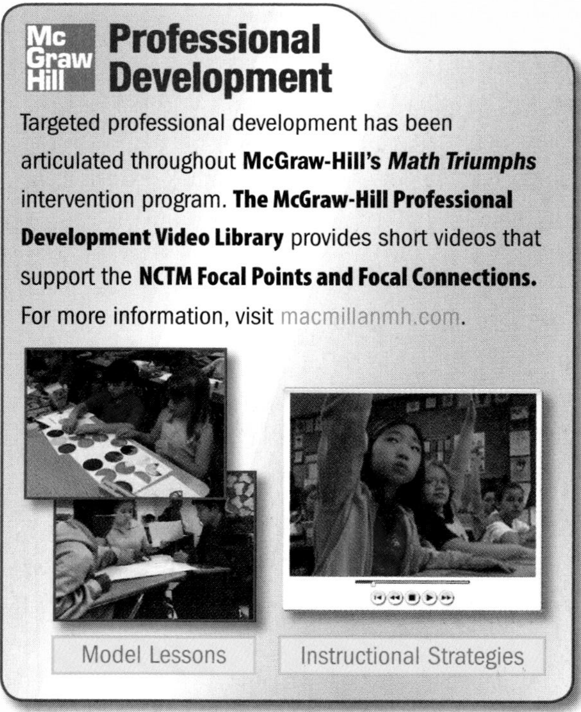

Professional Development

Targeted professional development has been articulated throughout **McGraw-Hill's *Math Triumphs*** intervention program. **The McGraw-Hill Professional Development Video Library** provides short videos that support the **NCTM Focal Points and Focal Connections.** For more information, visit macmillanmh.com.

Lesson 9-1 Lesson Notes

Lesson Planner

Objective Estimate the area of a figure using a grid.

Vocabulary **area, square unit**

Materials/Manipulatives coordinate plane/grid paper, geoboard, ruler

Chapter Resource Masters

- CRM Vocabulary and English Language Development (p. A186)
- CRM Skills Practice (p. A187)
- CRM Problem-Solving Practice (p. A188)
- CRM Homework Practice (p. A189)

Vocabulary

Explore Vocabulary Hand out a sheet of grid paper to each student. Inform students that one square is one *square unit.* Ask students to make a rectangle on grid paper and count the number of squares inside the rectangle. Guide students to realize that the number of squares inside the rectangle is the area. Explain nonexamples of *area*.

Key Concept

Foundational Skills and Concepts After students have read through the Key Concept box, have them try these exercises.

1. Which figure is easier to find the area?
   Possible answer: The figure on the left is easier, because it is a familiar figure.
2. What is the area of both figures combined?
   The area of both figures is $35\frac{1}{2}$ square units.
3. How is the area of each figure found?
   by counting the number of square units the figure covers.

Lesson 9-1 Introduction to Area

KEY Concept

The **area** of a figure is the number of **square units** needed to cover a surface.

To find the area of a figure, you can count the number of square units the figure covers.

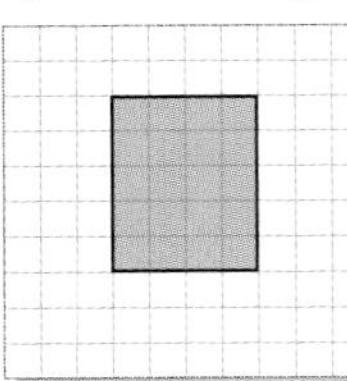

The area of the rectangle is 20 square units.

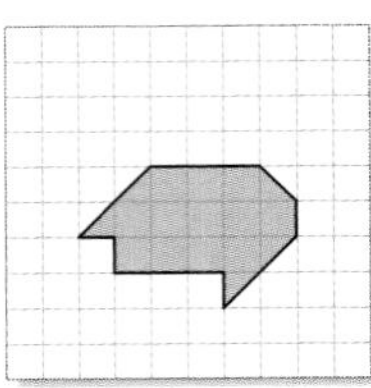

The area of the figure is about $14\frac{1}{2}$ square units.

VOCABULARY

area
the number of square units needed to cover a region or plane figure

square unit
a unit for measuring area

The units of area are square units.

Example 1

Find the area of the rectangle.

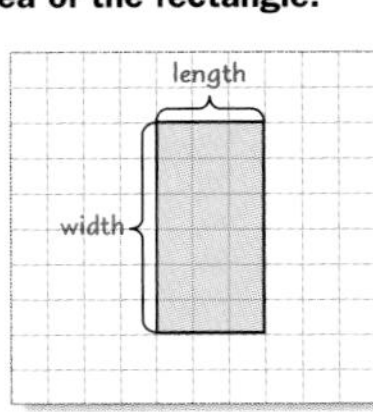

Count the number of squares the rectangle covers.

The area is 18 square units.

YOUR TURN!

Find the area of the rectangle.

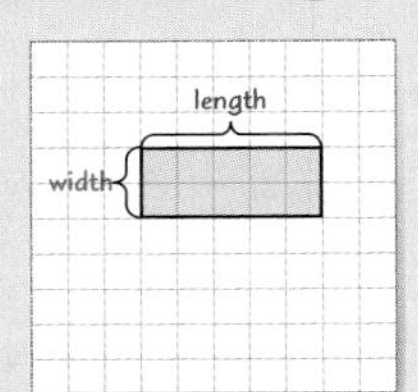

Count the number of squares the rectangle covers. The area is 10 square units.

Additional *Example 1*

Find the area of the rectangle.

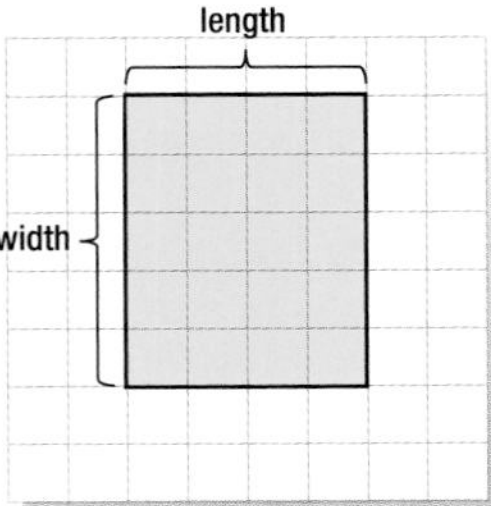

Count the number of squares the rectangle covers.

The area is 20 square units.

Example 2

Estimate the area of the figure.

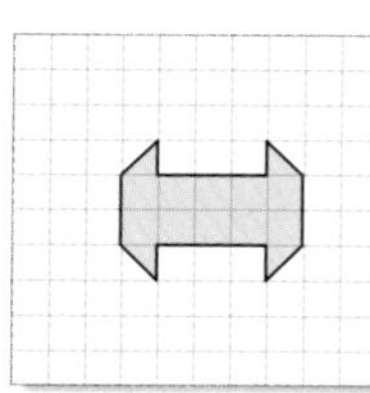

1. Count the number of whole squares the figure covers. 10 whole squares
2. Count the number of half squares the figure covers. 4 half squares

   Convert the half squares to whole squares.

   $\frac{1}{2}+\frac{1}{2}+\frac{1}{2}+\frac{1}{2}=2$
3. Add the number of whole squares.

   $10+2=12$

The area of the figure is about 12 square units.

YOUR TURN!

Estimate the area of the figure.

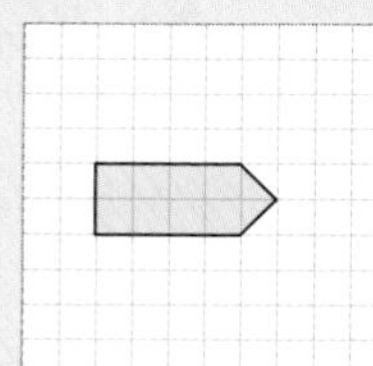

1. Count the number of whole squares the figure covers. __8__ whole squares
2. Count the number of half squares the figure covers.

   __2__ half square(s) = __1__ whole square(s)
3. Add the number of whole squares.

   __8__ + __1__ = __9__

The area of the figure is about __9__ square units.

Who is Correct?

Find the area of the square.

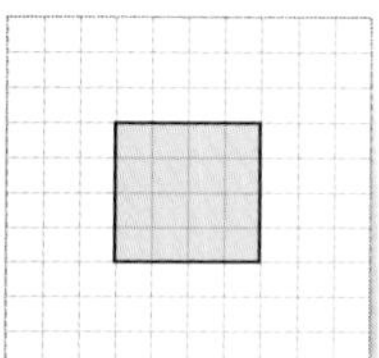

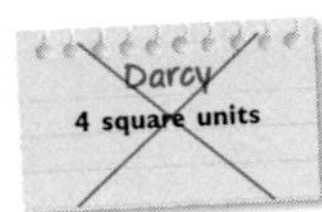

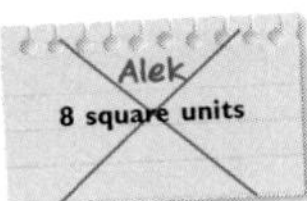

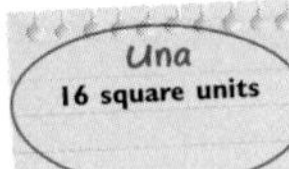

Circle correct answer(s). Cross out incorrect answer(s).

Additional *Example 2*

Estimate the area of the figure.

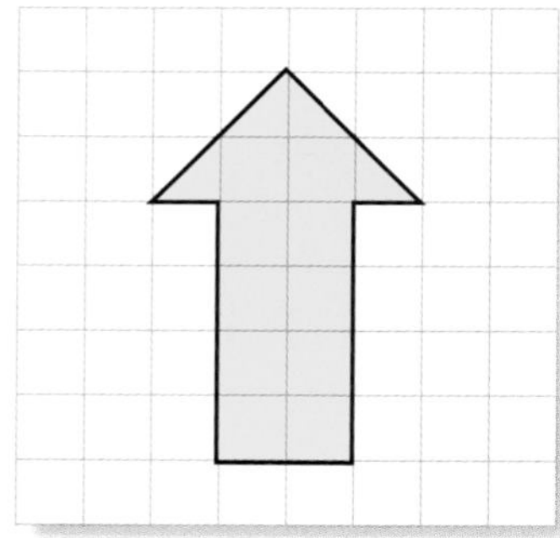

1. Count the number of whole squares the figure covers. 10 whole squares
2. Count the number of half squares the figure covers. 4 half squares

   Convert the half squares to whole squares.

   $\frac{1}{2}+\frac{1}{2}+\frac{1}{2}+\frac{1}{2}=2$
3. Add the number of whole squares.

   $10+2=12$

The area of the figure is about 12 square units.

Math Coach Notes

Common Error One of the most common errors students make is to believe that area is defined by formulas. If the students see a figure for which they do not know a formula for determining the area, they will have no idea how to proceed with finding the area.

Who *is Correct?*

Diagnostic Teaching

- Darcy is incorrect. She counted only one row of squares.
- Alek is incorrect. He added one row and one column.
- Una is correct.

Remind students to count the square units inside of the rectangle to find the area.

3 Practice

Using Manipulatives

Geoboard When assigning Exercise 1, model the two different ways to find the area of a rectangle and square. Use a geoboard and make a rectangle that is 2 units by 7 units. Point out to the students that they can either count the units or multiply the length by the width.

Coordinate Plane/Grid Paper When presenting Example 2, model the units on a grid. Emphasize to students that when they are asked to estimate, they need to count the whole units and then count the partial units.

On-Hand Manipulatives Draw figures or have students draw figures on grid paper to practice counting the units within the figures to find the areas. Cover flat surfaces with blocks to illustrate the area of each figure.

Math Coach Notes

Strategies

1. Start this lesson by identifying and drawing square units, and hand out a sheet of grid paper to each student. Have each student use a ruler and draw a diagonal line through a few square units. Make sure that the students know that each triangle made is one-half of a square unit. Model how to count partial square units.
2. Have students draw different figures that have partial square units and exchange drawings to see if they can find the areas.

Guided Practice

Draw a figure that has the given area.

1. 14 square units Sample answer:

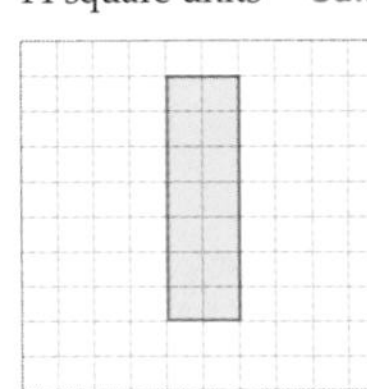

2. 25 square units Sample answer:

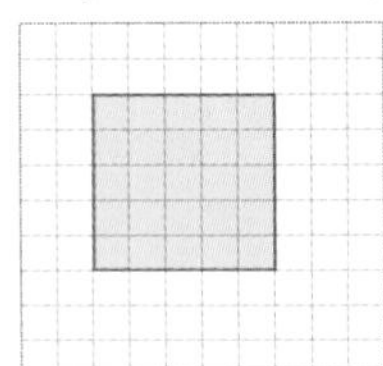

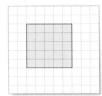

Step by Step Practice

3. Estimate the area of the figure.

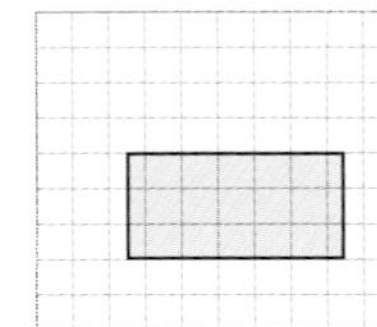

Step 1 Count the number of whole squares.

15 whole squares

Step 2 Count the number of half squares.

6 half square(s) = 3 whole square(s)

Step 3 Add the number of whole squares.

15 + 3 = 18

The area is about 18 square units.

Estimate the area of each figure.

4.

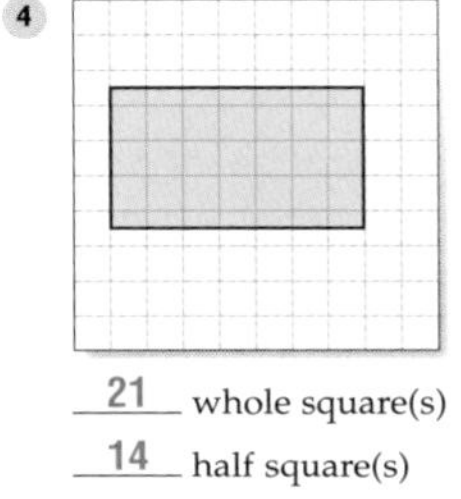

21 whole square(s)

14 half square(s)

The area is about 28 square units.

5. The area is about $18\frac{1}{2}$ square units.

Intervention Strategy

Visual/ Logical Learners

Find the Area Provide each student with a rectangular placemat or a plain sheet of paper. Distribute a set of congruent triangular tiles to each student. Instruct students to use the triangular tiles to determine the area of the placemat. Repeat the process with congruent square tiles and congruent rectangular tiles. Ask students to explain which type of tile was easier to use to find the area of the placemat.

Step by Step Problem-Solving Practice

Problem-Solving Strategies
- ☑ Draw a diagram.
- ☐ Look for a pattern.
- ☐ Guess and check.
- ☐ Act it out.
- ☐ Solve a simpler problem.

Solve.

6 GEOMETRY What is the area of a rectangle that has sides of 8 units and 6 units?

Understand Read the problem. Write what you know.
A rectangle has sides of 8 units and 6 units.

Plan Pick a strategy. One strategy is to draw a diagram. Draw a rectangle that has sides of 8 units and 6 units.

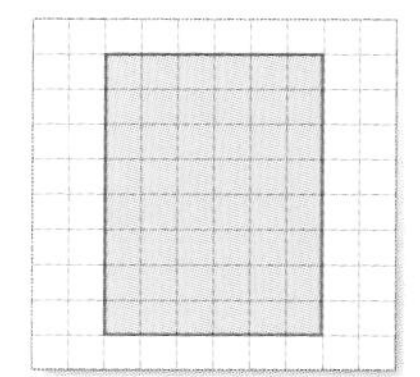

Solve Count the number of squares the figure covers.
The area of the rectangle is 48 square units.

Check Add the number of squares in each row.

7 ROOMS Talia's dining room floor measures 10 feet by 8 feet. What is the area of the floor?
Check off each step.

✔ Understand: I circled key words.

✔ Plan: To solve the problem, I will draw a diagram.

✔ Solve: The answer is 80 square feet.

✔ Check: I checked my answer by adding the number of squares in each row.

8 SHOPPING Howie bought a blanket. It is 7 meters wide and 8 meters long. What is the area of the blanket?
56 square meters

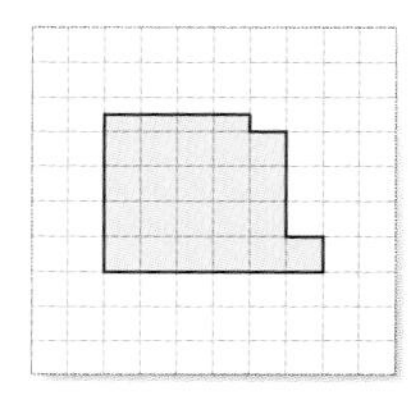

9 **Reflect** Look at the figure at the right. Is the area 23 square units? Explain.
yes; $4 \times 5 + 1 + \frac{1}{2} + \frac{1}{2} + \frac{1}{2} + \frac{1}{2} = 23$ square units

GO ON

Lesson 9-1 Introduction To Area 371

Math Coach Notes

Practice Tip Area is measured in square units. Remind students that their final answers should be labeled in square units.

Intervention Strategy — Visual/Linguistic Learners

State Areas Provide students with a map of the United States. Determine the scale of the map. Using square tiles, have students create and write a plan to determine the area of a state. Students should then use their plans to find the area of a state. States that resemble parallelograms, such as Colorado and Tennessee, may be easiest to determine area.

Intervention Strategy — Kinesthetic Learners

Classroom Objects Allow students to pick a classroom object and find the area of that object. Encourage them to use different methods to find the area.

Are They Getting It?

Check students' understanding of finding the area by writing these problems on the board. Ask students to point out each wrong answer. Tell them to use a grid to show why the answers are correct or incorrect.

Find the area of each figure.

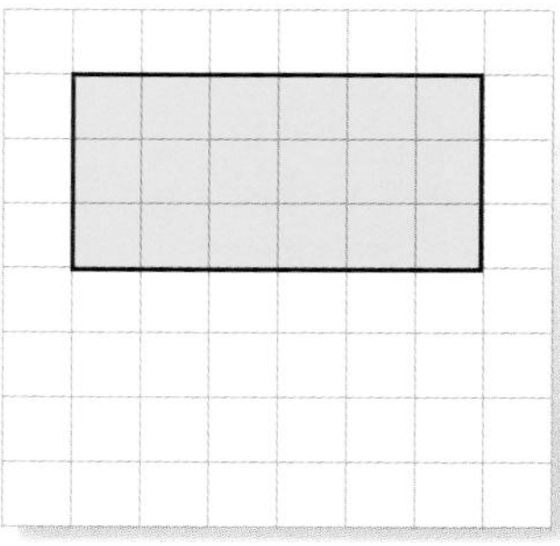

The area of the rectangle is 18 units. This is incorrect. The area is 18 *square* units.

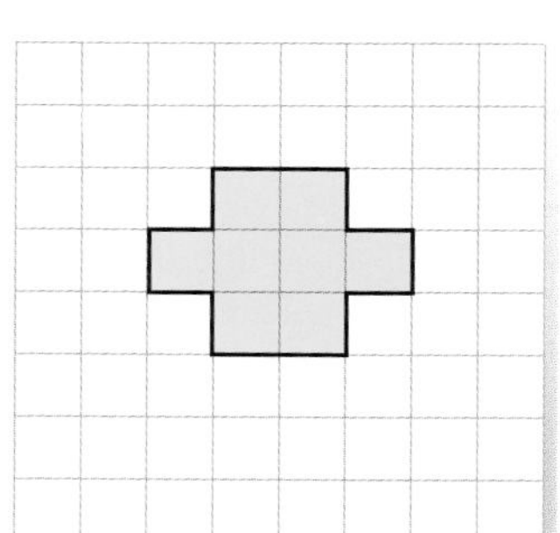

The area of the figure is 8 square units. This is correct.

Odd/Even Assignments

Exercises 10–14 are structured so that students practice the same concepts whether they are assigned the odd or even problems.

In-Class Assignment

Have students complete Exercises 12, 14, and 17 to ensure that they understand the concept.

See It, Do It, Say It, Write It

Step 1 Draw the following figure on the board.

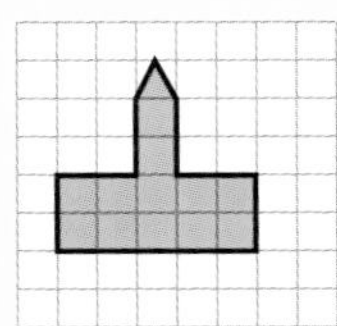

Step 2 Have students estimate the area of the figure on the board.

Step 3 Arrange the students in pairs and have them explain to each other how they found the area of the figure.

Step 4 Have students write in their journals how to find the area of a figure.

Looking Ahead: Pre-teach

Area of a Rectangle In the next lesson, students will learn how to find the area of a rectangle.

Example

What is the area of the rectangle?

1. The length is 4 centimeters, and the width is 10 centimeters.
2. Substitute these values into the formula. Multiply.

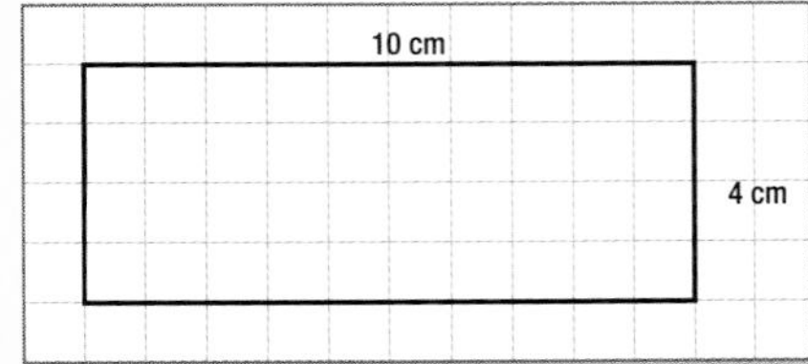

$A = \ell \times w$

$A = 4 \times 10$

$A = 40$

The area of the rectangle is 40 square centimeters.

Skills, Concepts, and Problem Solving

Draw a figure that has the given area.

10. 16 square units
Sample answer:

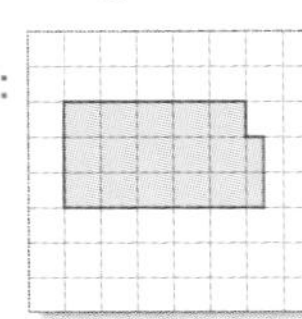

11. 30 square units
Sample answer:

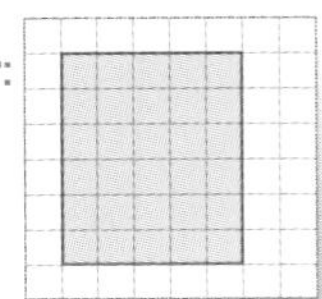

Find the area of each figure.

12. The area of the figure is about 12 square units.

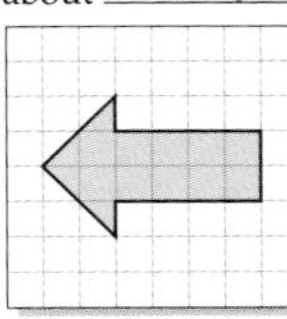

13. The area of the figure is 18 square units.

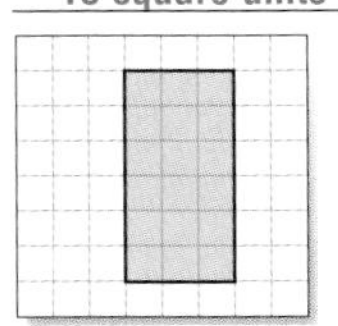

Solve.

14. ART Look at the photo at the right. It shows the largest picture Gregory painted. What is the area?
80 square inches

ART Gregory's painting is 8 inches by 10 inches.

Vocabulary Check **Write the vocabulary word that completes each sentence.**

15. A(n) square unit is a unit for measuring area.

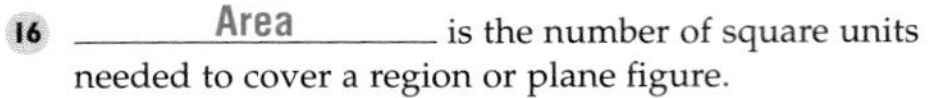

16. Area is the number of square units needed to cover a region or plane figure.

17. Writing in Math Explain how to find the length and width of a rectangle with an area of 24 square units.
The area of a rectangle is found by multiplying length times width. Any two factors of 24 can be the length and width of the rectangle. For example, 2×12, 3×8, or 6×4 could be the dimensions of the rectangle.

STOP

Ticket Out the Door

I Spy an Area Give students an example of a figure found in the class that has an area of 25 square inches. Have students find the objects that have an area of 25 square inches. Students turn in their results as they exit the classroom.

Lesson 9-2 Area of a Rectangle

KEY Concept

Find the **area** of a **rectangle** using the formula below.

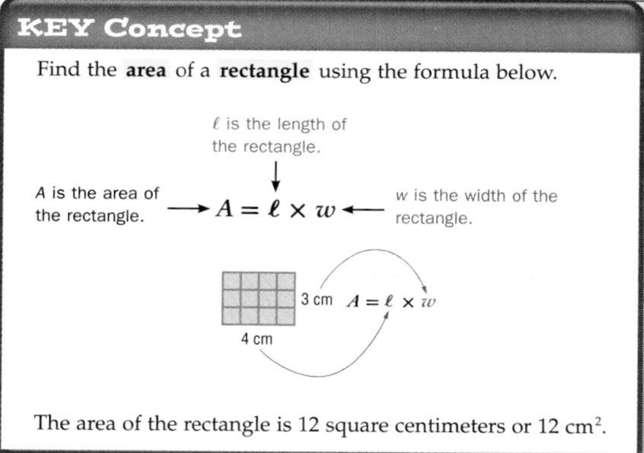

The area of the rectangle is 12 square centimeters or 12 cm^2.

VOCABULARY

area
the number of square units needed to cover a region or a plane figure

rectangle
a quadrilateral with four right angles; opposite sides are parallel and equal in length

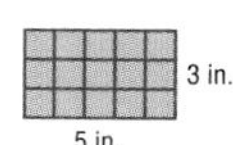

square
a rectangle with equal sides

square unit
a unit for measuring area

The units of area are **square units**. Remember that a square is a special rectangle because a square has four equal sides.

Example 1

Find the area of the rectangle.

1. The length is 5 inches.
   The width is 3 inches.

2. Substitute these values into the formula. Multiply.

$A = \ell \times w$
$A = 5 \text{ in.} \times 3 \text{ in.}$
$A = 15 \text{ in}^2$

The area of the rectangle is 15 square inches.

GO ON

Additional Example 1

Find the area of the rectangle.

1. The length is 5 meters.
   The width is 2 meters.

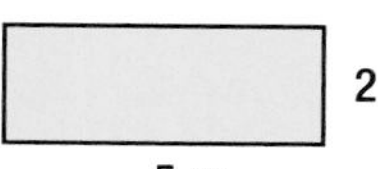

2. Substitute these values into the formula. Multiply.

$A = \ell \times w$
$A = 5 \text{ m} \times 2 \text{ m}$
$A = 10 \text{ m}^2$

The area of the rectangle is 10 square meters.

Lesson Notes

Lesson 9-2

Lesson Planner

Objective Find the area of a rectangle.

Vocabulary **area, rectangle, square, square unit**

Materials/Manipulatives base-ten blocks, connecting cubes, construction paper, geoboard, grid paper, index cards, toy blocks

Chapter Resource Masters

- CRM Vocabulary and English Language Development (p. A190)
- CRM Skills Practice (p. A191)
- CRM Problem-Solving Practice (p. A192)
- CRM Homework Practice (p. A193)

1 Introduce

Vocabulary

Vocabulary Review Draw two rectangles on the board. Fill the rectangles with an equal number of squares. What is the *area* of the rectangle? Guide students to see that each unit that fills the figure is a *square unit* of the same size. Now fill the other rectangle with squares or rectangles that are an unequal size. Challenge students to see this figure as a nonexample because the units are not of equal size.

2 Teach

Key Concept

Foundational Skills and Concepts After students have read through the Key Concept box, have them try these exercises.

1. What is the area of a rectangle with length 4 cm and width 3 cm? 12 cm^2
2. What is the formula for area of a rectangle? $A = \ell \times w$
3. What is another way to represent square centimeters? cm^2

Math Coach Notes

Length and Width When studying the area of a rectangle, suggest that students change the length and width of the rectangle. For example, the problem may say that the length is 5 and the width is 3. Switch the values so the length is 3 and the width is 5. Encourage students to explore the results of switching the values for the length and width.

Using Manipulatives

Geoboard When presenting Example 1, model the rectangle by using a geoboard.

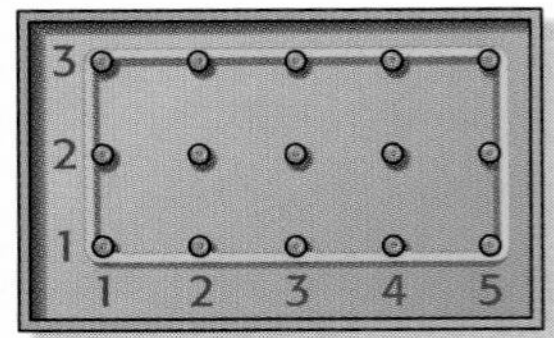

Base-Ten Blocks Base-ten blocks can be used in a single layer as square units.

Connecting Cubes Connecting cubes can be used in a single layer to represent the length and width of rectangles.

On-Hand Manipulatives Use children's toy blocks or squares cut out from construction paper to show square units of area.

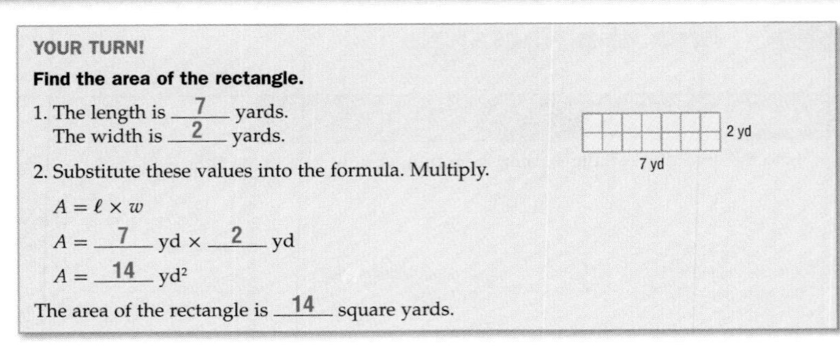

YOUR TURN!

Find the area of the rectangle.

1. The length is __7__ yards.
   The width is __2__ yards.
2. Substitute these values into the formula. Multiply.

$A = \ell \times w$

$A =$ __7__ yd × __2__ yd

$A =$ __14__ yd²

The area of the rectangle is __14__ square yards.

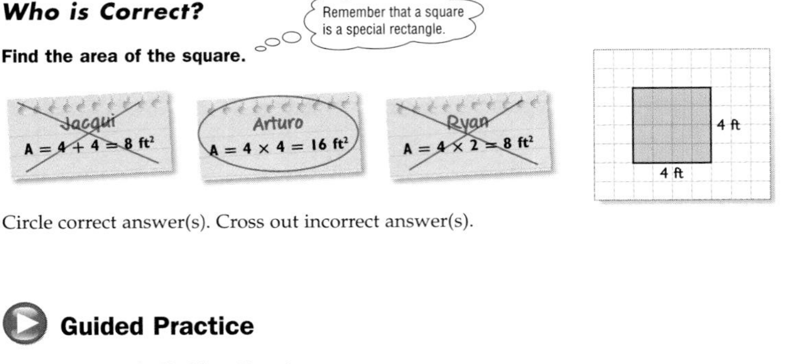

Circle correct answer(s). Cross out incorrect answer(s).

Guided Practice

Draw a rectangle that has the given area.

1. 18 square cm **Sample answer:**

   9 cm, 2 cm

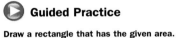

2. 4 cm² **Sample answer:**

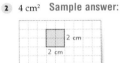

   2 cm, 2 cm

374 Chapter 9 Area

Who *is Correct?*

Diagnostic Teaching

- Jacqui wrote 8 ft². This is incorrect. She added the length and width.
- Arturo wrote 16 ft². This is correct.
- Ryan wrote 8 ft². This is incorrect. He multiplied the side length by 2.

Remind students that they can estimate their answers by counting the squares.

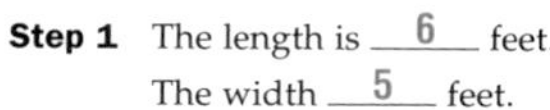

Step by Step Practice

3 Find the area of the rectangle.

Step 1 The length is 6 feet.
The width 5 feet.

Step 2 Substitute these values into the formula. Multiply.

$A = \ell \times w$
$A = 6 \text{ ft} \times 5 \text{ ft}$
$A = 30 \text{ ft}^2$

The area of the rectangle is 30 square feet.

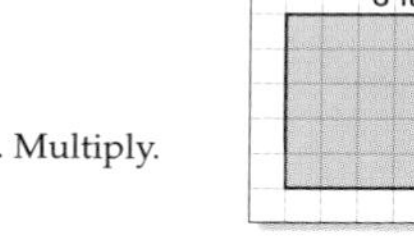

Find the area of each rectangle.

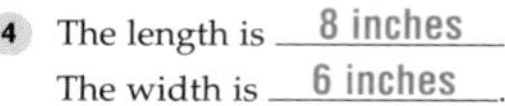

4 The length is 8 inches.
The width is 6 inches.

$A = \ell \times w$
$A = 8 \text{ in.} \times 6 \text{ in.}$
$A = 48 \text{ in}^2$

5 The length is 9 meters. The width is 3 meters.

$A = 9 \text{ m} \times 3 \text{ m}$
$A = 27 \text{ m}^2$

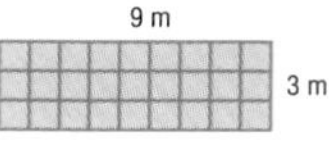

6 $A = 36 \text{ yd}^2$

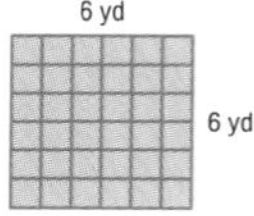

7 $A = 18 \text{ yd}^2$

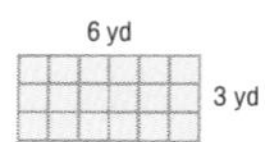

Intervention Strategy

Visual/Logical Learners

Floor Plans Have students use grid paper to create a floor plan for a house. Ask them to estimate the area by counting the squares and then find the exact area by dividing the floor plan into rectangles and adding the area of each individual rectangle. How do the areas compare?

Are They Getting It?

Check students' understanding of the area of rectangles by writing these problems on the board. Have students explain the incorrect information in each problem. Tell them to use a drawing or model to show why the answers are correct or are incorrect.

1. A rectangle that is 7 in. by 5 in. has an area of 35 in. This is incorrect. The area should be in square inches.
2. A rectangle with an area of 24 cm^2 could have a length of 8 cm and a width of 4 cm. This is incorrect because $8 \times 4 = 32$.
3. The area of this square is 16 in^2. This is correct.

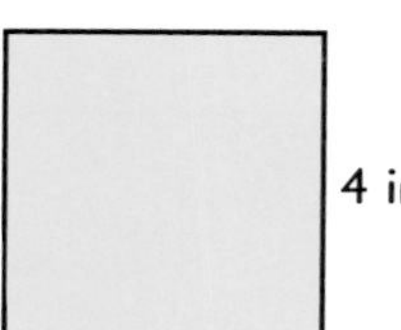

Math Coach Notes

Strategies

1. Start this lesson with a hands-on practice as an anchoring experience. Tell students to locate something that is the shape of a rectangle or square in the classroom. Have students measure the length and width using the unit of their choice. Have them represent their figure on grid paper. Guide them to find the area.
2. Area is the number of equal squares that covers a surface. Alternate using the words "cover" and "pave" to remind students of what the area really is.
3. When possible, present nonexamples. If a rectangle measures 10 by 5 units, why is the area not 100 square units? Continuously offering nonexamples reminds students of what area is not.
4. Point out when a student uses linear measurements to represent area that area is measured in square units while length is measured in linear units (like inches).

Note This!

Exponents Lead students to not overlook the exponent when writing square units in their notes. With practice it will become automatic.

8 $A =$ 40 mi^2

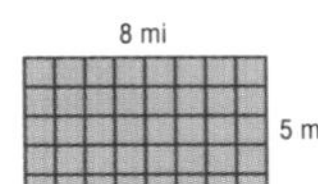

9 $A =$ 36 km^2

Step by Step Problem-Solving Practice

Problem-Solving Strategies
- ✓ Use a formula.
- ☐ Look for a pattern.
- ☐ Guess and check.
- ☐ Act it out.
- ☐ Solve a simpler problem.

Solve.

10 BASKETBALL A high-school basketball court is 94 feet long and 50 feet wide. What is the area of the court?

Understand Read the problem. Write what you know.

The length of the basketball court is 94 feet.
The width of the court is 50 feet.

Plan Pick a strategy. One strategy is to use a formula.

Substitute values for length and width into the area formula.

Solve Use the formula.

$A = \ell \times w$

$A =$ 94 ft $\times$ 50 ft

$A =$ 4,700 ft^2

The area of the high-school basketball court is 4,700 square feet.

Check Use division or a calculator to check your multiplication.

11 CONSTRUCTION A construction crew is pouring cement for sidewalk slabs. Each slab is a square that has sides that measure 70 centimeters. What is the area of each slab?

Check off each step.

✓ Understand: I circled key words.

✓ Plan: To solve the problem, I will use a formula.

✓ Solve: The answer is 4,900 cm^2.

✓ Check: I checked my multiplication with division or a calculator.

376 Chapter 9 Area

English Learner Strategy

Guiding Questions Use index cards that have been cut into squares. Then ask students the following questions.

- Cover your desk (or textbook) with the cards. How many cards did you use?
- How can you find the number of cards without counting them?
- Which formula do you use to find the area of a rectangle that has a length of 5 centimeters and a width of 4 centimeters?
- How would you find the area of the classroom (or the counter top)?

12 ART Mrs. Brady asked her class to use an entire sheet of paper to finger paint. Each sheet of paper measured 8.5 inches by 11 inches. What was the area of the finger painting?

93.5 in^2

13 **Reflect** Can two rectangles have the same area but different lengths and widths? Explain.

Sample answer: Yes; a rectangle with side lengths of 1 inch and 6 inches has an area of 6 in^2. A rectangle with side lengths of 2 inches and 3 inches also has an area of 6 in^2.

Skills, Concepts, and Problem Solving

Draw a rectangle that has the given area.

14 6 square units Sample answer:

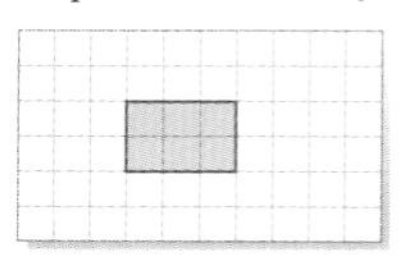

15 24 square units Sample answer:

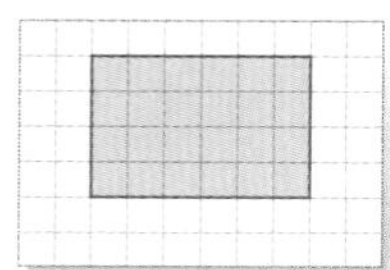

Find the area of each rectangle.

16 $A =$ 16 m^2

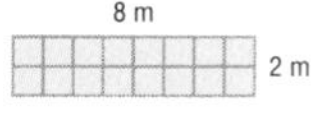

17 $A =$ 28 mi^2

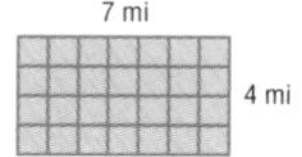

18 $A =$ 100 cm^2

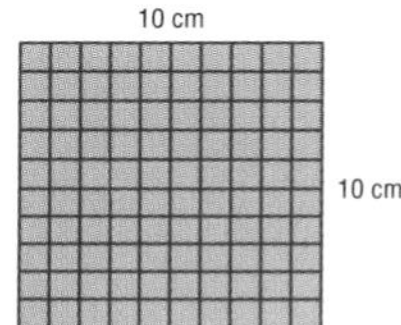

19 $A =$ 36 in^2

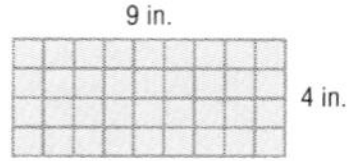

GO ON

Intervention Strategy

Kinesthetic/ Naturalist Learners

Draw the Classroom Instruct students to draw a picture of any part of the classroom with the stipulation that the picture contains at least four rectangles. After the picture is drawn, have students find the area of the rectangular objects in their drawings. Recommend that students number the rectangles in their picture.

Odd/Even Assignments

Exercises 14–21 are structured so that students practice the same concepts whether they are assigned the odd or even problems.

In-Class Assignment

Have students complete Exercises 15, 17, 21, and 25 to ensure that they understand the concept.

Math Coach Notes

Key Information Before a test, tell students to write a summary sheet that contains the key information in each lesson. Students should include vocabulary, definitions, and examples. They should also draw pictures to help them remember the examples.

Math Challenge

Rolling Rectangles Each pair of students will need two number cubes. The first student rolls both cubes. The numbers on the cubes are the dimensions of his or her rectangle. The other student then rolls. Whoever has the greatest area wins 1 point. The first student who earns 10 points wins.

4 Assess

See It, Do It, Say It, Write It

Step 1 Use an overhead to draw a rectangle on grid paper. Label the length and width. Show students how you can use the formula to find the area. Show them how the area can be verified counting the square units.

Step 2 Give students rectangular figures that they can measure or trace on grid paper. Tell them to find the areas. Have them share their methods with the class.

Step 3 Go around the classroom and ask students how they would find the area of something. For instance, how would you find the area of the gymnasium (or lunchroom)? What about this base-ten unit model? Have students share ideas.

Step 4 Have students write the definition of *area.* Tell them to imagine they are writing the information for another fifth grade student, and to use a lot of details, pictures, and examples.

Looking Ahead: Pre-teach

Area of a Parellelogram In the next lesson students will learn about the area of a parallelogram. A parallelogram looks like this:

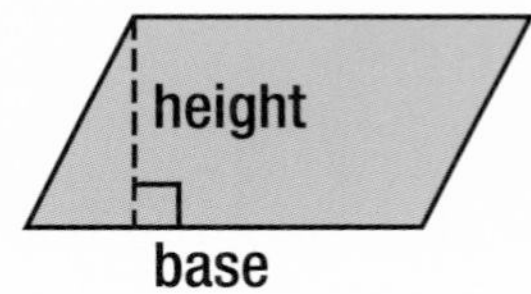

The formula for the area is $A = base \times height$.

Example

What is the area of a parallelogram with a base of 5 inches and a height of 3 inches? 15 in^2

Find the area of parallelograms with:

1. base 6 in., height 4 in. 24 in^2
2. base 12 cm, height 6 cm 72 cm^2
3. base 4 yd, height 2 yd 8 yd^2

Solve.

28 cm

36 cm

20 PHOTOS At the portrait studio, Ines ordered the picture of her family shown. What was the area of Ines's family portrait?

1,008 cm^2

21 DOORS The screen door at Ethan's house is 32 inches wide and 85 inches tall. What is the area of Ethan's screen door?

2,720 in^2

Vocabulary Check **Write the vocabulary word that completes each sentence.**

22 Area is the number of square units needed to cover a region or a plane figure.

23 A(n) square is a rectangle with four equal sides.

24 A(n) rectangle has opposite sides that are equal and parallel. It is a quadrilateral with four right angles.

25 Writing in Math Explain how to find the area of a rectangle.

Sample answer: Identify the length and width of the rectangle. Substitute values of the length and width into the formula for the area of a rectangle. Multiply to find the area of the rectangle. Express the answer in square units.

Spiral Review

Find the area of each figure. (Lesson 9-1, p. 368)

26
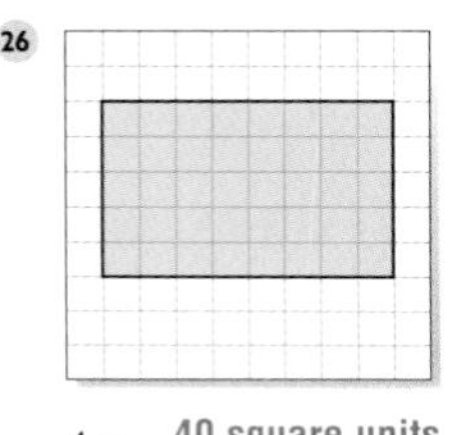

$A =$ 40 square units

27
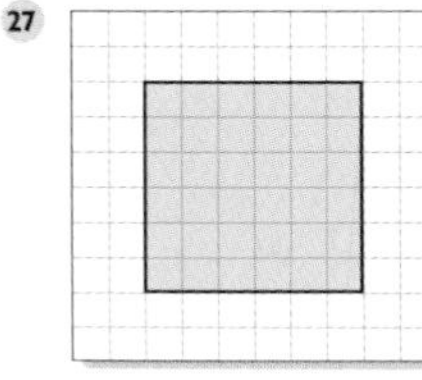

$A =$ 36 square units

Ticket Out the Door

Solve a Problem Tell students to write the answer to this question on paper: To complete an art project, Alissa needs to draw on a work space with an area of at least 84 square inches. If she chooses a table at the library that measures 12 inches by 5 inches, will it be large enough for her project? No, she needs a table that measures at least 12 inches by 7 inches. Have students turn in their answers as they exit the classroom.

Progress Check 1 (Lessons 9-1 and 9-2)

Find the area of each figure.

1 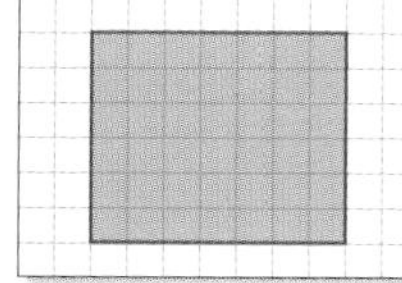

$A =$ 42 square units

2 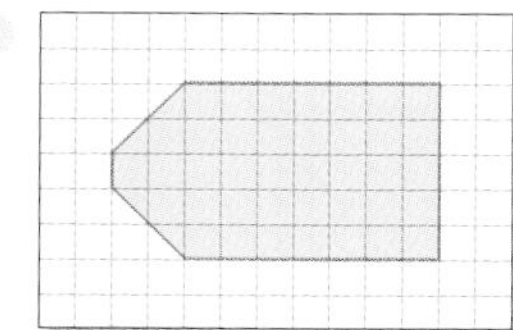

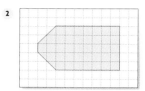

$A =$ 41 square units

3 

$A =$ 108 yd^2

4 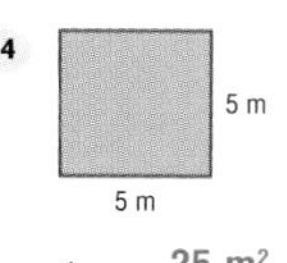

$A =$ 25 m^2

5 5 cm, 14 cm

$A =$ 70 cm^2

6 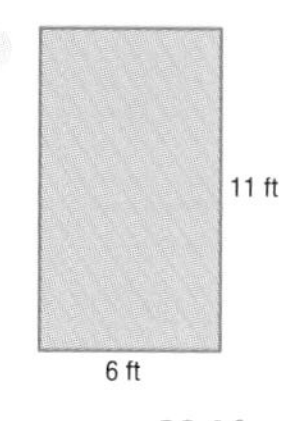

$A =$ 66 ft^2

Solve.

7 **DESIGN** Lena hung a rectangular mirror on her bathroom wall. The mirror was 85 centimeters high and 67 centimeters wide. What was the area of Lena's mirror? 5,695 cm^2

8 **TILES** Lamont decorated square-shaped tiles. Each tile was 80 millimeters long and 60 millimeters wide. What was the area of each tile? 4,800 square millimeters

Chapter 9 Area 379

Progress Check 1

Chapter 9

Formative Assessment

Use the Progress Check to assess students' mastery of the previous lessons. Have students review the lesson indicated for the problems they answered incorrectly.

Odd/Even Assignments

Exercises are structured so that students practice the same concepts whether they are assigned the odd or even problems.

Common Error *Alert*

Label Units If some of the students are not labeling their answers in square units when asked to find an area, remind them to do so. Reiterate that area is found by multiplying the dimensions of the rectangle, square, or parallelogram.

Exercise 2 Remind students to count the squares if needed for this figure. Now that they know how to compute the area of a rectangle using the formula, they can use the formula for the rectangular part of the picture and then add the rest of the approximate piece.

Data-Driven Decision Making

Students missing Exercises . . .	Have trouble with . . .	Should review and practice . . .
1–2	estimating the area of a rectangle on a grid.	SSG Lesson 9-1, p. 368 CRM Skills Practice, p. A187
3–6	finding the area of a rectangle with a formula.	SSG Lessons 9-1 and 9-2, pp. 368 and 373 CRM Skills Practice, p. A191
7–8	solving word problems involving the area of a rectangle.	CRM Problem-Solving Practice, pp. A188 and A192

Lesson 9-3

Lesson Notes

Lesson Planner

Objective Find the area of a parallelogram and derive a formula.

Vocabulary **area**, **parallelogram**, **rectangle**, **square unit**

Materials/Manipulatives cardstock, geoboard, grid paper, paper, tangram

Chapter Resource Masters

- CRM Vocabulary and English Language Development (p. A194)
- CRM Skills Practice (p. A195)
- CRM Problem-Solving Practice (p. A196)
- CRM Homework Practice (p. A197)

1 Introduce

Vocabulary

Reenact Vocabulary Draw a *parallelogram* on the board. Illustrate the example in the Key Concept box and show how the figure can be made into a *rectangle.* Ask students what unit would be used to express the area of a *parallelogram*.

2 Teach

Key Concept

Foundational Skills and Concepts After students have read through the Key Concept box, have them try these exercises.

1. The formula for the areas of a rectangle and parallelogram are similar: true or false. true
2. Describe the area of a parallelogram. base × height
3. What shape can you cut off and move on a parallelogram to form a rectangle? triangle
4. Are the areas of the parallelogram and rectangle the same? yes

Lesson 9-3

Area of a Parallelogram

KEY Concept

parallelogram

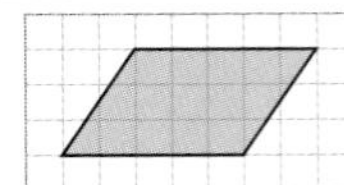

In a parallelogram, b represents the base, and h represents the height. Cut a triangle from the parallelogram along the dashed line. Place the triangle on the other side, next to the right edge of the parallelogram.

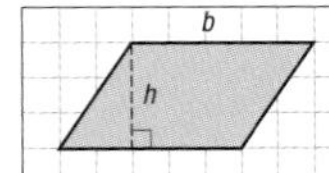
b
h

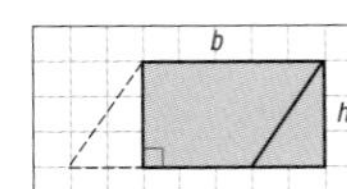
b
h

Notice that the new shape is a rectangle. So, the formulas for the areas of parallelograms and rectangles are similar.

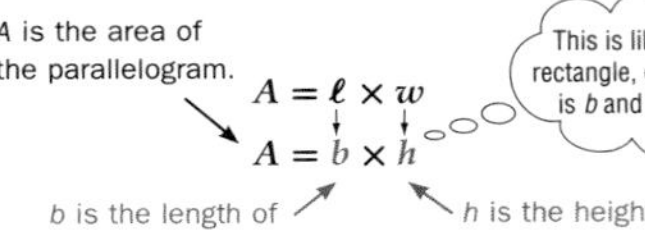
A is the area of the parallelogram.
$A = \ell \times w$
$A = b \times h$
This is like the area of a rectangle, except the length is b and the width is h.
b is the length of the base.
h is the height.

VOCABULARY

area the number of square units needed to cover a region or a plane figure

parallelogram a quadrilateral in which each pair of opposite sides is parallel and equal in length

rectangle a quadrilateral with four right angles; opposite sides are parallel and equal in length

square unit a unit for measuring area

Example 1

Find the area of the parallelogram.

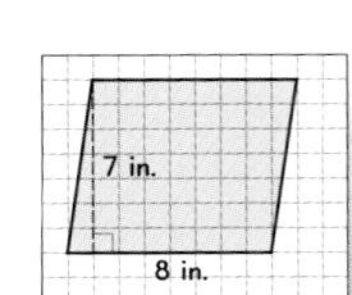
7 in.
8 in.

1. The base is 8 inches. The height is 7 inches.
2. Substitute these values into the formula. Multiply.

$A = b \times h$
$A = 8 \text{ in.} \times 7 \text{ in.}$
$A = 56 \text{ in}^2$

The area of the parallelogram is 56 square inches.

380 Chapter 9 Area

Additional Example 1

Find the area of the parallelogram.

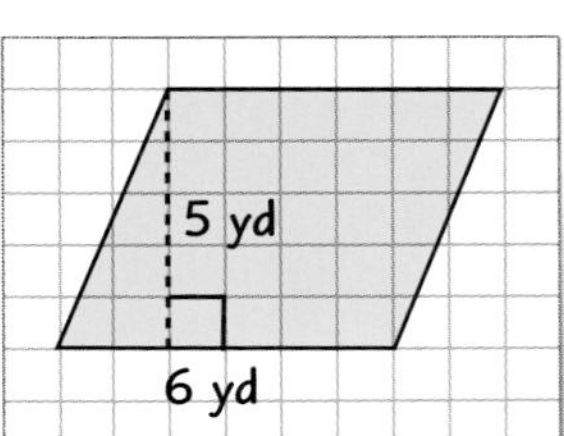
5 yd
6 yd

1. The base is 6 yards. The height is 5 yards.
2. Substitute these values into the formula. Multiply.

$A = b \times h$
$A = 6 \text{ yd} \times 5 \text{ yd}$
$A = 30 \text{ yd}^2$

The area of the parallelogram is 30 square yards.

YOUR TURN!

Find the area of the parallelogram.

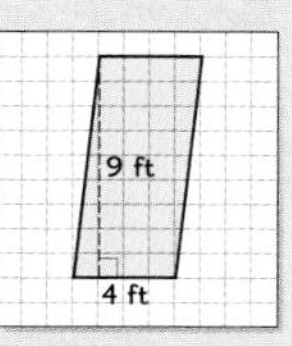

1. The base is __4__ feet. The height is __9__ feet.
2. Substitute these values into the formula. Multiply.

$A = b \times h$

$A =$ __4__ ft × __9__ ft

$A =$ __36__ ft^2

The area of the parallelogram is __36__ square feet.

Example 2

Find the area of the parallelogram.

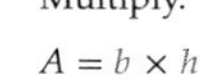

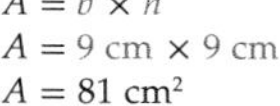

1. The base is 9 centimeters. The height is 9 centimeters.
2. Substitute these values into the formula. Multiply.

$A = b \times h$

$A = 9 \text{ cm} \times 9 \text{ cm}$

$A = 81 \text{ cm}^2$

The area of the parallelogram is 81 square centimeters.

YOUR TURN!

Find the area of the parallelogram.

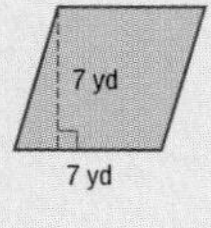

1. The base is __7__ yards. The height is __7__ yards.
2. Substitute these values into the formula. Multiply.

$A = b \times h$

$A =$ __7__ yd × __7__ yd

$A =$ __49__ yd^2

The area of the parallelogram is __49__ square yards.

Who is Correct?

Find the area of the parallelogram.

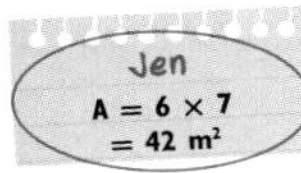

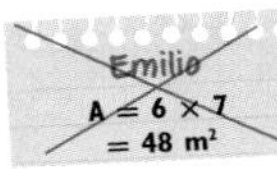

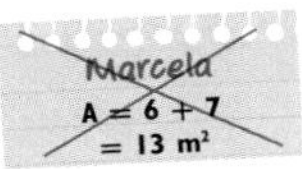

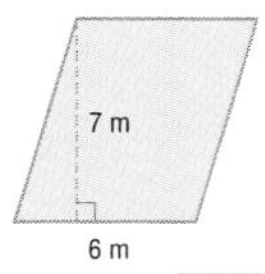

Circle correct answer(s). Cross out incorrect answer(s).

GO ON

Additional Example 2

Find the area of the parallelogram.

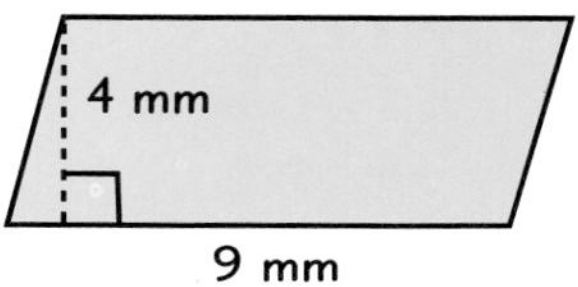

1. The base is 9 millimeters. The height is 4 millimeters.
2. Substitute these values into the formula. Multiply.

$A = b \times h$

$A = 9 \text{ mm} \times 4 \text{ mm}$

$A = 36 \text{ mm}^2$

The area of the parallelogram is 36 square millimeters.

Math Coach Notes

Area The most common error for students is that they define area by the formulas. Move figures around to show students where the formulas come from. Show them how the formulas are derived so they can always find the area.

Who is Correct?

- Jen wrote 42 m^2. This is correct.
- Emilio wrote 48 m^2. This is incorrect because $6 \times 7 = 42$, not 48.
- Marcela wrote 13 m^2. This is incorrect. She added the dimensions instead of multiplying them.

Remind students to do the calculations in a formula carefully.

3 Practice

Using Manipulatives

Geoboard When presenting Exercises 1 or 2, model the parallelogram using a geoboard.

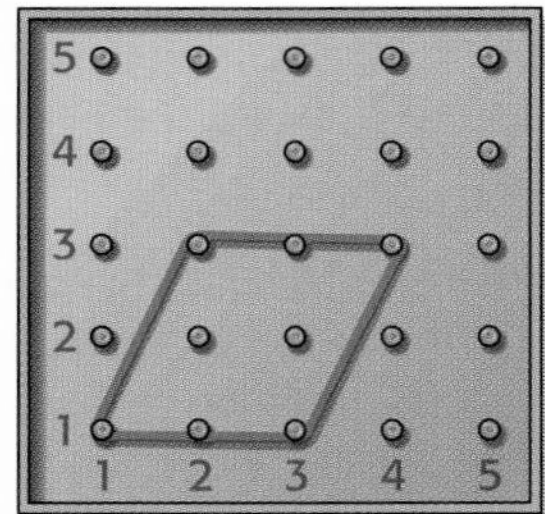

Tangram Tangram pieces can be used to show the relationships between areas of triangles, rectangles, and parallelograms.

On-Hand Manipulatives Cut out figures using paper to show the relationships between the areas of rectangles and parallelograms.

Common Error *Alert*

Exercises 1 and 2 If students do not arrive at the correct answers for Exercises 1 or 2, they might not understand how to proceed. Give the students grid paper. Have them practice making parallelograms and finding their areas. Ask what dimensions would be required for an area of 30 cm² or 200 mm². Guide students to realize that they are looking for two factors with a product of the required areas.

Guided Practice

Draw a parallelogram that has the given area.

1. 30 cm² Sample answer:

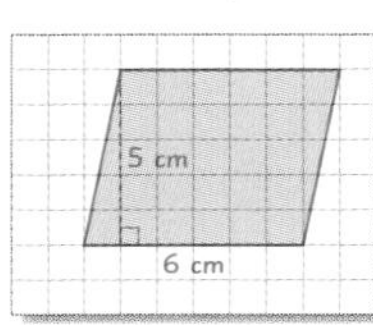

2. 200 mm² Sample answer:

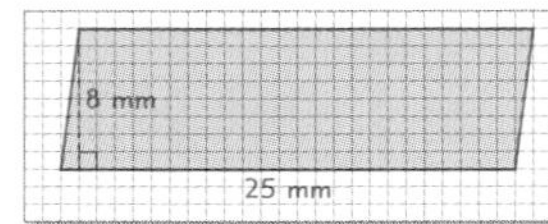

Step by Step Practice

Find the area of the parallelogram.

3.

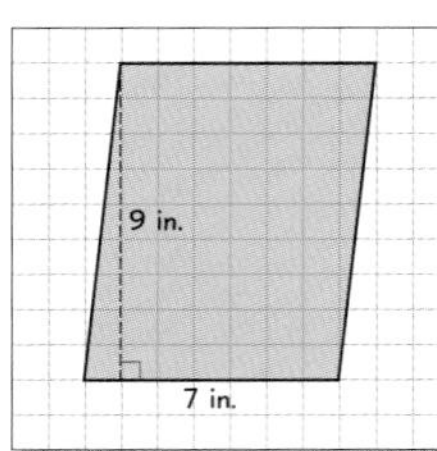

Step 1 The base is <u>7</u> inches.
The height is <u>9</u> inches.

Step 2 Substitute these values into the formula. Multiply.

$A = b \times h$

$A = \underline{7}$ in. $\times$ $\underline{9}$ in.

$A = \underline{63}$ in²

The area of the parallelogram is <u>63</u> square inches.

Intervention Strategy

Kinesthetic/ Visual Learners

Estimate Area Create several parallelograms cut from cardboard or cardstock. Distribute a parallelogram and several congruent square tiles to each student. Using the tiles, have students estimate the area of the parallelogram by placing the tiles on top of the cardboard parallelogram. Create a chart on the board in which students can fill in the estimated area of their parallelogram.

Find the area of each parallelogram.

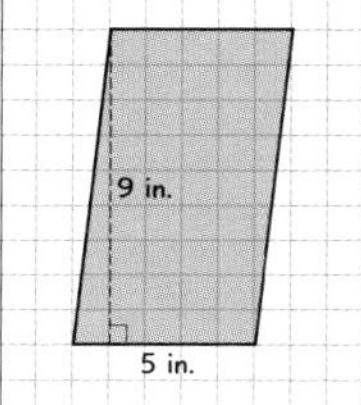

4 The base is 5 inches.
The height is 9 inches.

$A = b \times h$
$A =$ 5 in. $\times$ 9 in.
$A =$ 45 in^2

The area of the parallelogram is 45 square inches.

5 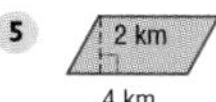

The base is 4 kilometers.
The height is 2 kilometers.

$A =$ 4 km $\times$ 2 km
$A =$ 8 km^2

6 
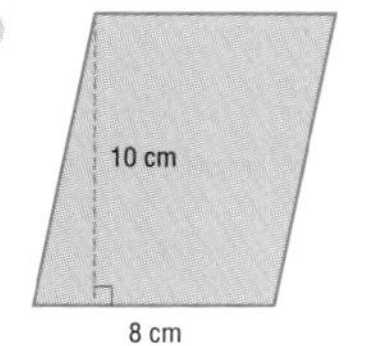

$A =$ 8 cm $\times$ 10 cm
$A =$ 80 cm^2

7 

$A =$ 11 mi $\times$ 6 mi
$A =$ 66 mi^2

8 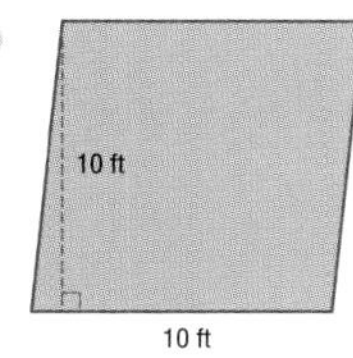

$A =$ 100 ft^2

9 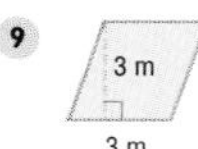

$A =$ 9 m^2

Math Coach Notes

Strategies

1. Start this lesson with hands-on practice as an anchoring experience. Give students grid paper. Have them draw a parallelogram and then cut it out. Tell them to snip off the end triangle and move it to make a rectangle. Have students find the areas of both the parallelogram and rectangle. Allow them to do this with a variety of different-sized figures.

2. Experiment with a tangram. If needed, make one using an online pattern. Tell students to cover the parallelogram in the puzzle with the two small triangles. What other shape can they cover with the two triangles (the square)? Use the square and the small triangles to form a rectangle, and move the triangles onto each end to make a parallelogram. Trace these on grid paper. Prove the area relationship between parallelograms and rectangles.

Note This!

Area Formula When reading the lesson on the area of a parallelogram, encourage students to write the formula for area in their notes. Also, have students list the characteristics of a parallelogram in their notes. Having a better understanding of parallelograms can help students determine which formula is appropriate for finding area.

Are They Getting It?

Check students' understanding of the area of parallelograms by writing these problems on the board. Ask students to point out wrong answers. Tell them to use a drawing or model to show why the answers are correct or are incorrect.

1. A parallelogram with a base of 10 mm and a height of 7 mm has an area of 17 mm^2. This is incorrect, because the dimensions were added and not multiplied.

2. A parallelogram with an area of 16 cm^2 could have a base of 8 cm and a height of 2 cm. This is correct.

3. The area of this parallelogram is 49 yd^2. This is incorrect. $7 \times 5 = 35$ The area is 35 yd^2.

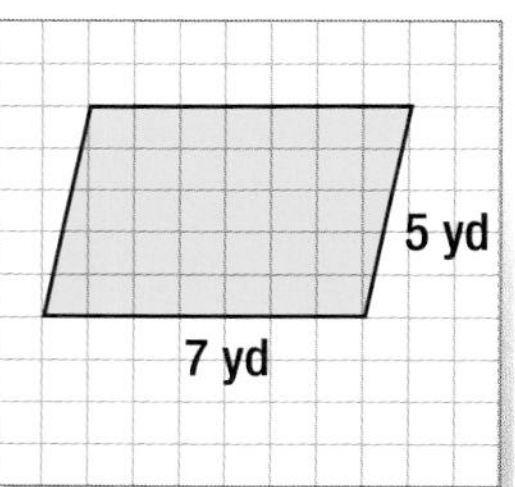

Intervention Strategy

Kinesthetic/ Auditory Learners

Create Parallelograms Prompt students to create a parallelogram on grid paper. Then have them cut out the parallelogram. Have students determine the area of their parallelogram. Encourage students to volunteer to orally describe their parallelogram to the class and to explain the steps they chose to find its area.

Note This!

Label Drawings When completing the area-of-a-parallelogram exercises, suggest that students draw and label a parallelogram with the given information. Next to the numeric values for base and height, have students write *b* next to the base and *h* next to the height. Labeling the dimensions can help when substituting the numbers into the formula.

Step by Step Problem-Solving Practice

Problem-Solving Strategies
- ☐ Draw a diagram.
- ☑ Use a formula.
- ☐ Guess and check.
- ☐ Solve a simpler problem.
- ☐ Work backward.

Solve.

10 HOBBIES Tony bought a sail for his boat. The sail is a parallelogram. It is 21 feet wide at the base and 42 feet tall. What is the area of the new sail?

Understand Read the problem. Write what you know.

The base of the sail is 21 feet.

The height of the sail is 42 feet.

Plan Pick a strategy. One strategy is to use a formula.

Substitute the values for base and height into the area formula.

Solve Use the formula.

$A = b \times h$

$A =$ 21 ft $\times$ 42 ft

$A =$ 882 ft^2

The area of the sail is 882 square feet.

Check Use division or a calculator to check your multiplication.

HOBBIES A sailboat can have sails shaped like parallelograms.

11 ART Part of the sculpture at Jacob Park is shaped like a parallelogram. The front of this piece is 13 feet tall. It has a base of 8 feet. What is the area of the front of the sculpture? Check off each step.

✔ Understand: I circled key words.

✔ Plan: To solve the problem, I will use a formula.

✔ Solve: The answer is 104 square feet.

✔ Check: I checked my answer by using division or a calculator.

12 ART Camila's class is making cardboard ornaments. Each ornament is shaped like a parallelogram with a height of 16 centimeters and a base of 9 centimeters. What is the area of each ornament?

144 cm^2

English Learner Strategy

Guiding Questions Give students two squares of equal size. Cut one in half diagonally. Then ask students the following questions.

- Point to the square. Move the four pieces together to make a rectangle. How do you form a parallelogram with the four pieces?
- Trace the rectangle and the parallelogram on grid paper. What are the areas of the two figures?
- How can you find the area without counting square units?
- What is the relationship between the area of the rectangle and the area of the parallelogram?
- How would you use the formula to find the area of a parallelogram with base length 5 mm and height 2 mm?

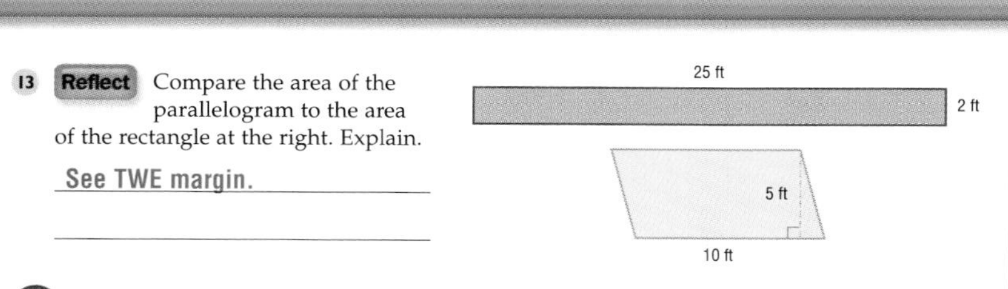

13 **Reflect** Compare the area of the parallelogram to the area of the rectangle at the right. Explain.

See TWE margin.

Skills, Concepts, and Problem Solving

Draw a parallelogram that has the given area.

14 220 mm² Sample answer:

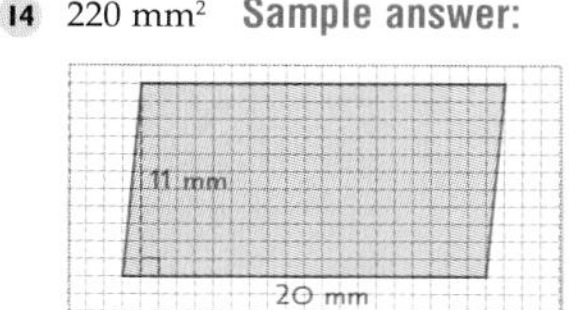

15 5 in² Sample answer:

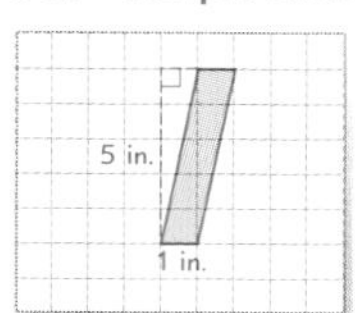

Find the area of each parallelogram.

16

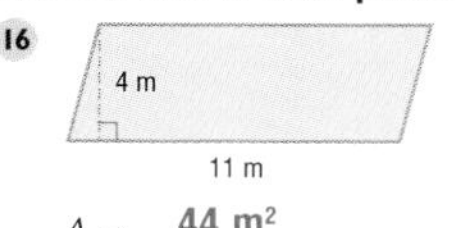

$A =$ 44 m²

17

$A =$ 45 ft²

18

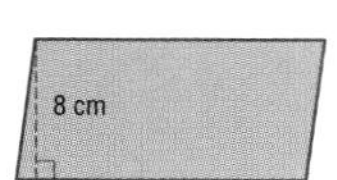

$A =$ 128 cm²

19

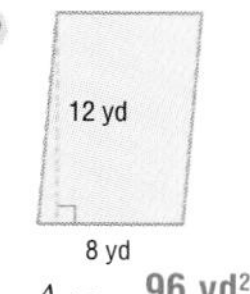

$A =$ 96 yd²

20

6 in.
12 in.

$A =$ 72 in²

21

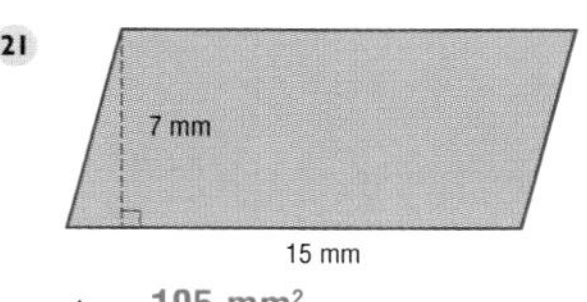

$A =$ 105 mm²

GO ON

Math Challenge

Draw a Dimension Make two sets of cards with the numbers 1 to 20 so there are 40 cards. Shuffle the deck and place the cards facedown. Each student will take turns picking one card from the deck. This is the base length of their parallelograms. Then they will each pick another card. This represents the height. Whoever has the greatest area wins the point. You can also instruct students to draw the parallelograms.

Odd/Even Assignments

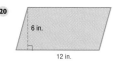

Exercises 14–24 are structured so that students practice the same concepts whether they are assigned the odd or even problems.

In-Class Assignment

Have students complete Exercises 15, 19, 23, and 27 to ensure that they understand the concept.

Additional Answer

Exercise 13 The area of the parallelogram is found by using the formula $A = b \times h$. Since $10 \times 5 = 50$, the area of the parallelogram is 50 ft². The area of the rectangle is found by using the formula $A = \ell \times w$. Since $25 \times 2 = 50$, the area of the rectangle is 50 ft². The areas of the two figures are equal, even though the lengths of their sides are different, because 25, 2, 10, and 5 are factors of 50.

Common Error Alert

Exercise 23 If a student struggles with Exercise 23, it might be because he or she is having difficulty visualizing the figure. Suggest he or she sketch a picture and label the dimensions.

See It, Do It, Say It, Write It

Step 1 Use an overhead projector to draw a parallelogram on grid paper. Draw a line that is perpendicular to the base and count the units of the height. Label the base and height. Ask a student what the area of the figure is. Verify by counting units.

Step 2 Give students geoboards. Challenge them to make rectangles and determine the areas. Then students can move the bands to make a parallelogram. Have students explain how they know what the area of the parallelogram is.

Step 3 Tell students to draw a parallelogram on grid paper. Ask them to draw a line where they would cut to make it into a rectangle. They can use an arrow to show where they would place the part they cut.

Step 4 On the same paper, ask students to write about what they have learned about area. Also tell them to write about the relationship between the areas of a rectangle and a parallelogram.

Looking Ahead: Pre-teach

Area of a Triangle In the next lesson, students will learn about the area of a triangle. You can cut a rectangle into two triangles like this.

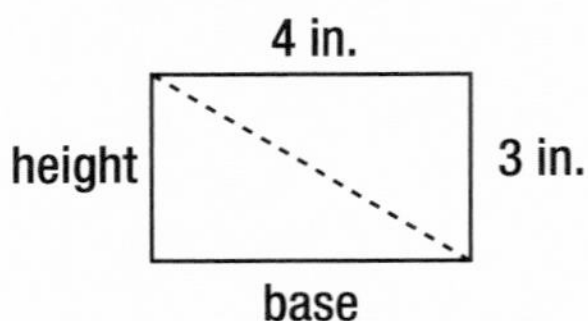

The formula for the area is $A = \frac{1}{2} \times base \times height$.

Example

What is the area of the triangle? 6 in^2

Additional Answer

Exercise 27 Substitute the values of the base and height into the formula for the area of a parallelogram. $A = b \times h$; $A = 9$ in. $\times$ 10 in. $= 90$ in^2. The area of the parallelogram is 90 square inches.

Solve.

22 FARMING Mrs. Rockwell's cornfield is in the shape of a parallelogram. Refer to the photo caption at the right. What is the area of the cornfield?
4,108 m^2

FARMING **The height of Mrs. Rockwell's cornfield is 79 meters. The base is 52 meters.**

23 HOBBIES Toby made toy wooden boats. He cuts each sail in the shape of a parallelogram. Each sail is 45 millimeters at the base and 65 millimeters tall. What is the area of each sail?
2,925 mm^2

24 POSTERS The cheerleaders make a Spirit Week sign in the shape of a parallelogram. The sign is 6 feet long and 4 feet tall. How many square feet of poster board do the cheerleaders use?
24 square feet

Vocabulary Check **Write the vocabulary word that completes each sentence.**

25 A(n) square unit is a unit for measuring area.

26 A(n) parallelogram is a quadrilateral in which each pair of opposite sides is parallel and equal in length.

27 Writing in Math Explain how to find the area of a parallelogram with a base of 9 inches and a height of 10 inches.
See TWE margin.

Spiral Review

Solve.

28 FITNESS A trampoline has a mat that is 10 feet wide and 14 feet long. What is the area of the mat? (Lesson 9-2, p. 373)
140 ft^2

29 Draw a figure that has an area of 18 square units. (Lesson 9-1, p. 368)
Sample answer:

3
6

STOP

Ticket Out the Door

Rectangles and Parallelograms Using grid paper, tell each student to draw a rectangle. Tell students to now draw a parallelogram that has the same area as the rectangle. Ask them to label the dimensions. Tell them to do this two more times, making the dimensions of each set of figures different. Students can hand in their papers when they exit the classroom.

Lesson 9-4

Area of a Triangle

KEY Concept

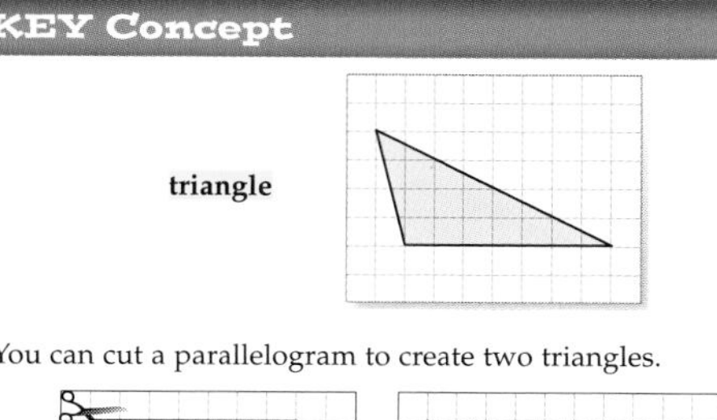

You can cut a parallelogram to create two triangles.

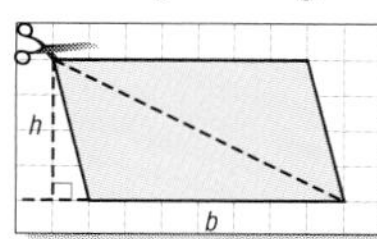

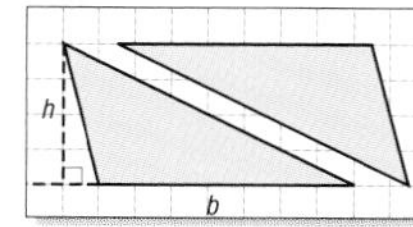

Notice you now have two triangles. Each triangle is one-half the size of the parallelogram. Remember the formula for the area of a parallelogram is $A = b \times h$

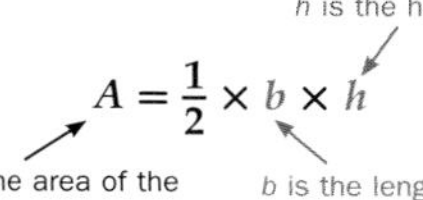

The location of the height of a triangle can vary. There are three possibilities.

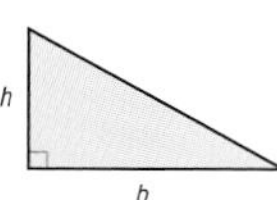

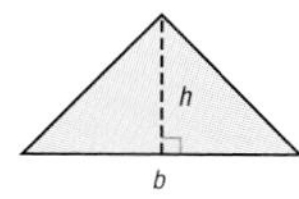

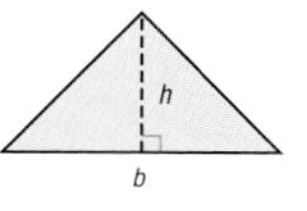

The height is one side of a triangle.	The height is inside the triangle.	The height is outside the triangle.

VOCABULARY

area
the number of square units needed to cover a region or a plane figure

parallelogram
a quadrilateral in which each pair of opposite sides is parallel and equal in length

rectangle
a quadrilateral with four right angles; opposite sides are parallel and equal in length

square unit
a unit for measuring area

triangle
a polygon with three sides and three angles

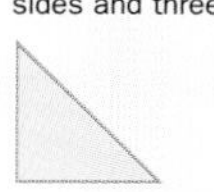

GO ON

Intervention Strategy — Linguistic Learners

Real-World Triangles Have students go through magazines, newspapers, and other printed material to find examples of triangles in the real world. Have students cut out or copy these examples and share their results with the class.

Lesson Notes

Lesson 9-4

Lesson Planner

Objective Find the area of a triangle.

Vocabulary **area**, **parallelogram**, **rectangle**, **square unit**, **triangle**

Materials/Manipulatives geoboard, grid paper, index cards, ruler, tangram

Chapter Resource Masters

- CRM Vocabulary and English Language Development (p. A198)
- CRM Skills Practice (p. A199)
- CRM Problem-Solving Practice (p. A200)
- CRM Homework Practice (p. A201)

Vocabulary

Relationships Draw a *triangle* on the board. Tell students that any two identical *triangles* will always form a *parallelogram.* If that is so, what is the formula for area of a *triangle?* $A = \frac{1}{2} \times \text{base} \times \text{height}$

Key Concept

Foundational Skills and Concepts After students have read through the Key Concept box, have them try these exercises.

1. Is the height of a triangle always on the inside? no
2. Which figure is used to derive the formula for the area of a triangle? parallelogram
3. What is the formula for the area of a triangle? $A = \frac{1}{2} \times b \times h$
4. True or false: The side length is always the height of a triangle. false

Additional Example 1

Find the area of the triangle.

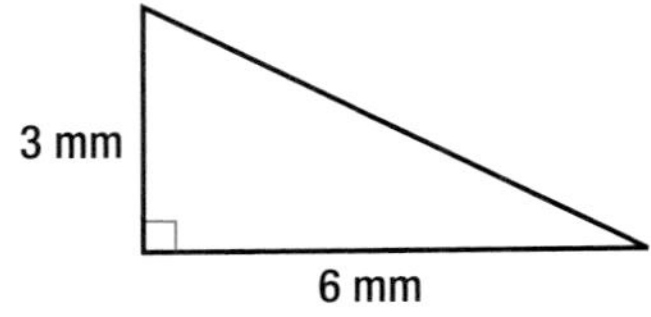

1. The base of the triangle is 6 millimeters. The height of the triangle is 3 millimeters.
2. Substitute these values into the formula.
   $A = \frac{1}{2} \times b \times h$
   $A = \frac{1}{2} \times 6 \text{ mm} \times 3 \text{ mm}$
3. Multiply to find the area of the triangle.
   $A = 9 \text{ mm}^2$

   The area of the triangle is 9 square millimeters.

Additional Example 2

Find the area of the triangle.

1. The base is 2 units long.

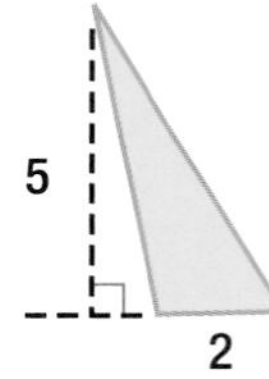

2. The height is 5 units long.
3. Substitute these values into the formula.
   $A = \frac{1}{2} \times b \times h$
   $A = \frac{1}{2} \times 2 \times 5$
4. Multiply to find the area of the triangle.
   $A = 5 \text{ units}^2$

   The area of the triangle is 5 square units.

Example 1

Find the area of the triangle.

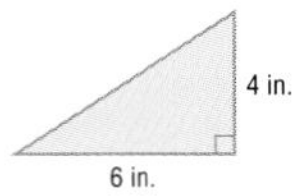

1. The base is 6 inches.
   The height is 4 inches.
2. Substitute these values into the formula.
   $A = \frac{1}{2} \times b \times h$
   $A = \frac{1}{2} \times 6 \text{ in.} \times 4 \text{ in.}$
3. Multiply to find the area of the triangle.
   $A = 12 \text{ in}^2$

   The area of the triangle is 12 square inches.

YOUR TURN!

Find the area of the triangle.

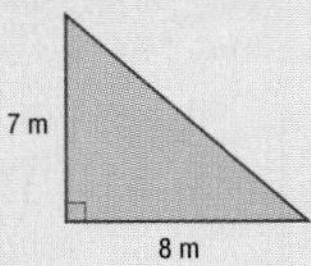

1. The base is __8__ meters.
   The height is __7__ meters.
2. Substitute these values into the formula.
   $A = \frac{1}{2} \times b \times h$
   $A = \frac{1}{2} \times$ __8__ m $\times$ __7__ m
3. Multiply to find the area of the triangle.
   $A =$ __28__ m^2

   The area of the triangle is __28__ square meters.

Example 2

Find the area of the triangle.

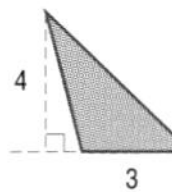

1. The base is 3 units long.
2. The height is 4 units long.
3. Substitute these values into the formula.
   $A = \frac{1}{2} \times b \times h$
   $A = \frac{1}{2} \times 3 \times 4$
4. Multiply to find the area of the triangle.
   $A = 6 \text{ units}^2$

   The area of the triangle is 6 square units.

Intervention Strategy — Linguistic Learners

Area of a Triangle Have students write a list of steps for determining the area of a triangle. They should use complete sentences, appropriate grammar, and punctuation. After their instructions are complete, student volunteers can share their directions with the class verbally and draw illustrations as needed on the board.

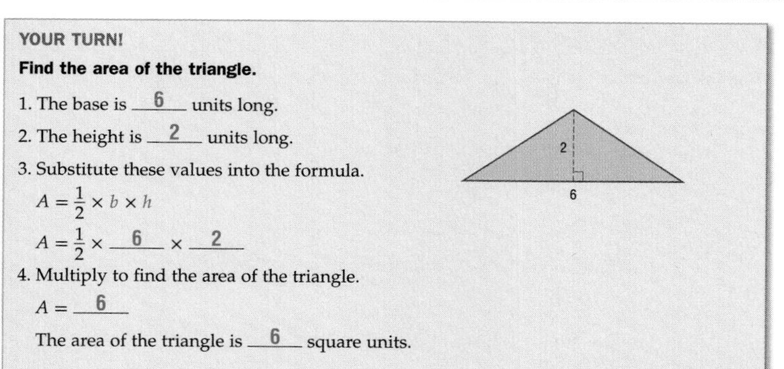
YOUR TURN!

Find the area of the triangle.

1. The base is 6 units long.
2. The height is 2 units long.
3. Substitute these values into the formula.

$A = \frac{1}{2} \times b \times h$

$A = \frac{1}{2} \times$ 6 $\times$ 2

4. Multiply to find the area of the triangle.

$A =$ 6

The area of the triangle is 6 square units.

Who is Correct?

Find the area of the triangle.

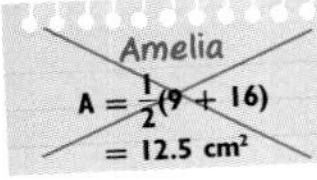

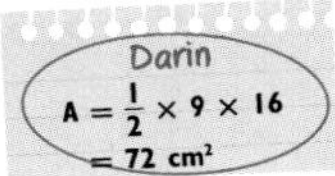

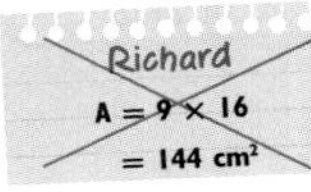

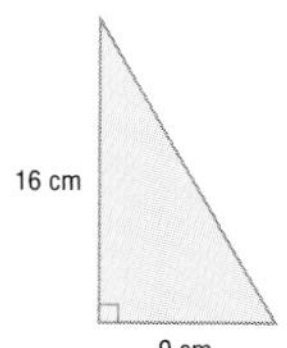

Circle correct answer(s). Cross out incorrect answer(s).

Guided Practice

Draw a triangle that has the given area.

1. 15 units² Sample answer:

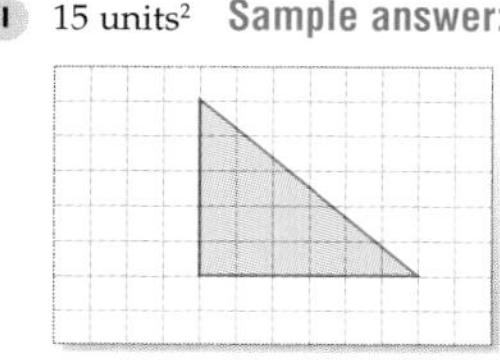

2. 100 units² Sample answer:

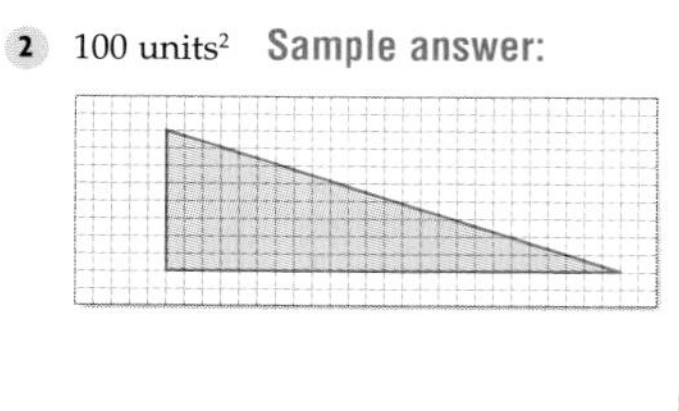

GO ON

Who *is Correct?*

Diagnostic Teaching

- Amelia wrote 12.5 cm². This is incorrect because she added the dimensions when she should have multiplied.
- Darin wrote 72 cm². This is correct.
- Richard wrote 144 cm². This is incorrect because he forgot to divide by 2.

Remind students that the area of a triangle is half the product of the base and height.

Math Coach Notes

Strategies

1. Start this lesson with hands-on practice as an anchoring experience. Give students grid paper. Have them draw a rectangle and then cut it out. Ask: What is the area? Next, have students cut along the diagonal. Ask: What is the area of the triangle? Tell them to write a formula. Challenge students to draw as many different rectangles and parallelograms as they can. Tell them to see if they can disprove the fact that all parallelograms (including rectangles and squares, which are parallelograms) can be divided along the diagonal to make two identical triangles.
2. A tangram will also prove these area relationships.

Using Manipulatives

Geoboard When presenting Example 2, use a geoboard to model the triangle with one color band. Model the rectangle that is twice the size of the triangle in another color band.

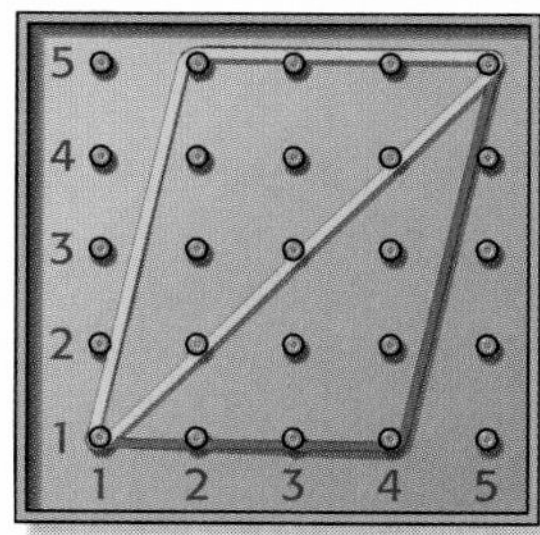

Tangram Tangram pieces can be used to show the relationships between areas of triangles, rectangles, and parallelograms.

On-Hand Manipulatives Cut out paper figures to show the relationships between the areas of triangles, rectangles, and parallelograms.

Math Coach Notes

Triangle Varieties Point out that not all triangles are right triangles. Suggest to students that they draw a variety of triangles (scalene acute, isosceles right, and so on) in their notes and label the base and height of each triangle.

Measurements Measurements are often taught as if they are exact. Stress to students that they may or may not be accurate. Errors in measurement and estimation can accumulate. Point these inaccuracies out to students.

Step by Step Practice

Find the area of the triangle.

3 **Step 1** The base is 5 miles. The height is 16 miles.

Step 2 Substitute these values into the formula.

$A = \frac{1}{2} \times b \times h$

$A = \frac{1}{2} \times$ 5 mi $\times$ 16 mi

Step 3 Multiply to find the area of the triangle.

$A =$ 40 mi²

The area of the triangle is 40 square miles.

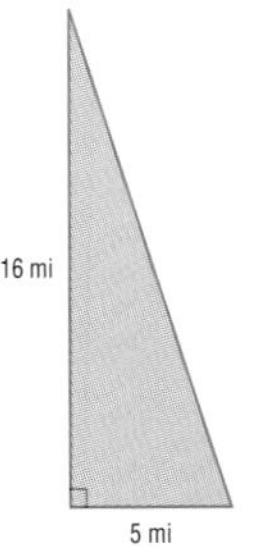

Find the area of each triangle.

4 The base is 10 meters. The height is 7 meters.

$A = \frac{1}{2} \times b \times h$

$A = \frac{1}{2} \times$ 10 m $\times$ 7 m

$A =$ 35 m²

The area of the triangle is 35 square meters.

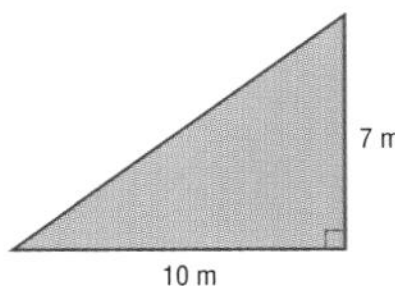

5 $A = \frac{1}{2} \times b \times h$

$A = \frac{1}{2} \times$ 8 ft $\times$ 11 ft

$A =$ 44 ft²

The area of the triangle is 44 square feet.

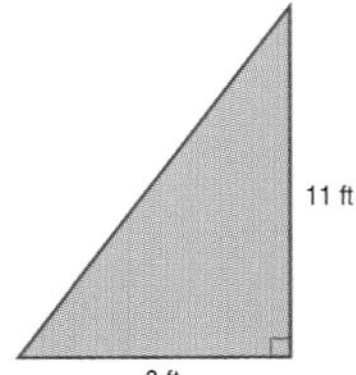

390 Chapter 9 Area

Are They Getting It?

Check students' understanding of the area of triangles by writing these problems on the board. Ask students to point out wrong answers and explain why they are wrong. Tell them to use a drawing or model to show why the answers are correct or are incorrect.

1. A triangle with base of 4 mm and height of 9 mm has area of 36 mm². This is incorrect. The area for a parallelogram was found. It must be divided in half to find the area of a triangle.

2. A triangle with area of 12 m² could have a base of 6 m and a height of 2 m. This is incorrect. The dimensions should be multiplied, then divided by 2. For example, $3 \times 8 = 24$, $24 \div 2 = 12$.

3. The area of this triangle is 12 in². This is correct.

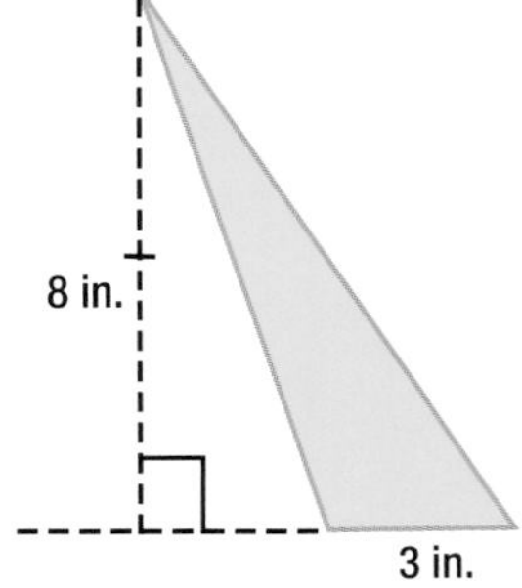

6 The area of the triangle is 45 square inches

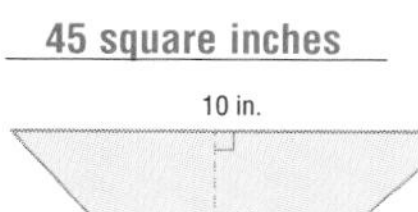

7 The area of the triangle is 20 square units

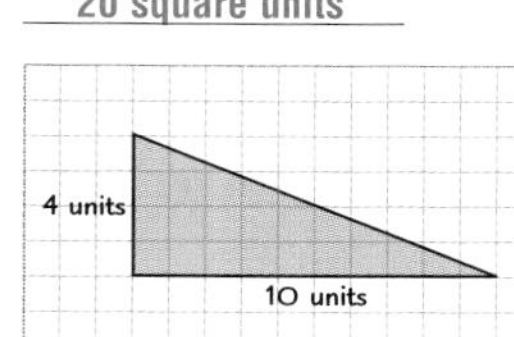

Step by Step Problem-Solving Practice

Problem-Solving Strategies
- ☐ Draw a diagram.
- ☐ Look for a pattern.
- ☐ Guess and check.
- ☑ Use a formula.
- ☐ Solve a simpler problem.

Solve.

8 VOLUNTEERING Lolita earned a club patch by volunteering last week. The patch is shaped like a triangle. It has a base of 53 millimeters and is 66 millimeters tall. What is the area of Lolita's patch?

Understand Read the problem. Write what you know.

The base of the patch is 53 millimeters.
The height of the patch is 66 millimeters.

Plan Pick a strategy. One strategy is to use a formula.

Substitute these values into the formula.

Solve Use the formula.

$A = \frac{1}{2} \times b \times h$

$A = \frac{1}{2} \times$ 53 mm $\times$ 66 mm

$A =$ 1,749 mm^2

The area of the patch is 1,749 square millimeters

Check Use a calculator to check your answer.

Common Error *Alert*

Exercises 6 and 7 If students multiply the base by the height but forget to divide by 2 in Exercises 6 and 7, have them practice with a geoboard. They can first form the triangle and then form the rectangle for which the triangle is half. Have these students physically work these problems as they verbally describe their techniques.

Intervention Strategy

Logical/ Visual Learners

Different Triangles, Same Area Give each student pair a ruler. Tell them to draw a triangle with an area of 20 square inches. Have students share their results. Guide students to see that the dimensions of the triangles can be different, while the areas are the same. Ask student volunteers to draw their triangles on the board. Note that the triangles can have different shapes and still have the same areas.

Odd/Even Assignments

Exercises 12–21 are structured so that students practice the same concepts whether they are assigned the odd or even problems.

In-Class Assignment

Have students complete Exercises 12, 15, 21, 23, and 24 to ensure that they understand the concept.

Note This!

Chart of Formulas In this chapter, students have learned three formulas. Tell students to make a content frame. Have them include a picture of the figure, its name, the formula, and examples. Students can add to their content frame after future lessons. An example is shown below for triangles.

Name	Picture	Area Formula	Example
Triangle	△	$A = \frac{1}{2} \times b \times h$	$b = 5; h = 4$ $A = \frac{1}{2} \times 5 \times 4 = 10$

9 FLAGS The Coleman Camp flag is raised every morning. The flag is in the shape of a triangle. It is 36 inches long at its base and has a height of 49 inches. What is the area of the camp flag?

Check off each step.

✔ Understand: I circled key words.

✔ Plan: To solve the problem, I will use a formula.

✔ Solve: The answer is 882 in².

✔ Check: I checked my answer by using a calculator.

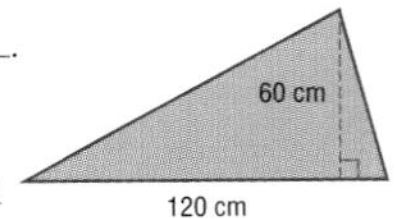

10 COSTUMES Marita bought a triangular-shaped bandanna for her costume in the school play. The bandanna is 60 centimeters tall and has a base of 120 centimeters. What is the area of the bandanna?

3,600 cm²

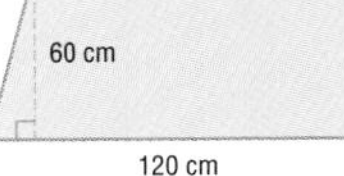

11  Reflect Compare the area of the triangular-shaped bandanna to the area of the parallelogram at the right.

The parallelogram's area is two times the triangle's area.

Skills, Concepts, and Problem Solving

Draw a triangle that has the given area.

12 12 units² Sample answer:

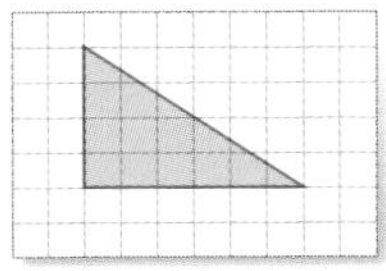

13 6 units² Sample answer:

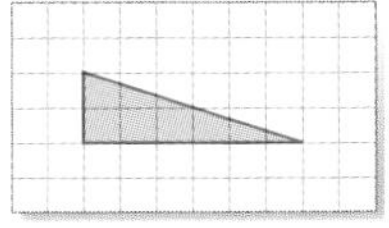

English Learner Strategy

Guiding Questions Give students two index cards each. Fold and cut one along the diagonal. Then ask the following questions.

- Which is the rectangle? Which is the triangle?
- How many of the triangles make a rectangle?
- What is the formula for the area of a rectangle?
- How can you use the formula for the area of a rectangle to write the formula for the area of a triangle?
- How would you use the area of a triangle formula to find the area of a triangle with a base length of 4 feet and a height of 5 feet?

Find the area of each triangle.

14 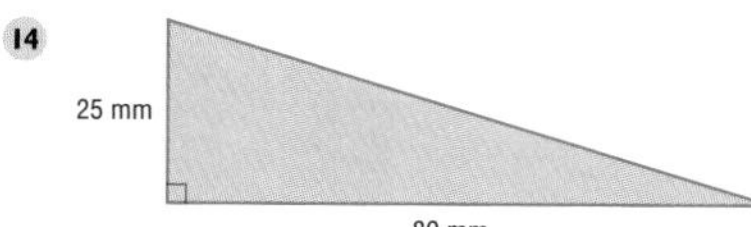

$A =$ 1,000 mm²

15 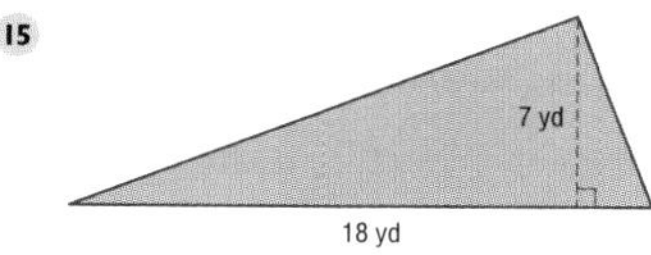

$A =$ 63 yd²

16 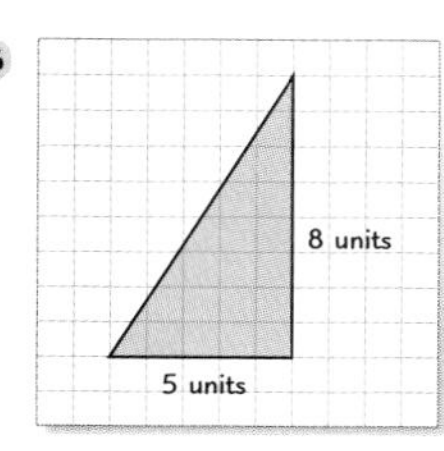

$A =$ 20 units²

17 3 units

6 units

$A =$ 9 units²

18 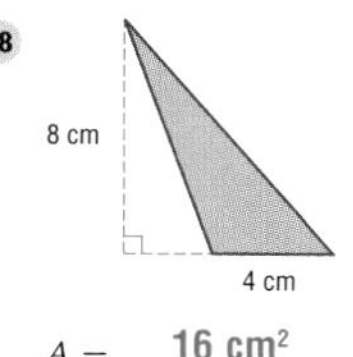

$A =$ 16 cm²

19 3 ft

10 ft

$A =$ 15 ft²

Solve.

20 WOODWORKING For a game, Wayne made triangular-shaped wooden blocks. Each block was 48 millimeters at the base and 51 millimeters tall. What was the area of each block?

1,224 mm²

Common Error *Alert*

Exercise 20 If a student struggles with Exercise 20, it might be because he or she is having difficulty visualizing the figure. Suggest the student sketch and label the triangle.

Intervention Strategy — Linguistic Learners

Draw and Find Area Distribute four index cards to each student. Ask students to draw triangles on each index card in which the height is not one of the sides of the triangle. These will be triangles that are not right triangles. Have students review the Key Concept box if needed. Collect all of the index cards and shuffle them. Distribute four random cards to each student. Instruct students to find the areas of the triangles on the index cards.

Math Challenge

Rolling Triangles Each pair of students will need two number cubes. Students take turns rolling both cubes. The product of these numbers is the area of a triangle. Now tell both students to draw as many triangles as possible that have that area. Each student gets one point for each correct triangle. The student with the most points wins.

4 Assess

See It, Do It, Say It, Write It

Step 1 Draw a right triangle on the board. Label its dimensions. Have a student volunteer explain how to find the area using a formula. Repeat using equilateral and acute triangles. Let students explain where the height would be measured.

Step 2 Draw a right triangle on the board. Extend the triangle to a rectangle. Have a student explain how to find the area using what he or she knows about the area of a rectangle. Do this with different types of triangles.

Step 3 Draw an equilateral, acute, and scalene triangle on the board. Discuss with students what is different and the same about the triangles. Tell students to copy the triangles onto graph paper. Tell them to find the area of each using two methods.

Step 4 Ask students to use one of the triangles from the step above. Tell them to describe in writing the two methods they used to find the area.

21 HORSES Earl searched for a missing horse near his uncle's ranch. He searched in an area that was shaped like a triangle. Refer to the photo caption at the right. What was the area of the piece of land that Earl searched?

306,556 yd^2

HORSES **The area in which Earl searched for the horse had a base of 886 yards and a height of 692 yards.**

Vocabulary Check **Write the vocabulary word that completes each sentence.**

22 __Area__ is the number of square units needed to cover a region or a plane figure.

23 A(n) __triangle__ is a polygon with three sides and three angles.

24 Writing in Math Explain how the area of a triangle is related to the area of a rectangle.

Sample answer: A rectangle can be cut into two equal triangles. So, the area of a triangle is half the area of a rectangle.

Spiral Review

Solve.

25 WEATHER Zing turned on the weather channel. He saw a region that had a tornado watch. The region was shaped like a parallelogram. It measured 82 miles across at the base and was 56 miles long. What was the area of the region with the tornado watch? (Lesson 9-3, p. 380)

4,592 mi^2

26 Find the area of the rectangle. (Lessons 9-1, p. 368 and 9-2, p. 373)

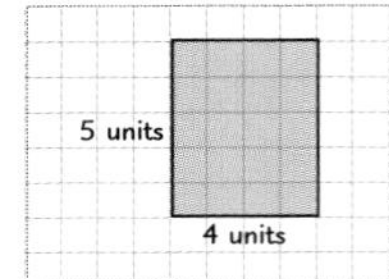

The area of the rectangle is __20__ square units.

STOP

394 **Chapter 9** Area

Ticket Out the Door

Partners Make Triangles Count off each student from 2 through 20. Then start over again until each student is assigned a number. Tell students to pair up with a partner. The number assigned to one student is the height, and the other number is the base of a triangle in inches. Tell students to draw their triangle on paper, labeling the height and base. After calculating the area, students can present their work. Students hand in their papers as they exit the classroom.

Progress Check 2 (Lessons 9-3 and 9-4)

Draw a figure that has the given area.

1 parallelogram, 60 square units sample answer:

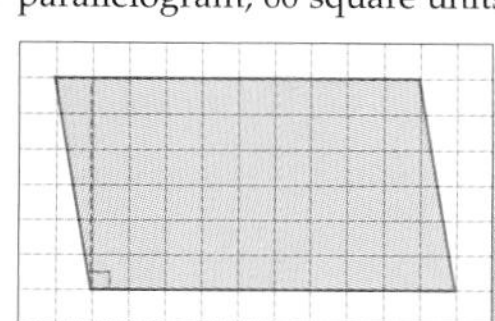

2 triangle, 15 square units sample answer:

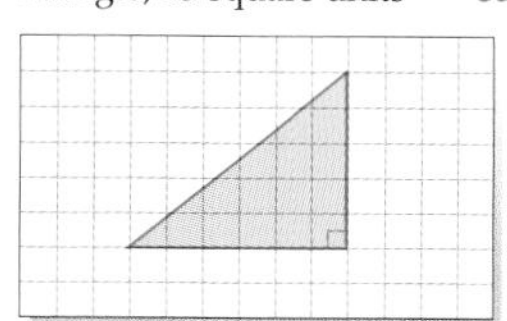

Find the area of each parallelogram.

3

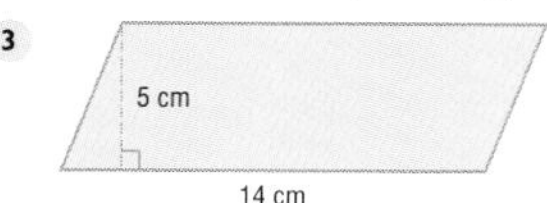

$A =$ 70 cm²

4

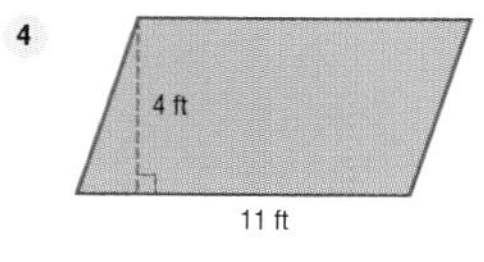

$A =$ 44 ft²

Find the area of each triangle.

5

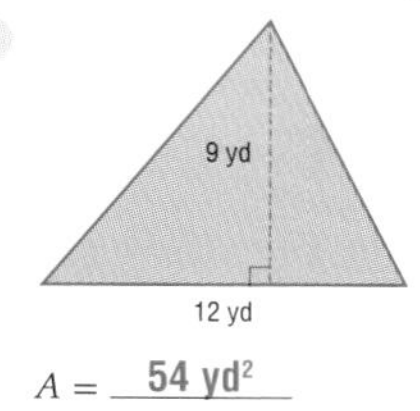

$A =$ 54 yd²

6

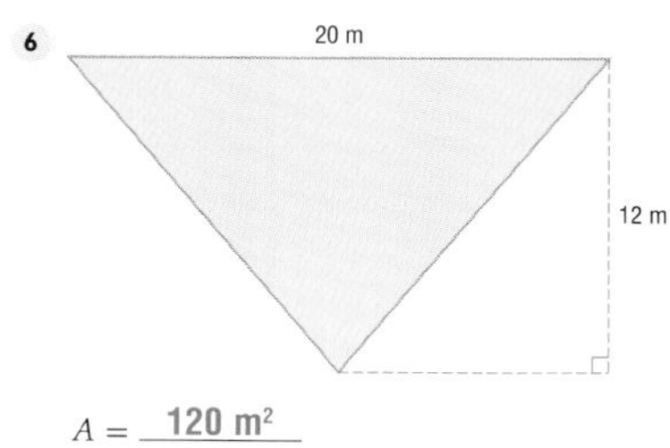

$A =$ 120 m²

Solve.

7 **DESIGN** Ngoko hung a triangular-shaped picture in her bedroom. The picture was 60 centimeters tall and 85 centimeters at the base. What was the area of the picture? 2,550 cm²

8 **ARCHITECTURE** A window is in the shape of a parallelogram. The window is 3 feet tall and 4 feet at the base. What is the area of the window? 12 ft²

Chapter 9 Area 395

Progress Check 2

Chapter 9

Formative Assessment

Use the Progress Check to assess students' mastery of the previous lessons. Have students review the lesson indicated for the problems they answered incorrectly.

Odd/Even Assignments

Exercises are structured so that students practice the same concepts whether they are assigned the odd or even problems.

Common Error Alert

Label Units If some of the students are not labeling their answers in square units when asked to find an area, remind them to do so. Reiterate that area is found by multiplying the dimensions of the rectangle, square, and parallelograms.

Exercise 1 Be sure students recognize the figure as a parallelogram. Be sure the students understand why the formulas for the area of a rectangle and a parallelogram are similar. Construct a sketch, if necessary.

Data-Driven Decision Making

Students missing Exercises . . .	Have trouble with . . .	Should review and practice . . .
1–2	drawing a figure with a given area.	SSG Lessons 9-3 and 9-4, pp. 380 and 387 CRM Skills Practice, pp. A195 and A199
3–4	finding the area of a parallelogram with a formula.	SSG Lesson 9-3, p. 380 CRM Skills Practice, p. A195
5–6	finding the area of a triangle with a formula.	SSG Lesson 9-4, p. 387 CRM Skills Practice, p. A199
7–8	solving word problems involving finding the area of a rectangle and/or parallelogram.	CRM Problem-Solving Practice, pp. A196 and A200

Chapter 9 Study Guide
Formative Assessment

Vocabulary and Concept Check

If students have difficulty answering Exercises 1–8, remind them that they can use the page references to refresh their memories about the vocabulary terms.

Vocabulary Review Strategies

Word Game Divide the class into small groups. Have each group design an answer-question-style game that they can use to review the vocabulary words. For example, the phrase might be "I am the number of square units in a figure or region." Then the proper response (in the form of a question) would be, "What is area?"

Lesson Review

Each example walks the students through the main concepts of this chapter. If the given examples are not sufficient to review the questions, remind students that the page reference tell them where to review the topic in their textbooks.

Find **Extra Practice** for these concepts in the Practice Worksheets, pages A186–A201.

Classroom Management

Early Finishers Have those students with extra time on their hands design a small lab for their classmates. You could give them a list of items around the classroom to measure and record. Then on the following day, some of the class time could be spent in small groups with the early finishers assigned as group leaders to guide the others through the lab they created.

Chapter 9 Study Guide

Vocabulary and Concept Check

area, *p. 368*
parallelogram, *p. 380*
rectangle, *p. 373*
square, *p. 373*
square unit, *p. 368*
triangle, *p. 387*

Write the vocabulary word that completes each sentence.

1. A(n) ___square___ is a rectangle with four equal sides.
2. The number of square units needed to cover a region or a plane figure is the ___area___.
3. A(n) ___parallelogram___ is a quadrilateral in which each pair of opposite sides is parallel and equal in length.
4. A(n) ___rectangle___ is a parallelogram with four right angles.
5. The unit used for measuring area is called a(n) ___square unit___.

Identify the correct figure for each area formula.

6. $A = \ell \times w$ ___rectangle___
7. $A = \frac{1}{2} \times b \times h$ ___triangle___
8. $A = b \times h$ ___parallelogram___

9-1 Introduction to Area (pp. 368–372)

9. Draw a figure that has an area of 23 square units.

sample answer:

Example 1

Draw a figure that has an area of 17 square units.

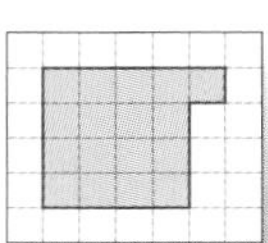

To cover an area of 17 square units, there are two options.

Cover 17 whole squares.

Cover a combination of whole and half squares that adds up to 17 squares.

Find the area of each figure.

10 

The area of the square is 16 square units.

11 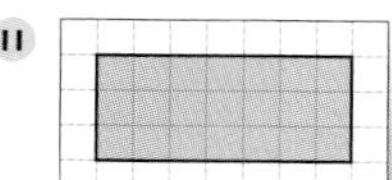

$A =$ 21 square units

Estimate the area of each figure.

12 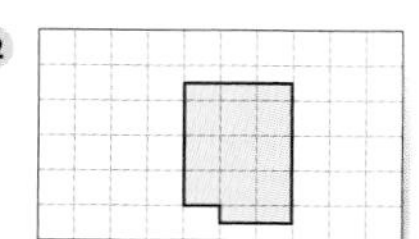

The area of the figure is about 12 square units.

13 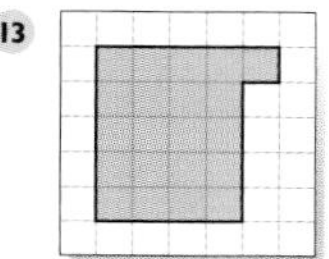

$A =$ 21 square units

Example 2

Estimate the area of the figure.

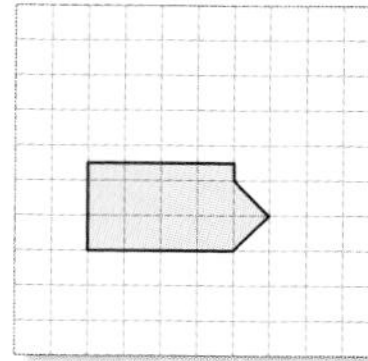

Count the number of whole squares the figure covers. The figure covers 8 whole squares.

Count the number of half squares the figure covers. The figure covers 6 half squares.

$\frac{1}{2}+\frac{1}{2}+\frac{1}{2}+\frac{1}{2}+\frac{1}{2}+\frac{1}{2}=3$

Add the number of whole squares.

$8 + 3 = \mathbf{11}$

The area of the figure is 11 square units.

Dinah Zike's Foldables®

Review Have students trade their completed Foldables with a partner. Then have partners give each other problems from each lesson of the chapter. Students solve the problems, using the information contained in the Foldables as an aid. (For complete instructions, see Chapter Resource Masters, p. A183)

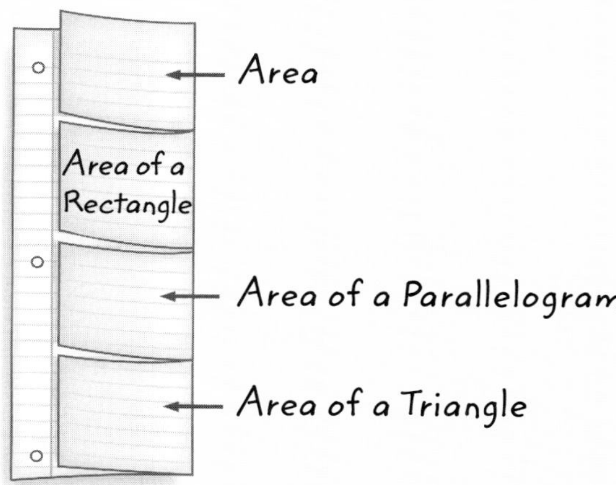

Note This!

Study Checklist Help students create a study checklist. The checklist should include the following items.

- State the formula for the area of a rectangle and parallelogram.
- Find the area of a rectangle.
- Find the area of a parallelogram.
- State the formula for the area of a triangle.
- Find the area of a triangle.

Students should put a check mark next to each topic when they feel they have a good grasp of the process.

Lesson Review

9-2 Area of a Rectangle (pp. 373–378)

Find the area of each square.

14 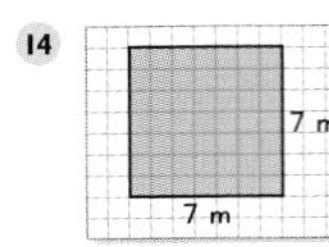

$A =$ 49 square meters or 49 m^2

15 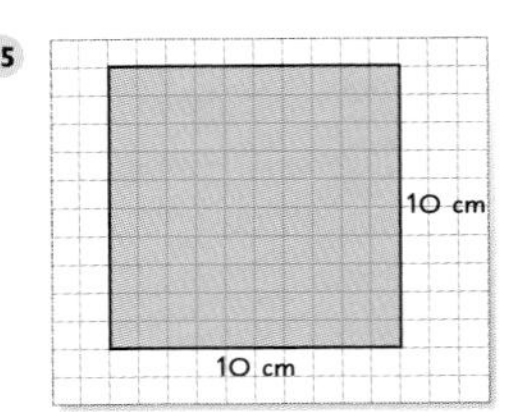

$A =$ 100 square centimeters or 100 cm^2

Find the area of each rectangle.

16 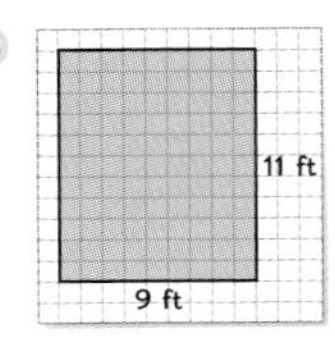

$A =$ 99 square feet or 99 ft^2

17 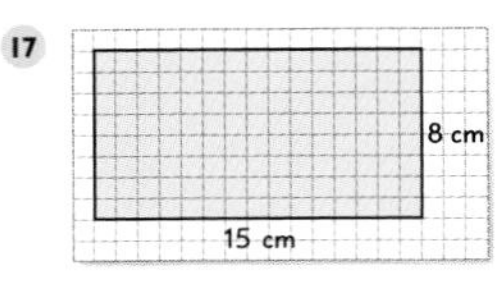

$A =$ 120 square centimeters or 120 cm^2

Example 3

Find the area of the square.

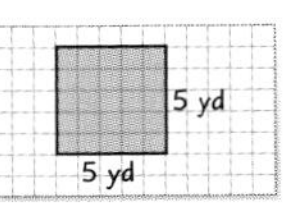

The length is 5 yards, and the width is 5 yards.

Substitute these values into the formula. Multiply.

$A = \ell \times w$
$A = 5 \text{ yd} \times 5 \text{ yd}$
$A = 25 \text{ yd}^2$

The area of the square is 25 square yards.

Example 4

Find the area of the rectangle using the formula $A = \ell \times w$.

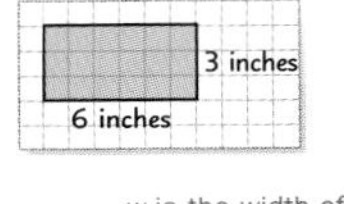

ℓ is the length of the rectangle.
w is the width of the rectangle.
A is the area of the rectangle.
$A = \ell \times w$

The length of the rectangle is 6 inches, and the width is 3 inches.

Substitute these values into the formula. Multiply.

$A = \ell \times w$
$A = 6 \text{ in.} \times 3 \text{ in.}$
$A = 18 \text{ in}^2$

The area of the rectangle is 18 square inches.

9-3 Area of a Parallelogram (pp. 380–386)

Find the area of each parallelogram.

18

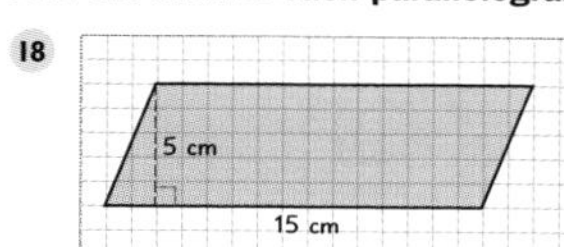

$A =$ 75 square centimeters or 75 cm^2

19

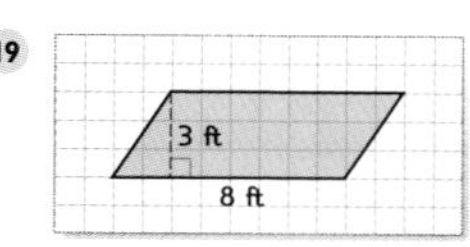

$A =$ 24 square feet or 24 ft^2

Example 5

What is the area of the parallelogram?

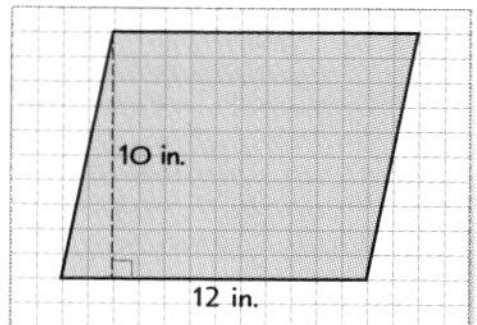

The base of the parallelogram is 12 inches, and the height is 10 inches.

Substitute these values into the formula. Multiply.

$A = b \times h$
$A = 12 \text{ in.} \times 10 \text{ in.}$
$A = 120 \text{ in}^2$

The area of the parallelogram is 120 square inches.

9-4 Area of a Triangle (pp. 387–394)

Find the area of each triangle.

20

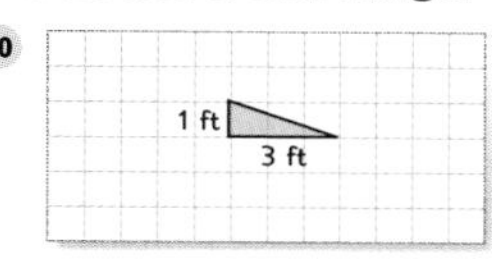

$A =$ 1.5 square feet, or 1.5 ft^2

21

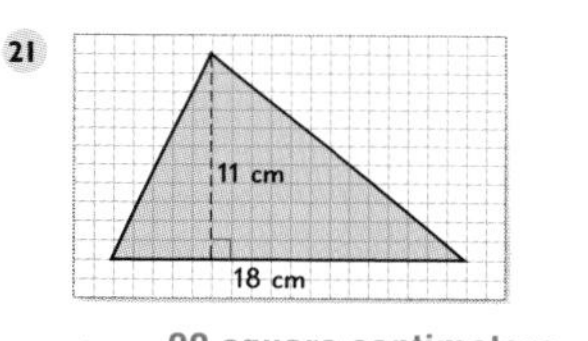

$A =$ 99 square centimeters, or 99 cm^2

Example 6

What is the area of the triangle?

The base of the triangle is 10 inches, and the height of the triangle is 16 inches.

16 in.

10 in.

Substitute values of the base and height into the area of a triangle formula.

$A = \frac{1}{2} \times b \times h$

$A = \frac{1}{2} \times 10 \text{ in.} \times 16 \text{ in.}$

Multiply to find the area of the triangle.

$A = 80 \text{ in}^2$

The area of the triangle is 80 square inches.

Common Error *Alert*

Exercises 20 and 21 If students are not finding the areas in Exercises 20 and 21, remind them to pay close attention to the $\frac{1}{2}$ that is in the formula for finding the area of a triangle. If they omitted the $\frac{1}{2}$, ask them what shape's area they actually found.

Ticket Out the Door

Review Area Have students answer a total of four questions that you give them on a half-sheet of paper. Have one question from each concept.

- How do you find the area of a figure using estimation?
- How do you find the area of a rectangle?
- How do you find the area of a parallelogram?
- How do you find the area of a triangle?

Students should hand you their papers as they exit the classroom.

Chapter 9

Chapter Test

Chapter Resource Masters

Additional forms of the Chapter 9 Tests are available.

Test Format	Where to Find it
Chapter 9 Test	Math Online macmillanmh.com
Blackline Masters	Assessment Masters, p. 114

Customize and create multiple versions of your chapter tests and their answer keys. All of these questions from the chapter tests are available on ExamView® Assessment Suite.

Online Assessment and Reporting

macmillanmh.com

This online assessment tool allows teachers to track student progress with easily accessible comprehensive reports available for every student. Assess students using any internet-ready computer.

Alternative Assessment

Use Portfolios Ask students to write examples of each type of problem from this chapter in their portfolios. Require them to include a diagram or picture with each example as well as the formulas.

Have students write the answer to each example in their portfolios and describe the steps taken (in their own words) to solve or simplify each one.

Chapter 9 **Chapter Test**

Find the area of each figure.

1 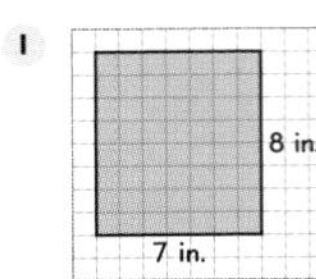

$A =$ 56 in^2

2 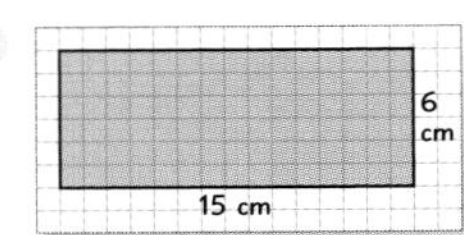

$A =$ 90 cm^2

3 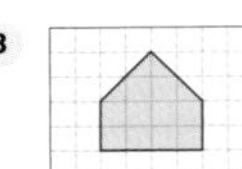

$A =$ 12 square units

4 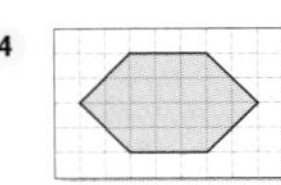

$A =$ 20 square units

Draw a rectangle that has the given area.

5 35 units^2 Sample answer:

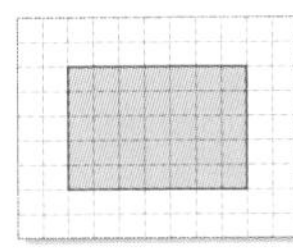

6 49 units^2 Sample answer:

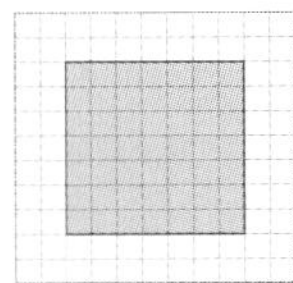

7 42 units^2 Sample answer:

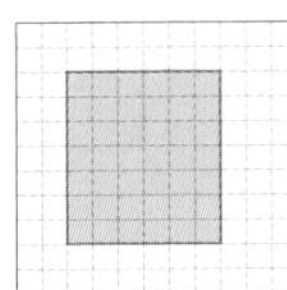

8 64 units^2 Sample answer:

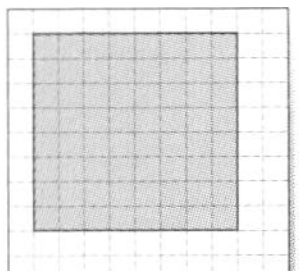

English Learner Strategy

Assessment Allow students time to look over the assessment. Have students take a close look at all the problem directions, as well as any terms in the word problems. Provide an opportunity for students to clarify any words they think they do not understand by conducting a brief question-and-answer period.

Find the area of each parallelogram.

9 

$A =$ 60 yd²

10 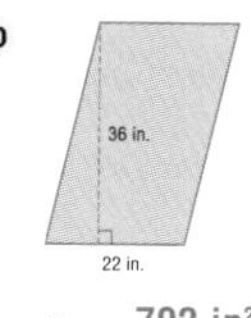

$A =$ 792 in²

Find the area of each triangle.

11 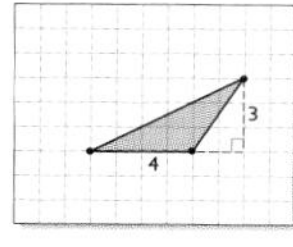

$A =$ 6 units²

12 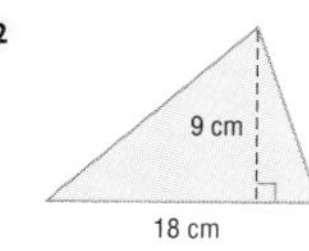

$A =$ 81 cm²

Solve.

13 **PETS** The floor of Jet's doghouse is a rectangle with a length of 32 inches and a width of 20 inches. What is the area of the floor of Jet's doghouse? 640 in²

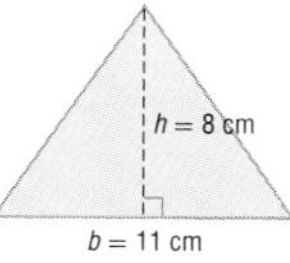

14 **BAKING** Betsy made dough cutouts in the form of triangles. Each had a base of 11 centimeters and a height of 8 centimeters. What was the area of each triangular dough cutout? 44 cm²

Correct the mistakes.

15 Margaret bought a square rug that measures 8 feet on each side. Later that day Margaret e-mailed her sister to describe the rug. What mistake did Margaret make?

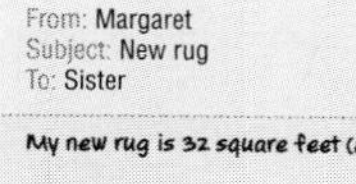

From: Margaret
Subject: New rug
To: Sister

My new rug is 32 square feet (8 ft × 4 = 32 square feet)

Margaret

Sample answer: The mistake Margaret made was that she found the perimeter of the rug rather than the area.

16 Show how Margaret should have found the area of the rug.

Sample answer: To find the area of the rug, you multiply the length and width. $8 \times 8 = 64$ square feet, or 64 ft².

Learning from Mistakes

Missed Questions Review commonly missed questions as a small group or class. Ask students to share their methods of answering each question. Try to point out when any errors occur and take corrective measures.

Data-Driven Decision Making

Students missing Exercises . . .	Have trouble with . . .	Should review and practice . . .
1–2, 5–8	finding the area of a rectangle.	SSG Lessons 9-1 and 9-2, pp. 368 and 373 CRM Skills Practice, pp. A187 and A191
3–4	estimating the area of a figure.	SSG Lesson 9-1, p. 368 CRM Skills Practice, p. A187
9–10	finding the area of a parallelogram.	SSG Lesson 9-3, p. 380 CRM Skills Practice, p. A195
11–12	finding the area of a triangle.	SSG Lessons 9-4, p. 387 CRM Skills Practice, p. A199
13–16	solving word problems involving finding area.	CRM Problem-Solving Practice, pp. A188, A192, and A200

Chapter 9 Test Practice

Diagnose Student Errors

Survey student responses for each item. Class trends may indicate common errors and misconceptions.

1. A added measurements instead of multiplying
B calculated perimeter instead of area
Ⓒ correct
D guess

2. A added measurements instead of multiplying
B calculated perimeter instead of area
Ⓒ correct
D guess

3. A miscalculated areas
B miscalculated areas
C miscalculated areas
Ⓓ correct

4. A guess
B added measurements instead of multiplying
C calculated perimeter
Ⓓ correct

5. A added measurements instead of multiplying
B guess
Ⓒ correct
D found area of square not one triangle

6. A added measurements instead of multiplying
B incorrect label
Ⓒ correct
D did not take half after multiplying

7. A calculated perimeter instead of area, incorrect label for area
B calculated perimeter instead of area, incorrect label
C wrong label
Ⓓ correct

8. A calculated perimeter instead of area, incorrect label
B calculated perimeter instead of area
C incorrect label
Ⓓ correct

Chapter 9 Test Practice

Choose the best answer and fill in the corresponding circle on the sheet at right.

1 What is the area of the rectangle?

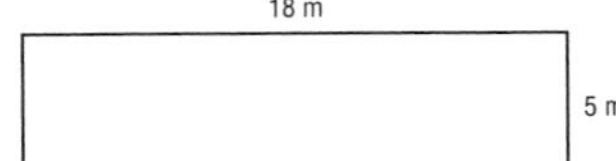

A 23 m^2
B 46 m^2
Ⓒ 90 m^2
D 100 m^2

2 One wall in Mr. Viera's classroom measures 35 feet by 14 feet. What is the area of this wall?

A 49 ft^2
B 98 ft^2
Ⓒ 490 ft^2
D 560 ft^2

3 Find the area of each figure. Which sentence is true?

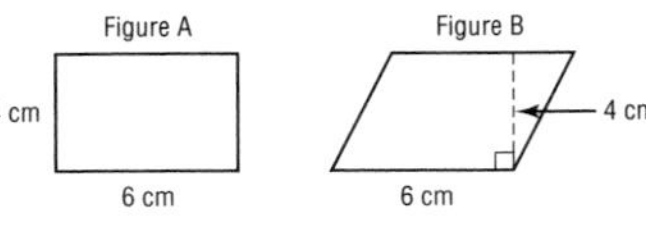

A Area A > Area B
B Area B > Area A
C Area A < Area B
Ⓓ Area A = Area B

4 Alyssa has a parallelogram-shaped mouse pad. It has a base length of 10 inches and a height of 8 inches. What is the area of the mouse pad?

A 9 in^2
B 18 in^2
C 36 in^2
Ⓓ 80 in^2

5 Find the area of each triangle in the figure.

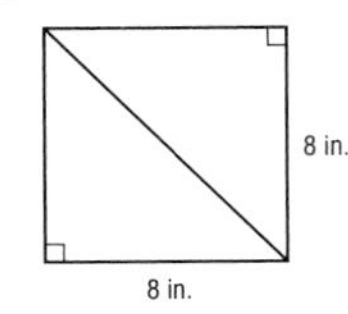

A 16 in^2
B 24 in^2
Ⓒ 32 in^2
D 64 in^2

6 What is the area of the triangle?

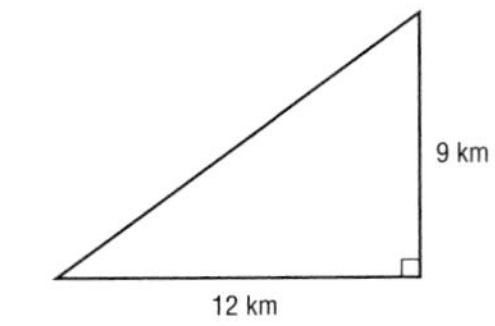

A 21 km
B 54 km
Ⓒ 54 km^2
D 108 km^2

GO ON

402 Chapter 9 Test Practice

9. A incorrect label
B forgot to multiply by $\frac{1}{2}$ & units must be squared
Ⓒ correct
D did not compute area properly, forgot to multiply by $\frac{1}{2}$

10. Ⓐ correct
B miscounted
C incorrectly found area of unshaded part
D found area of entire grid

7 What is the area of the rectangle?

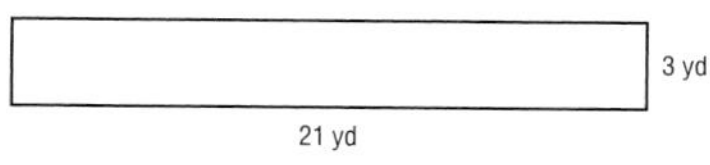

A 48 yards

B 48 yd^2

C 63 yards

(D) 63 yd^2

8 Malik wants to make a scarf. He buys a piece of fabric that is 36 inches long and 24 inches wide. How much fabric does he have?

A 120 inches

B 120 square inches

C 864 inches

(D) 864 square inches

9 What is the area of the triangle?

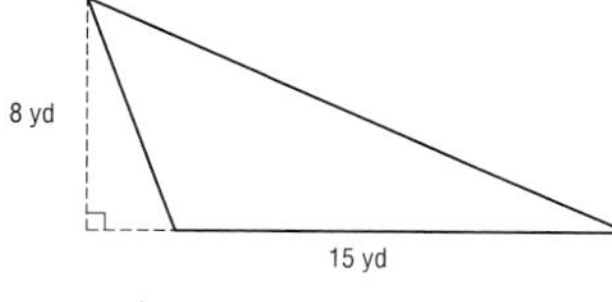

A 60 yd

B 120 yd

(C) 60 yd^2

D 120 yd^2

10 What is the area of the shaded figure?

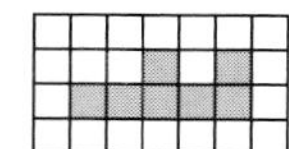

(A) 7 square units

B 8 square units

C 22 square units

D 28 square units

ANSWER SHEET

Directions: Fill in the circle of each correct answer.

1	A	B	● C	D
2	A	B	● C	D
3	A	B	C	● D
4	A	B	C	● D
5	A	B	● C	D
6	A	B	● C	D
7	A	B	C	● D
8	A	B	C	● D
9	A	B	● C	D
10	● A	B	C	D

Success Strategy

Try to answer every question. Work out the problem and eliminate answers you know are wrong. Do not change your answers unless you are very uncertain about your first answer choice.

STOP

Diagnosing Student Errors and Misconceptions

Scoring When working on the Test Practice problems, have students show their work on a separate sheet of notebook paper that can be used later as a reference as needed. After the class has completed the Test Practice problems, go over all the correct responses and have the students score their own responses.

Have students try to find and correct their mistakes. If they are still having trouble, try to determine whether the mistake was due to a basic computational error or whether there is a misunderstanding of the concept. Try to resolve as many of these errors as time permits.

Chapter 10

Chapter Overview

Chapter-at-a-Glance

Lesson	Math Objective	State/Local Standards
10-1 Unit Conversions: Metric Capacity and Mass (pp. 406–411)	Convert one metric unit of measure to a different metric unit of measure.	
10-2 Unit Conversions: Customary Capacity and Weight (pp. 412–417)	Convert one customary unit of measure to a different customary unit of measure.	
Progress Check 1 (p. 418)		
10-3 Surface Area of Rectangular Solids (pp. 419–427)	Find the surface area of a rectangular solid.	
10-4 Introduction to Volume (pp. 428–433)	Find the volume of a rectangular prism.	
10–5 Volume of Rectangular Solids (pp. 434–439)	Find the volume of a rectangular solid.	
Progress Check 2 (p. 440)		

Content-at-a-Glance

The diagram below summarizes and unpacks Chapter 10 content.

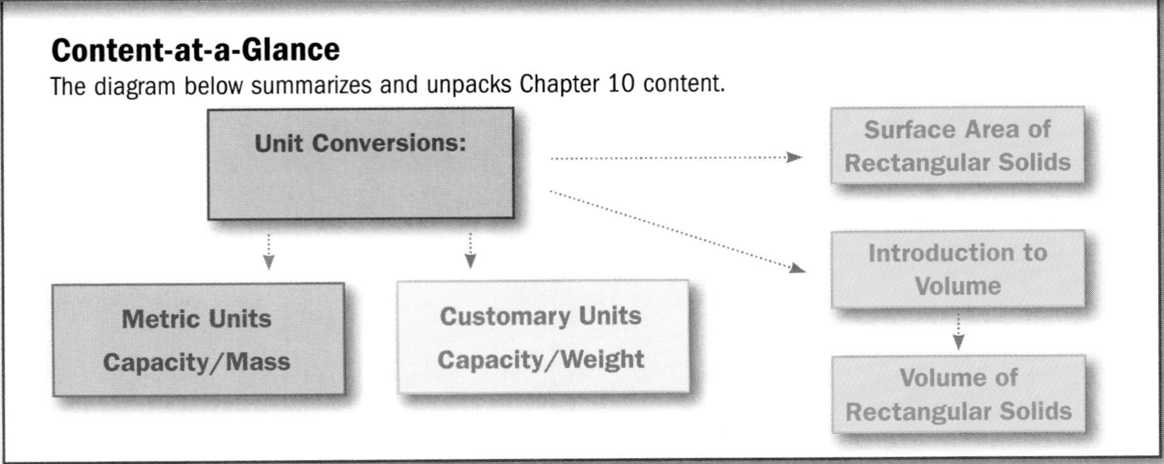

Chapter Assessment Manager

Diagnostic

Diagnose students' readiness.

	Student Study Guide/ Teacher Edition	Assessment Masters	Technology
Course Placement Test		1	ExamView® Assessment Suite
Book 3 Pretest		97	ExamView® Assessment Suite
Chapter 10 Pretest		122	ExamView® Assessment Suite
Quiz/Preview	SSG 405		Math Online macmillanmh.com StudentWorks™ Plus

Formative

Identify students' misconceptions of content knowledge.

	Student Study Guide/ Teacher Edition	Assessment Masters	Technology
Progress Checks	SSG 418, 440		Math Online macmillanmh.com StudentWorks™ Plus
Vocabulary Review	SSG 441		Math Online macmillanmh.com
Lesson Assessments			ExamView® Assessment Suite
Are They Getting It?	SSG 409, 415, 422, 431, 437		

Summative

Determine student success in learning the concepts in the lesson, chapter, or book.

	Student Study Guide/ Teacher Edition	Assessment Masters	Technology
Chapter 10 Test	SSG 446	125	ExamView® Assessment Suite
Test Practice	SSG 448	128	ExamView® Assessment Suite
Alternative Assessment	TE 446	131	
See It, Do It, Say It, Write It	TE 441, 417, 427, 433, 439		
Book 3 Test		133	ExamView® Assessment Suite

Back-mapping and Vertical Alignment **McGraw-Hill's *Math Triumphs*** intervention program was conceived and developed with the final result in mind: student success in grade-level mathematics, including Algebra 1 and beyond. The authors, using the **NCTM Focal Points and Focal Connections** as their guide, developed this brand-new series by backmapping from grade-level and Algebra 1 concepts, and vertically aligning the topics so that they build upon prior skills and concepts and serve as a foundation for future topics.

Chapter Resource Manager

	Lesson 10-1	Lesson 10-2	Lesson 10-3	Lesson 10-4
Concept	Unit Conversions: Metric Capacity and Mass	Unit Conversions: Customary Capacity and Weight	Surface Area of Rectangular Solids	Introduction to Volume
Objective	Convert one metric unit of measure to a different metric unit of measure.	Convert one customary unit of measure to a different customary unit of measure.	Find the surface area of a rectangular solid.	Find the volume of a rectangular prism.
Math Vocabulary	capacity gram liter mass metric system	benchmark capacity convert customary system weight	face net square unit surface area	cube cubic unit rectangular prism volume
Lesson Resources	**Materials** • Liter container • Place-value chart **Manipulatives** • Bucket balance **Other Resources** CRM Vocabulary and English Language Development CRM Skills Practice CRM Problem-Solving Practice CRM Homework Practice	**Materials** • Gallon container • Index cards **Manipulatives** • Bucket balance **Other Resources** CRM Vocabulary and English Language Development CRM Skills Practice CRM Problem-Solving Practice CRM Homework Practice	**Materials** • Grid paper • Index cards • Isometric dot paper **Manipulatives** • Base-ten blocks • Connecting cubes • Geometric solids **Other Resources** CRM Vocabulary and English Language Development CRM Skills Practice CRM Problem-Solving Practice CRM Homework Practice	**Materials** • Toy blocks **Manipulatives** • Connecting cubes • Unit cubes **Other Resources** CRM Vocabulary and English Language Development CRM Skills Practice CRM Problem-Solving Practice CRM Homework Practice
Technology	**Math Online** macmillanmh.com StudentWorks™ Plus ExamView® Assessment Suite	**Math Online** macmillanmh.com StudentWorks™ Plus ExamView® Assessment Suite	**Math Online** macmillanmh.com StudentWorks™ Plus ExamView® Assessment Suite	**Math Online** macmillanmh.com StudentWorks™ Plus ExamView® Assessment Suite

Student Study Guide
Chapter Resource Masters

Teacher Edition
DVD

Lesson 10-5

Concept	Volume of Rectangular Solids
Objective	Find the volume of a rectangular solid.
Math Vocabulary	cube cubic unit volume
Lesson Resources	**Materials** • Alphabet blocks • Grid paper • Isometric dot paper • Unit cubes **Manipulatives** • Base-ten blocks • Connecting cubes • Geometric solids **Other Resources** CRM Vocabulary and English Language Development CRM Skills Practice CRM Problem-Solving Practice CRM Homework Practice
Technology	Math Online macmillanmh.com StudentWorks™ Plus ExamView® Assessment Suite

Intervention Strategy

Volume

Step 1 Using unit cubes or toy blocks, have students build a rectangular prism, beginning with one cube and then increasing each dimension.

Step 2 Have them record the length, width, and height of the prism in the table below. Then have them find the product of the 3 numbers and record it in the table.

Length	Width	Height	Product

Step 3 Have students count the number of cubes or blocks they used. They can dismantle the prism to do that. How does the count compare to the product?

Step 4 Repeat Steps 1–3 until students realize that the product of the length, width, and height is the same as the number of cubes or blocks.

Chapter 10

Chapter Notes

Real-World Applications

Forecast the Weather Weather forecasters report the current weather conditions. These conditions may include the time, temperature, wind direction, wind speed, humidity percentage, and chance of precipitation. What tools are used to find these measurements? Have students research this topic and report back to the class. Students should include the units of measurement with their reports.

Intervention Strategy

Stair Diagrams

Step 1 Divide students into small groups.

Step 2 Review the five topics for the five lessons of the chapter. For each lesson they will need to come up with a diagram showing the relationships between the units. A common diagram used with measurement is a stair diagram. Each diagram should include the base unit and at least the three units above and the three units below the base unit.

Step 3 Students should also include next to each unit an example that describes the unit.

Step 4 Each group should present their diagrams and examples to the class. Students should compare diagrams for accuracy.

Chapter 10

Surface Area, Volume, and Measurement

How much does your backpack weigh?

How much does your dog's water dish hold? How much wrapping paper do you need to cover a box? These questions ask for measurements of weight and capacity.

Key Vocabulary

Find interactive definitions in 13 languages in the **eGlossary** at macmillanmh.com.

English **Español** *Introduce the most important vocabulary terms from Chapter 10.*

metric system **sistema métrico**
a measurement system that includes units such as meter, kilogram, and liter (p. 406)

capacity **capacidad**
the amount of dry or liquid material a container can hold (p. 406)
Examples: 1 liter 1 gallon

mass **masa**
the amount of matter in an object (p. 406)
Example: 1 kilogram

benchmark **parámetro**
an object or number used as a guide to estimate or reference (p. 412)

customary system **sistema inglés**
a measurement system that includes units such as foot, pound, quart, and degrees Fahrenheit (p. 412)

weight **peso**
a measurement that tells how heavy or light an object is (p. 412)
Example: 1 ton

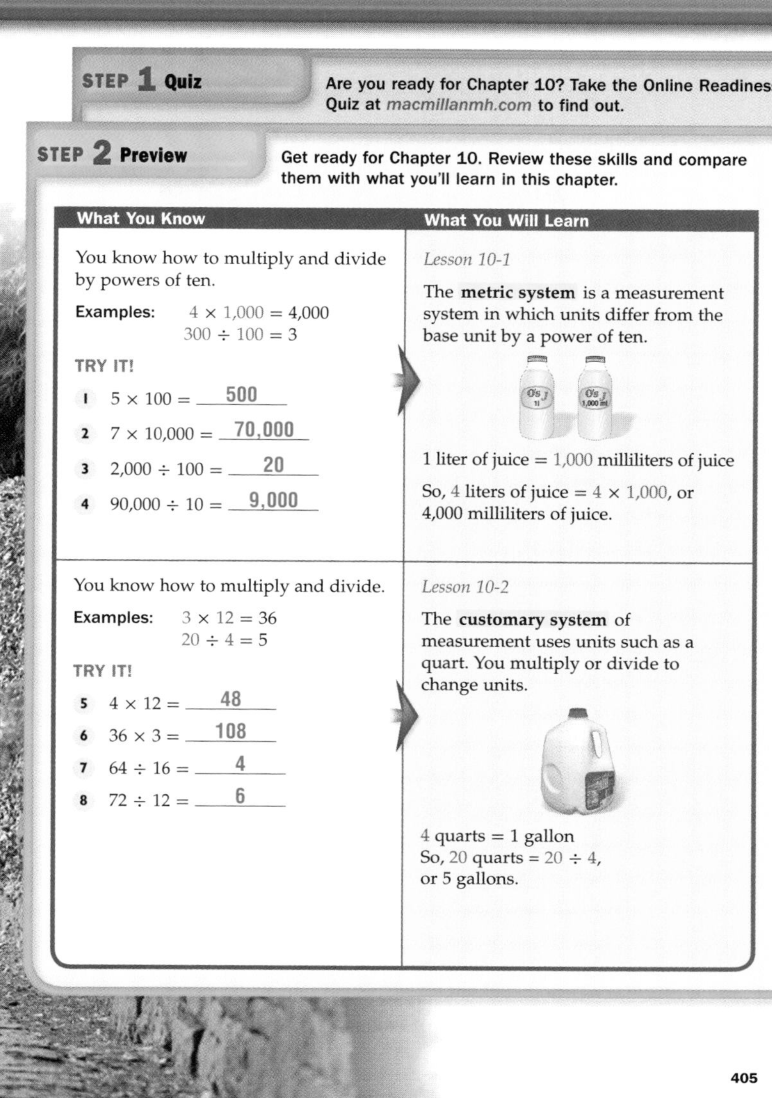

STEP 1 Quiz

Are you ready for Chapter 10? Take the Online Readiness Quiz at macmillanmh.com to find out.

STEP 2 Preview

Get ready for Chapter 10. Review these skills and compare them with what you'll learn in this chapter.

What You Know	What You Will Learn
You know how to multiply and divide by powers of ten. Examples: $4 \times 1{,}000 = 4{,}000$ $300 \div 100 = 3$ TRY IT! 1 $5 \times 100 =$ 500 2 $7 \times 10{,}000 =$ 70,000 3 $2{,}000 \div 100 =$ 20 4 $90{,}000 \div 10 =$ 9,000	*Lesson 10-1* The **metric system** is a measurement system in which units differ from the base unit by a power of ten. 1 liter of juice = 1,000 milliliters of juice So, 4 liters of juice = $4 \times 1{,}000$, or 4,000 milliliters of juice.
You know how to multiply and divide. Examples: $3 \times 12 = 36$ $20 \div 4 = 5$ TRY IT! 5 $4 \times 12 =$ 48 6 $36 \times 3 =$ 108 7 $64 \div 16 =$ 4 8 $72 \div 12 =$ 6	*Lesson 10-2* The **customary system** of measurement uses units such as a quart. You multiply or divide to change units. 4 quarts = 1 gallon So, 20 quarts = $20 \div 4$, or 5 gallons.

405

Vocabulary Preview

- As students complete the Chapter Preview, have them make a list of important terms and prefixes throughout the chapter.
- Using graph paper, have students create a stair diagram to define each prefix associated with unit measurement.
- Below the stair diagram, have them list the various base units and definitions.
- Once students are finished, pair them up and have them challenge each other to define words that are a combination of a prefix and base unit such as kilometer.

Step 1 Quiz

Pretest/Prescribe Students can take the Online Readiness Quiz or the Diagnostic Pretest in the Assessment Masters.

Step 2 Preview

Use this pre-chapter activity to activate students' prior knowledge, build confidence, and help students preview the lessons.

Dinah Zike's Foldables®

Guide students through the directions on p. A202 in the Chapter Resource Masters to create their own Foldable graphic organizer to use with this chapter.

Home Connections

- Find and name three tools that are used frequently in your home to measure. Tell what they measure and the units used for the measurement.

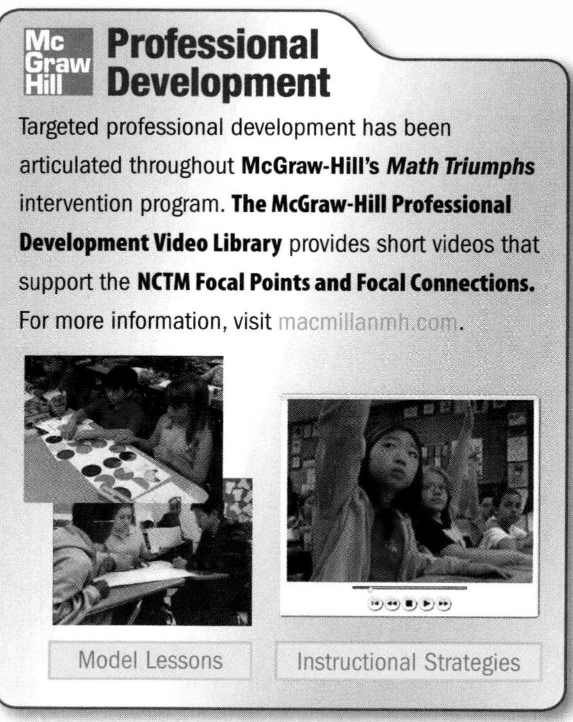

Mc Graw Hill **Professional Development**

Targeted professional development has been articulated throughout **McGraw-Hill's *Math Triumphs*** intervention program. **The McGraw-Hill Professional Development Video Library** provides short videos that support the **NCTM Focal Points and Focal Connections.** For more information, visit macmillanmh.com.

Model Lessons | Instructional Strategies

Lesson 10-1 Lesson Notes

Lesson Planner

Objective Convert one metric unit of measure to a different metric unit of measure.

Vocabulary **capacity**, **gram**, **liter**, **mass**, **metric sytem**

Materials/Manipulatives bucket balance, liter container, place-value chart

Chapter Resource Masters

- CRM Vocabulary and English Language Development (p. A204)
- CRM Skills Practice (p. A205)
- CRM Problem-Solving Practice (p. A206)
- CRM Homework Practice (p. A207)

1 Introduce

Vocabulary

Vocabulary Round-up Review the prefixes. What is *capacity*? Hold up a bottle and a cup. Which has the greater *capacity*? the greater *mass*? How do you know?

2 Teach

Key Concept

Foundational Skills and Concepts After students have read through the Key Concept box, have them try these exercises.

1. Which is a benchmark for 1 mL, a bottle or a drop of water? a drop of water
2. How many grams equal a milligram? 0.001g
3. How many liters in one kiloliter? 1,000 L

Lesson 10-1 Unit Conversions: Metric Capacity and Mass

KEY Concept

Prefixes used for standard units of measurement in the **metric system** always have the same meaning.

Metric prefixes indicate the place-value position of the measurement.

Prefix	Meaning in Words	Meaning in Numbers
kilo-	thousands	1,000
milli-	thousandths	0.001

The base unit of **capacity** in the metric system is the **liter**.

Metric Units for Capacity

Unit for Capacity	Abbreviation	Equivalents	Real-World Benchmark
milliliter	mL	1 mL = 0.001 L	drop of water
liter	L		sports water bottle
kiloliter	kL	1 kL = 1,000 L	bathtub filled with water

The base unit of **mass** in the metric system is the **gram**.

Metric Units for Mass

Unit for Capacity	Abbreviation	Equivalents	Real-World Benchmark
milligram	mg	1 mg = 0.001 g	grain of salt
gram	g		paper clip
kilogram	kg	1 kg = 1,000 g	digital camera

VOCABULARY

capacity the amount of dry or liquid material a container can hold

gram a metric unit for measuring mass

liter a metric unit for measuring volume or capacity

mass the amount of matter in an object

metric system a measurement system that includes units such as meter, gram, and liter

Sometimes it is necessary to convert from one unit of measure to another. Prefixes can help you understand the relationship between two units.

Intervention Strategy — Linguistic Learners

Remember Units Provide students with a list of unit conversions for the metric units for capacity. Prompt students to create a word phrase or sentence to help them remember the difference between each unit.

406 Chapter 10 Surface Area, Volume, and Measurement

Example 1

Convert 5,500 milliliters to liters.

1. Use a chart. Place 5,500 in the chart so the 0 that is farthest right is in the mL column.
2. Read the number from the chart for the conversion.

5,500 mL = 5.5 L

1,000	100	10	1	0.1	0.01	0.001
thousands	hundreds	tens	ones	tenths	hundredths	thousandths
			5.	5	0	0
kilo (kL)			liter (L)			milli (mL)

YOUR TURN!

Convert 270 milliliters to liters.

1. Use a chart. Place 270 in the chart so the 0 that is farthest right is in the mL column.
2. Read the number from the chart for the conversion.
   270 mL = 0.270 L

1,000	100	10	1	0.1	0.01	0.001
thousands	hundreds	tens	ones	tenths	hundredths	thousandths
			0.	2	7	0
kilo (kL)			liter (L)			milli (mL)

Multiply to convert from larger units to smaller units.
Divide to convert from smaller units to larger units.

× 1,000 × 1,000
kilogram kg → gram g → milligram mg
÷ 1,000 ÷ 1,000

Example 2

Convert.

0.0027 kg = 2.7 g

1. To convert from kilograms to grams, multiply by 1,000.
2. Convert.

0.0027 × 1,000 = 2.7 g

YOUR TURN!

Convert.

4,600,000 mg = 4,600 g

1. You are converting milligrams to grams. You need to divide by 1,000.
2. Convert.
   4,600,000 ÷ 1,000 = 4,600 kg

GO ON

Additional Example 1

Convert 1,750 milliliters to liters.

1. Use a chart. Place 1,750 in the chart so the 0 that is farthest right is in the mL column.

1,000	100	10	1	.	0.1	0.01	0.001
Thousands	Hundreds	Tens	ones		tenths	hundredths	thousandths
			1	.	7	5	0
kilo (KL)			liter (L)				milli (mL)

2. Read the number from the chart for the conversion.
   1,750 mL = 1.750 L

Additional Example 2

Convert.

0.0067 kg = ____ g

1. To convert from kilograms to grams, multiply by 1,000.
2. Convert.

   0.0067 × 1,000 = 6.7 g

Intervention Strategy — Interpersonal/Kinesthetic Learners

Measure Mass Provide a group of students with a metric scale and several classroom items such as a stapler, textbook, or box of chalk. Using the scale, instruct students to measure the items in grams. After they measure each object, instruct students to convert the measurements into other metric units of mass.

Intervention Strategy — Linguistic/Visual Learners

Prefix Chart Have students make a chart on poster board. Tell them to begin with the largest prefix, kilo-, to the smallest, milli-. Then have students place the meaning for each prefix on the chart. Tell them to color each line in the table a unique color. Point to the prefixes discussed in class to aid students in learning.

Using Manipulatives

Bucket Balance

You can demonstrate using a bucket balance (or balance scale) that 1000 milligrams equals 1 gram, and 1000 grams equals 1 kilogram.

On-Hand Manipulatives A liter container, such as a beaker or a graduated cylinder that also shows mL, can be used to show some capacity conversions.

Math Coach Notes

Strategies

1. Start this lesson with a hands-on activity. Show students capacity using a container that is marked in liters and milliliters. You can also have students use rice or lentils to show capacity.
2. Students can use a balance to put equivalent weights of differing units on either side. In order to anchor benchmarks, use a science scale and weigh a paper clip.
3. Once students understand the relative sizes of units, converting between metric units is a matter of moving the decimal point. Accelerated students can be taught this more abstract methodology.

Who is Correct?

Convert 650 liters to kiloliters.

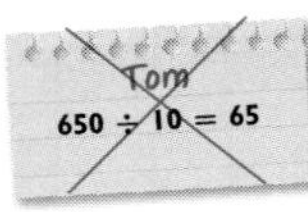

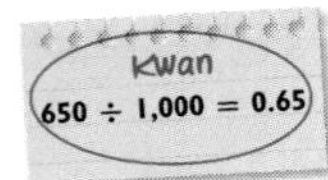

Circle correct answer(s). Cross out incorrect answer(s).

Guided Practice

Convert using a place-value chart.

1 3 kL = 3,000 L

1,000	100	10	1	0.1	0.01	0.001
thousands	hundreds	tens	ones	tenths	hundredths	thousandths
3	0	0	0.			
kilo (kL)			liter (L)			milli (mL)

2 6 mg = 0.006 g

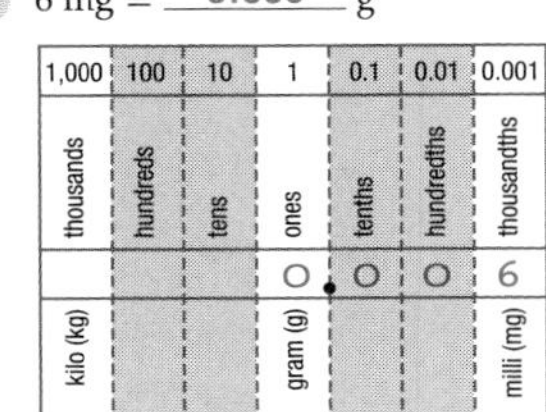

1,000	100	10	1	0.1	0.01	0.001
thousands	hundreds	tens	ones	tenths	hundredths	thousandths
			0.	0	0	6
kilo (kg)			gram (g)			milli (mg)

Step by Step Practice

Convert.

3 28 kg = 28,000,000 mg

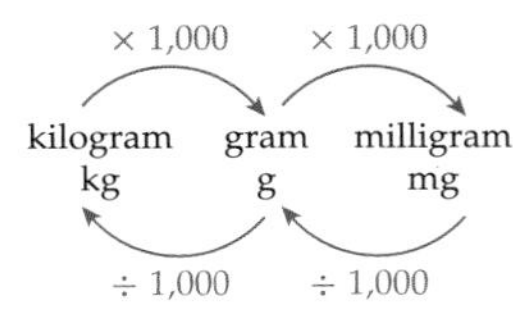

Step 1 You are converting kilo grams to milli grams.

Step 2 Since you are converting from kilograms to milligrams, you must multiply 28 by 1,000 twice.

Step 3 Convert.
28 × 1,000 × 1,000
28 kg = 28,000,000 mg

Who *is Correct?*

Diagnostic Teaching

- Hugo wrote 650,000 kL. This is incorrect because converting from a smaller unit to a larger unit indicates division, not multiplication.
- Tom wrote 65 kL. This is incorrect because 65 kL is one tenth of 650 L, and kilo- means one-thousandth.
- Kwan wrote 0.65 kL. This is correct.

Convert.

4. 1.2 L = 1,200 mL
1 L = 1,000 mL
1.2 × 1,000 = 1,200
1.2 L = 1,200 mL

5. 900 mg = 0.0009 kg
1 kg = 1,000,000 mg
900 ÷ 1,000,000 = 0.0009
900 mg = 0.0009 kg

6. 1,050 mL = 0.00105 kL

7. 0.25 g = 250 mg

8. 246 mg = 0.246 g

9. 2,010 L = 2.01 kL

10. 936 mL = 0.936 L

11. 880 g = 880,000 mg

12. 404 g = 404,000 mg

13. 31 kL = 31,000 L

Step by Step Problem-Solving Practice

Problem-Solving Strategies
- ☑ Use a table.
- ☐ Look for a pattern.
- ☐ Guess and check.
- ☐ Solve a simpler problem.
- ☐ Work backward.

Solve.

14. NUTRITION Roxanna bought a giant turkey sandwich for a party. The giant sandwich has 200,000 milligrams of protein. How many grams of protein are in the giant turkey sandwich?

Understand Read the problem. Write what you know. The giant sandwich has 200,000 milligrams of protein.

Plan Pick a strategy. One strategy is to use a table.

Solve Place 200,000 in the chart so the 0 that is farthest right is in the mL column. Read the number from the chart for the conversion.

Roxanna's giant sandwich has 200 grams of protein.

1,000	100	10	1	0.1	0.01	0.001
thousands	hundreds	tens	ones	tenths	hundredths	thousandths
	2	0	0.	0	0	0
kilo (kL)			gram (g)			milli (mL)

Check A milligram is a smaller unit of measure than a gram, so the number of milligrams of protein should be greater than the number of grams.

GO ON

Are They Getting It?

Check students' understanding of the metric system of capacity and mass by writing these problems on the board. Ask students to point out the wrong answers. Tell them to create a model or drawing to show why the answers are correct or incorrect.

1. 2 L = 500 mL This is incorrect, because 1 L = 1,000 mL. So, 2 L = 2,000 mL.
2. 30 g = 0.003 kg This is incorrect. 30 ÷ 1,000 = 0.03 kg
3. 6 mL = 0.006 L This is correct.

Note This!

Lists of Examples Encourage students to create a list of the different units of metric capacity and mass. Next to each unit, have students write an item that is best measured with that unit. Later, when they are choosing which unit to use in the exercises, they can refer back to this list.

Common Error *Alert*

Multiply or Divide? If students are having difficulty knowing whether to divide or multiply, encourage them to think about the size of the units. Demonstrate with a one-liter container or weights to show the relative sizes. Ask whether they would multiply or divide a number to get a larger number (with a smaller unit).

Math Coach Notes

Aspects of Measurement In measurement, students should learn the different measurement systems. They also need to learn when it is more appropriate to use one system over another. Eventually, students will learn to convert between systems so their foundation should be solid.

Odd/Even Assignments

Exercises 18–30 are structured so that students practice the same concepts whether they are assigned the odd or even problems.

In-Class Assignment

Have students complete Exercises 18, 20, 28, and 35 to ensure that they understand the concept.

Intervention Strategy

Visual/ Kinesthetic Learners

Compare Items Have students bring in examples of items that have capacity or mass in metric units. Write the masses of the items on the board. Have students put the items in order on a number line from the least to greatest mass. Repeat the activity using items with measures of capacity.

Math Coach Notes

Right or Left Encourage students to list the units of capacity and mass in order from greatest to least. Before completing the exercise, prompt students to study their list to determine if their conversions will require multiplication or division.

15 HEALTH Jaleesa weighs 45 kilograms. How many grams does she weigh? Check off each step.

✔ Understand: I circled key words.

✔ Plan: To solve this problem, I will use a table.

10,000	1,000	100	10	1	0.1	0.01	0.001
ten thousands	thousands	hundreds	tens	ones	tenths	hundredths	thousandths
4	5	0	0	0.			
	kilo (kg)			gram (g)			milli (mg)

✔ Solve: The answer is 45,000 g.

✔ Check: I checked my answer by multiplying.

16 NUTRITION Elijah drank all of the water in the bottle shown. How many milliliters of water did he drink?
1,200 mL

17 **Reflect** Are 65 liters equal to 0.065 kiloliters? Explain.
Yes; convert 65 liters to kiloliters: $65 \div 1000 = 0.065$; $0.065 = 0.065$.

Skills, Concepts, and Problem Solving

Convert using a place-value chart.

18 7 kg = 7,000 g

1,000	100	10	1	0.1	0.01	0.001
thousands	hundreds	tens	ones	tenths	hundredths	thousandths
7	0	0	0.			
kilo (kg)			gram (g)			milli (mg)

19 752 mL = 0.752 L

1,000	100	10	1	0.1	0.01	0.001
thousands	hundreds	tens	ones	tenths	hundredths	thousandths
			0.	7	5	2
kilo (kL)			liter (L)			milli (mL)

Math Challenge

Mass Challenge Make a list of items that can be measured in units of mass. Ask students to write the list on their papers, and then write next to it the best unit measure for each item. Then students will work with a partner and give him or her the list of items with the unit measures covered up. Then the student will say the unit of measure to his or her partner. The other student will guess what item it is. Each correct guess earns 1 point.

Convert.

20 0.0036 kL = 3,600 mL

21 1.09 g = 1,090 mg

22 0.01 kg = 10 g

23 15 L = 0.015 kL

24 0.2 mg = 0.0002 g

25 65 kL = 65,000 L

26 9.4 mL = 0.0000094 kL

27 4.8 g = 0.0048 kg

Solve.

28 COOKING Anoki needed 1,500 milliliters of vegetable oil to cook a chicken for the family reunion. He bought a 2-liter bottle of oil. How many liters of oil did Anoki have left over?
0.5 L

29 TRAVEL At the airport, you can only have 32 kilograms of mass per bag. How many grams are you able to carry in each bag?
32,000 g

30 DRINKS Kendra bought a bottle of strawberry-flavored water while she waited at the airport. The bottle contained 591 milliliters of water. How many liters of water did she purchase?
0.591 L

Vocabulary Check **Write the vocabulary word that completes each sentence.**

31 Mass is the amount of matter in an object.

32 Capacity is the amount of dry or liquid material a container can hold.

33 A(n) liter is a metric unit for measuring volume or capacity.

34 A(n) gram is a metric unit for measuring mass.

35 Writing in Math Explain how to convert 6.07 grams to kilograms.
See TE margin.

Ticket Out the Door

Design a Problem Separate the class into small groups. Each group will design a problem. The group should solve the problem correctly and then show a solution that is incorrect. At a later class time, use the problems with errors in problem solving or problem design as opportunities to model correct conversions. Groups will turn in their papers as they exit.

See It, Do It, Say It, Write It

Step 1 Write a conversion problem on the board, such as 145 mL = ___ L. Model how to solve the problem. Write several more problems on the board and have student volunteers tell you the steps in solving each one.

Step 2 Ask students to work in pairs. Give half of the class a capacity problem to model and the other half of the class a mass problem to model. Students can use either concrete materials or drawings.

Step 3 Have student presenters show their work. Use students' findings as teachable moments.

Step 4 Have students write about the metric system of capacity and mass. Tell them to define both, and describe the units used.

Additional Answer

Exercise 35 There are 1,000 grams in 1 kilogram. You would divide because you are going from a smaller unit to a larger unit: $6.07 \div 1{,}000 = 0.00607$. So, 6.07 grams = 0.00607 kilogram.

Looking Ahead: Pre-teach

Unit Conversions: Customary Capacity and Weight In the next lesson, students will learn about the customary system of capacity and weight.

Example

Convert 1 gallon to cups. 16 cups

Convert.

1. 3 lb to oz 48 oz
2. 4 c to pt 8 pt
3. 1 T to lb 2,000 lb

Lesson 10-2 Lesson Notes

Lesson Planner

Objective Convert one customary unit of measure to a different customary unit of measure.

Vocabulary **benchmark**, **capacity**, **convert**, **customary system**, **weight**

Materials/Manipulatives bucket balance, gallon container, index cards

Chapter Resource Masters

- CRM Vocabulary and English Language Development (p. A208)
- CRM Skills Practice (p. A209)
- CRM Problem-Solving Practice (p. A210)
- CRM Homework Practice (p. A211)

1 Introduce

Vocabulary

Relate Vocabulary Remind students what they learned in Lesson 10-1 about *capacity* and mass. Discuss how *weight* is different than *mass*. For instance, the same object weighed on Earth and on the Moon will have different weights but the same mass. Show ordinary items as *benchmarks* of *customary* units for both *weight* and *capacity*.

2 Teach

Key Concept

Foundational Skills and Concepts After students have read through the Key Concept box, have them try these exercises.

1. Which is a benchmark for a pint, a spoon, or a cereal bowl? a cereal bowl
2. How many ounces are in a pound? 16 oz
3. How many cups are in one gallon? 16 cups

Lesson 10-2 Unit Conversions: Customary Capacity and Weight

KEY Concept

The **customary system** of measurement is not based on powers of ten. It is based on numbers like 12 and 16, which have many factors.

Customary Units for Capacity

Unit for Capacity	Abbreviation	Equivalents	Real-World Benchmark
fluid ounce	fl oz		eye dropper
cup	c	1 c = 8 fl oz	coffee mug
pint	pt	1 pt = 2 c 1 pt = 16 fl oz	cereal bowl
quart	qt	1 qt = 2 pt 1 qt = 4 c 1 qt = 32 fl oz	large bottle of sports drink
gallon	gal	1 gal = 4 qt 1 gal = 8 pt 1 gal = 16 c 1 gal = 128 fl oz	milk carton

Customary Units for Weight

Unit for Capacity	Abbreviation	Equivalents	Real-World Benchmark
ounce	oz		a strawberry
pound	lb	1 lb = 16 oz	bunch of grapes
ton	T	1 T = 2,000 lb	car

VOCABULARY

benchmark an object or number used as a guide to estimate or reference

capacity the amount of dry or liquid material a container can hold

convert to find an equivalent measure

customary system a measurement system that includes units such as foot, pound, and quart

weight a measurement that tells how heavy or light an object is

Sometimes it is necessary to **convert** from one unit of measure to another. Knowing customary conversions can help you understand the relationship between two units.

Intervention Strategy — Linguistic/Visual Learners

Grocery Items Units of capacity and mass are used often to measure grocery store items. Have students explore a grocery store or their own kitchens to determine which items are measured by capacity or weight. Suggest that students make two lists, one list containing items measured by capacity, and another list of items measured by weight. For example, milk is sold by the gallon, a unit of capacity, and bananas are sold by the pound, a unit of weight.

Example 1

Convert 32 pints to gallons using a table.

gallons	1	2	3	4
pints	8	16	24	32

1. 8 pints is equal to 1 gallon.
2. Fill in the table.
   1 gallon $= 1 \times 8$ pints
   2 gallons $= 2 \times 8$ pints
   3 gallons $= 3 \times 8$ pints
   4 gallons $= 4 \times 8$ pints

32 pints is equal to 4 gallons.

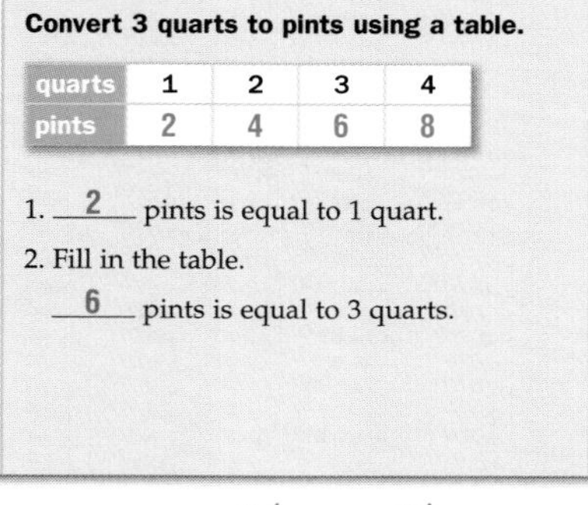

YOUR TURN!

Convert 3 quarts to pints using a table.

quarts	1	2	3	4
pints	2	4	6	8

1. __2__ pints is equal to 1 quart.
2. Fill in the table.
   __6__ pints is equal to 3 quarts.

To convert a larger unit to a smaller unit, multiply.
To convert a smaller unit to a larger unit, divide.

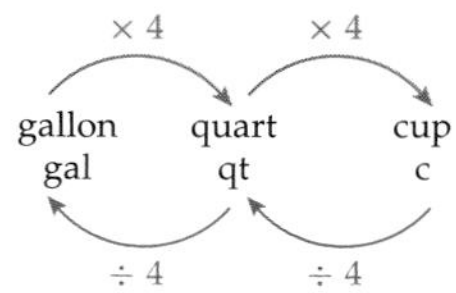

Example 2

Convert 56 fluid ounces to pints.

1. You are converting from fluid ounces to pints, which is a smaller unit to a larger unit. You need to divide.
2. 1 cup is equal to 8 fluid ounces. 1 pint is equal to 2 cups. So, 1 pint is equal to 16 fluid ounces.
   $56 \div 16 = 3.5$

So, 56 fluid ounces equals 3.5 pints.

YOUR TURN!

Convert 22 pints to gallons.

1. You are converting from __pints__ to __gallons__, which is a __smaller__ unit to a __larger__ unit. You need to __divide__.
2. 1 gallon is equal to __4 quarts__. 1 quart is equal to __2 pints__. So, 1 gallon is equal to __8 pints__.
   22 __÷ 8__ = __2.75__

So, 22 pints equals __2.75 gallons__.

GO ON

Additional Example 1

Convert 24 pints to gallons using a table.

Gallons	1	2	3
Pints	8	16	24

1. 8 pints is equal to 1 gallon.
2. Fill in the table.
   1 gallon $= 1 \times 8$ pints
   2 gallons $= 2 \times 8$ pints
   3 gallons $= 3 \times 8$ pints

24 pints is equal to 8 gallons.

Additional Example 2

Convert 72 fluid ounces to pints.

1. You are converting from fluid ounces to pints, which is a smaller unit to a larger unit. You need to divide.
2. 1 cup is equal to 8 fluid ounces. 1 pint is equal to 2 cups. So, 1 pint is equal to 16 fluid ounces.
   $72 \div 16 = 4.5$

So, 72 fluid ounces equals 4.5 pints.

English Learner Strategy

Guiding Questions Ask students the following questions to ensure that they understand the concept.

- How many ounces are in a pound? 16 ounces How many pounds are in a ton? 2,000 pounds
- How do you convert 16 pints to fluid ounces? 1 pint is equal to 16 fluid ounces. Multiply 16 by 16 fluid ounces to get 256 fluid ounces.
- How do you know whether to multiply or divide when converting from one unit to another? To convert a larger unit to a smaller unit, multiply. To convert a smaller unit to a larger unit, divide.

English Learner Strategy

Use Prior Knowledge It is possible that an English learner might be familiar with the metric system since it is widely used in other parts of the world. Use this opportunity to allow English learners to share their experiences with units of measure. Connect their experiences with customary measurements if possible.

Additional **Example 3**

Convert 10 tons to ounces.

1. You are converting from tons to ounces, which is a larger unit to a smaller unit. You need to multiply.
2. 1 ton is equal to 2,000 pounds.
   1 pound is equal to 16 ounces.
   $16 \times 2{,}000 = 32{,}000$ ounces

So, 1 ton is equal to 32,000 ounces.

$10 \times 32{,}000 = 320{,}000$ ounces

So, 10 tons equals 320,000 ounces.

Using Manipulatives

Bucket Balance Weight conversions can be demonstrated by placing two equivalent units on either side of the balance. Benchmarks for a pound and an ounce can also be shown.

On-Hand Manipulatives A container that also shows quarts, pints, cups, and fluid ounces can be used to convert capacity units.

Example 3

Convert 2 tons to ounces.

1. You are converting from tons to ounces, which is a larger unit to a smaller unit. You need to multiply.
2. 1 ton is equal to 2,000 pounds.
   1 pound is equal to 16 ounces.
   $16 \times 2{,}000 = 32{,}000$ ounces

So, 1 ton is equal to 32,000 ounces.

$2 \times 32{,}000 = 64{,}000$ ounces

So, 2 tons equals 64,000 ounces.

YOUR TURN!

Convert 3.2 tons to ounces.

1. You are converting from tons to ounces, which is a larger unit to a smaller unit. You need to multiply.
2. 1 ton is equal to 2,000 pounds.
   1 pound is equal to 16 ounces.
   $3.2 \times 32{,}000 = 102{,}400$

So, 3.2 tons equals 102,400 ounces.

Who is Correct?

Convert 64 fluid ounces to quarts.

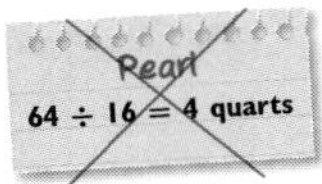

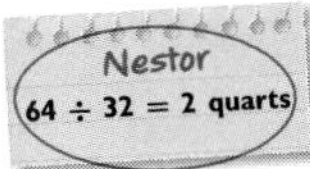

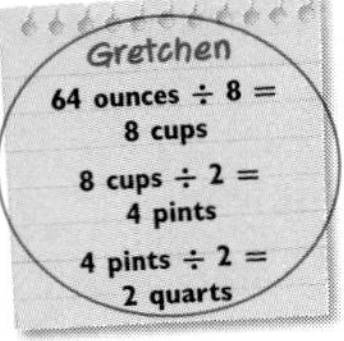

Circle correct answer(s). Cross out incorrect answer(s).

Guided Practice

Convert using a table.

1. 320 fl oz = 10 qt

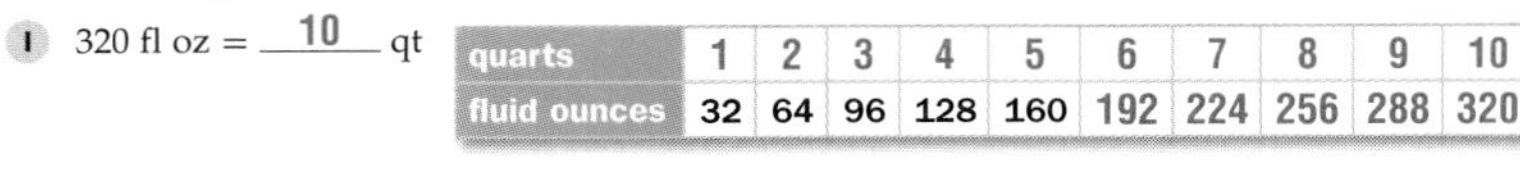

quarts	1	2	3	4	5	6	7	8	9	10
fluid ounces	32	64	96	128	160	192	224	256	288	320

2. 3 T = 96,000 oz

tons	1	2	3
ounces	32,000	64,000	96,000

Who *is Correct?*
Diagnostic Teaching

- Pearl wrote 4 quarts. This is incorrect because there are 32 fluid ounces in a quart, not 16. She should have divided by 32.
- Nestor wrote 2 quarts. This is correct.
- Gretchen wrote 2 quarts. This is correct.

Step by Step Practice

Convert.

3. 16 pt = ______ c

Step 1 You are converting from a __larger__ unit to a __smaller__ unit. You need to __multiply__.

Step 2 1 pint is equal to __2__ cups.

Step 3 So, 16 pints are 16 __×__ 2, or __32__ cups.

Convert.

4. 7 lb = __112__ oz
5. 2 gal = __8__ qt
6. 800 fl oz = __25__ qt
7. 10 pt = __20__ c

Step by Step Problem-Solving Practice

Problem-Solving Strategies
- ☑ Make a table.
- ☐ Look for a pattern.
- ☐ Write an equation.
- ☐ Solve a simpler problem.
- ☐ Work backward.

Solve.

8. MEASUREMENT A bathtub for a baby can hold 7 gallons of water. How many quarts of water can the bathtub hold?

Understand Read the question. Write what you know.
A baby bathtub holds __7__ gallons of water.

Plan Pick a strategy. One strategy is to make a table.

gallons	1	2	3	4	5	6	7
quarts	4	8	12	16	20	24	28

Solve The table begins with the numbers 4, 8, and 12.
Continue the pattern until you find the seventh term.
The seventh term is __28__. __28__ quarts = __7__ gal
The baby bathtub can hold __28__ quarts of water.

Check A quart is a smaller unit of measurement than a gallon. So the number of quarts of water is greater than the number of gallons of water.

GO ON

Are They Getting It?

Check students' understanding of the customary system of capacity and weight by writing these problems on the board. Have students explain the incorrect information in each problem. Tell them to use a model or drawing to show why the answers are correct or incorrect.

1. 20 qt = 30 pt This is incorrect, because 1 qt = 2 pt. So, 20 qt = 40 pt.
2. 0.5 lb = 8 oz This is correct.
3. 6 c = 48 fl oz This is correct.

Math Coach Notes

Strategies

1. Start this lesson with a hands-on activity. Represent capacity using a gallon container that is marked in ounces, cups, pints, and quarts. Have students work with nonliquids to keep water from spilling in the classroom.
2. Students can use a balance to put equivalent weights of differing units on either side. If possible, have two scales, one that weighs in ounces and one that weigh in pounds.
3. Have students use the same-sized cup and weigh a cupful of cotton balls and a cupful of sand or beans. Discuss their findings. Make connections between capacity, mass, and weight.

Note This!

Conversion Factors While studying unit conversions for the customary system of capacity and weight, encourage students to write the conversion factors between the various units and draw a picture to represent the conversion.

Intervention Strategy — Auditory Learners

Measure Song For liquid measures, teach students unit measures sung to the tune of the song "The Noble Duke of York."

8 ounces are in a cup,
2 cups are in a pint,
2 pints are in a quart,
and 4 quarts are in a gallon.

Odd/Even Assignments

Exercises 12–23 are structured so that students practice the same concepts whether they are assigned the odd or even problems.

In-Class Assignment

Have students complete Exercises 13, 21, 22, and 27 to ensure that students understand the concept.

Intervention Strategy

Visual/Kinesthetic Learners

Real-World Benchmarks Provide students with different objects to weigh, such as a pencil, a book, and a sports bottle with water. Have them weigh the items and record the results. Ask them to justify the units they used.

Math Coach Notes

Know the Units in Order Encourage students to list the units of capacity in order from smallest to largest. Show them how to draw a concept map or flow chart to represent the relationships between the units. When it is time for the test, tell them to cover up the chart and redraw the chart without looking.

Measurement Students should learn the different measurement systems. It is particularly important for students to be able to discern which system of measurement, metric or customary, may be best to use in different circumstances. They should be able to justify their selections.

9 ZOO ANIMALS A rhinoceros at the zoo weighs 7,000 pounds. How many tons does it weigh?

Check off each step.

✔ Understand: I circled key words.

✔ Plan: To solve this problem, I will make a table.

✔ Solve: The answer is 3.5 T.

✔ Check: I checked my answer by dividing.

10 COOKING For the baking contest this year, each baker will be given 48 ounces of flour. Galeno needs more flour than that for his recipes. He is bringing 32 ounces of flour. How many pounds of flour will Galeno have altogether? 5 lb

11 **Reflect** Are there 64 cups in 2 gallons? Explain.

No; find the number of cups in 2 gallons: $2 \times 16 = 32$; $64 \neq 32$.

Skills, Concepts, and Problem Solving

Convert using a table.

12 6 c = 48 fl oz

cups	1	2	3	4	5	6
fluid ounces	8	16	24	32	40	48

13 5 lb = 80 oz

pounds	1	2	3	4	5
ounces	16	32	48	64	80

Convert.

14 9,000 lb = 4.5 T

15 12 c = 3 qt

16 7 gal = 28 qt

17 256 oz = 16 lb

18 20 qt = 40 pt

19 8 pt = 128 fl oz

20 1.5 T = 48,000 oz

21 4 gal = 64 c

Math Challenge

Equivalent Cards Write equivalent capacity and weights on index cards. Have students shuffle the cards and deal 7 cards to each player, then place the deck facedown on the desk. Students will ask another player for one of the cards he or she is holding as play passes between players. For example, if the player says, "5 cups" and the other player has an equivalent card, he or she will give the card to the asking player. That player will lay down the pair and take another card from the deck. The game ends when all the pairs are made. The player with the most pairs wins.

Solve.

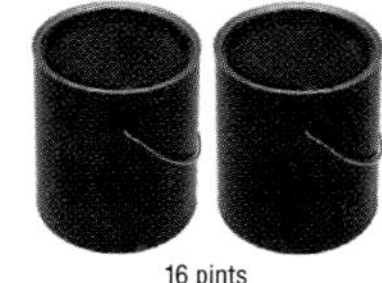

22 ART Lucas mixed the paint shown to make a shade of gray. How many gallons of gray paint did Lucas make? 3 gal

23 PETS Vincent feeds his dog 1 cup of dog food in the morning and 1 cup of dog food in the evening. How many ounces of food will Vincent's dog eat in 14 days? 224 ounces

Vocabulary Check **Write the vocabulary word that completes each sentence.**

24 A(n) benchmark is an object or number used as a guide for estimation or reference.

25 Weight is a measurement that tells how heavy or light an object is.

26 Capacity is the amount of dry or liquid material a container can hold.

27 Writing in Math Explain how to convert 12 fluid ounces to cups.

8 fluid ounces is equal to 1 cup. Divide because you are going from a smaller unit to a larger unit: $12 \div 8 = 1.5$. 1.5 cups is equal to 12 fluid ounces.

Spiral Review

Solve. (Lesson 10-1, p. 406)

28 NUTRITION If a person consumes 71,700 grams of sugar in a year, how many kilograms of sugar was consumed? 71.7 kg

Convert.

29 7 kL = 7,000,000 mL.

30 37 L = 0.037 kL

31 8,200 g = 8.2 kg

32 400 mg = 0.4 g

STOP

Ticket Out the Door

All One Unit Have students work in small groups. Write recipes on index cards that list ingredients with measures in only one unit like ounces or cups. Tell them to convert the ingredients to other units and rewrite the recipes. For example, the measures of a recipe may contain only ounces; ask that they be converted to pints. These recipes can be actual recipes or imaginary ones with "far out" ingredients. Give each group an assortment of units. Discuss their findings. Students should turn in their rewritten recipes when they exit the classroom.

4 Assess

See It, Do It, Say It, Write It

Step 1 Write a conversion problem on the board. For instance, 3 gallons is equal to ____ cups. Use a table to find the answer. Write other problems on the board that students can use a table to find answers. Have students fill out the tables and find the answers.

Step 2 Ask students to work in pairs. Give each set of students conversion problems to complete. Ask students to choose a problem they can model with a drawing or concrete materials.

Step 3 Have students present their problem to the class and demonstrate how they used their models to find the answer. Discuss other ways the answers could be found.

Step 4 Tell students to write down whether they think a cup of feathers would have the same capacity as a cup of marbles. Would they have the same weight? Tell them to explain their reasoning.

Looking Ahead: Pre-teach

Surface Area of Rectangular Solids In the next lesson, students will learn about the surface area of a rectangular solid. Show students a cube and a rectangular prism. The sum of the areas of each of the six faces equals the surface area.

Example

What is the surface area of a cube that has one face with an area of 10 square units? 60 square units

How many faces does a rectangular prism have? 6

Find the surface area of each prism.

1. 52 square units

2.

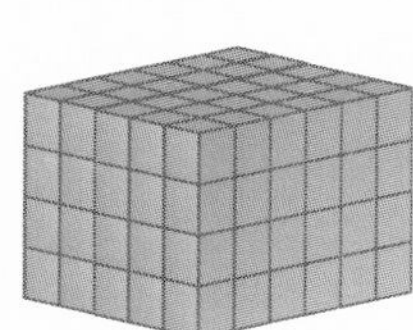

148 square units

Chapter 10 Progress Check 1

Formative Assessment

Use the Progress Check to assess students' mastery of the previous lessons. Have students review the lesson indicated for the problems they answered incorrectly.

Odd/Even Assignments

Exercises are structured so that students practice the same concepts whether they are assigned the odd or even problems.

Common Error Alert

Exercise Help

Exercises 1–6 Refer students to a metric chart and remind them that it works the same for units of mass measurements.

Exercise 9 Reiterate that there are 2,000 pounds in 1 ton.

Chapter 10 Progress Check 2 (Lessons 10-1 and 10-2)

Convert.

1. 3,400 mL = 0.0034 kL
2. 0.56 g = 560 mg
3. 332 mg = 0.332 g
4. 22 L = 22,000 mL
5. 6,050 L = 6.05 kL
6. 775 mL = 0.775 L

Convert using a table.

7. 4 gal = 64 c

gallons	1	2	3	4
cups	16	32	48	64

8. 4 qt = 128 fl oz

quarts	1	2	3	4	5
fluid ounces	32	64	96	128	160

Convert.

9. 400 lb = 0.2 T
10. 16 c = 4 qt
11. 5 gal = 20 qt
12. 160 oz = 10 lb
13. 15 qt = 30 pt
14. 1 pt = 16 fl oz
15. 1 T = 32,000 oz
16. 1 gal = 16 c

Solve.

17. **BABIES** Mora's little brother weighs 240 ounces. How many pounds does he weigh?
15 lb

18. **CONSTRUCTION** Edgar needs 5.3 liters of paint for his garage. How many milliliters of paint does he need?
5,300 mL

STOP

418 Chapter 10 Surface Area, Volume, and Measurement

Data-Driven Decision Making

Students missing Exercises . . .	Have trouble with . . .	Should review and practice . . .
1–6	converting metric capacity and mass.	SSG Lesson 10-1, p. 406 CRM Skills Practice, p. A205
7–16	converting customary capacity and weight.	SSG Lesson 10-2, p. 412 CRM Skills Practice, p. A209
17–18	solving word problems that require unit measure conversions.	CRM Problem-Solving Practice, pp. A206 and A210

Lesson 10-3

Surface Area of Rectangular Solids

KEY Concept

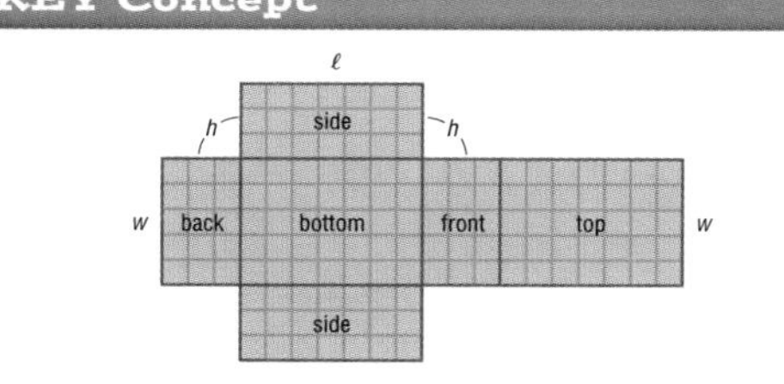

The **net** can be folded to make a rectangular prism.

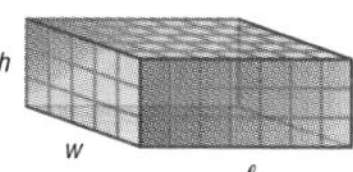

The **surface area** of a rectangular prism is the sum of the areas of all the **faces** of the figure. Surface area is measured in **square units.**

VOCABULARY

face
the flat part of a three-dimensional figure that is considered one of the sides

net
a flat pattern that can be folded to make a three-dimensional figure

square unit
a unit for measuring area

surface area
the area of the surface of a three-dimensional figure

A rectangular prism has six faces.

Example 1

What is the surface area of the rectangular prism?

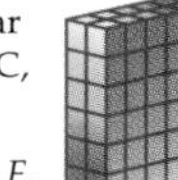

1. Draw a net of the rectangular prism. Label the faces A, B, C, D, E, and F.
2. Find the area of faces A and F.

   $A = \ell \times w$
   $A = 2 \times 5 = 10$
3. Find the area of faces B and D.

   $A = \ell \times w$
   $A = 5 \times 6 = 30$

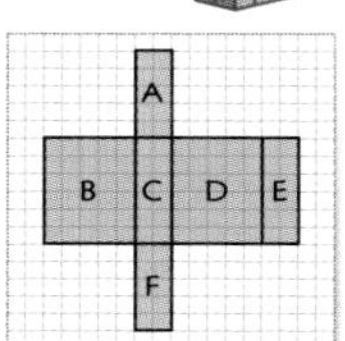

4. Find the area of faces C and E.

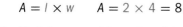

   $A = \ell \times w$
   $A = 2 \times 6 = 12$
5. Find the sum of all the areas of all the faces.

   $10 + 30 + 12 + 10 + 30 + 12 = 104$

The surface area of the rectangular prism is 104 square units.

GO ON

Additional Example 1

What is the surface area of the rectangular prism?

1. Draw a net of the rectangular prism. Label the faces A, B, C, D, E, and F.
2. Find the area of faces A and F.
   $A = l \times w \quad A = 2 \times 4 = 8$
3. Find the area of faces B and D.
   $A = l \times w \quad A = 3 \times 2 = 6$
4. Find the area of faces C and E.
   $A = l \times w \quad A = 3 \times 4 = 12$
5. Find the sum of all the areas of all the faces.
   $8 + 6 + 12 + 8 + 6 + 12 = 52$

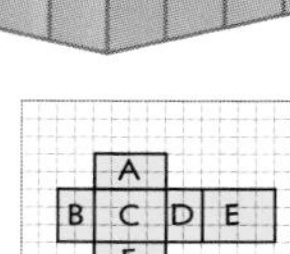

The surface area of the rectangular prism is 52 square units.

Lesson Notes

Lesson 10-3

Lesson Planner

Objective Find the surface area of a rectangular solid.

Vocabulary **face**, **net**, **square unit**, **surface area**

Materials/Manipulatives base-ten blocks, connecting cubes, geometric solids, grid paper, index cards, isometric dot paper

Chapter Resource Masters

- CRM Vocabulary and English Language Development (p. A212)
- CRM Skills Practice (p. A213)
- CRM Problem-Solving Practice (p. A214)
- CRM Homework Practice (p. A215)

1 Introduce

Vocabulary

Extend Vocabulary Draw a *net* of a cube on the board. What shape is each *face*? Draw a cube and a square on the board. Talk about the square in terms of area by connecting with past lessons. Relate the area of the square to the *surface area* of each *face* of the cube.

2 Teach

Key Concept

Foundational Skills and Concepts After students have read through the Key Concept box, have them try these exercises.

1. What is a net? a flat pattern that can be folded to make a three-dimensional object
2. What kind of units are used to find surface area? square units
3. True or false: The surface area is the sum of the areas of all the faces. true

Additional *Example 2*

What is the surface area of the cube?

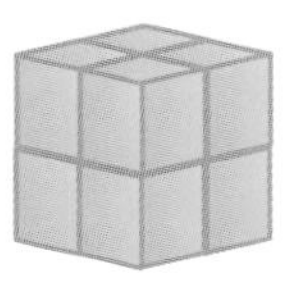

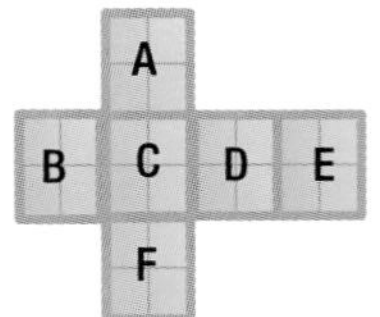

1. Draw a net of the cube.
2. Find the area of each face.

   $A = \ell \times w$
   $A = 2 \times 2 = 4$

3. There are six faces on the cube. Find the sum of the areas of all six faces.

   $4 + 4 + 4 + 4 + 4 + 4 = 24$
   A B C D E F

The surface area of the cube is 24 square units.

Math Coach Notes

Units The surface area of a prism can be shown as having the same units as the area of a polygon. Stress, as you add the areas of each face, the sum will be in *square* units. A parallel example can be linear units: 2 feet + 3 feet = 5 feet. The whole numbers are added, and the units remain the same.

YOUR TURN!

What is the surface area of the rectangular prism?

1. Draw a net of the rectangular prism. Label the faces A, B, C, D, E, and F.

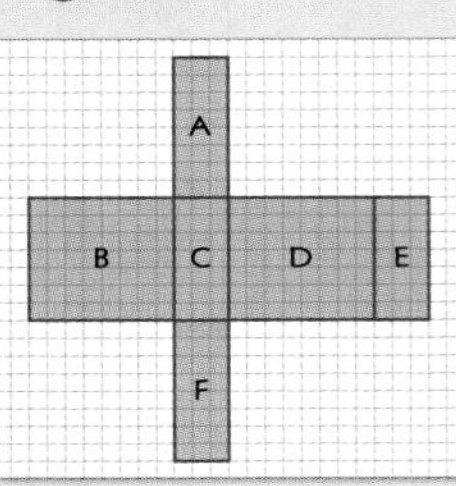

2. Find the area of faces A and F.

   $A = \ell \times w$
   $A = \underline{3} \times \underline{8} = \underline{24}$

3. Find the area of faces B and D.

   $A = \ell \times w$
   $A = \underline{8} \times \underline{7} = \underline{56}$

4. Find the area of faces C and E.

   $A = \ell \times w$
   $A = \underline{3} \times \underline{7} = \underline{21}$

5. Find the sum of the areas of all the faces.

   $\underline{24} + \underline{56} + \underline{21} + \underline{24} + \underline{21} + \underline{56} = \underline{202}$

The surface area of the rectangular prism is 202 square units.

Example 2

What is the surface area of the cube?

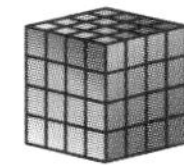

1. Find the area of each face.

   $A = \ell \times w$
   $A = 4 \times 4 = 16$

2. There are six faces on the cube. Find the sum of the areas of all six faces.

   $16 + 16 + 16 + 16 + 16 + 16 = 96$
   A B C D E F

The surface area of the cube is 96 square units.

YOUR TURN!

What is the surface area of the cube?

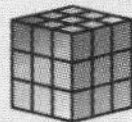

1. Find the area of each face.

   $A = \ell \times w$
   $A = \underline{3} \times \underline{3} = \underline{9}$

2. Find the sum of the areas of all six faces.

   $\underline{9} + \underline{9} + \underline{9} + \underline{9} + \underline{9} + \underline{9} = \underline{54}$

The surface area of the cube is 54 square units.

Intervention Strategy

Linguistic/ Interpersonal Learners

Real-World Objects Ask students to bring in items from home that are rectangular prisms. Students can share their items with the class. When the prisms are not cubes, ask the student to demonstrate which faces of the prism are congruent. Students can also measure their objects and approximate the surface area.

Who is Correct?

What is the surface area of the rectangular prism?

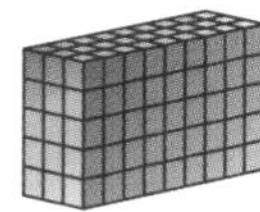

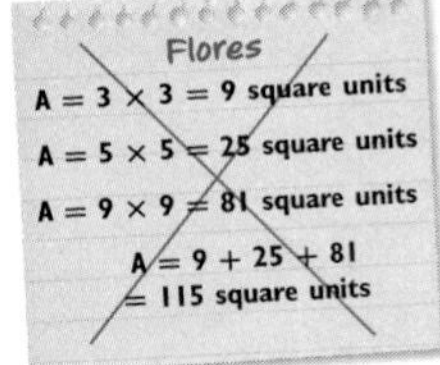

Flores
A = 3 × 3 = 9 square units
A = 5 × 5 = 25 square units
A = 9 × 9 = 81 square units
A = 9 + 25 + 81
= 115 square units

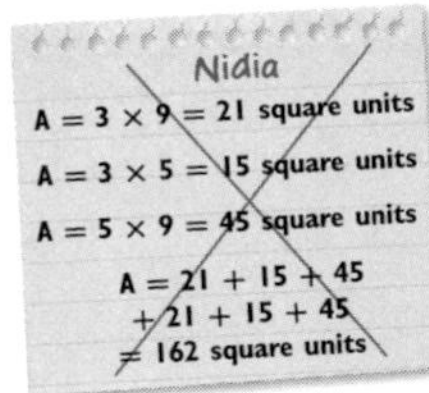

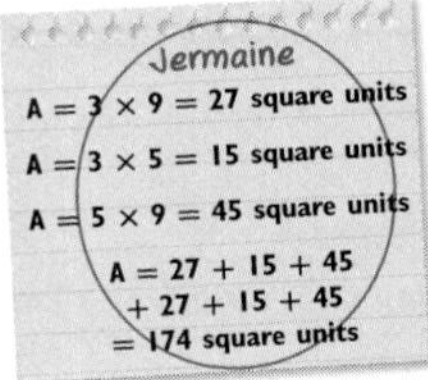

Circle correct answer(s). Cross out incorrect answer(s).

Guided Practice

Draw a net for a rectangular prism with the given length, width, and height.

1. $2 \times 8 \times 9$ Sample answer:

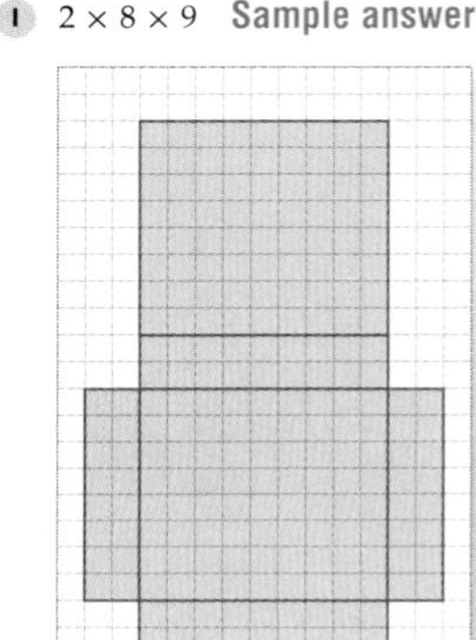

2. $5 \times 4 \times 7$ Sample answer:

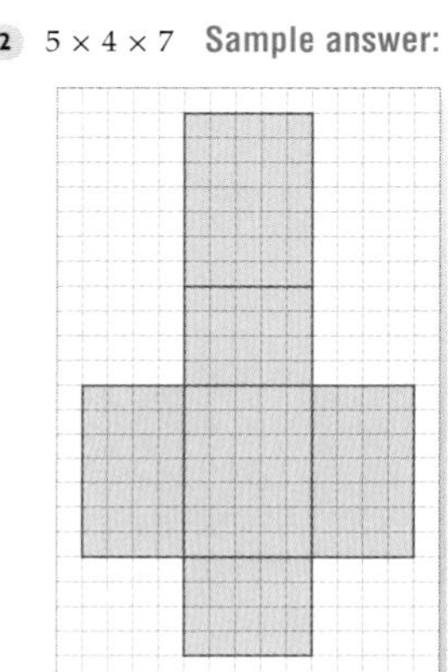

GO ON

Who *is Correct?*

Diagnostic Teaching

- Flores wrote 115 square units. This is incorrect because she did not find the sum of all six faces of the prism.
- Nidia wrote 162 square units. This is incorrect because she multiplied 3×9 for a product of 21, and it is 27.
- Jermaine wrote 174 square units. This is correct.

Remind students that rectangular prisms have six faces, so they will need to find the sum of six addends to find the surface area.

Using Manipulatives

Geometric Solids When presenting Examples 1 and 2, model the solids. Show students how you can trace the sides of the faces to make the net, and then fill in the square units.

Example 1

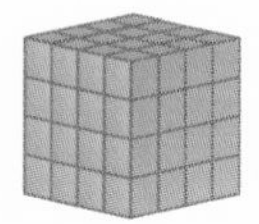

Example 2

Base-Ten Blocks Base-ten blocks can be useful in showing prisms and surface area.

Grid Paper Use a solid and grid paper to make a net.

Connecting Cubes Increase the number of connecting cubes and note how the surface area changes.

On-Hand Manipulatives Take six index cards and make a net. Use the net to make a prism.

Common Error *Alert*

Multi-Step Problems If students struggle with Exercises 1 and 2, it might be because they do not know what the dimensions of the figure represent. To remedy this problem, hold a prism and show students the height, the length, and the width. Now tell them to use blocks and build a prism with a height of 2 units, a length of 8 units, and a width of 9 units. Once they have made the figure, they can then draw the net. To check their work, encourage students to draw the answer on grid paper and use the net to make the prism. Does it match the figure they built? Does it have the correct dimensions?

Math Coach Notes

Strategies

1. Start this lesson with hands-on practice as an anchoring experience. Give students grid paper. Show them a cube. Count the faces. Demonstrate how to make a net. Have students make a net and then cut the net in order to make a cube.
2. Remind students that the unit for area is square units. Whenever they use linear units, ask them what a linear unit would measure.
3. Each time you hold up a rectangular solid, point out the height, the length, and the width.

Intervention Strategy

Interpersonal/ Kinesthetic Learners

Build a Prism Using dot or grid paper, tell students to make a net of a rectangular prism. Then trade with a partner. Students will cut out and build the prism with the net. Have students share their results.

Step by Step Practice

What is the surface area of the rectangular prism?

3 

Step 1 Use a net of the rectangular prism.

Step 2 Find the area of faces A and F.

$A = \ell \times w$
$A = \underline{2} \times \underline{4} = \underline{8}$

Step 3 Find the area of faces B and D.

$A = \ell \times w$
$A = \underline{4} \times \underline{3} = \underline{12}$

Step 4 Find the area of faces C and E.

$A = \ell \times w$
$A = \underline{2} \times \underline{3} = \underline{6}$

Step 5 Find the sum of the areas of all the faces.

$\underline{8} + \underline{12} + \underline{6} + \underline{8} + \underline{12} + \underline{6} = \underline{52}$

The surface area of the rectangular prism is $\underline{52}$ square units.

Find the surface area of each rectangular prism.

4 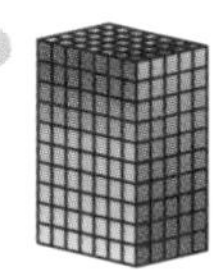

Sample answer:

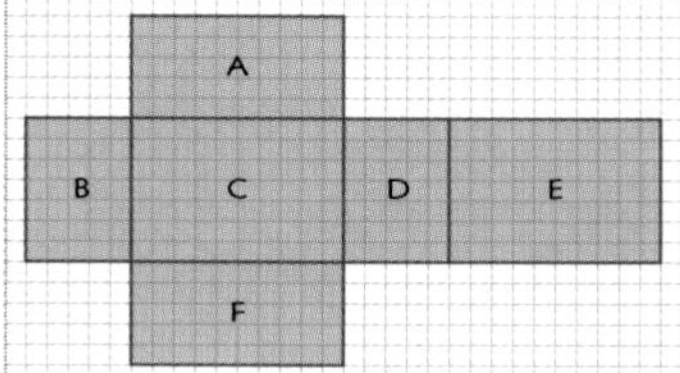

Use a net of the rectangular prism. Follow the steps at the top of page 422 to find the surface area.

Are They Getting It?

Check students' understanding of the surface area of rectangular solids by writing these problems on the board. Have students explain the incorrect information in each problem. Tell them to use a model or drawing to show why the answer is correct or incorrect.

1. A cube that has a face with area 7 square mm has a total surface area of 35 square mm. This is incorrect, because $6 \times 7 = 42$.
2. A rectangular prism with height 5 in., length 3 in., and width 4 in. has a surface area of 94 in. This is incorrect because the units should be square inches.
3. The surface area of this prism is 76 square m. This is correct.

Find the area of faces A and F.

$A = \ell \times w$

$A =$ 10 $\times$ 5 $=$ 50 sq. units

Find the area of faces B and D.

$A = \ell \times w$

$A =$ 5 $\times$ 7 $=$ 35 sq. units

Find the area of faces C and E.

$A = \ell \times w$

$A =$ 10 $\times$ 7 $=$ 70 sq. units

Find the sum of the area of all the faces.

50 (A) + 35 (B) + 70 (C) + 35 (D) + 70 (E) + 50 (F) = 310 sq. units

The surface area of the rectangular prism is 310 square units.

5

Find the area of faces A and F.

$A = \ell \times w$

$A =$ 9 $\times$ 4 $=$ 36 sq. units

Find the area of faces B and D.

$A = \ell \times w$

$A =$ 4 $\times$ 6 $=$ 24 sq. units

Find the area of faces C and E.

$A = \ell \times w$

$A =$ 6 $\times$ 9 $=$ 54 sq. units

Find the sum of the area of all the faces.

36 (A) + 24 (B) + 54 (C) + 36 (D) + 24 (E) + 54 (F) = 228 sq. units

The surface area of the rectangular prism is 228 square units.

6 The surface area of the rectangular prism is 174 square units.

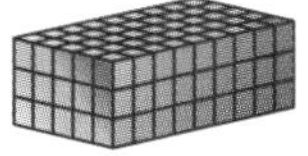

7 The surface area of the rectangular prism is 136 square units.

GO ON

Common Error *Alert*

Multi-Step Problem If students struggle with finding the surface area of the figure in Exercise 5, they may benefit from using a sheet of grid or dot paper and making a net. First have them number the sides of the figure. Then have them outline each one and create the net. Finally, have them find the area of each face, as directed, to solve the problem.

Intervention Strategy — Kinesthetic Learners

Find Surface Area Provide each student with a net of a three-dimensional prism on cardstock paper. Have students find the area of the net. Then students should cut out and fold the net to form the three-dimensional figure.

Have students trade figures so that they can unfold the net of a different prism and find its surface area. Tell students to share their findings. Did they arrive at the same measurement? Have the nets prenumbered and their surface areas recorded so you can check their answers.

Intervention Strategy

Kinesthetic/ Visual Learners

Wrap and Find Surface Area Provide each student with a three-dimensional prism and a section of wrapping paper large enough to wrap the figure. Instruct students to cut out pieces of wrapping paper that will fit each side of the figure. Once the wrapping paper is cut, ask students to determine the surface area of the figure.

Note This!

Figures Suggest to students that they write the different types of solids introduced in their notes. Next to each name, students should draw the figure and then think of some real-world examples that will help them remember the figure. They should also write in their own words the steps necessary to find the surface area of that figure.

Step by Step Problem-Solving Practice

Problem-Solving Strategies
- ☑ Draw a diagram.
- ☐ Look for a pattern.
- ☐ Guess and check.
- ☐ Solve a simpler problem.
- ☐ Work backward.

Solve.

8 PRESENTS Celia wrapped a present that was shaped like a cube. Each side measured 9 inches. What is the least amount of wrapping paper that Celia could have used to wrap the present?

Understand Read the problem. Write what you know. Each side of the present is __9__ inches.

Plan Pick a strategy. One strategy is to draw a diagram. Draw a net of the cube.

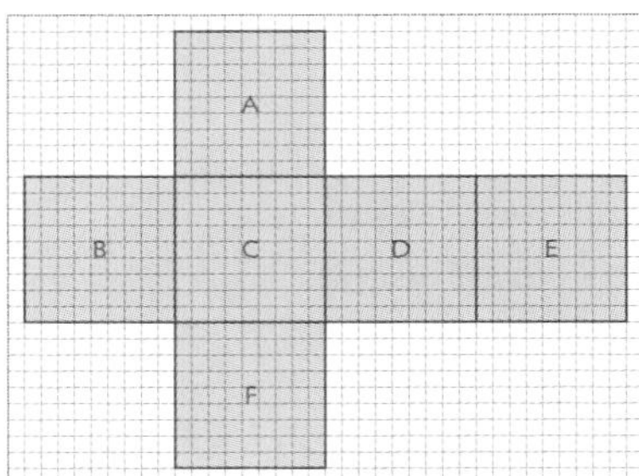

Solve Find the area of each face.

$A = \ell \times w$

$A =$ __9__ $\times$ __9__ $=$ __81__ sq. inches

Find the sum of the areas of all the faces.

__81__ + __81__ + __81__ + __81__ + __81__ + __81__ = __486__ sq. inches

Celia used at least __486__ square inches of wrapping paper.

Check Use division and subtraction to check your multiplication and addition.

English Learner Strategy

Guiding Questions Set out a rectangular prism and a cube. Then ask the following questions. Point to the rectangular prism.

- What are the sides called? How many sides are there?
- How is the area of a rectangle or square different than the surface area of a rectangular prism or solid?
- How do you find the surface area of a prism?
- How would you use a sheet of grid paper to construct a net?

9 DESIGN Chase put carpet on the floor, ceiling, and all of the walls in his video room. The video room has a length of 10 feet, a width of 15 feet, and a height of 10 feet. How much carpet did Chase use for his video room? Check off each step.

✓ Understand: I circled key words.

✓ Plan: To solve this problem, I will draw a diagram.

✓ Solve: The answer is 800 square feet.

✓ Check: I checked my answer by dividing and subtracting.

10 GEOMETRY What is the surface area of a number cube that has 15 millimeter edges?

1,350 mm^2

11 **Reflect** Use what you know about how to find the area of triangles and rectangles to find the surface area of this triangular prism. (Hint: This triangular prism has 2 sides that are triangles and 3 sides that are rectangles.)

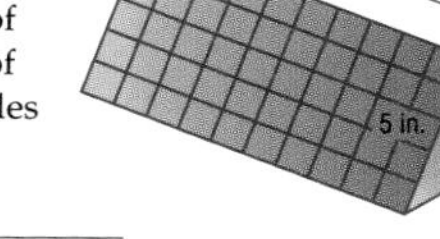

See TE margin.

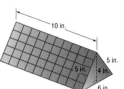

Skills, Concepts, and Problem Solving

Draw a net for a rectangular prism with the given length, width, and height. Label the faces A, B, C, D, E, and F.

12 $3 \times 7 \times 5$ Sample answer:

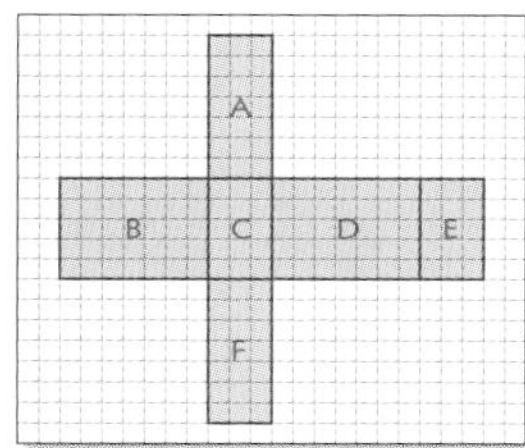

13 $4 \times 8 \times 4$ Sample answer:

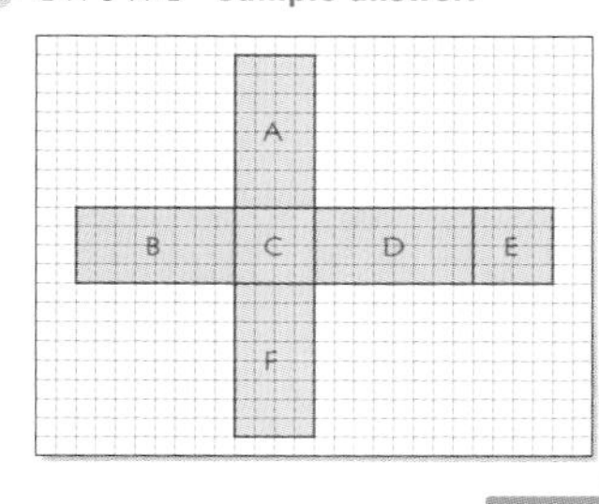

GO ON

Intervention Strategy

Kinesthetic/ Visual Learners

Connecting Cubes Have students begin with one connecting cube. Assume that one edge has a length of one unit. Find the surface area of one cube. Attach a second cube. Find the surface area. How has the surface area changed? Have students repeat this activity and keep track of their results. Can they predict the surface area when five cubes are connected?

Odd/Even Assignments

Exercises 12–20 are structured so that students practice the same concepts whether they are assigned the odd or even problems.

In-Class Assignment

Have students complete Exercises 12, 15, 19 and 24 to ensure that they understand the concept.

Math Coach Notes

Number the Sides When learning about surface area, encourage students to number the sides of the figure and write the area of that side next to the number. This will help students organize their work and determine which areas of the figure still need to be found.

Additional Answer

Exercise 11 To find the area of the triangles, use the formula $A = \frac{1}{2} \times b \times h$. Since $\frac{1}{2} \times 4 \times 6 = 12$, the area of each triangle is 12 square inches. To find the area of the rectangles, use the formula $A = l \times w$. One rectangle has a length of 6 inches and a width of 10 inches. Two rectangles have a length of 5 inches and a width of 10 inches. The areas are $6 \times 10 = 60$ square inches and $5 \times 10 = 50$ square inches, twice. To find the surface area of the triangular prism, add the area of each side. Since $12 + 12 + 60 + 50 + 50 = 184$, the surface area is 184 square inches.

Common Error *Alert*

Exercise 19 If a student struggles with Exercise 19, it might be because he or she is having difficulty visualizing the chest. Suggest he or she draw and label the figure.

Find the surface area of each rectangular prism.

14 The surface area of the rectangular prism is 168 square units.

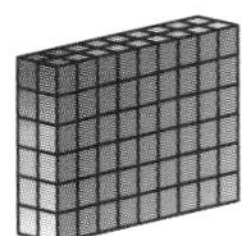

15 The surface area of the rectangular prism is 340 square units.

16 The surface area of the rectangular prism is 216 square units.

17 The surface area of the rectangular prism is 142 square units.

Solve.

18 JEWELRY Daisy made the jewelry box shown. The sides measure 18 centimeters each. What is the surface area of the jewelry box?
1,944 cm^2

JEWELRY Daisy's jewelry box is shaped like a cube.

19 ART Quinn decorated a rectangular-shaped chest with wallpaper. The length of the chest is 3 feet, the width is 5 feet, and the height is 2 feet. What is the least amount of wallpaper Quinn used?
62 ft^2

20 MOSAIC TILES Arleta is adding small tiles to a soap dish. It is in the shape of a rectangular prism. The soap dish is 10 centimeters long, 8 centimeters wide, and 3 centimeters tall. Each tile is a 1-centimeter square. How many tiles will Arleta need to decorate the surface area of the soap dish?
268 tiles

Math Challenge

Index Rectangles Cut index cards into a variety of different-sized rectangles. Make certain there are pairs of each size, and place an identical letter on each card in a pair. Fifteen pairs would be enough faces to make five prisms. Mix the cards up and give three cards to each student. Students try to get as many identical pairs of cards as possible by taking turns asking one another for a specific card. If no student has that card, the student picks up a card from the deck. Each time they have three matching cards, they can use tape and build a rectangular prism. Whoever builds three rectangular prisms first wins.

Vocabulary Check **Write the vocabulary word that completes each sentence.**

21 A(n) ___net___ is a flat pattern that can be folded to make a three-dimensional figure.

22 A(n) ___face___ is the flat side of a three-dimensional figure that is considered one of the sides.

23 ___Surface area___ is the area of the surface of a three-dimensional figure.

24 **Writing in Math** Explain how to find the surface area of a rectangular prism.

Sample answer: To find the surface area, find the sum of the areas of all the faces of the rectangular prism.

Spiral Review

Convert using a place value chart. (Lesson 10-1, p. 406)

25 0.49 L = ___490___ mL

1,000	100	10	1	0.1	0.01	0.001
thousands	hundreds	tens	ones	tenths	hundredths	thousandths
			0.	4	9	0
kilo (kL)			liter (L)			milli (mL)

26 78,000 mg = ___0.078___ kg

1,000	100	10	1	0.1	0.01	0.001
thousands	hundreds	tens	ones	tenths	hundredths	thousandths
0	0	7	8.	0	0	0
kilo (kg)			gram (g)			milli (mg)

Convert. (Lesson 10-2, p. 412)

27 3,000 lb = ___1.5___ T

28 16 pt = ___2___ gal

29 6 c = ___48___ fl oz

30 8 pt = ___16___ c

31 **PACKAGING** Sancho bought a 2-pound box of chocolates. How many ounces of chocolate did he buy? ___32 oz___

Ticket Out the Door

Sketches Ask students to carefully sketch a rectangular prism on grid paper. Have students trade papers. Then tell students to find the surface area and draw a net of the figure. Both students' names should be written on the paper before turning them in when they exit the classroom.

See It, Do It, Say It, Write It

Step 1 Draw a cube on grid paper. Show students how you can add the area of the faces to get the total surface area. Now draw a rectangular solid. Point out the dimensions. Have students help you calculate the surface area.

Step 2 Have students work in pairs. Give them rectangular prisms of varying dimensions. Ask them to draw a net. Then give them only the dimensions of another prism, and have them make another net.

Step 3 Ask students to discuss the steps for finding the surface area of a prism drawn as a net.

Step 4 Give each student a sheet with a rectangular prism on it. Ask students to write the method they would use to draw a net for the figure. Then have them draw the net and find the surface area.

Looking Ahead:

Introduction to Volume In the next lesson, students will learn how to determine the volume of a rectangular solid by counting the unit cubes that make up the solid.

Example

Find the volume of the rectangular prism.

- Count the number of cube layers in the prism. 3
- Count the number of cubes in the top layer. 12
- Each layer has the same number of cubes. The volume is 12 + 12 + 12 = 36 cubes.

Find the volume of each rectangular prism.

1. 18 cubes

16 cubes

Lesson 10-4

Lesson Notes

Lesson Planner

Objective Find the volume of a rectangular prism.

Vocabulary **cube**, **cubic unit**, **rectangular prism**, **volume**

Materials/Manipulatives connecting cubes, toy blocks, unit cubes

Chapter Resource Masters

- CRM Vocabulary and English Language Development (p. A216)
- CRM Skills Practice (p. A217)
- CRM Problem-Solving Practice (p. A218)
- CRM Homework Practice (p. A219)

1 Introduce

Vocabulary

Explore Vocabulary Hand out unit cubes to pairs of students. Explain to students that the *cube* is a three-dimensional figure because it has length, width, and height. Ask students to make a three-dimensional figure that is 2 cubes long, 2 cubes wide, and 2 cubes high. Guide students to realize that the number of units that take the space of the three-dimensional figure is the *volume.*

2 Teach

Key Concept

Foundational Skills and Concepts After students have read through the Key Concept box, have them try these exercises.

1. What is *volume?* the amount of space inside a three-dimensional figure
2. How do you find the volume of a solid figure? Count the number of cubic units the figure contains.

Lesson 10-4

Introduction to Volume

KEY Concept

The amount of space inside a three-dimensional figure is its **volume**. Volume is measured in **cubic units.** To find the volume of a solid figure, determine the number of cubic units the solid figure contains.

One way to determine the volume of a **rectangular prism** is to think about the number of **cubes** in each layer.

This figure has 2 layers. Each layer has 10 cubes.

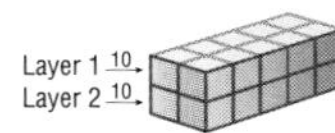

2 layers of 10 cubes = 10 + 10 = 20

This rectangular prism has a volume of 20 cubic units.

VOCABULARY

cube
a rectangular prism with six congruent square faces

cubic unit
a unit for measuring volume

rectangular prism
a three-dimensional figure with six faces that are rectangles

volume
the number of cubic units needed to fill a three-dimensional figure or solid figure

The volume of a figure is related to its dimensions, or length, width, and height.

Example 1

Find the volume of the rectangular prism.

1. Count the number of cube layers in the prism. There are 2 layers of cubes.

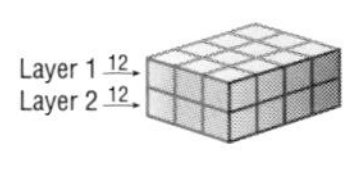

2. Count the number of cubes in the top layer. There are 12 cubes in the top layer.
3. Each layer has the same number of cubes. There are 12 + 12 = 24 cubes.

The volume of the rectangular prism is 24 cubic units.

YOUR TURN!

Find the volume of the rectangular prism.

1. How many layers of cubes are in the prism? 3

2. How many cubes are in the top layer? 2
3. There are 2 + 2 + 2 = 6 cubes.

The volume of the rectangular prism is 6 cubic units.

Additional Example 1

Find the volume of the rectangular prism.

1. Count the number of cube layers in the prism. There are 3 layers of cubes.
2. Count the number of cubes in the top layer. There are 8 cubes in the top layer.

8 Layer 1
8 Layer 2
8 Layer 3

3. Each layer has the same number of cubes. There are 8 + 8 + 8 = 24 cubes.

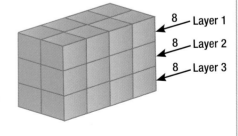

The volume of the rectangular prism is 24 cubic units.

Example 2

Find the volume of the rectangular prism.

1. Look at the top layer of cubes on the prism. Finding the area of the rectangle would tell you how many cubes are on that layer.
2. Area = $\ell \cdot w$, so the area of the top layer is $4 \times 5 = 20$. There are 20 cubes on the top layer.
3. Each layer has the same number of cubes. There are 2 layers, so there are $20 + 20 = 40$ cubes in the prism.
4. The volume of the rectangular prism is 40 cubic units.

height 2, width 4, length 5

YOUR TURN!

Find the volume of the rectangular prism.

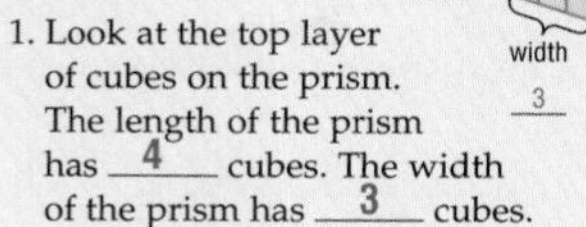

1. Look at the top layer of cubes on the prism. The length of the prism has __4__ cubes. The width of the prism has __3__ cubes.
2. Area = $\ell \cdot w$, so the area of the top layer is __4__ × __3__ = __12__. There are __12__ cubes on the top layer.
3. Each layer has the same number of cubes. There are __4__ layers, so there are __12__ + __12__ + __12__ + __12__ = __48__ cubes in the prism.
4. The volume of the rectangular prism is __48__ cubic units.

Who is Correct?

Find the volume of the rectangular prism.

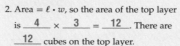

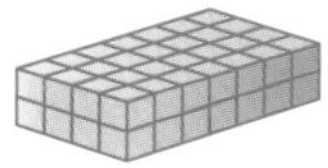

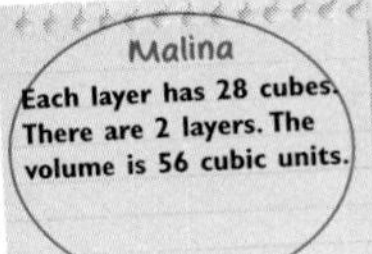

Malina
Each layer has 28 cubes. There are 2 layers. The volume is 56 cubic units.

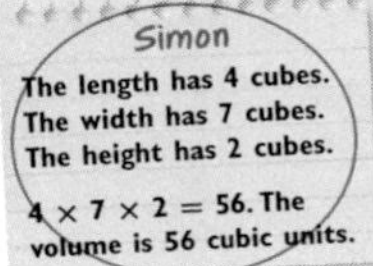

Erin
The length has 4 cubes. The width has 7 cubes. The height has 2 cubes.
4 + 7 + 2 = 13. The volume is 13 cubic units.

Circle correct answer(s). Cross out incorrect answer(s).

GO ON

Additional Example 2

Find the volume of the rectangular prism.

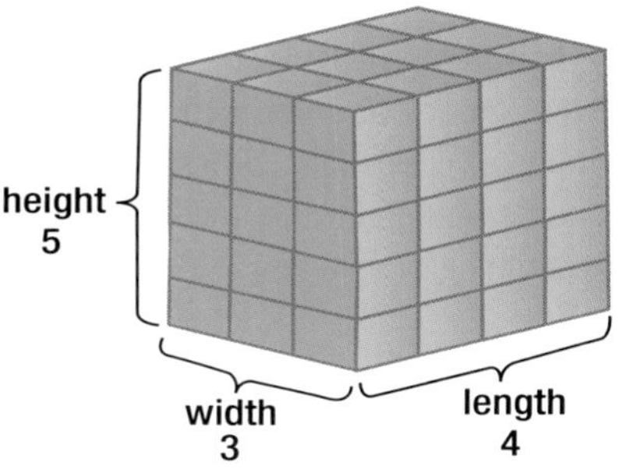

1. Look at the top layer of cubes on the prism. Finding the area of the rectangle would tell you how many cubes are on that layer.
2. Area = $\ell \times w$, so the area of the top layer is $4 \times 3 = 12$. There are 12 cubes on the top layer.
3. Each layer has the same number of cubes. There are 5 layers, so there are $12 + 12 + 12 + 12 + 12 = 60$ cubes in the prism.
4. The volume of the rectangular prism is 60 cubic units.

Who *is Correct?*

Diagnostic Teaching

- Malina is correct. She counted the cubic units the figure contains.
- Simon is correct. He found the area of the top layer then multiplied by the height.
- Erin is incorrect. She added instead of multiplying the length, width, and height.

Note This!

Sketches Encourage students to sketch and label the three-dimensional figures in this lesson. Labeling figures with the appropriate dimensions can help students in the future when they use them to find volume.

Math Coach Notes

Volume Another way to look at volume is to emphasize that the volume is the area of the base times the height. This is important because if the shape of the base is modified, the formula will still be based on the area of the base.

3 Practice

Using Manipulatives

Unit Cubes/Connecting Cubes When assigning Examples 1 and 2, model the three-dimensional figures by using unit cubes or connecting cubes. Allow students to model the figures and count the unit cubes to have a deeper understanding of volume.

On-Hand Manipulatives Use children's toy blocks instead of unit cubes.

Math Coach Notes

Strategies

1. Start this lesson identifying and drawing each dimension as you build to three dimensions. Have each student start with drawing a length, which is one dimension. Now have the students join the width to the length, which makes the figure two-dimensional. Finally, add height to make the figure three-dimensional.
2. Have students draw different three-dimensional figures by building the figure dimension by dimension.

Guided Practice

1 How many cubes are in this rectangular prism?

12

2 How many cubes are in this rectangular prism?

40

Remember, you can find the volume of a solid figure by counting the number of cubic units it contains.

Step by Step Practice

3 Find the volume of the rectangular prism.

Step 1 Count the number of cubes along the length.
The length of the rectangular prism has 5 cubes.

Step 2 Count the number of cubes along the width.
The width of the rectangular prism has 2 cubes.

Step 3 The area of the top layer is 5 × 2 = 10.

Step 4 There are 3 layers in the prism.
10 + 10 + 10 = 30 cubes in the prism.
The volume of the rectangular prism is 30 cubic units.

Find the volume of each rectangular prism.

4 Count the number of cubes along the length, width, and height of the rectangular prism.

Find the area of the top layer. Add that number four times. The volume of the rectangular prism is 72 cubic units.

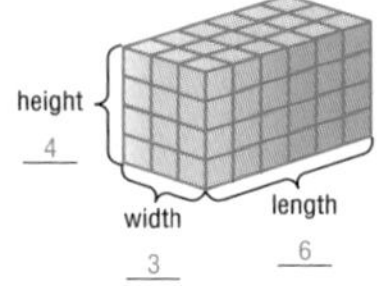

Intervention Strategy Kinesthetic Learners

Show Volume Provide students with a variety of clear, empty rectangular prisms and a container of cubic blocks. Have students fill the prism with the cubic blocks. Once they have filled the prism, have students count the number of blocks used to fill the prism.

5 Count the number of cubes along the length, width, and height of the rectangular prism.

Find the area of the top layer. Add that number eight times. The volume of the rectangular prism is 96 cubic units.

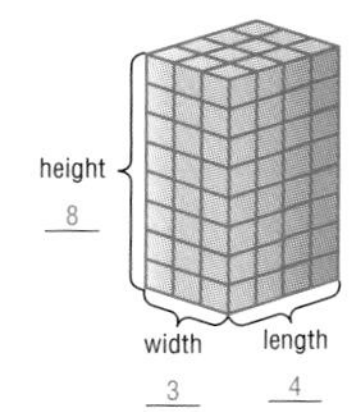

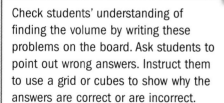

6 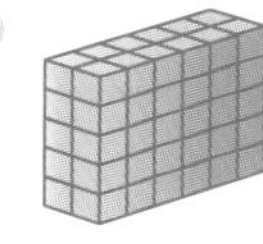 The volume of the rectangular prism is 45 cubic units.

7 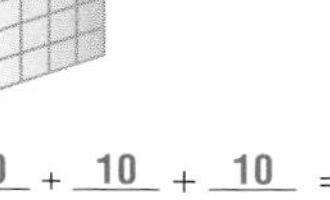 The volume of the rectangular prism is 60 cubic units.

Step by Step Problem-Solving Practice

Problem-Solving Strategies
- ☐ Draw a diagram.
- ☐ Look for a pattern.
- ☑ Use a model.
- ☐ Solve a simpler problem.
- ☐ Work backward.

Solve.

8 GIFTS A gift box that is shaped like a rectangular prism has a length of 5 feet, a width of 2 feet, and a height of 8 feet. What is its volume?

Understand Read the problem. Write what you know.
A gift box has a length of 5 feet,
a width of 2 feet, and a height of 8 feet.

Plan Pick a strategy. One strategy is to use a model.

Solve Use unit blocks to build the rectangular prism. Count the number of blocks used.

Check The length is 5 feet.
The width is 2 feet.
There are 8 layers.
Multiply then add.

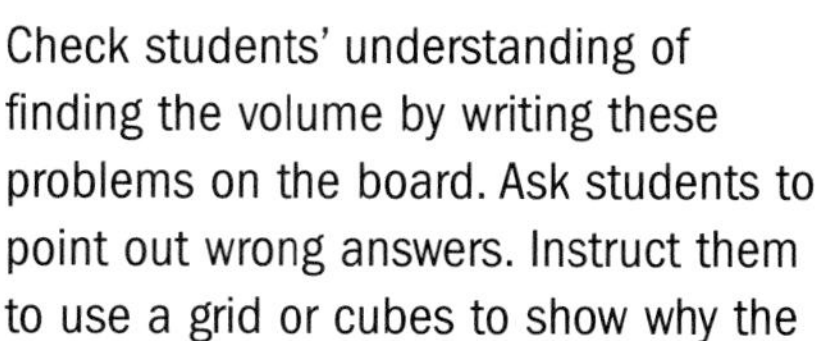

5 × 2 = 10

10 + 10 + 10 + 10 + 10 + 10 + 10 + 10 = 80

The volume of the gift box is 80 cubic feet.

GO ON

Common Error Alert

Remember the Units Volume is measured in cubic units. Remind students that their final answers should be described in cubic units.

Note This!

Example Lists While taking notes on volume, encourage students to notice what kind of figures have volume. In their notes, suggest students list examples of three-dimensional shapes that have volume.

Are They Getting It?

Check students' understanding of finding the volume by writing these problems on the board. Ask students to point out wrong answers. Instruct them to use a grid or cubes to show why the answers are correct or are incorrect.

Find the volume of each rectangular prism.

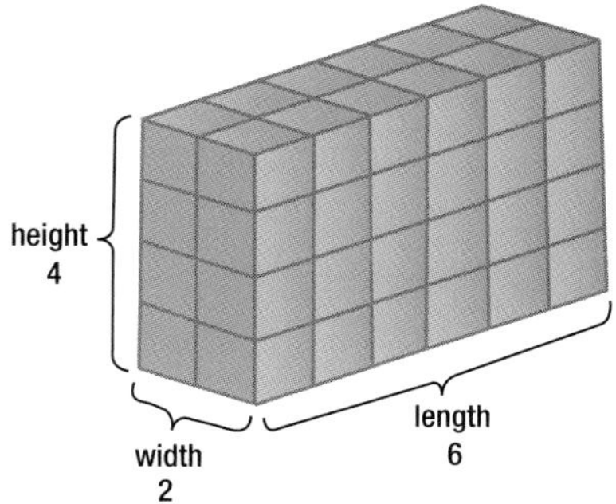

The volume of the rectangular prism is 48 cubic units. This is correct.

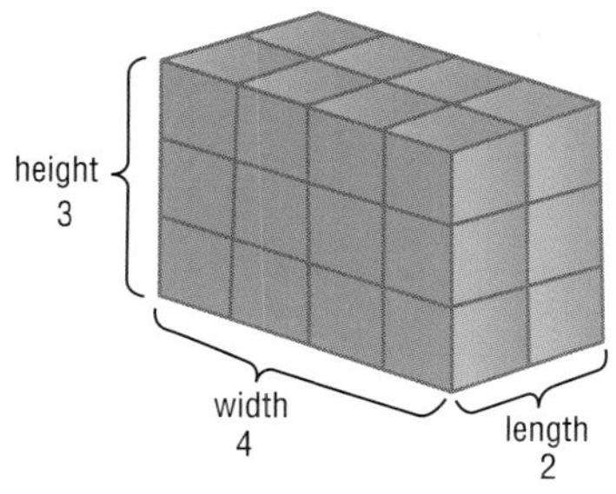

The volume of the rectangular prism is 28 cubic units. This is incorrect. The volume is 24 cubic units.

Odd/Even Assignments

Exercises 12–17 are structured so that students practice the same concepts whether they are assigned the odd or even problems.

In-Class Assignment

Have students complete Exercises 12, 16, 19, and 20 to ensure that they understand the concept.

Additional Answer

Exercise 11 Sample answer: A rectangular prism that has a volume of 36 cubic units could have a length of 9 units, a width of 1 unit, and a height of 4 units. Multiply the length and width to get the area of the top layer, $9 \times 1 = 9$. Then multiply the area by the height 4 to get 36 cubic units.

English Learner Strategy

Guiding Questions Ask students the following questions to ensure that they understand the concept.

- How do you find the dimensions of a prism?
- What is the length of the prism? What is the width of the prism? What is the height of the prism?
- How do you use these numbers to find the volume?
- How would you describe to another student how to find the volume of a prism? If another student of the same native language is available, have the student explain the process to him or her in the native language.

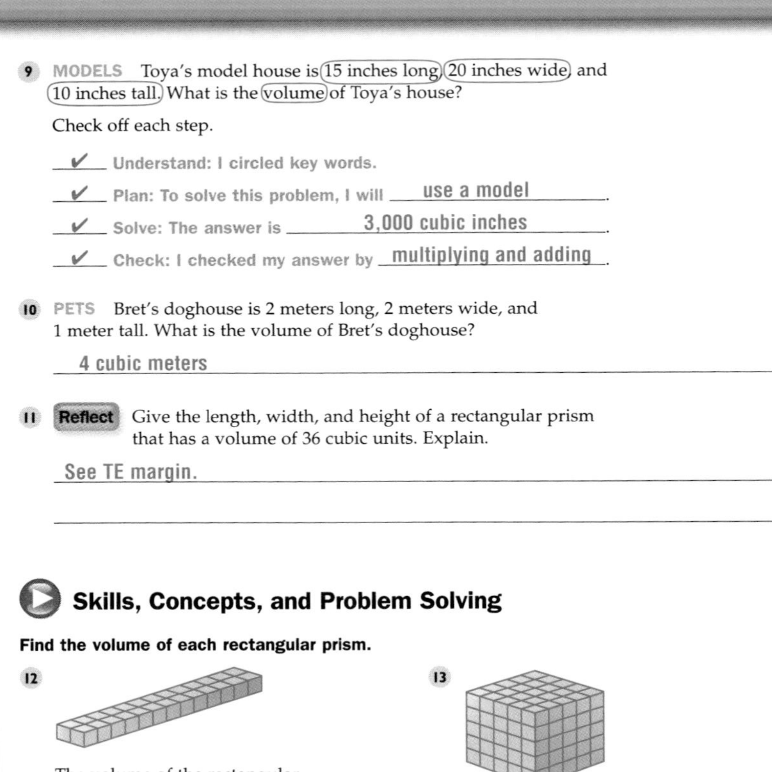

9 MODELS Toya's model house is 15 inches long, 20 inches wide, and 10 inches tall. What is the volume of Toya's house?

Check off each step.

✓ Understand: I circled key words.

✓ Plan: To solve this problem, I will use a model.

✓ Solve: The answer is 3,000 cubic inches.

✓ Check: I checked my answer by multiplying and adding.

10 PETS Bret's doghouse is 2 meters long, 2 meters wide, and 1 meter tall. What is the volume of Bret's doghouse?

4 cubic meters

11 **Reflect** Give the length, width, and height of a rectangular prism that has a volume of 36 cubic units. Explain.

See TE margin.

Skills, Concepts, and Problem Solving

Find the volume of each rectangular prism.

12 The volume of the rectangular prism is 26 cubic units.

13 The volume of the rectangular prism is 125 cubic units.

14 The volume of the rectangular prism is 40 cubic units.

15 The volume of the rectangular prism is 72 cubic units.

432 Chapter 10 Surface Area, Volume, and Measurement

Math Challenge

Irregular Solids Challenge students to make an irregular three-dimensional object by taping together faces that will form a solid. Then they can estimate the volume of that solid. Point out that the students may have to find the volume of parts of the solid and add the parts together.

Solve.

16 PACKAGING What is the volume of the package shown at the right?

210 cubic inches

17 ART A box of art tools is 8 centimeters long, 4 centimeters wide, and 5 centimeters tall. What is the volume of the art box?

160 cubic cm

PACKAGING The package is 10 inches long, 7 inches wide, and 3 inches tall.

Vocabulary Check **Write the vocabulary word that completes each sentence.**

18 A(n) cubic unit is a unit for measuring volume.

19 Volume is the number of cubic units needed to fill a three-dimensional figure or solid figure.

20 Writing in Math Explain how to find the volume of a rectangular prism.

See TE margin.

Spiral Review

Draw a net for a rectangular prism with the given length, width, and height. Label the faces A, B, C, D, E, and F. (Lesson 10-3, p. 419)

21 $3 \times 5 \times 6$ Sample answer:

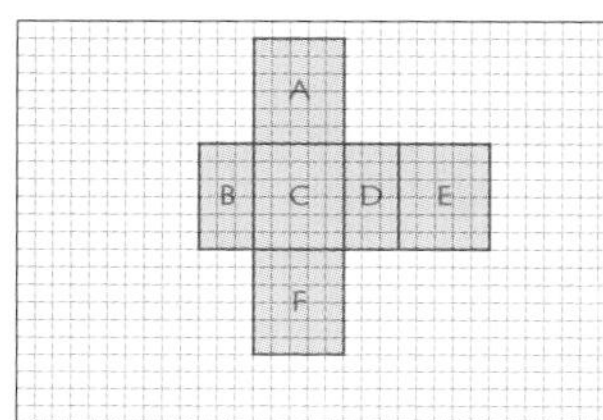

22 $2 \times 3 \times 1$ Sample answer:

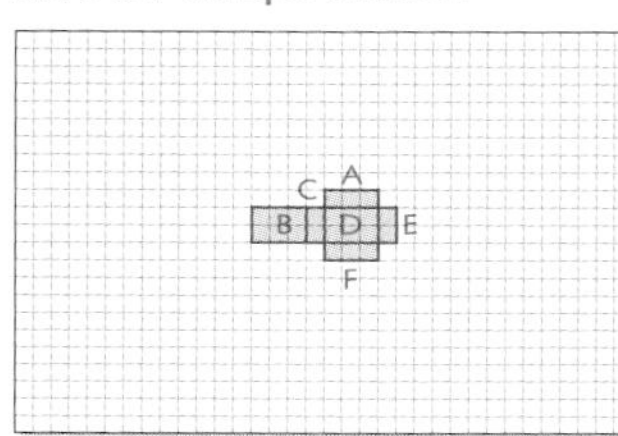

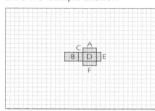

Ticket Out the Door

I Spy a Volume Give students an example of a figure found in the class that has a volume of 27 cubic centimeters. Have students find its volume. Students turn in their results as they exit the classroom.

See It, Do It, Say It, Write It

Step 1 Draw the following figure on the board:

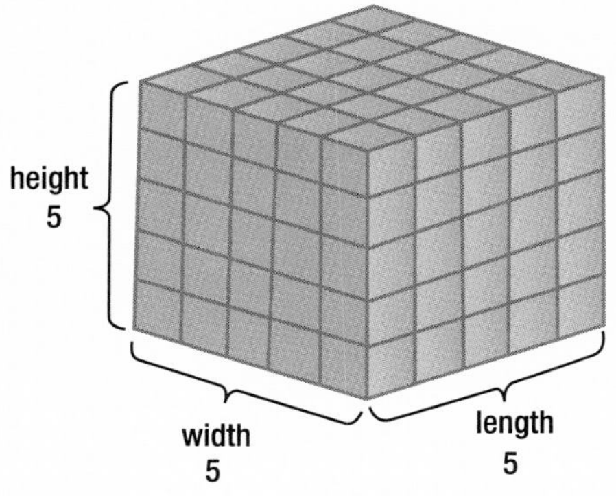

Step 2 Have students estimate the volume of the figure.

Step 3 Arrange the students into pairs and have them explain to each other how they found the volume of the figure.

Step 4 Have students write in their journals how to find the volume of a figure.

Additional Answer

Exercise 20 Count the number of cubes along the length, width, and height of the rectangular prism. Find the area of the top layer by multiplying length $\times$ width. Then multiply by the height. Place your answer in cubic units.

Looking Ahead:

Volume of Rectangular Solids In the next lesson, students will learn that the formula $V = l \times w \times h$ can be used to find the volume in cubic units.

Example

What is the volume of the cube shown at the top of the page? 125 cubic units

$$A = l \times w \times h$$
$$A = 5 \times 5 \times 5$$
$$A = 125 \text{ cubic units}$$

Find the volume of each rectangular prism.

1. length 6 cm, width 3 cm, height 5 cm 90 cubic cm
2. length 10 in., width 5 in., height 8 in. 400 cubic in.

Lesson 10-5

Lesson Notes

Lesson Planner

Objective Find the volume of a rectangular solid.

Vocabulary **cube, cubic unit, volume**

Materials/Manipulatives alphabet blocks, base-ten blocks, connecting cubes, geometric solids, grid paper, isometric dot paper, unit cubes

Chapter Resource Masters

- CRM Vocabulary and English Language Development (p. A220)
- CRM Skills Practice (p. A221)
- CRM Problem-Solving Practice (p. A222)
- CRM Homework Practice (p. A223)

1 Introduce

Vocabulary

Compare Vocabulary Draw a *cube* on the board. Ask: How do you know it is a *cube?* Write dimensions with units on the *cube* and ask how many *cubic units* would fit into the cube. How can you find out? This is the *volume.* Challenge students to compare surface area and square units with volume and cubic units.

2 Teach

Key Concept

Foundational Skills and Concepts After students have read through the Key Concept box, have them try these exercises.

1. What is volume? the amount of space inside a three-dimensional figure
2. A rectangular solid has length, width, and height. What is the volume? length × width × height
3. What is the unit for volume? cubic units

Lesson 10-5

Volume of Rectangular Solids

KEY Concept

The amount of space inside a three-dimensional figure is the **volume** of the figure.

The volume of a rectangular solid is the product of its length, width, and height.

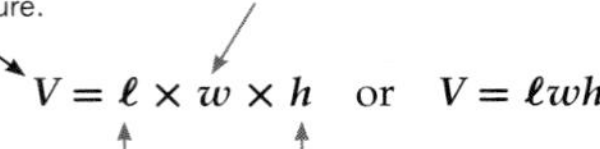

V is the volume of the solid figure.
w is the width.
$V = \ell \times w \times h$ or $V = \ell wh$
ℓ is the length.
h is the height.

VOCABULARY

cube a three-dimensional figure with six congruent square faces

cubic unit a unit for measuring volume

volume the number of cubic units needed to fill a three-dimensional figure or solid figure

Volume is measured in **cubic units.**

Example 1

What is the volume of the rectangular prism?

1. The length of the cube is 3 units.
   The width of the cube is 7 units.
   The height of the cube is 4 units.
2. Substitute the length, width, and height into the volume formula.
   $V = \ell \times w \times h$
   $V = 3 \times 7 \times 4$
3. Multiply.
   $V = 84$

The volume of the rectangular prism is 84 cubic units.

YOUR TURN!

What is the volume of the rectangular prism?

1. The length of the rectangular prism is 5 units.
   The width of the rectangular prism is 4 units.
   The height of the rectangular prism is 8 units.
2. Substitute the length, width, and height into the volume formula.
   $V = \ell \times w \times h$
   $V = 5 \times 4 \times 8$
3. Multiply.
   $V = 160$

The volume of the rectangular prism is 160 cubic units.

Additional Example 1

What is the volume of the rectangular prism?

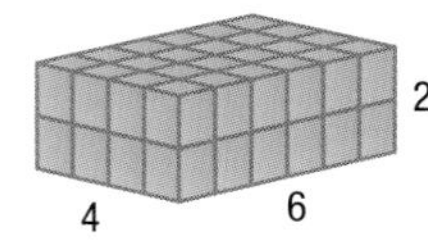

2
4
6

1. The length of the cube is 4 units.
   The width of the cube is 6 units.
   The height of the cube is 2 units.
2. Substitute the length, width, and height into the formula for volume.
   $V = \ell \times w \times h$
   $V = 4 \times 6 \times 2$
3. Multiply.
   $V = 48$

The volume of the rectangular prism is 48 cubic units.

Example 2

What is the volume of the cube?

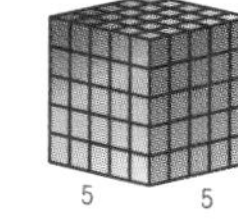

1. The length of the cube is 5 units.

   The width of the cube is 5 units.

   The height of the cube is 5 units.

2. Substitute the length, width, and height into the volume formula.

   $V = \ell \times w \times h$
   $V = 5 \times 5 \times 5$
   $V = 5^3$

3. Multiply.

   $V = 125$

The volume of the cube is 125 cubic units.

YOUR TURN!

What is the volume of the cube?

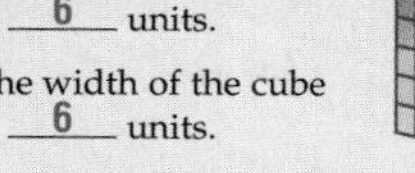

1. The length of the cube is 6 units.

   The width of the cube is 6 units.

   The height of the cube is 6 units.

2. Substitute the length, width, and height into the volume formula.

   $V = \ell \times w \times h$
   $V = 6 \times 6 \times 6$
   $V = 6^3$

3. Multiply.

   $V = 216$

The volume of the cube is 216 cubic units.

Who is Correct?

What is the volume of the rectangular prism?

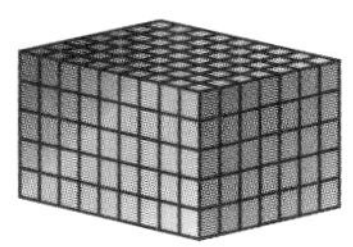

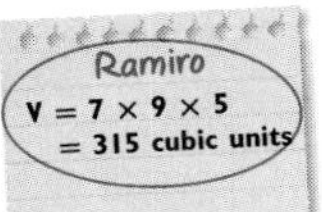

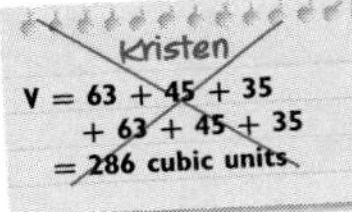

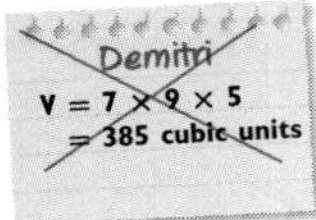

Circle correct answer(s). Cross out incorrect answer(s).

Additional ***Example 2***

What is the volume of the cube?

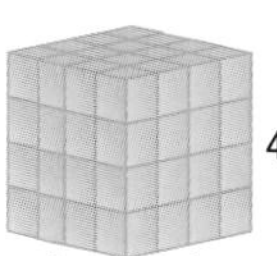

1. The length of the cube is 4 units.
   The width of the cube is 4 units.
   The height of the cube is 4 units.

2. Substitute the length, width, and height into the formula for volume.
   $V = \ell \times w \times h$
   $V = 4 \times 4 \times 4$
   $V = 4^3$

3. Multiply.
   $V = 64$

The volume of the cube is 64 cubic units.

Note This!

Make a Table Prompt students to make a table comparing the last lesson on surface area with this lesson on volume. The table will magnify the differences between the two concepts.

Who ***is Correct?***

Diagnostic Teaching

- Ramiro wrote 315 cubic units. This is correct.
- Kristen wrote 286 cubic units. This is incorrect. She found surface area instead of multiplying the dimensions to find the volume.
- Demitri wrote 385 cubic units. This is incorrect. He made an error in multiplying.

Remind students that the volume of a prism is the product of its length, width, and height.

Math Coach Notes

Volume The concept of volume is analogous to area and should be presented that way. The unit for area is fixed and called the unit square. The unit for volume is also fixed and called the unit cube. While area is the sum of the areas of the units that pave a surface, the volume of a figure is the sum of the volumes of the cubes that fill it.

3 Practice

Using Manipulatives

Geometric Solids When presenting Example 1, model it with geometric solids. Show students how to fill the solid with cubes to find the volume.

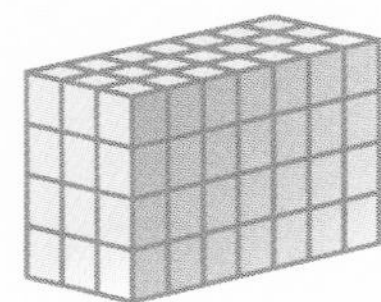

Base-Ten Blocks Base-ten blocks can be used to show how cubic units make up the volume of a prism.

Connecting Cubes Increase the number of connecting cubes and look at how the volume changes.

On-Hand Manipulatives Build solids with alphabet blocks and/or unit cubes.

Math Coach Notes

Exercises 1 and 2 If centimeter cubes are available, have students build the cube shown in Exercise 1. First, ask students to use a metric ruler to measure the length, width, and height of the prism. They should find that the length, width, and height of the cube are each 2 centimeters. (2 cm × 2 cm × 2 cm = 8 cubic cm) They will notice that they used 8 centimeter cubes to build the cube.

For Exercise 2:

7 cm × 5 cm × 1 cm = 35 cubic cm

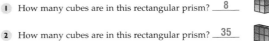

Guided Practice

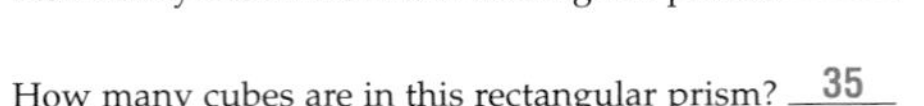

1 How many cubes are in this rectangular prism? 8

Check your answer. Remember, you can find the volume of a solid figure by counting the number of cubic units it contains.

2 How many cubes are in this rectangular prism? 35

Step by Step Practice

Find the volume of the rectangular prism.

3

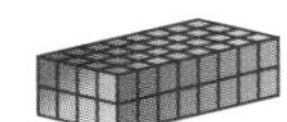

Step 1 The length of the rectangular prism is 4 units.

The width of the rectangular prism is 8 units.

The height of the rectangular prism is 2 units.

Step 2 Substitute the length, width, and height into the volume formula.

$V = \ell \times w \times h$

$V = 4 \times 8 \times 2$

Step 3 Multiply.

$V = 64$

The volume of the rectangular prism is 64 cubic units.

Find the volume of each rectangular prism.

4 Substitute the length, width, and height into the volume formula. Then multiply.

$V = \ell \times w \times h$

$V = 6 \times 10 \times 3$

$V = 180$

The volume of the rectangular prism is 180 cubic units.

Intervention Strategy

Kinesthetic/ Logical Learners

Fill a Shoebox Give students a rectangular solid (such as a shoebox) that can be filled. Using cubic blocks, have students determine the volume of the rectangular solid by filling the solid with the cubic blocks. Once they have determined the volume using the blocks, have students use the formula to determine the volume of the box.

5 $V = \ell \times w \times h$

$V =$ 2 $\times$ 12 $\times$ 5

$V =$ 120

The volume of the rectangular prism is 120 cubic units.

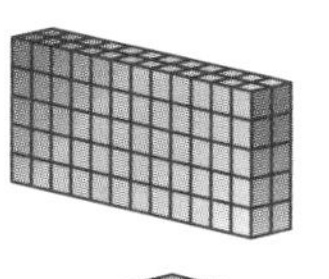

6 The volume of the rectangular prism is 288 cubic units.

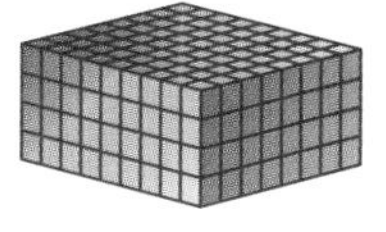

7 The volume of the rectangular prism is 168 cubic units.

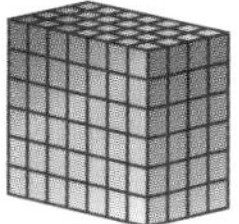

Step by Step Problem-Solving Practice

Problem-Solving Strategies
- ☑ Use a model.
- ☐ Look for a pattern.
- ☐ Guess and check.
- ☐ Act it out.
- ☐ Work backward.

Solve.

8 HOUSES Hillary has an air humidifier in her bedroom that is 10 inches long, 17 inches wide, and 10 inches tall. What is the volume of Hillary's air humidifier?

Understand Read the problem. Write what you know.

The air humidifier has a length of 10 inches, a width of 17 inches, and a height of 10 inches.

Plan Pick a strategy. One strategy is to use a model.

Stack cubes to model the air humidifier.

Solve Use the formula.

$V = \ell \times w \times h$

$V =$ 10 in. $\times$ 17 in. $\times$ 10 in.

$V =$ 1,700 cubic inches

The volume of Hillary's air humidifier is 1,700 cubic inches.

Check Use division to check your multiplication.

GO ON

Are They Getting It?

Check students' understanding of the volume of rectangular solids by writing these problems on the board. Have students explain the incorrect information in each problem. Tell them to use a model or drawing to show why the answer is correct or incorrect.

1. A cube that has a base of area 16 square mm has a volume of 64 cubic mm. This is correct.
2. A rectangular prism with width 5 in., length 4 in., and height 7 in. has a volume of 140 square in. This is incorrect because the units should be cubic inches.
3. The volume of this prism is 24 cubic m. This is incorrect. The volume is 120 cubic m.

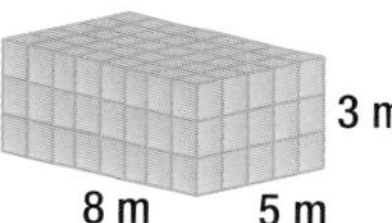

Math Coach Notes

Strategies

1. Start this lesson with a hands-on lab as an anchoring experience. Have students build different-sized rectangular prisms with blocks, beginning with one cube and then increasing a dimension. Have them keep track of the height, width, length, and the number of blocks or cubes they use. Repeat until students see that the product of the dimensions equals the number of blocks used in construction.
2. Students should realize that the base of a prism changes depending on which face it lies. Because of the Commutative Property, the order the dimensions are multiplied does not affect the result.

Note that the labels for length and width can be interchanged due to the Associative and Commutative Properties of Multiplication. When checking student answers, be mindful that students may label the width and length differently.

English Learner Strategy

Guiding Questions Use connecting cubes or blocks. Ask students the following questions.

- Which figure is a cube?
- What is the volume of one cube?
- Connect two cubes. What is the volume now?
- What is the difference between a cubic unit and a square unit?
- How do you use the formula for volume to find the volume of a rectangular solid that is 2 cubes high, 3 cubes long, and 4 cubes wide?

Odd/Even Assignments

Exercises 12–17 are structured so that students practice the same concepts whether they are assigned the odd or even problems.

In-Class Assignment

Have students complete Exercises 13, 16, 17, and 20 to ensure that they understand the concept.

Additional Answer

Exercise 11 The volume of the rectangular prism is found by using the formula $V = l \times w \times h$. Since $9 \times 1 \times 4 = 36$, the volume is 36 cubic units. The surface area of the rectangular prism is found by adding the areas of all six sides. Two sides have areas of $9 \times 1 = 9$ square units. Two sides have areas of $4 \times 1 = 4$ square units. The remaining two sides have areas of $9 \times 4 = 36$ square units. The surface area is $9 + 9 + 4 + 4 + 36 + 36$ or 98 square units. Volume describes how many cubic units are within the rectangular prism. Surface area describes how many square units cover the outside surface of the rectangular prism.

Common Error *Alert*

Exercises 9 and 10 If a student struggles with Exercises 9 or 10, it might be because he or she is having difficulty visualizing the figure. Suggest the student draw the figure and label the dimensions.

9 CONSTRUCTION Sanouk's family has a storage shed that is 5 yards wide, 28 yards long, and 5 yards high. What is the volume of the shed?

Check off each step.

✓ Understand: I circled key words.

✓ Plan: To solve this problem, I will use a model.

✓ Solve: The answer is 700 cubic yards.

✓ Check: I checked my answer by dividing.

10 PACKAGING Mrs. Reynolds put together a card box for her daughter's graduation party. The card box was shaped like a cube. Each side measured 50 centimeters. What was the volume of the card box? $125{,}000$ cm^3

11 **Reflect** Compare the volume of the rectangular prism shown at the right to its surface area.

See TE margin.

Skills, Concepts, and Problem Solving

Find the volume of each rectangular prism.

12 The volume of the rectangular prism is 30 cubic units.

13 The volume of the rectangular prism is 162 cubic units.

14 The volume of the rectangular prism is 80 cubic units.

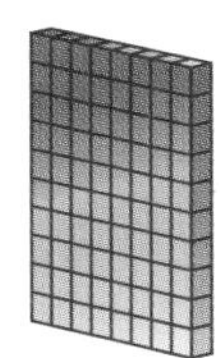

15 The volume of the rectangular prism is 225 cubic units.

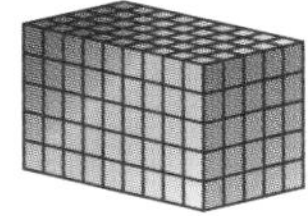

438 **Chapter 10** Surface Area, Volume, and Measurement

Math Challenge

Rolling Solids Students will take turns rolling a number cube. Each number will represent a dimension of a rectangular solid. After three rolls each, the players will calculate the volume of their solid. The play continues. The volumes are totaled after five plays. The student with the greater total volume wins.

Solve.

16 CONSTRUCTION Marco's father built the tree house shown at the right. What was the volume of the tree house?
420 ft^3

17 COLLECTIONS Brittany used a shoe box for her rock collection. The shoe box was 12 inches long, 6 inches wide, and 5 inches high. What was the volume of the shoe box?
360 in^3

CONSTRUCTION **The tree house that Marco's father built had a height of 7 feet, a length of 10 feet, and a width of 6 feet.**

Vocabulary Check **Write the vocabulary word that completes each sentence.**

18 Cubic unit is a unit for measuring volume.

19 Volume is the number of cubic units needed to fill a three-dimensional figure or solid figure.

20 Writing in Math Explain how to find the volume of a rectangular prism.
Sample answer: Find the length, width, and height of the rectangular prism. Substitute the length, width, and height into the formula for the volume of a rectangular prism. Then multiply.

Spiral Review

Solve. (Lesson 10-3, p. 419)

21 MUSIC Alvar's stereo speakers are cube shaped. Each side measures 20 millimeters. What is the surface area of each speaker?
2,400 mm^2

22 Draw a net for a rectangular prism with a length of 10, a width of 7, and a height of 4.

Sample answer:

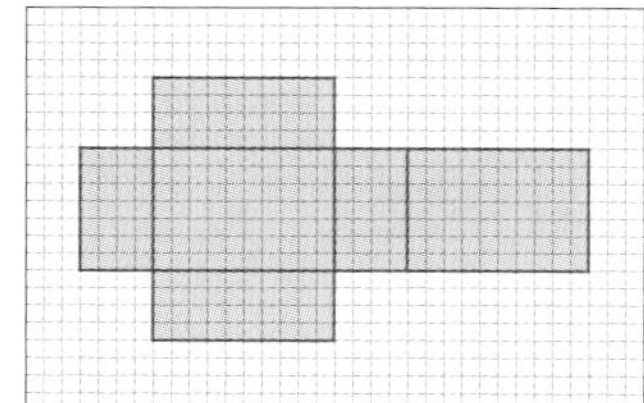

STOP

See It, Do It, Say It, Write It

Step 1 Hold a base-ten flat. What is the volume? Hold up a rod and ask the same question. Tell students to draw a rectangular solid on grid paper that has the same volume but different dimensions than the flat and the rod. Volunteers can share their answers.

Step 2 Draw a rectangular prism on the board. Label the height, width, and length. Tell students to find the volume. Change the dimensions and units and repeat.

Step 3 Students can work in pairs or small groups. Hand out a volume, such as "48 cubic units," written on an index card. Ask students to use a model to make a rectangular prism with that volume. After they draw the figure on dot or grid paper, tell them to make as many rectangular prisms as they can with that same volume. Have them sketch each figure.

Step 4 Discuss the results in class. Then have each student write about the activity they just completed.

Ticket Out the Door

Find Volume Ask students to carefully sketch a rectangular prism on grid paper. Students trade papers. Tell students to find the volume of the prism. Then have them write the definition of *volume.* Students turn in their papers when they exit the classroom.

Chapter 10

Progress Check 2

Formative Assessment

Use the Progress Check to assess students' mastery of the previous lessons. Have students review the lesson indicated for the problems they answered incorrectly.

Odd/Even Assignments

Exercises are structured so that students practice the same concepts whether they are assigned the odd or even problems.

Common Error *Alert*

Exercises

Exercises 1–2 Students may have difficulty visualizing how to draw a net when given the dimensions of a prism. Remind them of what the dimensions represent and how it will help to think of the net as several pieces or sides of the prism flattened out and laid together.

Exercises 3, 5 Students may forget one or more of the sides when totaling the prism's surface area.

Progress Check 2 (Lessons 10-3, 10-4, and 10-5)

Draw a net for a rectangular prism with the given length, width, and height.

1. $3 \times 7 \times 6$ Sample answer:

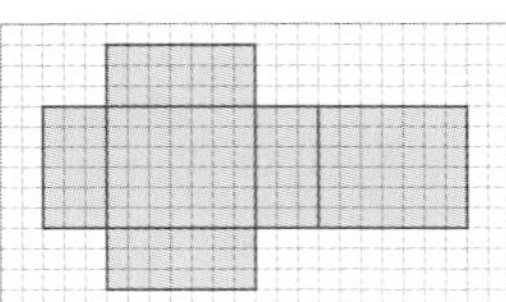

2. $2 \times 8 \times 5$ Sample answer:

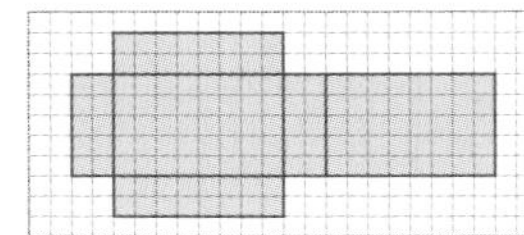

Find the surface area and the volume of each rectangular prism.

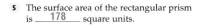

3. The surface area of the rectangular prism is 268 square units.
4. The volume of the rectangular prism is 240 cubic units.

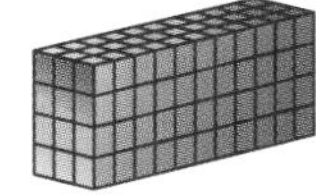

5. The surface area of the rectangular prism is 178 square units.
6. The volume of the rectangular prism is 132 cubic units.

Solve.

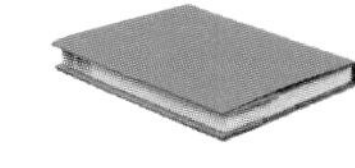

7. **GIFTS** Melinda is wrapping a present for her sister's graduation. The gift is a book that is 6 inches long, 5 inches wide, and 2 inches high. What is the surface area of the book?
104 square inches

8. **STORAGE** A storage cabinet is 24 inches wide, 26 inches long, and 40 inches high. What is the surface area of the storage cabinet?
5,248 square inches

Data-Driven Decision Making

Students missing Exercises . . .	Have trouble with . . .	Should review and practice . . .
1–2	drawing a net given its dimensions.	SSG Lesson 10-3, p. 419 CRM Skills Practice p. A213
3, 5	finding the surface area of a prism.	SSG Lesson 10-3, p. 419 CRM Skills Practice p. A213
4, 6	finding the volume of a rectangular prism.	SSG Lessons 10-5, pp. 428 and 434 CRM Skills Practice pp. A217 and A221
7–8	solving word problems involving area and volume of a prism.	CRM Problem-Solving Practice, pp. A214, A218 and A222

Chapter 10 Study Guide

Vocabulary and Concept Check

benchmark, *p. 412*
capacity, *p. 406*
cube, *p. 428*
cubic unit, *p. 428*
customary system, *p. 412*
face, *p. 419*
gram, *p. 406*
liter, *p. 406*
mass, *p. 406*
metric system, *p. 406*
net, *p. 419*
rectangular prism, *p. 428*
square unit, *p. 419*
surface area, *p. 419*
volume, *p. 428*
weight, *p. 412*

Write the vocabulary word that completes each sentence.

1. A ___gram___ is the metric unit for measuring mass.
2. ___Surface area___ is the area of the surface of a three-dimensional figure.
3. Volume is measured in ___cubic units___ .
4. The ___metric system___ is a measurement system that includes units such as grams and liters.
5. The ___customary system___ is a measurement system that includes units such as gallons and pounds.
6. A ___net___ is a flat pattern that can be folded to make a three-dimensional figure.

Label each diagram below. Write the correct vocabulary term in each blank.

7. The net shown is of a ___cube___ that has 6 ___faces___.

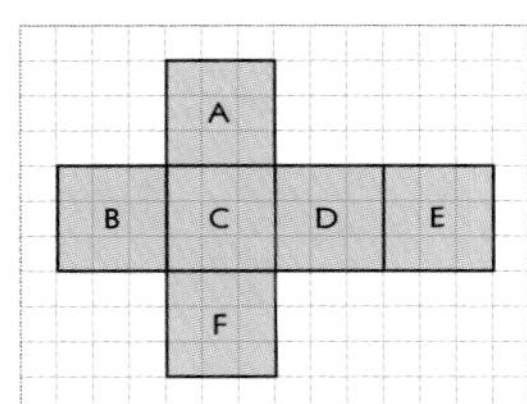

8. ___gram___ 9. ___milligram___

$1 \text{ g} = 1{,}000 \text{ mg}$

10. ___kiloliter___ 11. ___liter___

$1 \text{ kL} = 1{,}000 \text{ L}$

Chapter 10 Study Guide 441

Study Guide
Formative Assessment

Chapter 10

Vocabulary and Concept Check

If students have difficulty answering Exercises 1–11, remind them that they can use the page references to refresh their memories about the vocabulary terms.

Vocabulary Review Strategies

Have students make a crossword puzzle to help them review key vocabulary words. They should interlock the words in the Vocabulary and Concept Check and then write clues that are used to determine the correct word. Have them trade puzzles with another student.

Lesson Review

Each example walks the students through the main concepts of this chapter. If the given examples are not sufficient to review the questions, remind students that the page references tell them where to review that topic in their textbooks.

Find **Extra Practice** for these concepts in the Practice Worksheets, pages A204–A223.

Classroom Management

Pair and Share Pair a student who has a good grasp of the material with another student who could use some support. Have students take turns explaining the examples to each other. In this case they will both benefit, either by doing the explaining or having it explained to them.

Dinah Zike's Foldables®

Review Have students review their Foldables against the Study Guide to see if they have captured all of the key points on their Foldables. Have students exchange Foldables with a partner. The partner's job is to add one key concept or note to his or her partner's Foldable. (For complete instructions, see Chapter Resource Masters, p. A202.)

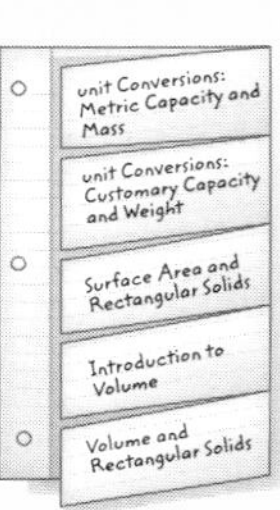

Common Error *Alert*

Exercises 18–23 If students are not converting the units in Exercises 18–23 correctly, have the students make a table like the one below and complete it to find multiples of unit measures. This may help to prevent the question: Should I multiply or divide to get my answer?

The table below is an example of a table that could be made to help answer Exercise 18.

Number of Quarts	4	8	12	16	20
Number of Gallons	1	2	3	4	5

Lesson Review

10-1 Unit Conversions: Metric Capacity and Mass (pp. 406–411)

Convert using a place-value chart.

12 9 kg = 9,000 g

1,000	100	10	1	0.1	0.01	0.001
thousands	hundreds	tens	ones	tenths	hundredths	thousandths
9	0	0	0.			
kilo (kg)			gram (g)			milli (mg)

13 30 L = 30,000 mL

14 2 g = 0.002 kg

15 15 kg = 15,000 g

16 45 g = 0.045 kg

17 12,400 mL = 12.4 L

Example 1

Convert 2,503 milliliters to liters.

Use a chart. Place 2,503 in the chart so the 3 that is farthest right is in the mL column.

1,000	100	10	1	0.1	0.01	0.001
thousands	hundreds	tens	ones	tenths	hundredths	thousandths
			2.	5	0	3
kilo (kL)			liters (L)			milli (mL)

Read the number from the chart for the conversion.

2,503 mL = 2.503 L

10-2 Unit Conversions: Customary Capacity and Weight (pp. 412–417)

Convert.

18 20 qt = 5 gal

19 3 T = 6,000 lb

20 2 c = 16 fl oz

21 16,000 lb = 8 T

22 16 c = 4 qt

23 224 oz = 14 lb

Example 2

Convert 5 pounds to ounces.

You are converting from a larger unit to a smaller unit. You need to multiply. There are 16 ounces in 1 pound.
5 × 16 = 80

5 lb = 80 oz

442 Chapter 10 Study Guide

Intervention Strategy — Visual Learners

Color Code Until the students have a grasp (especially with the metric system) of which units are larger and which are smaller, assign a color to each to aid them in determining whether to multiply or divide. For example, consistently code the smaller unit in blue and the larger unit in red.

10-3 Surface Area of Rectangular Solids (pp. 419–427)

Find the surface area of each rectangular prism.

24 

The surface area of the cube is 216 square units.

25 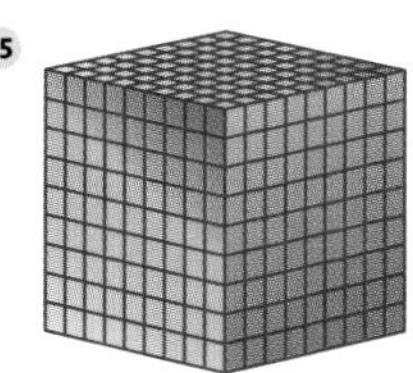

The surface area of the cube is 486 square units.

Example 3

What is the surface area of the rectangular prism?

Draw a net of the rectangular prism. Label the faces A, B, C, D, E, and F.

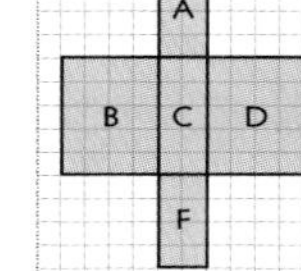

Find the area of faces A and F.

$A = \ell \times w$

$A = 2 \times 4 = 8$

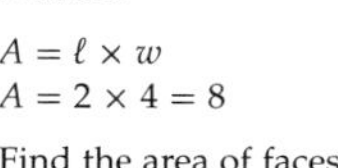

Find the area of faces B and D.

$A = \ell \times w$

$A = 4 \times 5 = 20$

Find the area of faces C and E.

$A = \ell \times w$

$A = 2 \times 5 = 10$

Find the sum of the areas of all the faces.

$8 + 20 + 10 + 8 + 20 + 10 = 76$

The surface area of the rectangular prism is 76 square units.

Find the surface area of each rectangular prism.

26 

The surface area of the rectangular prism is 248 square units.

27 

The surface area of the rectangular prism is 150 square units.

Note This!

Solids in the Real World Suggest students write the different types of solids introduced. Next to each name, students should draw the figure and then think of some real-world examples that will help them remember the figure. They should also write in their own words the steps necessary to find the volume of that figure.

Common Error *Alert*

Liquid or Solid Students are sometimes confused with the word *volume* because they have also seen it in science class. Explain to students that volume is a capacity and can be either a solid or a liquid.

Intervention Strategy — Visual/Linguistic Learners

Real-World Volume In a paragraph, have students describe in their own words how volume is used. Have students include examples of how they have used volume in their everyday life. The paragraph should be grammatically correct and have correct spelling.

10-4 Introduction to Volume

(pp. 428–433)

28 Find the volume of the rectangular prism.

The volume of the rectangular prism is 24 cubic units.

29 Find the volume of the rectangular prism.

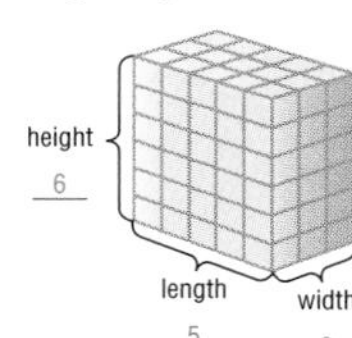

The volume of the rectangular prism is 90 cubic units.

30 Find the volume of the rectangular prism.

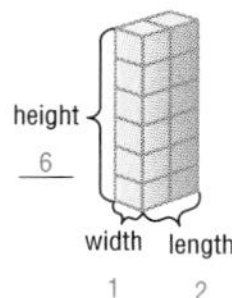

The volume of the rectangular prism is 12 cubic units.

Example 4

Find the volume of the rectangular prism.

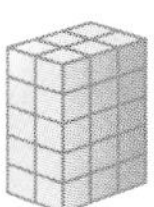

Count the number of layers of cubes in the prism. There are 5 layers of cubes in the rectangular prism.

Count the number of cubes in the top layer. There are 6 cubes in the top layer.

Each layer has the same number of cubes. There are 6 + 6 + 6 + 6 + 6 cubes.

The volume of the rectangular prism is 30 cubic units.

Example 5

Find the volume of the rectangular prism.

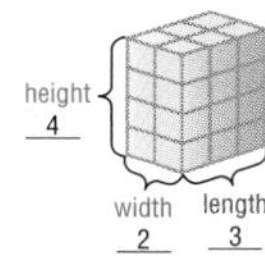

Count the number of cubes along the length. The length of the rectangular prism has 3 cubes.

Count the number of cubes along the width. The width of the rectangular prism has 2 cubes.

Count the number of cubes along the height. The height of the rectangular prism has 4 cubes.

Find the area of the top layer.

$3 \times 2 = 6$

Add that number 4 times.

$6 + 6 + 6 + 6 = 24$

The volume of the rectangular prism is 24 cubic units.

444 Chapter 10 Study Guide

10-5 Volume of Rectangular Solids (pp. 434–439)

Find the volume of each rectangular prism.

31 

The volume of the rectangular prism is 48 cubic units.

32 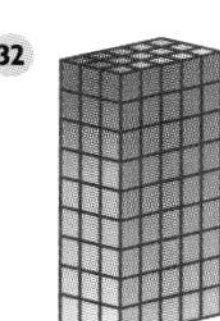

The volume of the rectangular prism is 135 cubic centimeters.

33 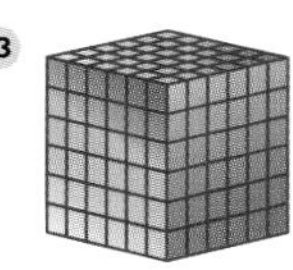

The volume of the rectangular prism is 216 cubic units.

34 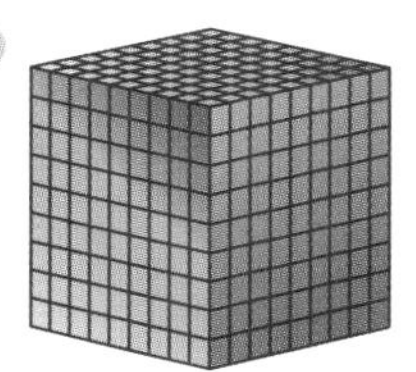

The volume of the rectangular prism is 729 cubic units.

Example 6

Find the volume of the rectangular solid using the formula below:

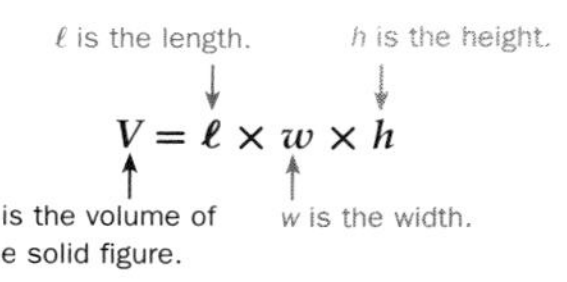

ℓ is the length.
h is the height.
V = ℓ × w × h
V is the volume of the solid figure.
w is the width.

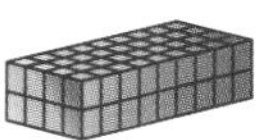

The length of the cube is 4 units.

The width of the cube is 9 units.

The height of the cube is 2 units.

Substitute the length, width, and height into the volume formula.

$V = \ell \times w \times h$
$V = 4 \times 9 \times 2$
$V = 72$

The volume of the rectangular prism is 72 cubic units.

Note This!

Study Checklist Help students create a study checklist. The checklist should include the following items:

- Do metric unit conversions for capacity and mass.
- Do customary unit conversion for capacity and weight.
- Find the surface area of a rectangular solid.
- Find the volume of a rectangular solid.

Students should put a check mark next to each topic when they feel they have a good grasp of the process.

Ticket Out the Door

Quick 4 Questions Have students answer a total of four questions that you give them on a half-sheet of paper. Have one question from each of the following: metric unit conversion for capacity and mass, customary unit conversion for capacity and weight, surface area of rectangular prisms, and volume of rectangular solids. Students should hand you the paper as they exit the classroom.

Chapter 10

Chapter Test

Chapter Resource Masters

Additional forms of the Chapter 10 Test are available.

Test Format	Where to Find it
Chapter 10 Test	Math Online macmillanmh.com
Blackline Masters	Assessment Masters, p. 125

Customize and create multiple versions of your chapter tests and their answer keys. All of these questions from the chapter tests are available on ExamView® Assessment Suite.

Online Assessment and Reporting
macmillanmh.com

This online assessment tool allows teachers to track student progress with easily accessible, comprehensive reports available for every student. Assess students using any internet-ready computer.

Alternative Assessment

Use Portfolios Ask students to write an example of each type of problem from this chapter in their portfolios. Make sure that the students include a picture or a model for each section. Encourage students to create a table of formulas so that they have easy access to them while they study.

Chapter 10 **Chapter Test**

Convert using a place-value chart or table.

1. 6,300 mg = 6.3 g

1000			1			0.001
thousands			ones			thousandths
			6	3	0	0
kilo (kg)			gram (g)			milli (mg)

2. 7 gal = 28 qt

gallons	1	2	3	4	5	6	7
quarts	4	8	12	16	20	24	28

Draw a net for a rectangular prism with the given length, width, and height.

3. 2 × 4 × 5 Sample answer:

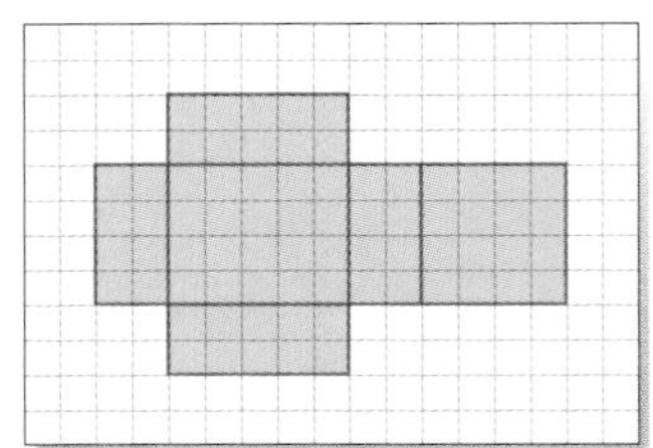

4. 3 × 3 × 3 Sample answer:

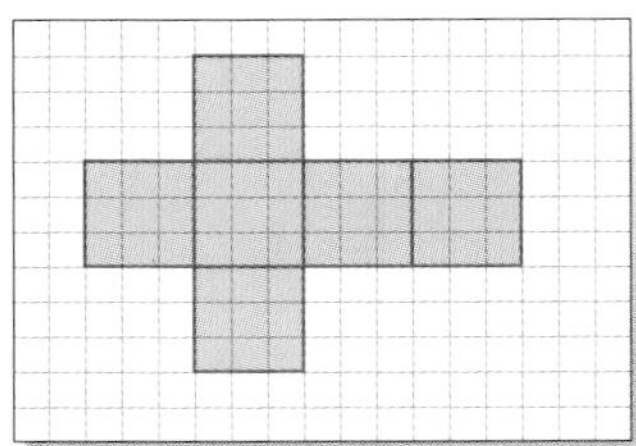

Convert.

5. 400 g = 0.4 kg
6. 2.2 L = 2,200 mL
7. 15 kL = 15,000 L
8. 11.2 g = 11,200 mg
9. 250 mL = .250 L
10. 0.049 kg = 49 g
11. 5 T = 160,000 oz
12. 10 gal = 1,280 fl oz
13. 16 pt = 8 qt
14. 5 lb = 80 oz
15. 6,000 lb = 3 T
16. 8 gal = 128 c

GO ON

446 Chapter 10 Test

English Learner Strategy

Assessment Allow students time to look over the assessment. Have students take a close look at all the problem directions and the word problems. If there are any words or phrases a student does not understand, provide a dictionary or a translation manual in the student's native language so that the words do not interfere with understanding the mathematics. If students made flashcards in their native language and English, allow them to use these on the test.

Find the surface area of each rectangular prism.

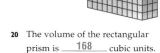

17 The surface area of the rectangular prism is 122 square units.

18 The surface area of the rectangular prism is 234 square units.

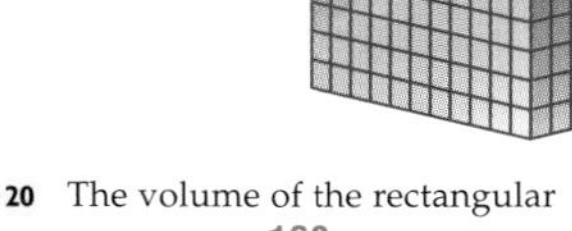

Find the volume of each rectangular prism.

19 The volume of the rectangular prism is 180 cubic units.

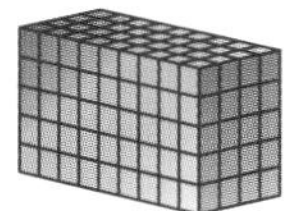

20 The volume of the rectangular prism is 168 cubic units.

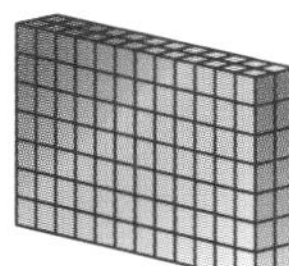

Solve.

21 **PETS** Jet's doghouse is a rectangular prism. It has a length of 30 inches, a width of 20 inches, and a height of 30 inches. What is the volume of Jet's doghouse?

18,000 cubic inches

22 **SEWING** Mrs. Larson is making a cloth cover for her daughter's storage trunk. The storage trunk is 4 feet long, 2 feet wide, and 3 feet high. How much cloth will Mrs. Larson need to cover the surface area of the trunk?

52 square feet

Correct the mistake.

23 Tyrell bought a 2-gallon container of laundry detergent. He told his sister that his purchase was equal to four 1-quart containers of laundry detergent. What mistake did Tyrell make?

One gallon is equal to 4 quarts. He forgot to multiply 2 times 4.

Show how to find how many quarts are equal to 2 gallons.

2 gallons $\times$ 4 quarts $=$ 8 quarts

Learning from Mistakes

Missed Questions Review commonly missed questions as a small group or class. Ask students to share their methods of answering each question. Try to point out when any errors occur and take corrective measures.

Data-Driven Decision Making

Students missing Exercises . . .	Have trouble with . . .	Should review and practice . . .
1–2	converting units of measure using place-value charts.	SSG Lessons 10-1, 10-2, pp. 406 and 412 CRM Skills Practice, pp. A205 and A209
3–4	drawing nets of rectangular prisms.	SSG Lesson 10-3, p. 419 CRM Skills Practice, p. A213
5–16	converting units of measure.	SSG Lessons 10-1, 10-2, pp. 406 and 412 CRM Skills Practice, pp. A205 and A209
17–18	finding the surface area of rectangular prisms.	SSG Lesson 10-3, p. 419 CRM Skills Practice, p. A213
19–20	finding the volume of rectangular prisms.	SSG Lessons 10-4, 10-5, pp. 428 and 434 CRM Skills Practice, pp. A217 and A221
21–23	solving word problems involving surface area and volume.	CRM Problem-Solving Practice pp. A214, A218, and A222

Chapter 10 Test Practice

Diagnose Student Errors

Survey student responses for each item. Class trends may indicate common errors and misconceptions.

1. A mass is about 1 milligram
(B) correct
C mass is about 1 gram
D mass is about 6 grams

2. A 2 quarts = 8 cups
(B) correct
C guess
D 16 cups = 8 pints

3. (A) correct
B 40 ounces > 32 ounces
C misinterpreted concept of comparison
D 40 ounces > 32 ounces

4. A miscalculated
(B) correct
C miscalculated
D miscalculated

5. A only counted cubes in front
B only counted cubes in top and side layers
C miscounted
(D) correct

6. A only counted cubes in front
B only counted cubes on top
C miscalculated
(D) correct

7. A miscalculated conversion
B miscalculated conversion
(C) correct
D miscalculated conversion

8. A miscalculated conversion
B miscalculated conversion
C miscalculated conversion
(D) correct

9. A used addition instead of multiplication
(B) correct
C misinterpreted units
D misinterpreted units

10. A used addition instead of multiplication
B miscalculated
(C) correct
D miscalculated

11. A miscalculated conversion
(B) correct
C misinterpreted concept of comparison
D miscalculated conversion

12. A miscalculated conversion
B miscalculated conversion
C miscalculated conversion
(D) correct

Chapter 10 Test Practice

Choose the best answer and fill in the corresponding circle on the sheet at the right.

1 Which has a mass of about 1 kilogram?

A a grain of salt
(B) a digital camera
C a small paper clip
D a granola bar

2 The pitcher can hold 16 cups. How many quarts can the pitcher hold?

A 2
(B) 4
C 6
D 8

3 Which symbol makes this sentence true?

2 pounds ☐ 40 ounces

(A) <
B >
C +
D =

4 Nathan sells lemonade in glasses that hold 12 fluid ounces. How many glasses can be filled with 3 gallons of lemonade?

A 22 glasses
(B) 32 glasses
C 28 glasses
D 34 glasses

5 What is the volume of the solid figure?

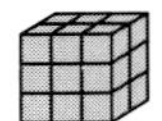

A 9 cubic units
B 12 cubic units
C 16 cubic units
(D) 18 cubic units

6 What is the volume of the solid figure?

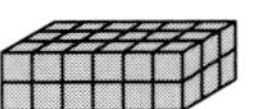

A 12 cubic units
B 18 cubic units
C 30 cubic units
(D) 36 cubic units

7 8,039 mL = _____ L

A 803.9
B 80.39
(C) 8.039
D 0.008039

8 A baby weighs 4 kilograms. How much does the baby weigh in grams?

A 1,200 grams
B 28 grams
C 400 grams
(D) 4,000 grams

GO ON

448 Chapter 10 Test Practice

9 Silvia has a closed shoe box that measures 10 inches by 7 inches by 5 inches. What is the volume of the shoe box?

A 22 cubic inches

(B) 350 cubic inches

C 350 square inches

D 350 inches

10 What is the surface area of the rectangular solid?

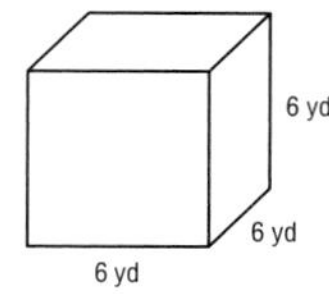

A 18 square yards

B 186 square yards

(C) 216 square yards

D 248 square yards

11 Which symbol makes this sentence true?

2 liters □ 200 milliliters

A <

(B) >

C −

D =

12 4 pounds = ______ ounces

A 2

B 8

C 16

(D) 64

ANSWER SHEET

Directions: Fill in the circle of each correct answer.

1	A	**B**	C	D
2	A	**B**	C	D
3	**A**	B	C	D
4	A	**B**	C	D
5	A	B	C	**D**
6	A	B	C	**D**
7	A	B	**C**	D
8	A	B	C	**D**
9	A	**B**	C	D
10	A	B	**C**	D
11	A	**B**	C	D
12	A	B	C	**D**

Success Strategy

Double check your answers after you finish. Read each problem and all of the answer choices. Put your finger on each bubble you filled in to make sure it matches the answer for each problem.

Diagnosing Student Errors and Misconceptions

Labels The most common error in measurement problems, other than computational mistakes, is the misuse of labels. Help students understand the differences in the units for each measure.

Perimeter is a measure in linear units.

- Examples are inches, feet, centimeters, meters.

Area is measured in square units.

- Examples are square inches, square yards.

Volume is measured in cubic units.

- Examples are cubic feet, cubic miles.

Index

Red type denotes items only in the Teacher's Wraparound Edition.

Photo Credits

ix Image Ideas/PictureQuest; **vi** Larry Brownstein/Getty Images; **vii** Comstock/PunchStock; **viii** Stockbyte/Gettty Images; **x** Donovan Reese/Getty Images; **xi** Robert Glusic/Getty Images; **xii** Steve Hamblin/Alamy; **xiii** Glen Allison/Getty Images; **xiv** Donovan Reese/Getty Images; **xv** Scenics of America/PhotoLink/Getty Images; **49** (cr)Michael Houghton/StudiOhio; **180D** Blend Images/SuperStock; **282** (bl)Michael Houghton/StudiOhio; **282** (bc)United States coin images from the United States Mint; **289** (l)Michael Houghton/StudiOhio; **289** (r)United States coin images from the United States Mint

Chapter Resource Masters

Chapter Resource Masters

NAME ________________ DATE ________

Foldables Study Organizer

Dinah Zike's Foldables

Make this Foldable to help you organize information about place value and number relationships.

1. Begin with one sheet of $8\frac{1}{2}'' \times 11''$ paper. Fold the paper into thirds from top to bottom as shown.

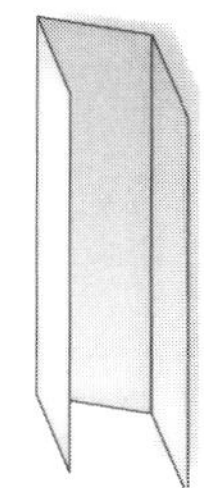

2. Fold the paper into fourths from side to side as shown. (Fold the paper in half, and then fold it in half again.)

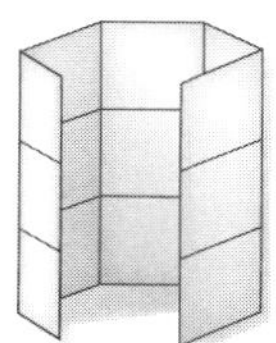

3. Unfold and draw lines along the folds.

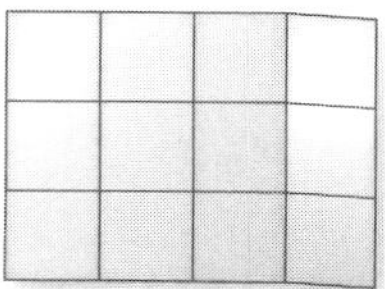

4. Label as shown. In the second now, write a number in word form. (Example: one thousand two hundred fifty three). In the third row write the number in expanded form. (Example: 1,000; 200; 50; 3).

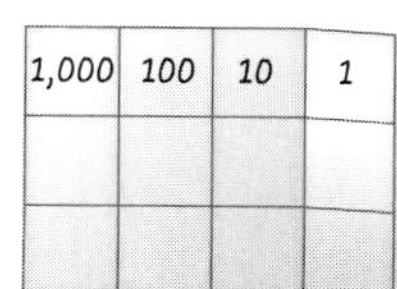

TAKING NOTES
As you read through the chapter, use your Foldable to write the word form and expanded form of numbers.

USING YOUR FOLDABLE
As you study, check your understanding by writing additional examples of writing numbers in word form and standard form.

USING YOUR FOLDABLE
Work in groups of four. Take turns choosing a number. Have each member of your group write numbers in word form and standard form.

NAME ______________________ DATE ______________

Chapter 1

Games and Puzzles

Place-Value War

GET READY: Each player needs ten game sheets, one for each of ten rounds.

What You Need

- Number Cube
- Place-Value War
- Game Sheets

Number of Players

2

DIRECTIONS

- One player rolls the number cube.
- Each player writes the number in one of the blanks on his or her game sheet.
- The other player rolls the cube, and each player writes the number in a blank.
- Play continues until all blanks are filled.
- The person with the greater number scores 1 point.
- Repeat for ten rounds.
- **Who Wins?** The person with the greater number of points after ten rounds is the winner.

NAME ______________________________ DATE ______________

Place-Value War Game Sheets

____, ____ ____ ____   ____, ____ ____ ____

____, ____ ____ ____   ____, ____ ____ ____

____, ____ ____ ____   ____, ____ ____ ____

____, ____ ____ ____   ____, ____ ____ ____

____, ____ ____ ____   ____, ____ ____ ____

NAME ______________________ DATE ______________

Lesson 1-1

Vocabulary and English Language Development

Activate Prior Knowledge

Complete the check by writing the dollar amount in digits and in word form.

1 Gary borrowed two 100-dollar bills and three 10-dollar bills from his mother. How should Gary complete the check to repay his mother?

Gary Midar
123 High Street,
Santa Cruz, CA 95064

001

DATE 9/14/2009

PAYEE Sarah Midar $ ______

______________________ 00 DOLLARS

BANK • Gary Midar

⑈001⑈12345⑈123⑈ 123456⑈123⑈

____

Definition Review

Place value is the value given to a digit by its position in a number.

Complete each statement.

2 The **place values** of a four-**digit** number, in order from greatest to least are ________, ________, ________, and ________.

3 The number 3,415 is written in ________ form. It is written as 3,000 + 400 + 10 + 5 in ________ form.

Application

Follow the directions to play the game.

- Form groups of three. Each group needs a number card deck.
- Place the cards facedown.
- Choose 2 to 4 cards each and make a number.
- Write and read your number to the group.
- Identify the highest place value in your number.
- Each group writes the numbers in expanded form.
- Replace the cards.
- Repeat steps until a variety of numbers have been written.

TRY THIS:
Follow the directions, but make the number even or odd.

NAME ______________________ DATE ____________

Lesson 1-1

Skills Practice

Chapter 1

Write the correct digits in the place-value chart.

1 4,982

1,000	100	10	1
thousands	hundreds	tens	ones

2 5,080

1,000	100	10	1
thousands	hundreds	tens	ones

Identify the digit in the thousands place of each number.

3 6,704 ____________

4 8,009 ____________

5 1,387 ____________

6 9,300 ____________

Identify the value of each underlined digit.

7 $\underline{2}$,458 ____________

8 3,0$\underline{7}$2 ____________

9 $\underline{8}$64 ____________

10 3$\underline{1}$7 ____________

11 54$\underline{3}$ ____________

12 $\underline{5}$,136 ____________

Write each number in expanded form.

13 5,124 ____________

14 3,078 ____________

15 2,300 ____________

16 1,203 ____________

17 8,904 ____________

18 9,978 ____________

Write each number in standard form.

19 2,000 + 800 + 7 ____________

20 6,000 + 100 + 20 + 4 ____________

21 1,000 + 50 ____________

22 8,000 + 600 + 10 + 9 ____________

23 5,000 + 30 + 1 ____________

24 4,000 + 3 ____________

Lesson 1-1

NAME ________________ DATE ________________

Problem-Solving Practice

Solve.

1 **PUZZLES** Use the digits 2, 5, 1, and 8 to make the largest possible four-digit number. Use each digit once. ________

2 **MOVIES** A small video rental store has 200 action DVDs, 70 comedy DVDs, and 5 foreign DVDs. What is the total number of DVDs in the store? ________

3 **AGE** Awar noticed that the digit in the hundreds place of his street address is the same as his age. His street address is 2915 Windy Way. What is Awar's age? ________

4 **DOWN PAYMENT** Tom and Irene paid six thousand, seven hundred five dollars as a down payment on a new house. What is this amount in standard form? ________

5 **PUZZLES** Use the digits 2, 5, 1, and 8 to make a number that is odd. Use each digit once. ________

6 **RENT** Reggie Hamilton just rented his first apartment. He wrote a check for the first and last months' rents. Write the dollar amount in expanded form. ________

Reggie Hamilton
123 High Street,
Santa Cruz, CA 95064
001
DATE 9/14/2007
PAYEE Apple Tree Apartments
$ 1,370.00
00 DOLLARS
BANK •
Reggie Hamilton
⑈001 ⑆12345⑈123⑆ 123456⑈123⑈

7 **FORESTRY** Javier, the owner of a tree farm, planted 50 trees in his first year of business. He planted 800 trees in his second year. Now in his third year, Javier planted 2,000 trees. What is the total number of trees Javier planted? ________

Lesson 1-1

NAME ______________________ DATE ____________

Homework Practice

Chapter 1

Write *true* or *false* for each statement. If the statement is false, change the statement to make it true.

1. In a four-digit number, the number on the far left is the thousands digit. ________

2. The ones place is to the right of the tens place. ________

Write the correct digits in the place-value chart.

3. seven thousand, two hundred, ninety-one

1,000	100	10	1
thousands	hundreds	tens	ones

4. two thousand, fifty-eight

1,000	100	10	1
thousands	hundreds	tens	ones

Write each number in standard form.

5. 7 thousands, 5 hundreds, 2 tens ________

6. 8 thousands, 3 tens, 6 ones ________

Write each number in expanded form.

7. 4,537 ________

8. 2,080 ________

9. 3,506 ________

10. 6,124 ________

Solve.

11. **PUZZLE** Use the digits 6, 5, 1, and 2 to make the smallest possible number. Use each digit only once. ________

Lesson 1-2

NAME ______________________ DATE ____________

Vocabulary and English Language Development

Activate Prior Knowledge

Consider the following results from a calculator screen. Write each number correctly in standard form, using commas to separate the periods. Write each number in word form also.

1. 2457000 ______________________

2. 5047892 ______________________

3. 3046670 ______________________

Definition Review

4. Complete the **place-value** chart by labeling the **place values**.

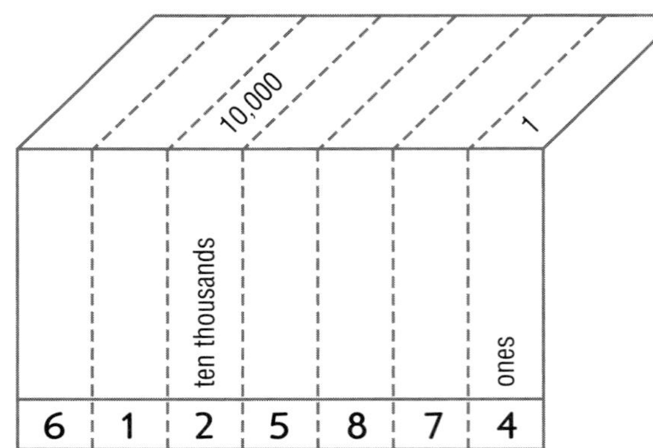

As the number of digits increases, the **place-value** chart has to get bigger. To help you read and write numbers, **place values** are grouped into **periods. Periods** are separated by commas.

Consider the number 3,456,789. Answer the questions.

5. In what **period** are the digits 456? ____________

6. In what **period** are the digits 789? ____________

7. What is used to separate **periods**? ____________

8. What is the **place value** of the 6? ____________

9. What is the **place value** of the 4? ____________

Lesson 1-2

NAME ______________________ DATE ______________

Skills Practice

Use a place-value chart. Fill in the digit for each place value.

1 two million, eight hundred thousand, two hundred forty-five

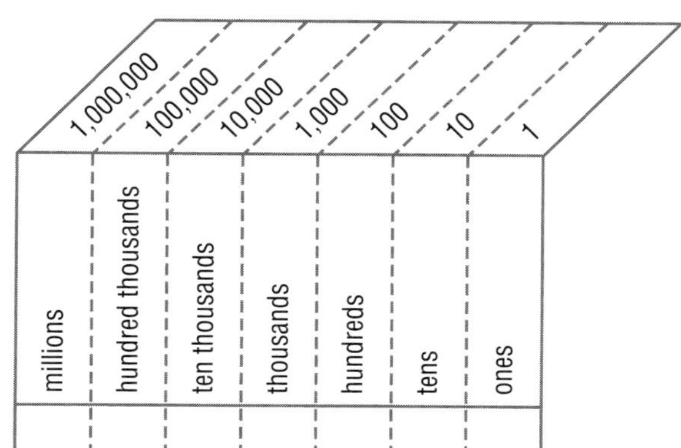

Write each number in word form.

2 5,216,000 ______________________

3 7,050,278 ______________________

4 3,800,000 ______________________

5 1,246,935 ______________________

6 5,045,540 ______________________

Write each number in standard form.

7 six million, two hundred fifty ______________

8 five million, two hundred thirty-seven thousand, forty ______________

9 three million, two hundred eighty-five thousand, one hundred ______________

10 three million, two hundred fifty thousand, two ______________

Answer each question.

11 How many zeros are in 4 millions? ______________

12 How many zeros are in 5 thousands? ______________

NAME ______________________ DATE ______________

Lesson 1-2

Problem-Solving Practice

Solve.

1 **PHYSICS** The speed of sound on a spring day is thirteen thousand, five hundred four inches per second. What is this speed in standard form? ______________

2 **AREA** The drainage basin for the Mississippi-Missouri River System is approximately 1,200,000 square miles. Write this area in word form. ______________

3 **WRITING** Juanita wrote 7,025,345 in words on her paper. What mistake did Juanita make if she wrote, "seven million, twenty-five, three hundred forty-five"? ______________

____

4 **AREA** Australia is the smallest continent in the world. It has an area of 7,617,930 square km. Write the area of Australia in word form. ______________

____

5 **GEOGRAPHY** The table shows the highest points in Asia, Africa, and North America.

Location	Height (in feet)
Kilimanjaro – Africa	19,340
Everest – Asia	29,035
McKinley – North America	20,320

What is the height of Everest in word form? ______________

____

Of these three locations, which is the lowest point? ______________

____

6 **AGE** Jeremy used a calculator to find his age in hours. The screen shows 197100. Write the number in standard form (with commas) and in word form. ______________

____

7 **SPACE** The population of Honolulu in 2000 was one million, two hundred eleven thousand, five hundred thirty-seven. Write the population in standard form. ______________

Homework Practice

Write the missing number in each equation.

1 2,000,000 + 30,000 + ______ + 400 = 2,035,400

2 ______ + 700,000 + 3,000 = 1,703,000

3 6,000,000 + ______ + 20 + 5 = 6,000,125

Write each number in standard form.

4 two million, three hundred fifty thousand, forty ______

5 seven million, three hundred fifty-eight ______

6 nine million, four hundred five thousand, seven ______

Write each number in word form.

7 3,215,700 ______

8 5,050,050 ______

9 140,013 ______

Solve.

10 **SCHOOL** In an answer to a math problem, Diego wrote, "six million, two hundred forty thousand, ninety." For the same problem, Tamera wrote, "6 millions, 2 hundred-thousands, 4 ten-thousands, 9 tens." Write each answer in standard form. Did they give the same answer? Explain.

______

11 **MONEY** ABC Company's check for this year's annual charity donation is shown below. Write the amount of the donation in word form.

______

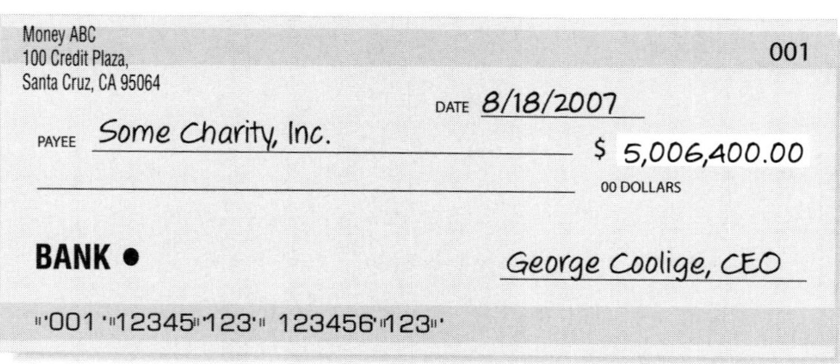

Money ABC
100 Credit Plaza,
Santa Cruz, CA 95064
001
DATE 8/18/2007
PAYEE Some Charity, Inc.
$ 5,006,400.00
00 DOLLARS
BANK •
George Coolige, CEO
⑈001⑈12345⑈123⑈ 123456⑈123⑈

Write the vocabulary word that completes each sentence.

12 A group of three digits in the place-value chart is a ______.

13 The digit 8 in the number 4,178,325 is in the ______ place.

NAME ______________________ DATE ______________

Lesson 1-3

Vocabulary and English Language Development

Activate Prior Knowledge

Complete each sentence using the words *add, subtract, multiply,* or *divide.*

1 Carlos brushes his teeth three times a day. To find the number of times he brushes his teeth in a week, we can use the rule: __________ 3 for each day.

2 Theo saves 2 pennies on Monday, 4 pennies on Tuesday, 8 pennies on Wednesday and so on. His rule for saving pennies is to __________ the previous day's savings by 2.

3 John buys a 32-ounce bottle of juice. He drinks 8 ounces of juice each day. To find the amount of juice left at the end of 3 days, use the rule: __________ 8.

4 Matilda is reading a book that is 240 pages long. After the first day of reading, she has 120 pages left. After the second day she has 60 pages left, and after the third day she has 30 pages left. To find the number of pages Matilda has left to read on the fourth day, we can __________ by 2.

Definition Review

A **rule** tells how numbers are related to each other.

Match the pattern to its rule.

5 6, 21, 36, 51	Divide by 4.
6 64, 16, 4, 1	Add 300.
7 100; 400; 700; 1,000	Subtract 4.
8 2,004; 2,000; 1,996; 1,992	Add 15.

Application

Follow the directions for the activity.

- A year is a leap year if it is divisible by 4. If the year is a year ending in 00, then it must be divisible by 400 to be a leap year.
- Determine if the following years are leap years:

  1976 __________ 1990 __________ 2000 __________
- Use the rule for leap years to find the number of days in the year you were born.

  Remember: A standard year has 365 days, and a leap year has 366 days. ______________

Lesson 1-3

NAME ________________________________ DATE ______________

Skills Practice

Find a rule for each pattern.

1 10, 20, 30, 40 ______________

2 100, 85, 70, 55 ______________

3 1,600, 400, 100, 25 ______________

4 25, 50, 100, 200 ______________

5 12, 17, 22, 27 ______________

Write the next three terms in each pattern.

6 11, 21, 31, 41

The next three terms are ________, ________, and ________.

7 2,400,000; 240,000; 24,000

The next three terms are ________; ________; and ________.

8 62, 74, 86, 98

The next three terms are ________, ________, and ________.

9 7, 28, 49, 70

The next three terms are ________, ________, and ________.

Write the next three conversions in each pattern.

10

Number of Quarts	1	2	3	4
Number of Pints	2			

11

Number of Years	1	2	3	4
Number of Months	12			

12

Number of Yards	1	2	3	4
Number of Inches	36			

NAME ______________________ DATE ______________

Lesson 1-3

Problem-Solving Practice

Solve.

1 **BANKING** Leo saves $4 each week. How much money does Leo save in 6 weeks? ________

Week	1	2	3	4	5	6
Amount Saved	$4					

2 **DESIGN** Candace created the pattern at the right. How many squares are in the fifth term of the pattern? ________

3 **PIZZA** The Pizza Place sells a large pizza for $7.50. You can buy a second large pizza for $7.25, and a third for $7.00. If this pattern continues, how much would the fifth large pizza cost? ________

4 **VIDEO** Dion rented 8 DVDs. Each rental costs $3. How much did Dion spend on all of the DVDs? ________

Number of DVDs	1	2	3	4	5	6	7	8
Cost	$3							

5 **COMMUTING** Mr. Harris drives 12 miles to and from work each weekday. After 4 weeks, not including the weekends, how many miles has Mr. Harris driven to and from work? ________

6 **PACKAGING** Jason bought 6 packages of cookies to share with the students in his grade. If each package contains 15 cookies, how many cookies did Jason buy? ________

7 **INTERIOR DESIGN** Cara is painting the following pattern on her kitchen wall.

 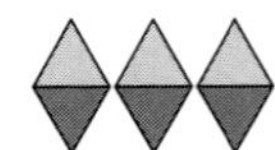 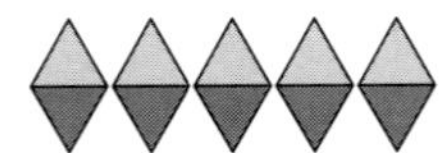 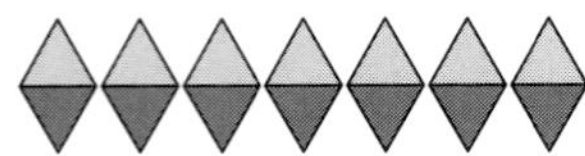

If the pattern continues, how many dark triangles are in the sixth term? ________

How many light triangles are in the sixth term? ________

How many triangles in all are in the sixth term? ________

Lesson 1-3

NAME ______________________ DATE ______________

Homework Practice

Find a rule for each pattern.

1. 7, 21, 63, 189 ______________

2. 125, 100, 75, 50 ______________

3. 234, 245, 256, 267 ______________

Write the next three terms in each pattern.

4. 189, 173, 157, 141

   The next three terms are ______, ______, and ______.

5. 729, 243, 81, 27

   The next three terms are ______, ______, and ______.

Write the next three conversions in each pattern.

6.

Number of Tricycles	1	2	3	4
Number of Wheels	3			

7.

Number Hours	1	2	3	4
Number of Minutes	60			

Solve.

8. **RACING** Lance is training for a bike race. Starting on Tuesday, each day he will bike 3 more miles than he did the day before. On Monday he bikes 3 miles. How many miles does he bike on Friday? ______________

Vocabulary Check

Write the vocabulary word that completes each sentence.

9. A ______________ tells how numbers are related to each other.

10. A ______________ is a sequence of numbers, figures, or symbols that follows a rule or design.

Lesson 1-4

NAME ______________________________ DATE ______________

Vocabulary and English Language Development

Activate Prior Knowledge

1. List three classroom rules. ______________________________

____

2. List three rules for numbers. ______________________________

____

3. What is the rule for the following sequence of numbers? ______________

12, 17, 22, 27, 32

Definition Review

A pattern follows a **rule.** A **rule** describes the relationship that one element of a sequence has with another element of the sequence.

What is the next element of each pattern?

4. ▲ ● ▲ ● ▲ ● ______

5. + + − − − + + ______

6. ● ◆ ■ ■ ● ◆ ■ ______

7. ♥ ♠ ♠ ♠ ♥ ♠ ♠ ♠ ♥ ______

8. ▲ ▼ ◀ ▶ ▲ ▼ ◀ ▶ ▲ ______

Application

Follow the directions for the activity.

- Work in groups of two or three.
- Each student chooses a different sound to make. Some suggestions are to use your hands for snapping or clapping, use a book and pencil for a drum, or whistle.
- Work together to create a pattern of sound for your group.
- Experiment with patterns of sound to create simple melodies.
- After practicing, have your group share its melody with the rest of the class.

NAME ____________________ DATE ____________

Skills Practice

Write a possible situation for each rule.

1. Add 5. ____________________

2. Multiply by 7. ____________________

Who is correct?

3. There are 9 buttons on a shirt. How many buttons are there on 6 shirts? Circle the correct answer(s). Cross out the incorrect answer(s).

   Nadia believes there are 56. Sanchez believes there are 54. Mark believes there are 15.

Solve.

4. There are 60 minutes in 1 hour. How many minutes are there in 6 hours?

   There are ________ minutes in 6 hours.

5. Kei types 35 words in 1 minute. How many words does Kei type in 3 minutes? Kei types ________ words in 3 minutes.

6. There are 8 batteries in 1 pack. How many batteries are there in 7 packs?

   There are ________ batteries in 7 packs.

7. Andy has 12 strawberries in 1 basket. How many strawberries does Andy have in 7 baskets? Andy has ________ strawberries in 7 baskets.

8. There are 64 ounces in 1 juice bottle. How many ounces are in 2 bottles?

   There are ________ ounces in 2 bottles.

9. Ruby reads 25 pages in 1 hour. Ruby reads ________ pages in 5 hours.

10. A spider has 8 legs. How many legs do 8 spiders have? There are ________ legs on 8 spiders.

11. There are 20 hexagons on 1 soccer ball. How many hexagons are there on 8 soccer balls? There are ________ hexagons on 8 soccer balls.

Lesson 1-4

NAME ______________________ DATE ____________

Problem-Solving Practice

Solve. Write in simplest form.

1 **RUNNING** Amanda is training for a marathon. She runs 8 miles each day. How many miles does Amanda run in 4 days? ____________

2 **MACHINERY** Mr. Diaz needs to order new belts for the machines on his company's production line. Each machine requires 3 belts. There are 7 machines on the production line. How many belts does Mr. Diaz need to order? ____________

3 **COOKING** Woo baked 12 loaves of bread for his parents' bakery. Each loaf required 3 cups of flour. How many cups of flour did Woo use in all? ____________

4 **FOOTBALL** At Friday night's game, the home team passed for 3 yards on each down. How many total yards had they gained after the third pass? ____________

5 **CELEBRATIONS** Every year Ana adds 6 more people to the guest list of her New Year's Eve party. Twenty-three people were on the original guest list for her first party from 2 years ago. How many people will she invite this year? ____________

6 **CHEMISTRY** Ms. Hawkins set up 7 test tubes for each student in her class. There are 21 students in her fifth-period chemistry class. How many test tubes did Ms. Hawkins set up during fifth period? ____________

7 **CONSTRUCTION** Patrick is building a fence. He needs two 8-foot sections for each side of the fence. He needs to fence in 3 sides of his property. How many feet of fencing does Patrick need? ____________

8 **GOLF** Mali has been taking golf lessons. With each week of lessons, her drive increases by 10 yards. Mali's drive was 190 yards the first week. How far did her drive go on the third week? How far did her drive go on the sixth week?

____

NAME ______________________ DATE ______________

Lesson 1-4

Homework Practice

Write a possible situation for each rule.

1 Multiply by 13. ______________________

2 Add 4. ______________________

Complete each sentence given the rule.

3 There are 6 sides on 1 cube. How many sides are there on 9 cubes? There are ________ sides on 9 cubes.

4 There are 4 tires on 1 car. How many tires are there on 6 cars? There are ________ tires on 6 cars.

5 Dion drives 45 miles in 1 hour. How many miles does Dion drive in 4 hours? Dion drives ________ miles in 4 hours.

6 There are 5 bananas in 1 bunch. How many bananas are there in 7 bunches? There are ________ bananas in 7 bunches.

7 Sandy needs 6 cups of water for 1 pitcher of lemonade. How many cups of water does she need for 4 pitchers of lemonade? Sandy needs ________ cups of water for 4 pitchers of lemonade.

Solve.

8 **CABINETRY** Nari is installing new cabinet doors in her kitchen. She needs 8 screws for each cabinet door. There are 15 doors. How many screws does Nari need? ____________

9 **WEIGHT LIFTING** Alonso started weight lifting. The first week he was able to lift 145 pounds. Each week he has been able to lift an additional 5 pounds. How much is Alonso able to lift in the seventh week? ____________

Write the vocabulary word that completes each sentence.

10 A(n) ____________ is a sequence of numbers, figures, or symbols that follows a rule or design.

11 A(n) ____________ tells how numbers are related to each other.

NAME ______________________ DATE ____________

Foldables Study Organizer

Dinah Zike's Foldables

Create the Foldable below to help study multiplication facts.

1 Fold a sheet of notebook paper in half from side to side.

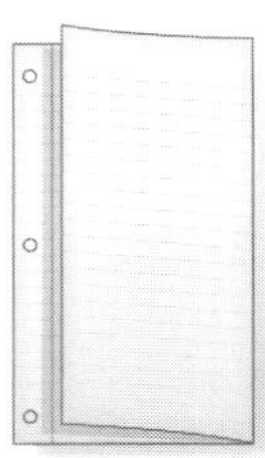

2 On one side, cut along every third line.

Tabs will form as you cut.

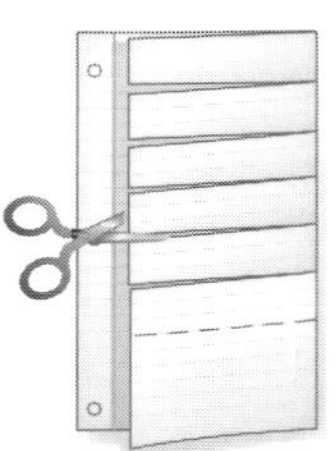

3 Turn and label your foldable as shown. As you read the chapter, list the basic multiplication facts on each tab. Write the products under each tab.

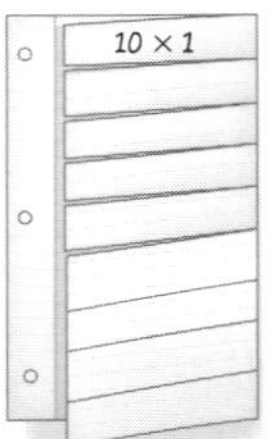

TAKING NOTES
As you read through the chapter, use your Foldable to explain and write an example of a problem with each multiplication fact you encounter. Solve the problem and write the product under the tab.

USING YOUR FOLDABLE
Create additional Foldables as an alternative form of the multiplication tables or flash cards. As you study, try to solve the problems that you wrote on your Foldable without looking at the answer. If you have any difficulties, go over that concept again.

USING YOUR FOLDABLE
Work with a partner. Quiz each other by stating the multiplication expressions written on your Foldable. Be sure to give your partner the correct answer if he or she gets it wrong.

Chapter 2

NAME ______________________ DATE ____________

Games and Puzzles
Multiplication Tic Tac Toe

DIRECTIONS With a partner, choose X's or O's to play **Multiplication Tic Tac Toe**. Take turns answering the questions below. If you answer the question correctly, you get to place an X or O. The first player with 3 X's or O's in a row wins the game.

Players choose even or odd. Answers have been divided into even and odd columns. As you play, check your opponents answers by using the Even or Odd Answer Sheet.

What You Need
- Question Sets
- tic tac toe boards

Number of Players
2

Chapter 2

QUESTIONS

SET 1

1. If $1 \times 3 = 3$, then what is 100×3?
2. If $2 \times 3 = 6$, then what is 20×3?
3. If $3 \times 3 = 9$, then what is 30×3?
4. If $4 \times 3 = 12$, then what is 40×3?
5. If $5 \times 3 = 15$, then what is 30×5?
6. If $6 \times 2 = 12$, then what is 60×2?
7. If $7 \times 3 = 21$, then what is 70×3?
8. If $8 \times 4 = 32$, then what is 80×4?
9. If $9 \times 3 = 27$, then what is 90×3?
10. If $10 \times 4 = 40$, then what is 100×4?

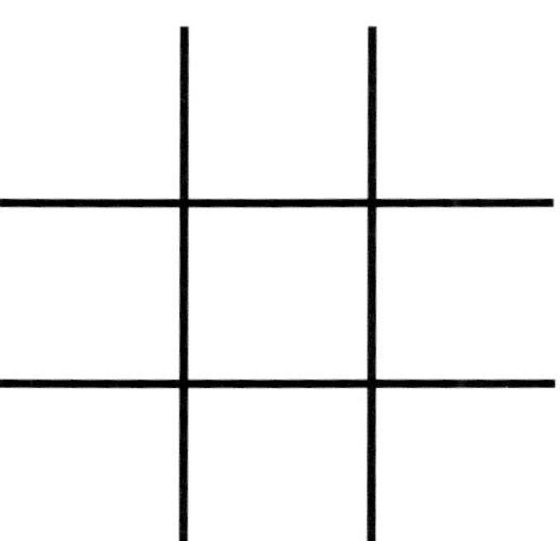

SET 2

1. What is $1{,}000 \times 3$?
2. What is 20×4?
3. What is 30×3?
4. What is 40×5?
5. What is 50×6?
6. What is 60×7?
7. What is 70×4?
8. What is 80×3?
9. What is 90×2?
10. What is 100×100?

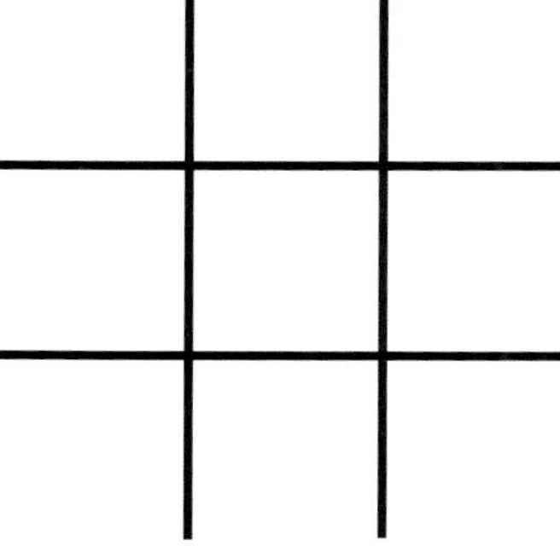

NAME ______________________ DATE ______________

Games and Puzzles

Multiplication Tic Tac Toe

SET 3

1. What is 10 × 1?
2. What is 10 × 3?
3. What is 10 × 5?
4. What is 10 × 6?
5. What is 10 × 10?
6. What is 10 × 100?
7. What is 10 × 20?
8. What is 10 × 50?
9. What is 10 × 600?
10. What is 10 × 55?

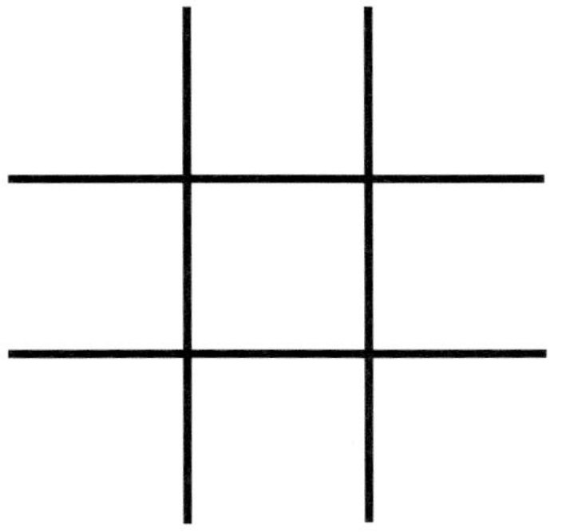

SET 4

1. What is 12 × 2?
2. What is 12 × 3?
3. What is 22 × 4?
4. What is 222 × 4?
5. What is 5 × 40?
6. What is 5 × 400?
7. What is 25 × 3?
8. What is 15 × 3?
9. What is 12 × 5?
10. What is 120 × 5?

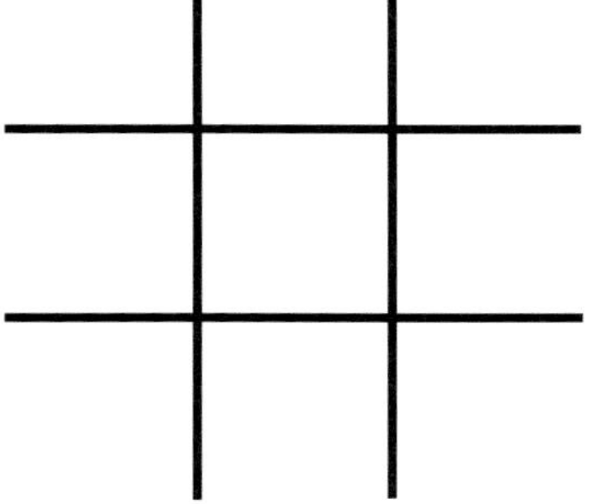

SET 5

Make up your own questions to challenge each other.

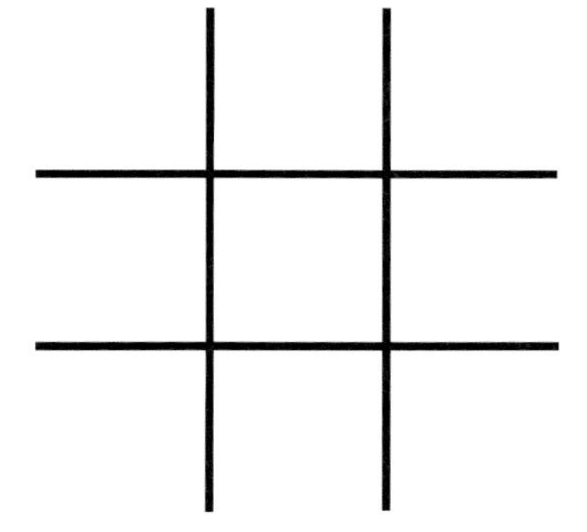

ANSWERS

Odd Number Answer Sheet

	SET 1	SET 2	SET 3	SET 4
1	300	3,000	10	24
3	90	90	50	88
5	150	300	100	200
7	210	280	200	75
9	270	180	6,000	60

Even Number Answer Sheet

	SET 1	SET 2	SET 3	SET 4
2	60	80	30	36
4	120	200	60	888
6	120	420	1,000	2,000
8	320	240	500	45
10	400	10,000	550	600

Lesson 2-1

NAME ______________________ DATE ______________

Vocabulary and English Language Development

Activate Prior Knowledge

Solve.

1 **FISHING** Jud caught 6 fish the first day, 8 fish the second day, and 2 fish the third day. In all, he caught 16 fish in four days. How many fish did he catch the fourth day? ________

Definition Review

The **Identity Property of Multiplication** says that any number times 1 is equal to that number.

The **Zero Property of Multiplication** says that any number times zero is zero.

- **Place an I next to an example of the Identity Property of Multiplication.**
- **Place a Z next to an example of the Zero Property of Multiplication.**
- **Place an N next to examples that are neither of these properties.**

2 $16 \times 1 = 16$ ________

3 $82 \times 0 = 0$ ________

4 $0 + 47 = 47$ ________

5 $1 \times 76 = 76$ ________

6 $0 \times 54 = 54$ ________

7 $67 + 1 = 68$ ________

Application

- Find a partner. Use 6 index cards each.
- Write 3 equations each that model the Identity Property of Multiplication and 3 equations each that model the Zero Property of Multiplication. Use separate cards.
- Exchange index cards and place them face down in front of you.
- Take turns turning over one of the index cards and identifying the property illustrated. Tell your partner to check your work. If it is incorrect, then you partner should explain why.
- The student who is correct gets to keep the card.
- Repeat until all of the cards have been used.
- The student with the most cards wins.

NAME ______________________ DATE ______________

Lesson 2-1

Skills Practice

Use skip counting to fill in the blanks by the number shown.

1. 5, ___, ___, ___, ___
2. 10, ___, ___, ___, ___

Use the Zero Property of Multiplication to find each product.

3. 0×21 ________
4. 72×0 ________
5. 37×0 ________
6. 0×44 ________
7. 0×86 ________
8. 19×0 ________

Use the Identity Property of Multiplication to find each product.

9. 27×1 ________
10. 1×77 ________
11. 1×52 ________
12. 39×1 ________
13. 11×1 ________
14. 1×62 ________

Find each product.

15. 5×14 ________
16. 37×5 ________
17. 29×10 ________
18. 10×76 ________
19. 52×5 ________
20. 5×61 ________
21. 10×88 ________
22. 47×10 ________
23. 0×53 ________
24. 1×99 ________
25. 59×1 ________
26. 47×0 ________
27. 1×649 ________
28. 302×10 ________

NAME ______________________________ DATE ______________

Problem-Solving Practice

Solve.

1 **TEST MATERIALS** Tayshia is helping her teacher pass out the answer sheets for the quiz. Her class has 22 students and each student gets 1 answer sheet. How many answer sheets will she pass out?

2 **MULTIPLICATION** As shown below, Jorie, Reed, and Demont are multiplying 10×72. Who is correct?

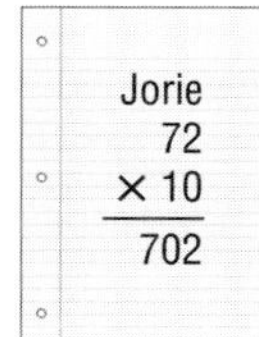

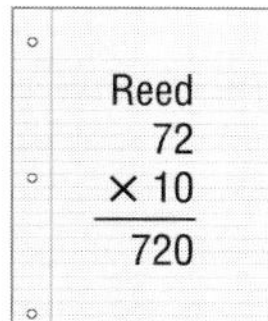

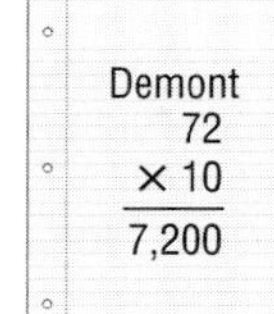

3 **FRIENDS** Each day Devon calls five of his friends. How many phone calls will he make in 6 days?

4 **PUZZLE** Manuel wrote the following multiplication sentences on a piece of paper and showed them to Allen. What number makes each sentence true?

$$5 \times \textbf{?} = 0$$
$$\textbf{?} \times 20 = 0$$
$$97 \times \textbf{?} = 0$$

5 **SOUP** If Darlene buys 12 times the amount of soup shown in the figure below, how many cans of soup does she buy?

6 **PETS** Karen feeds each of her rabbits 1 carrot before she goes to school. If Karen has 17 rabbits, how many carrots does she need?

NAME ______________________ DATE ______________

Lesson 2-1 Homework Practice

Consider the product 72×0 when answering the following two questions.

1 What is the first factor? ________

2 What is the second factor? ________

Write a multiplication fact for each of the following products.

3 $5 \times 83 = 415$ ____________

4 $97 \times 1 = 97$ ____________

Find each product.

5 10×66 ________

6 33×5 ________

7 48×1 ________

8 0×21 ________

9 5×88 ________

10 1×74 ________

11 27×10 ________

12 81×0 ________

Solve.

13 **NUTRITION** Lucy eats 2 pieces of fresh fruit each day. How many pieces does she eat in 5 days? ____________

14 **CARNIVAL RIDES** Ride tickets at the carnival come in packages of 10. If Eli and his 7 friends purchase 14 packages, how many tickets did they buy? ____________

Write the vocabulary word that completes each sentence.

15 The Zero Property of Multiplication states that any number times ________ is ________.

16 The ________ Property of Multiplication states that any number times 1 is equal to that number.

NAME ______________________ DATE ______________

Vocabulary and English Language Development

Activate Prior Knowledge

Use mental math to simplify each expression.

1. $5 + 11$ ________
2. $28 - 23$ ________
3. $5 \times (3 + 2)$ ________
4. $1 \times 4 \times 1$ ________
5. $(6 \times 2) + (2 \times 2)$ ________
6. $7 \times 0 \times 8$ ________

Definition Review

The **Commutative Property of Multiplication** says that the order of factors does not change the product.

- **Write C next to an example of the Commutative Property of Multiplication.**
- **Write N next to an example that is not the Commutative Property of Multiplication.**

7. $43 \times 9 = 9 \times 43$ ________
8. $7 \times 22 = 7 \times (20 + 2)$ ________
9. $78 + 2 = 2 + 78$ ________
10. $21 \times 37 = 37 \times 21$ ________
11. $0 \times 61 = 61 \times 0$ ________
12. $18 \times 40 = 8 \times 40 + 400$ ________
13. $0 \times 12 = 0$ ________
14. $12 \times 2 = 2 \times 12$ ________

Application

- Find a partner.
- Roll two six-sided number cubes.
- Write a multiplication problem using the two numbers.
  Example: If you roll 2 and 5, write $2 \times 5 = 10$ or $5 \times 2 = 10$.
- Write the related multiplication fact.
- Repeat four times.

NAME ______________________ DATE ______________

Lesson 2-2

Skills Practice

Use skip counting to fill in the blanks by the number shown.

1. 2, ___, ___, ___, ___

2. 6, ___, ___, ___, ___

Write the related multiplication fact for each product.

3. $2 \times 41 = 82$ ________ $= 82$

4. $98 \times 3 = 294$ ________ $= 294$

5. $18 \times 4 = 72$ ________ $= 72$

6. $6 \times 12 = 72$ ________ $= 72$

7. $3 \times 51 = 153$ ________ $= 153$

8. $4 \times 86 = 344$ ________ $= 344$

Write an equation using repeated addition that represents each product.

9. 2×7 ____________________

10. 3×5 ____________________

11. 4×8 ____________________

12. 6×9 ____________________

Find each product.

13. 2×26 ________

14. 87×3 ________

15. 47×4 ________

16. 6×28 ________

17. 3×19 ________

18. 4×99 ________

19. 6×37 ________

20. 55×2 ________

21. 68×4 ________

22. 3×72 ________

23. 77×2 ________

24. 29×6 ________

NAME ______________________ DATE ______________

Problem-Solving Practice

Solve.

1 **HEALTH** Every day Matilda and her three brothers each take a multi-vitamin. What is the total number of multi-vitamins they take in all for one week? ____________

2 **ARRAYS** What multiplication problem is modeled by the array below? ____________

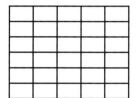

3 **SHOPPING** Chochmo bought 3 boxes of golf balls. If each box contains 12 balls, how many balls did he buy?

4 **FORESTRY** Mr. Rodriquez owns a tree farm. He planted several ash trees as seen in the figure below. How many Ash trees did he plant?

5 **TRAVEL** Adam drove from Jacksonville, Florida to Atlanta, Georgia. If he averaged 58 miles per hour while completing the 6 hour trip, approximately how far did he travel?

6 **GEOMETRY** Each side of a cube is called a face. What is the total number of faces shown in the figure below?

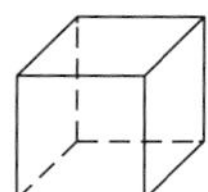 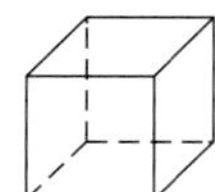 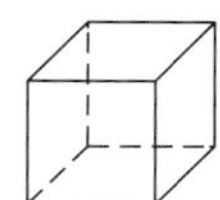 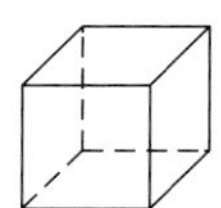

Lesson 2-2

Homework Practice

NAME ______________________ DATE ______________

Write the equation that represents each product using repeated addition.

1. 3×8 ______________________

2. 6×5 ______________________

Rewrite each multiplication problem in vertical format.

3. 2×29 __________

4. 4×72 __________

Find each product.

5. 6×29 __________

6. 17×4 __________

7. 75×3 __________

8. 2×38 __________

9. 4×29 __________

10. 3×61 __________

Solve.

11. **POULTRY** Harold raises chickens and sells the eggs they lay. If he packages the eggs in groups of 6 and sells on average 19 packages per day, how many eggs does he sell per day? __________

12. **COLLECTING** Melinda collects dolls. How many dolls are in her collection, if she has 13 shelves in her room each containing 2 dolls? __________

Write the vocabulary word that completes each sentence.

13. The __________ Property of Multiplication says that the order in which two numbers are multiplied does not change the product.

14. Multiplication is an operation on two numbers to find their __________.

NAME ______________________ DATE ______________

Lesson 2-3

Vocabulary and English Language Development

Activate Prior Knowledge

Solve.

1 Drake has 6 identical square tiles. He wants to create a rectangular design using all of them. How many different designs can he create if at least one edge of each tile must touch at least one edge of a second tile? ________

Definition Review

A **factor** is a number that is multiplied by another number, or a number that divides into a whole number evenly.

A **product** is the answer or result of a multiplication problem.

In each of the problems, identify the product and each of the factors.

		Product	First Factor	Second Factor
2	$27 \times 8 = 216$	________	________	________
3	$369 = 9 \times 41$	________	________	________
4	$7 \times 0 = 0$	________	________	________
5	$72 = 8 \times 9$	________	________	________

Application

- Work in a group.
- Write the following numbers on the board: 6, 30, 70, and 89.
- List all whole number factors of each of the numbers.

6 :

30:

70:

89:

Chapter 2

NAME ______________________ DATE ______________

Lesson 2-3 Skills Practice

Use skip counting to fill in the blanks by the number shown.

1. 7, ___, ___, ___, ___

2. 9, ___, ___, ___, ___

Use doubling to find each product.

3. 8 × 42

   Double 42: ______

   Double the result: ______

   Double the result again: ______

4. 26 × 8

   Double 26: ______

   Double the result: ______

   Double the result again: ______

5. 91 × 8

   Double 91: ______

   Double the result: ______

   Double the result again: ______

6. 8 × 63

   Double 63: ______

   Double the result: ______

   Double the result again: ______

Use a pattern to find each product.

7. 9 × 6

   9 × 1 = ______

   9 × 2 = ______

   9 × 3 = ______

   9 × 4 = ______

   9 × 5 = ______

   9 × 6 = ______

8. 5 × 7

   5 × 1 = ______

   5 × 2 = ______

   5 × 3 = ______

   5 × 4 = ______

   5 × 5 = ______

   5 × 6 = ______

   5 × 7 = ______

Find each product.

9. 8 × 52 ______

10. 65 × 7 ______

11. 47 × 9 ______

12. 74 × 8 ______

13. 7 × 97 ______

14. 9 × 24 ______

15. 8 × 77 ______

16. 36 × 7 ______

17. 84 × 9 ______

18. 8 × 8 ______

Lesson 2-3

NAME ____________________ DATE ____________

Problem-Solving Practice

Solve.

1 **CHECKING ACCOUNT** Cindy's bank charges $2 per check to pay her bills from her checking account. If she wrote 9 checks last month, how much did the bank charge her? ____________

2 **FENCING** Aaron is building a dog pen for his three dogs. How much fencing does he need to build the pen seen in the figure below? ____________

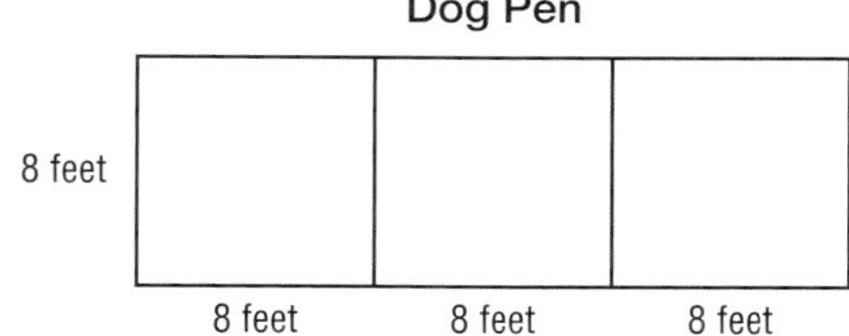

3 **RUNNING** Jenna has a 7 mile route that she runs each Saturday. If she runs all 52 Saturdays during the year, how many miles will she run? ____________

4 **TOURISM** Lake Front Tours charges $7 per person for a boat tour of Lake Michigan. Complete the table below to find the revenue generated based on the number of passengers on the tour.

Number of Passengers	1	2	3	4	5	6	7	8	9
Revenue	$7								

5 **EARNINGS** Jessica earns $8 an hour working at the Ernie's pet shop. If Jessica worked 36 hours last week, how much did she earn? ____________

6 **THEATER SEATING** The seating arrangement in row 1 of a movie theater is shown in the figure below. If there are 40 rows in the theater and they all contain the same number of seats, how many seats are in the theater? ____________

Row 1 ☐☐ Aisle ☐☐☐☐☐ Aisle ☐☐

NAME ______________________ DATE ____________

Lesson 2-3

Homework Practice

Use doubling to find each product.

1. 8×73

   Double 73: ________

   Double the result: ________

   Double the result again: ________

2. 35×8

   Double 35: ________

   Double the result: ________

   Double the result again: ________

Use a pattern to find each product.

3. 8×7

   $8 \times 1 =$ ________

   $8 \times 2 =$ ________

   $8 \times 3 =$ ________

   $8 \times 4 =$ ________

   $8 \times 5 =$ ________

   $8 \times 6 =$ ________

   $8 \times 7 =$ ________

4. 9×5

   $9 \times 1 =$ ________

   $9 \times 2 =$ ________

   $9 \times 3 =$ ________

   $9 \times 4 =$ ________

   $9 \times 5 =$ ________

Find each product.

5. 9×71 ________

6. 45×7 ________

7. 82×8 ________

8. 9×67 ________

Solve.

9. **READING** Each month Heather expects to read 6 books. If she meets her expectations, how many books does she read in 9 months? ________

Write the vocabulary word that completes each sentence.

10. A number that divides into a whole number evenly is called a ________.

Lesson 2-4

NAME ______________________ DATE ______________

Vocabulary and English Language Development

Activate Prior Knowledge

Solve.

1 Taylor's bedroom measures 12 feet by 9 feet, while Puna's bedroom measures 11 feet by 10 feet. If both bedrooms are rectangular, whose room has more area? ________

Definition Review

A **pattern** is a sequence of numbers, figures, or symbols that follows a rule or design.

The **Distributive Property of Multiplication** says that to multiply a sum by a number, multiply each addend by the number and add the products. For example: $3 \times (5 + 2) = 3 \times 5 + 3 \times 2 = 15 + 6 = 21$

- **Write D next to an example of the Distributive Property.**
- **Write N next to an example that is not the Distributive Property.**

2 $25 \times (8 + 3) = 25 \times 8 + 25 \times 3$ ________

3 $12 \times (4 + 11) = 12 \times 4 + 11$ ________

4 $(18 + 5) \times 7 = 18 \times 7 + 5 \times 7$ ________

5 $(2 \times 6) \times 4 = 2 \times (6 \times 4)$ ________

6 $5 \times (3 + 9) = 5 \times 3 + 5 \times 9$ ________

7 $(6 + 8) \times 5 = 6 \times 5 + 8 \times 5$ ________

Application

- Write the following problems on the board or overhead.

12×15 11×37 40×12

- Solve the problems using the traditional method.
- Solve the problems using the Distributive Property.
- Compare your answers.

Chapter 2

Lesson 2-4

NAME ______________________ DATE ____________

Skills Practice

Rewrite the factors in distributive form.

1. 12×9 ______________
2. 12×6 ______________
3. 12×4 ______________
4. 12×5 ______________

Use a pattern to find 7 × 11. Use the table to complete the pattern.

5.

1	× 11 =	
2	× 11 =	
3	× 11 =	
4	× 11 =	
5	× 11 =	
6	× 11 =	
7	× 11 =	

$7 \times 11 =$ ________

Find each product.

6. 12×15 ________
7. 11×88 ________
8. 12×4 ________
9. 10×11 ________
10. 11×11 ________
11. 25×12 ________
12. 13×11 ________
13. 19×12 ________
14. 16×11 ________
15. 6×12 ________
16. 12×80 ________
17. 11×24 ________
18. 12×35 ________
19. 11×18 ________

NAME ______________________ DATE ______________

Lesson 2-4

Problem-Solving Practice

Solve.

1 **MEASUREMENT** A *gross* is equal to a dozen dozen, or 12 times 12. A hotel manager ordered 3 gross of light bulbs. How many light bulbs did she order in all? ______

2 **DECORATING** Eric is decorating his deck for a party. He is hanging strings of lights that have 12 lights on each string. If he hangs 9 strings of lights, how many lights are there in all? ______

3 **MONEY** José saved $25 each month this year. How much did he save in all? ______

4 **NUTRITION** A bag of pita chips contains 15 servings. Each serving is about 11 pita chips. About how many chips are in the bag? ______

5 **FOOD SERVICE** The price of a large pizza is $11. Today the Pizza Place sold 129 large pizzas. How much money did they make from the sale of large pizzas? ______

6 **EXERCISE** Carlo biked 12 miles per day for 22 days. Rosa biked 11 miles per day for 24 days. Who biked the greater number of miles? Explain how you found your answer.

______

7 **PACKAGING** A package of crackers contains 12 crackers. There are 8 packages of crackers in a box. How many crackers are there in all? ______

8 **CONTEST** Each month every fifth grade student has to read 11 books. There are 110 students. How many books are read in all? ______

NAME ______________________ DATE ______________

Lesson 2-4

Homework Practice

Rewrite the factors in distributive form. Then find each product.

1 $11 \times 6 = (10 \times \_\_\_\_) + (1 \times \_\_\_\_)$
$= \_\_\_\_ + \_\_\_\_$
$= \_\_\_\_$

2 $9 \times 12 = (\_\_\_\_ \times 10) + (\_\_\_\_ \times 2)$
$= \_\_\_\_ + \_\_\_\_$
$= \_\_\_\_$

Find each product.

3 11×65 ________

4 33×11 ________

5 12×55 ________

6 19×12 ________

7 12×12 ________

8 11×19 ________

9 23×11 ________

10 7×12 ________

Solve.

11 **FOOD** Laurel owns a restaurant. She bought 15 cartons of eggs. Each carton holds a dozen eggs. How many eggs did she buy in all? ________

12 **MONEY** Carlton has 12 quarters. How much money does he have? ________

Write the vocabulary word that completes each sentence.

13 The ________ Property of Multiplication can be illustrated using the following example: $5 \times (10 + 2) = 5 \times 10 + 5 \times 2 = 50 + 10 = 60$.

14 A ________ is a sequence of numbers, figures, or symbols that follows a rule or design.

Lesson 2-5

NAME ________________________ DATE ____________

Vocabulary and English Language Development

Chapter 2

Activate Prior Knowledge

Give 3 examples of when you might use estimation in your daily life.

1 ________________________

2 ________________________

3 ________________________

Definition Review

List all factors for each number.

4 32 ________________________

5 56 ________________________

6 45 ________________________

7 96 ________________________

8 12 ________________________

9 100 ________________________

10 63 ________________________

Application

- Write the following problems on the board or overhead.
  - 58×87
  - 62×16
  - 48×59
  - 81×73
  - 20×41
- Solve three of the problems using each of the following methods: the traditional method and the partial products method.
- Use calculators to check your work if you get different answers for any single problem.

NAME ______________________ DATE ______________

Lesson 2-5

Skills Practice

Estimate each product.

1. $82 \times 79 =$ ______________
2. $33 \times 62 =$ ______________
3. $504 \times 28 =$ ______________
4. $396 \times 61 =$ ______________

Find each product. Use the traditional method and the partial products method.

5. $23 \times 58 =$ ______________
6. $17 \times 46 =$ ______________
7. $15 \times 92 =$ ______________
8. $12 \times 84 =$ ______________
9. $18 \times 39 =$ ______________
10. $14 \times 103 =$ ______________
11. $21 \times 65 =$ ______________
12. $19 \times 43 =$ ______________

Find each product.

13. $42 \times 75 =$ ______________
14. $37 \times 86 =$ ______________
15. $94 \times 29 =$ ______________
16. $28 \times 51 =$ ______________
17. $63 \times 36 =$ ______________
18. $59 \times 47 =$ ______________
19. $12 \times 474 =$ ______________
20. $15 \times 825 =$ ______________
21. $18 \times 320 =$ ______________
22. $20 \times 950 =$ ______________

Lesson **2-5**

NAME ______________________ DATE ____________

Problem-Solving Practice

Solve.

1 **CHEMISTRY** Darnell ordered 16 boxes of test tubes for his chemistry lab. Each box contains 65 test tubes. How many test tubes did Darnell order? ____________

2 **FLOWERS** Jeremy owns a flower shop. On Valentine's Day he sold 74 bouquets with a dozen roses in each bouquet. How many roses did Jeremy sell on Valentine's Day? ____________

3 **RUNNING** Dakota has been preparing for a marathon for the past 18 weeks. She has run 23 miles each week. How many miles has Dakota run during her training? ____________

4 **TRAVEL** Zach is driving from Los Angeles to New York City. He has driven for 29 hours and his average speed is 59 mph. How many miles has Zach driven? ____________

5 **EMPLOYMENT** Ivan has a summer job as a painter. He makes $23 per hour. On Monday Ivan worked 7 hours, on Tuesday 8 hours, on Wednesday he worked 7 hours, on Thursday 7 hours, and on Friday Ivan worked 7 hours. How much did Ivan make last week? ____________

6 **TYPING** Leah can type 65 words per minute. Her boss asked her to estimate how many words were in a report she just typed. The report took Leah 15 minutes to type. Approximately how many words are in the report? ____________

7 **BAKING** Amelia owns a bakery. Every Tuesday she bakes 14 batches of cookies. Each batch makes the same number of cookies. If 1 batch makes 36 cookies, how many cookies does Amelia bake every Tuesday? ____________

8 **SCHOOL** The principal has set a goal for each homeroom class in the school to sell 134 raffle tickets. The school has 28 homeroom classes. What is the goal of total raffle tickets to be sold for the whole school? ____________

NAME ______________________ DATE ______________

Lesson 2-5

Homework Practice

Estimate each product.

1. 34 × 77 = ____________
2. 58 × 93 = ____________
3. 104 × 31 = ____________
4. 45 × 190 = ____________

Find each product. Use the traditional method and the partial products method.

5. 39 × 54 = ____________
6. 68 × 63 = ____________
7. 86 × 42 = ____________
8. 27 × 95 = ____________

Find each product. Use the partial products method.

9. 71 × 37 = ____________
10. 44 × 43 = ____________
11. 198 × 29 = ____________
12. 17 × 256 = ____________

Find each product.

13. 52 × 19 = ____________
14. 73 × 84 = ____________
15. 38 × 32 = ____________
16. 97 × 61 = ____________

Solve.

17. **HEALTH** Suki measured her heart rate. It was 74 beats per minute at rest. How many times does her heart beat at rest for 1 hour? ____________

18. **TRANSPORTATION** The Speedy Ride Company provides transportation from the train station to the airport. Their shuttle bus can hold 32 passengers. The shuttle makes 19 trips each day. How many passengers can Speedy Ride take to the airport each day? ____________

Write the vocabulary word that completes the sentence.

19. A ____________ is a number that divides into a whole number evenly.

20. In the ____________ products method, the value of each digit in one factor is multiplied by the value of each digit in the other factor. The product is the sum of its partial products.

NAME ______________________ DATE ______________

Lesson 2-6

Vocabulary and English Language Development

Chapter 2

Activate Prior Knowledge

Use mental math to simplify each expression.

1. 0×23 __________
2. 10×15 __________
3. 3×30 __________
4. 7×40 __________
5. 9×20 __________
6. 11×7 __________
7. 10×10 __________
8. 10×20 __________
9. 8×80 __________
10. 70×60 __________

Definition Review

Inverse operations are operations that undo each other. Multiplication and division are inverse operations.

Use a fact family to match each of the three sentences with one or more of the five sentences on the right.

11. $5 \times 17 = 85$ __________
12. $76 \div 4 = 19$ __________
13. $21 \times 5 = 105$ __________

A $4 \times 19 = 76$

B $85 \div 17 = 5$

C $76 \div 19 = 4$

D $5 \times 21 = 105$

E $105 \div 21 = 5$

Application

- Find a partner.
- Write a division or multiplication sentence.
- Your partner writes a sentence that illustrates the inverse operation.
- Check your partner's work.
- Interchange roles and repeat the process as time permits.

Lesson 2-6

NAME ______________________ DATE ______________

Skills Practice

Write a different but equivalent multiplication sentence for each sentence below.

1. $17 \times 4 = 68$ ______________
2. $42 \times 21 = 882$ ______________
3. $63 \times 13 = 819$ ______________
4. $33 \times 29 = 957$ ______________

Write a different but equivalent division sentence for each sentence below.

5. $64 \div 4 = 16$ ______________
6. $77 \div 7 = 11$ ______________
7. $54 \div 18 = 3$ ______________
8. $54 \div 6 = 9$ ______________

Write a division sentence with the same numbers.

9. $43 \times 11 = 473$ ______________________________
10. $29 \times 18 = 522$ ______________________________
11. $37 \times 21 = 777$ ______________________________

Complete each equation using the numbers in the fact family.

12. $15 \times 14 =$ ______________
    $14 \times$ ______________ $= 210$
    $210 \div 14 =$ ______________
    $210 \div$ ______________ $= 14$

13. $37 \times 5 =$ ______________
    $5 \times$ ______________ $= 185$
    $185 \div 5 =$ ______________
    $185 \div$ ______________ $= 5$

Fill in the blank to make each equation correct.

14. $25 \times 7 =$ ______________
15. $88 \div 11 =$ ______________
16. ______________ $\div 3 = 31$
17. $13 \times$ ______________ $= 156$
18. ______________ $\times 11 = 121$
19. $16 \times$ ______________ $= 160$
20. $120 \div 12 =$ ______________
21. ______________ $\div 6 = 22$

NAME ______________________ DATE ____________

Problem-Solving Practice

Solve.

1 **SEATING ARRANGEMENTS** Kitchi has invited 42 friends to his party. He will be renting tables that seat six people. How many tables does he need to rent?

2 **PRODUCE** Patty went shopping at the local grocery store for apples. When she arrived she saw the sign shown below. What is the cost for 1 apple?

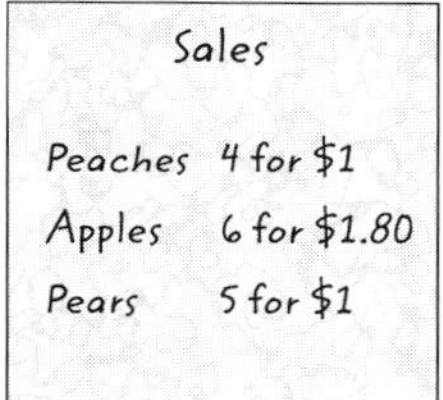

3 **GAS MILEAGE** Mrs. Torres drove 1080 miles on her vacation and used 40 gallons of gas. How many miles per gallon did her car average during the trip?

4 **PACKAGING** The Cherries-4-U company packages cherries in a box similar to the one shown below. If each box contains only one layer of cherries, how many cherries are in the box?

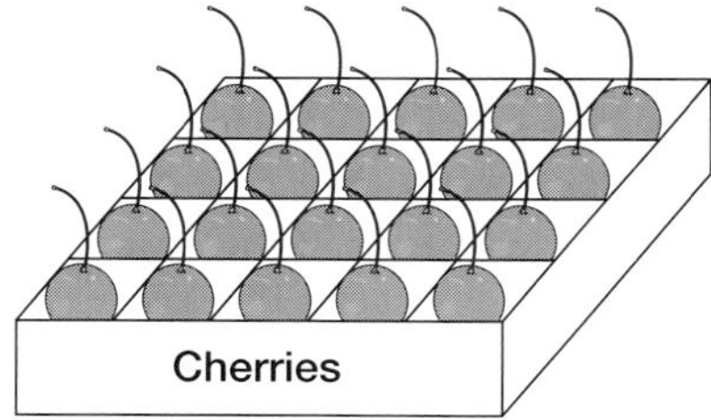

5 **INDUSTRIAL TECH** Jimmy's woodworking class built 32 four-legged stools. In all, how many legs were used to build the stools?

6 **PATTERN** The pattern you see below is row 1 of a painting which contains 19 more identical rows. How many triangles are in the painting?

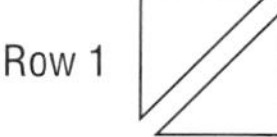

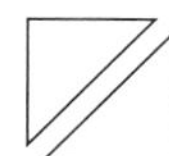

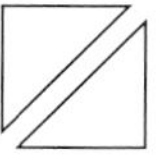

Lesson 2-6

NAME ______________________ DATE ____________

Homework Practice

Write a different but equivalent multiplication sentence for each sentence below.

1. $42 \times 23 = 966$ ____________

2. $97 \times 8 = 776$ ____________

Write a different but equivalent division sentence for each sentence below.

3. $84 \div 12 = 7$ ____________

4. $108 \div 27 = 4$ ____________

Write a division sentence with the same numbers.

5. $93 \times 3 = 279$ ____________

6. $48 \times 22 = 1{,}056$ ____________

Solve.

7. **SHARING** Kelly has 60 long stem roses which she would like to share equally with herself and four friends. How many roses should each person get? ____________

8. **READING** If Kyle reads 32 pages a day, how many pages will he read in 21 days? ____________

9. **DECORATING** Sharyln and five of her friends cut out 120 stars to decorate the gym. Each of them cuts the same numbers of stars. How many stars did each cut out? ____________

Write the vocabulary word that completes each sentence.

10. An operation on two numbers to find their __________ is a multiplication sentence.

11. Operations that undo one another are called __________ operations.

NAME ______________________ DATE ______________

Foldables Study Organizer

Dinah Zike's Foldables

Create the Foldable below to help study division facts.

1. Fold a sheet of notebook paper in half from side to side.

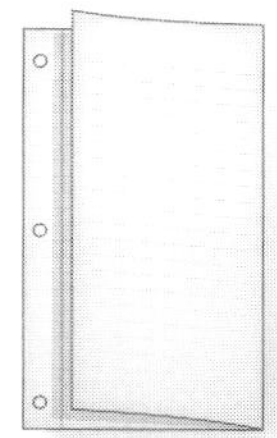

2. On one side, cut along every third line.

Tabs will form as you cut.

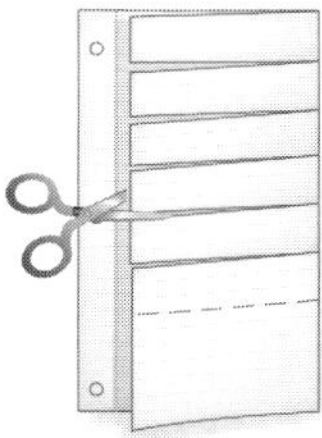

3. Turn and label your foldable as shown. As you read the chapter, list a division fact on each tab. Write the quotients under each tab.

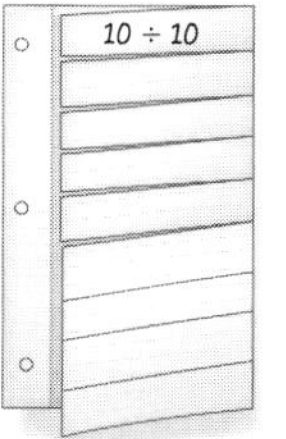

TAKING NOTES

As you read through the chapter, use your Foldable to explain and write an example of a problem with each division fact you encounter. Solve the problem and write the product under the tab.

USING YOUR FOLDABLE

Create additional Foldables as an alternative form of the division tables or flashcards. As you study, try to solve the problems that you wrote on your Foldable without looking at the answer. If you have any difficulties, then go over that concept again.

USING YOUR FOLDABLE

Trade Foldables with a partner. Check each other's work. Did your partner write the correct quotient under each tab with a division problem? If not, provide the correct answer.

NAME ______________________ DATE ____________

Chapter 3

Games and Puzzles

Find the Greatest Quotient

DIRECTIONS

- The object is to make the **greatest quotient** possible.
- Players take turns spinning the spinner.
- During his or her turn, each player writes the number the spinner lands on in one of the boxes.
- A player may not move the digits after they have been placed in a box.
- Once all the boxes have been filled, divide. The player with the greatest quotient wins.
- Draw more boxes to play more rounds.
- Also play this game to find the least quotient.

What You Need

- 1–9 Spinner
- "find the greatest quotient" game sheet

Number of Players

2 or more

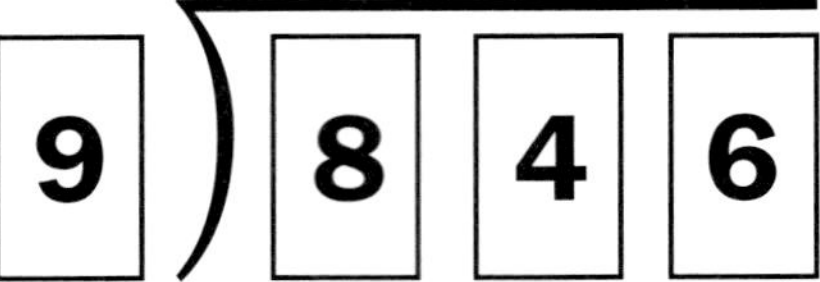

NAME _______________ DATE _______________

Find the Greatest Quotient Game Sheet

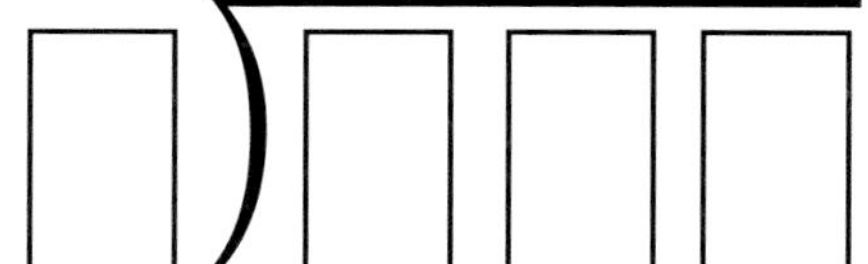

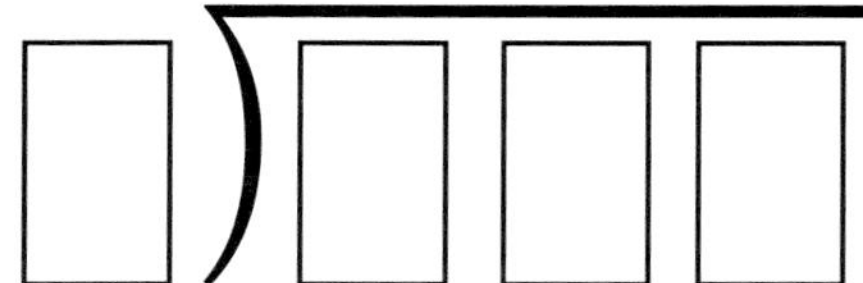

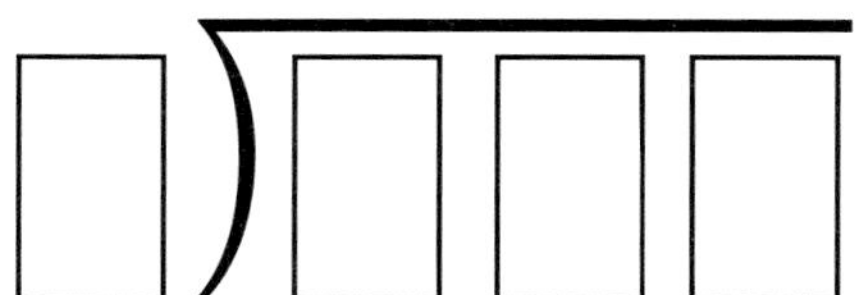

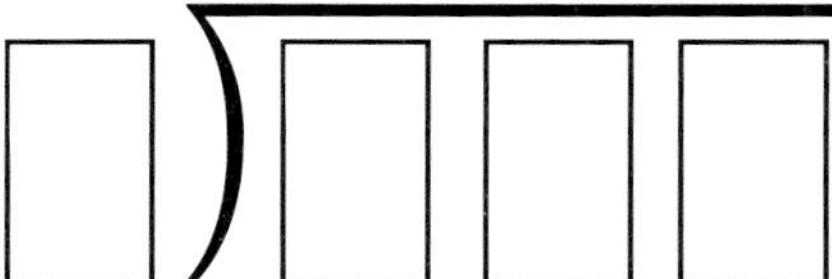

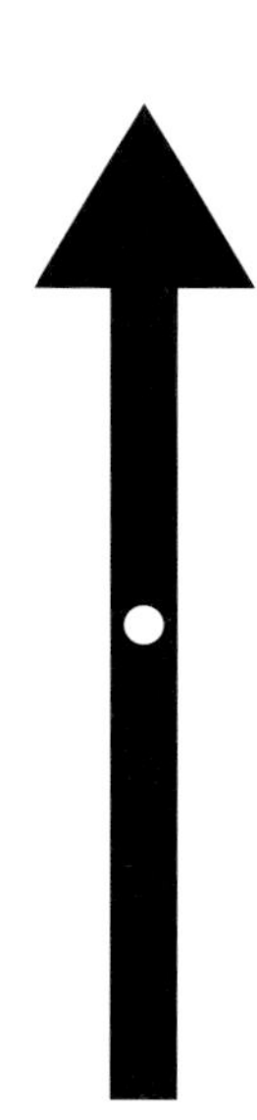

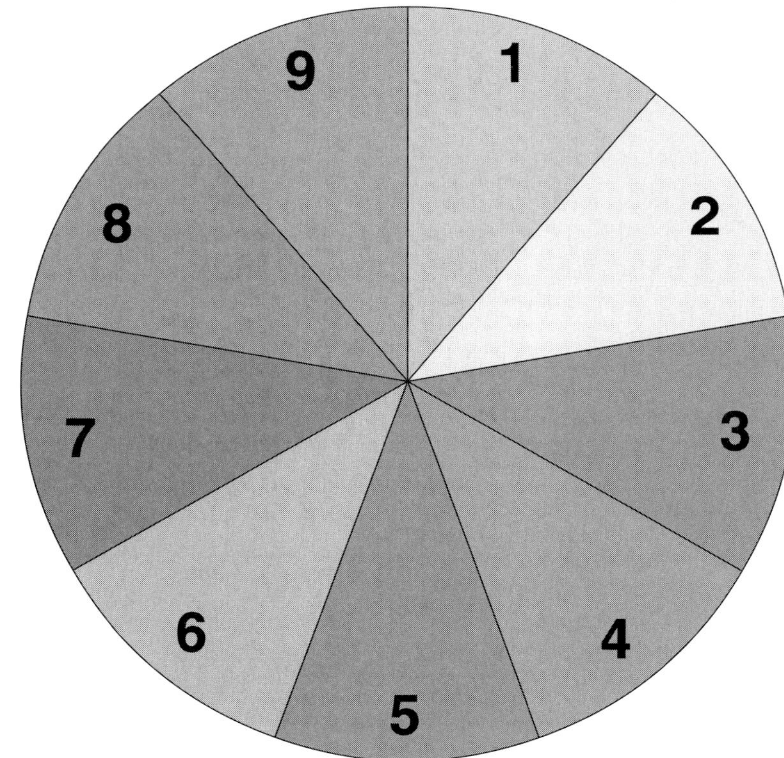

Lesson 3-1

NAME ________________ DATE ________________

Vocabulary and English Language Development

Activate Prior Knowledge

Group like items in separate columns.

1 Group these objects by hot or cold.

sun, fire, iceberg, ice-cream, stove, snow, sleet ________________

____

2 Group the numbers by even and odd numbers.

58, 15, 69, 137, 47, 155, 36, 200 ________________

____

3 Group the letters by vowels and consonants.

C, E, O, X, R, P, A ________________

Definition Review

A(n) **array** is the display of objects or symbols in rows of the same length and columns of the same length.

The answer or result of a division problem is the **quotient**.

A number that is being divided is the **dividend**.

Label each as the *dividend*, *divisor*, or *quotient*.

$\frac{8}{4} = 2$

4 8 is the ________

5 4 is the ________

6 2 is the ________

$2\overline{)12}$ with 6 above

7 2 is the ________

8 6 is the ________

9 12 is the ________

$10 \div 5 = 2$

10 10 is the ________

11 5 is the ________

12 2 is the ________

Application

- Create classroom floor plans showing all possible arrays using 12 desks.
- Each array must have all rows the same length and all columns the same length, although the length of the rows may be different from the lengths of the columns.
- The arrangements do not have to be practical.
- Repeat the activity with 16, 18, and 24 desks.

Lesson 3-1

NAME ______________________ DATE ______________

Skills Practice

Chapter 3

Write the division facts from each fact family.

1. $6 \times 2 = 12$ ______ ______

2. $3 \times 10 = 30$ ______ ______

3. $7 \times 4 = 28$ ______ ______

4. $2 \times 11 = 22$ ______ ______

5. $9 \times 4 = 36$ ______ ______

6. $1 \times 7 = 7$ ______ ______

Draw a model using circles and tally marks for each division fact.

7. $10 \div 2$

8. $8 \div 4$

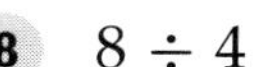

9. $9 \div 3$

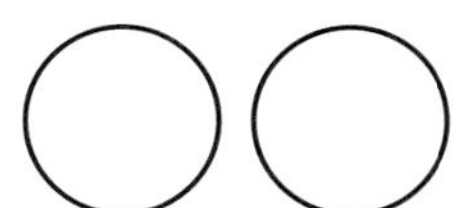

10. $25 \div 5$

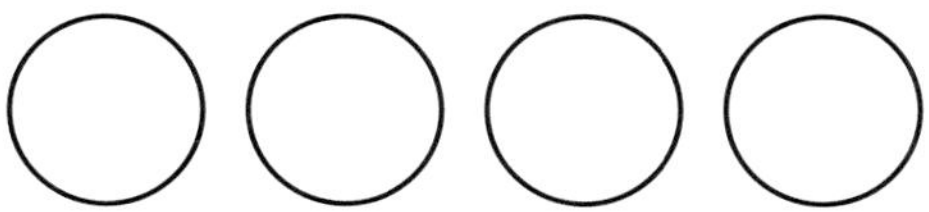

11. $6 \div 2$

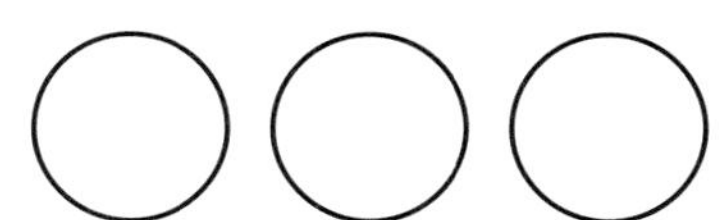

12. $21 \div 3$

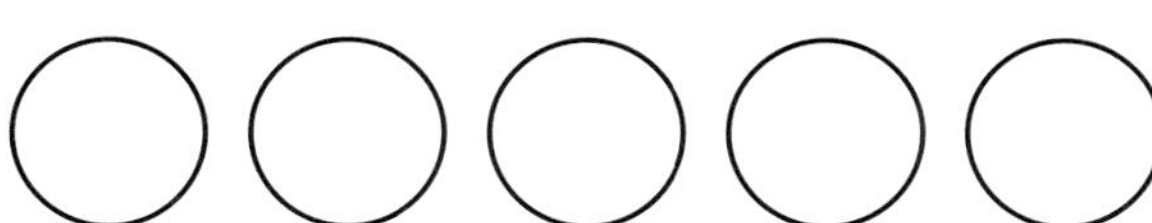

Draw an array to model each division fact.

13. $6 \div 1$

14. $4 \div 2$

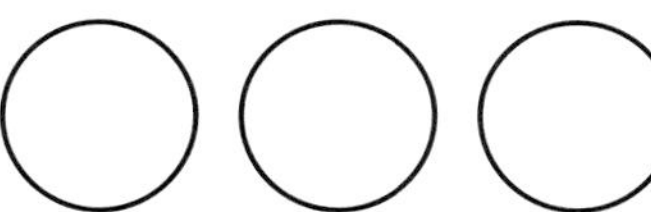

15. $14 \div 7$

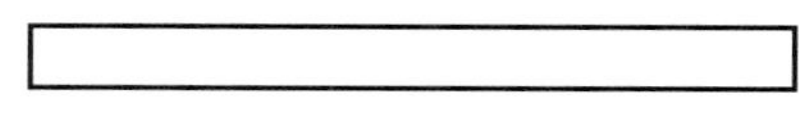

16. $15 \div 5$

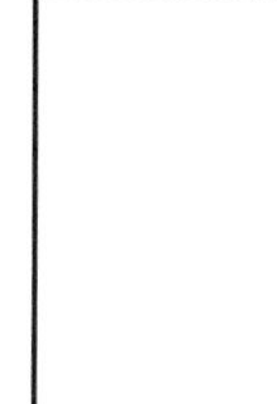

NAME ______________________ DATE ______________

Lesson 3-1

Problem-Solving Practice

Solve.

1. **GROCERY** Frozen yogurt is on sale 3 for $12. How much does one container of frozen yogurt cost? ______

2. **TECHNOLOGY** Rashid has 24 MB of free space on his MP3 player. The songs he puts on it usually take up 3 MB of space. How many more songs can Rashid put on his MP3 player? ______

3. **EMPLOYMENT** Bill works 40 hours each week. He works the same number of hours, 4 days a week. How many hours does Bill work each workday? ______

4. **RESTAURANT** Tania and five of her friends go out to lunch. The final bill including tax and tip is $48. They decide to split the bill evenly. How much does each person owe? ______

5. **WOODWORK** Wapi needs to make 4 legs for a small stool. If he uses an entire 48″ piece of wood to make the 4 legs, how long is each leg? ______

6. **FOOTBALL** Emilio ran the ball 7 times for 35 yards. Each time he ran for the same number of yards. How many yards did he carry the ball each time? ______

7. **FARMING** Ruby is designing an egg flat to hold eggs produced at a farm. She wants the flat to hold 56 eggs with 7 eggs in each row. How many rows does the egg flat need to have? ______

8. **COUNTING** Betty wants to know how many floors there are in her friend's apartment building. There are 48 windows on one side of the building with 8 windows per floor. How many floors are there in this building? ______

NAME ______________________ DATE ______________

Lesson 3-1

Homework Practice

Write each expression in two different formats.

1. $5 \div 1$ ____________ ____________

2. $\frac{100}{2}$ ____________ ____________

3. $\frac{16}{4}$ ____________ ____________

4. $1\overline{)10}$ ____________ ____________

Draw a model using circles and tally marks for each expression.

5. $35 \div 5$

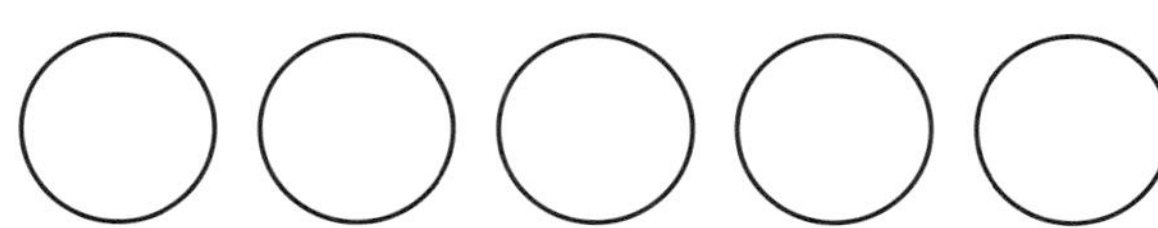

6. $14 \div 2$

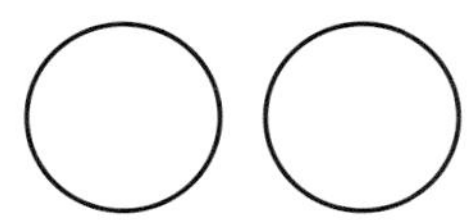

7. $10 \div 5$

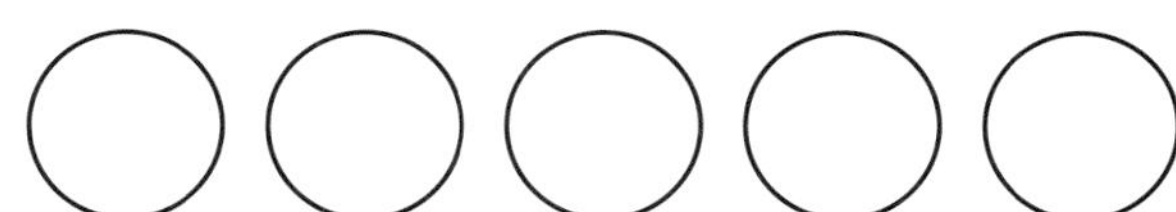

8. $18 \div 3$

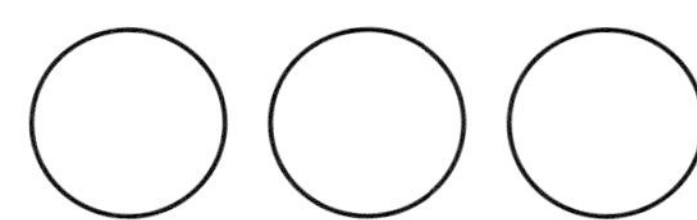

Write the division expression represented by each model.

9. ____________

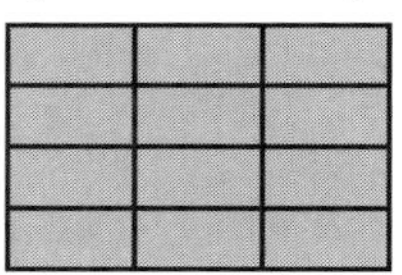

10. ____________

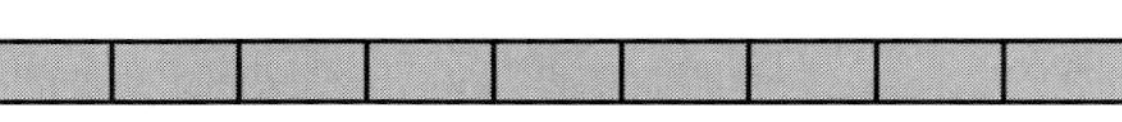

11. ____________

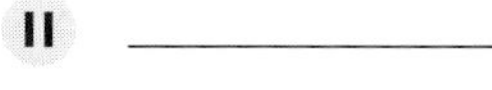

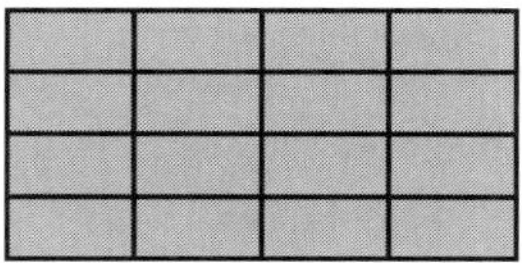

12. ____________

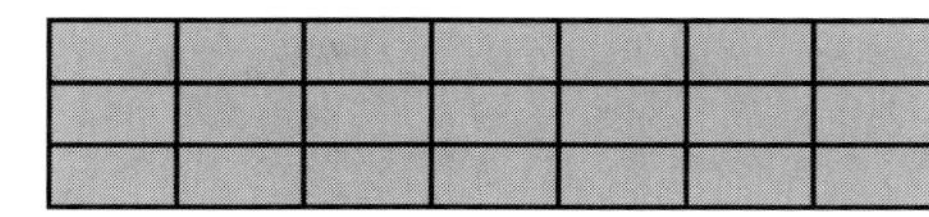

Write the division facts from each fact family.

13. $2 \times 10 = 20$ ____________ ____________

14. $5 \times 3 = 15$ ____________ ____________

15. $9 \times 3 = 27$ ____________ ____________

16. $8 \times 4 = 32$ ____________ ____________

Solve.

17. **MUSIC** Ms. Harada wants to arrange her chorus of 72 students into 8 rows. How many students are in each row? ____________

18. **PHOTOGRAPHS** Anil is painting a checkerboard pattern on the floor. He wants to have 64 squares on the floor with 8 rows. How many squares will be in each row? ____________

Chapter 3

NAME ______________________ DATE ______________

Lesson 3-2

Vocabulary and English Language Development

Activate Prior Knowledge

Find the number of coins in each amount.

1. How many pennies are in 50¢? ________
2. How many dimes are in $3.00? ________
3. How many dimes are in $7.40? ________
4. How many dimes are in 90¢? ________
5. How many pennies are in $2.37? ________
6. How many dimes are in $2.10? ________
7. How many pennies are in $1.00? ________
8. How many dimes are in $1.50? ________

Definition Review

Inverse operations are operations that undo each other.
A **factor** is a number that divides into a whole number evenly.

Match each with its inverse operation.

9	$+ 7$	$+ 3$
10	$- 3$	$\times 2$
11	$\times 6$	$- 7$
12	$\div 2$	$\div 6$

Application

- Form groups of 4 or 5 students.
- Gather 50–100 pennies. (You may substitute pennies with marbles, tokens, or any other small items.)
- Using different amounts, experiment to see what numbers of pennies can be evenly divided by 10 or 1.
- Share your findings with the class.

NAME ______________________ DATE ______________

Lesson 3-2

Skills Practice

Find each quotient.

1. $2 \div 2 =$ ________
2. $60 \div 6 =$ ________
3. $50 \div 5 =$ ________
4. $0 \div 1 =$ ________
5. $0 \div 10 =$ ________
6. $9 \div 9 =$ ________
7. $80 \div 8 =$ ________
8. $3 \div 3 =$ ________
9. $70 \div 7 =$ ________
10. $0 \div 4 =$ ________

Use a model to find each quotient.

11. $5 \div 1 =$ ________
12. $8 \div 1 =$ ________
13. $6 \div 1 =$ ________
14. $90 \div 10 =$ ________

Find each quotient. If finding the quotient is not possible, write *not possible*.

15. $70 \div 10 =$ ________
16. $4 \div 1 =$ ________
17. $1 \div 1 =$ ________
18. $3 \div 0 =$ ________
19. $80 \div 10 =$ ________
20. $19 \div 19 =$ ________
21. $5 \div 0 =$ ________
22. $10 \div 10 =$ ________

NAME ______________________ DATE ______________

Lesson 3-2

Problem-Solving Practice

Solve.

1. **CHANGE** Lucy has 70 pennies. How many dimes could she trade for the pennies ? ____________

2. **FLOWERS** Kimiko planted 150 marigolds in rows of 10. How many rows did she plant? ____________

3. **TELEPHONES** Felipe wants to know how much time he spends per phone call on his cell phone. On Monday, he made 10 phone calls and talked for a total of 40 minutes. How many minutes did he spend on each call? ____________

4. **TECHNOLOGY** Dave purchased a new MP3 player for $80. He only had 10-dollar bills in his wallet. How many of the bills did he need to give the cashier? ____________

5. **SAVINGS** Carlos saved $4 each week for 8 weeks. Juan saved $2 each week for 16 weeks. Who saved more. Explain your answer.

____

____

6. **HARDWARE** Shenequa measured a screw to be 20 millimeters long. If 10 mm = 1 cm, how long is the screw in centimeters? ____________

7. **BAKING** Oya baked 110 cookies to give to 10 of her teachers. How many cookies did she give each teacher? ____________

8. **CHARITY** Ms. Dixon gives money to charities of her choice each year. She is able to donate $100 this year and has decided to give to one charity. How much will each of her selected charities get this year? ____________

Lesson 3-2

NAME ____________________ DATE ____________

Homework Practice

Use a model to find each quotient.

1. $12 \div 1 =$ ________

2. $4 \div 4 =$ ________

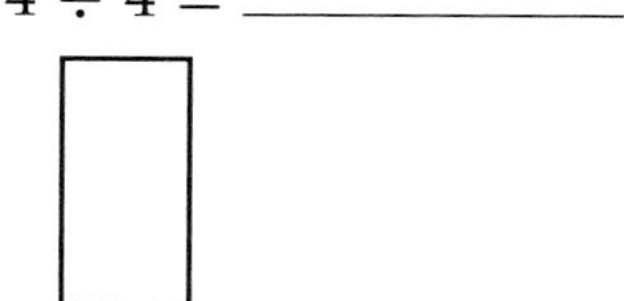

Find each quotient. If finding the quotient is not possible, write *not possible*.

3. $40 \div 10 =$ ________
4. $190 \div 10 =$ ________
5. $70 \div 10 =$ ________
6. $110 \div 10 =$ ________
7. $10 \div 0 =$ ________
8. $6 \div 6 =$ ________
9. $8 \div 1 =$ ________
10. $11 \div 11 =$ ________
11. $9 \div 1 =$ ________
12. $8 \div 0 =$ ________
13. $0 \div 1 =$ ________
14. $2 \div 1 =$ ________

Chapter 3

Solve.

15. **GROCERY** One brand of yogurt comes in 10-oz containers. Terrell bought 60 ounces of the yogurt. How many containers did he buy? ________

16. **BASEBALL** Nadish was calculating the batting average for the school baseball team. He noticed Keith had 0 hits from 0 at bats. ________

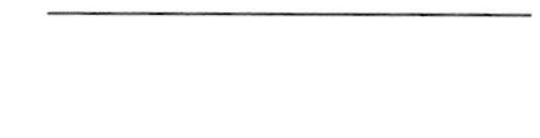

What is Keith's batting average? ________

17. **INTERIOR DESIGN** Ferrell is laying tiles in his bathroom. Each tile is one square foot. If his bathroom is 90 square feet, how many boxes of 10 tiles each does he need to buy? ________

Write the vocabulary word that completes the sentence.

18. The ________ is a number that is being divided.

19. The answer or result of a division problem is the ________.

Lesson 3-3

NAME ______________________ DATE ______________

Vocabulary and English Language Development

Activate Prior Knowledge

Complete the series following the pattern.

1 5, 10, 15, 20, ________, ________, ________, ________

2 2, 4, 6, 8, ________, ________, ________, ________

3 80, 85, 90, 95, ________, ________, ________, ________

4 28, 30, 32, 34, ________, ________, ________, ________

Definition Review

A **quotient** is the answer or result of a division problem.

A **dividend** is the number that is being divided.

A **divisor** is the number by which the dividend is being divided.

Label each number as *dividend, divisor,* or *quotient*.

$5\overline{)35}$ with quotient 7 | $\frac{18}{2} = 9$ | $8 \div 2 = 4$

5 7 is the ________.

6 5 is the ________.

7 35 is the ________.

8 18 is the ________.

9 9 is the ________.

10 2 is the ________.

11 8 is the ________.

12 2 is the ________.

13 4 is the ________.

Application

- Work individually or in small groups.
- Understand that all numbers with an even number in the ones place are divisible by 2.
- Test this rule. Can you find any number that contradicts this rule?
- Understand that all numbers with a 0 or 5 in the ones place are evenly divisible by 5.
- Test this rule. Can you find any exceptions?
- Discuss your findings. What were some of the numbers you tested?

Lesson 3-3

NAME ______________________ DATE ____________

Skills Practice

Find each quotient by using the related multiplication fact.

1. 6 ÷ 2 ________
2. 10 ÷ 5 ________
3. 15 ÷ 5 ________
4. 12 ÷ 2 ________
5. 4 ÷ 2 ________
6. 8 ÷ 2 ________
7. 35 ÷ 5 ________
8. 10 ÷ 2 ________

Draw a model to find each quotient.

9. 8 ÷ 2 = ________

10. 20 ÷ 5 = ________

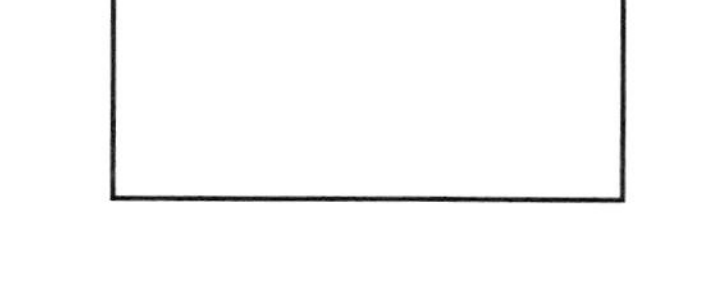

11. 5 ÷ 5 = ________

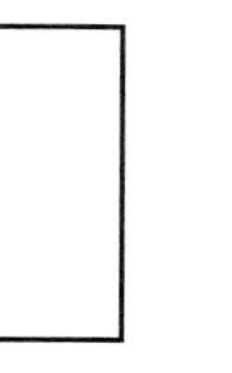

12. 6 ÷ 2 = ________

Find each quotient.

13. 10 ÷ 2 = ________
14. 15 ÷ 5 = ________
15. 25 ÷ 5 = ________
16. 48 ÷ 2 = ________
17. 55 ÷ 5 = ________
18. 22 ÷ 2 = ________
19. 100 ÷ 2 = ________
20. 45 ÷ 5 = ________
21. 16 ÷ 2 = ________
22. 40 ÷ 5 = ________

NAME ______________________ DATE ______________

Lesson 3-3

Problem-Solving Practice

Solve.

1. **RETAIL** Ren bought a new DVD player that cost $40. How many 5-dollar bills did Ren give the sales clerk? ________

2. **FOOD SERVICE** Sarai and her friend went out for lunch. They decided to each pay an equal share. The restaurant bill was a total of $22. How much does each girl owe? ________

3. **BASKETBALL** Tito has scored the same number of points during each of the first 5 basketball games of the year. He has scored 60 points total. How many points has Tito scored during each game? ________

4. **TECHNOLOGY** Nikki's hard drive is 30 GB. She wants to divide it into 2 equal parts. What size should Nikki make each section of her hard drive? ________

5. **BIOLOGY** LaBron needed to split his cell cultures into 5 new Petri dishes. After preparing the cell cultures, he has 20 milliliters of cell solution. How many milliliters does he need to add to each new dish? ________

6. **COOKING** Sanjay is making pancakes. The recipe card says that he needs 4 cups of flour. He wants to make the batter in 2 batches. How many cups of flour should Sanjay add to each batch? ________

7. **MODELS** Jonathan made a model of his car. The car is 15 feet long and 5 times larger than the model car. How long was Jonathan's model? ________

8. **EMPLOYMENT** Fala worked 50 hours last week. She worked the same number of hours each day for 5 days. How many hours did Fala work each day? ________

NAME ______________________ DATE ______________

Lesson 3-3

Homework Practice

Draw a model to find each quotient.

1. $28 \div 2 =$ ______

2. $45 \div 5 =$ ______

3. $30 \div 5 =$ ______

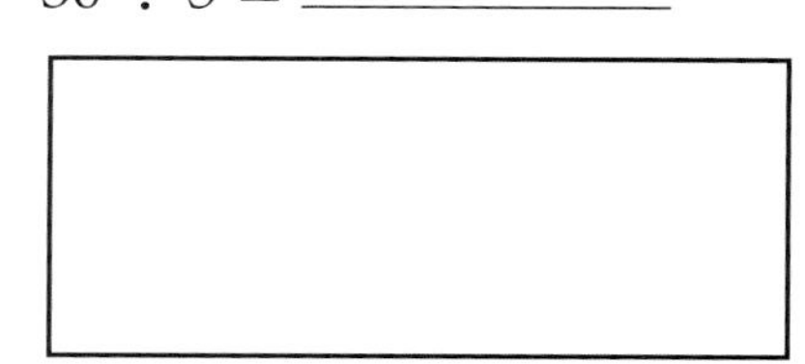

4. $20 \div 2 =$ ______

Find each quotient.

5. $40 \div 5 =$ ______
6. $35 \div 5 =$ ______
7. $14 \div 2 =$ ______
8. $20 \div 5 =$ ______
9. $18 \div 2 =$ ______
10. $14 \div 2 =$ ______
11. $30 \div 5 =$ ______
12. $22 \div 2 =$ ______
13. $10 \div 5 =$ ______
14. $16 \div 2 =$ ______
15. $50 \div 5 =$ ______
16. $10 \div 2 =$ ______

Solve.

17. **GROCERY** Marjorie bought 2 boxes of the same kind of cookie. She spent a total of $4. How much was each box of cookies? ______

18. **ENGINEERING** Eva designed a sprinkler system with one pump with 5 different lines. Each line is designed to get the same flow of water. The pump produces 25 gallons of water per minute. How many gallons of water should each line get per minute? ______

Write the vocabulary word that completes the sentence.

19. The ______ is the number being divided.

20. The answer or result of a division problem is the ______.

Chapter 3

NAME _______________ DATE _______________

Lesson 3-4

Vocabulary and English Language Development

Activate Prior Knowledge

Fill in the blanks to make both sides of the equation equal.

1. $7 \times 4 =$ ___ + ___ + ___ + ___ + ___ + ___ + ___
2. $6 \times 3 =$ ___ + ___ + ___ + ___ + ___ + ___
3. $5 \times 4 =$ ___ + ___ + ___ + ___ + ___
4. $8 \times 3 =$ ___ + ___ + ___ + ___ + ___ + ___ + ___ + ___

Definition Review

A **multiple** of a number is the product of that number and any whole number.

The number that is left after one whole number is divided by another whole number is the **remainder**.

Circle the expressions that *will* have a remainder.

$16 \div 4$ $89 \div 4$

$17 \div 3$ $28 \div 4$

$75 \div 3$ $32 \div 3$

$26 \div 4$ $81 \div 3$

Application

- Work individually or in small groups.
- Understand that all numbers that can be divided by 2 twice are evenly divisible by 4.
- Test this rule. Can you find any number that contradicts this rule?
- Understand that all numbers are divisible by 3 when the digits of that number are added together and the sum is divisible by 3.
- Test this rule. Can you find any exceptions for this rule?
- Discuss your findings. What were some of the numbers you tested?

NAME ______________________ DATE ______________

Lesson 3-4

Skills Practice

Draw an array to model each quotient.

1 $8 \div 4 =$ ______

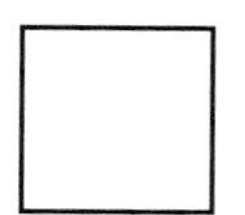

2 $20 \div 4 =$ ______

3 $21 \div 3 =$ ______

4 $12 \div 3 =$ ______

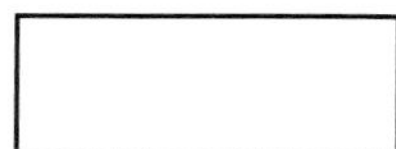

Chapter 3

Find each quotient.

5 $36 \div 4 =$ ______

6 $30 \div 3 =$ ______

7 $4 \div 4 =$ ______

8 $16 \div 4 =$ ______

9 $24 \div 3 =$ ______

10 $28 \div 4 =$ ______

11 $6 \div 3 =$ ______

12 $40 \div 4 =$ ______

13 $27 \div 3 =$ ______

14 $24 \div 4 =$ ______

15 $12 \div 3 =$ ______

16 $9 \div 3 =$ ______

Find each quotient. Show the remainder.

17 $20 \div 3 =$ ______

18 $17 \div 4 =$ ______

19 $14 \div 3 =$ ______

20 $26 \div 3 =$ ______

21 $11 \div 4 =$ ______

22 $16 \div 3 =$ ______

23 $22 \div 4 =$ ______

24 $27 \div 4 =$ ______

25 $20 \div 3 =$ ______

26 $21 \div 4 =$ ______

27 $28 \div 3 =$ ______

28 $33 \div 4 =$ ______

NAME ______________________ DATE ______________

Lesson 3-4

Problem-Solving Practice

Solve.

1 **ENTERTAINMENT** Uma and her 2 brothers want to buy a new game together. The game costs $27. How much does each sibling need to contribute to buy the game? ____________

2 **NUTRITION** Amanda is only allowed to eat 21 grams of fat each day. If she eats an equal number of grams at each of her 3 meals, how many grams of fat can she eat at lunch? ____________

3 **SAFETY** Mato and 3 of his friends are in an elevator. The elevator sign says that the maximum weight allowable is 400 pounds. If the weight is split evenly among the friends, what is the maximum allowable weight of each of the people in the elevator? ____________

4 **WOODWORK** Jamal is going to make a table with 3 legs. The piece of wood that he wants to use to make the legs is 12 feet long. What is the longest length Jamal can make each leg? ____________

5 **MANUFACTURING** The Clean Machine plant makes 33 washing machines each day. Each of the 3 work shifts produces the same number of washing machines. How many machines does each shift make at the Clean Machine plant? ____________

6 **INTERIOR DESIGN** Lydia is going to make curtains for 4 windows. She has 32 yards of fabric. How much fabric does Lydia have for each curtain? ____________

7 **RETAIL** Rai goes to a clothing store. The store is having a $\frac{1}{3}$ off sale. She finds a shirt she wants to buy for $24.00. How much will Rai save? What will be the sale price of the shirt? ____________ ____________ ____________

8 **INDUSTRY** An assembly line can make 12 toy trains per hour. If 3 people box the trains, how many does each have to pack to keep up with the assembly line? ____________

NAME ______________________________ DATE ______________

Lesson 3-4

Homework Practice

Draw an array to model each quotient.

1 $8 \div 4 =$ ________

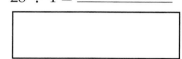

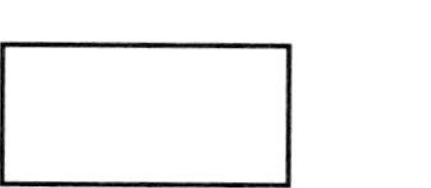

2 $27 \div 3 =$ ________

3 $9 \div 3 =$ ________

4 $28 \div 4 =$ ________

Find each quotient.

5 $44 \div 4 =$ ________

6 $36 \div 3 =$ ________

7 $12 \div 4 =$ ________

8 $0 \div 4 =$ ________

9 $6 \div 3 =$ ________

10 $3 \div 3 =$ ________

Find each quotient. Show the remainder.

11 $10 \div 4 =$ ________

12 $14 \div 3 =$ ________

13 $29 \div 4 =$ ________

14 $5 \div 3 =$ ________

15 $15 \div 4 =$ ________

16 $26 \div 3 =$ ________

Solve.

17 **MONEY** Omar collected 28 quarters to donate to a local charity. How many dollars did Omar collect? (There are 4 quarters in a dollar.) ________

18 **FOOTBALL** Aiden had 3 catches for 24 yards in the last game. How many yards did he average per catch? ________

Write the vocabulary word that completes the sentence.

19 A ________ of a number is the product of that number and any whole number.

20 The number that is left after one whole number is divided by another whole number is the ________.

NAME ______________________ DATE ______________

Lesson 3-5

Vocabulary and English Language Development

Activate Prior Knowledge

Find each total price.

A teddy bear has a price tag of $7, and a ball has a price tag of $6.

1. 3 balls ______________
2. 2 teddy bears ______________
3. 5 balls ______________
4. 8 teddy bears ______________

Definition Review

A **multiple** of a number is the product of that number and any whole number.

The number that is left after one whole number is divided by another whole number is called the **remainder**.

List 6 multiples for each number.

5. 2: ______________________
6. 4: ______________________
7. 6: ______________________
8. 7: ______________________
9. 20: ______________________

Application

- Work individually or in small groups.
- Understand that all *even* numbers that are divisible by 3 are also divisible by 6.
- Test this rule. Can you find any number that contradicts this rule?
- You can take the last digit of a number, multiply it by 2, and then subtract it from the rest of the number. If the new number is divisible by 7, then the original number is as well.
- Test this rule. Can you find any exceptions for this rule?
- Discuss your findings. What were some of the numbers you tested?

Lesson 3-5

NAME ____________________ DATE ____________

Skills Practice

Write the division problem represented by the model.

1 ____________

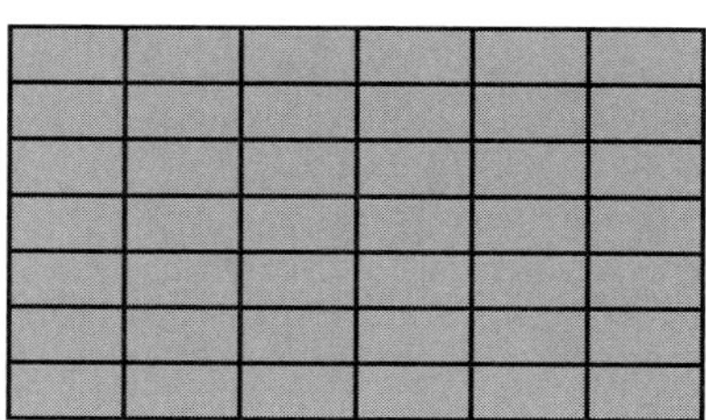

2 ____________

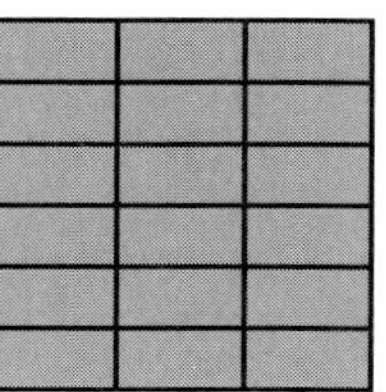

3 ____________

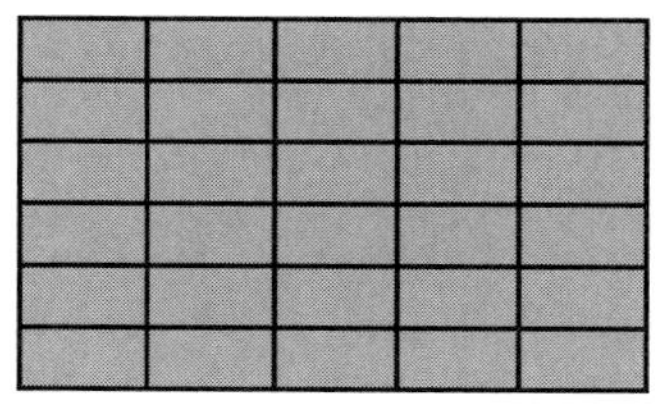

4 ____________

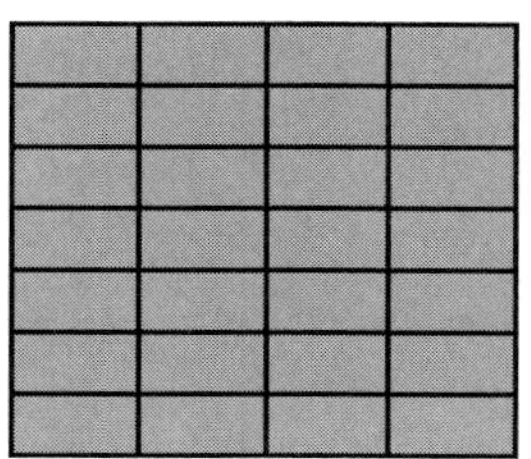

Find each quotient.

5 $0 \div 7 =$ ____________

6 $48 \div 6 =$ ____________

7 $42 \div 6 =$ ____________

8 $35 \div 7 =$ ____________

9 $60 \div 6 =$ ____________

10 $70 \div 7 =$ ____________

11 $56 \div 7 =$ ____________

12 $6 \div 6 =$ ____________

13 $14 \div 7 =$ ____________

14 $36 \div 6 =$ ____________

15 $66 \div 6 =$ ____________

16 $84 \div 7 =$ ____________

Find each quotient. Show the remainder.

17 $40 \div 6 =$ ____________

18 $27 \div 7 =$ ____________

19 $33 \div 6 =$ ____________

20 $16 \div 7 =$ ____________

21 $54 \div 7 =$ ____________

22 $25 \div 6 =$ ____________

23 $31 \div 7 =$ ____________

24 $53 \div 6 =$ ____________

25 $44 \div 6 =$ ____________

26 $13 \div 7 =$ ____________

27 $58 \div 6 =$ ____________

28 $37 \div 7 =$ ____________

NAME ______________________ DATE ______________

Lesson 3-5

Problem-Solving Practice

Solve.

1 **FUNDRAISING** Toru sells tins of popcorn to raise money for the school band. Each tin of popcorn sells for $7. He has raised $644 so far. How many tins of popcorn has he sold? ____________

2 **EMPLOYMENT** Kwam works for a landscaping company. He works 36 hours per week. If he decides to split his time equally over 6 days, how many hours should Kwam work each day? ____________

3 **FITNESS** Ines has been working out every day for the past 49 days. How many weeks has Ines been working out? ____________

4 **GROCERY** Dean has been stacking egg flats into boxes. Each box will hold 6 egg flats of 30 eggs. He was told to load 192 egg flats in a shipment for a local grocery store. How many boxes should Dean load onto the truck for this shipment? ____________

5 **CELEBRATION** A group of 8 people went out to lunch for Chantal's birthday. Seven of them decided to treat Chantal to lunch. The total restaurant bill was $63. How much does each person owe? ____________

6 **MAINTENANCE** Trevor needs to make sure there is enough cleaning solution to run a processing machine. He has three 10-liter bottles of cleaning solution. The machine uses 6 liters of cleaning solution every day. How many days can Trevor run the machine before he runs out of cleaning solution? ____________

7 **TRAVEL** Gen is driving from Atlanta, Georgia, to Salt Lake City, Utah. She estimates it will take her 28 hours to drive this distance. She decides to drive an average of 7 hours per day. How many days will it take Gen to complete her trip? ____________

8 **BIOLOGY** Sara needs to run tests to determine if the DNA she is looking for is present in her samples. The machine can hold a total of 30 samples in rows of 6. How many samples are in each row? ____________

Lesson 3-5

NAME ______________________ DATE ______________

Homework Practice

Write the division problem represented by each model.

1 ____________

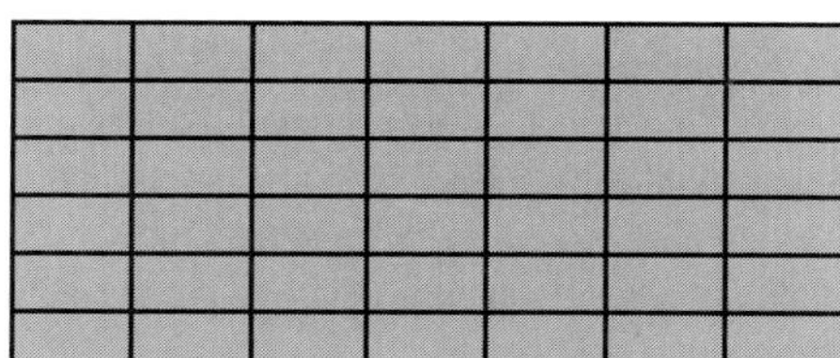

2 ____________

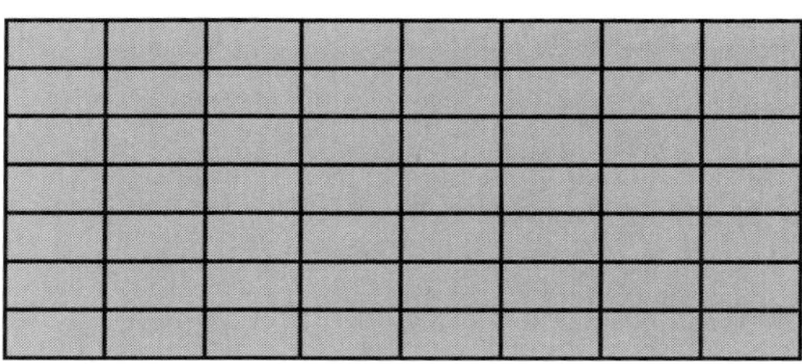

3 ____________

4 ____________

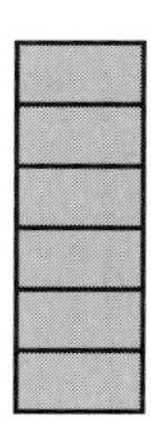

Find each quotient.

5 $7 \div 7 =$ ____________

6 $54 \div 6 =$ ____________

7 $30 \div 6 =$ ____________

8 $24 \div 6 =$ ____________

9 $21 \div 7 =$ ____________

10 $63 \div 7 =$ ____________

11 $18 \div 6 =$ ____________

12 $49 \div 7 =$ ____________

13 $0 \div 6 =$ ____________

14 $28 \div 7 =$ ____________

Find each quotient. Show the remainder.

15 $149 \div 7 =$ ____________

16 $365 \div 6 =$ ____________

17 $282 \div 7 =$ ____________

18 $425 \div 6 =$ ____________

Solve.

19 **TECHNOLOGY** Vito is downloading a file from the Internet at a speed of 6 MB/sec. The file is 60 MB. How long will it take the file to download? ____________

20 **ENGINEERING** Anaba is designing an electrical system to power 7 motors. The maximum amount of current all 7 motors can use is 35 amps. If each motor uses the same amount of current, what is the maximum amount of current each motor can use? ____________

Chapter 3

NAME ______________________ DATE ______________

Lesson 3-6

Vocabulary and English Language Development

Activate Prior Knowledge

Find each product.

1. $8 \times 9 =$ ______________
2. $9 \times 6 =$ ______________
3. $9 \times 9 =$ ______________
4. $8 \times 8 =$ ______________

Definition Review

A **multiple** of a number is the product of that number and any whole number.

Adding, subtracting, multiplying, or dividing in your head without using manipulatives, fingers, or pencil and paper is using **mental math**.

Use mental math to solve.

5. $75 + 29 = 75 + 25 + 4 =$ ______
6. $423 + 256 = 400 + 200 + 20 + 50 + 3 + 6 =$ ______
7. $157 + 158 = 150 + 150 + 7 + 8 =$ ______
8. $125 \times 5 = 100 \times 5 + 25 \times 5 =$ ______
9. $83 \times 4 = 80 \times 4 + 3 \times 4 =$ ______
10. $27 \times 11 = 27 \times 10 + 27 \times 1 =$ ______

Application

- Work individually or in small groups.
- Understand that all numbers that can be divided by 2 three times are evenly divisible by 8. For example, $32 \div 2 \div 2 \div 2 = 4$ and $32 \div 8 = 4$.
- Test this rule. Can you find any number that contradicts this rule?
- Understand that all numbers are divisible by 9 when the digits of that number are added together and that sum is divisible by 9. For example, the number 63 is divisible by 9 and $6 + 3 = 9$ is divisible by 9.
- Test this rule. Can you find any exceptions for this rule?
- Discuss your findings. What were some of the numbers you tested?

Lesson 3-6

NAME ______________________ DATE ____________

Skills Practice

Write the division problem represented by the model.

1 ______________

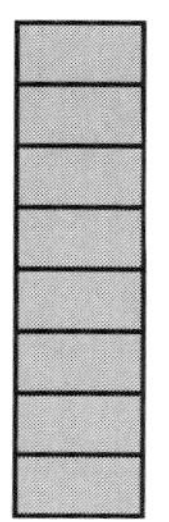

2 ______________

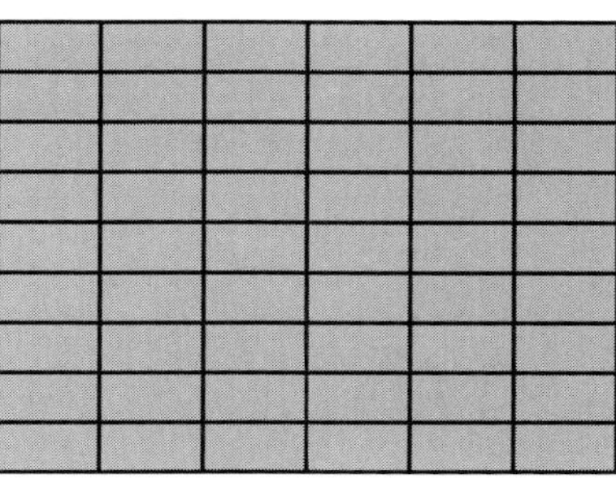

3 ______________

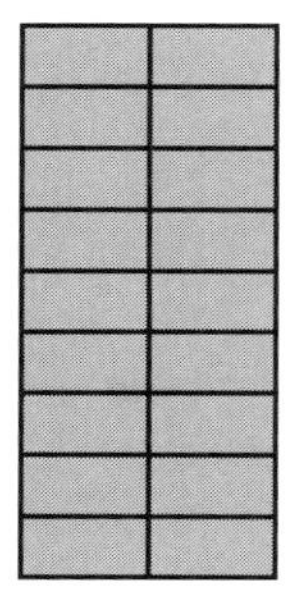

4 ______________

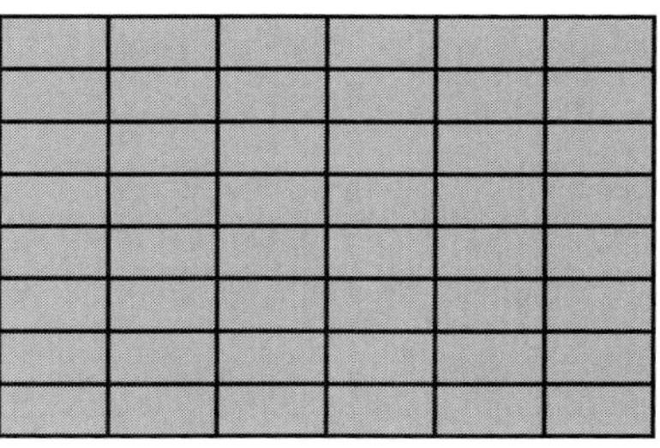

Find each quotient. Use short division.

5 $189 \div 9 =$ ______________

6 $120 \div 8 =$ ______________

7 $153 \div 9 =$ ______________

8 $176 \div 8 =$ ______________

Find each quotient. Show the remainder.

9 $51 \div 8 =$ ______________

10 $43 \div 9 =$ ______________

11 $29 \div 8 =$ ______________

12 $65 \div 9 =$ ______________

13 $43 \div 8 =$ ______________

14 $82 \div 9 =$ ______________

15 $62 \div 8 =$ ______________

16 $62 \div 9 =$ ______________

NAME ______________________ DATE ______________

Lesson 3-6

Problem-Solving Practice

Solve.

1. **TECHNOLOGY** Chelsea gets paid $9 per hour. How many hours does Chelsea need to work to buy an MP3 player that costs $63? ______

2. **DOG SLEDS** Shim and his team of sled dogs can run 9 miles per hour in rough winter weather. They need to travel 54 miles. How long will it take? ______

3. **EMPLOYMENT** Pearl is working on her time sheet. She has determined that she worked 24 hours last week and 48 hours this week. She always works 8 hours each day. How many days did she work each week? ______

4. **CONSTRUCTION** Anton is making two work tables for his shop. He has one long piece of wood that is 32 feet long. He wants to use the piece of wood for all 8 legs. How long will Anton make each of the legs of his tables? ______

5. **CELEBRATION** Sarita used 100 ounces of punch to fill 9 glasses equally. How many ounces of punch were left over? ______

6. **FURNITURE** It takes Amal 9 hours to make one chair. A customer asks him for a rush order of 6 chairs. He has only 48 available hours to work on this order. Is this enough to satisfy the customer's order? ______

7. **MOVIES** Hama and 7 of her friends went to the movies. The total cost of their tickets was $56. How much was each ticket? ______

8. **RETAIL** Carlos has $72 to spend for a DVD movie collection. There are 4 movies in the selection. How much did each movie cost? ______

Lesson 3-6

NAME ____________________ DATE ____________

Homework Practice

Write the division problem represented by each model.

1 ____________

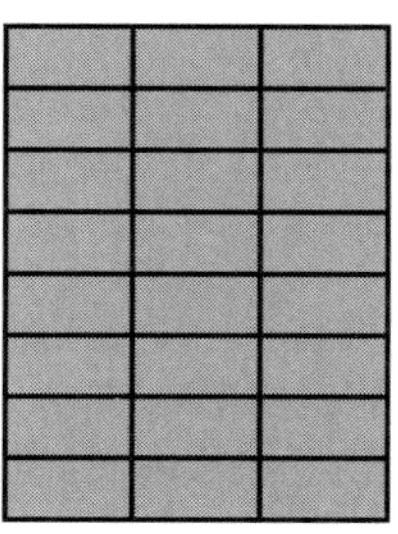

2 ____________

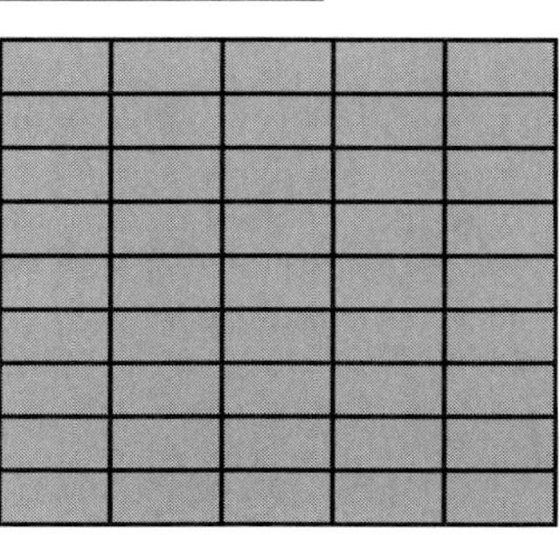

Find each quotient.

3 $27 \div 9 =$ ____________

4 $48 \div 8 =$ ____________

5 $0 \div 8 =$ ____________

6 $81 \div 9 =$ ____________

7 $64 \div 8 =$ ____________

8 $45 \div 9 =$ ____________

9 $80 \div 8 =$ ____________

10 $63 \div 9 =$ ____________

11 $18 \div 9 =$ ____________

12 $72 \div 8 =$ ____________

13 $99 \div 9 =$ ____________

14 $32 \div 8 =$ ____________

15 $72 \div 9 =$ ____________

16 $56 \div 8 =$ ____________

Solve.

17 **TECHNOLOGY** Julian's average music file uses 9 MB of space. He has 72 MB of free space left on his music player. How many more songs can Julian store? ____________

18 **COLLECTIBLES** Cheng is creating an album to hold the stamps he collects. He wants each page to hold 64 stamps. The pages have enough room for 8 columns of stamps. How many rows does Cheng need on each page? ____________

Write the vocabulary word that completes the sentence.

19 A ____________ of a number is the product of that number and any whole number.

20 Adding, subtracting, multiplying, or dividing in your head without using manipulatives, fingers, or pencil and paper is using ____________.

Chapter 3

NAME ______________________ DATE ______________

Chapter 4

Foldables Study Organizer

Dinah Zike's Foldables

Create the Foldable below to help study the properties of operations.

1 Fold a sheet of paper in half from side to side, leaving a $\frac{1}{2}$-inch tab along the side.

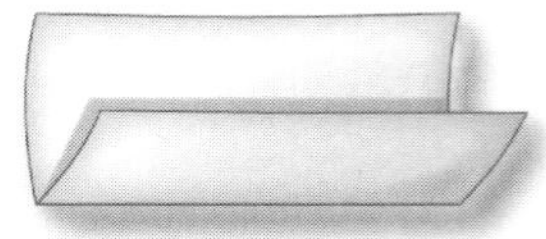

2 Turn the paper and fold it into fourths.

3 Unfold and cut up along the three fold lines.

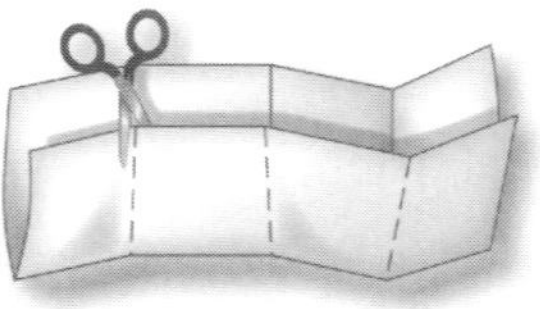

4 Label as shown. As you read the chapter, take notes under each tab. Write the definition and an example under each tab.

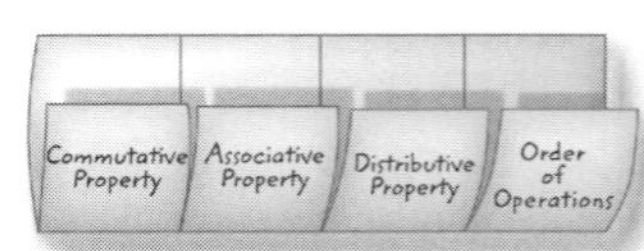

TAKING NOTES
As you read through the chapter, use your Foldable to write several examples for each topic.

 **USING YOUR FOLDABLE**
As you study, check your understanding by writing an additional example for each topic without lifting the tabs. Then, lift the tab to check yourself.

 **USING YOUR FOLDABLE**
Work with a partner. Take turns explaining your examples to one another. Alternate until you have both discussed each topic on your Foldables.

NAME ______________________ DATE ______________

Chapter 4

Games and Puzzles

Who Has My Number?

GET READY

- Cut along the lines on the **Who Has My Number?** game sheet, and glue or tape the numbers and clues to index cards. Make sure that the numeral is on one side of the card and the corresponding clue is on the back of the card.
- Give each student one card. If extra cards are available, some students can have two, or the teacher can play, but all cards must be distributed.

What You Need

- Who Has My Number? game sheet
- 25 index cards
- scissors
- tape or glue

Number of Players

2

DIRECTIONS

- The students begin by reading the number on the front of their card and the clue on the back. Their task is to find the person whose number matches their clue.
- For example, if the clue is **Who has twice my number?** and the number is 5, the student must find the person with the number 10.
- Eventually, the students should form a circle with each student standing next to the person who "matches" them.

VARIATION

- After a round of play, you may want to guide students into creating their own set of cards. First, have each student select two numbers. (No number can be used more than once.) Each student should think of directions that will lead from one of the numbers to the second number. Then all of the students' numbers can be put together to form a new deck.

NAME ______________________ DATE ______________

Chapter 4

Who Has My Number? Game Sheet

Number Cards A

FRONT	BACK
17	Subtract 1 and add 11.
27	Who has my number increased by 3, divided by 10, multiplied by 7, divided by 3, and multiplied by 7?
49	Who has 20 less than twice my number?
78	Who has 3 less than this number, divided by the product of 5 and 5?
3	Who has 3 less than 27 times this number, then halved?
39	Who has twice one third of this number?
26	Take this number, subtract 1, subtract the product of 3 and 3, and divide by 8.
2	Take this number, times 18 and divide what you get by 1.
36	Who has 28 more than 36 less than this number?
28	Divide this number by 4 and add 36.
43	Who has 15 less than 14 more than this number?
42	Divide this number by 42.
1	Who has 1 less than the product of this number and 3 times 6?

Number Cards B

FRONT	BACK
17	Who has my number times 3, minus 10?
41	Add 7 to the quotient of this number divided by 41.
8	Who has this number multiplied by 7?
56	Divide 4 more than this number by the number of minutes in a half hour.
2	Who has this number times itself, times 4?
16	Who has this number divided by 4, increased by 1, and multiplied by 5?
25	Who has 5 more, divided by 5?
6	Who has 3 times my number, increased by 2?
20	Who has my number times itself, divided by 10?
40	Who has twice this value, divided by 16?
5	Who has 3 times this number, times itself?
75	Divide this number by 15 and add 4 to the quotient.
9	Who has 10 less than the product of this number and 3?

Lesson 4-1

NAME ______________________ DATE ______________

Vocabulary and English Language Development

Activate Prior Knowledge

Complete the diagrams below to show the Commutative Property for the equations.

1 (6 squares) + ______ = (3 squares) + ______

2 (12 squares) = ______

Definition Review

The **Commutative Property of Addition** says that the order in which two numbers are added does not change the sum. Example: $5 + 3 = 3 + 5$

The **Commutative Property of Multiplication** says that the order in which two numbers are multiplied does not change the product. Example: $8 \times 4 = 4 \times 8$

Write A next to an example of the Commutative Property of Addition.
Write M next to an example of the Commutative Property of Multiplication.
Write N next to an expression that is neither property.

3 $8 + 4 = 4 + 8$ ______

4 $16 \times 2 = 2 \times 16$ ______

5 $4 \times (5 + 2) = 4 \times 5 + 4 \times 2$ ______

6 $12 + (7 + 2) = 12 + (2 + 7)$ ______

7 $3 \times (9 \times 2) = (9 \times 2) \times 3$ ______

8 $10 + 6 = 2 \times 8$ ______

Application

Complete the graphic organizer.

Commutative Property of Addition		**Commutative Property of Multiplication**	
Examples	Non-Examples	Examples	Non-Examples
$6 + 4 = 4 + 6$	$6 + 7 = 7 + 7$	$4 \times 5 = 5 \times 4$	$6 \times 2 = 5 \times 2$

Chapter 4

NAME ______________________ DATE ______________

Lesson 4-1 Skills Practice

Draw a model to show each equation.

1. $4 + 2 = 2 + 4$. Which property did you show?

____

2. $3 \times 5 = 5 \times 3$. Which property did you show?

____

Use the Commutative Property to fill in each blank. Check your answer.

3. $8 + 7 =$ ______ $+ 8$

   ______ = ______

4. $5 +$ ______ $= 4 + 5$

   ______ = ______

5. ______ $\times 9 = 9 \times 4$

   ______ = ______

6. $9 + 22 = 22 +$ ______

   ______ = ______

7. $3 \times 5 = 5 \times$ ______

   ______ = ______

8. $15 +$ ______ $= 45 + 15$

   ______ = ______

9. ______ $\times 7 = 7 \times 11$

   ______ = ______

10. $2 \times 8 =$ ______ $\times 2$

   ______ = ______

Lesson 4-1

NAME ________________ DATE ________________

Problem-Solving Practice

Solve.

1 **SAVINGS** Mandy saved $15 in January and $22 in February. Dasan saved $22 in January. How much money does Dasan need to save in February to have the same amount of money as Mandy?

2 **NUTRITION** Darla ate a whole-wheat bagel and $\frac{1}{2}$ cup of broccoli with lunch. Simon ate $\frac{1}{2}$ cup of raspberries and a whole-wheat pita with lunch. The chart below shows the amount of fiber in each food item. Who ate more grams of fiber?

Fiber Grams in Different Foods	
Food	**Fiber (grams)**
Whole-wheat pita	4
Whole-wheat bagel	4
Broccoli ($\frac{1}{2}$ cup)	3
Raspberries ($\frac{1}{2}$ cup)	3

3 **FITNESS** Nari walked 5 miles each day for 3 days. If Lawrence walks 3 miles each day, how many days will it take for Lawrence to walk the same number of miles as Nari?

4 **INTERIOR DESIGN** Sleepy Time Hotel and Overnight Stay Inn are putting new curtains in each room. Each room has 1 window. Sleepy Time Hotel has 10 floors and each floor has 12 rooms. Overnight Stay Hotel has 12 floors and each floor has 10 rooms. Which hotel put up the greater number of curtains?

5 **FLOORING** Mr. Garcia and Mrs. Lansing laid tiles on their porches in the patterns shown below. Who used the greater number of tiles?

Mr. Garcia's Porch

Mrs. Lansing's Porch

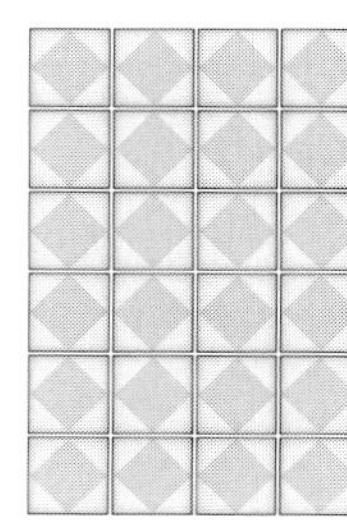

Chapter 4

NAME ______________________ DATE ______________

Lesson 4-1

Homework Practice

Draw a model to show each equation.

1. $2 \times 4 = 4 \times 2$. Which property did you show?

____

2. $5 + 8 = 8 + 5$. Which property did you show?

____

Use the Commutative Property to fill in each blank. Check your answer.

3. ______ $\times 4 = 4 \times 8$

   ______ = ______

4. $15 +$ ______ $= 75 + 15$

   ______ = ______

5. $3 + 41 = 41 +$ ______

   ______ = ______

6. $12 \times 2 = 2 \times$ ______

   ______ = ______

Solve.

7. **GARDENS** Silvia's garden has 5 rows of tomato plants with 6 plants in each row. Veronica's garden has 6 rows of tomato plants with 5 plants in each row. Whose garden has the greater number of tomato plants?

____

8. **MOVIES** Miguel watched a movie that ran 120 minutes. Then he watched a movie that ran 70 minutes. Lily watched a movie that ran 70 minutes. Then she watched a movie that ran 120 minutes. Who spent more time watching movies?

____

Lesson 4-2

NAME ________________ DATE ________________

Vocabulary and English Language Development

Activate Prior Knowledge

Solve.

1 Jorge opened a savings account. The table shows how much money he saved each month. Find the balances in February and March.

Jorge's Savings Account		
Date	**Amount Deposited**	**Balance**
January	$25	**$25**
February	$20	$______
March	$12	$______

Definition Review

The **Associative Property of Addition** says that the grouping of the **addends** does not change the sum. Example: $3 + (4 + 5) = (3 + 4) + 5$

The **Associative Property of Multiplication** says that the grouping of the **factors** does not change the product. Example: $6 \times (4 \times 2) = (6 \times 4) \times 2$

Name the property shown in each equation.

2 (4 rows of 5 apples) = (5 rows of 4 apples)

____

3 ( + ) + 1 stamp =  + (8 stamps + )

____

Application

Complete the graphic organizer.

Associative Property of Addition		Associative Property of Multiplication	
Examples	Non-Examples	Examples	Non-Examples
$4 + (6 + 2) = (4 + 6) + 2$	$(5 + 3) + 4 = 8 + 4$	$7 \times (4 \times 2) = (7 \times 4) \times 2$	$(8 \times 3) + 1 = 24 + 1$

Chapter 4

NAME ______________________ DATE ____________

Lesson 4-2

Skills Practice

Draw a model to show $(2 + 4) + 4 = 2 + (4 + 4)$.
Which property did you show?

1

____

Draw two different arrays to show the equation $(3 \times 5) \times 2 = 3 \times (5 \times 2)$.
Which property did you show?

2

____

Use the Associative Property to fill in the blank.

3 $4 + 5 + 8$

$= (\_\_\_\_ + \_\_\_\_) + \_\_\_\_$

$= \_\_\_\_ + \_\_\_\_$

$= \_\_\_\_$

4 $7 \times 2 \times 3$

$= (\_\_\_\_ \times \_\_\_\_) \times \_\_\_\_$

$= \_\_\_\_ \times \_\_\_\_$

$= \_\_\_\_$

5 $8 + 1 + 12$

$= (\_\_\_\_ + \_\_\_\_) + \_\_\_\_$

$= \_\_\_\_ + \_\_\_\_$

$= \_\_\_\_$

6 $6 \times 2 \times 5$

$= (\_\_\_\_ \times \_\_\_\_) \times \_\_\_\_$

$= \_\_\_\_ \times \_\_\_\_$

$= \_\_\_\_$

NAME ______________________ DATE ______________

Problem-Solving Practice

Solve.

1 **LANDSCAPING** Mr. Batista planted 15 tulip bulbs, 25 daffodil bulbs, and 12 iris bulbs. How many bulbs did he plant in all? ______________

2 **PENS** Rachel bought the packages of pens shown below. How many pens did Rachel buy in all? ______________

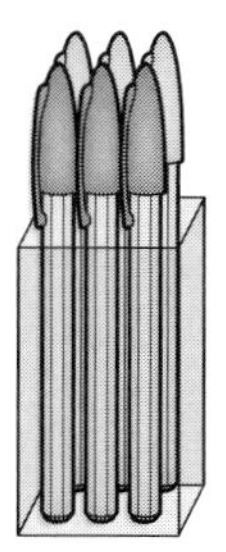
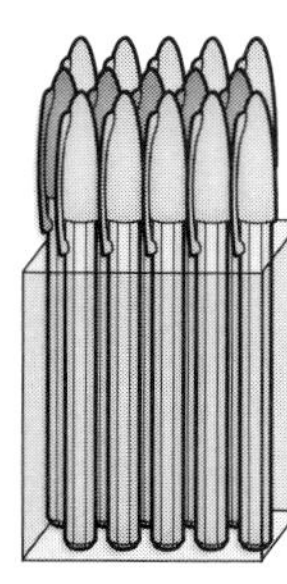
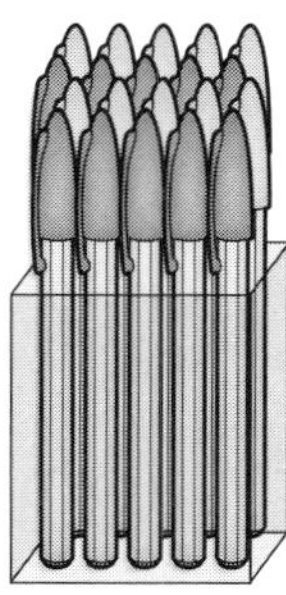
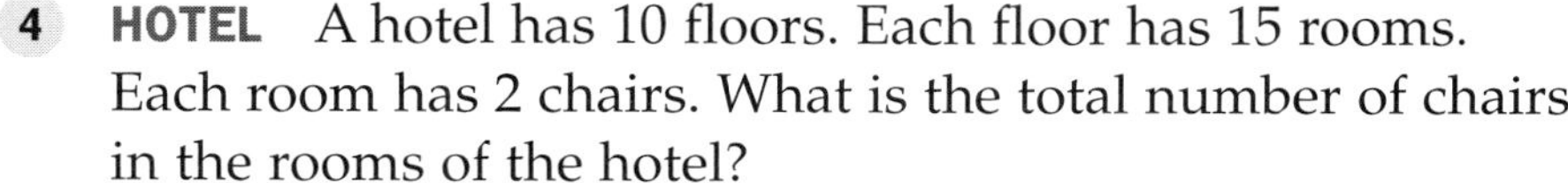

3 **PIANO** Delilah practiced the piano for 1 hour on Monday, 45 minutes on Tuesday and 1 hour 15 minutes on Wednesday. How many hours did Delilah practice in all? ______________

4 **HOTEL** A hotel has 10 floors. Each floor has 15 rooms. Each room has 2 chairs. What is the total number of chairs in the rooms of the hotel? ______________

5 **OLYMPICS** During the 2004 Summer Olympic Games, the United States won 36 gold medals, 39 silver medals, and 27 bronze medals. How many medals did the United States win in all? ______________

6 **PHOTOS** Lionel filled an album with photographs. Each page has 2 rows of photographs and 4 photographs in each row. The album has 15 pages. How many photographs are in the album? ______________

NAME ______________________ DATE ______________

Lesson 4-2 Homework Practice

Draw a model to show $(3 + 2) + 6 = 3 + (2 + 6)$. Which property did you show?

1 ______________________________

Draw two different arrays to show $(6 \times 2) \times 4 = 6 \times (2 \times 4)$. Which property did you show?

2 ______________________________

Use the Associative Property to fill in each blank.

3 $7 + 5 + 2$

= (_____ + _____) + _____

= _____ + _____

= _____

4 $9 \times 2 \times 1$

= (_____ × _____) × _____

= _____ × _____

= _____

5 $3 \times 2 \times 10$

= (_____ × _____) × _____

= _____ × _____

= _____

6 $14 + 12 + 3$

= (_____ + _____) + _____

= _____ + _____

= _____

Solve.

7 **BOOKS** Josefina read 10 books during her summer vacation. Then she read 3 books in September and 5 books in October. How many books did Josefina read in all? ______________

NAME ______________________ DATE ______________

Lesson 4-3

Vocabulary and English Language Development

Activate Prior Knowledge

Complete the diagram below to model how the Distributive Property can be used to simplify 5 × (10 + 3).

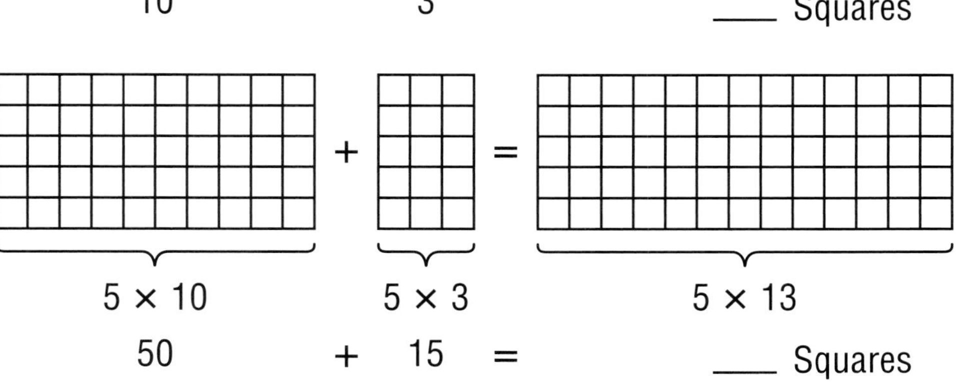

Definition Review

The **Distributive Property of Multiplication** says that to **multiply** a **sum** by a number, you can **multiply** each addend by the number and add the products.

1 Shown below is an example of the Distributive Property.

$$16 \times (6 + 2) = 128$$

$$16 \times 6 + 16 \times 2 = 128$$

2 Fill in the blanks to show the Distributive Property.

$$8 \times (9 + 6) = 120$$

______ × ______ + 8 × ______ = ______

Application

- Gather 30 counters, 10 in one color and 20 in another color.
- Using the Distributive Property, arrange the counters on your desk to demonstrate the following expressions. You can use different colors to represent each addend.

• 2 × (7 + 1)	• 4 × (4 + 2)
• 3 × (2 + 4)	• 3 × (6 + 3)
• 5 × (2 + 4)	• 6 × (1 + 2)

Chapter 4

NAME ______________________ DATE ______________

Lesson 4-3

Skills Practice

Use the Distributive Property and a model to find each product.

1 $13 \times 4 =$ ______

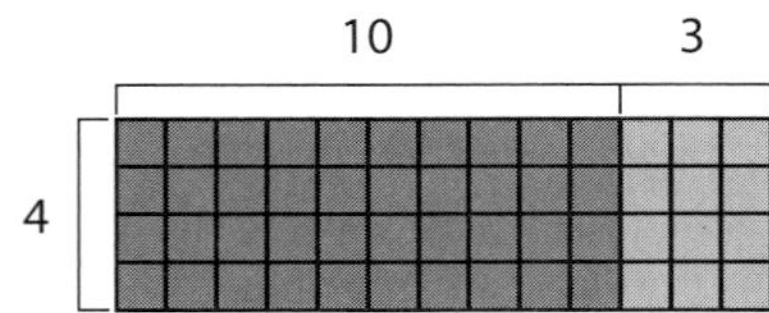

2 $16 \times 5 =$ ______

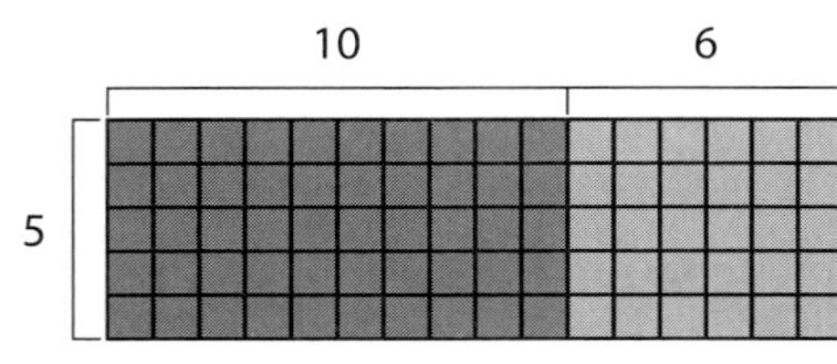

Use the Distributive Property to find each product.

3 $3(4 + 8)$

$=$ ______ $+$ ______

$=$ ______

4 $4(5 + 7)$

$=$ ______ $+$ ______

$=$ ______

5 $10(12 + 2)$

$=$ ______ $+$ ______

$=$ ______

6 $9(3 - 1)$

$=$ ______ $-$ ______

$=$ ______

7 $9(11 - 5)$

$=$ ______ $-$ ______

$=$ ______

8 $2(15 + 4)$

$=$ ______ $+$ ______

$=$ ______

9 $8(3 + 11)$

$=$ ______ $+$ ______

$=$ ______

10 $7(14 - 9)$

$=$ ______ $-$ ______

$=$ ______

NAME ______________________ DATE ______________

Lesson 4-3

Problem-Solving Practice

Solve.

1 **GARDEN** A farmer plants tomato plants using the plan shown below. How many tomato plants does she plant in all? ______________

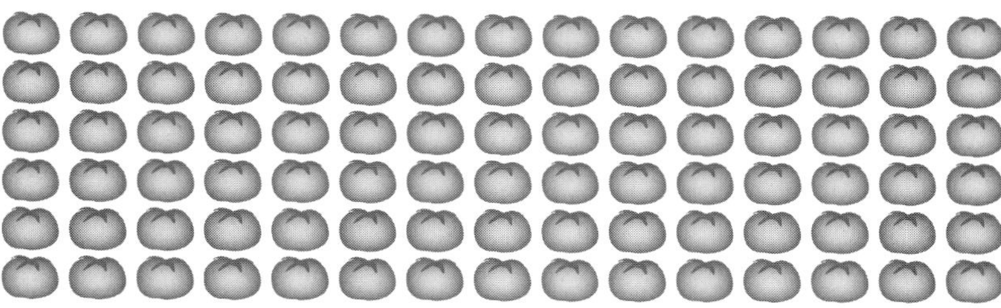

2 **FOOTBALL** A football team scored 4 touchdowns (each worth 6 points) and 4 extra points (each worth 1 point). How many total points did the football team score? ______________

3 **KNITTING** Lavelle knitted 12 scarves and 12 hats. Each scarf used 300 yards of yarn. Each hat used 150 yards of yarn. How many yards of yarn did Lavelle use in all? ______________

4 **FITNESS** Alano jogged 16 miles each week for 3 weeks, then he jogged 20 miles each week for 3 weeks. How many miles did Alano jog in all? ______________

5 **BASKETBALL** Willa made four 2-point baskets in the basketball game. Jenna made five 2-point baskets in the game. How many points did Willa and Jenna score in all? ______________

6 **SAVINGS** Larisa saved $10 each month for 3 months. Then she saved $15 each month for 3 months. She wants to buy a digital camera that costs $100. How much more money does Larisa need to save? ______________

7 **FLOORING** Mrs. Bateman is putting tiles on her kitchen floor in the design shown below. How many tiles does she need to buy? ______________

NAME ______________________ DATE ______________

Lesson 4-3

Homework Practice

Use the Distributive Property and a model to find each product.

1. $14 \times 2 =$ ______

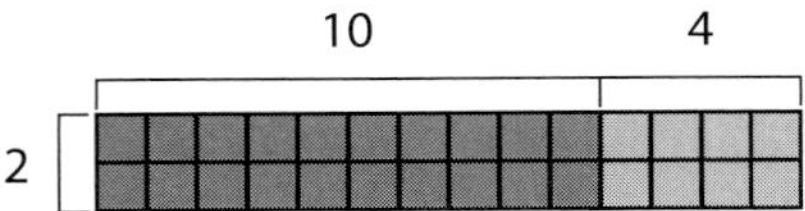

2. $17 \times 6 =$ ______

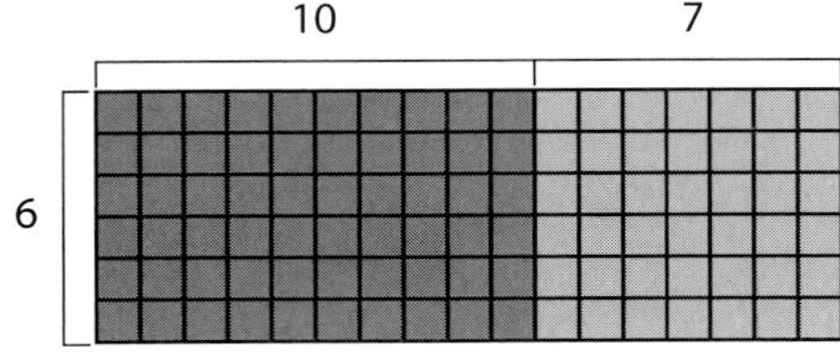

Use the Distributive Property to find each product.

3. $4(3 + 9)$

$=$ ______ $+$ ______

$=$ ______

4. $7(15 - 4)$

$=$ ______ $-$ ______

$=$ ______

5. $9(3 + 7)$

$=$ ______ $+$ ______

$=$ ______

6. $8(7 - 4)$

$=$ ______ $-$ ______

$=$ ______

Solve.

7. **EARNINGS** April earned \$20 each week for 8 weeks. She spent \$5 each week for 8 weeks. How much money does April have left? ______________

8. **CEREAL** Ramiro ate 7 servings of cereal this week. Alex ate 5 servings of cereal this week. A serving of cereal is 30 grams. How many total grams of cereal did Ramiro and Alex eat this week? ______________

NAME ______________________________ DATE ______________

Vocabulary and English Language Development

Activate Prior Knowledge

Simplify.

1. $9 \div 1 + 2$ ________
2. $9 \div 3$ ________
3. $24 \div 6 - 2$ ________
4. $24 \div 4$ ________

Definition Review

The **order of operations** are the rules that tell what order to use when evaluating expressions.

Simplify $6 \overset{②}{\times} 4 \overset{④}{-} 12 \overset{③}{\div} (8 \overset{①}{-} 2)$ by following the order shown above each operation.

Find the value in parentheses: $6 \times 4 - 12 \div (8 - 2) = 6 \times 4 - 12 \div$ ______

Multiply and divide left to right: $=$ ______ $- 12 \div 6$

Multiply and divide left to right: $= 24 -$ ______

Add and subtract left to right: $= 24 - 2 =$ ______

$$6 \times 4 - 12 \div (8 - 2) = 22$$

Application

- Work with a partner. Have each person get 8 index cards.
- On 4 cards write problems that include add, subtract, multiply, and divide.
- Add one set of parentheses to each problem.
- On the remaining 4 cards, write the answers to the problems you created.
- Place your cards and your partner's cards face down on a table and mix them up.
- Have one person start by flipping over two cards. If the cards are a problem and answer that match, that player gets to keep the cards.
- If the cards are not a match, flip them back over.
- The other person takes a turn.
- Continue the exercise until each card has been collected. The player with the most pairs wins.

NAME _______________ DATE _______________

Lesson 4-4

Skills Practice

Name the step that should be performed first.

1 $8 \times 6 \div (4 + 2) - 4$

____

2 $3 \times 6 + 9 \div 3$

____

3 $1 \div 5 - 3 + 2 \times 6$

____

4 $9 - 2 + (12 \times 6) + 9$

____

5 $8 + 12 \div 12 - 2 \times 6$

____

6 $10 \div 2 \times 5 - 1 + 4$

____

Find the value of each expression.

7 $4 \times (2 + 6) - 30$

parentheses: $4 \times$ _______ $- 30$

multiply/divide: _______ $- 30$

add/subtract: _______

8 $9 + 7 \times 2 + (1 \times 8)$

parentheses: $9 + 7 \times 2 +$ _______

multiply/divide: $9 +$ _______ $+$ _______

add/subtract: _______ $+$ _______

____

9 $7 - 4 \div 2$

____

10 $12 \div 4 \times 4 - (3 + 2)$

____

11 $14 \times 2 \div (8 - 4) + 9$

____

12 $10 - (2 + 4) + 2 \times 5$

____

13 $6 + 2 \times 5 + (5 \times 3)$

____

14 $(4 \times 3) - (7 - 3) + (10 \div 2)$

____

Lesson 4-4

NAME ______________________ DATE ______________

Problem-Solving Practice

Solve.

1. **KITTENS** Carla has 2 cats. Each cat had 5 kittens. She found homes for 7 kittens. How many cats and kittens does Carla have now? ______________

2. **BAKERY** A baker made 15 loaves of white bread, 12 loaves of wheat bread, and 10 loaves of rye bread. A customer bought 2 loaves of each of the 3 kinds of breads. How many loaves of bread are left? ______________

3. **EARNINGS** On Monday, Colin worked 3 hours, earned $10 per hour, and spent $5 for lunch. On Tuesday, Colin worked 7 hours, earned $8 per hour, and spent $6 for lunch. How much money does Colin have now? ______________

4. **COOKIES** Shamika baked 60 oatmeal cookies for a bake sale. She divided the cookies equally among 12 bags. At the bake sale she sold 7 bags of cookies. How many cookies does Shamika have left? ______________

5. **COMPUTERS** Emilio received a $15 discount when he bought an ink-jet printer. He also bought 2 black printer cartridges, 1 color printer cartridge, and 5 packages of paper. His receipt is shown below. How much did Emilio spend in all? ______________

Computer World

Ink-jet printer	1 @ $125.00
– Discount	–$15.00
Black printer cartridges	2 @ $35.00
Color printer cartridges	1 @ $35.00
Paper	5 @ $5.00

6. **AMUSEMENT PARK** Lalana paid $12 for admission to an amusement park. She rode the roller coaster 3 times and the Ferris wheel 2 times. Each ride cost $2. She also bought a hamburger and 2 lemonade drinks during the day. How much money did Lalana spend in all? ______________

Lunch Menu

Hot Dog	$2.00
Hamburger	$3.00
French Fries	$1.00
Lemonade	$1.50
Water	$1.00

NAME ______________________ DATE ______________

Lesson 4-4 Homework Practice

Name the step that should be performed first in each expression.

1. $7 + 9 - 2 + 4 \times 4$

   ____

2. $3 \times 18 + (9 - 2) \div 3$

   ____

3. $(9 + 4 \times 2) - 12 \div 3$

   ____

4. $20 \div 4 \times 2 - 9 \times 2 + 5$

   ____

Find the value of each expression.

5. $13 + (9 - 1) \times 2$

   ______

6. $15 \div (4 + 1) + 5 \times 2$

   ______

7. $11 + 3 \times 2 + 8 - 8 \div 2$

   ______

8. $(3 + 8 \times 2) - (18 - 9) + 1$

   ______

Solve.

9. **SNACKS** Marla bought 4 boxes of granola bars. Each box contains 6 granola bars. Marla ate 3 granola bars, and she gave her brother 4 granola bars. Marla then bought 2 more boxes of granola bars. How many granola bars does Marla have now?

   ____

10. **BOOKS** Daniel has 65 books on a book shelf. He divides the books equally among 5 shelves. He then moves 5 books on the top shelf to the bottom shelf. He also buys 3 new books and puts them on the top shelf. How many books are on the top shelf?

   ____

NAME ______________________ DATE ____________

Foldables Study Organizer

Dinah Zike's Foldables

Create this Foldable to help organize information about fractions.

1 Stack six sheets of paper, one on top of the other. On the top sheet of paper, trace a large circle.

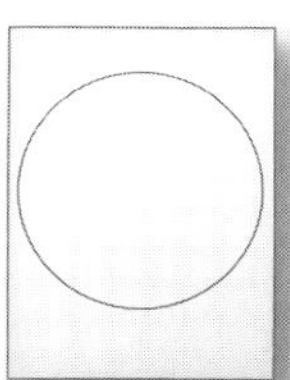

2 With the papers still stacked, cut out all six circles at the same time.

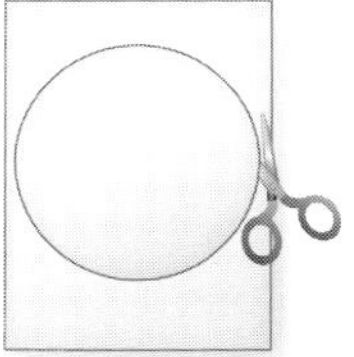

3 Staple the paper circles together at one point around the edge.

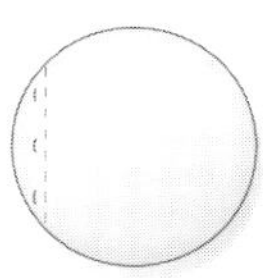

4 Label the top circle: Fractions. On this sheet of paper, define *fraction* and explain the parts of a fraction.

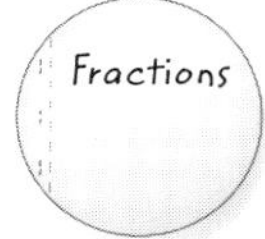

5 Write down the important concepts and vocabulary terms in each lesson in the remaining pages of your circular Foldable.

TAKING NOTES

As you read through the chapter, use your Foldable to explain and write an example of each of the following:

- Numerator and Denominator
- Equivalent fractions
- Mixed Number
- Improper Fraction
- Least Common Denominator
- Greatest Common Factors

USING YOUR FOLDABLE

As you study, check your understanding by writing additional examples of each type of fraction.

USING YOUR FOLDABLE

Work with a partner. One student should name a type of fraction. The other student should write an example of that type of fraction.

Chapter 5

NAME ____________________ DATE ____________

Games and Puzzles

That's Not Proper

What You Need

- Spinners
- Arrows
- Brads

Number of Players

3

DIRECTIONS

- Cut out That's Not Proper spinners and arrows.
- Use a brad to attach each arrow to a spinner.
- One person spins both spinners and names an improper fraction using the numbers from the spinners. For 13 and 4, the fraction would be $\frac{13}{4}$.
- The remaining players express the fraction as a mixed number.
- The first player to give the correct mixed number wins the round.

NAME ______________________ DATE ____________

That's Not Proper Spinners

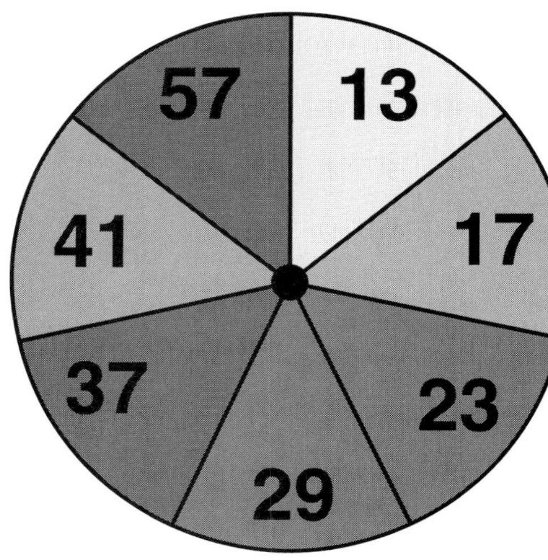

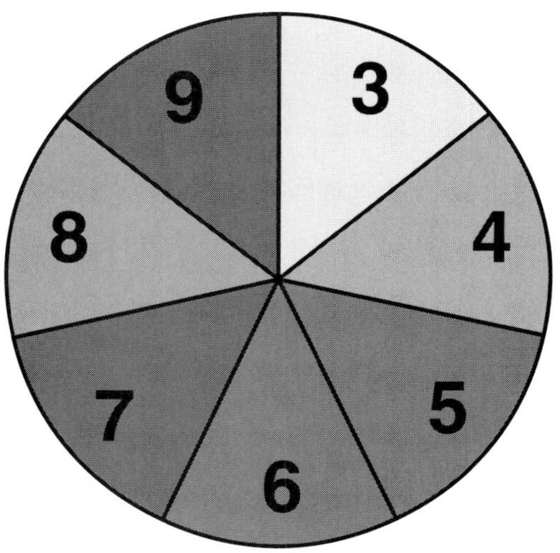

Lesson 5-1

NAME ______________________ DATE ______________

Vocabulary and English Language Development

Activate Prior Knowledge

Complete each sentence with the word *part or whole*.

1 Marty and his brother made a pizza and cut it into 6 slices. They ate all 6 slices of the pizza. Marty and his brother ate the ________________ pizza.

2 Nelia and her friends also made a pizza and cut it into 6 slices. They only ate 4 slices, so they only ate ________________ of the pizza.

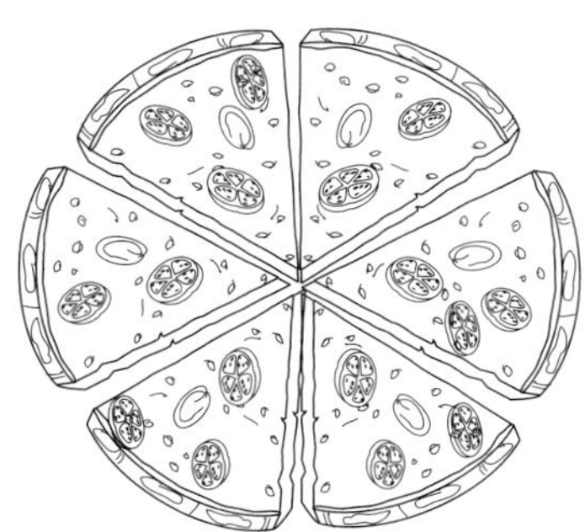

Definition Review

Fractions represent parts of a whole or part of a set. The number $\frac{5}{6}$ is an example of a fraction.

The **denominator** is the number below the bar in a fraction; it tells how many equal parts are in the whole or the set. The denominator of $\frac{5}{6}$ is 6.

The **numerator** is the number above the bar in a fraction; it tells how many of the equal parts are being used. The numerator of $\frac{5}{6}$ is 5.

Suppose 15 out of 25, or $\frac{15}{25}$ students in your class are girls.

Fill in the blanks with *denominator, fraction or numerator*.

3 15 is the ________________.

4 25 is the ________________.

5 $\frac{15}{25}$ is an example of a ________________.

Application

Follow the directions to play the game.

- Work in groups of 4. Number yourselves 1 – 4.
- Place 10 red chips and 10 blue chips in a bag.
- Student #1 pulls a handful of chips out of the bag.
- Student #2 writes a fraction to describe the number of red chips pulled.
- Student #3 identifies the numerator and the denominator of the fraction.
- Student #4 writes a fraction to describe the number of blue chips pulled.
- Continue the game until you each have a turn pulling handfuls of chips and identifying the fraction, numerator, and denominator.

Lesson **5-1**

NAME ______________________ DATE ______________

Skills Practice

Write a fraction to represent each situation.

1 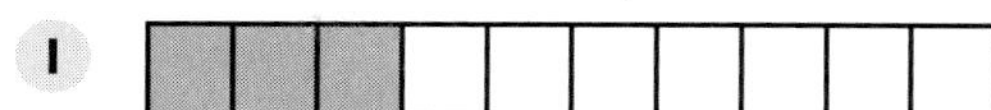

the shaded region ______________

2 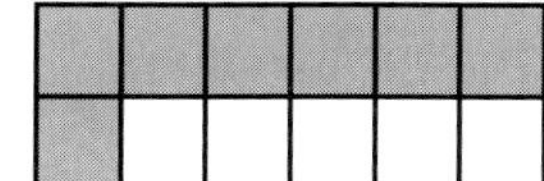

the shaded region ______________

3 

the shaded region ______________

4 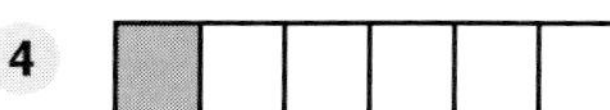

the shaded region ______________

5      

the number of hearts in the set

____

the number of happy faces in the set

____

6 M M M M M S S S

the number of Ms in the set

____

7  

the number of ball caps in the set

____

8 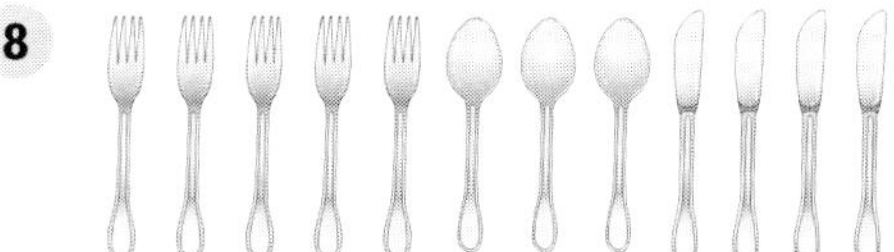

the number of spoons in the set

____

Draw a picture to model the fraction. Use a set of objects.

9 $\frac{5}{9}$

10 $\frac{2}{3}$

Draw a picture to model each fraction. Use equal parts of a whole.

11 $\frac{4}{7}$

12 $\frac{3}{12}$

Chapter 5

NAME ______________________ DATE ______________

Lesson 5-1

Problem-Solving Practice

Solve.

1 **FRUIT** Leon brought a bag of fruit to his after-school meeting. There were 4 apples, 3 bananas, and 6 pears in the bag. What fraction of the fruit were bananas? ______

2 **SHIRTS** Carla bought 5 new sweatshirts. Three sweatshirts were red, 1 sweatshirt was blue, and 1 sweatshirt was green. What fraction of the sweatshirts was blue? ______

What fraction of the sweatshirts were red? ______

3 **BALLOONS** Angie bought the following balloons for the party:

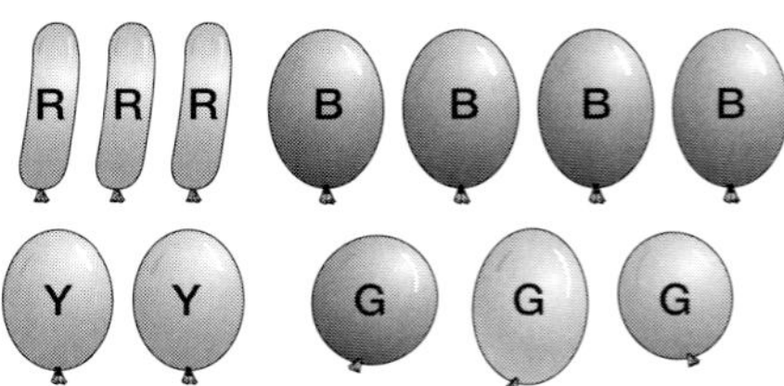

What fraction of the balloons is labeled B? ______

What fraction of the balloons is labeled R? ______

What fraction of the balloons is not labeled G? ______

4 **SCHOOL** Savannah brought in 20 cupcakes to share at snack time. She gave 12 cupcakes to the students and 3 cupcakes to the teachers. What fraction of the cupcakes did Savannah give out? ______

5 **PUZZLES** I am a fraction that has a denominator of 7 and a numerator of 3. What fraction am I? ______

NAME ______________________________ DATE ______________

Lesson 5-1 Homework Practice

Write a fraction for the shaded region.

1 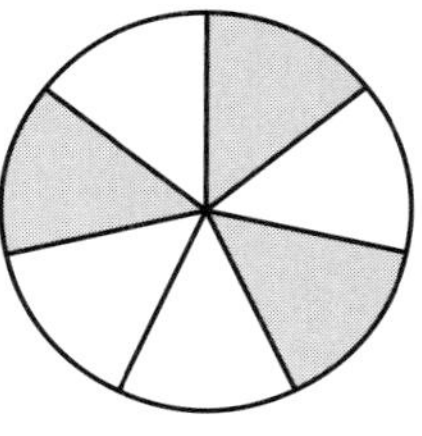

____

2 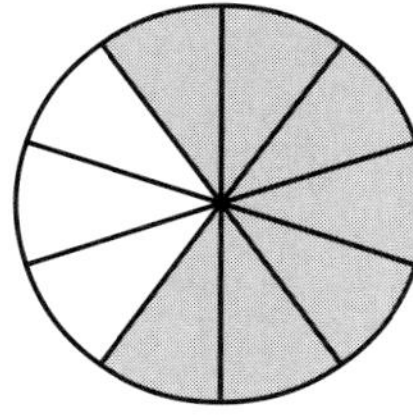

____

3 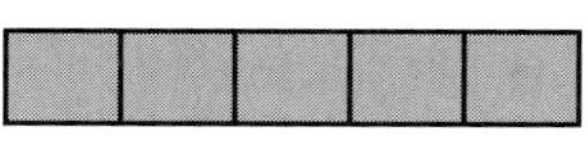

____

4 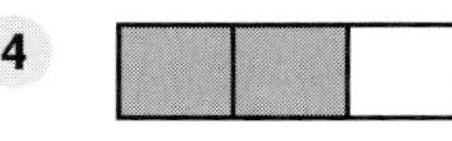

____

Draw a picture to model each fraction. Use equal parts of a whole or set.

5 $\frac{4}{7}$

6 $\frac{1}{8}$

Solve.

7 **PETS** A dog had 7 puppies. If 3 of the puppies are female, what fraction of them are male?

____

8 **ENGLISH** What fraction of the letters in the word Mississippi are vowels? ______________

9 **SCHOOL** This shows Sharika's score on her math exam. What fraction of the questions did she answer incorrectly?

____

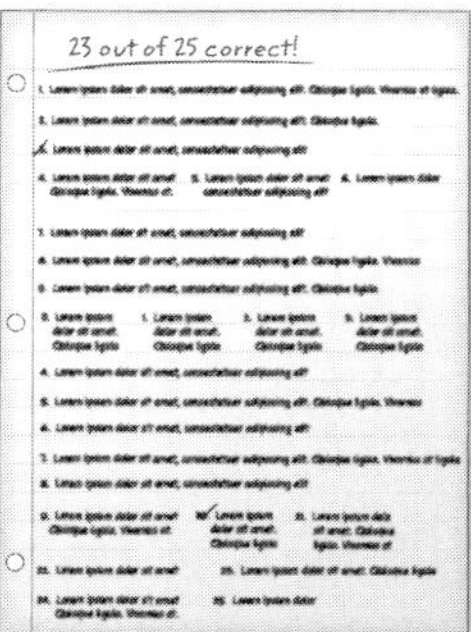

Write the vocabulary word that completes the sentence.

10 Six-sevenths $\left(\frac{6}{7}\right)$ is an example of a ______________. The ______________ is 6 and the ______________ is 7.

11 The entire amount or object is called the ______________.

Lesson 5-2

NAME ______________________ DATE ______________

Vocabulary and English Language Development

Activate Prior Knowledge

Solve.

Sara, Carmen, and Josh each ate a whole quesadilla, which they each cut differently. Their quesadillas are shown below. Which fraction expresses the amount eaten by each person?

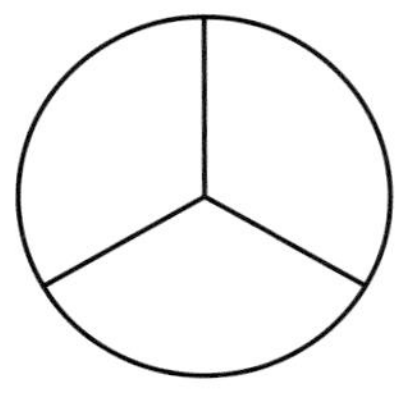

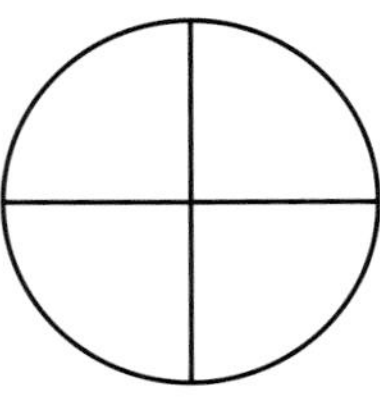

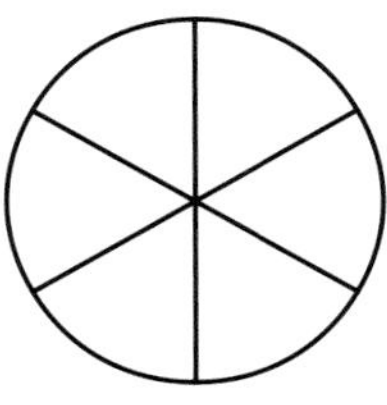

1 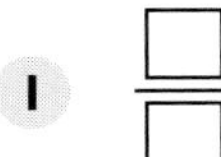

2 $\frac{\square}{\square}$

3 $\frac{\square}{\square}$

Definition Review

Equivalent fractions are fractions that represent the same number. Example: $\frac{1}{2} = \frac{2}{4}$

An **equivalent form of one** is a different expression that represents the number one. Example: $\frac{3}{3} = 1$

Fill in the blank with *equivalent fractions* or *equivalent forms of one*.

4 $\frac{3}{8}$ and $\frac{6}{16}$ are ______________________.

5 $\frac{7}{7}$ and $\frac{8}{8}$ are ______________________.

Application

- **Use fraction strips to model each fraction.**
- **Tell whether each pair of fractions is equivalent or not.**

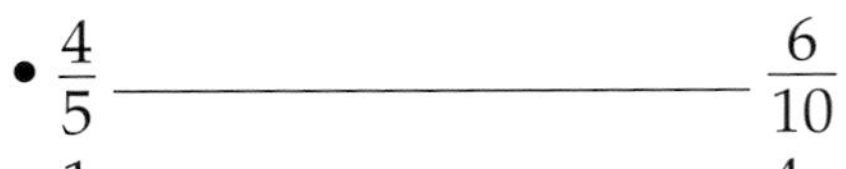

- $\frac{4}{5}$ ______________________ $\frac{6}{10}$
- $\frac{1}{2}$ ______________________ $\frac{4}{8}$
- $\frac{3}{8}$ ______________________ $\frac{4}{9}$
- $\frac{6}{10}$ ______________________ $\frac{3}{5}$
- $\frac{4}{6}$ ______________________ $\frac{2}{3}$

NAME ______________________________ DATE ______________

Skills Practice

Complete the models to name an equivalent fraction.

1. $\frac{3}{4}$ ______________

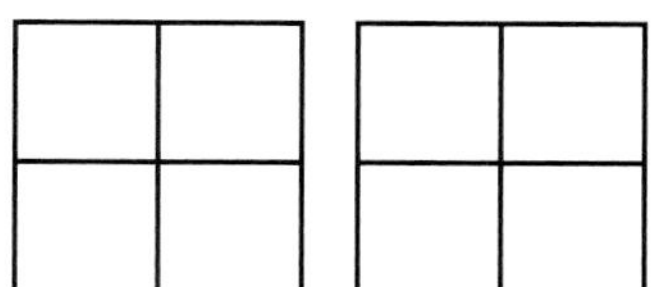

2. $\frac{4}{5}$ ______________

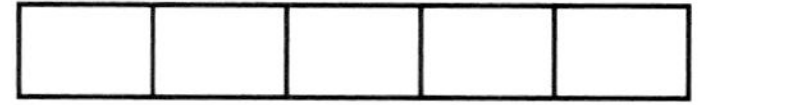

Complete to name an equivalent form of one.

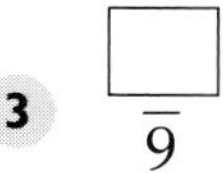

3. $\frac{\square}{9}$

4. $\frac{24}{\square}$

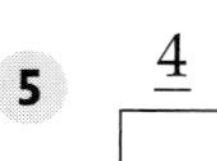

5. $\frac{4}{\square}$

6. $\frac{\square}{3}$

Complete to name an equivalent fraction.

7. $\frac{3}{8} = \frac{6}{\square}$

8. $\frac{2}{9} = \frac{\square}{18}$

9. $\frac{1}{7} = \frac{3}{\square}$

10. $\frac{4}{10} = \frac{16}{\square}$

11. $\frac{20}{25} = \frac{\square}{5}$

12. $\frac{5}{11} = \frac{\square}{66}$

13. $\frac{5}{12} = \frac{10}{\square}$

14. $\frac{7}{9} = \frac{28}{\square}$

NAME ______________________________ DATE ______________

Lesson 5-2

Problem-Solving Practice

Solve.

1 **KNITTING** Rachel and Lionel each knit a scarf 60 inches long. The scarves are shown below. What fraction of Rachel's scarf is white? ____________

What fraction of Lionel's scarf is white? Do Rachel and Lionel have equal amounts of white in their scarves? Explain. ____________

____

Rachel's Scarf

Lionel's Scarf

2 **LUNCH** John cut his 12-inch submarine sandwich into 12 equal pieces. He ate 2 pieces. Juanita cut her 12-inch submarine sandwich into 6 equal pieces. She ate the same amount as John. How many pieces of her sandwich did Juanita eat? ____________

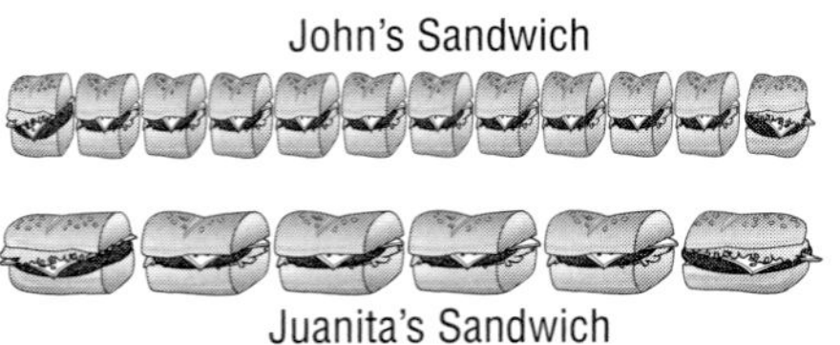

3 **DESSERT** Sylvia made a blueberry pie and cut it into 6 pieces. Thelma made a blueberry pie that is the same size and cut it into 12 pieces. How many pieces of Thelma's pie equal 2 pieces of Sylvia's pie? ____________

4 **BASEBALL** Anton and Julian both pitched in Friday's little league game. Anton threw 20 pitches; 8 were strikes. Julian threw 40 pitches; 16 were strikes. Who threw the greater fraction of strikes in Friday's game?

____

____

Lesson 5-2

NAME ______________________ DATE ______________

Homework Practice

Complete to name equivalent forms of one.

1. $\frac{6}{\square}$

2. $\frac{15}{\square}$

Complete to name an equivalent fraction.

3. $\frac{10}{17} = \frac{20}{\square}$

4. $\frac{4}{16} = \frac{\square}{4}$

Name two equivalent fractions for each fraction.

5. $\frac{1}{9}$ ______________________

6. $\frac{6}{10}$ ______________________

7. $\frac{5}{7}$ ______________________

8. $\frac{2}{3}$ ______________________

9. $\frac{8}{20}$ ______________________

10. $\frac{15}{25}$ ______________________

11. $\frac{7}{11}$ ______________________

12. $\frac{9}{36}$ ______________________

Solve.

13. **CRAFTS** Keisha had two pieces of ribbon of equal length. She cut the first piece of ribbon into 15 equal parts. She also cut the second piece of ribbon into equal parts. Nine parts of the first piece are equal in length to 3 parts of the second piece. Into how many parts did she cut the second piece of ribbon? ______________

14. **GARDENING** Lisa and Calvin have herb gardens of equal size. Oregano takes up $\frac{2}{9}$ of Lisa's garden and $\frac{4}{18}$ of Calvin's garden. Do Lisa and Calvin use equal amounts of their gardens for oregano? Explain your answer.

____

Chapter 5

NAME ______________________________ DATE ______________

Lesson 5-3

Vocabulary and English Language Development

Activate Prior Knowledge

Solve.

Mr. Sanchez made two cheesecakes for his family. Each cheesecake has 12 slices. He served a total of 14 slices. Use the diagram below to model the number of slices he served. Then write an improper fraction and a mixed number to represent the total number of slices Mr. Sanchez served.

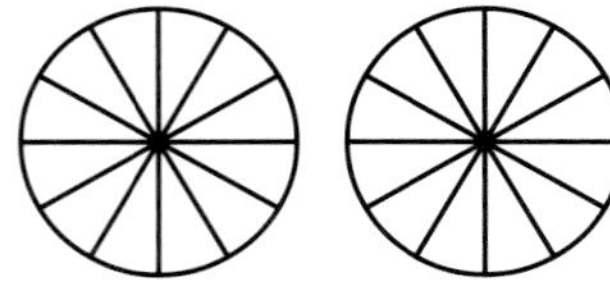

1 improper fraction ______________

2 mixed number ______________

Definition Review

An **improper fraction** has a numerator that is greater than or equal to the denominator. Example: $\frac{8}{5}$

A **mixed number** has a whole number part and a fraction part. Example: $2\frac{4}{5}$

Label each number as an *improper fraction* or a *mixed number*.

3 $1\frac{7}{8}$ ______________

4 $\frac{12}{10}$ ______________

5 $\frac{7}{7}$ ______________

6 $8\frac{8}{9}$ ______________

Application

- Roll two number cubes and write down the sum of the numbers.
- Roll two number cubes again and write down the sum of the numbers.
- Write an improper fraction using the two numbers you rolled.
- Write the improper fraction as a mixed number.
- If the numbers are equal, roll again to find a new number.

Fraction : $\frac{9}{7}$

NAME _______________ DATE _______________

Lesson 5-3

Skills Practice

1 Change $2\frac{1}{3}$ to an improper fraction using drawings. $2\frac{1}{3}$ = _______________

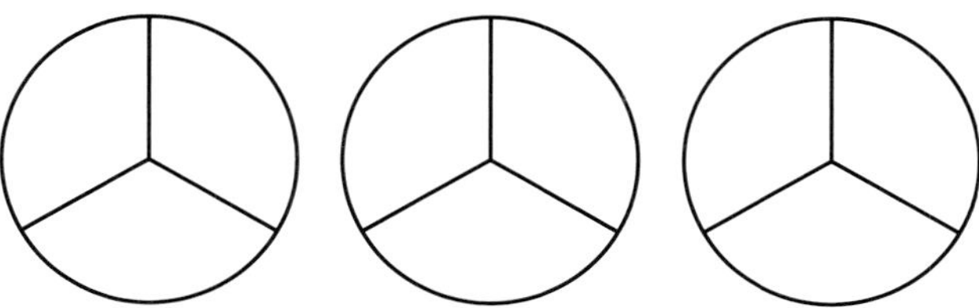

2 Change $\frac{5}{2}$ to a mixed number using drawings. $\frac{5}{2}$ = _______________

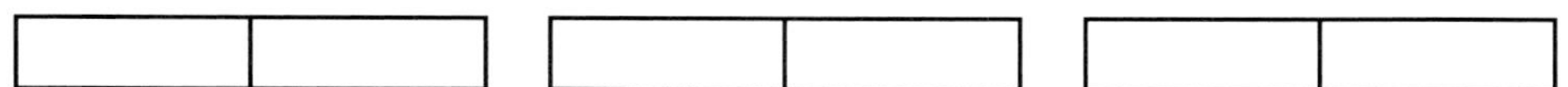

Chapter 5

Write each mixed number as an improper fraction.

3 $3\frac{2}{5} = \frac{\square \quad \square \quad \square}{\square} = \frac{\square}{\square}$

4 $6\frac{2}{15} = \frac{\square \quad \square \quad \square}{\square} = \frac{\square}{\square}$

5 $9\frac{1}{2}$ = _______________

6 $4\frac{3}{7}$ = _______________

7 $1\frac{3}{8}$ = _______________

8 $5\frac{3}{10}$ = _______________

Write each improper fraction as a mixed number.

9 $\frac{9}{5}$ = _______________

10 $\frac{17}{3}$ = _______________

11 $\frac{19}{4}$ = _______________

12 $\frac{35}{6}$ = _______________

NAME ______________________ DATE ______________

Lesson 5-3

Problem-Solving Practice

Solve.

1. **DESSERT** Jenna baked apple pies for a family reunion. Each pie was cut into 9 pieces. Her family ate 28 pieces of pie. Write an improper fraction and a mixed number to represent the number of pies Jenna's family ate. ______________

2. **SNACKS** Jamal had a bag of oranges to share with his friends. He divided each orange into four equal pieces. Sixteen orange sections were eaten. How many whole oranges did Jamal and his friends eat? ______________

3. **HOBBIES** Michele used strips of wood to make square picture frames. Each strip of wood was of equal length. She cut each strip into 7 equal pieces and used a total of 20 pieces for the frames. Write an improper fraction and a mixed number to represent the number of strips of wood Michele used. ______________ ______________

4. **PACKAGING** Carlotta bought boxes of snack bars at the grocery store. Each box contained 6 snack bars. During the week, her family ate 15 snack bars. How many whole boxes of snack bars did her family eat? ______________

5. **PACKAGING** Henry bought 3 packs of tomatoes to make salsa. Each pack has 4 tomatoes in it. He used a total of 9 tomatoes. Write an improper fraction and a mixed number to represent the number of packs of tomatoes Henry used. ______________ ______________

6. **PICNIC** Mrs. Meyers bought three jugs of lemonade for a school picnic. Each jug contained 16 cups of lemonade. Students drank a total of 39 cups of lemonade at the picnic. Write an improper fraction and a mixed number to represent the number of jugs of lemonade the students drank. ______________ ______________

Lesson 5-3

NAME ______________________ DATE ______________

Homework Practice

Write each mixed number as an improper fraction.

1 $5\frac{2}{3} = \frac{\square \times \square + \square}{\square} = \frac{\square}{\square}$

2 $4\frac{5}{7} = \frac{\square \times \square + \square}{\square} = \frac{\square}{\square}$

3 $1\frac{1}{12} =$ ______________

4 $2\frac{11}{12} =$ ______________

5 $8\frac{2}{9} =$ ______________

6 $6\frac{2}{5} =$ ______________

Write each improper fraction as a mixed number.

7 $\frac{21}{8} =$ ______________

8 $\frac{13}{2} =$ ______________

9 $\frac{45}{7} =$ ______________

10 $\frac{11}{4} =$ ______________

11 $\frac{39}{5} =$ ______________

12 $\frac{53}{12} =$ ______________

Solve.

13 **CRAFTS** Denise is making stuffed animals. She uses buttons for decoration on the animals. She bought 9 packages of buttons. Each package has 6 buttons. Denise used a total of 33 buttons. Write an improper fraction and a mixed number to represent the number of packages Denise used. ______________________________

Write the vocabulary word that completes each sentence.

14 The number $\frac{17}{5}$ is an example of an ______________________________.

Chapter 5

NAME ________________ DATE ________________

Lesson 5-4

Vocabulary and English Language Development

Activate Prior Knowledge

Write an equivalent form of one to represent the whole object.

1  ______

2  ______

3 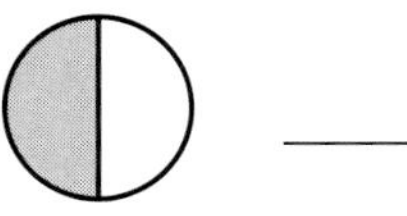 ______

Definition Review

A **common denominator** is the same denominator (bottom number) used in two or more fractions. Example: $\frac{2}{5}$ and $\frac{1}{10}$ have common denominator 10.

Equivalent forms of one are different expressions that represent one.

Example: $\frac{2}{2}$ is an equivalent form of one.

Find a common denominator for each pair of fractions.

4 $\frac{3}{5}$ and $\frac{7}{8}$ ______________

5 $\frac{1}{2}$ and $\frac{2}{9}$ ______________

6 $\frac{7}{16}$ and $\frac{3}{8}$ ______________

7 $\frac{2}{3}$ and $\frac{9}{15}$ ______________

Application

- Find a partner. You will need 2 number cubes.
- Roll the number cubes. Use the lesser number as the numerator and the greater number as the denominator of a fraction. Write down the fraction.
- Both of you then write down three common denominators of the two fractions. If the two fractions already have the same denominator, roll again.
- Check each other's common denominators and repeat the exercise.

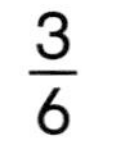

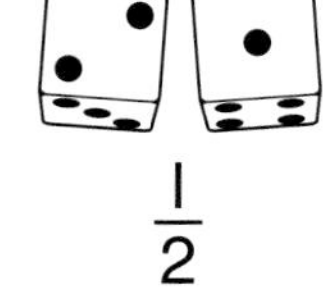

$\frac{3}{6}$ $\frac{1}{2}$

Common denominators: 6, 12, 18

Lesson 5-4

NAME ______________________ DATE ______________

Skills Practice

Find the Least Common Multiple.

1 Find the LCM of 2, 4, and 5 ______________

Multiples of 2: ☐, ☐, ☐, ☐, ☐, ☐, ☐, ☐, ☐, ☐, ☐, . . .

Multiples of 4: ☐, ☐, ☐, ☐, ☐, ☐, ☐, ☐, . . .

Multiples of 5: ☐, ☐, ☐, ☐, ☐, ☐, ☐, ☐, . . .

2 Find the LCM of 3, 4, and 8 ______________

Multiples of 3: ☐, ☐, ☐, ☐, ☐, ☐, ☐, ☐, ☐, ☐, . . .

Multiples of 4: ☐, ☐, ☐, ☐, ☐, ☐, ☐, ☐, . . .

Multiples of 8: ☐, ☐, ☐, ☐, ☐, ☐, . . .

Chapter 5

Find the LCM of each set of numbers.

3 2, 4, and 6 ______________

4 2, 4, and 25 ______________

5 3, 5, and 6 ______________

6 5, 15, and 25 ______________

Find the least common denominator for each set of fractions.

7 $\frac{2}{3}, \frac{1}{5}, \frac{1}{10}$ ______________

8 $\frac{1}{2}, \frac{1}{6}, \frac{3}{8}$ ______________

NAME ______________________ DATE ______________

Lesson 5-4

Problem-Solving Practice

Solve.

1 **BAKING** Brooke is using a recipe to make cookies. She needs $\frac{2}{3}$ cup of sugar. She also needs $\frac{3}{4}$ cup of brown sugar. Write each of the fractions for the amounts of sugar and brown sugar with a common denominator.

2 **FOOD** Jeremy bought $\frac{3}{4}$ pounds of American cheese and $\frac{5}{6}$ pounds of roast beef. What is the least common denominator of the two deli products?

3 **SNOW** Center City received $6\frac{1}{4}$ inches of snow. Leonardtown received $6\frac{3}{8}$ inches of snow. How much snow did each city receive using a common denominator?

4 **TRANSPORTATION** Two cars on a train contain an equal number of seats. Three-fourths of the seats in the first car are filled. Eleven-twelfths of the seats in the second car are filled. What is the least common denominator of the fractions representing the filled seats in each car?

5 **PIZZA** Mrs. Tyler ordered two pizzas. One pizza was cheese and one was pepperoni. The cheese pizza was cut into 12 pieces. The pepperoni pizza was cut into 8 pieces. Her family ate 10 pieces of the cheese pizza and 7 pieces of the pepperoni pizza. What is the fraction of each pizza eaten using a common denominator?

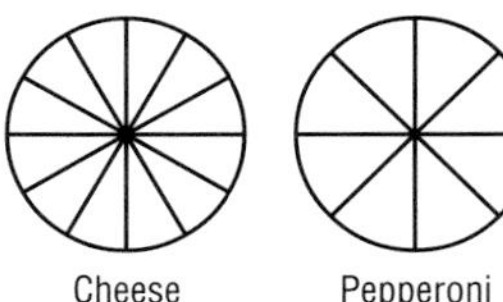

NAME ________________ DATE ________________

Lesson 5-4

Homework Practice

Find the LCM of each set of numbers.

1. 4, 8, 11 ________

2. 3, 9, 15 ________

3. 7, 8, 14 ________

4. 4, 25, 50 ________

Find the least common denominator of each set of fractions.

5. $\frac{1}{3}, \frac{1}{6}, \frac{1}{8}$ ________

6. $\frac{1}{4}, \frac{1}{8}, \frac{1}{16}$ ________

7. $\frac{1}{4}, \frac{2}{5}, \frac{3}{8}, \frac{1}{20}$ ________

8. $\frac{1}{3}, \frac{3}{5}, \frac{7}{10}, \frac{2}{15}$ ________

Solve.

9. **COMPUTERS** Shannon's flash drive is $\frac{2}{5}$ full of data. Alejandro's flash drive is $\frac{1}{2}$ full of data. Anna's flash drive is $\frac{3}{4}$ full of data. Show each flash drive data amount with a common denominator.

____

10. **DINNER** Leo ate $\frac{1}{4}$ serving of green beans. Lincoln ate $\frac{3}{8}$ serving of green beans. Pedro ate $\frac{1}{5}$ serving of green beans. Show each person's serving of green beans with a common denominator.

____

Write the vocabulary term that completes the sentence.

11. The ________________ (LCM) is the smallest whole number greater than 0 that is a common multiple of each of two or more numbers.

Chapter 5

Lesson 5-5

NAME ______________________ DATE ______________

Vocabulary and English Language Development

Activate Prior Knowledge

Use the designs to answer the questions.

Design A ★ ○ □ ★ □ □ ★ ○ □ ★ ○ □ ★

Design B ★ ○ □ ★ ○ □ ○ ★ ○ □ ★ ○

Design C □ ○ ★ ★ ○ □ ○ ★ ★

1. Which design has the greatest fraction of stars? ______________

2. Which design has the least fraction of circles? ______________

3. List the designs in ascending order according to the fraction of squares in each.

____

Definition Review

Ascending order means moving from least to greatest. Example: 1, 2, 3 ,4 ,5

Descending order means moving from greatest to least. Example: 5, 4, 3, 2, 1

Complete each sentence using the words *ascending* or *descending*.

4. Juan wrote $\frac{3}{4}, \frac{2}{3}, \frac{1}{4}$.
Juan wrote the fractions in ______________ order.

5. Laura wrote $\frac{1}{4}, \frac{2}{3}, \frac{3}{4}$.
Laura wrote the fractions in ______________ order.

Application

Use a scissors to cut 4 strips of paper, each 12 inches long. Divide each strip of paper into equal parts to show the fractions below. Then write the fractions in order from least to greatest.

$\frac{1}{2}$

$\frac{1}{3}$

$\frac{1}{12}$

$\frac{1}{4}$

NAME ______________________ DATE ______________

Skills Practice

Use <, =, or > to compare the fractions. Shade the models given.

1. $\frac{2}{5} \bigcirc \frac{5}{8}$

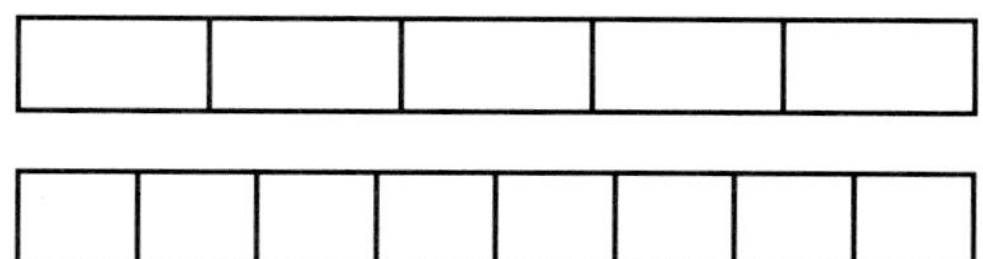

2. $\frac{4}{8} \bigcirc \frac{1}{3}$

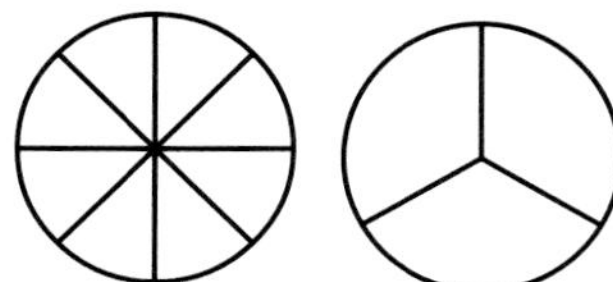

Use <, =, or > to compare the fractions.

3. $\frac{3}{4} \bigcirc \frac{7}{8}$

4. $\frac{1}{3} \bigcirc \frac{2}{9}$

5. $\frac{2}{9} \bigcirc \frac{4}{15}$

6. $\frac{2}{3} \bigcirc \frac{4}{6}$

Use <, =, or > to compare the fractions. Rename the fractions using a common denominator.

7. $\frac{5}{7} \bigcirc \frac{5}{6}$

____

8. $\frac{3}{11} \bigcirc \frac{1}{4}$

____

9. $\frac{5}{8} \bigcirc \frac{4}{5}$

____

10. $\frac{8}{10} \bigcirc \frac{7}{9}$

____

Order the fractions from least to greatest.

11. $\frac{8}{14}, \frac{5}{7}, \frac{3}{4}$ ______________________

12. $\frac{1}{2}, \frac{7}{18}, \frac{4}{9}$ ______________________

Lesson 5-5

NAME ______________________ DATE ______________

Problem-Solving Practice

Solve.

1 **MUSIC** Chris listened to three songs. The lengths of the songs are shown in the table below. Which song has the greatest length? ____________

Songs	
Name	**Length (min.)**
The Long Road	$3\frac{5}{6}$
Skateboard	$3\frac{3}{4}$
Climb High	$3\frac{1}{2}$

2 **SHOPPING** Maria bought $\frac{1}{2}$ pound of white potatoes, $\frac{3}{4}$ pound of red potatoes, and $\frac{7}{8}$ pound of sweet potatoes. Which kind of potatoes weighed the least? ____________

3 **HARVEST** Three friends went to a farm to pick strawberries. The table shows the amount each person picked. Who picked the greatest amount of strawberries? ____________

Strawberries Picked	
Name	**Weight (lbs.)**
Lionel	$1\frac{7}{8}$
Duncan	$1\frac{5}{6}$
Jorge	$1\frac{3}{4}$

4 **PIZZA** Three friends each ordered a small cheese pizza for lunch. Carolina ate $\frac{4}{9}$ of her pizza. Sharona ate $\frac{3}{8}$ of her pizza. Leona ate $\frac{1}{3}$ of her pizza. Who ate the least amount of pizza? ____________

5 **GARDENING** Manuel plants a vegetable garden every spring. Tomato plants use $\frac{1}{3}$ of the garden space. Pepper plants use $\frac{1}{6}$ of the garden space. Squash plants use $\frac{1}{2}$ of the garden space. Which vegetable takes up the greatest amount of space in the garden? ____________

6 **BASKETBALL** Melanie and Alicia both played in last week's basketball game. Melanie threw 10 foul shots and made 6 of them. Alicia threw 8 foul shots and made 6 of them. Who made the greater fraction of foul shots? ____________

Lesson 5-5

NAME ______________________ DATE ____________

Homework Practice

Use <, =, or > to compare the fractions. Shade the models given.

1. 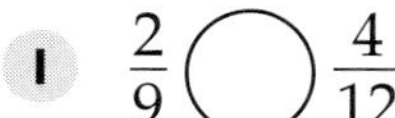 $\frac{2}{9} \bigcirc \frac{4}{12}$

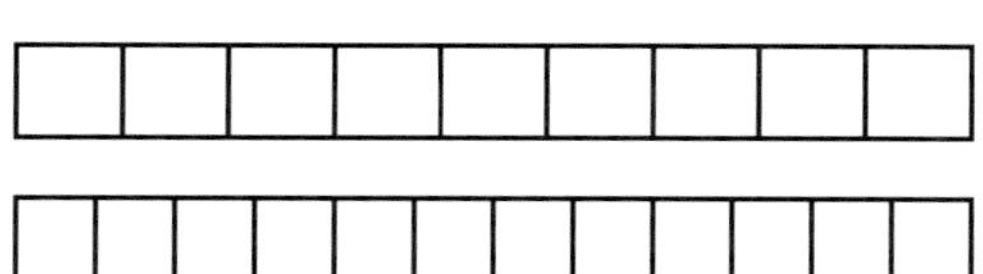

2. $\frac{4}{6} \bigcirc \frac{5}{8}$

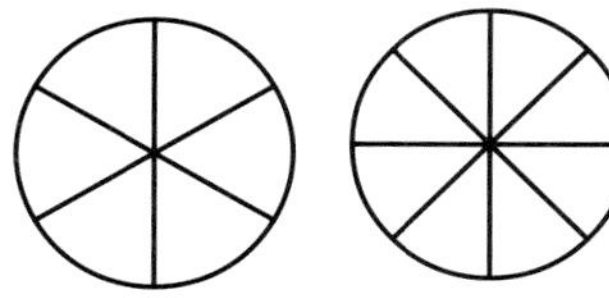

Use <, =, or > to compare the fractions. Rename the fractions using a common denominator.

3. $\frac{13}{20} \bigcirc \frac{7}{10}$ ______________________

4. $\frac{5}{14} \bigcirc \frac{1}{3}$ ______________________

Solve.

5. **PETS** Amelia has two dogs, Daisy and Rover. Daisy weighs $12\frac{5}{8}$ pounds and Rover weighs $12\frac{3}{4}$ pounds. Which dog weighs more? ______________

6. **CRAFTS** Bonita is using ribbon to decorate the perimeter of the flag shown below. The perimeter is found by adding the lengths of the sides of the triangle. She buys $7\frac{3}{8}$ feet of ribbon. Does she have enough ribbon to decorate the perimeter of the flag? Explain how you found your answer. ______________

____

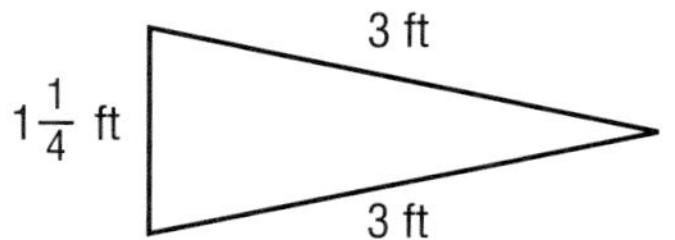

NAME ____________________ DATE ____________

Lesson 5-6

Vocabulary and English Language Development

Activate Prior Knowledge

Answer.

List the names of ten friends or family members. Out of the people you listed, what fraction of them has a dog as a pet? Write your answer in simplest form.

____

Definition Review

Match each term with its definition.

_______ simplest form
Example: $\frac{2}{4} = \frac{1}{2}$

_______ greatest common factor
Example: GCF of 6 and 9 is 3

_______ prime number
Example: 5 (factors are 1 and 5)

_______ composite number
Example: 8 (factors are 1, 2, 4, 8)

A. any whole number greater than 1 with exactly two factors, 1 and itself

B. a fraction in which the numerator and the denominator have no common factor greater than 1

C. a number greater than 1 with more than two factors

D. the largest number that divides evenly into two or more numbers

Application

Complete the graphic organizer.

Show the Prime Factorization for each number.	Find the Greatest Common Factor for each set of numbers.
20 __________	20 and 75 __________
35 __________	35 and 42 __________
42 __________	42 and 20 __________
75 __________	75 and 42 __________

Lesson 5-6

NAME _______________ DATE _______________

Skills Practice

Write each fraction in simplest form.

1 Write $\frac{4}{6}$ in simplest form. Use models to shade an equivalent area and name the simplified fraction.

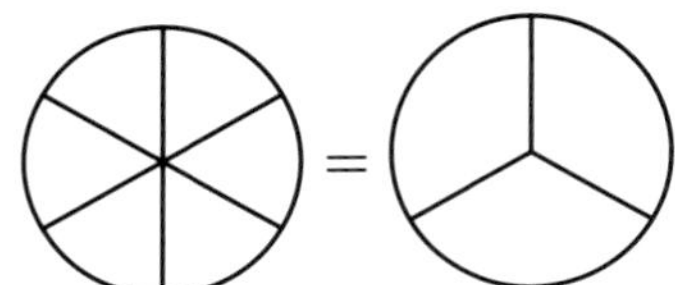

$\frac{4}{6}$ = _______

2 Write $\frac{9}{12}$ in simplest form. Solve by finding the greatest common factor.

Factors of 9: ☐ ☐ 9

Factors of 12: ☐ ☐ ☐ ☐ ☐ 12

____

Chapter 5

Write each fraction in simplest form. Use prime factorization.

3 $\frac{12}{24}$ _______________

4 $\frac{8}{32}$ _______________

5 $\frac{27}{81}$ _______________

6 $\frac{10}{45}$ _______________

7 $\frac{12}{28}$ _______________

8 $\frac{22}{55}$ _______________

Write each fraction in simplest form. Divide by the greatest common factor.

9 $\frac{9}{15}$ _______________

10 $\frac{6}{14}$ _______________

11 $\frac{18}{24}$ _______________

12 $\frac{50}{100}$ _______________

13 $\frac{5}{25}$ _______________

14 $\frac{18}{27}$ _______________

Lesson 5-6

NAME ______________________ DATE ____________

Problem-Solving Practice

Solve.

1 **RAIN** During the month of April, it rained on 8 days. What is the fraction of days it rained in April in simplest form? (Hint: There are 30 days in April.) ____________

2 **BRACELETS** Laurie is making two bracelets using heart-shaped and triangle-shaped beads. She wants to use an equal number of beads on each bracelet, with no beads left over. What is the greatest number of each shape she can use on both bracelets? ____________

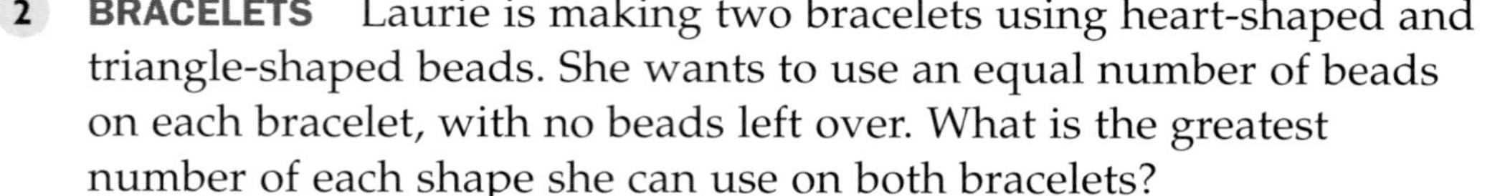

3 **BOOKS** Hector divided the books he read last year into four categories. In simplest form, what fraction of the books are mystery books? ____________

Book Categories	
Category	**Number**
Mystery	8
Science Fiction	12
History	4
Biography	4

4 **BASEBALL** A baseball pitcher threw a total of 75 pitches in a ballgame. Forty of those pitches were strikes. In simplest form, what fraction of the pitches were strikes? ____________

5 **MUSIC** The school orchestra contains 32 musicians. There are 10 musicians in the brass section. In simplest form, what fraction of the orchestra is the brass section? ____________

6 **TESTS** A math test has a total of 100 questions. Darla got 84 questions correct. A science test has 25 questions. Darla got the same fraction of questions correct on the science test as she did on the math test. How many questions did Darla answer correctly on the science test? ____________

Lesson 5-6

NAME ______________________ DATE ______________

Homework Practice

Write each fraction in simplest form. Use models. Shade an equivalent area and name the simplified fraction.

1. $\frac{5}{10}$ =

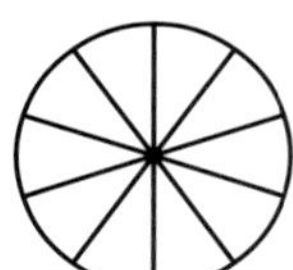
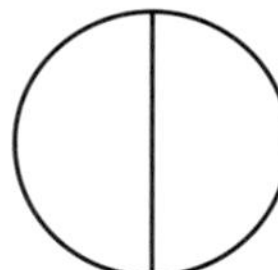

☐ = ☐

2. $\frac{9}{12}$ =

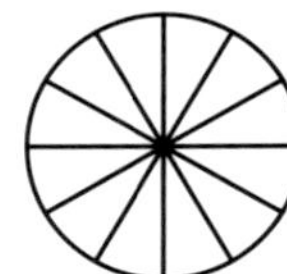
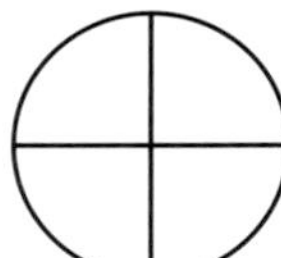

☐ = ☐

Write each fraction in simplest form. Use the GCF.

3. $\frac{5}{50}$ ______________

4. $\frac{8}{36}$ ______________

5. $\frac{12}{70}$ ______________

6. $\frac{18}{42}$ ______________

Write each fraction in simplest form. Use prime factorization.

7. $\frac{15}{100}$ ______________

8. $\frac{20}{30}$ ______________

9. $\frac{54}{81}$ ______________

10. $\frac{8}{44}$ ______________

Solve.

11. **PHOTOGRAPHS** Millie took 36 pictures using her digital camera. She deleted 8 pictures. In simplest form, what fraction of the pictures did Millie keep?

____

12. **SURVEY** A supermarket surveyed 100 people about their favorite brand of orange juice. Thirty-five people said Sunshine State orange juice is their favorite brand. In simplest terms, what fraction of the people surveyed did ***not*** say Sunshine State orange juice was their favorite brand?

____

Write the vocabulary word that completes each sentence.

13. A ______________ number is any whole number greater than 1 with exactly two factors, 1 and itself.

14. A ______________ number is a number greater than 1 with more than two factors.

Chapter 5

NAME ______ DATE ______

Chapter 6

Foldables Study Organizer

Dinah Zike's Foldables

Make this Foldable to help you organize information about adding and subtracting fractions.

1. Begin with three sheets of $8\frac{1}{2}'' \times 11''$ paper. Stack the paper about three inches apart.

2. Roll up the bottom so all tabs are the same size.

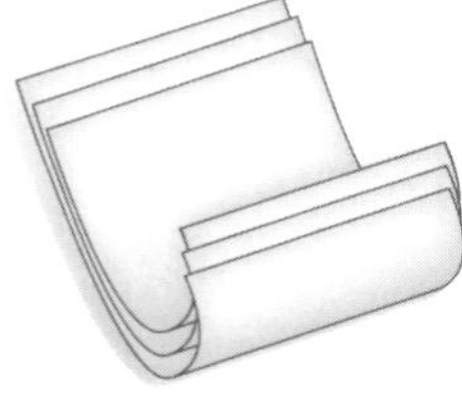

3. Crease and staple along the fold as shown.

4. Label as shown. Take notes as you move through the chapter.

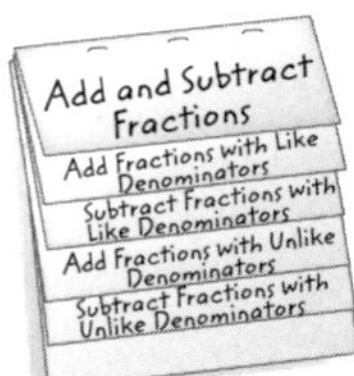

TAKING NOTES

As you read through the chapter, use your Foldable to write instructions on how to do each of the following:

- Add fractions with like denominators
- Subtract fractions with like denominators
- Add fractions with unlike denominators
- Subtract fractions with unlike denominator

USING YOUR FOLDABLE

As you study, use the information in your Foldable to write and solve problems that involve adding and subtracting fractions.

USING YOUR FOLDABLE

Work with a group of three or four students. Sit in a circle. One student starts by saying the first step in adding a fraction. The student to the right then says the next step. Continue until the steps are complete. Then do the same for subtracting fractions.

Chapter 6

NAME ______ DATE ______

Games and Puzzles

Fraction Subtraction

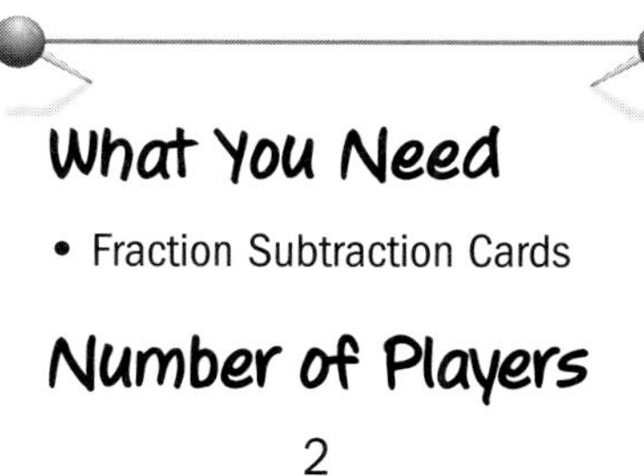

What You Need
• Fraction Subtraction Cards
Number of Players
2

DIRECTIONS

- Shuffle the cards. Then spread out the cards facedown on the table.
- Player 1 turns over any two cards.
- If the solutions to both cards are equivalent, Player 1 keeps the cards and receives one point. Player 1 continues his or her turn.
- If the solutions are *not* equivalent, the cards are turned over and Player 2 takes a turn.
- Play continues until all matches are made. The players add up the point value on their cards. The player with most points wins.

Answer Cards

$\frac{1}{3}$	$\frac{1}{7}$	$\frac{1}{2}$
$\frac{1}{5}$	$\frac{1}{6}$	$\frac{3}{4}$

Chapter 6

Chapter 6

NAME ______________________ DATE ______________

$\frac{3}{4} - \frac{1}{4}$	$\frac{9}{10} - \frac{7}{10}$	$\frac{7}{12} - \frac{5}{12}$
$\frac{10}{12} - \frac{1}{12}$	$\frac{5}{6} - \frac{2}{6}$	$\frac{7}{9} - \frac{4}{9}$
$\frac{6}{15} - \frac{3}{15}$	$\frac{6}{7} - \frac{5}{7}$	$\frac{7}{8} - \frac{1}{8}$
$\frac{11}{14} - \frac{9}{14}$	$\frac{9}{24} - \frac{5}{24}$	$\frac{4}{6} - \frac{2}{6}$

NAME ________________________________ DATE ______________

Lesson 6-1

Vocabulary and English Language Development

Activate Prior Knowledge

Solve.

1 Rama and Todd each ate the pizzas shown below for lunch. Rama ate $\frac{3}{8}$ of his pizza, and Todd ate $\frac{4}{8}$ of his pizza. Fill in the circle below to represent the total number of pieces eaten by the boys.

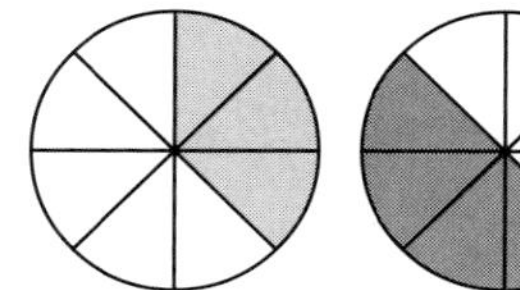

Definition Review

A fraction is in **simplest form** when the numerator and denominator have no common factor other than 1.
Like fractions are fractions that have the same denominator.

Write *yes* or *no* to tell if each fraction is in simplest form. If it is not in simplest form, write the fraction in simplest form.

2 $\frac{5}{8}$ ________

3 $\frac{12}{15}$ ________

4 $\frac{16}{36}$ ________

5 $\frac{11}{21}$ ________

Write *yes* or *no* to tell if each is a pair of like fractions.

6 $\frac{5}{7}$ and $\frac{5}{9}$ ________

7 $\frac{3}{4}$ and $\frac{4}{8}$ ________

8 $\frac{2}{5}$ and $\frac{1}{5}$ ________

9 $\frac{3}{7}$ and $\frac{4}{7}$ ________

Application

Follow the directions for the activity.

- Find a partner. Assemble a bag of 24 assorted marbles.
- Arrange the marbles into groups of each color.
- Write fractions to represent the fraction of the marbles that is each color.
- Find the fractional sum of 2 colors, and write this fraction in simplest form.
- Continue until you find the fractional sums for all colors.

Chapter 6

NAME ____________________ DATE ____________

Lesson 6-1

Skills Practice

Use drawings to help you add. Write each sum in simplest form.

1 $\frac{1}{3} + \frac{2}{3} =$ ____________

2 $\frac{2}{9} + \frac{4}{9} =$ ____________

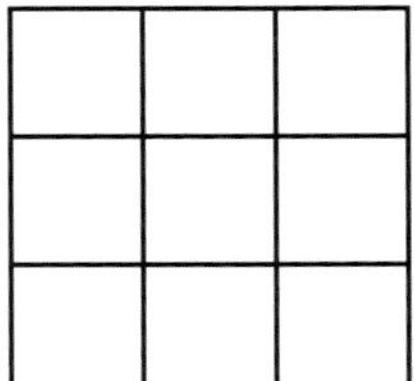

3 $\frac{4}{6} + \frac{5}{6} =$ ____________

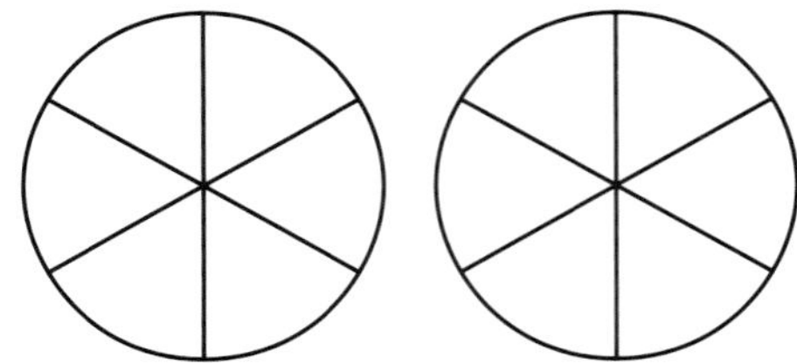

4 $\frac{3}{10} + \frac{5}{10} =$ ____________

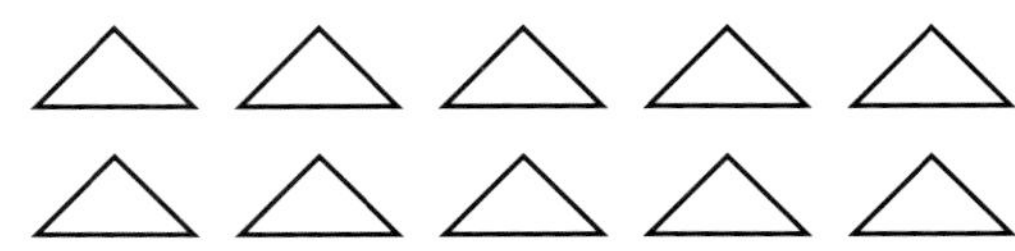

Circle the correct answer in simplest form.

5 $\frac{2}{7} + \frac{4}{7} =$ $\frac{6}{7}$ $\frac{6}{14}$

6 $\frac{3}{12} + \frac{3}{12} =$ $\frac{6}{12}$ $\frac{1}{2}$

7 $\frac{1}{6} + \frac{5}{6} =$ 1 $\frac{6}{6}$

8 $\frac{7}{9} + \frac{5}{9} =$ $\frac{12}{9}$ $1\frac{1}{3}$

Add. Write each sum in simplest form.

9 $\frac{3}{8} + \frac{1}{8} =$ ____________

10 $\frac{4}{11} + \frac{8}{11} =$ ____________

11 $\frac{6}{15} + \frac{4}{15} =$ ____________

12 $\frac{1}{4} + \frac{2}{4} =$ ____________

13 $\frac{6}{9} + \frac{4}{9} =$ ____________

14 $\frac{2}{5} + \frac{3}{5} =$ ____________

15 $\frac{19}{49} + \frac{23}{49} =$ ____________

16 $\frac{14}{30} + \frac{11}{30} =$ ____________

Lesson 6-1

NAME ____________________ DATE ____________

Problem-Solving Practice

Solve. Write your answer in simplest form.

1 **FOOD SERVICE** The Family Restaurant is offering the blueberry pie shown below. The waiter serves 4 pieces to one table and 2 pieces to another table. How much of the whole pie has been served? ____________

2 **DRINKS** Toshiro is making 10 liters of punch. He adds 2 liters of apple juice, 5 liters of orange juice, and 3 liters of soda. What fraction of the punch is juice? ____________

3 **BIOLOGY** Ines is looking at a total of 100 cells with a fluorescent microscope. She notices $\frac{20}{100}$ are glowing red, $\frac{35}{100}$ are glowing green, and $\frac{45}{100}$ are glowing blue. What fraction of the cells is glowing either red or blue? ____________

4 **AGRICULTURE** Elan collected 36 eggs. Of the 36, 4 eggs are dirty and 8 are cracked. If he must throw out all the dirty and cracked eggs, what fraction of eggs does he need to throw out? ____________

5 **CONSTRUCTION** Samir buys 50 pieces of wood to begin building a deck. Using the table below, what fraction of the wood is 2 inches wide? ____________

Size of Wood	Number of Pieces
2 × 6	5
2 × 4	20
1 × 4	25

6 **FOOTBALL** At the football game, the home team got a total of 20 first downs. During the first quarter they got 3 first downs. They got 2 first downs in the second quarter, 7 first in the third, and 8 first in the fourth. What fraction of first downs did the home team get in the first two quarters? ____________

7 **PACKAGING** Mr. Flores packs 48 books into a box. The box contains $\frac{19}{48}$ novels, $\frac{13}{48}$ biographies, and $\frac{16}{48}$ children's books. What fraction of the books are novels and biographies? ____________

Chapter 6

NAME ______________________ DATE ______________

Lesson 6-1

Homework Practice

Use drawings to help you add. Write each sum in simplest form.

1 $\frac{1}{7} + \frac{4}{7} =$ ____________

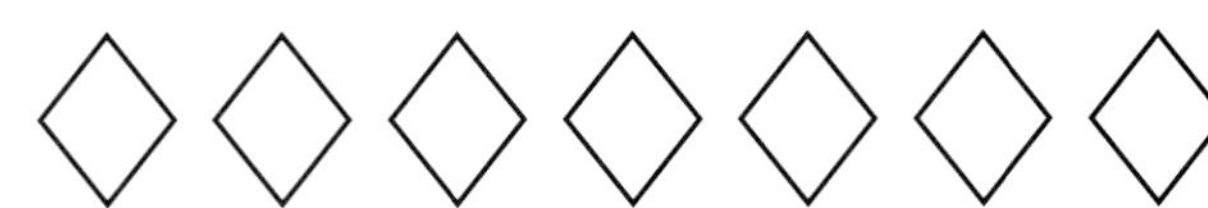

2 $\frac{3}{8} + \frac{3}{8} =$ ____________

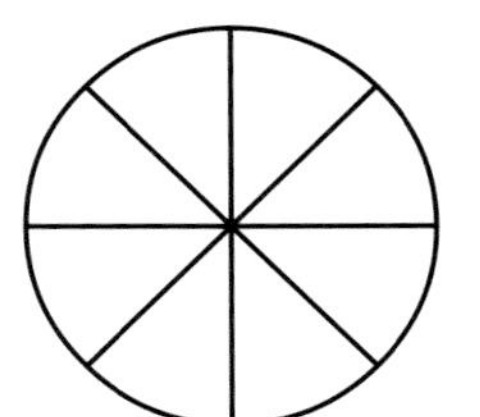

3 $\frac{8}{9} + \frac{7}{9} =$ ____________

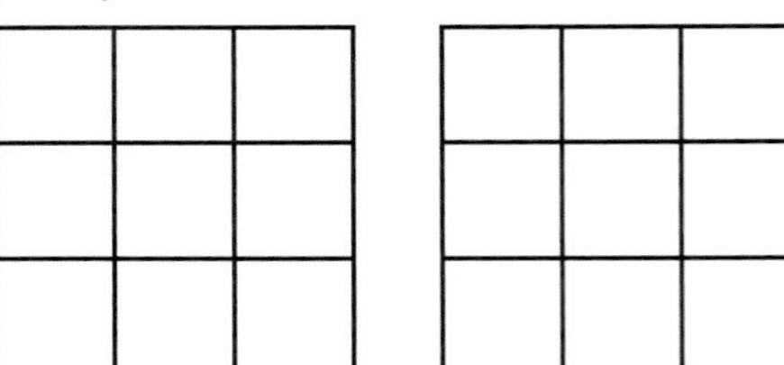

4 $\frac{3}{4} + \frac{1}{4} =$ ____________

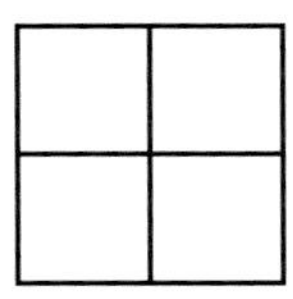

Add. Write each sum in simplest form.

5 $\frac{4}{5} + \frac{5}{5} =$ ____________

6 $\frac{6}{7} + \frac{3}{7} =$ ____________

7 $\frac{2}{10} + \frac{4}{10} =$ ____________

8 $\frac{17}{22} + \frac{5}{22} =$ ____________

9 $\frac{5}{8} + \frac{6}{8} =$ ____________

10 $\frac{5}{6} + \frac{5}{6} =$ ____________

11 $\frac{4}{14} + \frac{3}{14} =$ ____________

12 $\frac{4}{9} + \frac{8}{9} =$ ____________

Solve. Write in simplest form.

13 **FOOD** Mala cuts a watermelon into 12 equal pieces. She gives $\frac{3}{12}$ of the pieces to Samuel, $\frac{1}{12}$ of the pieces to Alana, $\frac{2}{12}$ of the pieces to Tyrone, and $\frac{3}{12}$ of the pieces to Silvia.
What fraction did she give to the boys? ____________

Write the vocabulary word that completes each sentence.

14 A fraction is in ____________ when the numerator and the denominator have no common factor greater than 1.

15 Fractions that have the same bottom numbers have ____________.

Lesson 6-2

NAME ______________________ DATE ______________

Vocabulary and English Language Development

Activate Prior Knowledge

Use each sentence to answer the question.

1 Rita bought 3 of the 5 books she needs for her book club.

How many more books does she need to buy? ______________

2 Sanjay delivered 8 of the 15 newspapers on his route.

How many newspapers does he have left to deliver? ______________

3 Lucy unpacked 4 of 9 boxes.

How many boxes does Lucy have left to unpack? ______________

Definition Review

A fraction is in **simplest form** when the numerator and denominator have no common factor greater than 1.
Fractions that have the same bottom number have **common denominators**.

Write *yes* or *no* to tell if each fraction is in simplest form. If it is not in simplest form, write the fraction in simplest form.

4 $\frac{3}{8}$ ________

5 $\frac{18}{48}$ ________

6 $\frac{28}{35}$ ________

7 $\frac{11}{21}$ ________

Write yes or no to tell if each pair of fractions have common denominators.

8 $\frac{2}{5}$ and $\frac{5}{10}$ ________

9 $\frac{1}{6}$ and $\frac{2}{12}$ ________

10 $\frac{3}{8}$ and $\frac{5}{8}$ ________

11 $\frac{1}{9}$ and $\frac{5}{9}$ ________

Application

- Make a fraction strip with 10 sections. Cut out the 10 sections.
- Gather 10 plastic markers.
- Create and solve 10 subtraction problems using the fraction tiles. Write the problems and record the difference in simplest form.
- For example, if the problem is $\frac{3}{5} - \frac{1}{5}$, place 5 tiles on the desk and put markers on 3 of the tiles. Then take off 1 marker and count the tiles that contain the remaining markers. This number is the numerator of the difference.

Chapter 6

Lesson 6-2

NAME ______________________ DATE ____________

Skills Practice

Use drawings to subtract. Write each difference in simplest form.

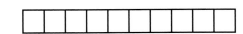

1. $\frac{3}{4} - \frac{1}{4} =$ ______________

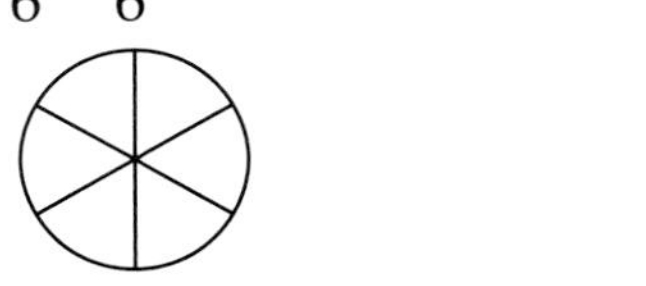

2. $\frac{5}{7} - \frac{2}{7} =$ ______________

3. $\frac{4}{6} - \frac{2}{6} =$ ______________

4. $\frac{9}{10} - \frac{2}{10} =$ ______________

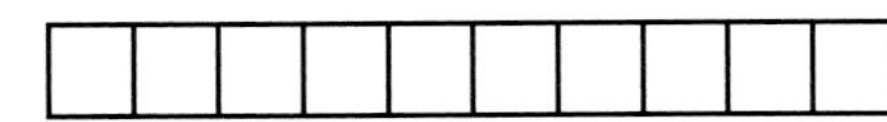

Circle the simplest form of the correct answer.

5. $\frac{6}{11} - \frac{3}{11} =$ $\frac{3}{11}$ 3

6. $\frac{9}{24} - \frac{1}{24} =$ $\frac{1}{3}$ $\frac{8}{24}$

7. $\frac{8}{9} - \frac{2}{9} =$ $\frac{6}{9}$ $\frac{2}{3}$

8. $\frac{25}{36} - \frac{7}{36} =$ $\frac{2}{4}$ $\frac{1}{2}$

Subtract. Write each difference in simplest form.

9. $\frac{14}{18} - \frac{6}{18} =$ ______________

10. $\frac{6}{8} - \frac{1}{8} =$ ______________

11. $\frac{3}{5} - \frac{2}{5} =$ ______________

12. $\frac{13}{22} - \frac{2}{22} =$ ______________

13. $\frac{9}{12} - \frac{6}{12} =$ ______________

14. $\frac{80}{100} - \frac{25}{100} =$ ______________

15. $\frac{11}{12} - \frac{6}{12} =$ ______________

16. $\frac{7}{9} - \frac{1}{9} =$ ______________

17. $\frac{15}{16} - \frac{3}{16} =$ ______________

18. $\frac{8}{14} - \frac{3}{14} =$ ______________

NAME ______________________ DATE ______________

Lesson 6-2

Problem-Solving Practice

Solve. Write in simplest form.

1. **FOOD** Kimoko buys 45 apples at an apple farm. Of these, $\frac{5}{9}$ are Gala apples. He decides to give three of the Gala apples to Roberta. Write a fraction to represent the number of Gala apples Kimoko has remaining out of the total number of apples. ______

2. **LANDSCAPING** Ravi is designing a pump to deliver water to two sprinklers. The pump can deliver $\frac{5}{8}$ gallon of water per minute. One of the sprinklers uses $\frac{2}{8}$ gallon of water per minute. How many gallons of water will the other sprinkler receive per minute? ______

3. **MUSIC** Makalla's CDs take up $\frac{4}{5}$ of the shelves on her CD shelf. At a yard sale, she sells 1 full shelf of her CDs. What fraction of the CD shelves is full after the yard sale? ______

4. **COOKING** Yahto has $\frac{7}{8}$ cup of milk. He needs $\frac{2}{8}$ cup of milk to make macaroni and cheese. How much milk will Yahto have left to make chocolate milk? ______

5. **HOBBIES** Annie collected 23 of the 50 state quarters, but she lost 5 of the quarters. What fraction of the state quarters does Annie have now? Write the fraction in simplest form. ______

6. **MOVIES** Russell has 32 DVDs in his collection. Eighteen of his DVDs are Westerns. What fraction of his collection is not Westerns? ______

7. **SEWING** Keisha bought $\frac{9}{10}$ yard of fabric to make a dress. She measures and uses $\frac{7}{10}$ yard for the dress. How many yards of fabric does Keisha have left after she makes the dress? ______

8. **COOKING** Masan buys $\frac{5}{6}$ pound of carrots at the market. He uses $\frac{3}{6}$ pound to make stew. How many pounds of carrots does Masan have left? ______

Chapter 6

Lesson 6-2

NAME ______________________ DATE ______________

Homework Practice

Use drawings to subtract. Write each difference in simplest form.

1. $\frac{7}{8} - \frac{4}{8} =$ ____________

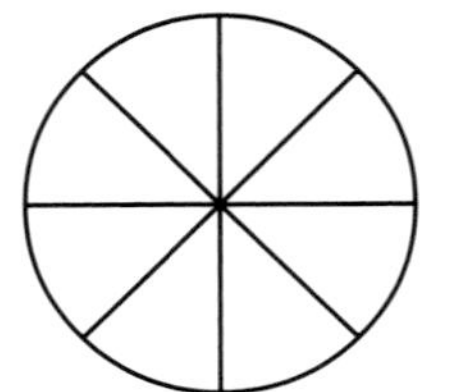

2. $\frac{11}{15} - \frac{2}{15} =$ ____________

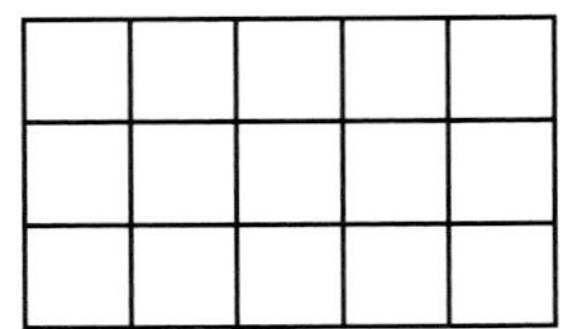

3. $\frac{13}{16} - \frac{1}{16} =$ ____________

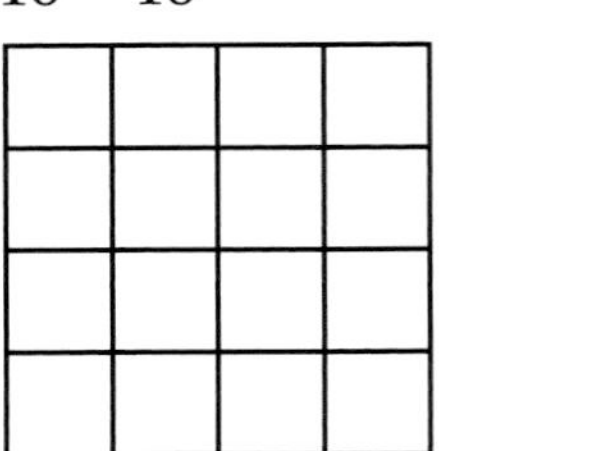

4. $\frac{5}{9} - \frac{3}{9} =$ ____________

Subtract. Write each difference in simplest form.

5. $\frac{9}{11} - \frac{5}{11} =$ ____________

6. $\frac{7}{8} - \frac{5}{8} =$ ____________

7. $\frac{7}{9} - \frac{2}{9} =$ ____________

8. $\frac{9}{12} - \frac{3}{12} =$ ____________

9. $\frac{1}{3} - \frac{1}{3} =$ ____________

10. $\frac{30}{45} - \frac{15}{45} =$ ____________

Solve. Write in simplest form.

11. **CONSTRUCTION** Cody is building a half-pipe in his backyard. For the frame, he buys beams that are $\frac{5}{6}$ yard long. After cutting the beams to fit the frame, he has $\frac{2}{6}$ -yard-long pieces remaining. How many yards long was the beam he used for the half-pipe frame?

____

Write the vocabulary word that completes each sentence.

12. A fraction is in ______________ when the numerator and the denominator have no common factor greater than 1.

13. Fractions that have ______________ are also called *like fractions*.

Lesson 6-3

NAME ______________________________ DATE ____________

Vocabulary and English Language Development

Activate Prior Knowledge

Identify a category in which each is alike. Add to find the number of items in each category.

1 pens and pencils ____________________

2 socks and shirts ____________________

Definition Review

Prime factorization is a way of writing a composite number as a product of its prime factors.

Name the LCD for each set of fractions.

3 $\frac{5}{6}, \frac{1}{9}$ ________

4 $\frac{3}{5}, \frac{2}{7}$ ________

5 $\frac{9}{10}, \frac{7}{8}$ ________

6 $\frac{20}{21}, \frac{6}{7}$ ________

Write the prime factorization for each composite number.

7 16 = ____________________

8 56 = ____________________

9 45 = ____________________

10 12 = ____________________

11 33 = ____________________

12 27 = ____________________

Application

- Find a partner. Gather 2 quarters, 2 dimes, 2 nickels, and 2 pennies. (If these are unavailable, use counters and assign coin values to different colors.)
- Determine the value of each coin as a fraction of $1.
- Create 5 different addition problems using different combinations of coins. (Example: 2 quarters + 2 dimes = 70 cents)
- Represent each sum using the fraction of $1 that each coin represents.

  (Example: $\frac{2}{4} + \frac{2}{10} = \frac{7}{10}$)
- Multiply the sum by 100 to check your answers.

  (Example: $\frac{7}{10} \times 100 = 70$ cents)

Chapter 6

NAME _______________ DATE _______________

Lesson 6-3

Skills Practice

Add using models. Write each sum in simplest form.

1. $\frac{1}{4} + \frac{1}{3} =$ ______________

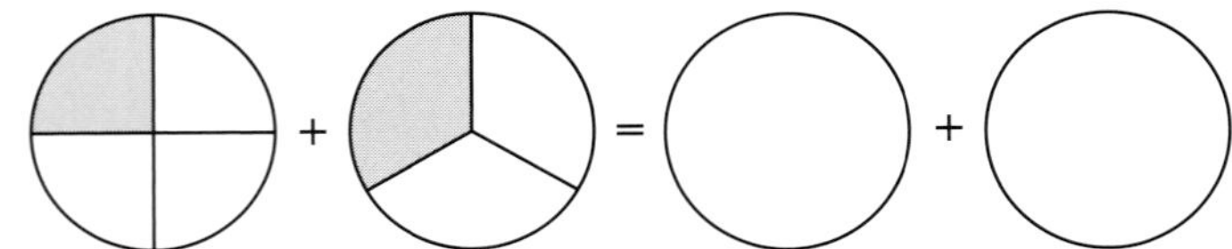

2. $\frac{2}{3} + \frac{1}{9} =$ ______________

3. $\frac{6}{12} + \frac{5}{6} =$ ______________

Name the LCD for each pair of fractions.

4. $\frac{1}{7}, \frac{1}{2}$ ______________

5. $\frac{7}{6}, \frac{3}{8}$ ______________

6. $\frac{1}{9}, \frac{2}{5}$ ______________

7. $\frac{5}{12}, \frac{2}{3}$ ______________

Add. Write each sum in simplest form.

8. $\frac{7}{8} + \frac{2}{3} =$ ______________

9. $\frac{3}{6} + \frac{2}{9} =$ ______________

10. $\frac{2}{5} + \frac{3}{4} =$ ______________

11. $\frac{1}{2} + \frac{3}{5} =$ ______________

12. $\frac{2}{7} + \frac{2}{3} =$ ______________

13. $\frac{1}{5} + \frac{1}{3} =$ ______________

14. $\frac{3}{9} + \frac{8}{18} =$ ______________

15. $\frac{5}{15} + \frac{8}{10} =$ ______________

NAME ______________________ DATE ______________

Lesson 6-3

Problem-Solving Practice

Solve.

1. **ENGINEERING** Hakan is designing a prototype using two metal plates. One plate is $\frac{1}{32}$ inch thick and the other is $\frac{3}{8}$ inch thick. If Hakan places one plate on top of the other, what is the overall thickness of the plates? ____________

2. **FITNESS** Mi-Lin walked $\frac{3}{4}$ mile in the morning, $\frac{5}{8}$ mile during lunch, and $\frac{1}{2}$ mile after dinner. How many miles did Mi-Lin walk in all? ____________

3. **CHEMISTRY** Tracy is mixing an alcohol solution in the lab. She adds $\frac{1}{4}$ liter of rubbing alcohol to a beaker of water filled to $\frac{7}{10}$ liters. What is the total volume of Tracy's solution? ____________

4. **HOBBIES** Sook is making a model airplane and decides that the balsa wood he is using is not thick enough. He glues together two pieces of wood to make a thicker piece. One is $\frac{3}{16}$ inch thick, and the other is $\frac{1}{8}$ inch thick. How thick is Sook's new piece of wood? ____________

5. **FINANCES** Mr. Hawkins gets two bonuses every year. This year, his first bonus was $\frac{1}{6}$ of his base salary. His second bonus was $\frac{1}{8}$ of his base salary. As a fraction of his base salary, what was Mr. Hawkins total bonus for this past year? ____________

6. **LANDSCAPING** Kaga connected two small sprinklers to water her front lawn. The first sprinkler delivers $\frac{5}{16}$ gallon per minute. The second sprinkler delivers $\frac{7}{8}$ gallon per minute. If both sprinklers are running at full pressure, how many gallons of water per minute will she be using? ____________

7. **DESSERT** Mario is making bran muffins and a fruit tart for a bake sale. He needs $\frac{3}{4}$ cup of sugar for the muffins, and $\frac{2}{3}$ cup of sugar for the crust of the tart. How much sugar does Mario need in all? ____________

NAME ______________________ DATE ______________

Lesson 6-3

Homework Practice

Add using models. Write each sum in simplest form.

1 $\frac{1}{6} + \frac{2}{4} =$ ______________

2 $\frac{9}{12} + \frac{3}{4} =$ ______________

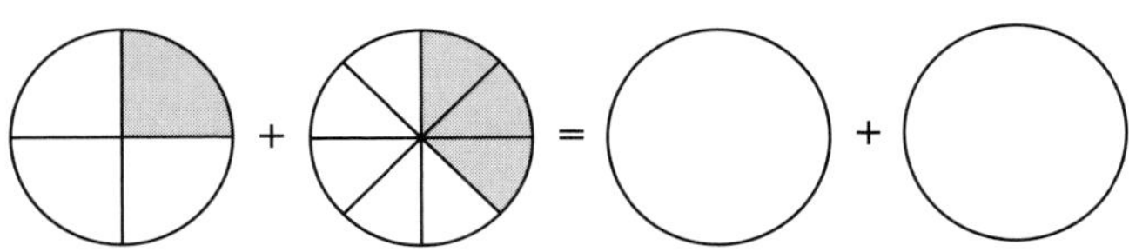

3 $\frac{1}{4} + \frac{3}{8} =$ ______________

Add. Write each sum in simplest form.

4 $\frac{4}{12} + \frac{3}{6} =$ ______________

5 $\frac{1}{7} + \frac{3}{4} =$ ______________

6 $\frac{2}{5} + \frac{1}{9} =$ ______________

7 $\frac{3}{12} + \frac{4}{5} =$ ______________

8 $\frac{2}{6} + \frac{4}{5} =$ ______________

9 $\frac{3}{6} + \frac{1}{12} =$ ______________

Solve.

10 **FASHION** Shada is mixing colors to dye fabric. She wants to mix $\frac{3}{5}$ quart of red with $\frac{1}{4}$ quart of blue to make purple. How much purple dye will Shada make?

____

11 **DINNER** Yo has a recipe which requires at least $1\frac{1}{2}$ pounds of salmon. She bought two salmon fillets, one weighing $\frac{5}{8}$ pound and the other weighing $\frac{8}{9}$ pound. How much salmon did Yo buy? Does she have enough for her recipe?

____

____

Lesson 6-4

NAME ______________________ DATE ____________

Vocabulary and English Language Development

Activate Prior Knowledge

Identify a category in which each of these items is alike. Add to find the number of items in each category.

1 squares and circles ______________

2 apples and pears ______________

Definition Review

Prime factorization is a way of expressing a composite number as a product of its prime factors.

Name the LCD for each set of fractions.

3 $\frac{2}{5}, \frac{5}{6}$ ________

4 $\frac{3}{4}, \frac{2}{3}$ ________

5 $\frac{3}{8}, \frac{1}{7}$ ________

6 $\frac{5}{16}, \frac{7}{8}$ ________

Write the prime factorization for each composite number.

7 21 = ______________

8 28 = ______________

9 25 = ______________

10 32 = ______________

11 42 = ______________

12 8 = ______________

Application

- Find a partner. Assemble 2 quarters, 2 dimes, 2 nickels, and 2 pennies. (If these are unavailable, use counters, assigning coin values to different colors.)
- Determine the value of each coin as a fraction of $1.
- Create 5 different subtraction problems using different combinations of coins. (Example: 2 quarters – 2 dimes = 30 cents)
- Represent each difference using the fraction of $1 that each coin represents. (Example: $\frac{2}{4} - \frac{2}{10} = \frac{3}{10}$)
- Multiply the difference by 100 to check your answers. (Example: $\frac{3}{10} \times 100 = 30$ cents)

Chapter 6

Lesson 6-4

NAME ______________________ DATE ______________

Skills Practice

Use models to subtract. Write each difference in simplest form.

1 $\frac{3}{4} - \frac{1}{8} =$ ______________

2 $\frac{2}{3} - \frac{2}{5} =$ ______________

3 $\frac{5}{6} - \frac{1}{2} =$ ______________

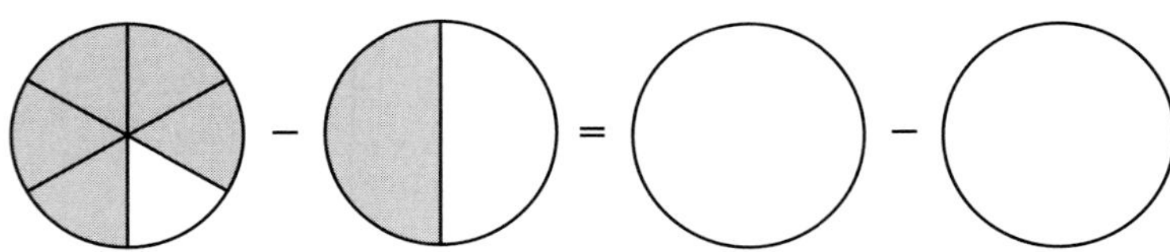

Name the LCD for each pair of fractions.

4 $\frac{1}{5}, \frac{1}{3}$ ______________

5 $\frac{1}{7}, \frac{1}{6}$ ______________

6 $\frac{1}{4}, \frac{1}{10}$ ______________

7 $\frac{1}{3}, \frac{1}{9}$ ______________

Subtract. Write each difference in simplest form.

8 $\frac{3}{5} - \frac{1}{9} =$ ______________

9 $\frac{3}{4} - \frac{4}{6} =$ ______________

10 $\frac{5}{8} - \frac{3}{6} =$ ______________

11 $\frac{1}{2} - \frac{3}{7} =$ ______________

12 $\frac{8}{9} - \frac{5}{6} =$ ______________

13 $\frac{6}{7} - \frac{2}{3} =$ ______________

14 $\frac{8}{12} - \frac{2}{6} =$ ______________

15 $\frac{5}{6} - \frac{2}{9} =$ ______________

16 $\frac{3}{10} - \frac{1}{5} =$ ______________

17 $\frac{2}{3} - \frac{4}{6} =$ ______________

NAME ______________________________ DATE ______________

Problem-Solving Practice

Solve.

1. **PHOTOGRAPHY** The useable space on Rohan's digital camera is $\frac{7}{8}$ full. He clears $\frac{9}{64}$ of the total space on the digital camera. How full is Rohan's camera now? ____________

2. **DRINKS** Twyla has $\frac{1}{2}$ gallon of milk. She pours $\frac{1}{6}$ gallon into a glass. How much milk is left in the carton? ____________

3. **HOBBIES** Ting is trying to make a model car that has a $\frac{3}{7}$ horsepower motor. He decides to combine a $\frac{1}{3}$ horsepower motor, which he already has, with a new motor. What is the smallest motor he must buy so that the car's motor has $\frac{3}{7}$ total horsepower? ____________

4. **TECHNOLOGY** Shada's battery on her laptop will last for $\frac{3}{4}$ hour. She uses it for $\frac{2}{5}$ hour. How much longer will Shada's battery last? ____________

5. **FINANCES** Peyton won $\frac{3}{4}$ million dollars in the state lottery. He has to pay $\frac{2}{7}$ million dollars in federal and state taxes. How much money does Peyton get to keep? ____________ ____________

6. **PARKS** Noah is designing a new park on a strip of land that is $\frac{3}{8}$ mile long. The entrance and parking area will take up $\frac{1}{10}$ mile. How much land remains for the fields and other structures in the park? ____________

7. **CONSTRUCTION** Shareef built a birdhouse with a piece of wood that was $\frac{7}{12}$ meters long. If he has a $\frac{1}{3}$-meter-long piece of wood left over, how much wood did he use for the birdhouse? ____________

Chapter 6

NAME ______________________ DATE ______________

Lesson 6-4

Homework Practice

Subtract using models. Write each difference in simplest form.

1. $\frac{1}{2} - \frac{3}{10} =$ ____________

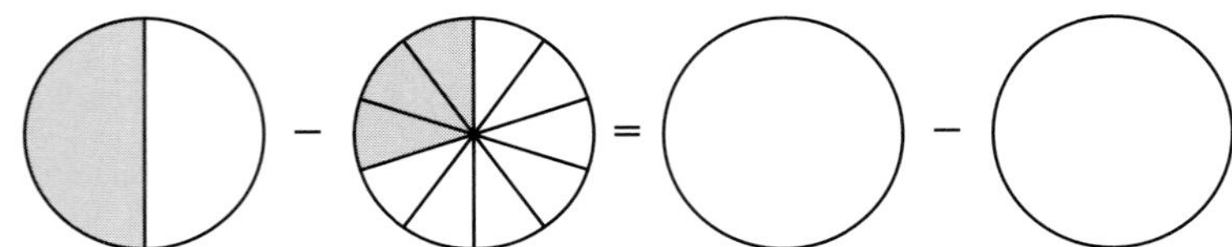

2. $\frac{2}{3} - \frac{1}{4} =$ ____________

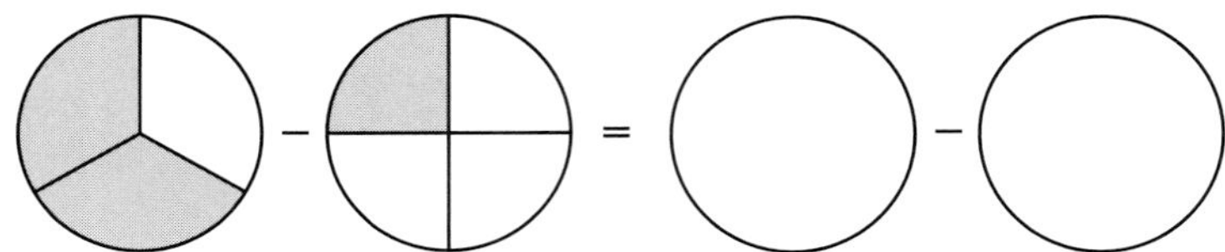

Subtract. Write each difference in simplest form.

3. $\frac{3}{7} - \frac{2}{5} =$ ____________

4. $\frac{4}{5} - \frac{1}{3} =$ ____________

5. $\frac{3}{4} - \frac{4}{8} =$ ____________

6. $\frac{5}{9} - \frac{2}{6} =$ ____________

7. $\frac{2}{3} - \frac{3}{5} =$ ____________

8. $\frac{8}{9} - \frac{4}{5} =$ ____________

Solve.

9. **POOLS** Mingan is draining his pool. When he began, the pool was $\frac{3}{4}$ full of water. After an hour, the pool is $\frac{1}{5}$ full of water. What fraction of the pool water has drained out over the first hour?

____

10. **INTERIOR DESIGN** Marisa painted her room periwinkle blue. She started with $\frac{9}{10}$ gallon of paint. After she was finished, she had $\frac{1}{5}$ gallon left over. How much paint did Marisa use?

____

Write the vocabulary word(s) that completes the sentence.

11. ____________ is a way of expressing a composite number as a product of its prime factors.

NAME ______________________ DATE ______________

Foldables Study Organizer

Dinah Zike's Foldables

Create this Foldable to help you study about decimals.

1. Fold a sheet of notebook paper in half from side to side.

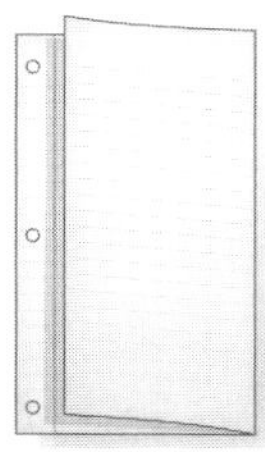

2. On one side, cut along every third line.

Tabs will form as you cut.

3. Label your Foldable as you read the chapter. The first vocabulary term is labeled on the model below.

You should have 10 tabs.

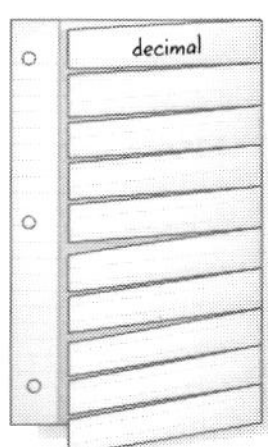

4. As you read the chapter, select and write key vocabulary terms on the front tabs of your Foldable. Then write the definition of each term under the tabs. After each definition, write a sentence or example using each vocabulary term correctly.

TAKING NOTES
As you read through the chapter, use your Foldable to write each key term, its definition, and an example.

USING YOUR FOLDABLE
As you study, open each tab of your Foldable and read the definitions and examples that you have written. State the term for the definitions and the examples. Check yourself by looking at the front of the tab.

USING YOUR FOLDABLE
Work with a partner. Take turns saying a term or a definition. If you say a term, your partner must state the definition. If you give a definition, your partner must state the term.

NAME ______________________ DATE ______________

Games and Puzzles
Countdown

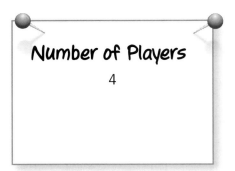

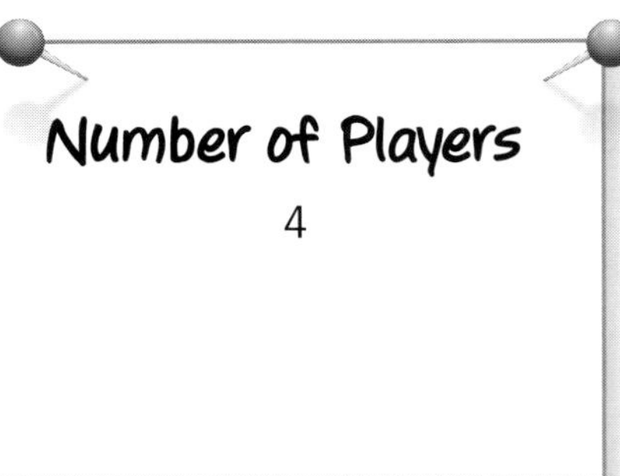

DIRECTIONS

- The first player begins with any number and counts down by subtracting the same number repeatedly. For example, the player may choose 67 and count 67, 64, 61. Each player stops after three numbers.
- The next player continues the countdown where the preceding player left off. In our example, that would be 58, 55, 52. Each player continues the countdown until one makes a mistake or until a team reaches the lowest whole number greater than or equal to zero.
- A player who makes a mistake is penalized 1 point. A player with 3 penalty points is eliminated from the round. The winner is the last survivor and gets to choose the next number.

VARIATION

- Count down by decimals. For example, a player may choose 42 and count 42, 41.5, 40, and so on.

NAME ______________________ DATE ______________

Lesson 7-1

Vocabulary and English Language Development

Activate Prior Knowledge

Complete the sentence with *right*, *left*, *first*, or *second*.

1

The shirt is to the ______________ of the hat.

2 410.78

The 8 is to the ______________ of the 7.

Definition Review

Identify the place value for each digit in the number 95.26.

3 9 ______________

4 5 ______________

5 2 ______________

6 6 ______________

Application

Fill in the place value and the words for the digits of each number.

	tens	ones		tenths	hundredths	thousandths
76.385			.			
words	seventy-six		and	three hundred and eighty-five thousandths		
29.5			.			
words	twenty-nine		and	five tenths		

Lesson 7-1

NAME ______________________ DATE ______________

Skills Practice

Write a decimal and a fraction or mixed number for each model.

1 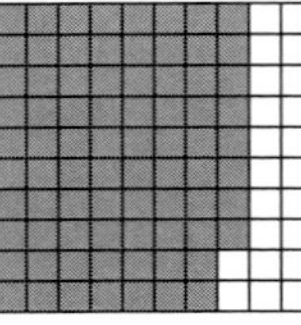

______ = ______

2 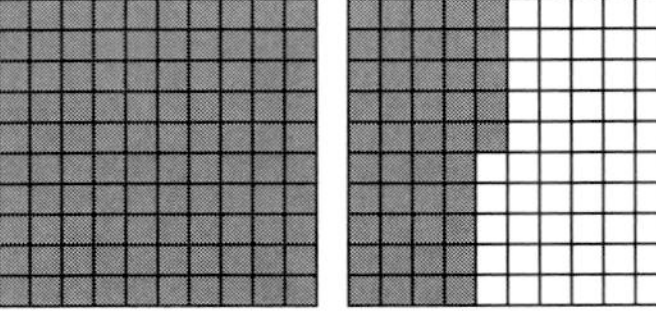

______ = ______

Write each number as a decimal.

3 twelve and sixty-five hundredths ______

4 nine tenths ______

5 seven and fourteen hundredths ______

6 eighteen and three hundredths ______

7 fifty-one hundredths ______

8 six and seven tenths ______

Write each number in words.

9 20.3 ______

10 0.89 ______

11 3.078 ______

12 17.4 ______

13 19.56 ______

Write the place of each underlined digit.

14 $\underline{6}7.4$ ______

15 $13.82\underline{5}$ ______

16 $5.\underline{4}$ ______

17 $2\underline{8}.4$ ______

18 $8\underline{6}.7$ ______

19 $\underline{4}4.5$ ______

20 $59.56\underline{4}$ ______

21 $7\underline{1}.2$ ______

NAME ______________________ DATE ______________

Lesson 7-1

Problem-Solving Practice

Solve. Write in simplest form.

1 **RACING** Judy is racing her dragster on a $\frac{1}{4}$-mile track. If she resets her odometer to 0.00, what should her odometer read after 1 lap around the track?

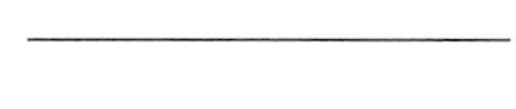

2 **TOOLS** Brandon needs to make a 0.625 -inch hole in a piece of wood. The drill bits he has are $\frac{3}{8}$ inch, $\frac{5}{8}$ inch, and $\frac{7}{8}$ inch in diameter. Which one should he use to drill the hole?

3 **TRIATHLON** Becky is training for a triathlon. To practice, she swims three-fourths of a kilometer 3 times a week. Use decimal notation to represent the number of kilometers Becky swims per week.

4 **HORSEBACK RIDING** Sergio rode his horse for $3\frac{14}{25}$ miles. What is the decimal equivalent of this distance?

5 **RUNNING** Sabrina and Aashi raced each other in a 100m sprint. Their stop watches are shown below. Who won the race and by how many hundredths of a second?

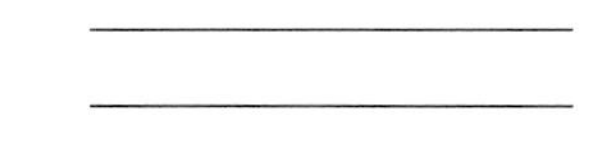

Sabrina

Aashi

6 **ENGINEERING** Andre is designing a power system that uses a motor with rating of $\frac{3}{4}$ hp. If his testing device reads horsepower in decimal units, what value should the testing device read?

7 **TRAVEL** Tia's mother told her they would need to drive four hundred eighty-two and sixty-three hundredths miles to Mount Rushmore. What is the distance as a decimal?

8 **BIOLOGY** In Biology class, Adita's frog weighed $1\frac{4}{10}$ kg. What is the decimal equivalent of the frog's weight?

Chapter 7

NAME ______________________ DATE ______________

Lesson 7-1

Homework Practice

Write a decimal and a fraction or mixed number for each model.

1 ____________ = ____________

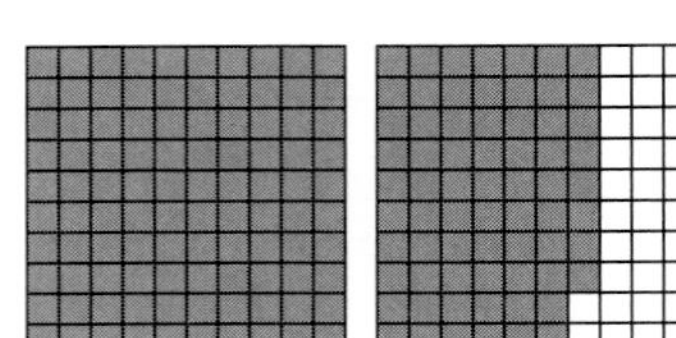

2 ____________ = ____________

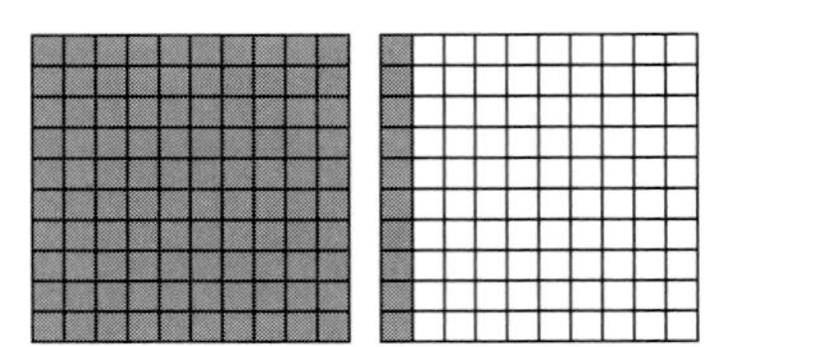

Write each number as a decimal.

3 two and thirty-six hundredths ____________

4 ninety-four and nine thousandths ____________

5 twelve and four tenths ____________

Write each number in words.

6 63.19 ____

7 5.8 ____

8 21.246 ____

Write the place of each underlined digit.

9 $3\underline{9}.8$ ____________________

10 $41.52\underline{7}$ ____________________

11 $\underline{2}4.1$ ____________________

12 $83.\underline{6}$ ____________________

Solve.

13 **SWIMMING** Khalid is a competitive swimmer. His best time in the backstroke is 32.34 seconds. At the meet on Saturday, his time was 31.97 seconds. Did Khalid beat his best time? If so, by how many hundredths of a second?

____

Write the vocabulary word(s) that completes each sentence.

14 One of ten equal parts is called a(n) ____________. One of one hundred equal parts is called a(n) ____________.

15 A(n) ____________ is a number that represents whole numbers and fractions.

A(n) ____________________ separates the whole number from the fraction.

Lesson 7-2

NAME ______________________ DATE ______________

Vocabulary and English Language Development

Activate Prior Knowledge

What number is being modeled?

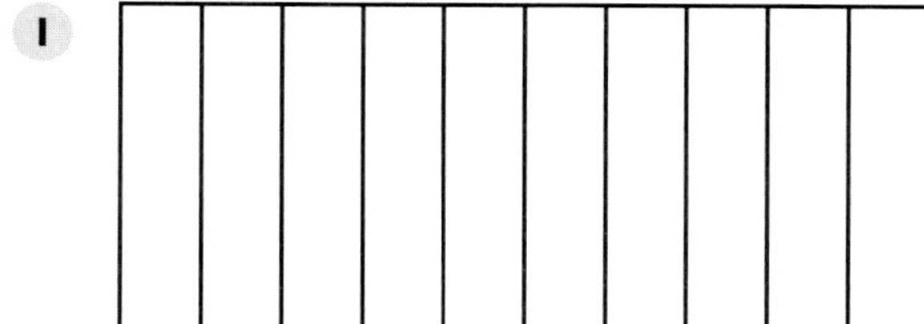

1 ______

2 ______

Definition Review

Equivalent decimals are decimals that have the same value.

Match each decimal in Column 1 with the equivalent decimal in Column 2.

	Column 1		Column 2
3	3.09	______	A 3.900
4	3.90	______	B 3.009
5	3.009	______	C 3.090

Application

- Find a partner.
- Write a number between 1 and 10 with up to three digits past the decimal point on a piece of paper.
- Your partner creates a place-value chart and completes the chart with the given number.
- Check your partner's work by saying the number in words.
- Alternate roles and repeat the process as time permits.

NAME ______________________ DATE ______________

Lesson 7-2

Skills Practice

Write equivalent decimals using hundredths.

1 12.4 ______________

2 72 ______________

3 0.9 ______________

4 6.23 ______________

5 1.2 ______________

6 0.370 ______________

Write equivalent decimals using thousandths.

7 23.06 ______________

8 37.1 ______________

9 4.002 ______________

10 19 ______________

11 6.8 ______________

12 0.1 ______________

Use place-value charts to show equivalent decimals for each pair of numbers.

13 8.2 and 8.200

ones	tenths
.	

ones	tenths	hundredths	thousandths
.			

14 7.05 and 7.050

ones	tenths	hundredths
.		

ones	tenths	hundredths	thousandths
.			

Write equivalent decimals to the indicated places.

	tenths	**hundredths**	**thousandths**
15	83.5	______	______
16	______	25.10	______
17	______	______	85.900
18	______	7.20	______

NAME ______________________________ DATE ______________

Lesson 7-2

Problem-Solving Practice

Solve.

1 **TRACK AND FIELD** Rosalinda, Li Ming, and Totsi were timing a race at a track meet each using a different type of stopwatch. At the end of the race Rosalinda's stopwatch read 15.02 seconds, Li Ming's stopwatch read 15.2 seconds, and Totsi's stopwatch read 15.020 seconds. Whose stopwatch recorded a different time from the other two? ____________

2 **EQUIVALENT DECIMALS** Connie, Nate, and Kite were each given a number to rewrite to the thousandths place. Who completed the task correctly? ____________

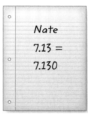

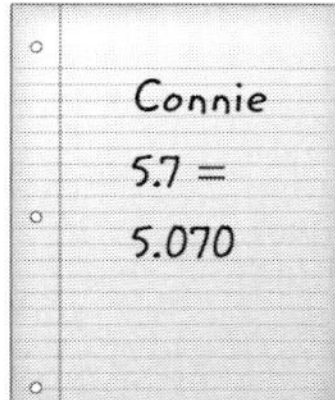

Nate
7.13 =
7.130

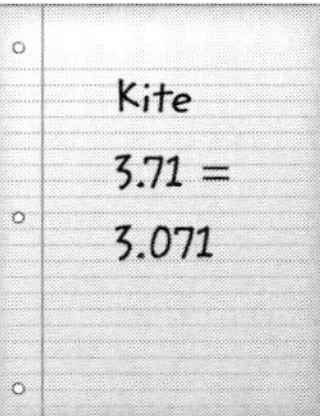

3 **REPRESENTING DECIMALS** Miller shaded 4 whole frames and 3 sections of a tenths frame. What number does this represent? ____________

4 **PLACE VALUE CHARTS** Kyle looked at the place-value chart shown below and said that it represented the number 17.1. Is Kyle correct? If not, what number does it represent? ____________ ____________

tens	ones	tenths	hundredths	thousandths

5 **TEMPERATURES** Jamila took her temperature and found it to be 101.07°. Since it seemed high, she asked her mother if she would retake it for her. Her mother found Jamila's temperature to be 101.7°. Are the temperatures the same? ____________

6 **DECIMAL REPRESENTATION** What number is being modeled in the figure below? ____________

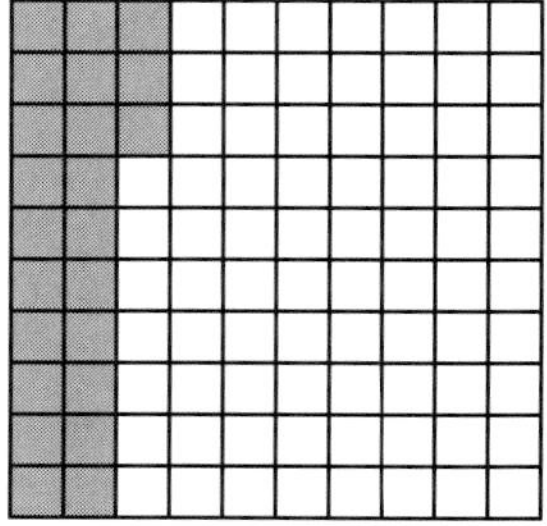

Chapter 7

Lesson 7-2

NAME ________________________ DATE ____________

Homework Practice

Use place-value charts to show equivalent decimals for each pair of numbers.

1 6.1 and 6.100

ones	tenths

ones	tenths	hundredths	thousandths

2 9.72 and 9.720

ones	tenths	hundredths

ones	tenths	hundredths	thousandths

Write equivalent decimals to the indicated place.

3 76.2 – thousandths ____________

4 18.1 – hundredths ____________

5 0.2 – hundredths ____________

6 1.9 – thousandths ____________

Solve.

7 **RAIN FALL** Beth looked at the rain gauge in the morning and told her mother that last night it rained 0.1 inches. Her brother Charlie looked at the same rain gauge and thought that 0.01 inches of rain fell last night. Could they both be correct? ______ If you answered no to the question, explain your answer. ____________________________

8 **GROCERY** Pedro went to the grocery store to buy 1.7 pounds of hamburger. When the grocery clerk handed him the hamburger it was labeled to the thousandths place. What number is on the label? ______

Write the vocabulary word that completes each sentence.

9 The amount of a number is called its ____________.

10 Decimals that represent the same number are called ____________ decimals.

11 The second decimal place to the right of the decimal point is called ______________ .

Lesson 7-3

NAME ______________________________ DATE ______________

Vocabulary and English Language Development

Activate Prior Knowledge

Complete each sentence with *more than or less than*.

1. 1.2 is ______________________ 1.8
2. 3.1 is ______________________ 3.11
3. 2.75 is ______________________ 2.71
4. 0.4 is ______________________ 0.14

Definition Review

Identify the place value of the underlined digit.

5. 48.<u>7</u>6 ______________________
6. 39<u>1</u>.27 ______________________
7. <u>6</u>52.48 ______________________
8. 77.3<u>1</u> ______________________
9. 8<u>4</u>6.59 ______________________
10. 29.19<u>5</u> ______________________

Application

Follow the directions for the activity.

- Teacher writes two consecutive whole numbers on the board.
- Write down a decimal (not to exceed the thousandths place) between the two numbers.
- Teacher selects six students to stand in front of the room.
- If you are selected, bring your number to display and order yourself from least to greatest.
- If you are seated, check if you are ordered correctly with other students who are also seated.
- Repeat the process as time permits with new numbers and students.

Chapter 7

NAME ______________________________ DATE ______________

Lesson 7-3

Skills Practice

Compare each pair of decimals using models. Write <, =, or > in each circle to make a true statement.

1 0.43 and 0.34

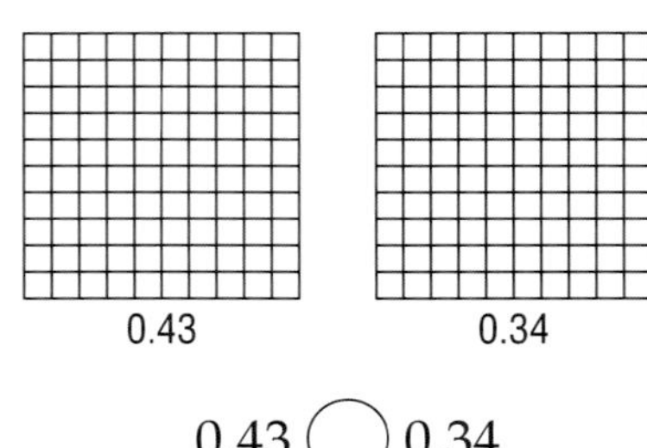

0.43 ◯ 0.34

2 0.1 and 0.11

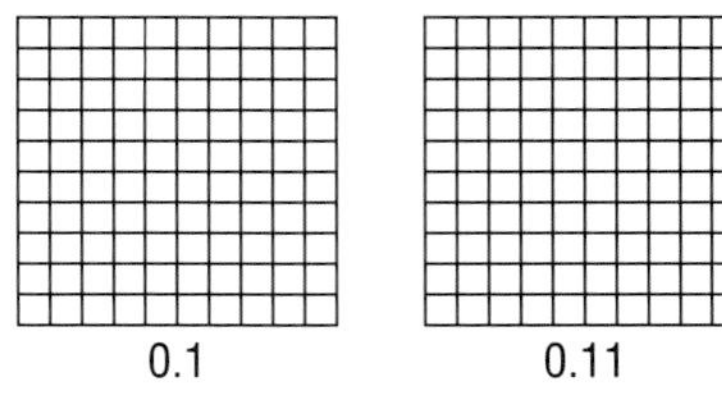

0.1 ◯ 0.11

Write <, =, or > in each circle to make a true statement.

3 5.50 ◯ 5.66

4 4.3 ◯ 4.23

5 8.96 ◯ 8.960

6 2.47 ◯ 2.44

7 4.54 ◯ 5.4

8 12.35 ◯ 12.6

9 11.56 ◯ 10.56

10 8.911 ◯ 9.0

11 0.02 ◯ 0.207

12 3.77 ◯ 3.77

13 12.06 ◯ 12.60

14 8.6 ◯ 8.35

Write <, =, or > in each circle to make a true statement. Check your answer by graphing the decimals on a number line.

15 3.53 ◯ 3.45

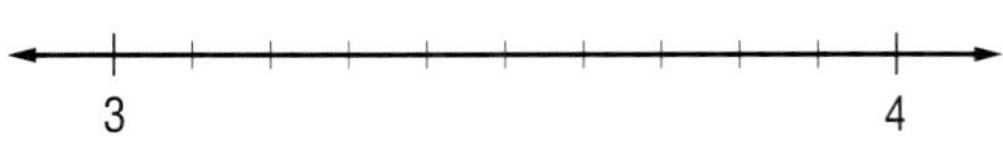

16 29.71 ◯ 29.9

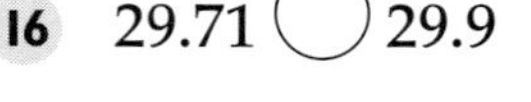

29 30

17 58.6 ◯ 58.60

18 42.70 ◯ 42.075

42 43

NAME _______________ DATE _______________

Lesson 7-3

Problem-Solving Practice

Solve.

1 **MANUFACTURING** Amalia works in a factory. She measures parts as they come off an assembly line. No part should measure more than 1.65 cm. She measures six parts to be 1.01 cm, 1.09 cm, 0.58 cm, 1.58 cm, 1.73 cm, and 1.64 cm. Order these parts from least to greatest. Are all of the parts within the requirement?

____

____

2 **MEASUREMENT** Coach Torres measured the heights of his players for the basketball team photo. The players were 78.5 inches, 73.2 inches, 75.7 inches, 79.2 inches, 71.3 inches, 73.1 inches, 78.7 inches, and 79.5 inches. What is the correct order of the players' heights from shortest to tallest?

____

____

3 **BASEBALL** Marcos wants to know which of his friends has the best batting average and which has the worst batting average. Look at the list below. Which is the highest batting average and which is the lowest?

highest: _______________

lowest: _______________

Batting Averages
0.273
0.325
0.371
0.313
0.269

4 **BIOLOGY** Makalla has four test tubes, each containing a different volume. Write the volumes from least to greatest.

____

Volume
3.9 mL
3.7 mL
3.5 mL
3.8 mL

Chapter 7

NAME ______________________________ DATE ______________

Lesson 7-3

Homework Practice

Compare each pair of decimals using models. Write $<$, $=$, or $>$ in each circle to make a true statement.

1. 0.12 and 0.21

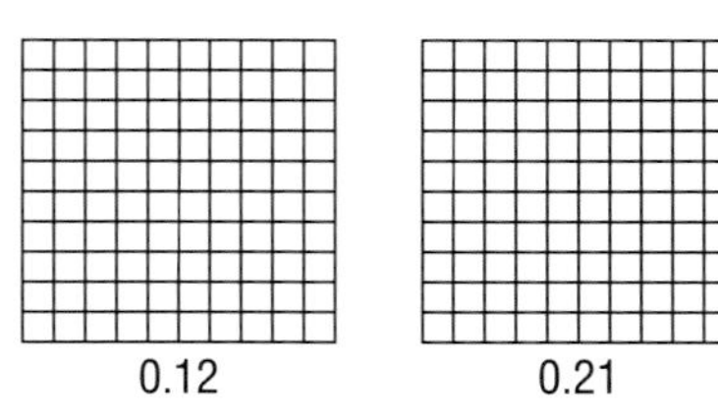

0.12 ◯ 0.21

2. 0.44 and 0.4

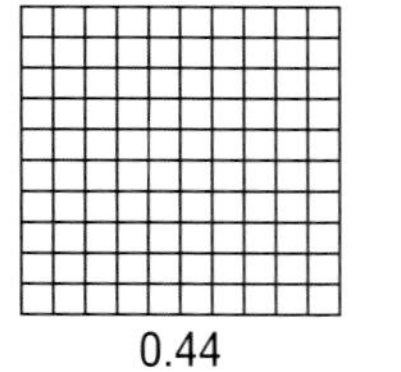

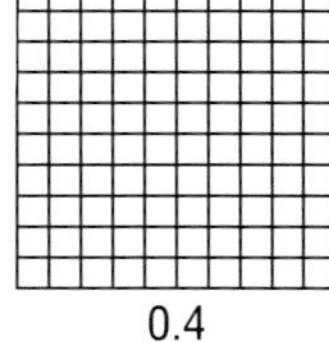

0.44 ◯ 0.4

Write $<$, $=$, or $>$ in each circle to make a true statement.

3. 21.78 ◯ 21.089

4. 10.6 ◯ 10.17

5. 5.24 ◯ 5.42

6. 29.5 ◯ 29.50

Write the numbers in order from least to greatest.

7. 11.6, 10.205, 10.05, 11.076

____

8. 63.54, 65.32, 58.62, 56.24

____

Solve.

9. **HEALTHCARE** A nurse is monitoring Lian's temperature. If it goes over 104.5 °F, she needs to page the doctor. Lian's chart lists the last four readings as 102.5 °F, 104.1°F, 103.7 °F, and 102.9 °F. Does the nurse need to call the doctor?

____

10. **STOCK MARKET** Nita follows the stock market. It has continued to go up for the past five days. On Monday, the market increased 12.5 points; on Tuesday, 37.8 points; on Wednesday, 11.7 points; on Thursday, 37.2 points; and on Friday, 22.5 points. Which day did the market go up the most? Which day did it go up the least?

____

____

Write the vocabulary word that completes the sentence.

11. A(n) __________ is a number that represents whole numbers and fractions.

12. The first number to the right of a decimal point is in the __________ place.

Lesson 7-4

NAME ______________________ DATE ______________

Vocabulary and English Language Development

Activate Prior Knowledge

Graph each number on the number line. Then tell which whole number it is closer to.

1 13.2

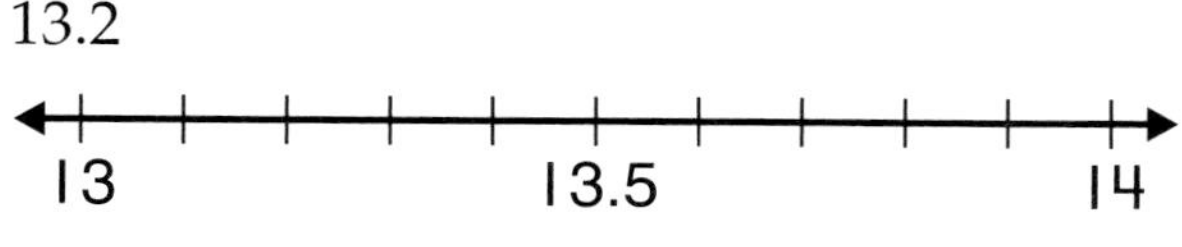

______

2 7.92

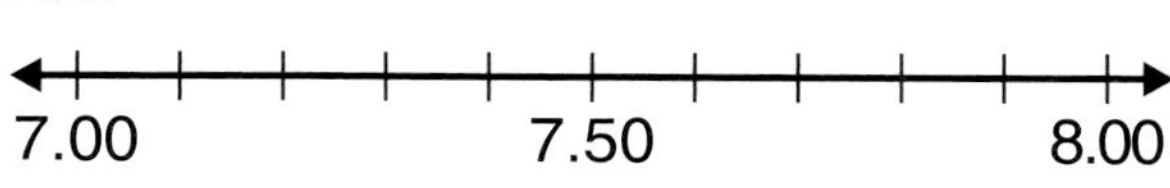

______

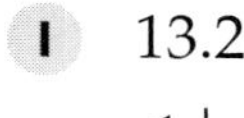

Definition Review

An **estimate** is a number close to an exact value; it indicates about how much.

Estimate the sum or difference for each set of numbers.

3 Estimate the sum of 47.2 and 22.9

Round each decimal to the tens place. ______ ; ______

add the rounded numbers. ______ + ______ = ______

4 Estimate the difference of $19.09 and $14.07.

Round to the nearest dollar. ______ ; ______

subtract the rounded numbers. ______ − ______ = ______

Application

- Find a partner.
- Write an addition or subtraction problem on a piece of paper. The problem should be the sum or difference of two numbers greater than zero but less than 100. Numbers should have at least one digit but no more than two digits to the right of the decimal point.
- Your partner estimates the sum or difference.
- Check your partner's work.
- Alternate roles and repeat the process as time permits.

Chapter 7

NAME ______________________ DATE ____________

Lesson 7-4

Skills Practice

Identify the greatest place value for each number.

1 47.2 ________

2 3.68 ________

3 112.1 ________

4 0.13 ________

Round each number to the nearest whole number.

5 56.9 ________

6 43.01 ________

7 34.09 ________

8 70.2 ________

9 11.81 ________

10 19.73 ________

Estimate the sum of difference for each set of numbers.

11 Estimate the sum of 31.6 and 17.

Round each decimal to the tens place ________ ; ________

and the rounded numbers ________ + ________ = ________

12 Estimate the difference of $47.90 and $18.

Round to the nearest dollar, ________ ;________

subtract the rounded numbers ________ – ________ = ________

Round each pair of numbers. Estimate the sum.

13 47.2 + 13.1 = ________

14 31.6 + 17 = ________

15 21.5 + 18.45 = ________

16 67.6 + 27.8 = ________

17 84.2 + 12.6 = ________

18 67.2 + 7.15 = ________

Round each pair of numbers. Estimate the difference.

19 23.4 – 14.5 = ________

20 47.9 – 18 = ________

21 98.07 – 29.1 = ________

22 54.3 – 33.6 = ________

23 81 – 6.52 = ________

24 72.8 – 19.2 = ________

NAME ______________________ DATE ______________

Problem-Solving Practice

Solve.

1 **WEIGHT** Kyle weighs 132.7 pounds and Kurt weighs 147.1 pounds. Estimate the difference between their weights. ______________

2 **PERIMETER** The perimeter of the picture frame shown below can be found by adding the lengths of all four sides. Estimate the perimeter.

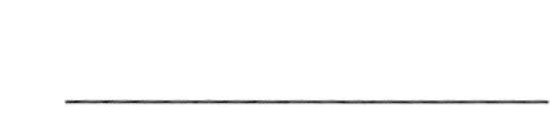

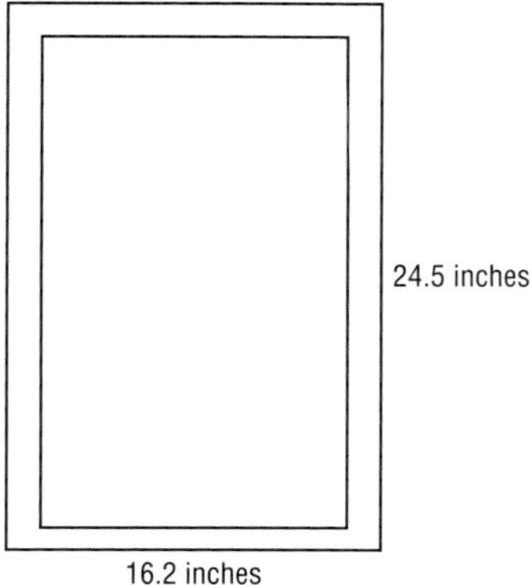

3 **WALKING DISTANCE** Noelle walks to school and walks back home every day. The distance from her house to school is 3.7 miles. Estimate the total distance she walks each day. ______________

4 **RECEIPT** Malik went to lunch and received the receipt shown below. What is the estimated total cost for his lunch? ______________

Receipt

Tea	$ 1.50
Sandwich	$ 3.30
Dessert	$ 2.75
Total	

5 **GARAGE SALE** Mr. Lopez had a garage sale. The table below shows how much money he earned daily. Estimate his total earnings ______________

Thursday	$47.50
Friday	$31.20
Saturday	$52.17

6 **WAGES** Tulip earned $67.39 last week and $86.53 this week. Estimate her total earnings from last week and this week. ______________

NAME ______________________ DATE ______________

Lesson 7-4 Homework Practice

Identify the greatest place value for each number.

1. 8.62 __________
2. 63.5 __________
3. 247.3 __________
4. 18.31 __________

Round each number to the nearest whole number.

5. 47.31 __________
6. 18.2 __________
7. 0.92 __________
8. 24.09 __________
9. 8.47 __________
10. 6.98 __________

Estimate each sum or difference.

11. 13.6 + 21.2 = __________
12. 48.1 – 21.6 = __________
13. 48 – 33.2 = __________
14. 18 + 21.3 = __________
15. 76.8 + 14.33 = __________
16. 91.2 – 56.7 = __________
17. 101.1 – 91.1 = __________
18. 51.9 + 51.9 = __________

Solve.

19. **SHOPPING EXPENSES** Sal spent $14.52, $23.71, and $12.22 at three different clothing stores. Estimate the amount that he spent. __________

20. **SAVINGS** Cricket saved $15.31 this week and wants to save $21.50 next week. What is the estimated difference between the two amounts? __________

Write the vocabulary word that completes each sentence.

21. To __________ a number is to find the nearest number based on a given place value.

22. A number that is close to the exact value is called an __________ .

Lesson 7-5

NAME ______________________ DATE ______________

Vocabulary and English Language Development

Activate Prior Knowledge

Add the money.

1    = ______________

2  = ______________

Definition Review

Write each number as a decimal.

3 Six and thirty-five hundredths ______

4 Four and seven thousandths ______

5 Twenty and three tenths ______

6 Ten and eighty-one hundredths ______

Application

- Bring in various receipts from home. Make sure you have at least one receipt.
- Work in groups of 3 or 4.
- Tear off the bottom of each receipt just above the total charge so that all of the individual prices are still on the top portion.
- Trade receipts within your group.
- Find the total of each receipt.
- Check with each other to see if answers are correct.
- Repeat the process by trading receipts and finding the new sums.

Chapter 7

NAME ______________________ DATE ______________

Lesson 7-5

Skills Practice

Add using decimal models.

1. 1.23 + 0.48 = ______________

2. 0.59 + 0.76 = ______________

Find each sum.

3. 3.45 + 10.82 = ______________

4. 8.13 + 2.07 = ______________

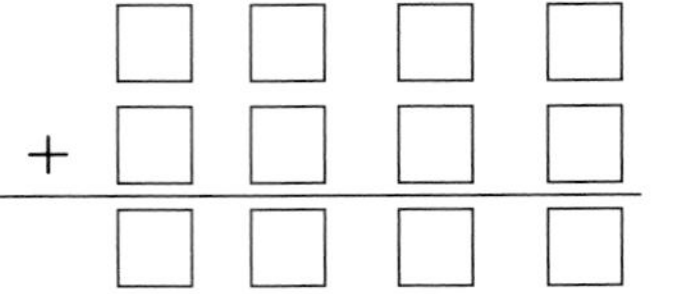

5. 12.06 + 5.9 = ______________

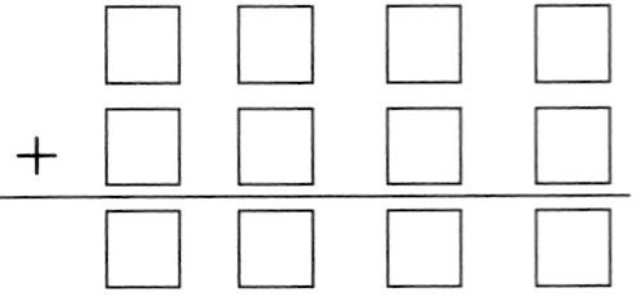

6. 6.31 + 9.2 = ______________

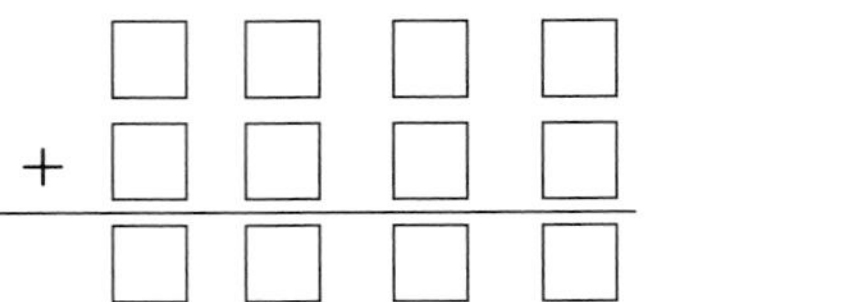

7. 1.56 + 10.28 = ______________

8. 8.9 + 3.35 = ______________

9. 5.92 + 7.3 = ______________

10. 5.07 + 2.5 = ______________

11. 12.19 + 3.70 = ______________

12. 4.3 + 9.84 = ______________

13. 12.05 + 10.34 = ______________

14. 2.77 + 4.15 = ______________

NAME ______________________ DATE ______________

Lesson 7-5

Problem-Solving Practice

Solve.

1. **BIKING** Yesterday, Angelica biked 6.73 miles from her house to the park. Then she biked 14.62 miles from the park to a lake. Then she biked 11.15 miles back to her house. How many miles did Angelica bike? ______________

2. **CHEMISTRY** Diego mixed 10.37 mL of solution with 1.28 mL of water. How much liquid does Diego have now? ______________

3. **WELDING** Ella welded a 2.465 inches thick piece of steel to a 0.75-inch thick piece of steel. How many inches thick is the new piece of welded steel? ______________

4. **COMPUTERS** Sanson needs to put two files on his flash drive. One file is 63.8 MB and the other file is 62.77 MB. His flash drive can hold 128 MB of data. Will both files fit on the flash drive? Explain.

____

____

5. **ENGINEERING** Yada is designing a sprinkler system with two lines. One of the lines will have a flow of 2.175 gallons per minute. The other line will have a flow of 1.645 gallons per minute. What will be the total flow of water when both lines are running? ______________

6. **BAKING** Yong needs 7 pounds of apples to make four apple pies. He buys two bags of apples—one is 3.28 lbs. and the other is 3.73 lbs. Does Yong have enough apples to make four pies? Explain.

____

____

7. **BUSINESS** Kasa keeps track of her mileage for her expense reports. On Monday she drives to the AB company and her odometer reads 88.2 miles. On Thursday she drives to the ZY Corporation and her odometer reads 45.9 miles. How many total miles did Kasa travel on business this week? ______________

Chapter 7

NAME ________________ DATE ________________

Lesson 7-5

Homework Practice

Add using decimal models.

1 $1.05 + 1.27 =$ ________

2 $0.96 + 1.25 =$ ________

Find each sum.

3 $\begin{array}{r} 35.29 \\ +16.54 \\ \hline \end{array}$

4 $\begin{array}{r} 63.47 \\ +59.38 \\ \hline \end{array}$

5 $\begin{array}{r} 28.765 \\ +\ 1.055 \\ \hline \end{array}$

6 $4.35 + 0.84 =$ ________

7 $15.6 + 2.03 =$ ________

8 $7.49 + 1.27 =$ ________

9 $9.18 + 6.4 =$ ________

10 $3.021 + 8.729 =$ ________

11 $11.656 + 5.39 =$ ________

Solve.

12 **NUTRITION** Neil is keeping track of his food intake for his Health class. On Wednesday, he ate 3.8 grams of fat at breakfast, 16.1 grams of fat at lunch, and 21.3 grams of fat at dinner. How many grams of fat did Neil consume on Wednesday? ________

13 **LANDSCAPING** Pilan used 1.7 gallons of gas to mow lawns on Saturday, and 0.6 gallons of gas to mow lawns on Sunday. How many gallons of gas did Pilan use this weekend? ________

Write the vocabulary word that completes the sentence.

14 A(n) ________ is a number that can represents whole numbers and fractions.

15 The answer or result of an addition problem is called the ________.

NAME ______________________________ DATE ______________

Lesson 7-6

Vocabulary and English Language Development

Activate Prior Knowledge

Write a decimal for each model.

1 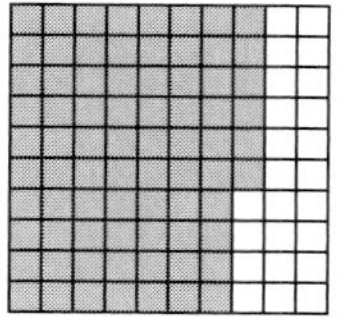

____

2 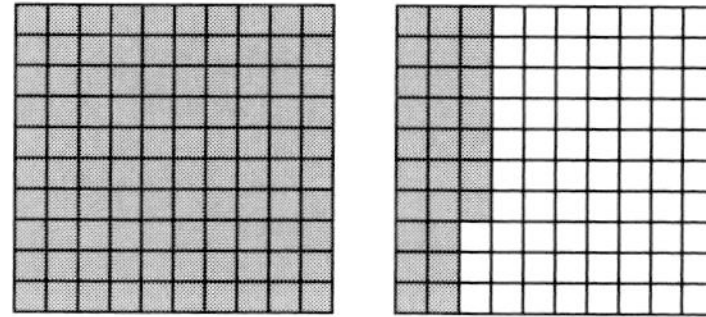

____

Definition Review

Decimal models can be used to subtract **decimals.**

Fill in the blanks with one of the following words: decimal, decimal point, regrouped, difference.

3 To subtract decimals, you can write the numbers vertically and line up the ______________.

4 When there is not a large enough number in a certain place value from which to subtract, the number must be ______________.

5 The answer to a subtraction problem is the called the ______________.

6 A ______________ is a number that represents both whole numbers and fractions.In such a number, the ______________ separates the whole number and fraction parts.

Application

- Find a partner.
- Create 5 subtraction problems with decimals, and write them on a piece of paper. Decimal numbers must be between 0 and 10 with up to three digits to the right of the decimal point.
- Trade papers with another pair and solve the decimal subtraction problems.
- Discuss answers and check solutions on a calculator. The pair with the most correct responses wins.

NAME _______________ DATE _______________

Lesson 7-6

Skills Practice

Subtract using decimal models.

1. 2.46 – 0.3 = ____________

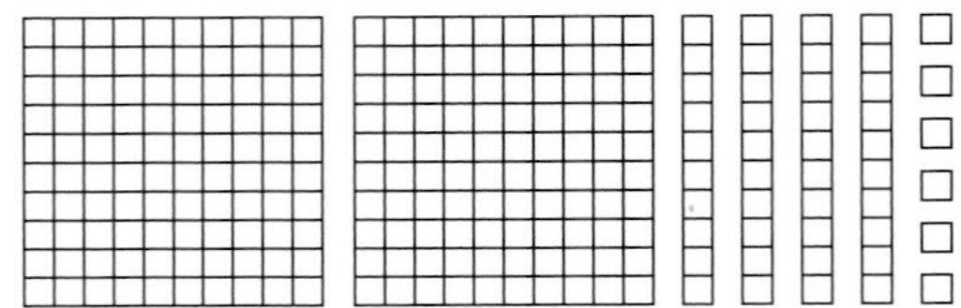

2. 1.8 – 0.79 = ____________

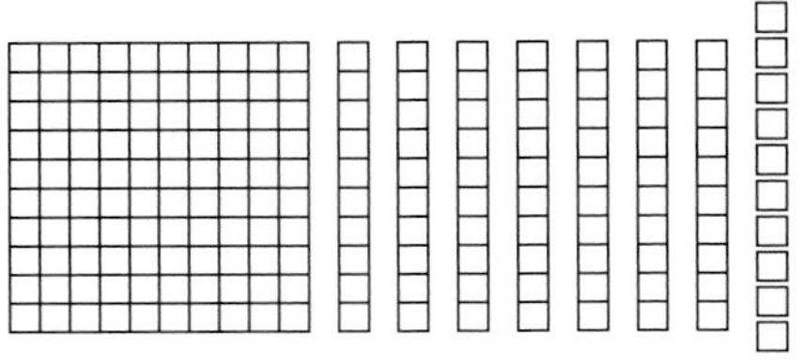

3. 0.87 – 0.56 = ____________

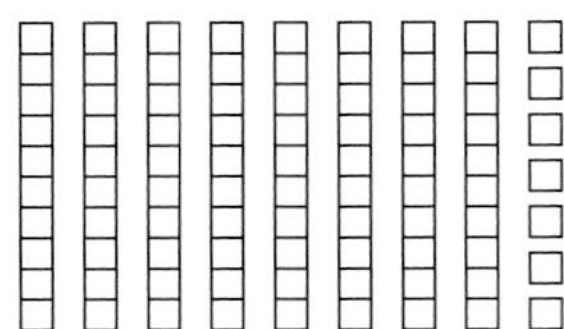

4. 2.35 – 1.74 = ____________

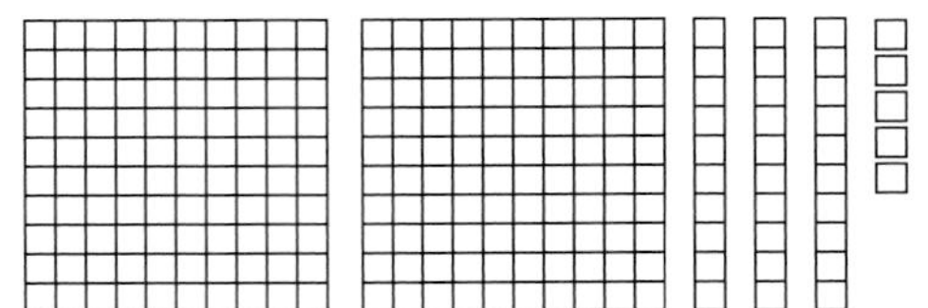

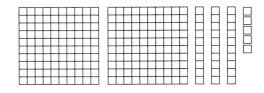

Subtract.

5. 14.86 – 9.315 = ____________

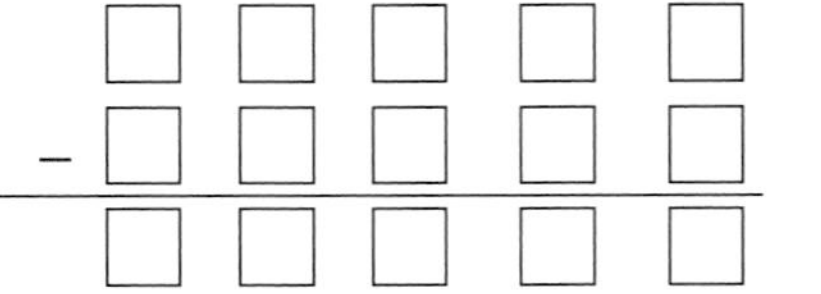

6. 7 – 4.25 = ____________

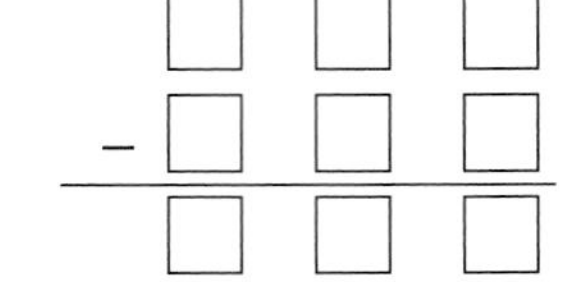

7. 23.81 – 14.29

8. 20.01 – 9.98

9. $16.00 – $ 7.05

10. 8.42 – 0.478

11. 59.84 – 2.71

12. $80.25 – $31.04

13. $42.73 – $11.24

14. 4.378 – 3.62

15. 37.04 – 15.3

16. 23.46 – 8.58

NAME ______________________ DATE ______________

Problem-Solving Practice

Solve.

1. **GROCERY** Emma bought several items at the grocery store. She gave the clerk $20 to pay for her total bill of $12.54. How much change did Emma receive? ______________

2. **GYMNASTICS** Imani earned a score of 38.68 in her qualifying event. She later earned a score of 39.82 in the final event round. How much did Imani improve her score from the qualifying round to the final round? ______________

3. **BASEBALL** In his junior year of high school, Charo had an earned run average of 6.19. In his senior year he had an earned run average of 5.43. How much better was Charo's earned run average in his senior year than in his junior year? ______________

4. **GROCERY STORE** Lorena needs 3 pounds of ground beef for a new spaghetti recipe. The grocery scale reads 2.855 pounds. How much more ground beef should the grocery clerk put on the scale to get the amount of ground beef that Lorena needs? ______________

5. **COMMUNITY SERVICE** To earn a badge in her service organization, Kate is working 24 hours at a local hospital. The first weekend, she works 8.25 hours. The second and third weekends she works 6 hours and 5.5 hours. If Kate completes her work to earn her badge, how many hours will she work during her last weekend? ______________

6. **POPULATION** China and India have the largest populations of any country in the world. The population of China is approximately 1.32 billion people. The population of India is approximately 1.13 billion people. How many more people live in China than in India? ______________

7. **GEOGRAPHY** Russia has the largest land area in the world. Its land area covers 17 million square kilometers. The land area of the United States is 9.16 million square kilometers. How much larger is Russia than the United States in land area? ______________

Lesson 7-6

NAME ______ DATE ______

Homework Practice

Subtract using decimal models.

1 1.67 – 0.52 = ______

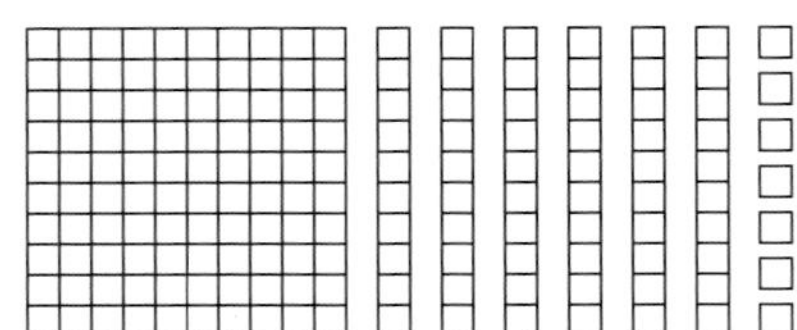

2 0.91 – 0.43 = ______

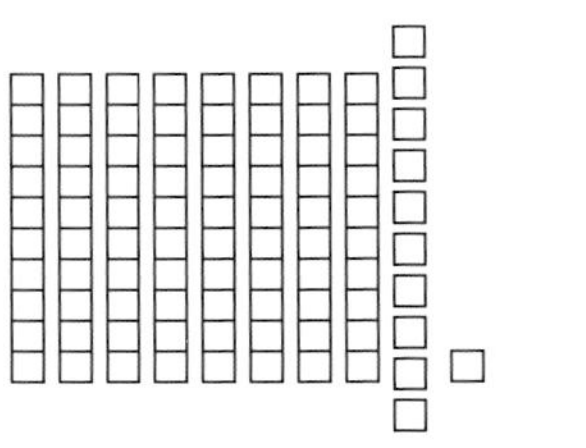

3 2.4 – 1.26 = ______

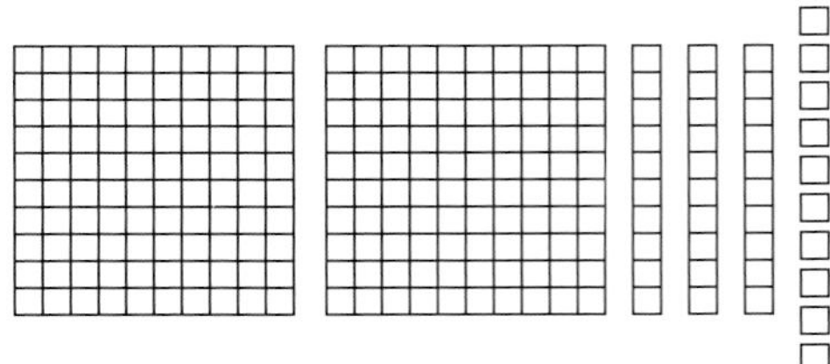

4 1.03 – 0.72 = ______

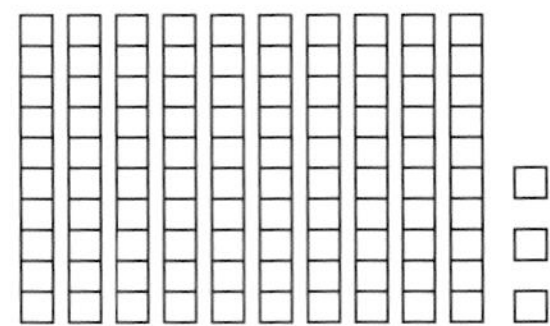

Subtract.

5 6.08 – 2.4 = ______

6 13.47 – 5.49 = ______

7 $8.42
– $7.31

8 16.21
– 11.47

9 25.17– 13.28 = ______

10 $12.40
– $ 3.16

Solve.

11 **GEOGRAPHY** The size of the North American continent is approximately 24.26 million square kilometers. The size of the South American continent is approximately 17.82 million square kilometers. How much larger is North America than South America?

______

Write the vocabulary word that completes the sentence.

12 Using place value to exchange equal amounts when renaming a number is called ______.

Chapter 8

NAME ____________________ DATE ____________

Foldables Study Organizer

Dinah Zike's Foldables

Make this Foldable to help you organize information about geometry.

1 Begin with one sheet of 11″ × 17″ paper. Fold the short sides so they meet in the middle.

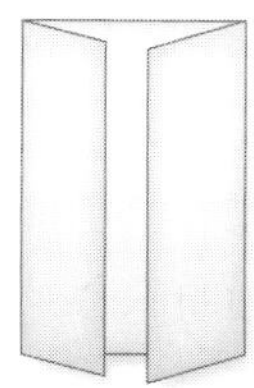

2 Fold the top to the bottom.

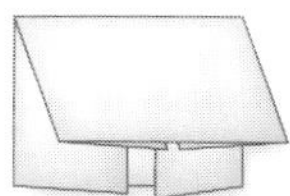

3 Unfold and cut to make four tabs.

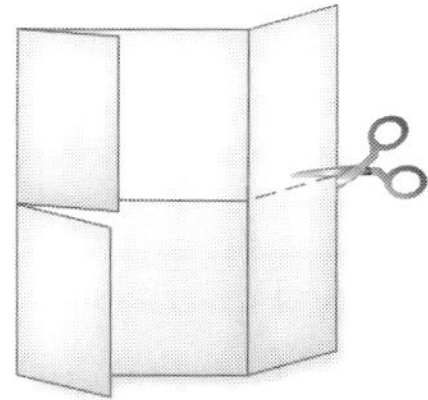

4 Label the tabs as shown.

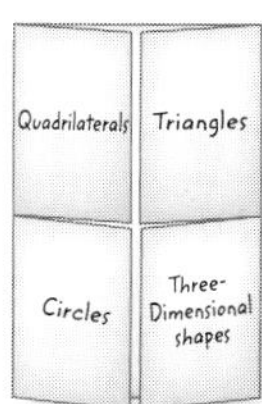

TAKING NOTES
As you read through the chapter, write a key fact for each lesson in your Foldable.

USING YOUR FOLDABLE
As you study, check your understanding by writing an additional fact for each lesson without lifting the tabs.

USING YOUR FOLDABLE
Work with a partner. Take turns explaining your examples to one another. Alternate until you have both discussed each topic in your Foldables.

Chapter 8

NAME ______________________ DATE ______________

Games and Puzzles

Guess the Figure

DIRECTIONS

- Player 1 chooses a quadrilateral, triangle, or three-dimensional figure.
- This player describes the figure by its properties. For example, "I am thinking of a quadrilateral with exactly one pair of parallel sides".
- The other players guess what the figure is.
- The first player to correctly identify the figure gets one point.
- Player 2 then describes a figure.
- Players take turns describing a figure and guessing its identity.
- **Who Wins?** The first player to get five points is the winner.

NAME ____________________ DATE ____________

Lesson 8-1

Vocabulary and English Language Development

Activate Prior Knowledge

1 **Label each figure below with *right angle, square,* or *rectangle.***

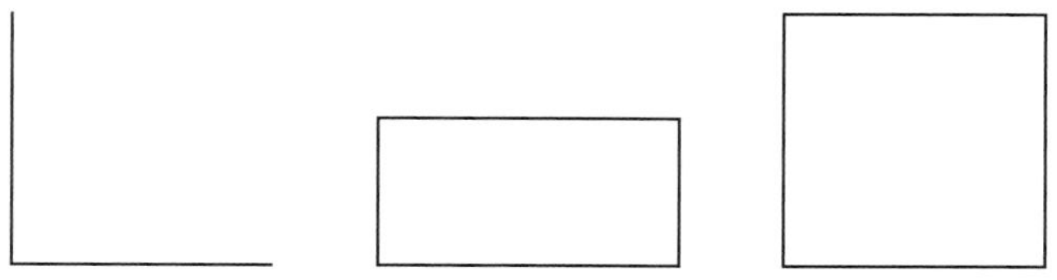

Definition Review

A **quadrilateral** is a shape with four sides and four angles.

Complete each statement.

2 A quadrilateral with four right angles is called a ____________________.

3 A rectangle with four equal sides is called a ____________________.

4 A parallelogram with four equal sides is called a ____________________.

Application

Follow the directions to play the game.

- Work in groups of three. Gather a deck of cards with diagrams of the five kinds of quadrilaterals.
- Pick one card.
- Name the quadrilateral shown on the card.
- Each student in the group tells something about the quadrilateral you have named.
- Replace the cards.
- Alternate roles and repeat the steps as time permits.

Chapter 8

NAME ______________________ DATE ______________

Lesson 8-1

Skills Practice

Classify the shape in as many ways as possible.

1 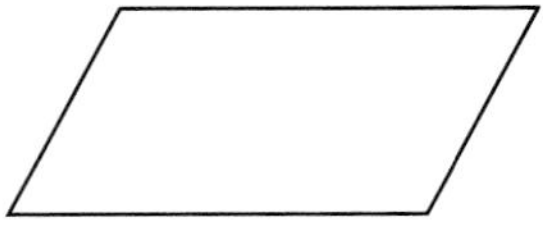

____

2 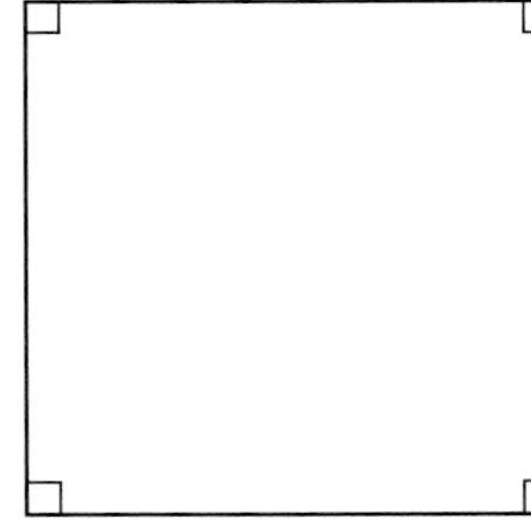

____

____

3 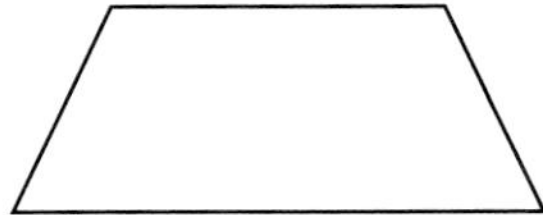

____

4 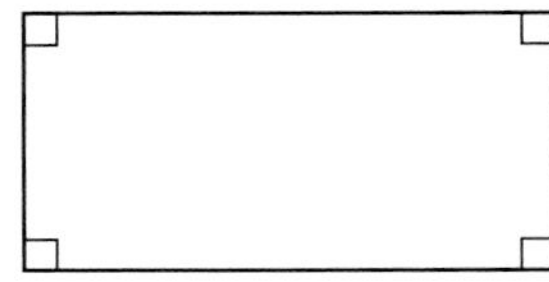

____

Identify each figure.

5 

____

6 

____

7 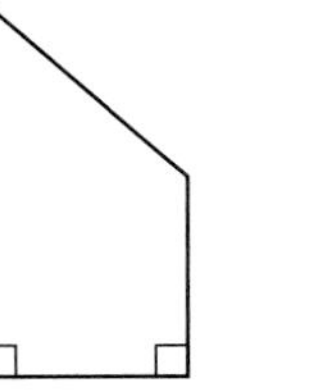

____

8 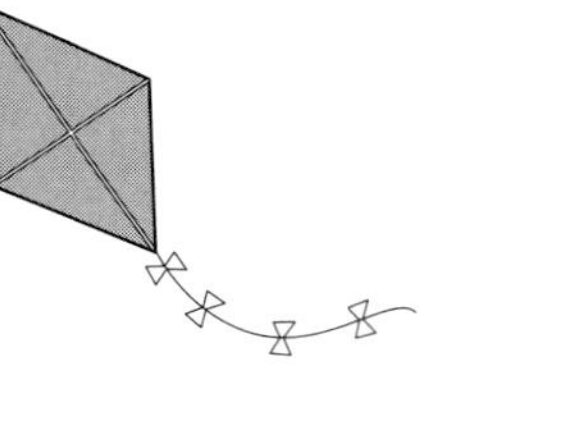

____

Tell whether each statement is true or false.

9 A square is a rhombus. ______________

10 A parallelogram is a rectangle. ______________

11 A square is a rectangle. ______________

12 A rectangle is a square. ______________

Lesson 8-1 NAME ______________________ DATE ____________

Problem-Solving Practice

Solve.

1 **QUADRILATERAL** A quadrilateral has four equal sides and four right angles. What is the quadrilateral? ____________

2 **RECTANGLE** Circle all the rectangles.

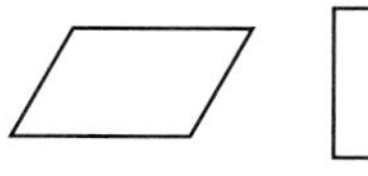 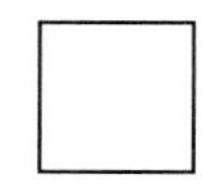 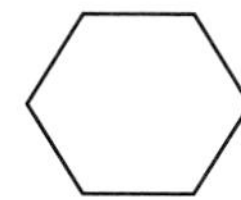 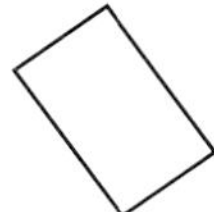 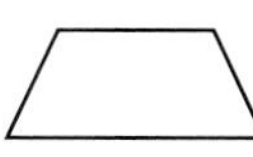

3 **QUADRILATERAL** Gregg draws a quadrilateral. Each pair of opposite sides are parallel. Two sides are longer than the other two. What is the quadrilateral?

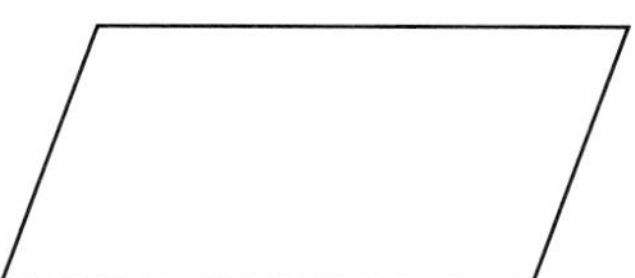

____

4 **WINDOW** Marsha found these shapes in a stained glass window. She said three were parallelograms. Bill said four were parallelograms. Who is correct?

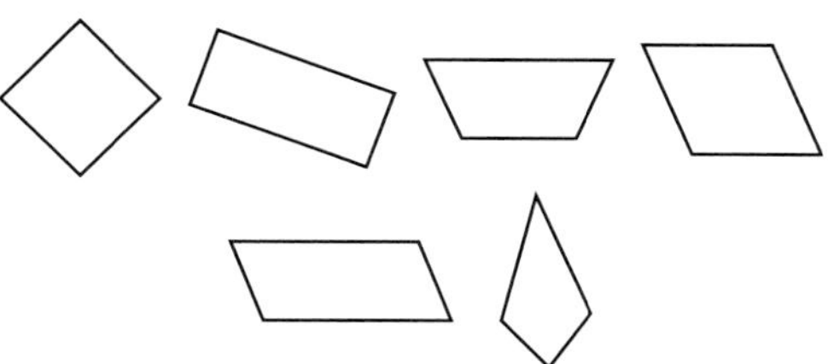

____

5 **MAP** What shape is the state of Colorado?

____

6 **TABLE** What shape is the table shown?

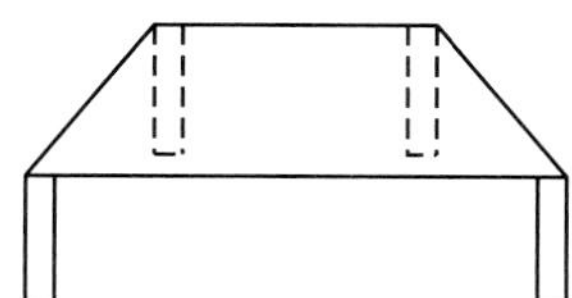

____

Chapter 8

NAME ______________________ DATE ______________

Lesson 8-1

Homework Practice

Identify the figure.

1 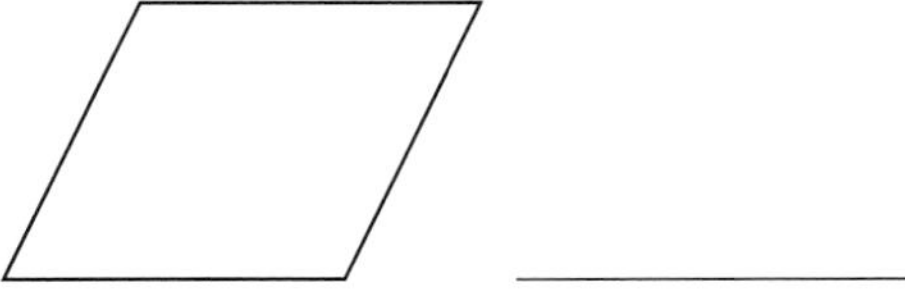 ______________

2 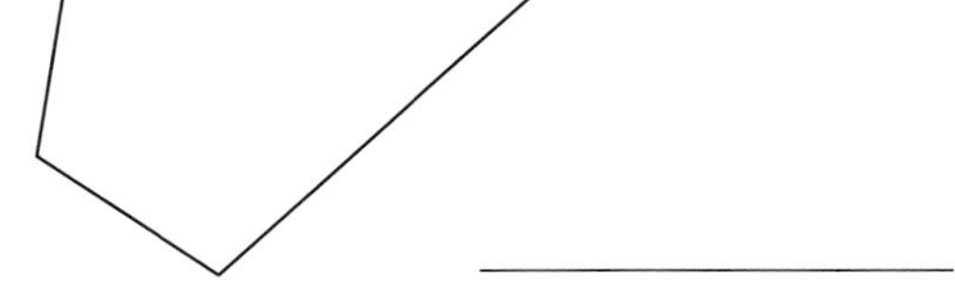 ______________

3 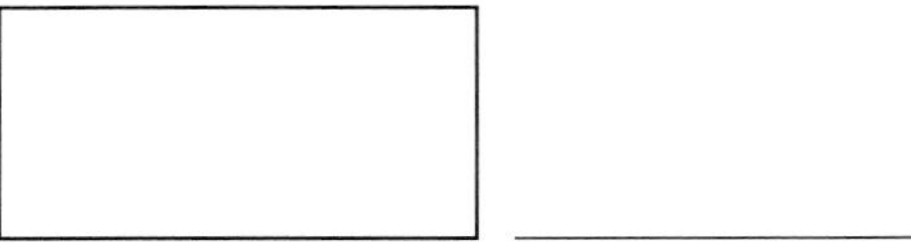 ______________

4 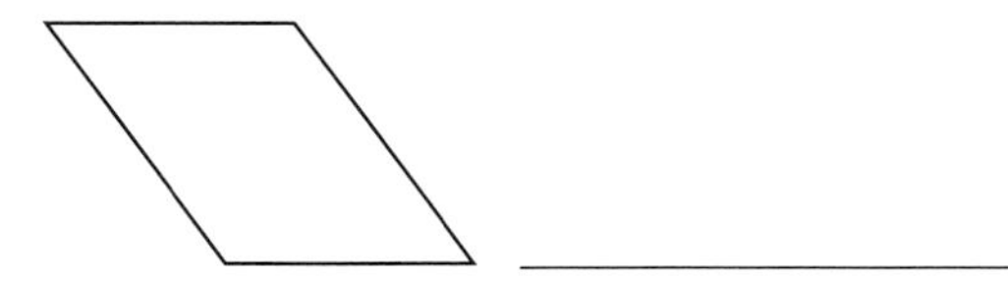 ______________

5 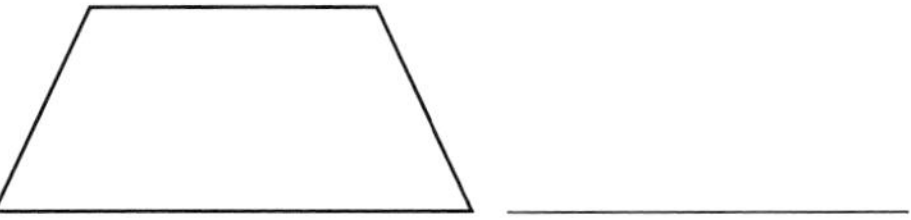 ______________

6 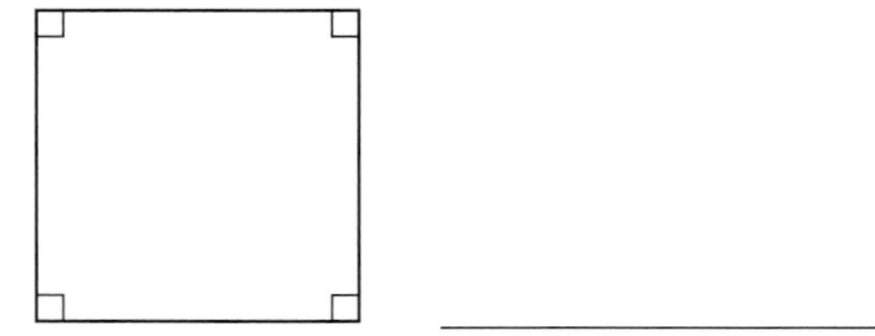 ______________

Classify the shape in as many ways as possible.

7  ______________

8 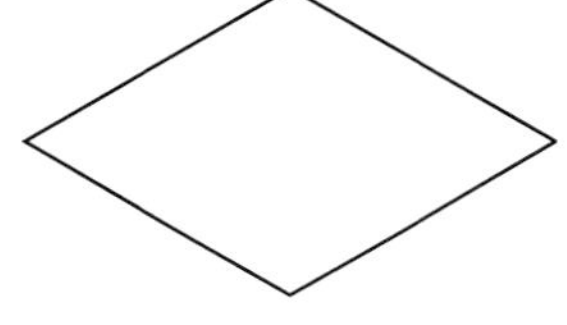 ______________

9 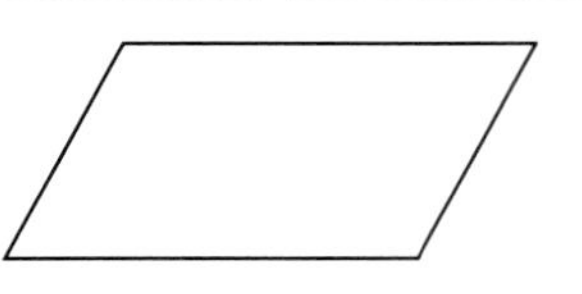 ______________

10 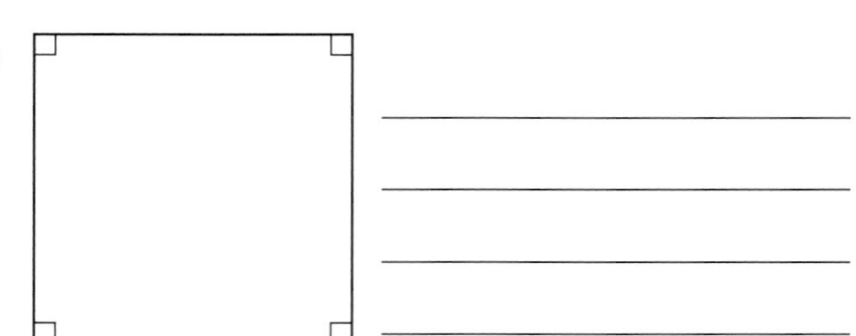 ______________

Draw the shape.

11 rhombus

12 trapezoid

13 rectangle

14 parallelogram

Lesson 8-2

NAME ______________________________ DATE ____________

Vocabulary and English Language Development

Activate Prior Knowledge

1 Which of the figures below are triangles? Draw a circle around each.

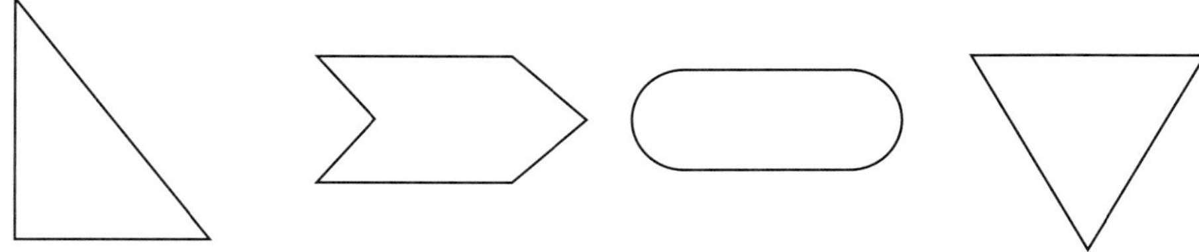

Definition Review

Complete each statement.

2 A triangle with all three angles less than 90° is an ______________ triangle.

3 A triangle with three congruent sides is an ______________ triangle.

4 A triangle with one obtuse angle is an ______________ triangle.

5 A triangle with one right angle is a ______________ triangle.

6 A triangle with no congruent sides is a ______________ triangle.

7 A triangle with at least two sides of the same length is an ________ triangle.

Application

- Pick a partner.
- Draw a picture of a triangle.
- Ask your partner to identify the triangle as equilateral, isosceles, or scalene.
- Your partner draws a triangle.
- Identify the triangle as right, acute, or obtuse.
- Continue drawing different triangles and identifying them by sides or angles, as time permits.

NAME ______________________________ DATE ______________

Lesson 8-2

Skills Practice

Identify each angle as acute, obtuse, or right.

1 117° ____________________

2 90° ____________________

3 3° ____________________

4 87° ____________________

5 164° ____________________

6 111° ____________________

Name the triangle by its sides.

7

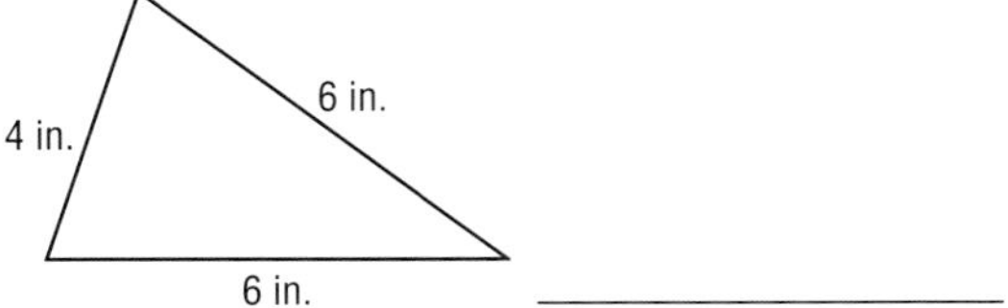

____

8

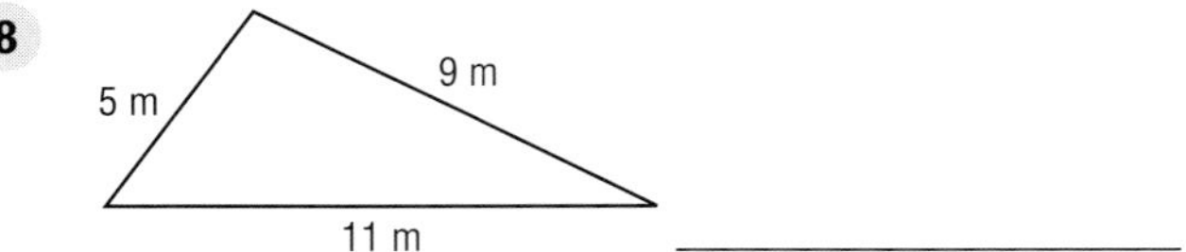

____

9

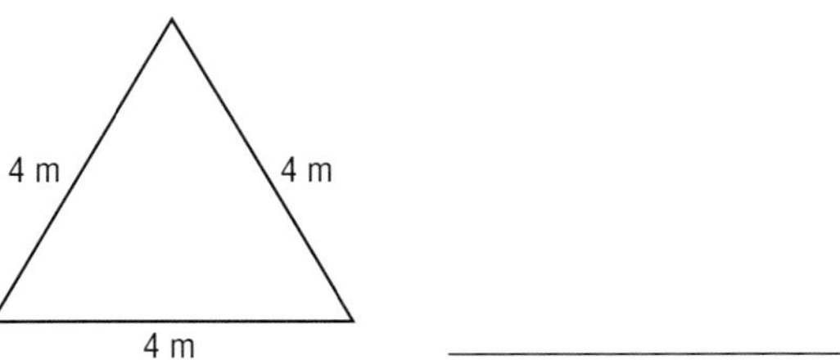

____

10

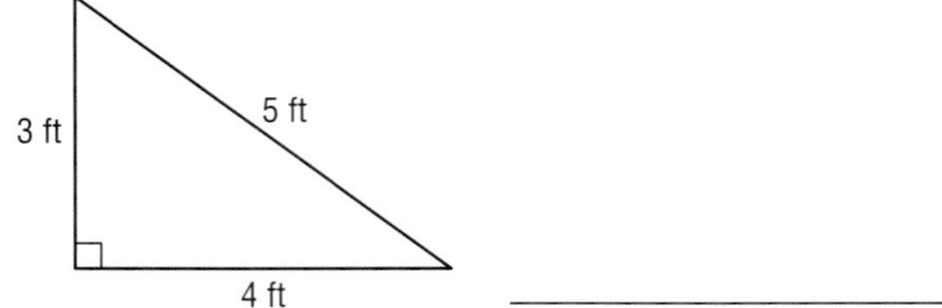

____

Name the triangle by its angles.

11

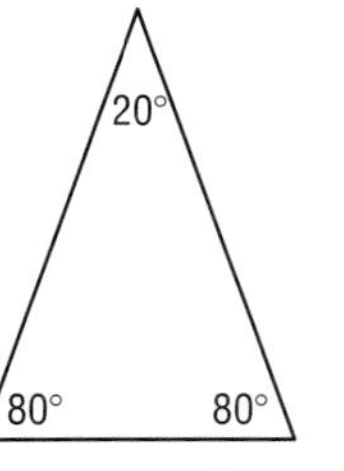

____

12

____

13

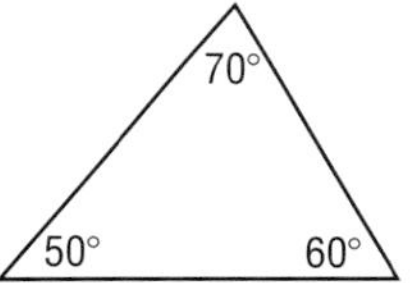

____

14

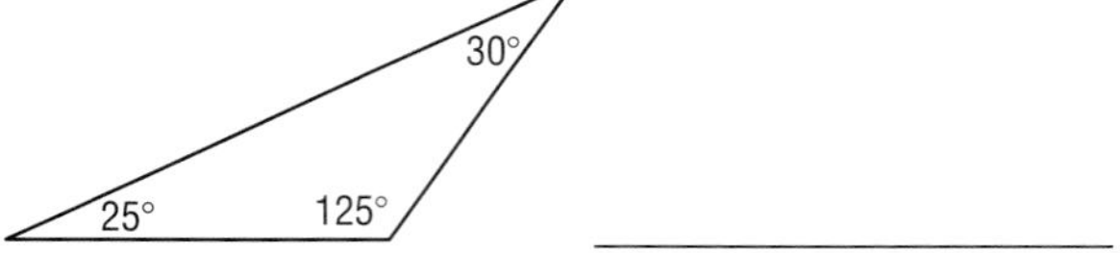

____

Name the triangle by its angles and sides.

15

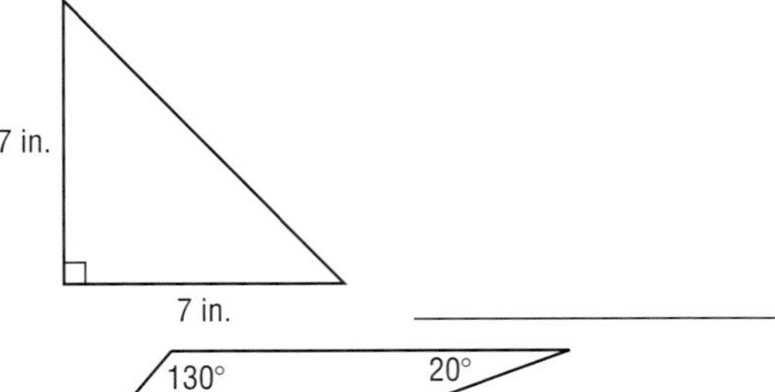

____

16

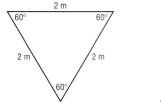

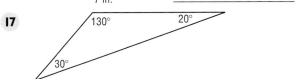

2 m, 60°, 60°, 2 m, 2 m, 60°

____

17

130°, 20°, 30°

____

18

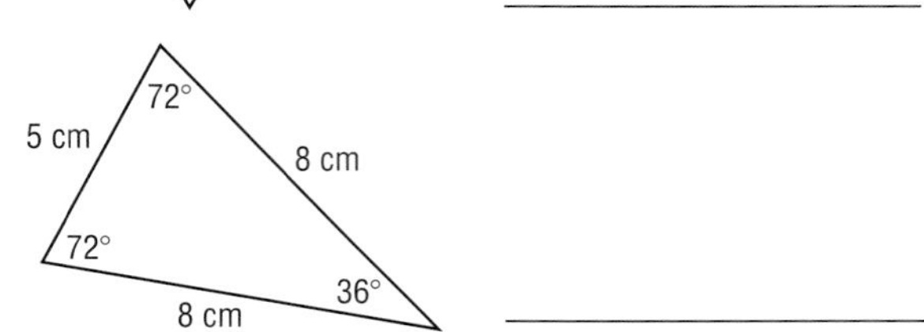

____

NAME ____________________ DATE ____________

Lesson 8-2

Problem-Solving Practice

Solve.

1 **PENNANT** Viktorio had a pennant that looked like the one shown below. Name the pennant by its sides.

____

____

2 **YARD** Eric's yard is in the shape of a triangle. One side is 100 feet, one side is 150 feet, and one side is 220 feet. Name the shape of the yard by its sides.

____

____

3 **GARDEN** Elias planted a garden of tulips as shown below. Name the shape of the garden by its sides.

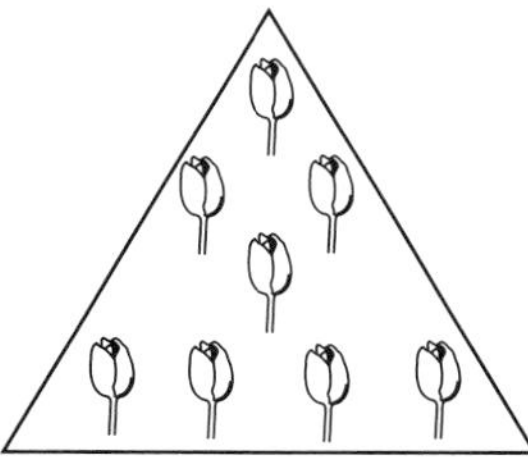

____

____

4 **RAMP** Orville made a ramp for his miniature cars as shown. Name the ramp by its sides.

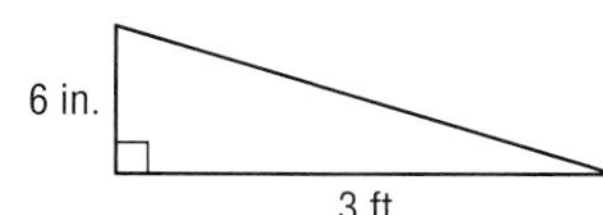

____

____

5 **STREET MAP** Apple Lane, Peach Place, and Vine Street are shown below. Name the shape of the figure formed by these three streets.

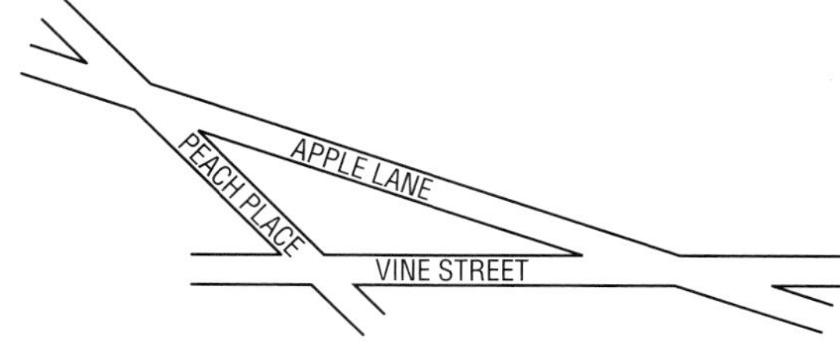

____

____

Chapter 8

Lesson 8-2

NAME ______________________ DATE ______________

Homework Practice

Identify each angle as acute, obtuse, or right.

1. 56° ______________

2. 157° ______________

3. 92° ______________

4. 90° ______________

Name the triangle by its sides.

5. 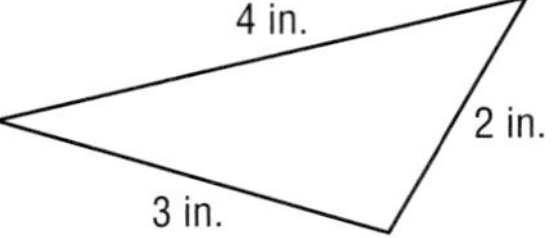

____

6. 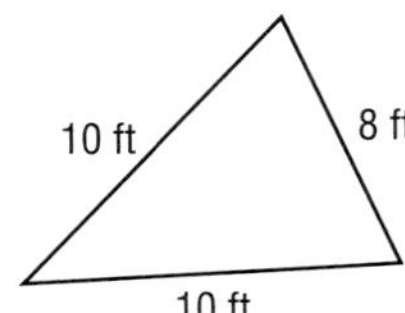

____

7. 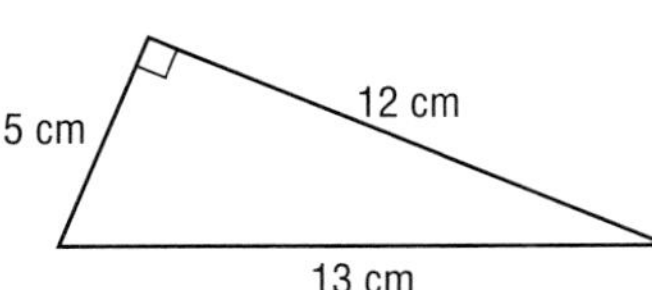

____

8. 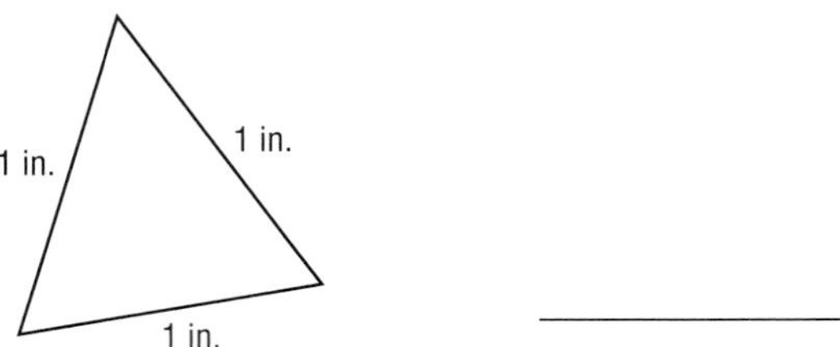

____

Name the triangle by its angles.

9. 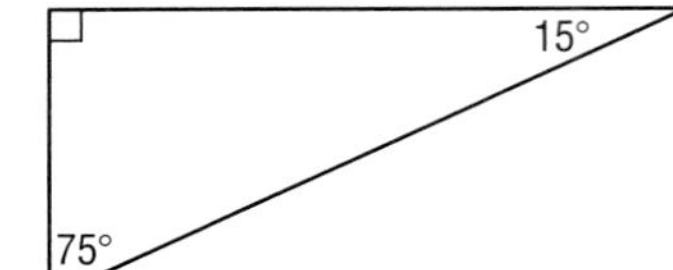

____

10. 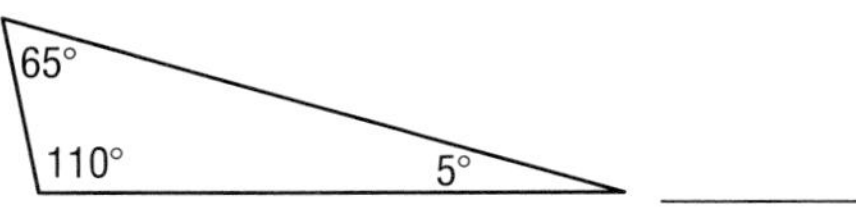

____

11. 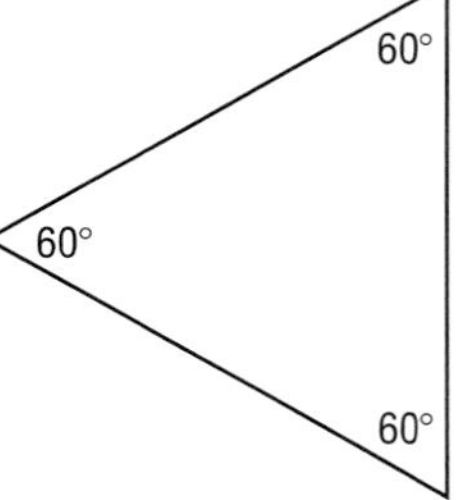

____

12. 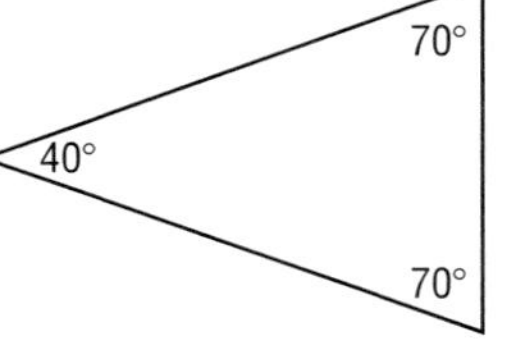

____

Name the triangle by its sides and angles.

13. 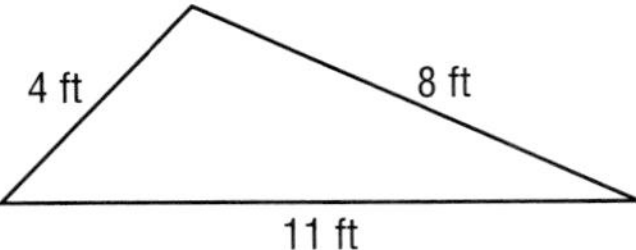

____

14. 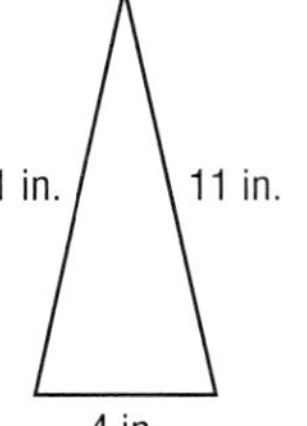

____

15. 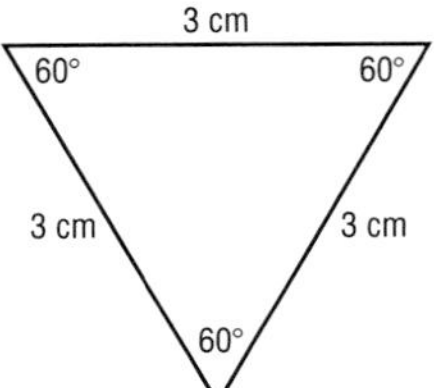

____

16. 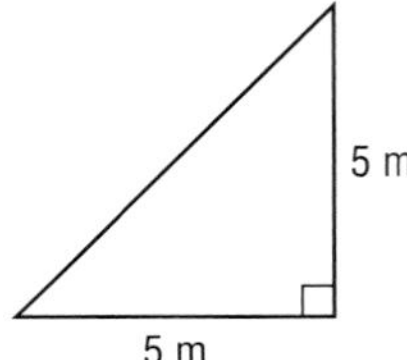
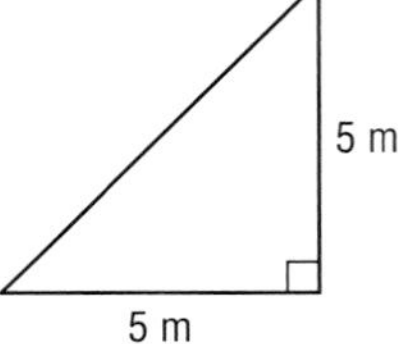

____

NAME ______________________ DATE ______________

Lesson 8-3

Vocabulary and English Language Development

Activate Prior Knowledge

1 Which of the following shapes are circles? Draw a circle around each.

Definition Review

Complete each statement.

2 The distance from the center of a circle to any point on a circle is the ______________.

3 The distance across a circle through its center is the ______________.

4 A closed figure in which all points are the same distance from a fixed point is called a ______________.

Application

- Find two examples of circles in the classroom, such as a clock or the top of a can.
- Measure the diameter of each circle.
- Measure the radius of each circle.
- Compare the measures of the radius and diameter.
- Fill in the blanks using the following words: *diameter, radius, two times.*
  The diameter is ______________ the ______________.
  The radius is one-half the ______________.

Chapter 8

NAME _______________ DATE _______________

Lesson 8-3

Skills Practice

Find the radius of each circle.

1

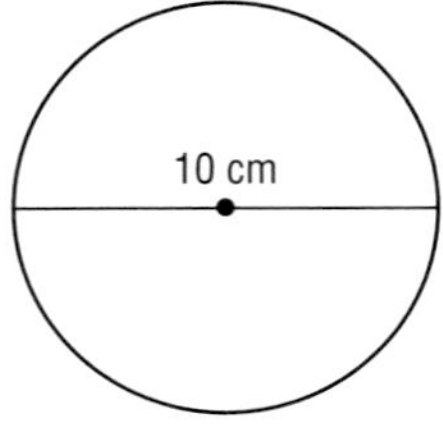

____

2

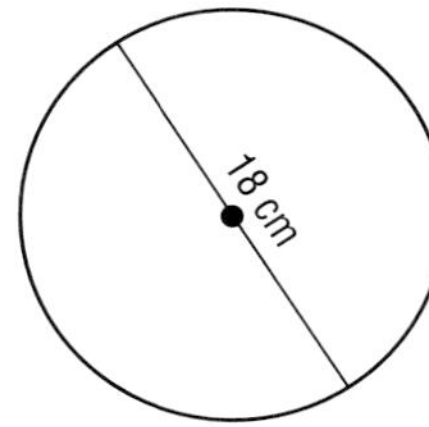

____

3

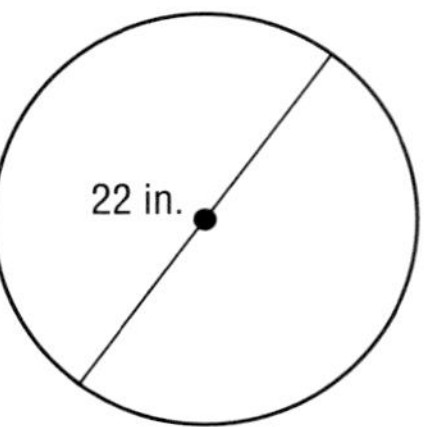

____

4

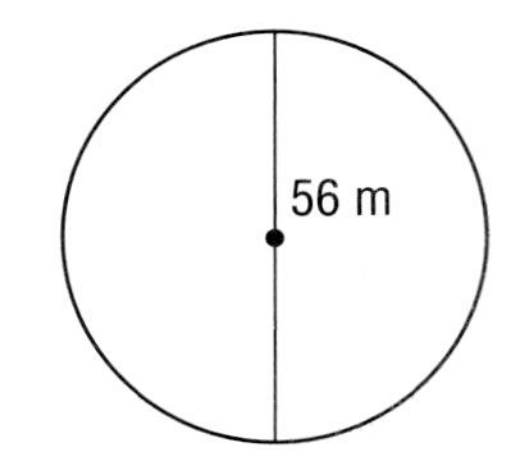

____

Find the diameter of each circle.

5

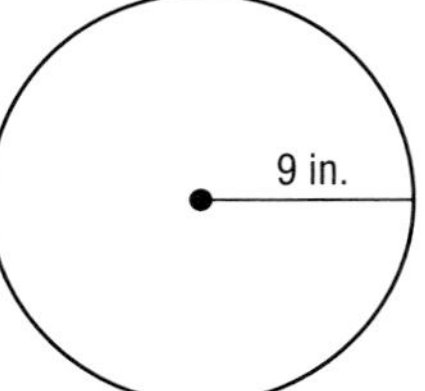

____

6

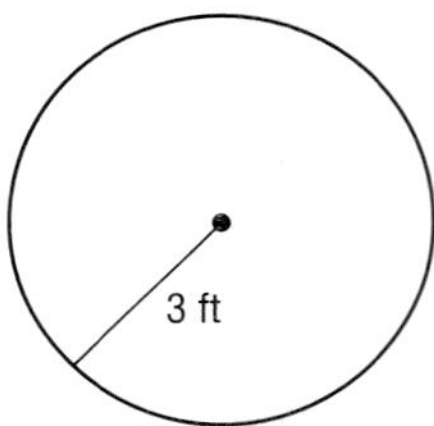

____

7

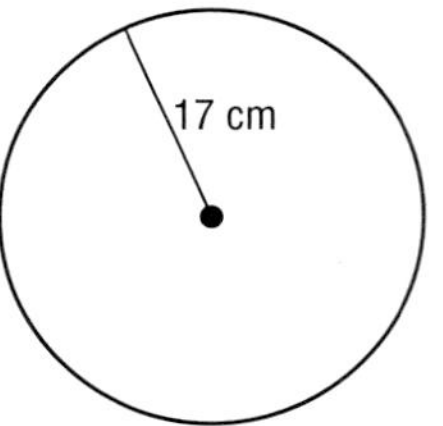

____

8

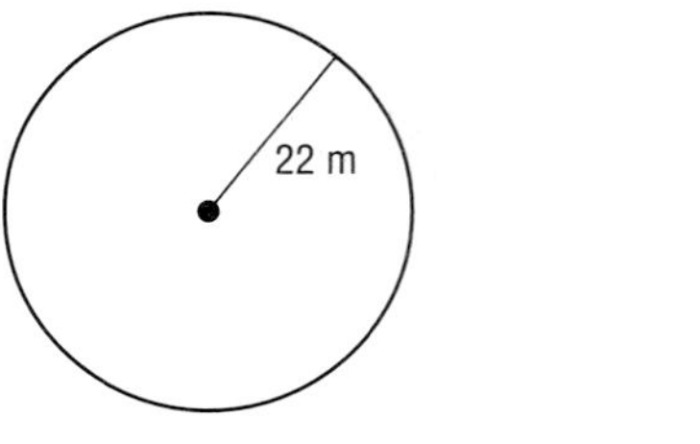

____

Find the radius or diameter of each circle.

9 $d = 24$ cm _______________

10 $d = 76$ yd _______________

11 $r = 2$ in. _______________

12 $r = 34$ ft _______________

13 $r = 7$ m _______________

14 $d = 46$ mi _______________

NAME ______________________ DATE ______________

Lesson 8-3

Problem-Solving Practice

Solve.

1 **SWIMMING POOL** Julie's swimming pool has a radius of 14 feet. What is the diameter of her pool?

2 **FOUNTAIN** Vance built a circular fountain. The diameter of his fountain is 30 feet. What is the radius?

3 **DANCE** The girls in a dance class formed a circle as shown. What is the diameter of the circle?

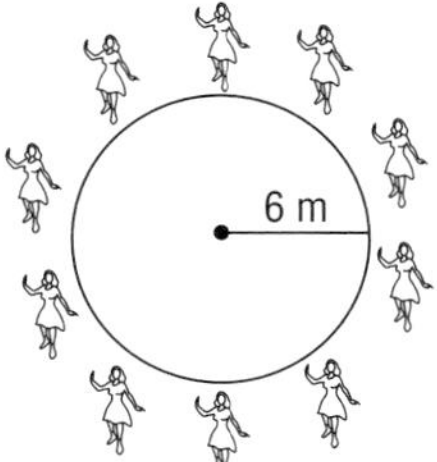

4 **HOOP** Lula was twirling a hoop. The diameter of the hoop is 100 centimeters. What is the radius?

5 **EMBROIDERY** Luigi was using this embroidery hoop. What is the radius of the hoop?

6 **PIZZA** Kathleen made a pizza with a radius of 8 inches. What is the diameter of the pizza?

7 **MOON** The radius of the Moon is about 1,738 kilometers. What is the diameter of the Moon?

8 **DISK** Matilda threw this flying disk to her puppy. What is the radius of the flying disk?

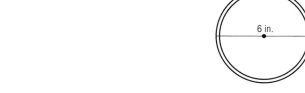

Chapter 8

NAME ____________________ DATE ____________

Lesson 8-3

Homework Practice

Find the radius of each circle.

1 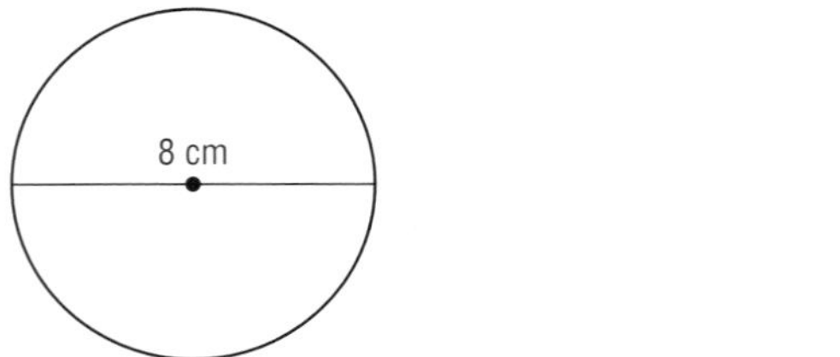

______

2 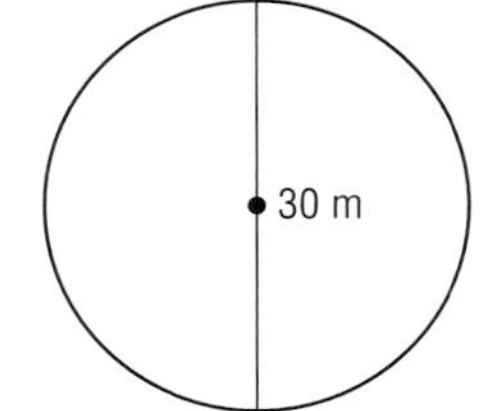

______

3 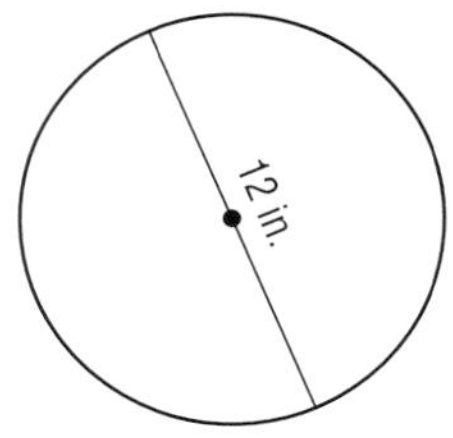

______

4 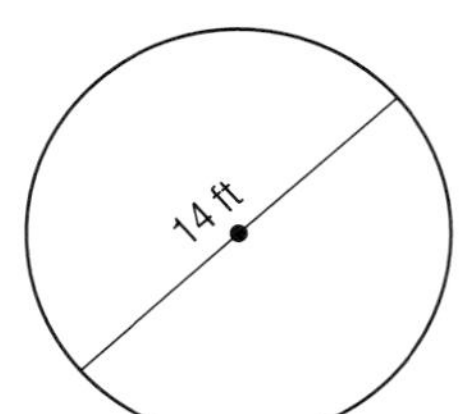

______

Find the diameter of each circle.

5 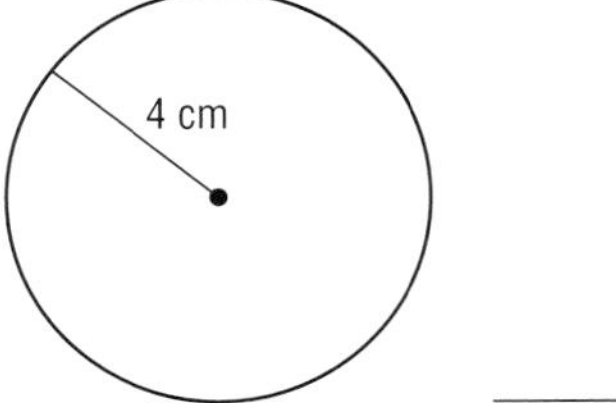

______

6 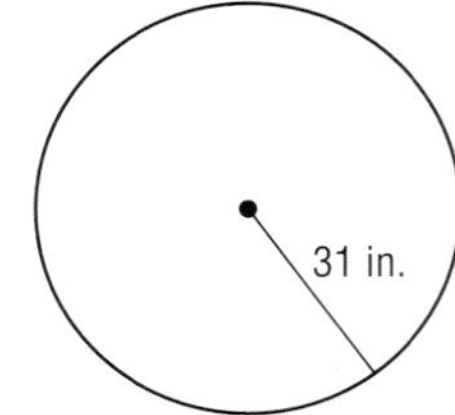

______

7 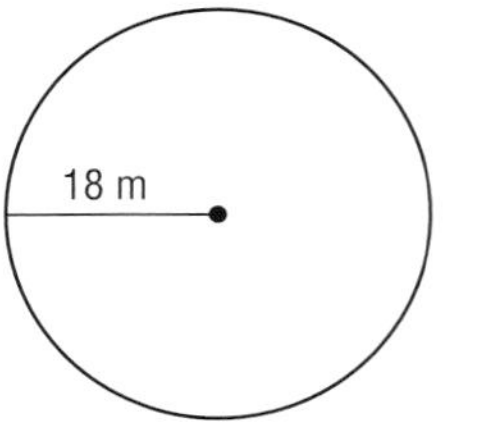

______

8 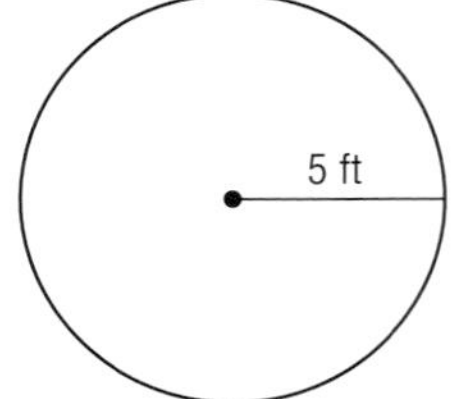

______

Find the radius or the diameter of each circle.

9 $r = 9$ in. ______

10 $d = 70$ m ______

11 $d = 16$ ft ______

12 $r = 13$ cm ______

13 **CORN** The radius of the top of a can of corn is 2 inches. What is the diameter of the can?

14 **FLOWER POT** Winnie bought a flower pot with a diameter of 24 centimeters. What is the radius of the flower pot?

15 **BAND** The band members from South School formed a circle in the center of the football field. If the radius of the circle was 24 feet, what was the diameter? ______

Lesson 8-4

NAME ______________________ DATE ______________

Vocabulary and English Language Development

Activate Prior Knowledge

Draw each figure.

1 rectangle

2 square

3 trapezoid

4 rhombus

Definition Review

Complete each statement.

5 The flat part of a three-dimensional figure is called a ______________.

6 The line segment where two faces of a three-dimensional figure meet is called an ______________.

7 The point on a three-dimensional figure where three or more edges meet is called a ______________.

Application

Draw a line matching each object below with the figure listed at the right.

rectangular prism

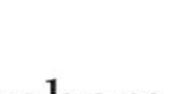

sphere

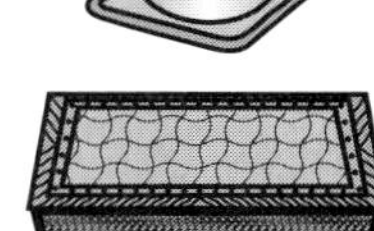

cone

cube

cylinder

Chapter 8

Lesson **8-4**

NAME ________________ DATE ________________

Skills Practice

Find the number of edges.

1 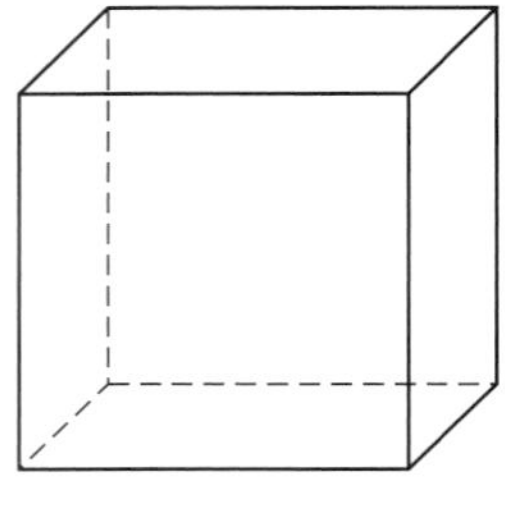

____

2 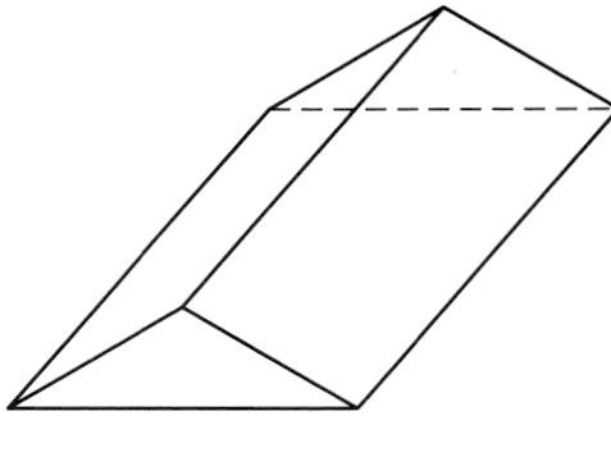

____

Find the number of faces.

3 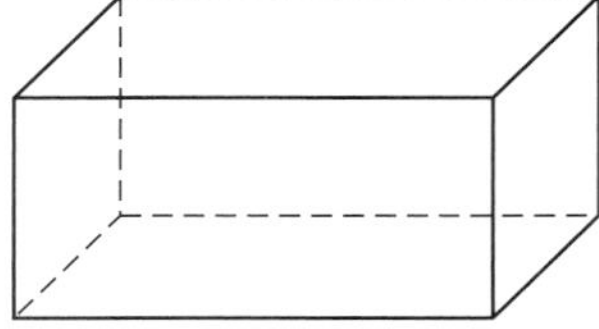

____

4 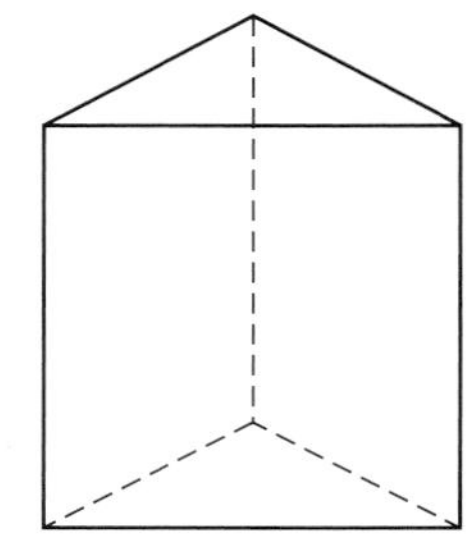

____

Identify the three-dimensional figure.

5 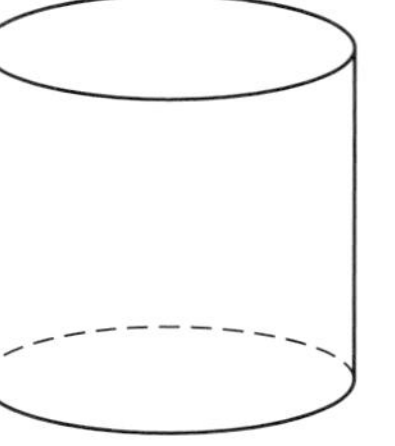

____

6 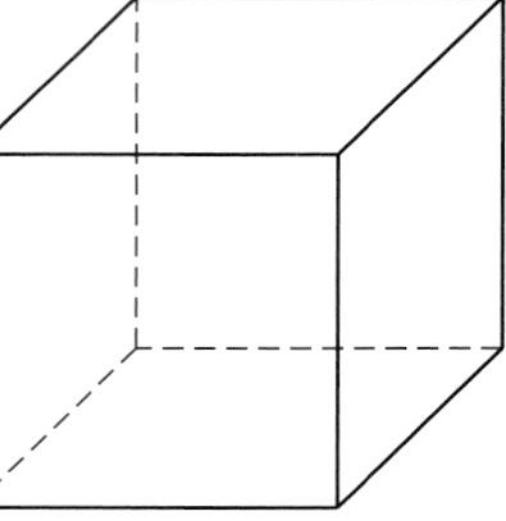

____

7 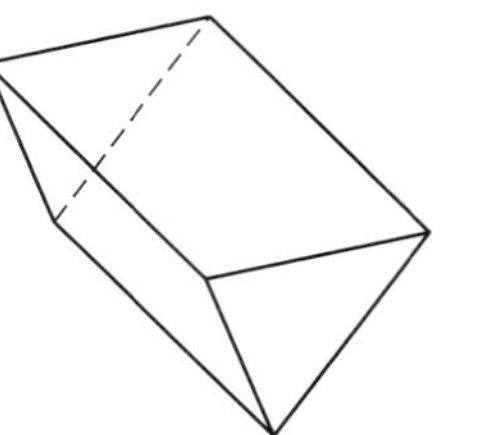

____

8 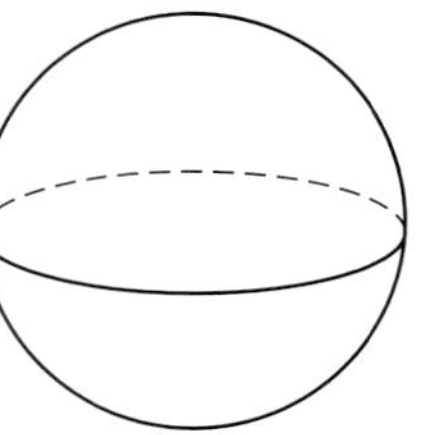

____

9 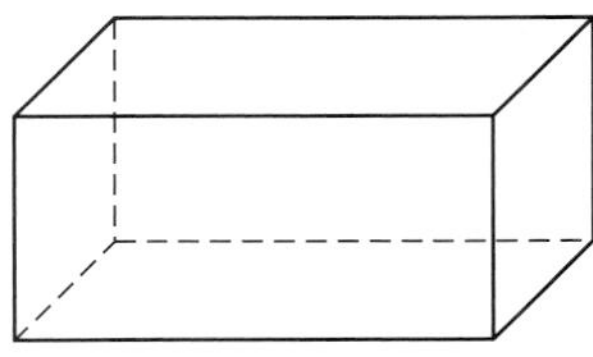

____

10 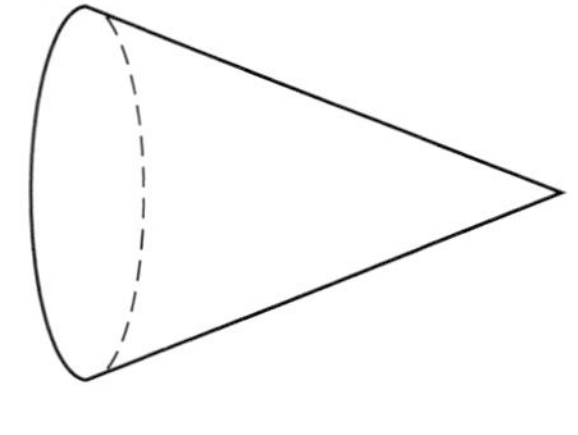

____

Lesson 8-4

NAME ____________________ DATE ____________

Problem-Solving Practice

Solve.

1 **DRAWING** Keela drew the figure below. What figure did Keela draw? ____________

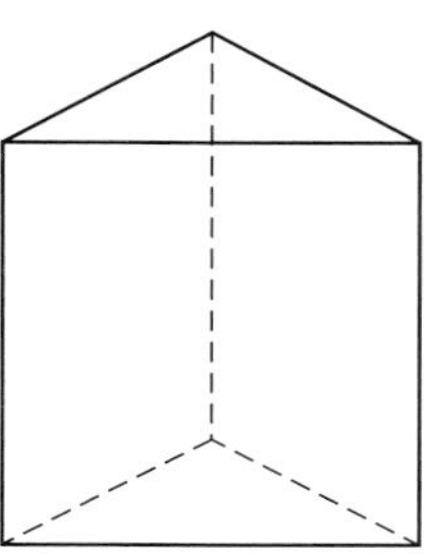

2 **GROCERY STORE** Max was stacking the shelves in the grocery store with cans of tomato sauce. What figure is a can of tomato sauce? ____________

3 **TISSUE BOX** What figure is this tissue box? ____________

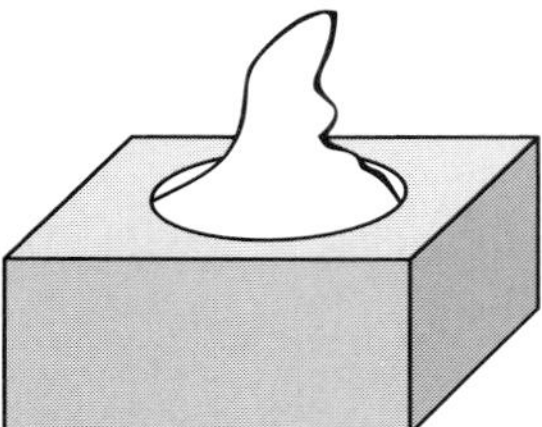

4 **SOCCER** Alexi was playing soccer. What figure is a soccer ball? ____________

5 **BIRTHDAY PRESENT** Kendra was wrapping a birthday present for her sister. The box has six congruent square faces. What figure is the box? ____________

6 **PENCIL BOX** Gary made this pencil box in shop class. What figure is the pencil box? ____________

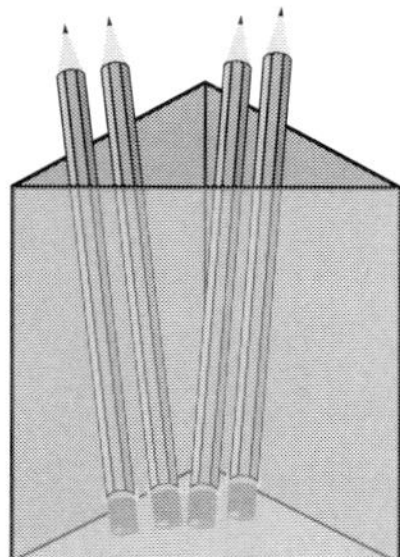

7 **PARTY HAT** Irma made party hats for her friends. Each hat has a circular base and one curved surface from the base to the vertex. What figure are the party hats? ____________

Lesson 8-4

NAME ______________________ DATE ____________

Homework Practice

Find the number of edges.

1 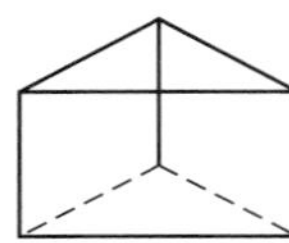 ________

2 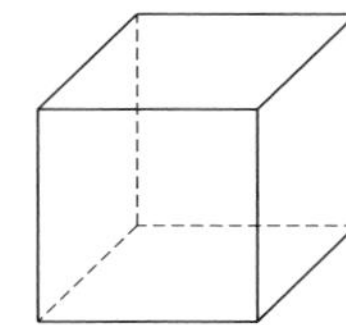 ________

3 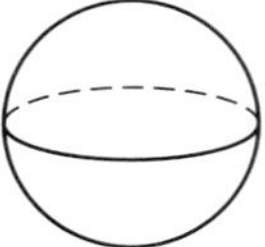 ________

4 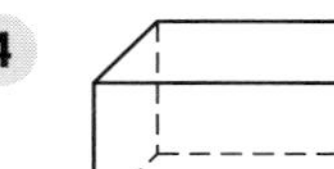 ________

Identify the three-dimensional figure.

5 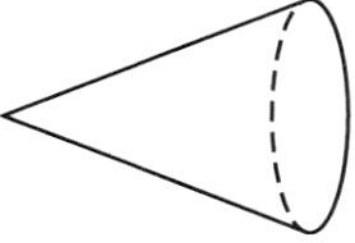 ________

6 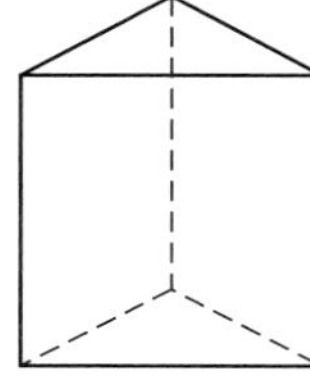 ________

7 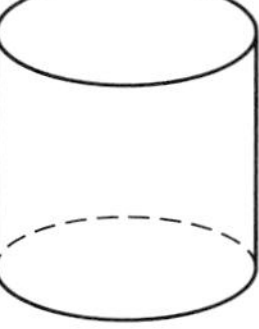 ________

8 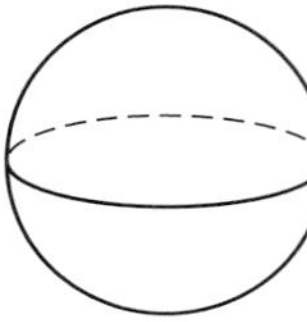 ________

9 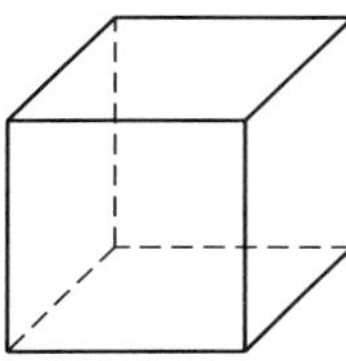 ________

10 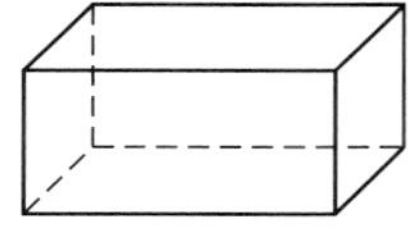 ________

Draw the three-dimensional figure.

11 cone

12 cube

13 **LAMP SHADE** Maria's lamp shade has two circular bases and a curved surface connecting them. What shape is the lamp shade? ________

14 **BUILDING** Ralph works in a building that has two congruent triangular faces and three congruent rectangular faces. What shape is Ralph's building? ________

NAME ______________________ DATE ____________

Foldables Study Organizer

Dinah Zike's Foldables

Follow the steps below to create a Foldable.

1 Fold a sheet of paper in half from side to side, leaving a $\frac{1}{2}$-inch tab along the side.

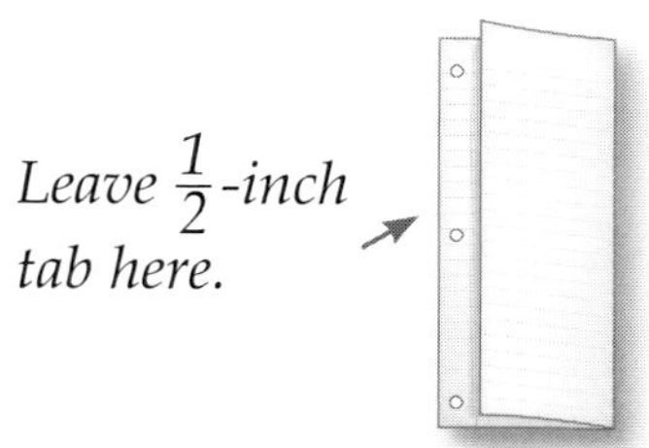

2 Turn the paper and fold it into fourths.

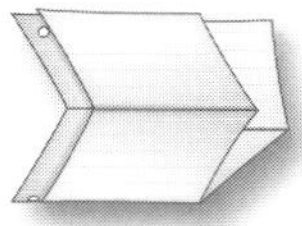

Fold in half, then fold in half again.

3 Unfold and cut up along the three fold lines.

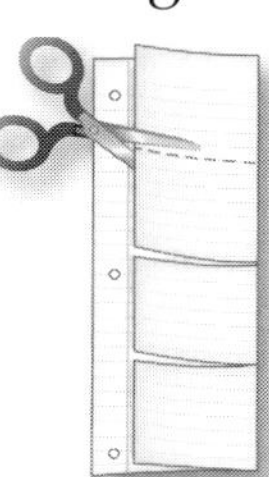

This will make four tabs.

4 Label as shown. As you read, write the important information under each tab. Include a description of the formula.

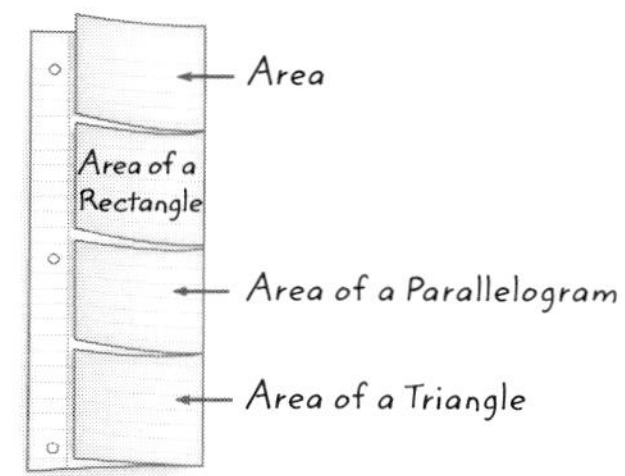

TAKING NOTES
As you read through the chapter, write the formulas to find each of the following in your Foldable:

- Area of a rectangle
- Area of a parallelogram
- Area of a triangle

USING YOUR FOLDABLE
As you study, write an example that uses each of the formulas you have written in your Foldable. Show all the steps to find the solution. Also sketch the figure.

USING YOUR FOLDABLE
Work in groups of three. One student sketches a figure from the chapter. The second student states a relevant formula. The third student writes and solves a problem using the figure and the formula. Do this several times until each student has solved a problem.

Chapter 9

NAME ________________________ DATE ____________

Games and Puzzles

Make the Greatest Area!

DIRECTIONS

- One player cuts out and assembles the **Greatest Area** spinner while the other player cuts out and assembles the shape cube.
- Player 1 rolls the shape cube. The shape that is on top is the shape for which the player is going to find the area.
- Player 1 then spins the spinner. This number is going to be the length of the base of the shape.
- Player 1 spins the spinner again. This number is going to be the height of the shape.
- Player 1 then finds the area of the shape.
- Player 2 takes a turn.
- Whoever has the largest area gets one point.
- Continue playing until a player has five points.

What You Need

- Greatest Area spinner
- Shape cube

Number of Players

2

Greatest Area Spinner

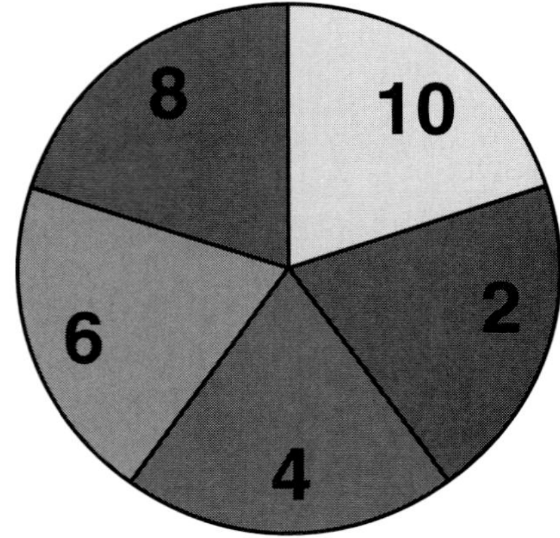

NAME ______________________ DATE ______________

Shape Cube

Cut along the solid black lines.

Fold along the dashed lines.

Tape or glue tabs.

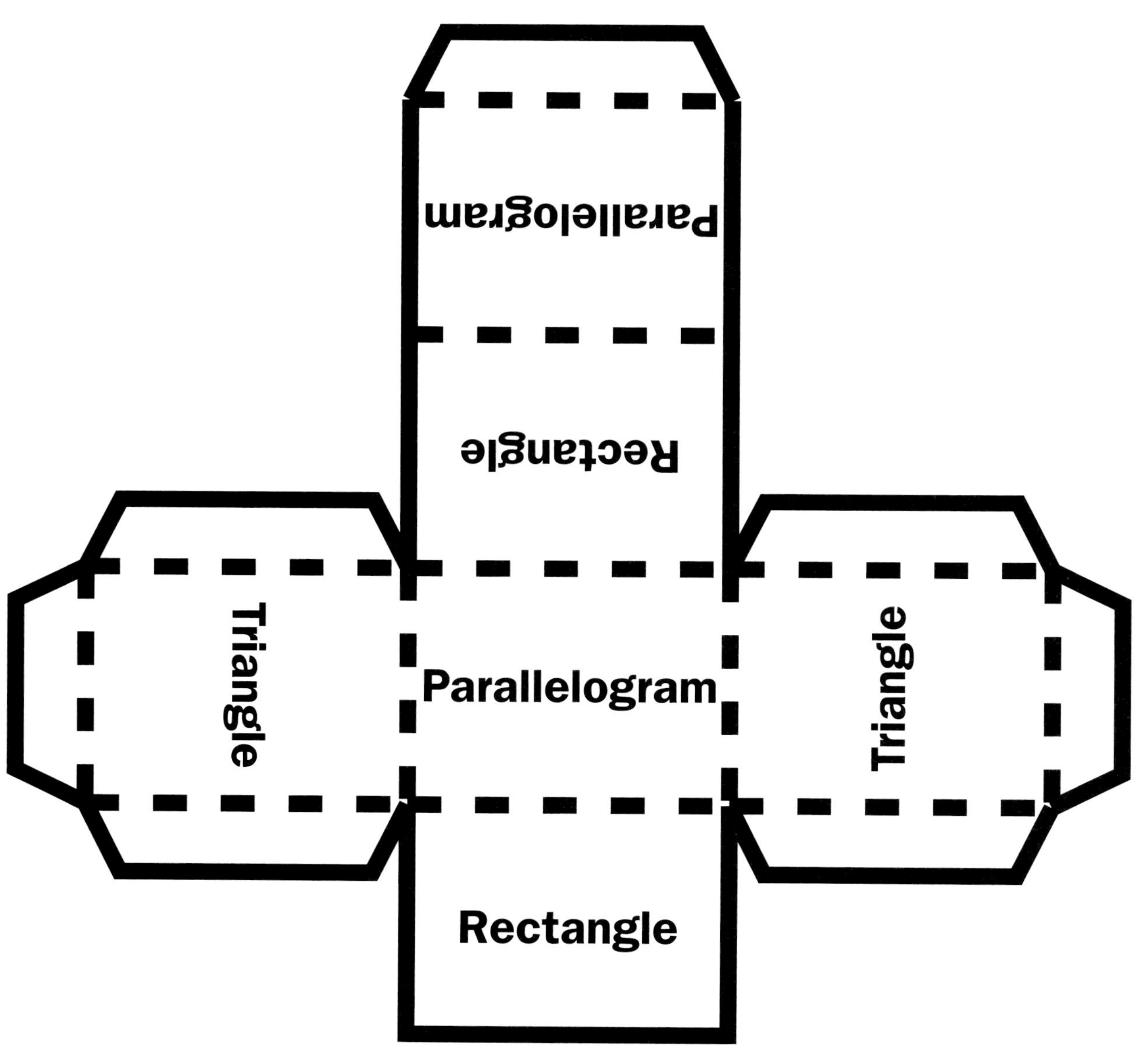

NAME ______________________ DATE ______________

Lesson 9-1

Vocabulary and English Language Development

Activate Prior Knowledge

Find the area of each shape.

1 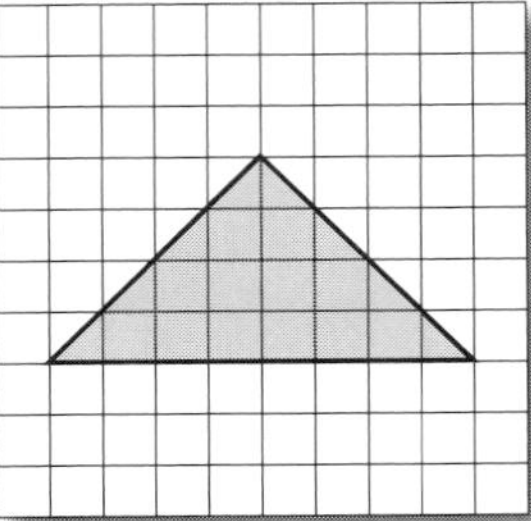

Area = ____________ square units

2 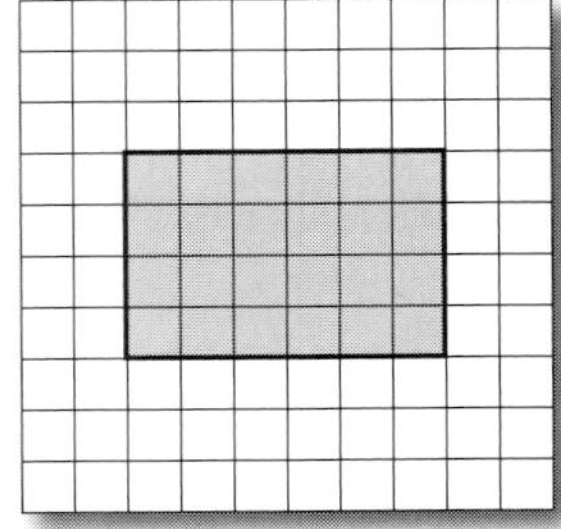

Area = ____________ square units

3 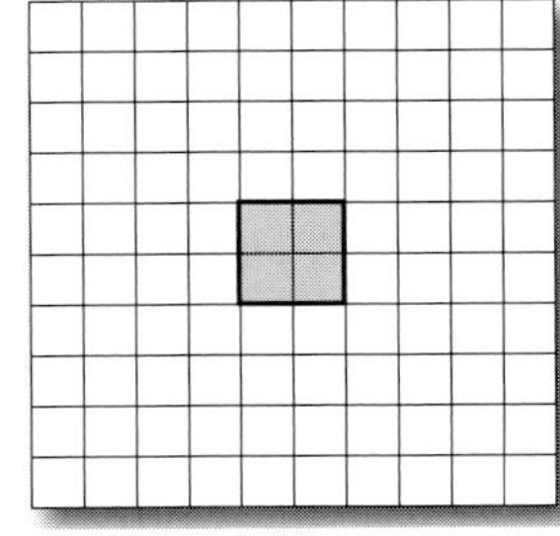

Area = ____________ square units

4 Write a number sentence, using the areas above to find the area of this figure. ____________

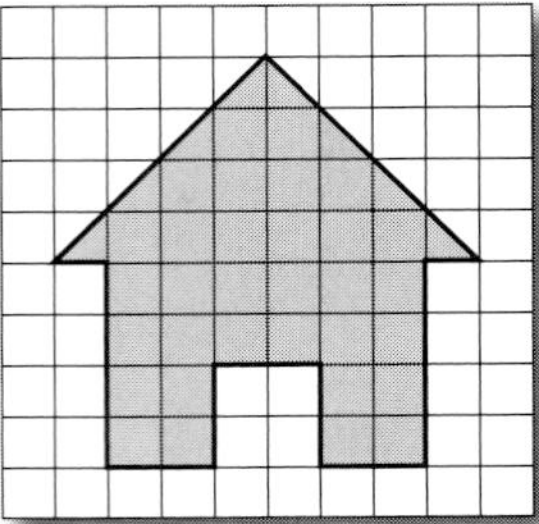

5 What is the area of this figure?

Area = ____________ square units

Definition Review

Fill in the blanks.

6 ____________ is the number of ____________ units needed to cover a plane figure.

7 ____________ is the number of units needed to go around the edge of a figure.

Application

Follow the directions for the activity.

- Work with a partner.
- Each person draws a picture on a piece of grid paper.
- Find the approximate area of your figure.
- Trade papers with your partner and find the approximate area of your partner's picture.
- Compare answers for each picture.

Lesson 9-1

NAME ______________________ DATE ____________

Skills Practice

Draw a figure that has the given area.

1. 20 square units

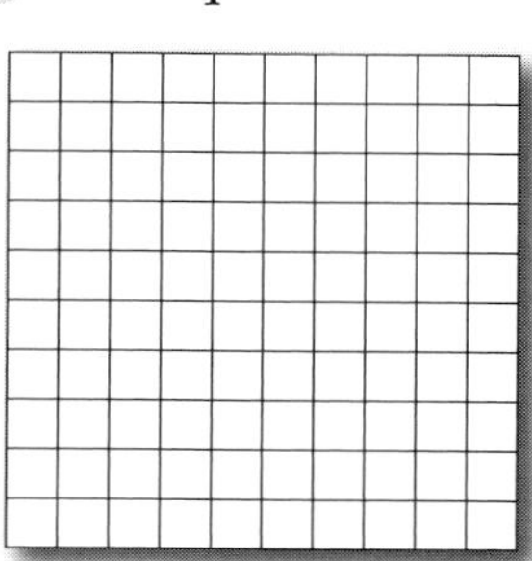

2. 64 square units

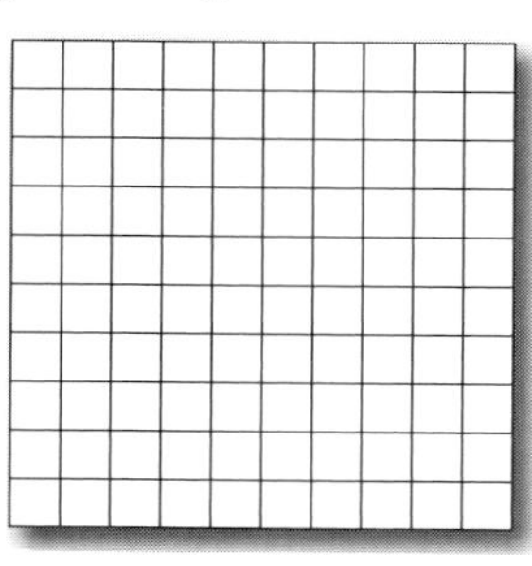

3. 40 square units

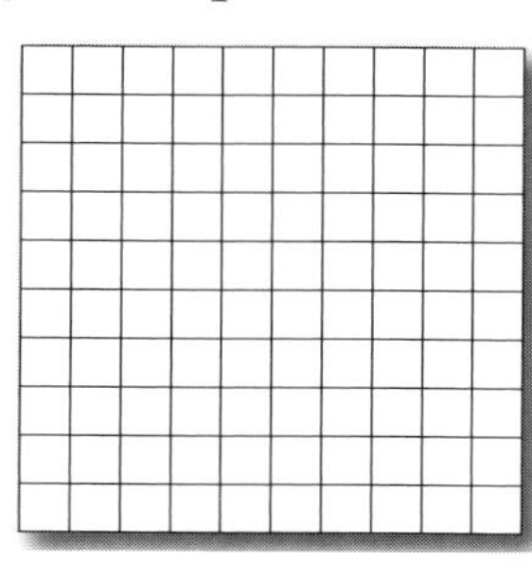

4. 12 square units

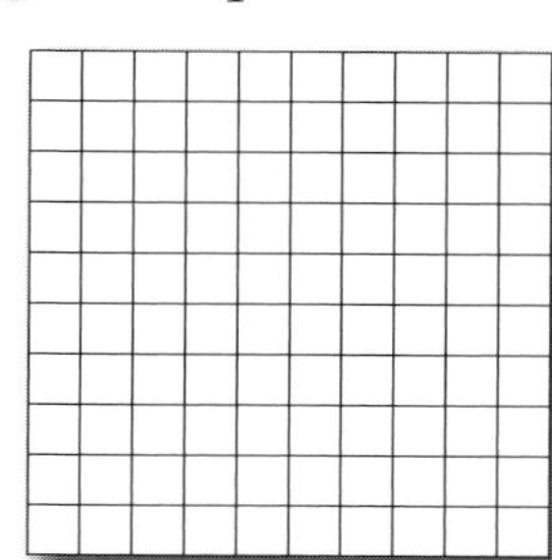

Estimate the area of each figure.

5.

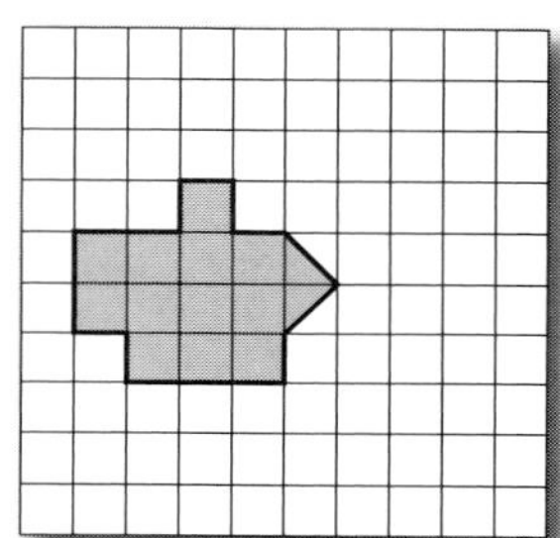

The area of the figure is about ________ square units.

6.

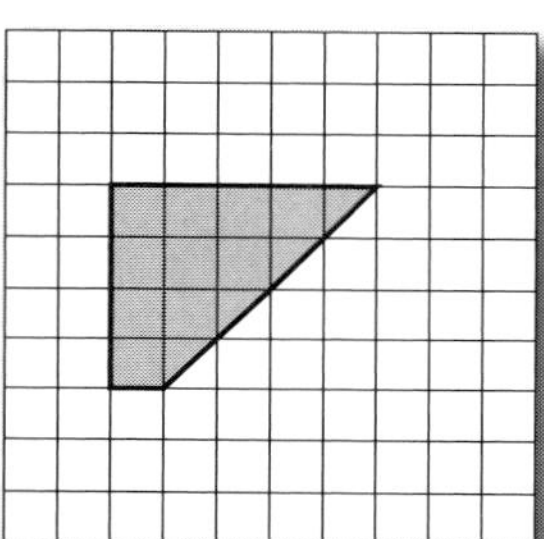

The area of the figure is about ________ square units.

7.

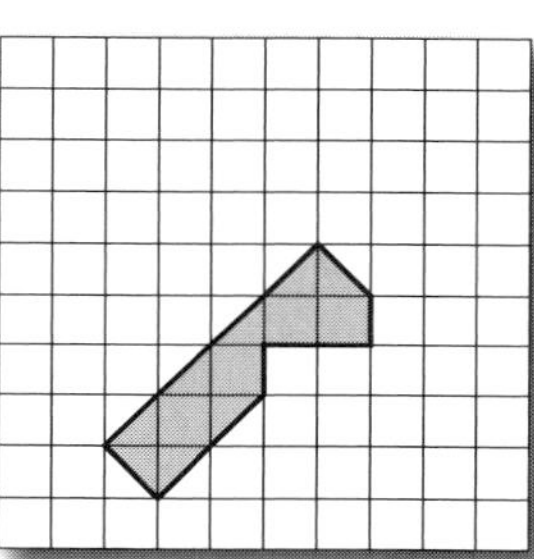

The area of the figure is about ________ square units.

8.

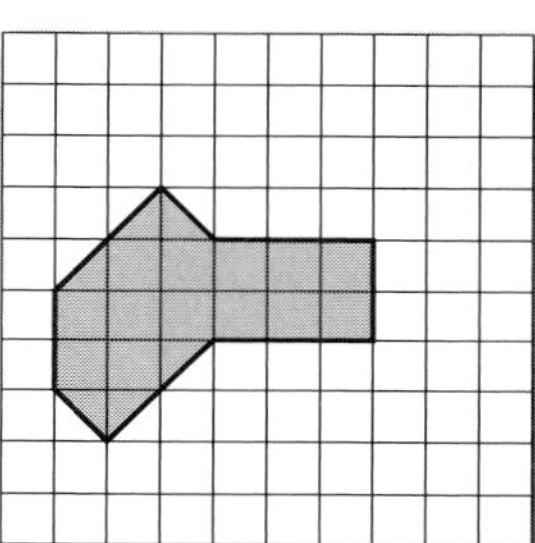

The area of the figure is about ________ square units.

Find the area of each figure.

9.

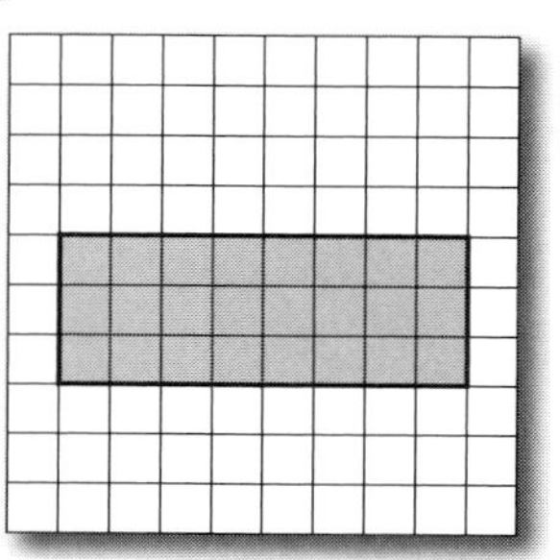

The area of the figure is ________ square units.

10.

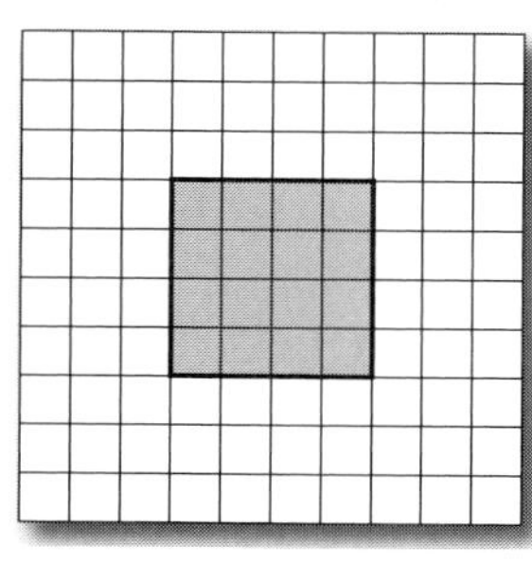

The area of the figure is ________ square units.

11.

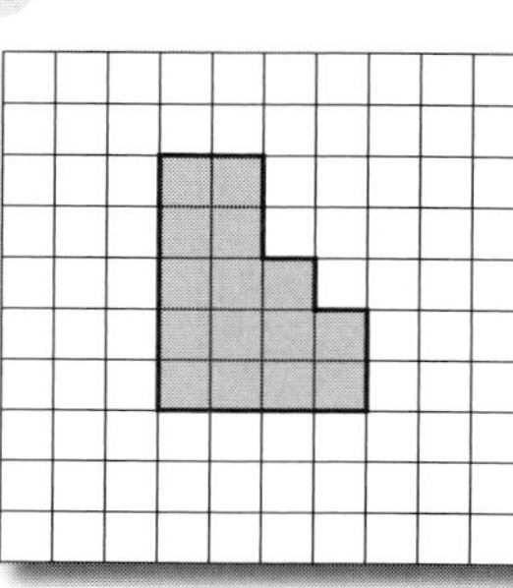

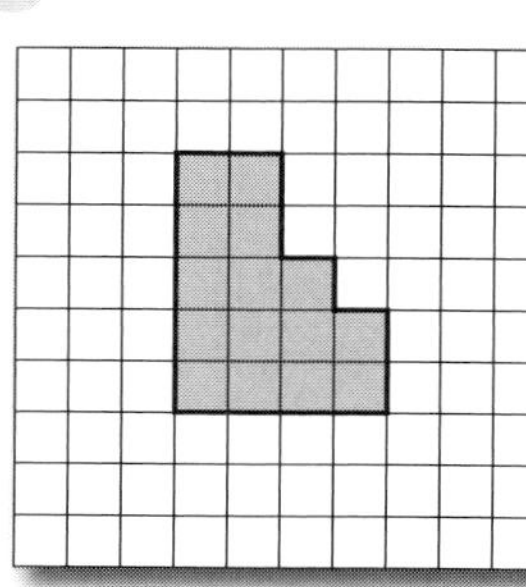

The area of the figure is ________ square units.

12.

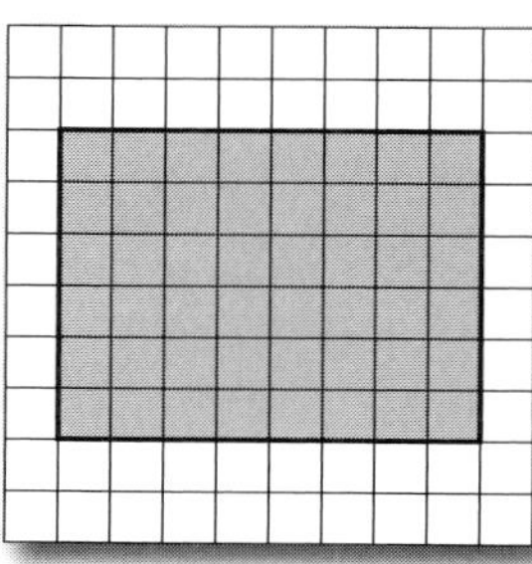

The area of the figure is ________ square units.

NAME ______________________ DATE ______________

Lesson 9-1

Problem-Solving Practice

Solve.

1. **GEOMETRY** What is the area of a rectangle that has sides of 6 units and 9 units? ________

2. **GAMES** Keisha and Halley are playing a memory game. The cards are laid out in a rectangular pattern, 4 cards by 6 cards. How many cards make up the game area? ________

3. **CONSTRUCTION** The kitchen in Alicia's home has a wall that is 12 feet long and 8 feet tall. What is the area of this wall? ________

4. **SCHOOL** Mr. Valez has a bulletin board in his classroom. The bulletin board is 7 feet long and 4 feet tall. What is the area of the bulletin board? ________

5. **LANDSCAPING** Mrs. Kincaid has hired a crew to place squares of grass sod in her front yard. The crew can fit 20 squares along the width of the yard and 10 squares along the length of the yard. How many squares of sod will fit in Mrs. Kincaid's yard? ________

6. **CONSTRUCTION** Josie is putting new tile in her kitchen. She can put 9 tiles along the length and 6 tiles along the width. How many tiles can Josie fit in the kitchen? ________

7. **GEOMETRY** What is the area of a square that has sides 9 units long? ________

8. **COOKING** Fidel is cooking brownies. The pan is a rectangle measuring 8 inches on one side and 11 inches on the other side. What is the area of the pan? ________

9. **CONSTRUCTION** Brandon wants to create a snowman-shaped yard sign for winter. He began by drawing a scale model on centimeter grid paper. What is the area of his drawing? ________

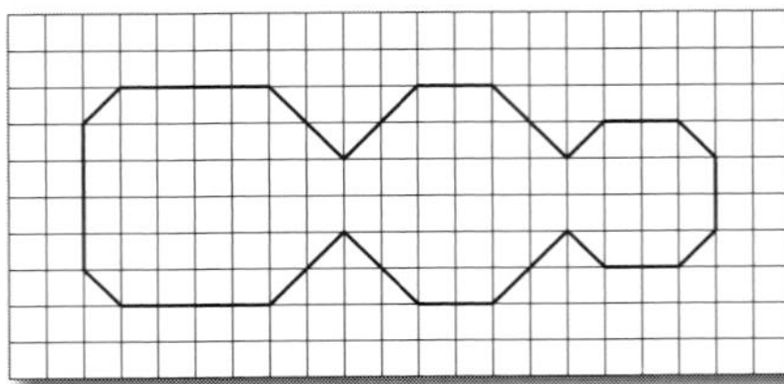

Lesson 9-1

NAME ______________________ DATE ______________

Homework Practice

Draw a figure that has the given area.

1 42 square units

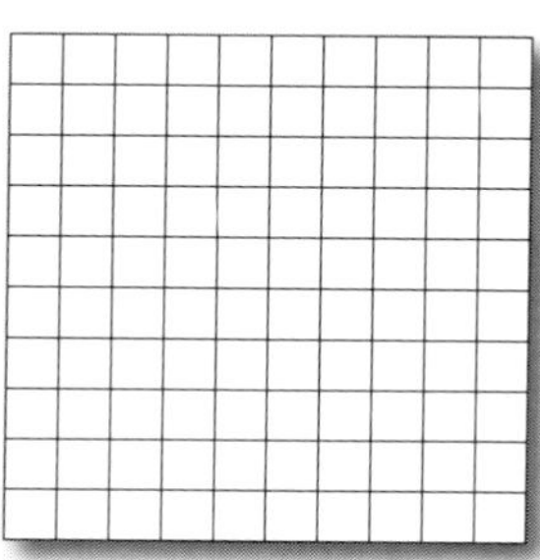

2 18 square units

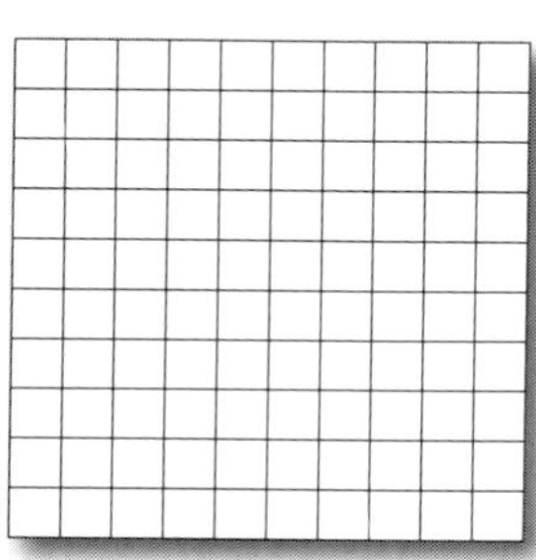

3 10 square units

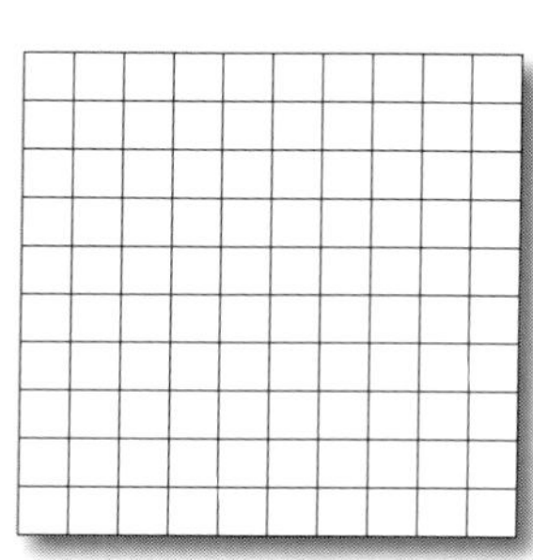

4 49 square units

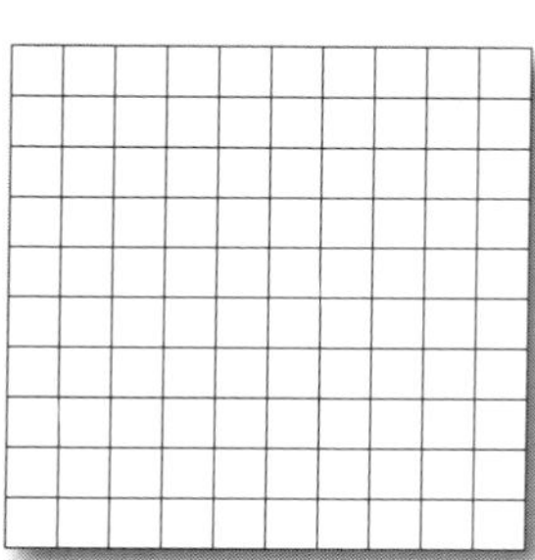

Find the area of each figure.

5

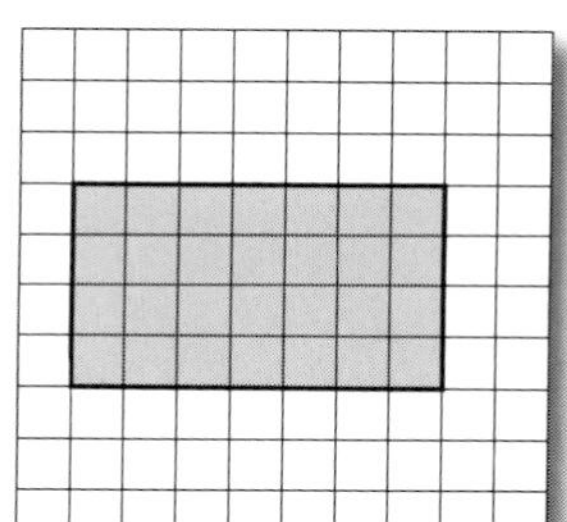

The area of the figure is ______ square units.

6

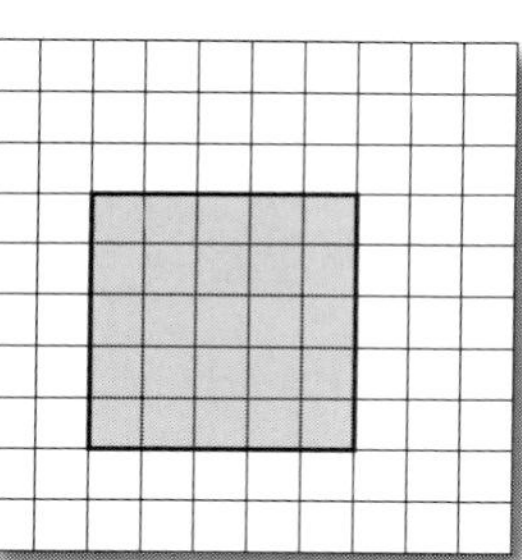

The area of the figure is ______ square units.

7

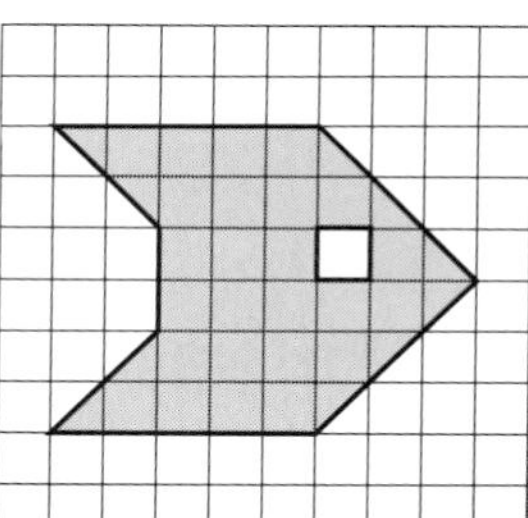

The area of the figure is ______ square units.

8

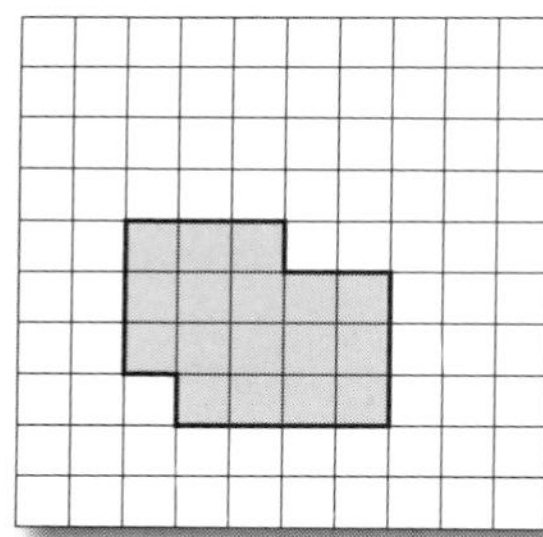

The area of the figure is ______ square units.

Solve.

9 **CONSTRUCTION** Craig is laying tile on his bathroom floor. The bathroom is a rectangle. He can place 10 tiles along one wall and 6 tiles along another. How many tiles will fit on Craig's bathroom floor? ______________

Write the vocabulary word that completes the sentence.

10 The number of square units needed to cover a region or plane figure is the ______________.

Chapter 9

NAME ____________________ DATE ____________

Lesson 9-2

Vocabulary and English Language Development

Activate Prior Knowledge

Find the area of each of the following.

1

3 cm

12 cm

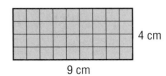

Area = ______

2

4 cm

9 cm

Area = ______

3

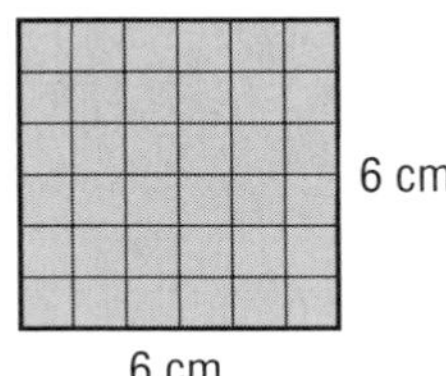

Area = ______

Definition Review

Complete each sentence by filling in the blanks.

4 A ____________________ is a quadrilateral with four right angles and opposite sides equal.

5 A ____________________ is a rectangle with equal sides.

6 The number of **square units** necessary to cover a **rectangle** or **square** is the ____________________ of that figure.

7 The units for measuring the **area** of a **rectangle** or **square** are ____________________.

8 The formula for the **area** of a **rectangle** is $A =$ ____________________.

Application

Follow the directions for the activity.

- Work with a partner.
- Measure the length and width of your classroom to the nearest foot.
- On grid paper, draw a model of your classroom using the measurements you found.
- Label the length and width.
- Find the area of your classroom based on your measurements.

NAME ______________________ DATE ______________ PERIOD ______

Lesson 9-2

Skills Practice

Find the area.

1 Find the area of a rectangle with a length of 12 centimeters and a width of 5 centimeters. ____________

2 Find the area of a rectangle with a length of 5 inches and a width of 7 inches. ____________

3

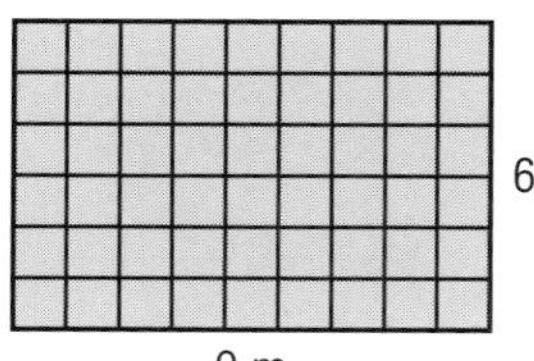

The area of the rectangle is ____________.

4

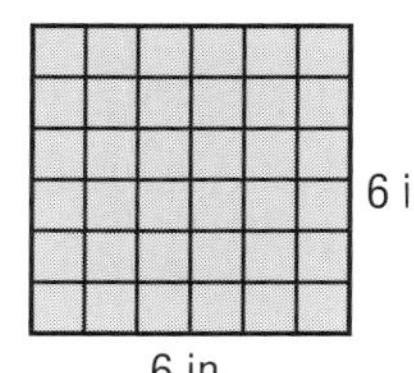

The area of the square is ____________.

5 Find the area of a square with side lengths of 7 feet. ____________

6 Find the area of a square with side lengths of 9 yards. ____________

Draw a rectangle that has the given area.

7 24 square cm

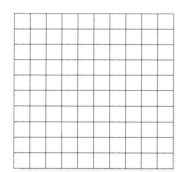

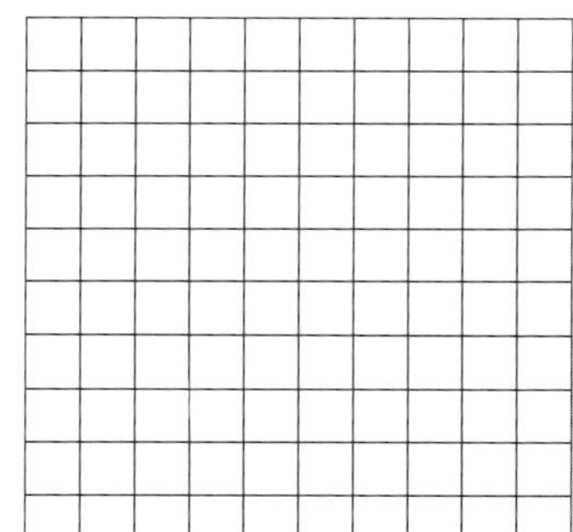

8 56 in^2

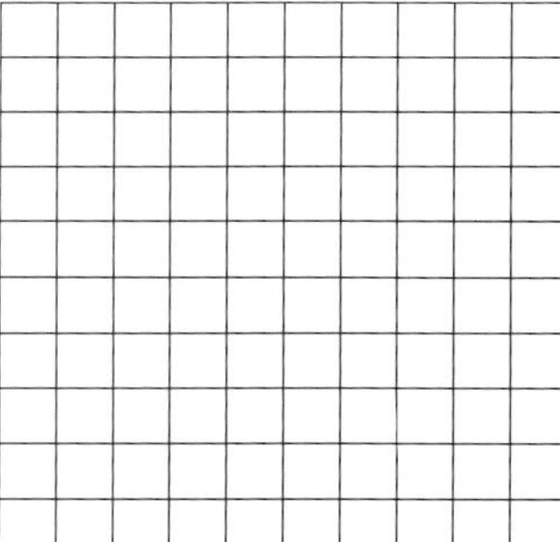

9 25 ft^2

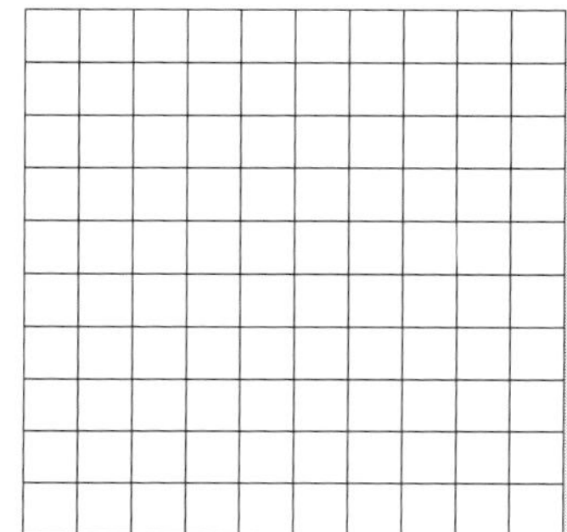

10 42 m^2

NAME ______________________ DATE ______________

Lesson **9-2**

Problem-Solving Practice

Solve.

1 **POSTERS** Mr. Lopez asked his students to create posters for their final projects. The poster boards measured 51 centimeters by 76 centimeters. What was the area of each poster board? ____________

2 **PHOTOGRAPHY** Jane and her brother posed for a formal portrait. Jane will use the 11 inch by 14 inch framed portrait as a gift for her grandmother. What is the area of the framed portrait? ____________

3 **CONSTRUCTION** The opening of a typical doorway is 3 feet wide and 7 feet tall. What is the area of the opening of a typical doorway? ____________

4 **TABLE CLOTHS** Tom purchased a tablecloth for his rectangular dining room table. The tablecloth measures 60 inches by 102 inches. What is the area of the tablecloth? ____________

5 **GOLF** The fairway of a golf course is rectangular in shape. Its width is 22 yards and its length is 280 yards. What is the area of the fairway? ____________

6 **AIRPORT** A small airport has a runway that is 900 meters long and 75 meters wide. What is the area of the runway? ____________

7 **CONSTRUCTION** Malik is building an additional 12 feet by 16 feet bedroom onto his house. What is the area of the new bedroom? ____________

8 **BILLIARDS** The surface of a billiards table is 44 inches wide and 88 inches long. What is the area of the surface of the billiards table? ____________

9 **COUNTERTOP** A new kitchen countertop has dimensions of 244 centimeters by 76 centimeters. What is the area of the countertop? ____________

10 **NOTE CARDS** Simon has an oral report for biology class. He made several notes on note cards measuring 3 inches by 5 inches. What is the area of each note card? ____________

NAME ______________________ DATE ____________

Homework Practice

Find the area.

1. Find the area of a square with side lengths of 4 inches. ____________

2. 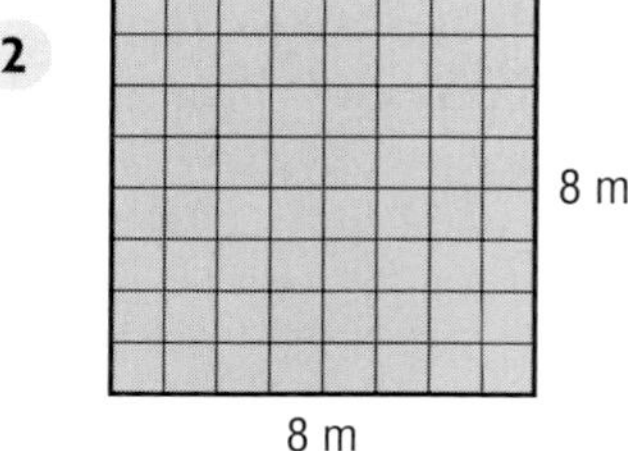

The area of the square is ____________.

3. Find the area of a rectangle with a length of 2 yards and a width of 6 yards.

____

4. Find the area of a rectangle with a length of 12 centimeters and a width of 7 centimeters. ____________

Draw a rectangle that has the given area.

5. 30 yd^2

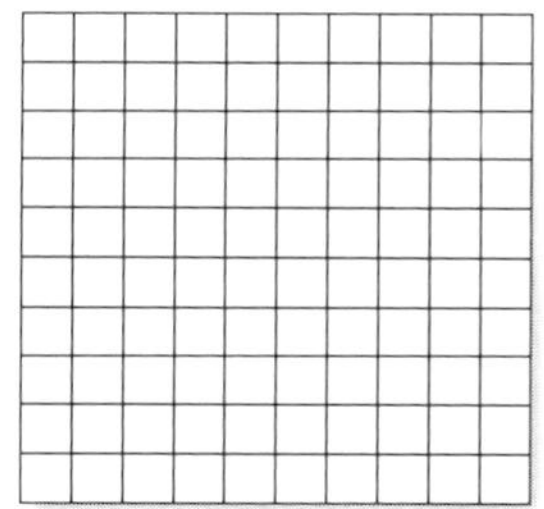

6. 15 cm^2

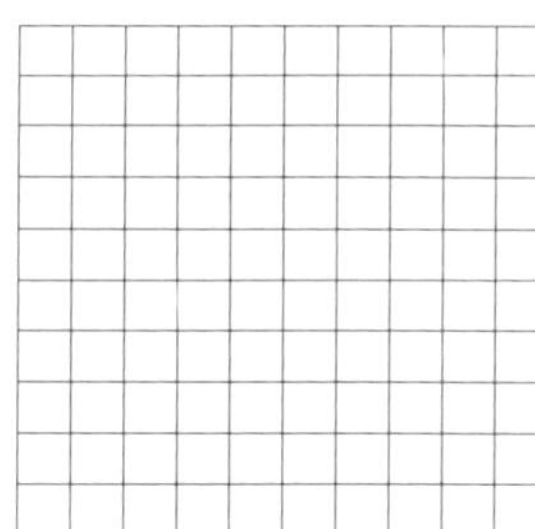

7. 8 cm^2

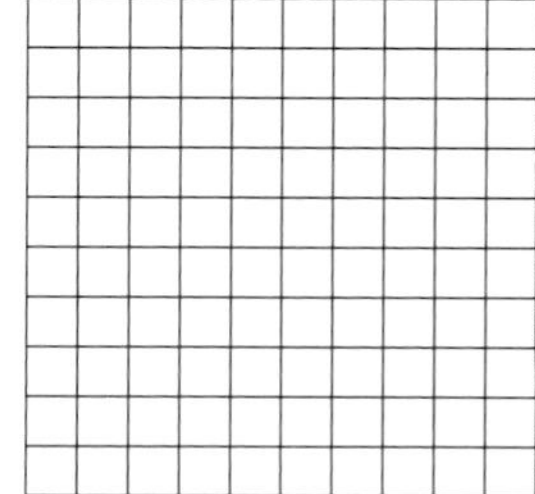

8. 36 ft^2

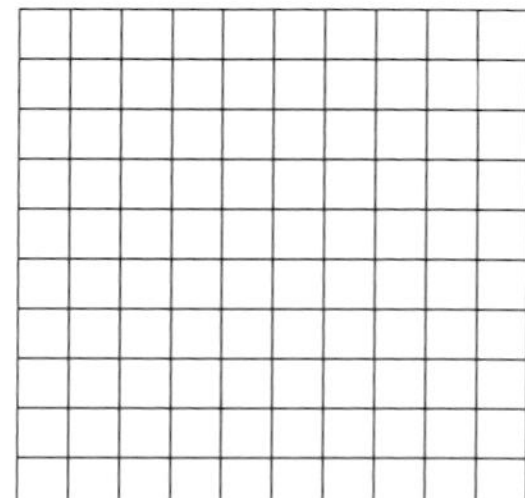

Solve.

9. **RUGS** Lydia bought an area rug for her living room. The rug is a rectangle that measures 42 inches wide by 66 inches long. What is the area of Lydia's rug?

____

Write the vocabulary word that completes the sentence.

10. A ____________ unit is a unit for measuring area.

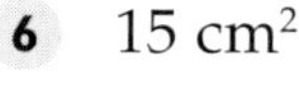

Lesson 9-3

NAME ______________________ DATE ______________

Vocabulary and English Language Development

Activate Prior Knowledge

Use the points on the grid to complete the following.

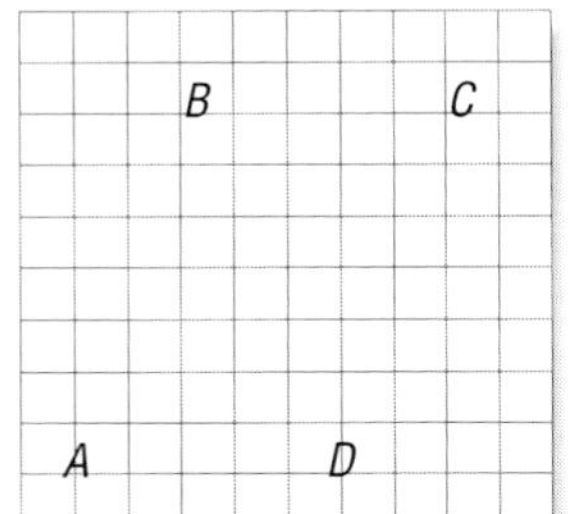

1 Draw line segments connecting points A and B, B and C, C and D, and D and A. What shape do the points form?

____

2 What is the length of this polygon's base? ______________

3 What is the length of this polygon's height? ______________

4 What is the area of this polygon? ______________

Definition Review

Complete the sentences by filling in the blanks.

5 The ______________ of a shape is the number of **square units** needed to cover the shape.

For a **parallelogram**, this is found using the formula $A =$ ______________.

Application

Follow the directions for the activity.

- Work in pairs. Use paper, a pencil, and a ruler to draw a parallelogram.
- Trade drawings with your partner.
- Measure the parallelograms and find their areas. Write down the areas.
- Cut out the parallelograms. Using scissors and tape, cut a triangle from one end of a parallelogram and tape it to the other end to form a rectangle.
- Check one another's shapes to make sure they form rectangles. (If rectangles are formed, all four angles must be right angles.)
- Measure and find the area of the rectangles.
- Discuss the relationship between the formula for the area of a rectangle and the formula for the area of a parallelogram.
- Repeat the activity three times.

NAME ____________________ DATE ____________

Lesson 9-3

Skills Practice

Find the area of each parallelogram.

1

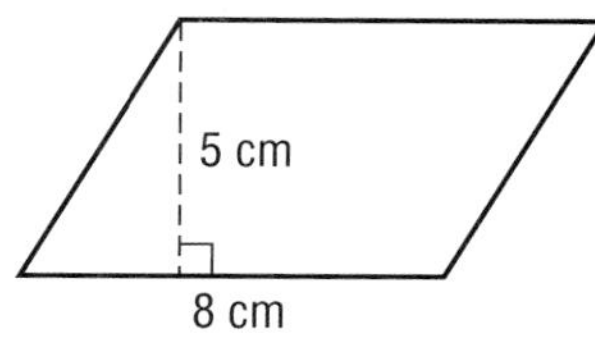

The base of the parallelogram is ________ and the height is ________.

The area of the parallelogram is ________.

2

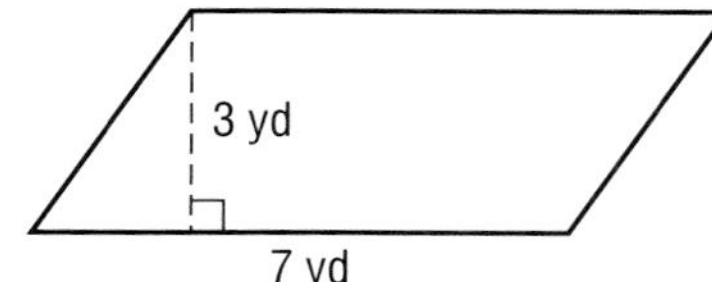

The base of the parallelogram is ________ and the height is ________.

The area of the parallelogram is ________.

3 If a parallelogram has a base of 6 inches and a height of 10 inches, then the area of the parallelogram is ________.

4 If a parallelogram has a base of 12 meters and a height of 3 meters, then the area of the parallelogram is ________.

Draw a parallelogram that has the given area.

5 15 cm^2

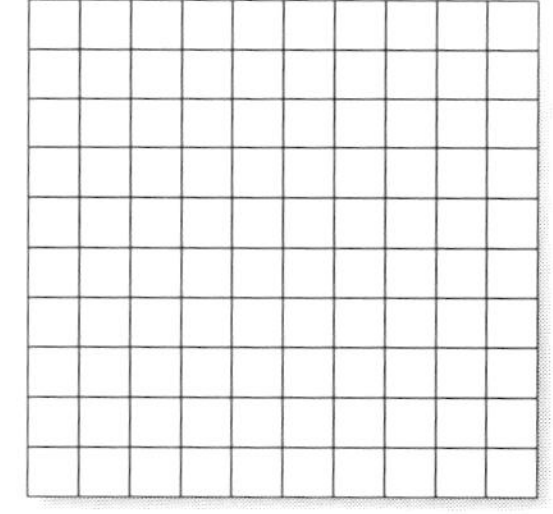

6 32 in^2

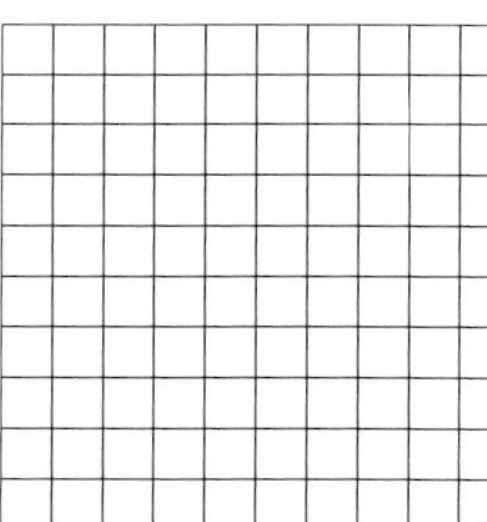

7 7 ft^2

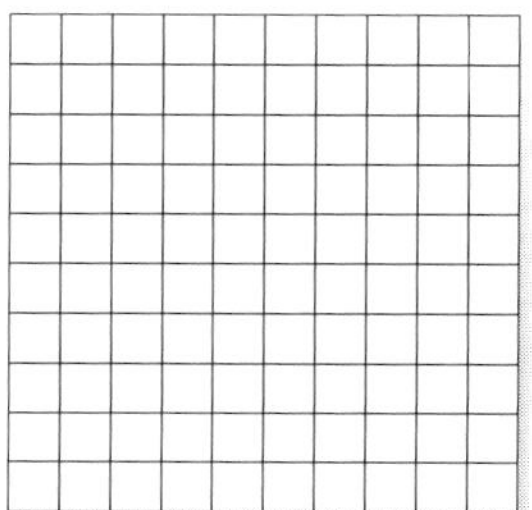

8 18 m^2

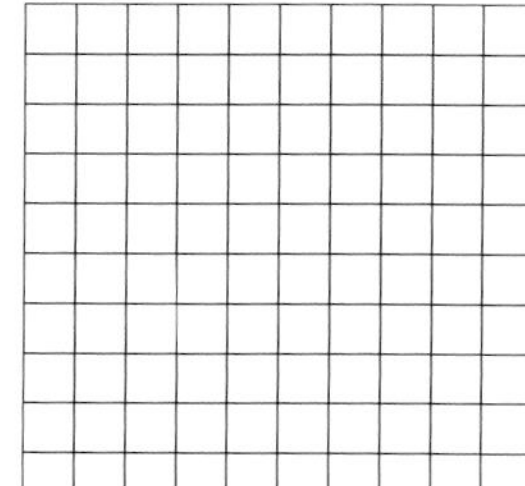

Chapter 9

NAME ______________________ DATE ______________

Lesson 9-3

Problem-Solving Practice

Solve.

1 **PICTURES** While on vacation, Luke bought a wall hanging in the shape of a parallelogram with a base of 18 inches and a height of 24 inches. What is the area of the wall hanging? ______________

2 **GEOMETRY** What is the area of a parallelogram with a base of 11 meters and a height of 8 meters? ______________

3 **STATES** Nodin is creating a flower bed in the shape of a parallelogram. The parallelogram is 5 yards long and 2 yards high. What is the area of the flower bed? ______________

4 **GEOGRAPHY** On the map, the shape of Tennessee is similar to a parallelogram. Approximate the area of Tennessee by using the formula for the area of a parallelogram, if the base of the state is about 385 miles and the height of the state is about 110 miles. ______________

5 **SNAKES** Many snakes have scales shaped like tiny parallelograms. If a snake has a scale with a base length of 3 millimeters and a height of 2 millimeters, what is the area of that scale? ______________

6 **BANNER** For a friend's 30th birthday party, Dario made a banner in the shape of a parallelogram. It had a base of 8 feet and a height of 1 foot. What is the area of the banner? ______________

7 **SCRAPBOOKING** In her scrapbooking workshop, Lindsey learned to use pictures cut into unusual shapes. She cut one picture into a parallelogram with a base of 4 inches and a height of 5 inches. What is the area of the picture? ______________

8 **GEOMETRY** A parallelogram has a base of 12 centimeters and a height of 9 centimeters. What is the area of the parallelogram? ______________

Lesson 9-3

NAME ______________________ DATE ____________

Homework Practice

Find the area of each parallelogram.

1

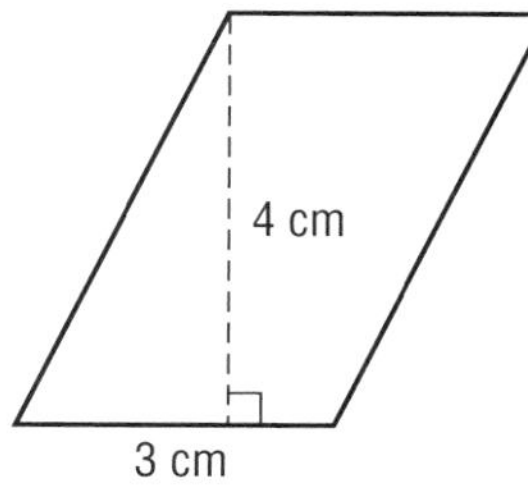

The base of the parallelogram is ______________ and the height is ______________. The area of the parallelogram is ______________.

2

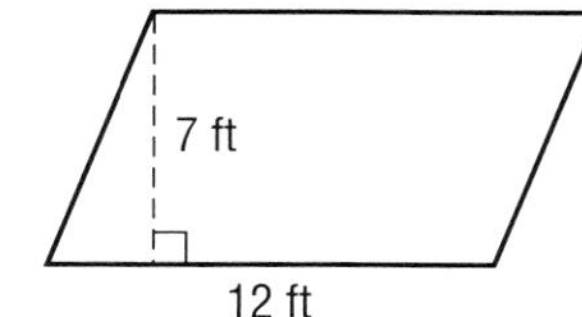

The base of the parallelogram is ______________ and the height is ______________. The area of the parallelogram is ______________.

3

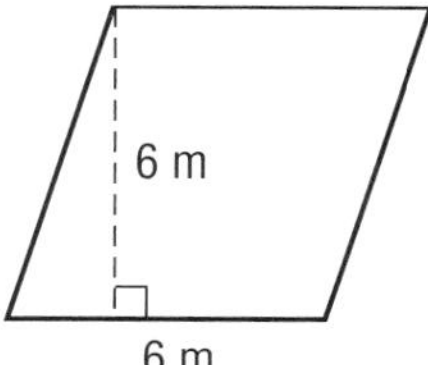

The area of the parallelogram is ______________.

4

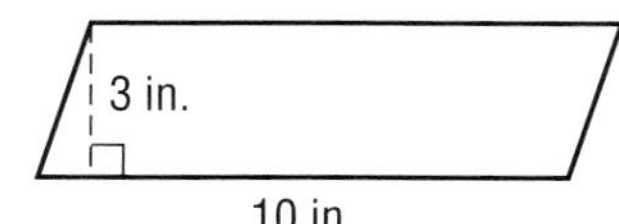

The area of the parallelogram is ______________.

Draw a parallelogram that has the given area.

5 20 m^2

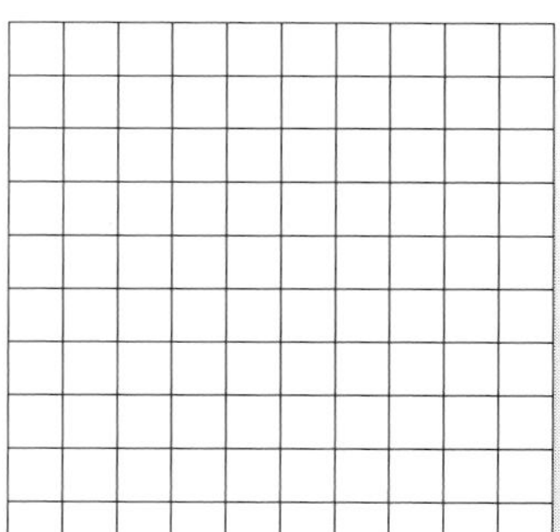

6 6 yd^2

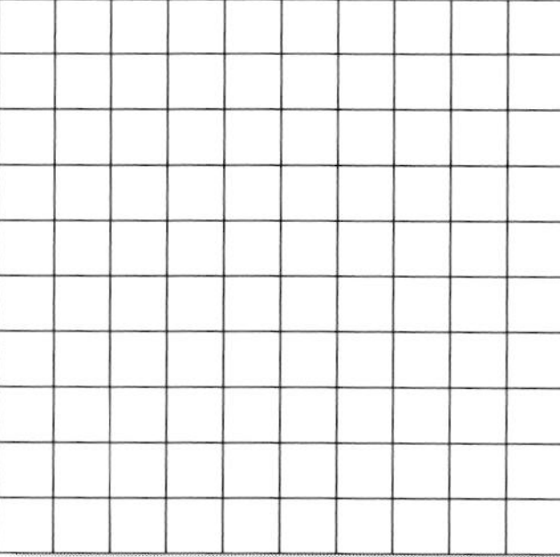

Solve.

7 **PENDANTS** Ratana made a metal pendant for a necklace. The pendant was shaped like a parallelogram. It had a base of 2 centimeters and a height of 6 centimeters. What was the area of the pendant?

____

Write the vocabulary word that completes the sentence.

8 ______________ is the number of square units needed to cover a region or a plane figure.

Chapter 9

Lesson 9-4

NAME ______________________ DATE ____________

Vocabulary and English Language Development

Activate Prior Knowledge

Find the total area.

1 What is the area of the triangular front of the tent? ____________

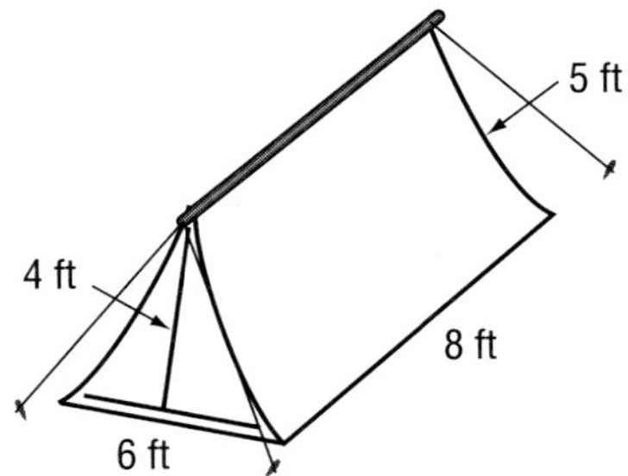

Definition Review

The formula for finding the area of a triangle is $A = \frac{1}{2}b \times h$.

Find the area of each triangle.

2 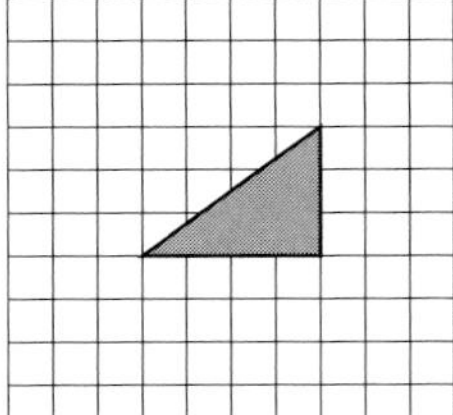

The base of the triangle measures ____________

The height of the triangle measures ____________

The area of the triangle is ____________

3 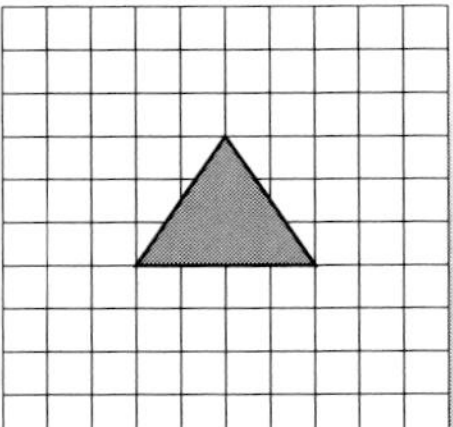

The base of the triangle measures ____________

The height of the triangle measures ____________

The area of the triangle is ____________

4 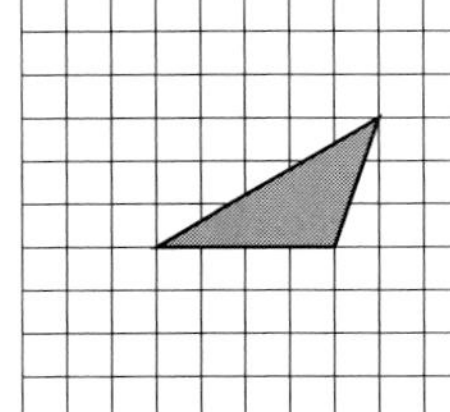

The base of the triangle measures ____________

The height of the triangle measures ____________

The area of the triangle is ____________

5 What is the area of each of these triangles? ____________

Application

Follow the directions for the activity.

- Work individually. Use a 3×5 note card.
- Draw a triangle on the note card, using one side of the card as the base and touching the opposite side as the height. (See the card shown.)
- Cut out the drawn triangle and keep the cut pieces.
- Tape together the pieces remaining from the rectangle to form another triangle. This triangle should be congruent to the one that was cut out.
- Compare triangles and discuss how the area formula for a triangle relates to the area formula of a rectangle.

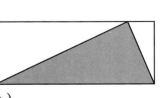

NAME ______________________ DATE ____________

Lesson 9-4

Skills Practice

Find the area of each triangle.

1 a triangle with a base of 7 centimeters and a height of 4 centimeters

The area of the triangle is ____________.

2 a triangle with a base of 4 inches and a height of 4 inches

The area of the triangle is ____________.

3

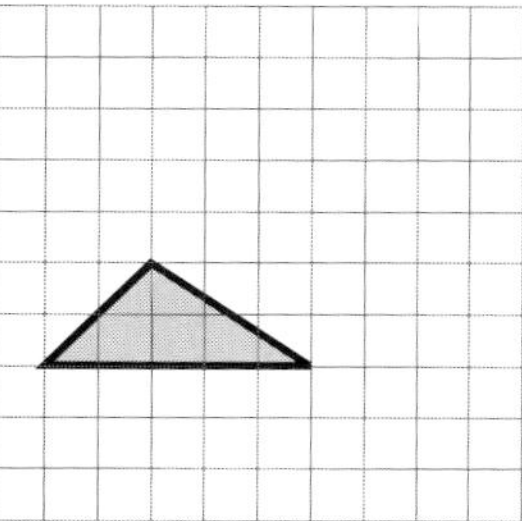

The base of the triangle measures

____________.

The height of the triangle measures

____________.

The area of the triangle is ____________.

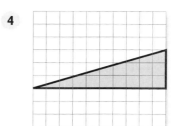

4

The base of the triangle measures

____________.

The height of the triangle measures

____________.

The area of the triangle is ____________.

5 a triangle with a base of 10 feet and a height of 6 feet

The area of the triangle is ____________.

6 a triangle with a base of 18 feet and a height of 8 feet

The area of the triangle is ____________.

Draw a triangle that has the given area.

7 16 in^2

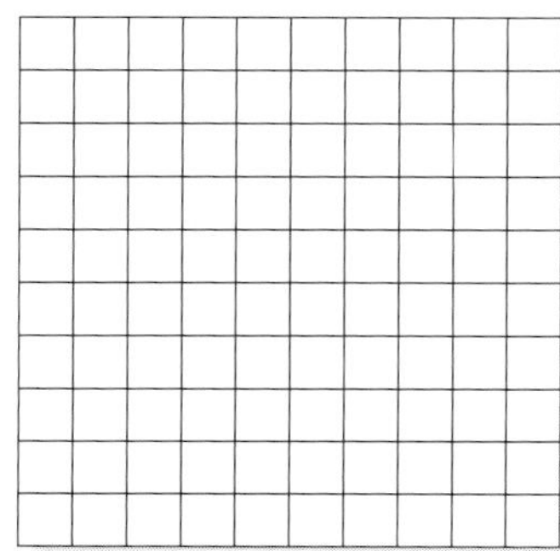

8 24 m^2

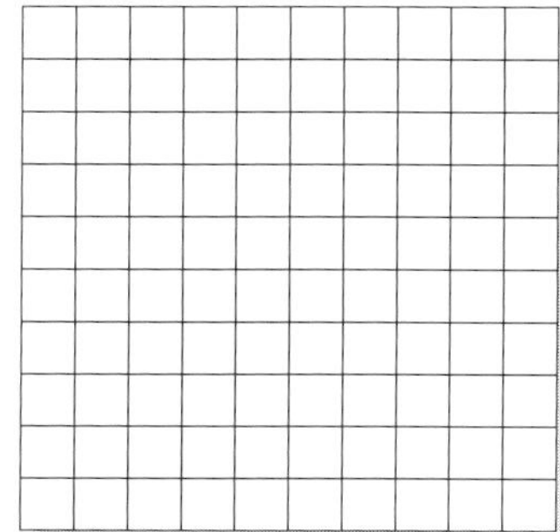

Chapter 9

NAME ______________________ DATE ______________

Lesson 9-4 Problem-Solving Practice

Solve.

1 **SIGNS** A yield sign is in the shape of an equilateral triangle (a triangle with three equal sides). What is the area of a yield sign if it has a base of 76 centimeters and a height of 65 centimeters?

2 **LOGOS** A company's logo is the shape of a right triangle. The base and height of the logo are each 2 yards long. What is the area of the logo?

3 **GRAPHING** Mrs. Simmons gave her students the grid below. What is the area of the triangle?

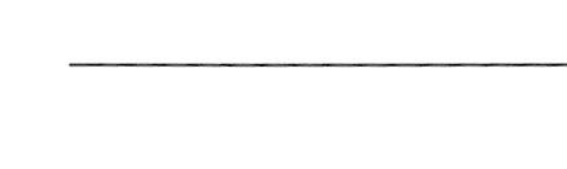

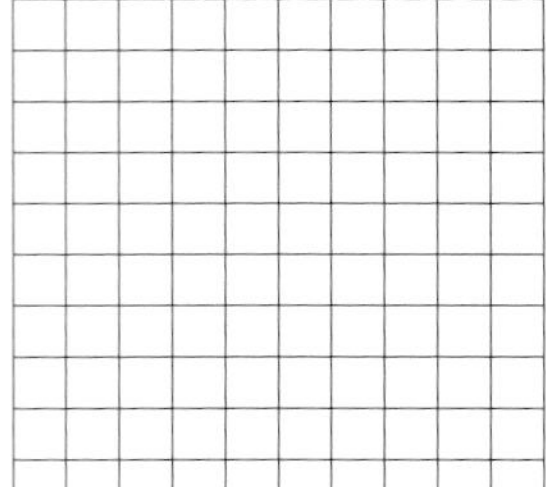

4 **SCRAPBOOKING** Eva is decorating a page in her scrapbook. She took a rectangle measuring 6 centimeters by 9 centimeters and cut it in half along its diagonal to make 2 triangles. What is the area of each triangle?

5 **BILLIARDS** A 15-ball rack used for playing billiards has the shape of an equilateral triangle. The sides of the rack measure 14 inches, and the height of the rack measures about 12 inches. What is the approximate area of the billiards rack?

6 **DRAWING** Kyle drew a right triangle on his paper. He then measured two sides and found that the base had a length of 6 centimeters and the height had a length of 11 centimeters. What is the area of the triangle that Kyle drew?

____

Lesson 9-4

NAME ______________________ DATE ____________

Homework Practice

Find the area of each triangle.

1. a triangle with a base of 6 inches and a height of 8 inches

   The area of the triangle is __________.

2. a triangle with a base of 5 meters and a height of 8 meters

   The area of the triangle is __________.

3. 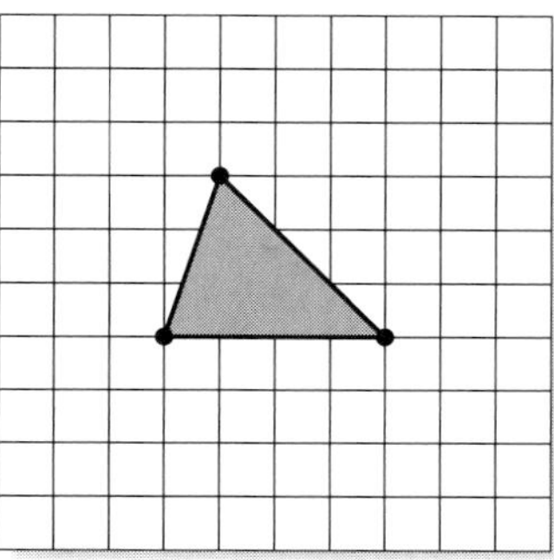

   The base of the triangle measures __________.

   The height of the triangle measures __________.

   The area of the triangle is __________.

4. 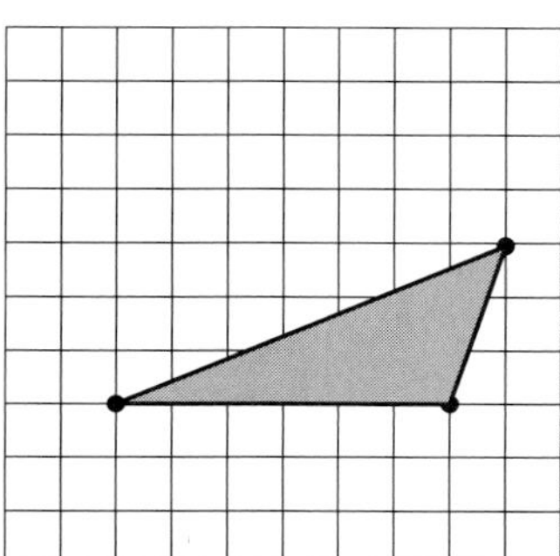

   The base of the triangle measures __________.

   The height of the triangle measures __________.

   The area of the triangle is __________.

Draw a triangle that has the given area.

5. 12 cm^2

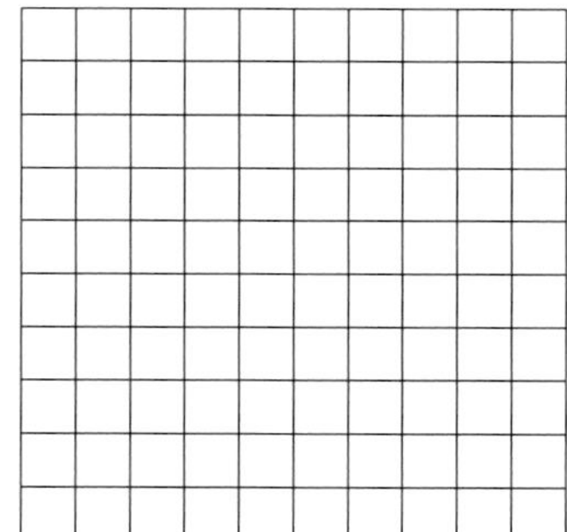

6. 18 mm^2

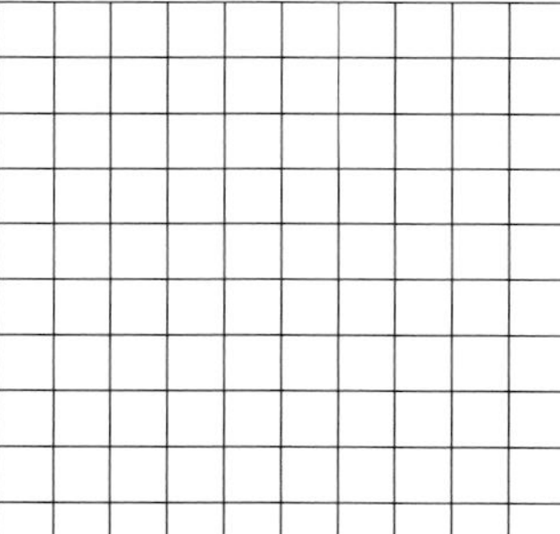

Solve.

7. **BANNER** For the school parade, Mrs. Murrilo's class made a triangular banner. The base of the banner was 4 feet long, and the height of the banner was 5 feet long. What was the area of the banner?

   ____

Write the vocabulary word that completes the sentence.

8. A __________ unit is used to measure the area of a figure.

Chapter 9

NAME ____________________ DATE ____________

Foldables Study Organizer

Dinah Zike's Foldables

Make this Foldable to help you organize information about surface area, volume, and measurement.

1. Begin with one sheet of notebook paper. Fold the sheet of paper in half as shown.

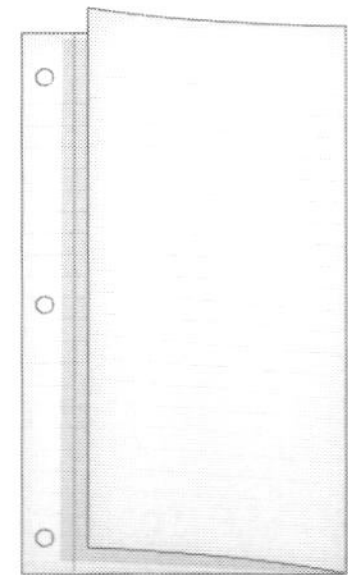

2. Cut every sixth line on one side. The result is five tabs.

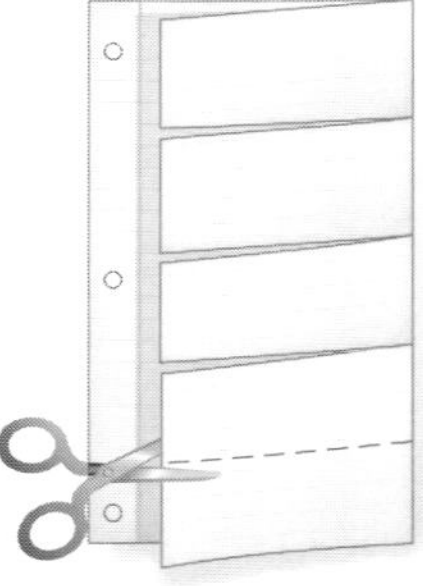

3. Label each tab as shown.

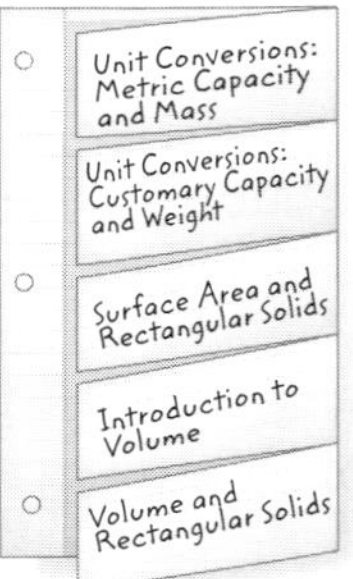

TAKING NOTES
As you read through the chapter, use your Foldable to explain and write an example of each key term.

USING YOUR FOLDABLE
As you study, try to solve the problems that you wrote on your Foldable without looking at the answer. If you have any difficulties, then go over that concept again.

USING YOUR FOLDABLE
Trade Foldables with a partner. Check each other's work. Did your partner solve the problem correctly under each tab? If not provide the correct answer.

NAME ______________________ DATE ____________

Games and Puzzles

Mystery Measurements

What You Need

- 2 yardsticks
- 12 index cards
- scissors

Number of Players

2

GET READY

- Working alone, each player secretly measures the length or width of six objects in the classroom and records them on a piece of paper. The measures may be in inches or feet. This will serve as the answer sheet at the end of the game.
- Each player takes 6 index cards and cuts them in half, making 12 cards.
- For each object, the measurement is recorded on one card. A description of what was measured is recorded on another card. Make sure each measurement is different.

DIRECTIONS

- Each player shuffles his or her cards.
- Keeping the cards facedown, players exchange cards.
- At the same time, players turn over all the cards given to them.
- Each player attempts to match each object with its measure.
- The player with more correct matches after 5 minutes is the winner.

NAME ______________________ DATE ______________

Lesson **10-1**

Vocabulary and English Language Development

Activate Prior Knowledge

1 Circle each item for which you could find the capacity. Put a square around the items for which you could only find the mass.

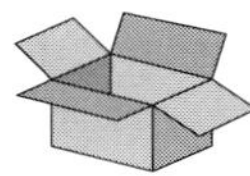

Definition Review

The **metric system** is a measurement system that includes units such as meter, gram, and liter.

Complete each sentence using the words *multiply* or *divide*.

2 To convert a smaller unit to a larger unit, you should ______________.

3 To convert a larger unit to a smaller unit, you should ______________.

Complete each sentence using the words *larger* or *smaller*.

4 A **liter** is ______________ than a kiloliter.

5 A **kilogram** is ______________ than a milligram.

6 A **liter** is ______________ than a milliliter.

7 A **gram** is ______________ than a kilogram.

Application

Follow the directions for the activity.

- Work in groups of 4.
- Find a container and a solid object in the classroom.
- In your group, order the containers from one that can hold the most capacity to the one that can hold the least capacity.
- In your group, order the solid objects from one that has the greatest mass to the one that has the least mass.
- Look at another other group's ordered items. Decide if you agree or disagree with the order.

NAME ________________________ DATE ____________

Lesson 10-1

Skills Practice

Convert using a place-value chart.

1. 1,261 mL = ____________ L

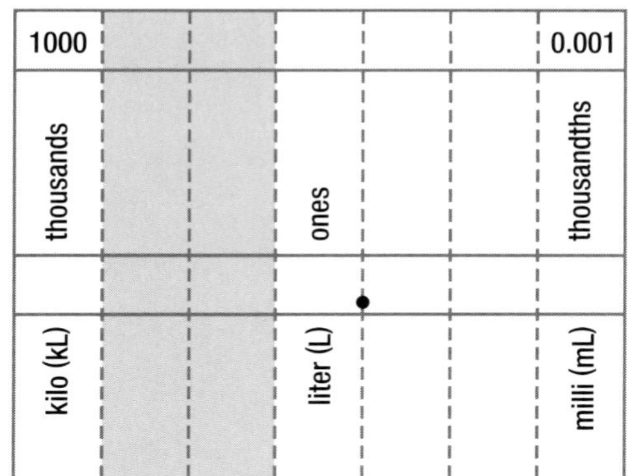

1000
0.001
thousands
ones
thousandths
kilo (kL)
liter (L)
milli (mL)

2. 5.98 kg = ____________ g

1000			1			0.001
thousands			ones			thousandths
			•			
kilo (kg)			gram (g)			milli (mg)

Convert.

3. 2.9 g = ________________ mg

   1 g = ________________ mg

   Multiply or divide? ________________

   2.9 ____________ 1000 = ____________

   2.9 g = ________________ mg

4. 106 mL = ________________ L

   1 L = ________________ mL

   Multiply or divide? ________________

   106 ____________ 1,000 = ____________

   106 mL = ________________ L

5. 6,300 kg = ________________ g

6. 465 mg = ________________ g

7. 0.019 kL = ________________ L

8. 93,500 L = ________________ kL

9. 1.04 g = ________________ kg

10. 200,010 mg = ________________ g

11. 25 mL = ________________ L

12. 0.0006 kL = ________________ L

13. 0.79 kg = ________________ g

14. 8,390 mL = ________________ L

Chapter 10

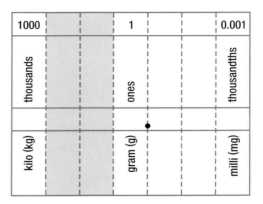

NAME ______________________ DATE ______________

Lesson 10-1 Problem-Solving Practice

Solve.

1 **FOOD** Molly ate a granola bar that was wrapped in the label shown below. How many milligrams of sugar did Molly eat? ______________

Nutrition Facts	
Serving Size 1 bar	
Amount Per Serving	
Calories 130	
Total Fat 2.5g	4%
Saturated Fat 1.5g	8%
Cholesterol 15mg	5%
Sodium 170mg	6%
Total Carbohydrate 17 g	6%
Dietary Fiber 0g	0%
Sugars 16g	
Protein 10g	

2 **BOWLING** Sipatu uses a 7 kilogram bowling ball when he bowls. How many grams does his bowling ball weigh? ______________

3 **MILK** Mr. Larson's tanker truck has 2.6 kiloliters of milk. How many liters of milk are in Mr. Larson's truck? ______________

4 **CUPS** Ling sells cups that hold 400 milliliters of liquid. How many liters does each cup hold? ______________

5 **PHOTOGRAPHY** Omar is developing film. He needs to use 0.85 liter of developing solution. How many milliliters of developing solution has he measured? ______________

6 **CONCRETE** Kelly is making concrete and needs to add 12 liters of water to reach the correct consistency. How many kiloliters of water does Kelly need? ______________

7 **GARDEN** Felix feeds his tomato plant with 1,320 milliliters of water each week. With how many liters of water does Felix feed his plant each week? ______________

8 **ANIMALS** At the zoo, Dakota feeds a baby giraffe 2,100,000 milligrams of food each day. How many grams of food does Dakota feed the baby giraffe each day? ______________

9 **CHEMISTRY** Fatima needs to make a solution with 100 milligrams of sodium chloride and 390 milliliters of water. How many grams of sodium chloride does Fatima need? How many liters of water does she need? ______________ ______________

NAME _______________ DATE _______________

Lesson 10-1

Homework Practice

Convert using a place-value chart.

1 0.04 kL = __________ L

1000			1			0.001
thousands			ones			thousandths
			•			
kilo (kL)			liter (L)			milli (mL)

2 680,000 mg = __________ g

1000			1			0.001
thousands			ones			thousandths
			•			
kilo (kg)			gram (g)			milli (mg)

Convert.

3 0.0092 kL = __________ L

4 3,510 mg = __________ g

5 0.0237 kg = __________ g

6 2.3 L = __________ mL

7 18 mL = __________ L

8 54,250 mg = __________ g

Solve.

9 **WEIGHT** A baby chick has a mass of 35,000 milligrams after it hatches. How many grams does the chick weigh? __________

10 **WATER** Jorge is designing a large tank to hold 209.1 kiloliters of water. How many liters of water will the tank hold? __________

Write the vocabulary word that completes each sentence.

11 A __________ is a metric unit for measuring mass.

12 A __________ is a metric unit for measuring volume or capacity.

NAME ______________________________ DATE ______________

Lesson 10-2

Vocabulary and English Language Development

Activate Prior Knowledge

Complete each sentence using the words *greater than*, *less than*, or *the same as*.

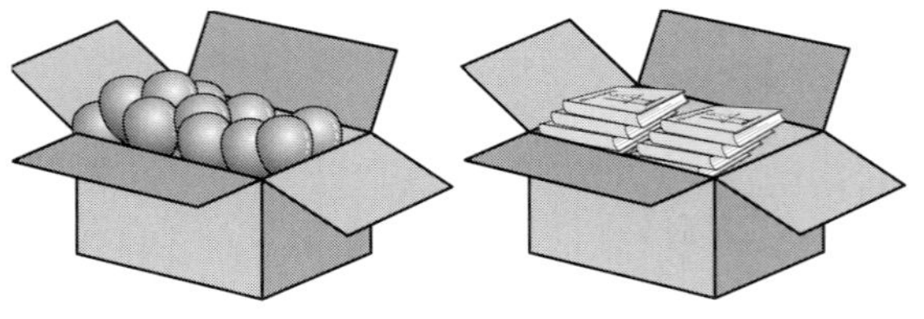

Bowl A

Bowl B

1. The weight of the box of balloons is __________ the weight of the box of books.
2. The capacity of the box of books is __________ the capacity of the box of balloons.
3. The weight of Bowl B is __________ the weight of Bowl A.
4. The capacity of Bowl A is __________ less than the capacity of Bowl B.

Definition Review

Weight is a measurement that tells how heavy or light an object is.
Capacity is the amount of dry or liquid material a container can hold.

Complete each sentence using the words *capacity* or *weight*.

5. A pint is a unit for measuring __________.
6. A ton is a unit for measuring __________.
7. A gallon is a unit for measuring __________.
8. An ounce is a unit for measuring __________.

Application

- Work in groups of 3 or 4.
- Bring from home a variety of containers such as empty juice bottles and milk jugs. Each group of students needs a plastic measuring cup.
- Experiment to see if the bottles and jugs hold as much water as their label claims.
- Test conversion amounts:
  - Do 2 cups equal 1 pint?
  - Do 4 quarts equal 1 gallon?
- Discuss your findings with the class.

Lesson 10-2

NAME ______________________ DATE ______________

Skills Practice

Convert using a table.

1. 8 c = ________ fl oz

cups								
fluid ounces	8	16	24	32	40	48	56	64

2. 5 tons = ________ lb

tons					
pounds	2,000	4,000	6,000	8,000	10,000

Convert.

3. 80 fl oz = ________ c
   1 c = ________ fl oz
   Multiply or divide? ________
   80 ________ 8 = ________
   80 fl oz = ________ c

4. 7 gal = ________ qt
   1 gal = ________ qt
   Multiply or divide? ________
   7 ________ 4 = ________
   7 gal = ________ qt

5. 96 oz = ________ lb

6. 13 pt = ________ c

7. 3 qt = ________ fl oz

8. 16,000 oz = ________ T

9. 3 pt = ________ fl oz

10. 5 gal = ________ pt

11. 9 qt = ________ pt

12. 512 fl oz = ________ gal

13. 32 c = ________ gal

14. 11 qt = ________ c

15. 5 gal = ________ fl oz

16. 6 c = ________ fl oz

17. 256 fl oz = ________ pt

18. 1 T = ________ oz

19. 42 c = ________ pt

20. 16 pt = ________ gal

NAME ______________________ DATE ____________

Lesson 10-2 Problem-Solving Practice

Solve.

1 **STRAWBERRIES** The grocery store received a delivery of 96 pints of strawberries. How many gallons of strawberries did the store receive? ____________

2 **LEMONADE** Lydia is making lemonade for a lemonade stand. She wants to fill all 4 of the pitchers shown below. How many cups of lemonade will she need? ____________

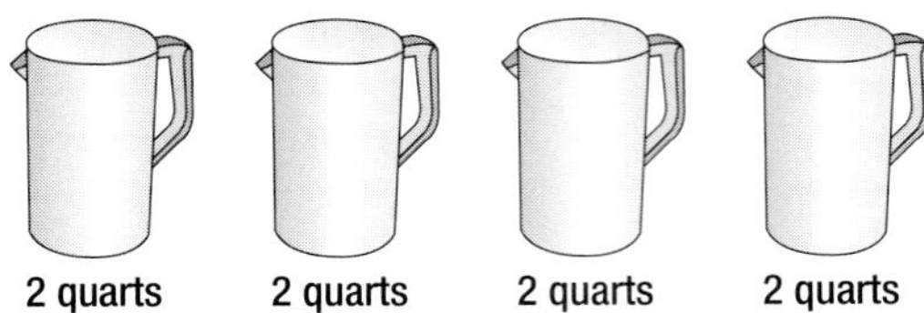

3 **NUTS** Kenyon bought 64 ounces of mixed nuts at the store. How many pounds of nuts did Kenyon buy? ____________

4 **SOUP** Erin needs 4 cups of vegetable broth to make her favorite soup. How many gallons of broth does she need? ____________

5 **GASOLINE** Ms. Harada poured an entire 3-gallon can of gasoline into her lawnmower. How many fluid ounces of gasoline did Ms. Harada put in the lawnmower? ____________

6 **DOGS** At the veterinarian's office, Sharon's dog weighs 10 pounds. How many ounces does Sharon's dog weigh? ____________

7 **ANIMALS** Casandra gives 15 gallons of water to the bears at the zoo each day. How many quarts of water does Casandra give the bears each day? ____________

8 **GRAVEL** Brian's truck can hold up to 6,000 pounds of gravel. How many tons of gravel can it hold? ____________

9 **COOKOUT** Emmett bought 80 ounces of ground beef for a cookout. How many pounds of ground beef did Emmett buy? ____________

10 **BRIDGES** Samir designed a bridge that will require 20 tons of steel. How many pounds of steel will the bridge require? ____________

Lesson **10-2** NAME ______________________ DATE ____________

Homework Practice

Convert using a table.

1 9 gal = __________ qt

gallons									
quarts	4	8	12	16	20	24	28	32	36

2 768 fl oz = __________ gal

gallons						
fluid ounces	128	256	384	512	640	768

3 4 lb = __________ oz

pounds	1	2	3	4
ounces				

Convert.

4 10 gal = __________ qt

5 14 pt = __________ qt

6 17 T = __________ lb

7 2 gal = __________ fl oz

8 64 c = __________ gal

9 3 lb = __________ oz

10 64,000 oz = __________ T

11 15 qt = __________ c

Solve.

12 **PIZZA** Angelos is making vegetable pizzas and needs 32 ounces of cheese. How many pounds of cheese does Angelos need? __________

13 **FISH** The fish tank in Mr. Moseley's classroom holds 20 gallons of water. How many quarts of water does the tank hold? __________

Write the vocabulary word that completes the sentence.

14 The __________ system is a measurement system that includes units such as feet, pounds, and quarts.

NAME ______________________ DATE ______________

Lesson **10-3**

Vocabulary and English Language Development

Activate Prior Knowledge

Find the surface area.

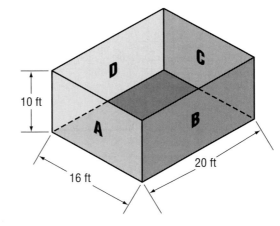

1 Find the area of wall *A*. ____________

2 Which wall has an area equal to wall *A*? ____________

3 Find the area of wall *B*. ____________

4 Which wall has an area equal to wall *B*? ____________

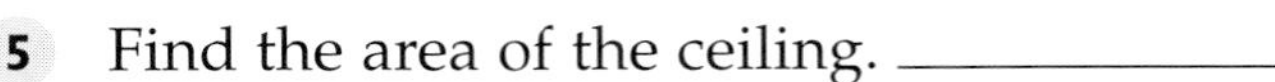

5 Find the area of the ceiling. ____________

6 Aurelia is going to paint all four walls and the ceiling of this room. What is this surface area of the room, *not* including the floor? ____________

Definition Review

7 A ______________ is a flat pattern that can be folded to make a rectangular prism.

8 The ______________ of a rectangular prism is the sum of the areas of all the faces of the figure.

Application

Follow the directions to create a cube.

- Get a piece of thick, colored paper.
- Using a pencil and a ruler, draw the net of a cube with sides of length 10 centimeters.
- For each exterior side of the net, draw a tab which can be used to connect the sides of the cube.
- Using a pair of scissors, cut out the net along exterior sides and tabs.
- Fold along all lines for sides and tabs.
- Using tape, connect tabs to form the cube.

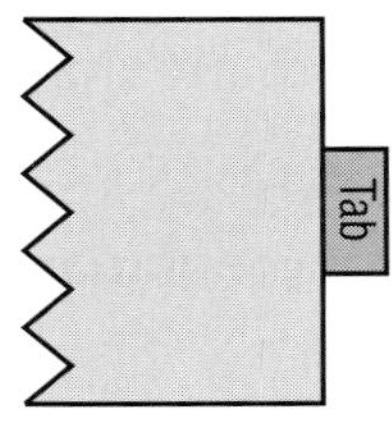

NAME ______________________ DATE ____________

Lesson 10-3 Skills Practice

Draw a net for a rectangular prism with the given length, width, and height.

1 $2 \times 4 \times 8$

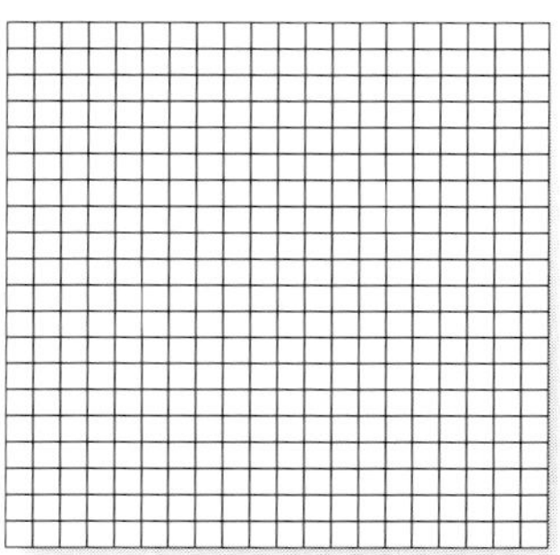

2 $5 \times 5 \times 10$

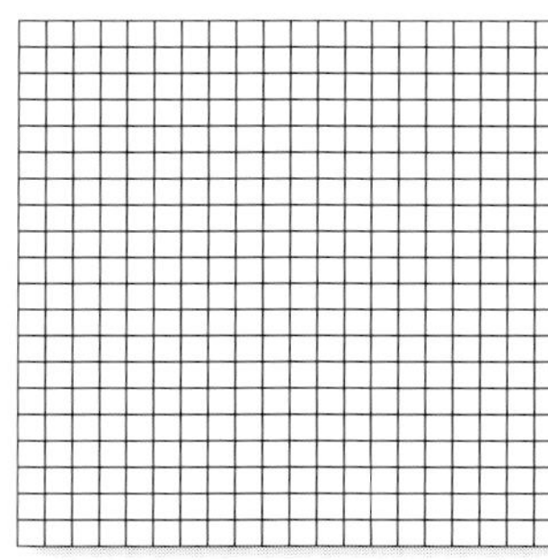

3 $9 \times 2 \times 4$

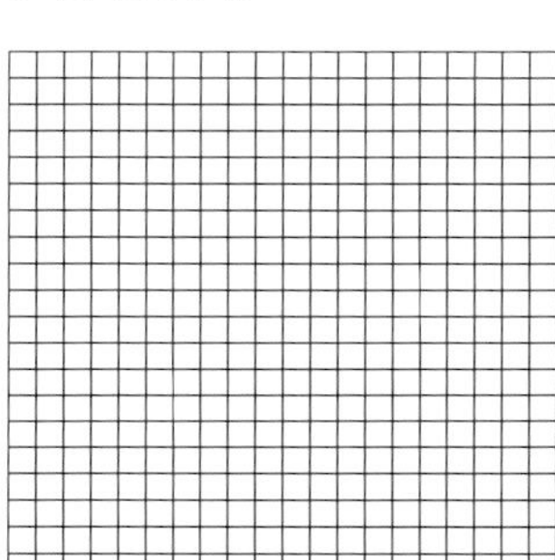

4 $3 \times 4 \times 5$

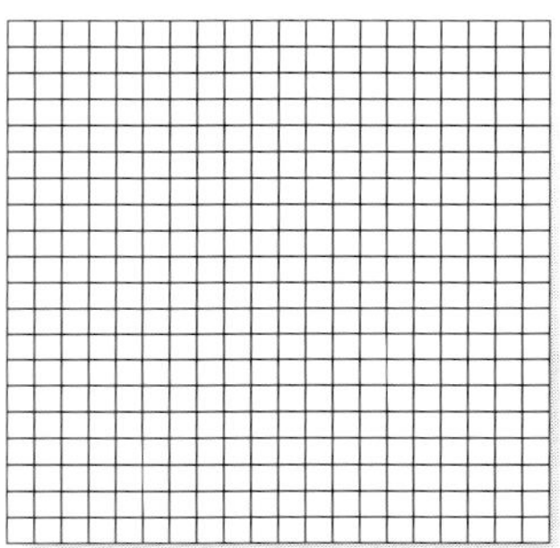

Find the surface area of each rectangular prism.

5

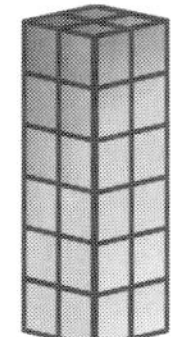

The surface area of the rectangular prism is ________ square units.

6

The surface area of the cube is ________ square units.

7

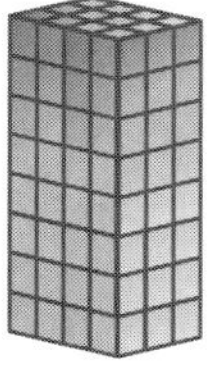

The surface area of the rectangular prism is ________ square units.

8

The surface area of the rectangular prism is ________ square units.

Lesson 10-3

NAME ______________________ DATE ______________

Problem-Solving Practice

Solve.

1 **PANELING** A practice room in a school music department is in the shape of a cube. Each wall has a length of 8 feet. Sound proof panels must be placed on all four walls, the floor, and the ceiling of the room. How much paneling will the room require? ____________

2 **COLORS** Gregory is helping his brother learn the names of colors. He makes a color cube with a different color on each side. If each side measures 2 inches, what is the surface area of the cube? Draw a net for the number cube. ____________

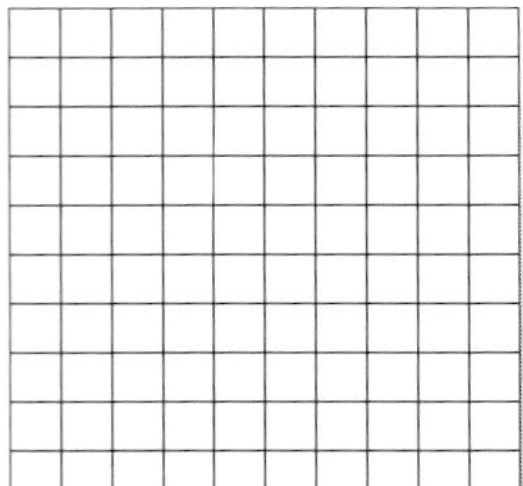

3 **GIFTS** Kenyi bought a birthday present for her friend. She placed it in a box. The box was 30 cm × 30 cm × 5 cm. She then wrapped the present with paper. How much wrapping paper did she need? Assume there was no overlap. ____________

4 **PAINTING** Nalin has converted his garage into a den. When decorating the room, Nalin decided to paint all the surfaces, including the floor and ceiling, using different shades of blue. The dimensions of the room are 22 feet wide, 20 feet long, and 9 feet high. What surface area did he paint? ____________

5 **GEOMETRY** A number cube has sides of length 3 centimeters. What is the surface area of the number cube? ____________

6 **CHEESE** A block of cheese has dimensions 3 cm × 10 cm × 15 cm. After cutting the block of cheese, the grocer must wrap it in plastic. What is the least amount of plastic wrap the grocer needs to wrap the block of cheese? ____________

7 **RACQUETBALL** When playing racquetball, the entire surface area of the room is used. A racquetball court has a width of 20 feet, a length of 40 feet, and a height of 20 feet. What is the total surface area of the racquetball court? ____________

NAME _______________ DATE _______________

Homework Practice

Draw a net for a rectangular prism with the given length, width, and height.

1. $6 \times 2 \times 8$

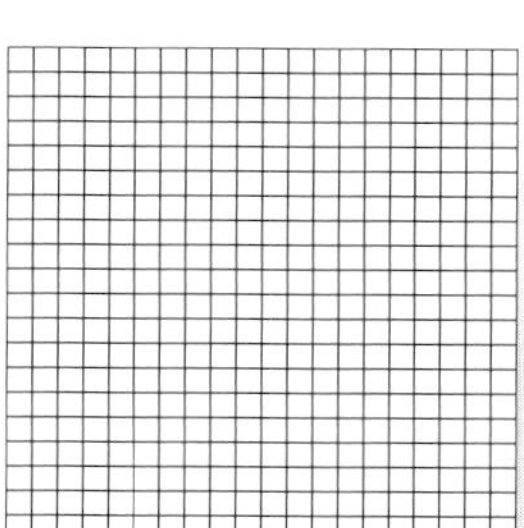

2. $3 \times 3 \times 5$

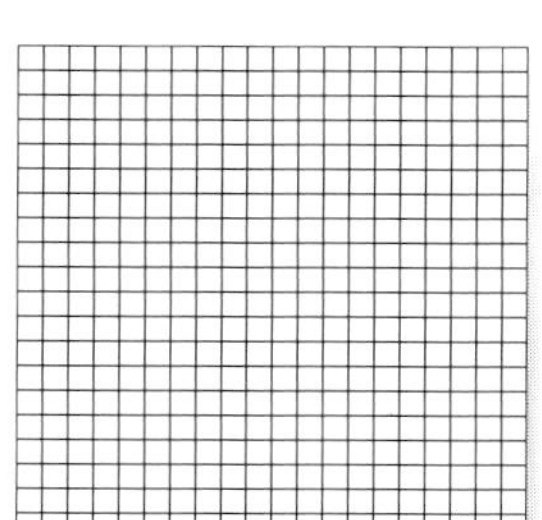

3. $2 \times 6 \times 4$

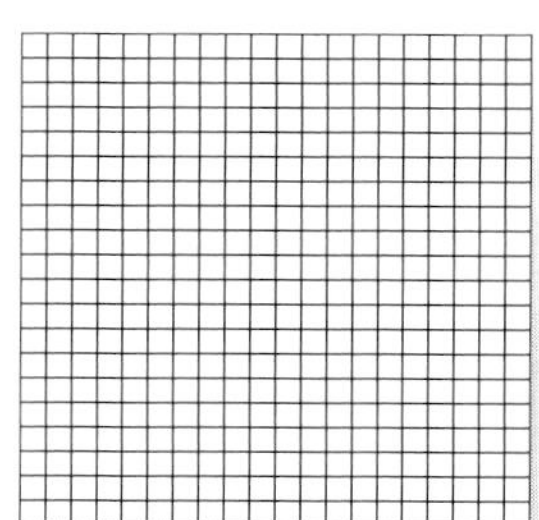

Find the surface area of each rectangular prism.

4. 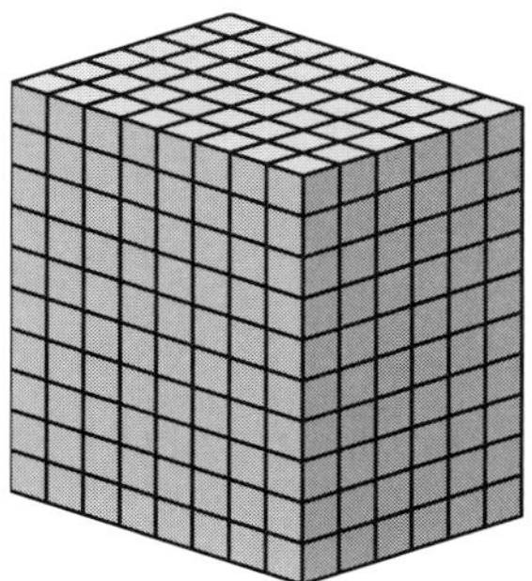

The surface area of the rectangular prism is _______ square units.

5. 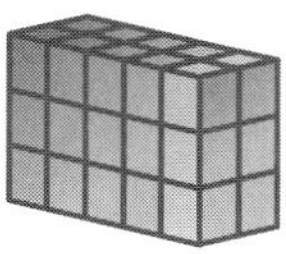

The surface area of the rectangular prism is _______ square units.

6. 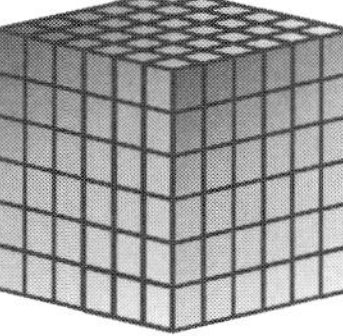

The surface area of the cube is _______ square units.

Solve.

7. **BLOCKS** Lourdes is playing with building blocks. One block is shaped like a rectangular prism with a length of 14 mm, a width of 40 mm, and a height of 80 mm. What is the surface area of the block? _______

8. **GEOMETRY** A cube has sides of length 7 feet. What is the total surface area of the cube? _______

Write the vocabulary term that completes the sentence.

9. The area of the surface of a three-dimensional figure is called

____

Lesson 10-4

NAME ________________________________ DATE ______________

Vocabulary and English Language Development

Activate Prior Knowledge

Create rectangular prisms with the given volume.

1 Measure, draw, and label three different rectangular prisms, each with a volume of 48 cubic inches.

Definition Review

2 The amount of space inside a three-dimensional figure is the ______________ of the figure.

To find the volume of a solid figure, count the number of cubic units the solid figure contains.

Refer to figures A-E to answer the questions.

A

B

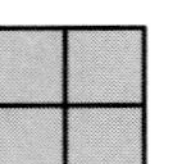

C

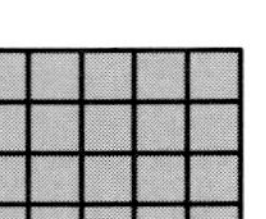

D

E

3 Which figures are three-dimensional? ______________

4 Which figures are cubes? ______________

5 Which figures are rectangular prisms? ______________

6 What is the volume of figure D? ______________

7 What is the volume of figure A? ______________

8 What is the volume of figure E? ______________

Lesson **10-4** NAME ________________ DATE ________________

Skills Practice

Count the number of cubes in each rectangular prism.

1 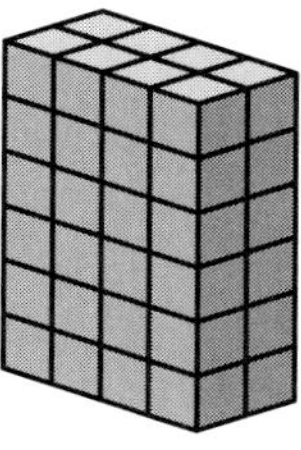

There are _______ cubes in the rectangular prism.

2 

There are _______ cubes in the rectangular prism.

Find the volume of each rectangular prism.

3 

The length of the prism has _______ cubes.
The width of the prism has _______ cubes.
The area of the top layer is _______ × _______ = _______.
There are _______ layers in the prism.
The volume of the cube is _______ cubic units.

4 

The length of the rectangular prism has _______ cubes.
The width of the rectangular prism has _______ cubes.
The area of the top layer is _______ × _______ = _______.
There are _______ layers in the rectangular prism.
The volume of the rectangular prism is _______ cubic units.

5 

The length of the rectangular prism has _______ cubes.
The width of the rectangular prism has _______ cubes.
The area of the top layer is _______ × _______ = _______.
There are _______ layers in the rectangular prism.
The volume of the rectangular prism is _______ cubic units.

NAME ______________________ DATE ______________

Lesson **10-4**

Problem-Solving Practice

Solve.

1 **GEOMETRY** What is the volume of a rectangular prism that has a length of 4 meters, a width of 6 meters, and a height of 5 meters? ____________

2 **APPLIANCES** The size of an appliance is determined by the volume of its interior space. What is the size of a microwave oven with a width of 20 inches, height of 10 inches, and depth of 13 inches? ____________

3 **MODELS** Valerie's father built her a dollhouse that is 40 inches long, 10 inches wide, and 30 inches tall. What is the volume of Valerie's dollhouse? ____________

4 **TOYS** Macaro is playing with building blocks. He made the structure shown below. How many blocks are in Macaro's structure? ____________

5 **PACKAGING** A package is 6 inches by 6 inches by 8 inches. What is the volume of the package? ____________

6 **RECREATION** What is the volume of an Olympic-size pool that has a length of 25 meters, a width of 50 meters, and a depth of 2 meters? ____________

7 **GEOMETRY** What is the volume of a cube with side lengths of 8 feet? ____________

NAME ____________________ DATE ____________

Homework Practice

How many cubes are in each rectangular prism?

1

There are ______ cubes in the rectangular prism.

2

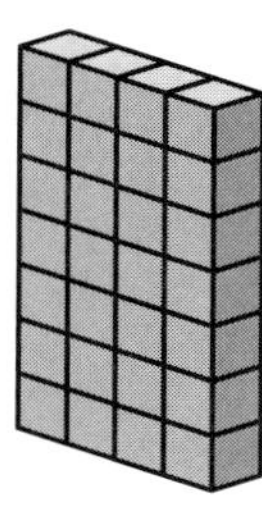

There are ______ cubes in the rectangular prism.

3

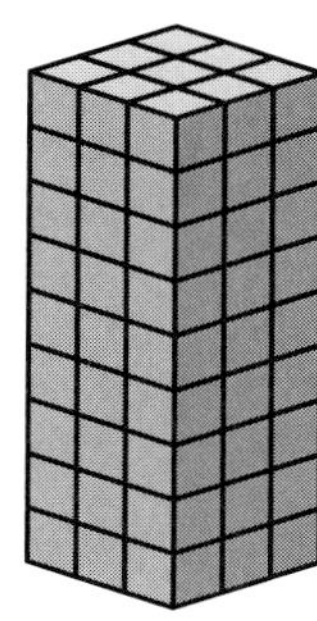

There are ______ cubes in the rectangular prism.

Find the volume of each rectangular prism.

4

The length of the prism has ______ cubes.
The width of the prism has ______ cubes.
The area of the top layer is ______ × ______ = ______.
There are ______ layers in the prism.
The volume of the rectangular prism is ______ cubic units.

5

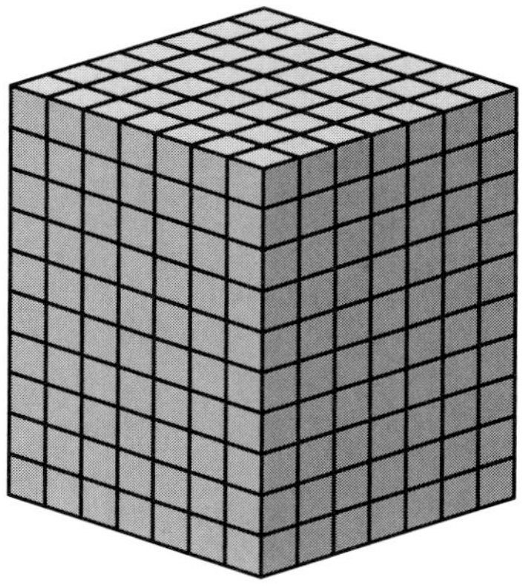

The volume of the rectangular prism is ______ cubic units.

6

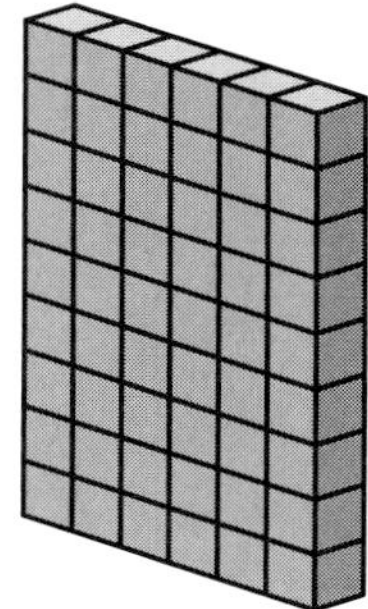

The volume of the rectangular prism is ______ cubic units.

Solve.

7 **APPLIANCES** The size of an appliance is determined by the volume of its interior space. What is the size of a refrigerator whose interior space has a height of 7 feet, a width of 2 feet, and a depth of 5 feet? ____________

NAME ______________________ DATE ______________

Lesson 10-5

Vocabulary and English Language Development

Activate Prior Knowledge

Find the surface area and volume of the rectangular prism using correct units.

1 What shape can be formed from the net?

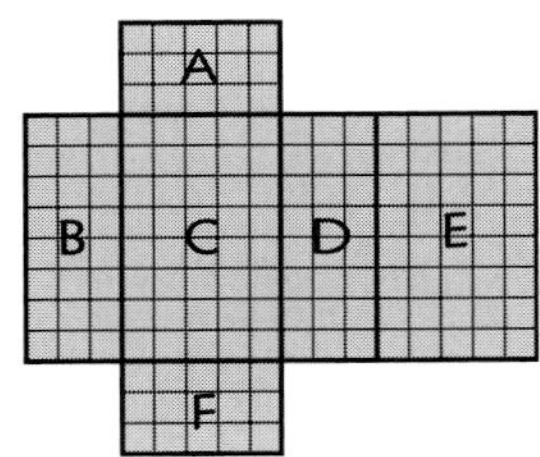

____

What is the surface area of the figure?

____

What is the volume of the figure?

____

Definition Review

Match each vocabulary word to the description that best fits it.

2 cube ______

3 face ______

4 net ______

5 parallelogram ______

6 rectangular prism ______

7 surface area ______

A. flat, four-sided polygon with opposite sides equal and parallel

B. total of areas of all flat surfaces of a solid figure

C. flat surface of a solid figure

D. flat pattern that can be folded to make a solid figure

E. solid figure with six rectangular sides

F. solid figure with six square sides

Application

Follow the directions to play the game.

- Form a group of 3 or 4.
- Choose a rectangular prism for which the volume can be found (for example: the room itself, a drawer, or a box).
- Examine the prism and estimate its volume. Write your estimated volume.
- Use a ruler or yardstick to determine the actual volume of the prism.
- The student with the closest estimate wins the game.
- Repeat the game until all students choose and measure a prism.

NAME _______________ DATE _______________

Lesson 10-5 Skills Practice

Find the number of cubes in each rectangular prism.

1 

How many cubes are in the rectangular prism?

____

2 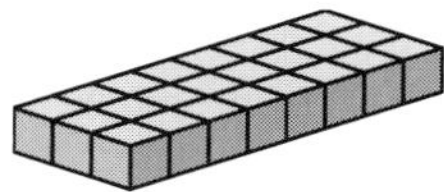

How many cubes are in the rectangular prism?

____

3 

How many cubes are in the rectangular prism?

____

Find the volume of each rectangular prism.

4 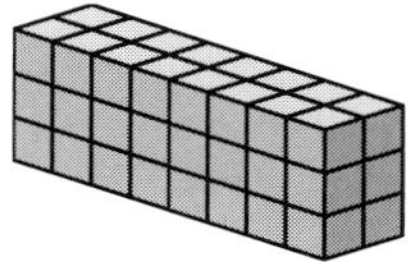

The length of the rectangular prism is _______ units.

The width of the rectangular prism is _______ units.

The height of the rectangular prism is _______ units.

The volume of the rectangular prism is _______ cubic units.

5 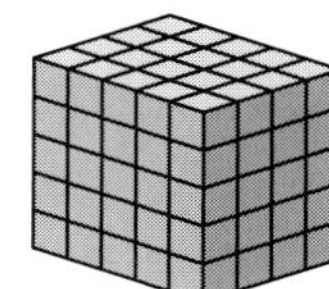

The length of the rectangular prism is _______ units.

The width of the rectangular prism is _______ units.

The height of the rectangular prism is _______ units.

The volume of the rectangular prism is _______ cubic units.

6 

The volume of the rectangular prism is _______ cubic units.

7 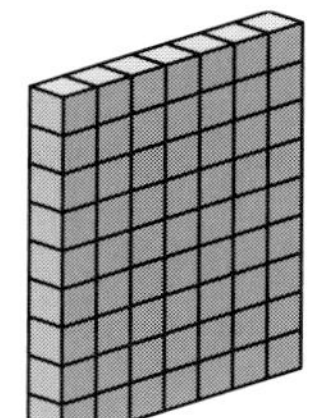

The volume of the rectangular prism is _______ cubic units.

8 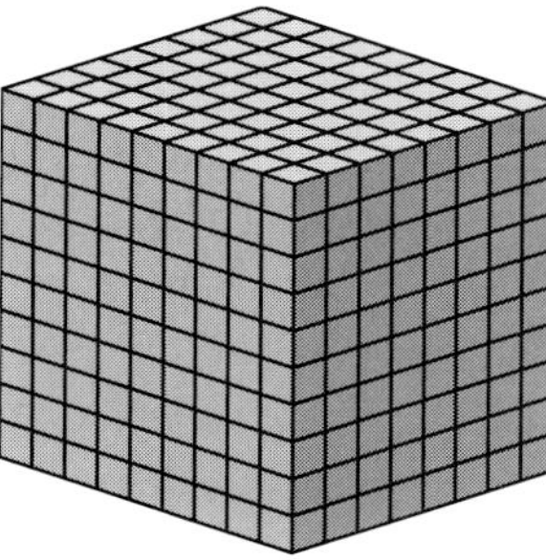

The volume of the rectangular prism is _______ cubic units.

NAME ______________________ DATE ______________

Lesson 10-5 Problem-Solving Practice

Solve.

1. **TOYS** Lina has a toy box in her room. The box is 4 feet long, 2 feet wide, and 3 feet tall. What is the volume of the toy box? ____________

2. **CEREAL** A cereal box has a length of 20 centimeters, a width of 4 centimeters, and a height of 30 centimeters. What is the volume of the cereal box? ____________

3. **MOVING TRUCK** The Morris family is moving. To transport some of their belongings to the new house, they rent a moving truck 5 feet wide, 8 feet long, and 10 feet tall. What is the volume of the truck? ____________

4. **CLOSET** Robin has a large closet in her bedroom. The closet measures 2 feet by 10 feet, and it is 8 feet tall. What is the volume of Robin's closet? ____________

5. **MUSIC BOX** Kenji collects music boxes. Her favorite one has a length of 4 inches, a width of 4 inches, and a height of 4 inches. What is the volume of Kenji's favorite music box? ____________

6. **AQUARIUM** The Batista family has pet fish in a medium-sized aquarium with dimensions of 62 centimeters long, 30 centimeters wide, and 30 centimeters high. What is the volume of their aquarium? ____________

7. **SANDBOX** Scott is playing in his sandbox. He digs a rectangular hole that measures 5 inches wide, 11 inches long, and 1 inch deep. What is the volume of the hole? ____________

8. **GEOMETRY** A number cube measures 5 millimeters on each side. What is the volume of the cube? ____________

9. **TRASH** A city provides commercial trash bins in several sizes. One common trash bin measures 10 feet long, 8 feet wide, and 7 feet high. What is the volume of the trash bin? ____________

Lesson 10-5

NAME ______________________________ DATE ______________

Homework Practice

Find the number of cubes in each rectangular prism.

1 

How many cubes are in the rectangular prism? ____________

2 

How many cubes are in the rectangular prism? ____________

Find the volume of each rectangular prism.

3 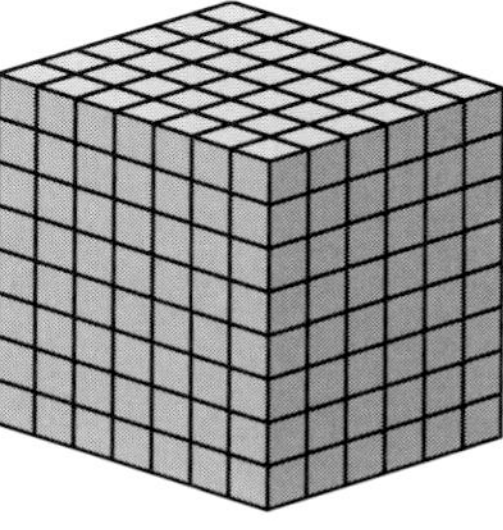

_______ cubic units

4 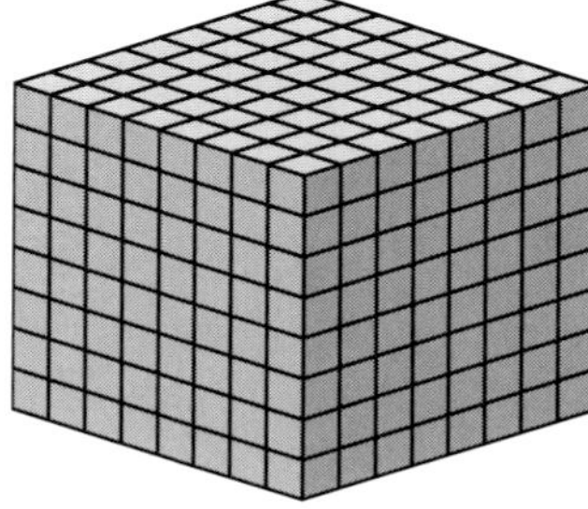

_______ cubic units

5 

_______ cubic units

6 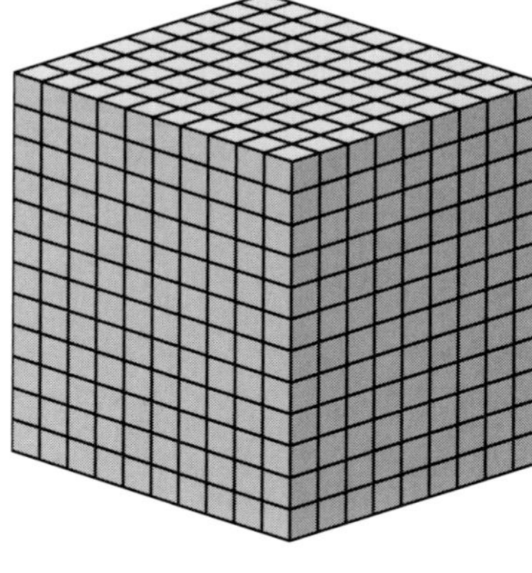

_______ cubic units

Solve.

7 **COTTON** A bale of cotton is measured by its width, length, and height. If the width of the bale is 20 inches, the length is 50 inches, and the height is 33 inches, what is the volume of the cotton bale? ____________

8 **GEOMETRY** A number cube measures 6 millimeters on each side. What is the volume of the cube? ____________

Answer Key (Lesson 1-1)

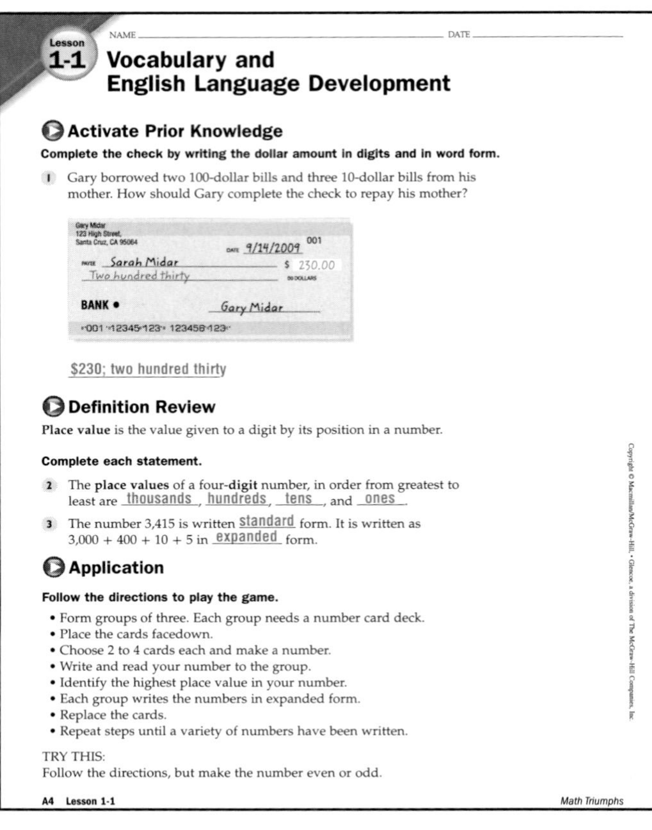

Lesson 1-1 NAME ______ DATE ______

Vocabulary and English Language Development

Activate Prior Knowledge

Complete the check by writing the dollar amount in digits and in word form.

1 Gary borrowed two 100-dollar bills and three 10-dollar bills from his mother. How should Gary complete the check to repay his mother?

Gary Midar
123 High Street,
Santa Cruz, CA 95064
DATE 9/14/2009 001
PAYEE Sarah Midar $ 230.00
Two hundred thirty DOLLARS
BANK • Gary Midar
⑆001⑆12345⑆123⑈ 123458⑆123⑈

$230; two hundred thirty

Definition Review

Place value is the value given to a digit by its position in a number.

Complete each statement.

2 The **place values** of a four-**digit** number, in order from greatest to least are thousands, hundreds, tens, and ones.

3 The number 3,415 is written standard form. It is written as 3,000 + 400 + 10 + 5 in expanded form.

Application

Follow the directions to play the game.

- Form groups of three. Each group needs a number card deck.
- Place the cards facedown.
- Choose 2 to 4 cards each and make a number.
- Write and read your number to the group.
- Identify the highest place value in your number.
- Each group writes the numbers in expanded form.
- Replace the cards.
- Repeat steps until a variety of numbers have been written.

TRY THIS:
Follow the directions, but make the number even or odd.

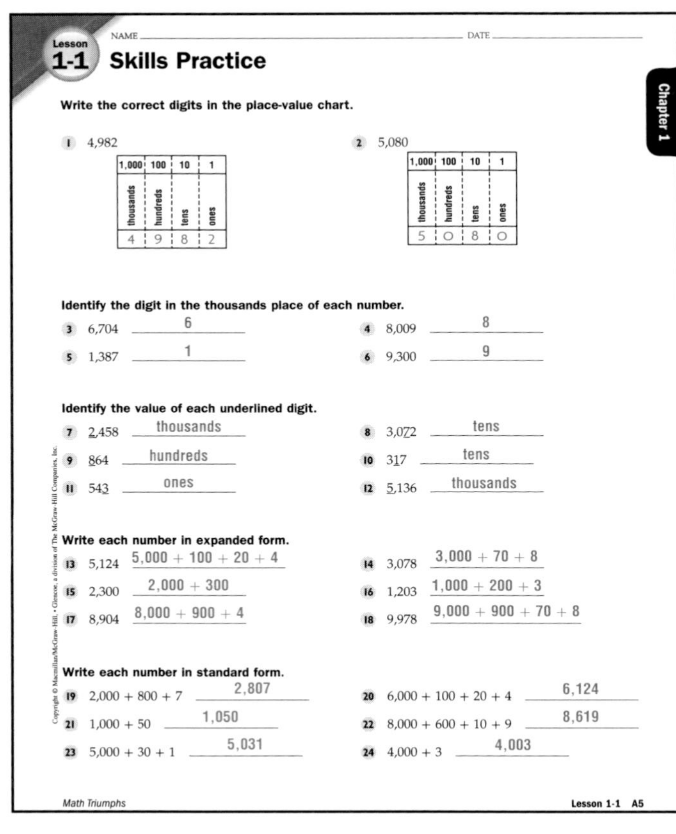

Lesson 1-1 NAME ______ DATE ______ Chapter 1

Skills Practice

Write the correct digits in the place-value chart.

1 4,982

1,000 thousands	100 hundreds	10 tens	1 ones
4	9	8	2

2 5,080

1,000 thousands	100 hundreds	10 tens	1 ones
5	0	8	0

Identify the digit in the thousands place of each number.

3 6,704 6
4 8,009 8
5 1,387 1
6 9,300 9

Identify the value of each underlined digit.

7 2,458 thousands
8 3,072 tens
9 864 hundreds
10 317 tens
11 543 ones
12 5,136 thousands

Write each number in expanded form.

13 5,124 5,000 + 100 + 20 + 4
14 3,078 3,000 + 70 + 8
15 2,300 2,000 + 300
16 1,203 1,000 + 200 + 3
17 8,904 8,000 + 900 + 4
18 9,978 9,000 + 900 + 70 + 8

Write each number in standard form.

19 2,000 + 800 + 7 2,807
20 6,000 + 100 + 20 + 4 6,124
21 1,000 + 50 1,050
22 8,000 + 600 + 10 + 9 8,619
23 5,000 + 30 + 1 5,031
24 4,000 + 3 4,003

Lesson 1-1 NAME ______ DATE ______

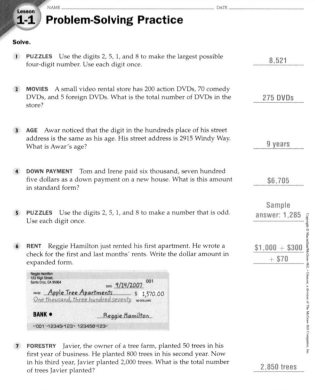

Problem-Solving Practice

Solve.

1 PUZZLES Use the digits 2, 5, 1, and 8 to make the largest possible four-digit number. Use each digit once. 8,521

2 MOVIES A small video rental store has 200 action DVDs, 70 comedy DVDs, and 5 foreign DVDs. What is the total number of DVDs in the store? 275 DVDs

3 AGE Awar noticed that the digit in the hundreds place of his street address is the same as his age. His street address is 2915 Windy Way. What is Awar's age? 9 years

4 DOWN PAYMENT Tom and Irene paid six thousand, seven hundred five dollars as a down payment on a new house. What is this amount in standard form? $6,705

5 PUZZLES Use the digits 2, 5, 1, and 8 to make a number that is odd. Use each digit once. Sample answer: 1,285

6 RENT Reggie Hamilton just rented his first apartment. He wrote a check for the first and last months' rents. Write the dollar amount in expanded form. $1,000 + $300 + $70

Reggie Hamilton
123 High Street,
Santa Cruz, CA 95064
DATE 9/14/2007 001
PAYEE Apple Tree Apartments $ 1,370.00
One thousand, three hundred seventy DOLLARS
BANK • Reggie Hamilton
⑆001⑆12345⑆123⑈ 123458⑆123⑈

7 FORESTRY Javier, the owner of a tree farm, planted 50 trees in his first year of business. He planted 800 trees in his second year. Now in his third year, Javier planted 2,000 trees. What is the total number of trees Javier planted? 2,850 trees

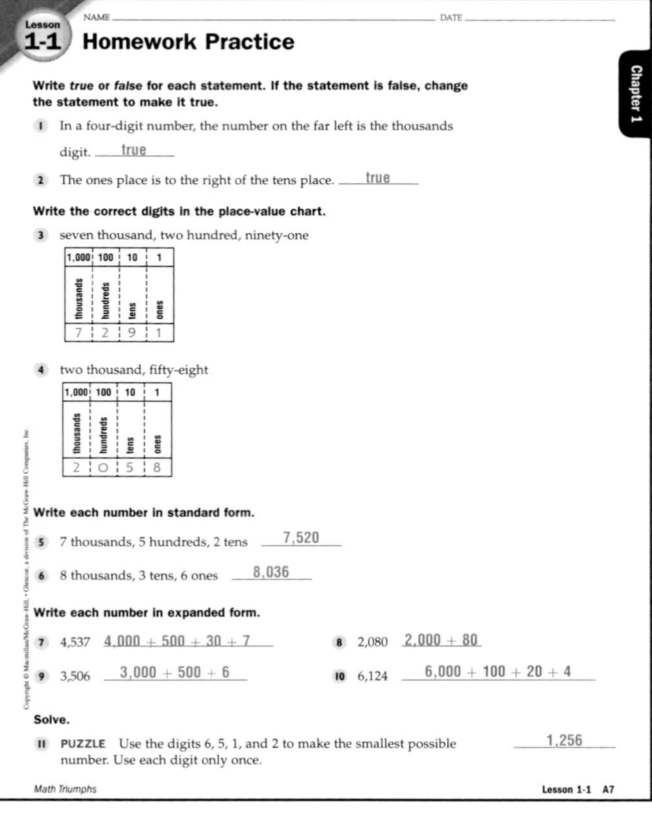

Lesson 1-1 NAME ______ DATE ______ Chapter 1

Homework Practice

Write *true* or *false* for each statement. If the statement is false, change the statement to make it true.

1 In a four-digit number, the number on the far left is the thousands digit. true

2 The ones place is to the right of the tens place. true

Write the correct digits in the place-value chart.

3 seven thousand, two hundred, ninety-one

1,000 thousands	100 hundreds	10 tens	1 ones
7	2	9	1

4 two thousand, fifty-eight

1,000 thousands	100 hundreds	10 tens	1 ones
2	0	5	8

Write each number in standard form.

5 7 thousands, 5 hundreds, 2 tens 7,520

6 8 thousands, 3 tens, 6 ones 8,036

Write each number in expanded form.

7 4,537 4,000 + 500 + 30 + 7
8 2,080 2,000 + 80
9 3,506 3,000 + 500 + 6
10 6,124 6,000 + 100 + 20 + 4

Solve.

11 PUZZLE Use the digits 6, 5, 1, and 2 to make the smallest possible number. Use each digit only once. 1,256

Answer Key (Lesson 1-2)

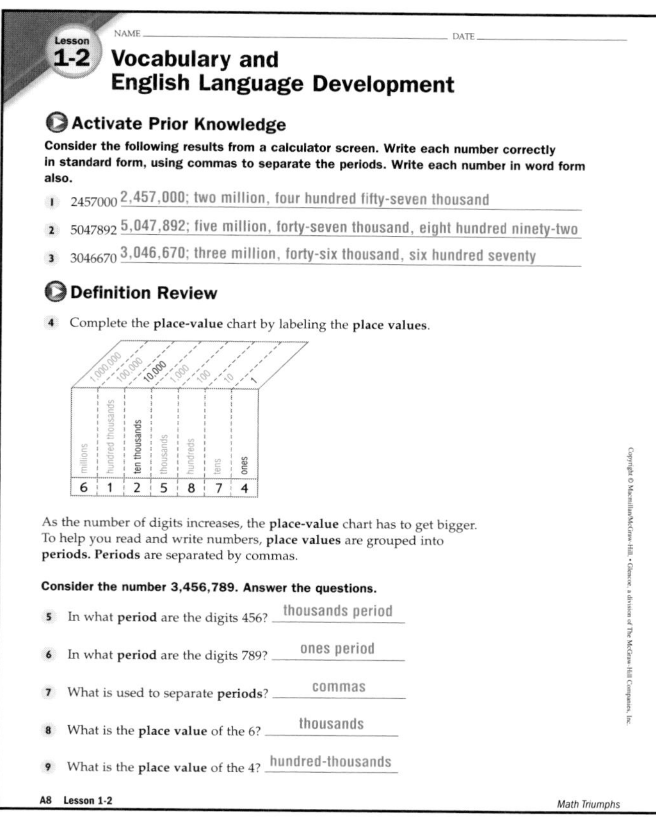

NAME ______ DATE ______

Lesson 1-2 **Vocabulary and English Language Development**

Activate Prior Knowledge

Consider the following results from a calculator screen. Write each number correctly in standard form, using commas to separate the periods. Write each number in word form also.

1. 2457000 2,457,000; two million, four hundred fifty-seven thousand
2. 5047892 5,047,892; five million, forty-seven thousand, eight hundred ninety-two
3. 3046670 3,046,670; three million, forty-six thousand, six hundred seventy

Definition Review

4. Complete the **place-value** chart by labeling the **place values**.

As the number of digits increases, the **place-value** chart has to get bigger. To help you read and write numbers, **place values** are grouped into **periods. Periods** are separated by commas.

Consider the number 3,456,789. Answer the questions.

5. In what **period** are the digits 456? thousands period
6. In what **period** are the digits 789? ones period
7. What is used to separate **periods**? commas
8. What is the **place value** of the 6? thousands
9. What is the **place value** of the 4? hundred-thousands

A8 Lesson 1-2 Math Triumphs

NAME ______ DATE ______

Chapter 1

Lesson 1-2 **Skills Practice**

Use a place-value chart. Fill in the digit for each place value.

1. two million, eight hundred thousand, two hundred forty-five

1,000,000	100,000	10,000	1,000	100	10	1
millions	hundred thousands	ten thousands	thousands	hundreds	tens	ones
2	8	0	0	2	4	5

Write each number in word form.

2. 5,216,000 five million, two hundred sixteen thousand
3. 7,050,278 seven million, fifty thousand, two hundred seventy-eight
4. 3,800,000 three million, eight hundred thousand
5. 1,246,935 one million, two hundred forty-six thousand, nine hundred thirty-five
6. 5,045,540 five million, forty-five thousand, five hundred forty

Write each number in standard form.

7. six million, two hundred fifty 6,000,250
8. five million, two hundred thirty-seven thousand, forty 5,237,040
9. three million, two hundred eighty-five thousand, one hundred 3,285,100
10. three million, two hundred fifty thousand, two 3,250,002

Answer each question.

11. How many zeros are in 4 millions? 6
12. How many zeros are in 5 thousands? 3

Math Triumphs Lesson 1-2 A9

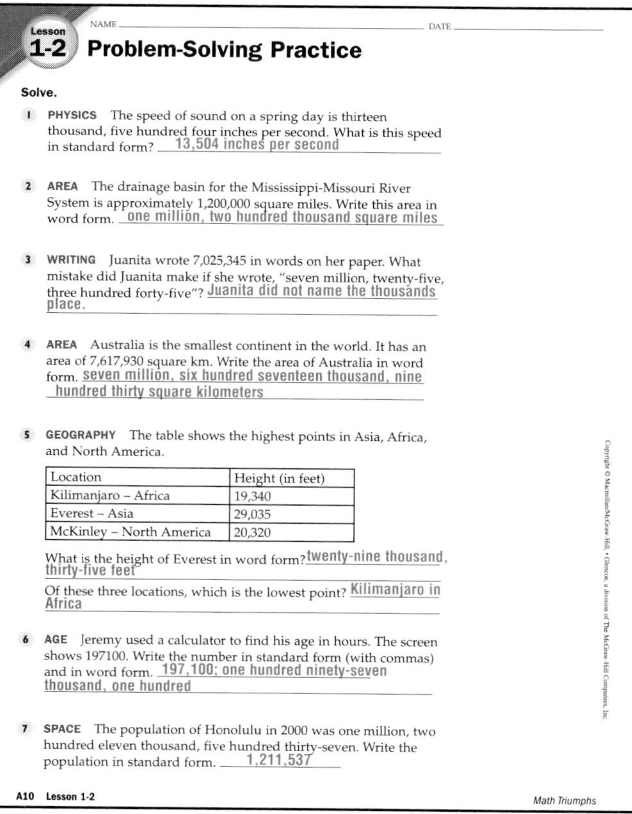

NAME ______ DATE ______

Lesson 1-2 **Problem-Solving Practice**

Solve.

1. **PHYSICS** The speed of sound on a spring day is thirteen thousand, five hundred four inches per second. What is this speed in standard form? 13,504 inches per second
2. **AREA** The drainage basin for the Mississippi-Missouri River System is approximately 1,200,000 square miles. Write this area in word form. one million, two hundred thousand square miles
3. **WRITING** Juanita wrote 7,025,345 in words on her paper. What mistake did Juanita make if she wrote, "seven million, twenty-five, three hundred forty-five"? Juanita did not name the thousands place.
4. **AREA** Australia is the smallest continent in the world. It has an area of 7,617,930 square km. Write the area of Australia in word form. seven million, six hundred seventeen thousand, nine hundred thirty square kilometers
5. **GEOGRAPHY** The table shows the highest points in Asia, Africa, and North America.

Location	Height (in feet)
Kilimanjaro – Africa	19,340
Everest – Asia	29,035
McKinley – North America	20,320

What is the height of Everest in word form? twenty-nine thousand, thirty-five feet

Of these three locations, which is the lowest point? Kilimanjaro in Africa

6. **AGE** Jeremy used a calculator to find his age in hours. The screen shows 197100. Write the number in standard form (with commas) and in word form. 197,100; one hundred ninety-seven thousand, one hundred
7. **SPACE** The population of Honolulu in 2000 was one million, two hundred eleven thousand, five hundred thirty-seven. Write the population in standard form. 1,211,537

A10 Lesson 1-2 Math Triumphs

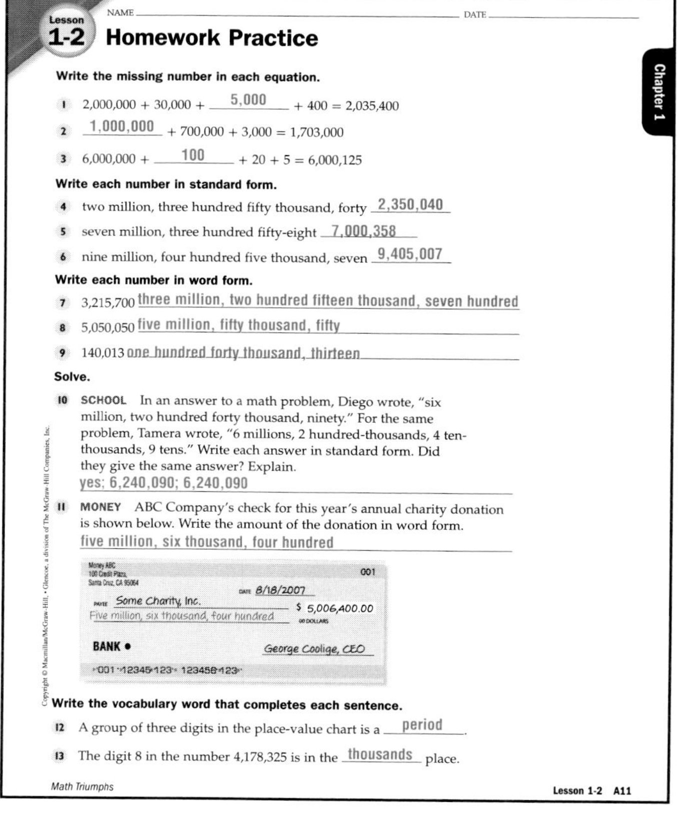

NAME ______ DATE ______

Chapter 1

Lesson 1-2 **Homework Practice**

Write the missing number in each equation.

1. 2,000,000 + 30,000 + 5,000 + 400 = 2,035,400
2. 1,000,000 + 700,000 + 3,000 = 1,703,000
3. 6,000,000 + 100 + 20 + 5 = 6,000,125

Write each number in standard form.

4. two million, three hundred fifty thousand, forty 2,350,040
5. seven million, three hundred fifty-eight 7,000,358
6. nine million, four hundred five thousand, seven 9,405,007

Write each number in word form.

7. 3,215,700 three million, two hundred fifteen thousand, seven hundred
8. 5,050,050 five million, fifty thousand, fifty
9. 140,013 one hundred forty thousand, thirteen

Solve.

10. **SCHOOL** In an answer to a math problem, Diego wrote, "six million, two hundred forty thousand, ninety." For the same problem, Tamera wrote, "6 millions, 2 hundred-thousands, 4 ten-thousands, 9 tens." Write each answer in standard form. Did they give the same answer? Explain. yes; 6,240,090; 6,240,090
11. **MONEY** ABC Company's check for this year's annual charity donation is shown below. Write the amount of the donation in word form. five million, six thousand, four hundred

Write the vocabulary word that completes each sentence.

12. A group of three digits in the place-value chart is a period.
13. The digit 8 in the number 4,178,325 is in the thousands place.

Math Triumphs Lesson 1-2 A11

Answer Key (Lesson 1-3)

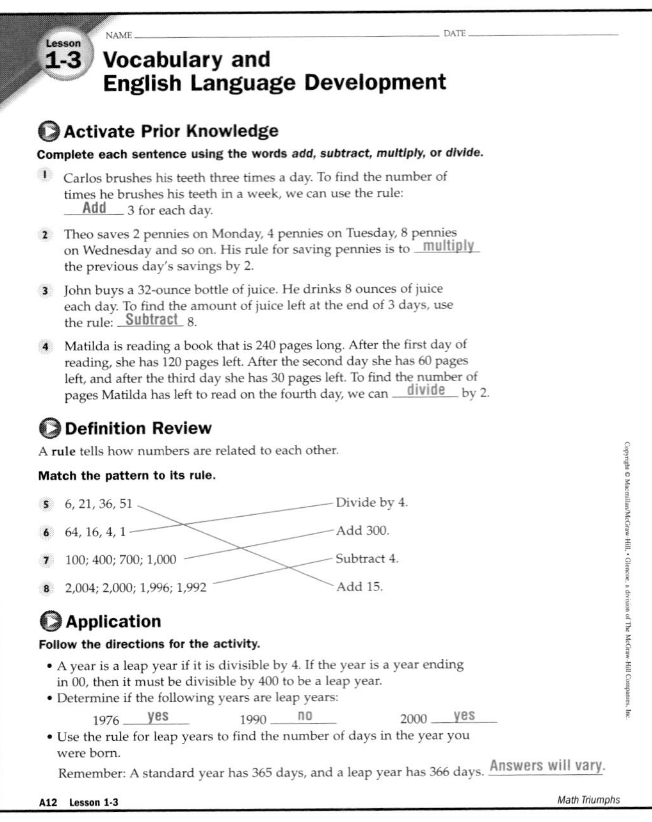

NAME ______ DATE ______

Lesson 1-3

Vocabulary and English Language Development

Activate Prior Knowledge

Complete each sentence using the words *add, subtract, multiply,* or *divide.*

1. Carlos brushes his teeth three times a day. To find the number of times he brushes his teeth in a week, we can use the rule: __Add__ 3 for each day.
2. Theo saves 2 pennies on Monday, 4 pennies on Tuesday, 8 pennies on Wednesday and so on. His rule for saving pennies is to __multiply__ the previous day's savings by 2.
3. John buys a 32-ounce bottle of juice. He drinks 8 ounces of juice each day. To find the amount of juice left at the end of 3 days, use the rule: __Subtract__ 8.
4. Matilda is reading a book that is 240 pages long. After the first day of reading, she has 120 pages left. After the second day she has 60 pages left, and after the third day she has 30 pages left. To find the number of pages Matilda has left to read on the fourth day, we can __divide__ by 2.

Definition Review

A **rule** tells how numbers are related to each other.

Match the pattern to its rule.

5. 6, 21, 36, 51 — Divide by 4.
6. 64, 16, 4, 1 — Add 300.
7. 100; 400; 700; 1,000 — Subtract 4.
8. 2,004; 2,000; 1,996; 1,992 — Add 15.

Application

Follow the directions for the activity.

- A year is a leap year if it is divisible by 4. If the year is a year ending in 00, then it must be divisible by 400 to be a leap year.
- Determine if the following years are leap years:

  1976 __yes__ 1990 __no__ 2000 __yes__
- Use the rule for leap years to find the number of days in the year you were born.

Remember: A standard year has 365 days, and a leap year has 366 days. __Answers will vary.__

NAME ______ DATE ______

Lesson 1-3

Skills Practice

Chapter 1

Find a rule for each pattern.

1. 10, 20, 30, 40 __Add 10.__
2. 100, 85, 70, 55 __Subtract 15.__
3. 1,600, 400, 100, 25 __Divide by 4.__
4. 25, 50, 100, 200 __Multiply by 2.__
5. 12, 17, 22, 27 __Add 5.__

Write the next three terms in each pattern.

6. 11, 21, 31, 41

   The next three terms are __51__, __61__, and __71__.
7. 2,400,000; 240,000; 24,000

   The next three terms are __2,400__; __240__; and __24__.
8. 62, 74, 86, 98

   The next three terms are __110__, __122__, and __134__.
9. 7, 28, 49, 70

   The next three terms are __91__, __112__, and __133__.

Write the next three conversions in each pattern.

10.

Number of Quarts	1	2	3	4
Number of Pints	2	4	6	8

11.

Number of Years	1	2	3	4
Number of Months	12	24	36	48

12.

Number of Yards	1	2	3	4
Number of Inches	36	72	108	144

NAME ______ DATE ______

Lesson 1-3

Problem-Solving Practice

Solve.

1. **BANKING** Leo saves $4 each week. How much money does Leo save in 6 weeks? __$24__

Week	1	2	3	4	5	6
Amount Saved	$4	$8	$12	$16	$20	$24

2. **DESIGN** Candace created the pattern at the right. How many squares are in the fifth term of the pattern? __25 squares__
3. **PIZZA** The Pizza Place sells a large pizza for $7.50. You can buy a second large pizza for $7.25, and a third for $7.00. If this pattern continues, how much would the fifth large pizza cost? __$6.50__
4. **VIDEO** Dion rented 8 DVDs. Each rental costs $3. How much did Dion spend on all of the DVDs? __$24__

Number of DVDs	1	2	3	4	5	6	7	8
Cost	$3	$6	$9	$12	$15	$18	$21	$24

5. **COMMUTING** Mr. Harris drives 12 miles to and from work each weekday. After 4 weeks, not including the weekends, how many miles has Mr. Harris driven to and from work? __480 miles__
6. **PACKAGING** Jason bought 6 packages of cookies to share with the students in his grade. If each package contains 15 cookies, how many cookies did Jason buy? __90 cookies__
7. **INTERIOR DESIGN** Cara is painting the following pattern on her kitchen wall.

   If the pattern continues, how many dark triangles are in the sixth term? __11 dark triangles__

   How many light triangles are in the sixth term? __11 light triangles__

   How many triangles in all are in the sixth term? __22 triangles__

NAME ______ DATE ______

Lesson 1-3

Homework Practice

Chapter 1

Find a rule for each pattern.

1. 7, 21, 63, 189 __Multiply by 3.__
2. 125, 100, 75, 50 __Subtract 25.__
3. 234, 245, 256, 267 __Add 11.__

Write the next three terms in each pattern.

4. 189, 173, 157, 141

   The next three terms are __125__, __109__, and __93__.
5. 729, 243, 81, 27

   The next three terms are __9__, __3__, and __1__.

Write the next three conversions in each pattern.

6.

Number of Tricycles	1	2	3	4
Number of Wheels	3	6	9	12

7.

Number Hours	1	2	3	4
Number of Minutes	60	120	180	240

Solve.

8. **RACING** Lance is training for a bike race. Starting on Tuesday, each day he will bike 3 more miles than he did the day before. On Monday he bikes 3 miles. How many miles does he bike on Friday? __15 miles__

Vocabulary Check

Write the vocabulary word that completes each sentence.

9. A __rule__ tells how numbers are related to each other.
10. A __pattern__ is a sequence of numbers, figures, or symbols that follows a rule or design.

Answer Key (Lesson 1-4)

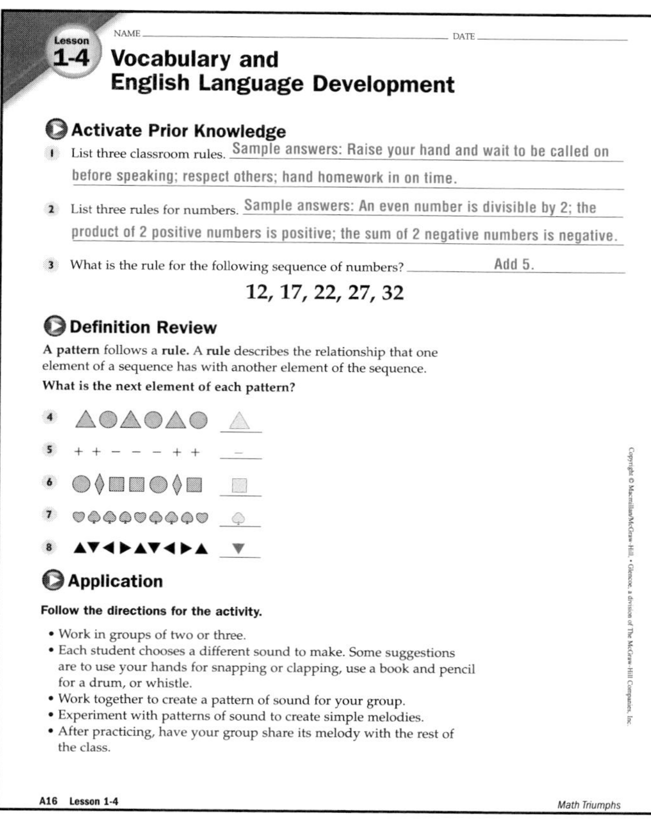
Lesson 1-4

NAME ______ DATE ______

Vocabulary and English Language Development

Activate Prior Knowledge

1. List three classroom rules. Sample answers: Raise your hand and wait to be called on before speaking; respect others; hand homework in on time.
2. List three rules for numbers. Sample answers: An even number is divisible by 2; the product of 2 positive numbers is positive; the sum of 2 negative numbers is negative.
3. What is the rule for the following sequence of numbers? Add 5.

12, 17, 22, 27, 32

Definition Review

A **pattern** follows a **rule.** A **rule** describes the relationship that one element of a sequence has with another element of the sequence.

What is the next element of each pattern?

4. △ ○ △ ○ △ ○ — △
5. + + − − − + + — −
6. ○ ◊ □ □ ○ ◊ □ — □
7. ♡ ♧ ♧ ♧ ♡ ♧ ♧ ♧ ♡ — ♧
8. ▲ ▼ ◀ ▶ ▲ ▼ ◀ ▶ ▲ — ▼

Application

Follow the directions for the activity.

- Work in groups of two or three.
- Each student chooses a different sound to make. Some suggestions are to use your hands for snapping or clapping, use a book and pencil for a drum, or whistle.
- Work together to create a pattern of sound for your group.
- Experiment with patterns of sound to create simple melodies.
- After practicing, have your group share its melody with the rest of the class.

A16 Lesson 1-4 *Math Triumphs*

Lesson 1-4

NAME ______ DATE ______

Skills Practice

Chapter 1

Write a possible situation for each rule.

1. Add 5. Sample answer: the number of pennies in a nickel
2. Multiply by 7. Sample answer: the number of days in a week

Who is correct?

3. There are 9 buttons on a shirt. How many buttons are there on 6 shirts? Circle the correct answer(s). Cross out the incorrect answer(s).

~~Nadia believes there are 56.~~ (Sanchez believes there are 54.) ~~Mark believes there are 15.~~

Solve.

4. There are 60 minutes in 1 hour. How many minutes are there in 6 hours? There are 360 minutes in 6 hours.
5. Kei types 35 words in 1 minute. How many words does Kei type in 3 minutes? Kei types 105 words in 3 minutes.
6. There are 8 batteries in 1 pack. How many batteries are there in 7 packs? There are 56 batteries in 7 packs.
7. Andy has 12 strawberries in 1 basket. How many strawberries does Andy have in 7 baskets? Andy has 84 strawberries in 7 baskets.
8. There are 64 ounces in 1 juice bottle. How many ounces are in 2 bottles? There are 128 ounces in 2 bottles.
9. Ruby reads 25 pages in 1 hour. Ruby reads 125 pages in 5 hours.
10. A spider has 8 legs. How many legs do 8 spiders have? There are 64 legs on 8 spiders.
11. There are 20 hexagons on 1 soccer ball. How many hexagons are there on 8 soccer balls? There are 160 hexagons on 8 soccer balls.

Math Triumphs Lesson 1-4 A17

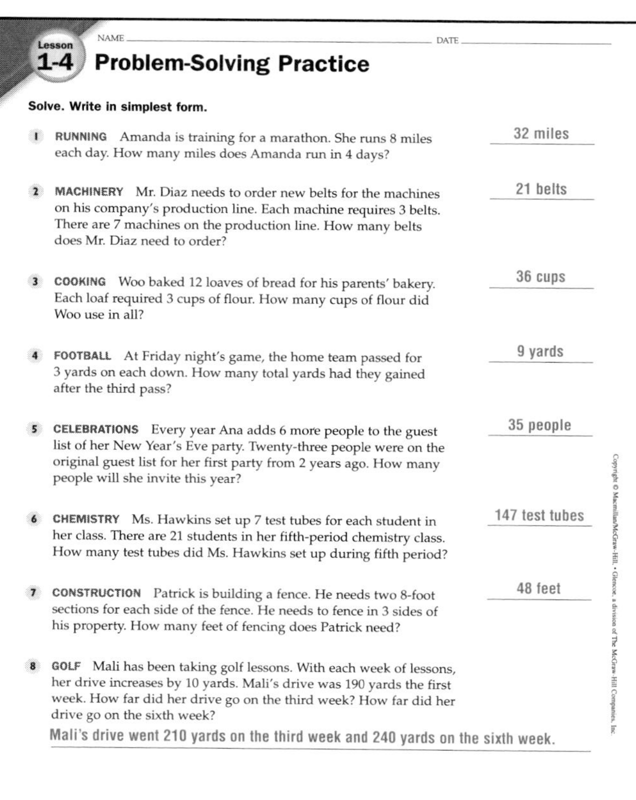
Lesson 1-4

NAME ______ DATE ______

Problem-Solving Practice

Solve. Write in simplest form.

1. **RUNNING** Amanda is training for a marathon. She runs 8 miles each day. How many miles does Amanda run in 4 days? 32 miles
2. **MACHINERY** Mr. Diaz needs to order new belts for the machines on his company's production line. Each machine requires 3 belts. There are 7 machines on the production line. How many belts does Mr. Diaz need to order? 21 belts
3. **COOKING** Woo baked 12 loaves of bread for his parents' bakery. Each loaf required 3 cups of flour. How many cups of flour did Woo use in all? 36 cups
4. **FOOTBALL** At Friday night's game, the home team passed for 3 yards on each down. How many total yards had they gained after the third pass? 9 yards
5. **CELEBRATIONS** Every year Ana adds 6 more people to the guest list of her New Year's Eve party. Twenty-three people were on the original guest list for her first party from 2 years ago. How many people will she invite this year? 35 people
6. **CHEMISTRY** Ms. Hawkins set up 7 test tubes for each student in her class. There are 21 students in her fifth-period chemistry class. How many test tubes did Ms. Hawkins set up during fifth period? 147 test tubes
7. **CONSTRUCTION** Patrick is building a fence. He needs two 8-foot sections for each side of the fence. He needs to fence in 3 sides of his property. How many feet of fencing does Patrick need? 48 feet
8. **GOLF** Mali has been taking golf lessons. With each week of lessons, her drive increases by 10 yards. Mali's drive was 190 yards the first week. How far did her drive go on the third week? How far did her drive go on the sixth week?

Mali's drive went 210 yards on the third week and 240 yards on the sixth week.

A18 Lesson 1-4 *Math Triumphs*

Lesson 1-4

NAME ______ DATE ______

Homework Practice

Chapter 1

Write a possible situation for each rule.

1. Multiply by 13. Sample answer: the number of doughnuts in a baker's dozen
2. Add 4. Sample answer: the number of tires on a car

Complete each sentence given the rule.

3. There are 6 sides on 1 cube. How many sides are there on 9 cubes? There are 54 sides on 9 cubes.
4. There are 4 tires on 1 car. How many tires are there on 6 cars? There are 24 tires on 6 cars.
5. Dion drives 45 miles in 1 hour. How many miles does Dion drive in 4 hours? Dion drives 180 miles in 4 hours.
6. There are 5 bananas in 1 bunch. How many bananas are there in 7 bunches? There are 35 bananas in 7 bunches.
7. Sandy needs 6 cups of water for 1 pitcher of lemonade. How many cups of water does she need for 4 pitchers of lemonade? Sandy needs 24 cups of water for 4 pitchers of lemonade.

Solve.

8. **CABINETRY** Nari is installing new cabinet doors in her kitchen. She needs 8 screws for each cabinet door. There are 15 doors. How many screws does Nari need? 120 screws
9. **WEIGHT LIFTING** Alonso started weight lifting. The first week he was able to lift 145 pounds. Each week he has been able to lift an additional 5 pounds. How much is Alonso able to lift in the seventh week? 175 pounds

Write the vocabulary word that completes each sentence.

10. A(n) pattern is a sequence of numbers, figures, or symbols that follows a rule or design.
11. A(n) rule tells how numbers are related to each other.

Math Triumphs Lesson 1-4 A19

Answer Key (Lesson 2-1)

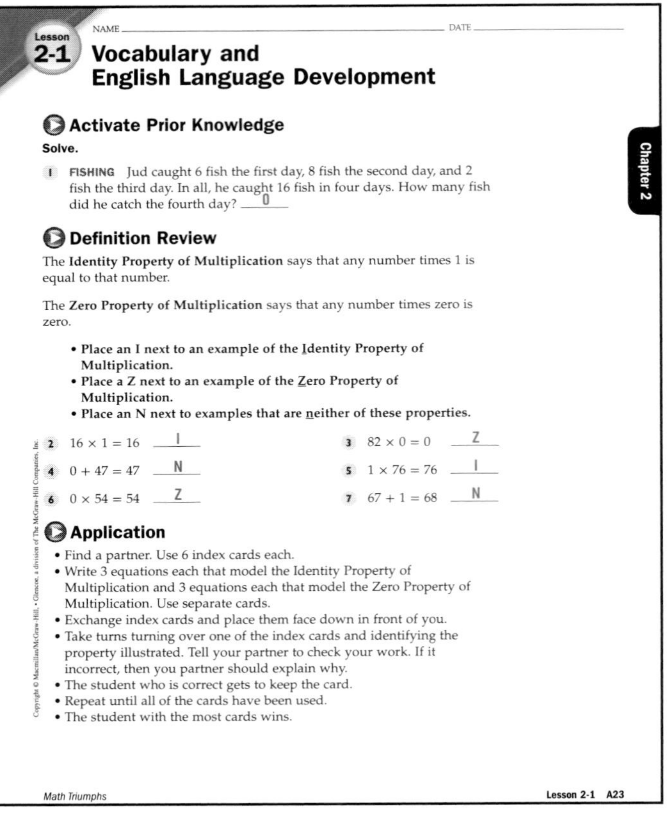

NAME ______ DATE ______

Lesson 2-1

Vocabulary and English Language Development

Chapter 2

Activate Prior Knowledge

Solve.

1 **FISHING** Jud caught 6 fish the first day, 8 fish the second day, and 2 fish the third day. In all, he caught 16 fish in four days. How many fish did he catch the fourth day? 0

Definition Review

The **Identity Property of Multiplication** says that any number times 1 is equal to that number.

The **Zero Property of Multiplication** says that any number times zero is zero.

- **Place an I next to an example of the Identity Property of Multiplication.**
- **Place a Z next to an example of the Zero Property of Multiplication.**
- **Place an N next to examples that are neither of these properties.**

2 $16 \times 1 = 16$ I

3 $82 \times 0 = 0$ Z

4 $0 + 47 = 47$ N

5 $1 \times 76 = 76$ I

6 $0 \times 54 = 54$ Z

7 $67 + 1 = 68$ N

Application

- Find a partner. Use 6 index cards each.
- Write 3 equations each that model the Identity Property of Multiplication and 3 equations each that model the Zero Property of Multiplication. Use separate cards.
- Exchange index cards and place them face down in front of you.
- Take turns turning over one of the index cards and identifying the property illustrated. Tell your partner to check your work. If it incorrect, then you partner should explain why.
- The student who is correct gets to keep the card.
- Repeat until all of the cards have been used.
- The student with the most cards wins.

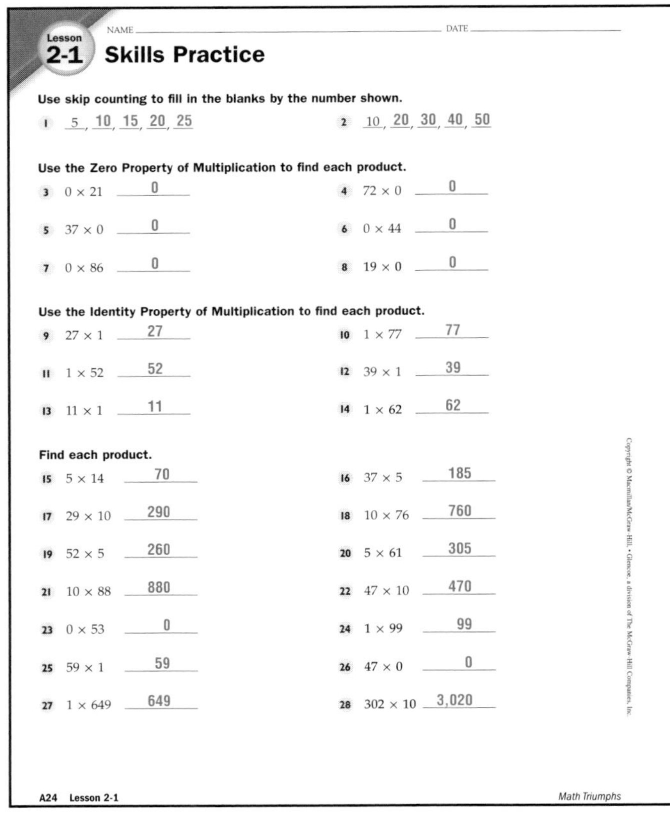

NAME ______ DATE ______

Lesson 2-1

Skills Practice

Use skip counting to fill in the blanks by the number shown.

1 5, 10, 15, 20, 25

2 10, 20, 30, 40, 50

Use the Zero Property of Multiplication to find each product.

3 0×21 0

4 72×0 0

5 37×0 0

6 0×44 0

7 0×86 0

8 19×0 0

Use the Identity Property of Multiplication to find each product.

9 27×1 27

10 1×77 77

11 1×52 52

12 39×1 39

13 11×1 11

14 1×62 62

Find each product.

15 5×14 70

16 37×5 185

17 29×10 290

18 10×76 760

19 52×5 260

20 5×61 305

21 10×88 880

22 47×10 470

23 0×53 0

24 1×99 99

25 59×1 59

26 47×0 0

27 1×649 649

28 302×10 3,020

NAME ______ DATE ______

Lesson 2-1

Problem-Solving Practice

Chapter 2

Solve.

1 **TEST MATERIALS** Tayshia is helping her teacher pass out the answer sheets for the quiz. Her class has 22 students and each student gets 1 answer sheet. How many answer sheets will she pass out? 22

2 **MULTIPLICATION** As shown below, Jorie, Reed, and Demont are multiplying 10×72. Who is correct? Reed

Jorie	Reed	Demont
$72 \times 10 = 702$	$72 \times 10 = 720$	$72 \times 10 = 7{,}200$

3 **FRIENDS** Each day Devon calls five of his friends. How many phone calls will he make in 6 days? 30

4 **PUZZLE** Manuel wrote the following multiplication sentences on a piece of paper and showed them to Allen. What number makes each sentence true? 0

$5 \times ? = 0$
$? \times 20 = 0$
$97 \times ? = 0$

5 **SOUP** If Darlene buys 12 times the amount of soup shown in the figure below, how many cans of soup does she buy? 60

SOUP SOUP SOUP SOUP SOUP

6 **PETS** Karen feeds each of her rabbits 1 carrot before she goes to school. If Karen has 17 rabbits, how many carrots does she need? 17

NAME ______ DATE ______

Lesson 2-1

Homework Practice

Consider the product 72×0 when answering the following two questions.

1 What is the first factor? 72

2 What is the second factor? 0

Write a multiplication fact for each of the following products.

3 $5 \times 83 = 415$ $83 \times 5 = 415$

4 $97 \times 1 = 97$ $1 \times 97 = 97$

Find each product.

5 10×66 660

6 33×5 165

7 48×1 48

8 0×21 0

9 5×88 440

10 1×74 74

11 27×10 270

12 81×0 0

Solve.

13 **NUTRITION** Lucy eats 2 pieces of fresh fruit each day. How many pieces does she eat in 5 days? 10

14 **CARNIVAL RIDES** Ride tickets at the carnival come in packages of 10. If Eli and his 7 friends purchase 14 packages, how many tickets did they buy? 140

Write the vocabulary word that completes each sentence.

15 The Zero Property of Multiplication states that any number times zero is zero.

16 The Identity Property of Multiplication states that any number times 1 is equal to that number.

Answer Key (Lesson 2-2)

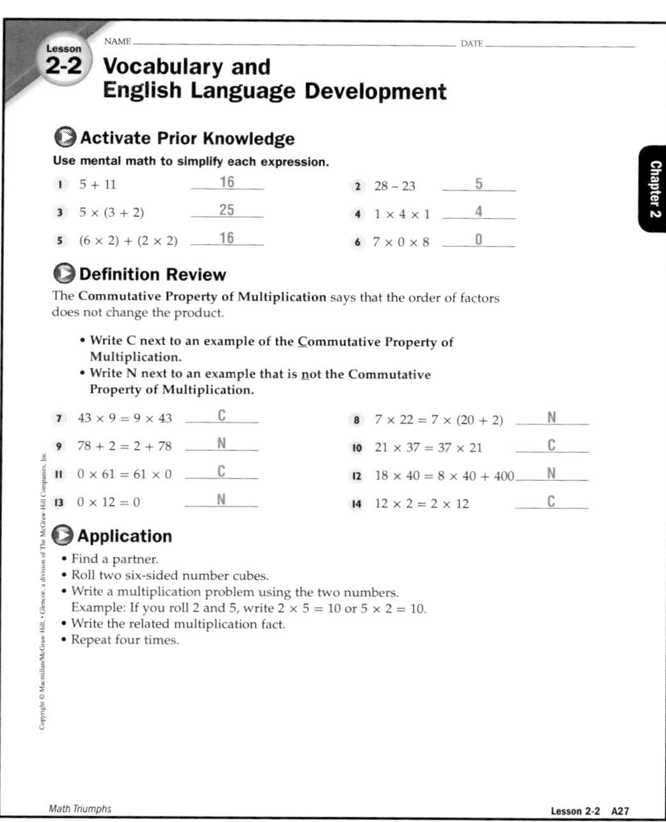

Lesson 2-2

NAME ______________ DATE ______________

Vocabulary and English Language Development

Activate Prior Knowledge

Use mental math to simplify each expression.

1. 5 + 11 16
2. 28 − 23 5
3. 5 × (3 + 2) 25
4. 1 × 4 × 1 4
5. (6 × 2) + (2 × 2) 16
6. 7 × 0 × 8 0

Definition Review

The **Commutative Property of Multiplication** says that the order of factors does not change the product.

- **Write C next to an example of the Commutative Property of Multiplication.**
- **Write N next to an example that is not the Commutative Property of Multiplication.**

7. 43 × 9 = 9 × 43 C
8. 7 × 22 = 7 × (20 + 2) N
9. 78 + 2 = 2 + 78 N
10. 21 × 37 = 37 × 21 C
11. 0 × 61 = 61 × 0 C
12. 18 × 40 = 8 × 40 + 400 N
13. 0 × 12 = 0 N
14. 12 × 2 = 2 × 12 C

Application

- Find a partner.
- Roll two six-sided number cubes.
- Write a multiplication problem using the two numbers. Example: If you roll 2 and 5, write 2 × 5 = 10 or 5 × 2 = 10.
- Write the related multiplication fact.
- Repeat four times.

Chapter 2

Lesson 2-2

NAME ______________ DATE ______________

Skills Practice

Use skip counting to fill in the blanks by the number shown.

1. 2, 4, 6, 8, 10
2. 6, 12, 18, 24, 30

Write the related multiplication fact for each product.

3. 2 × 41 = 82 41 × 2 = 82
4. 98 × 3 = 294 3 × 98 = 294
5. 18 × 4 = 72 4 × 18 = 72
6. 6 × 12 = 72 12 × 6 = 72
7. 3 × 51 = 153 51 × 3 = 153
8. 4 × 86 = 344 86 × 4 = 344

Write an equation using repeated addition that represents each product.

9. 2 × 7 2 + 2 + 2 + 2 + 2 + 2 + 2 = 14
10. 3 × 5 3 + 3 + 3 + 3 + 3 = 15
11. 4 × 8 4 + 4 + 4 + 4 + 4 + 4 + 4 + 4 = 32
12. 6 × 9 6 + 6 + 6 + 6 + 6 + 6 + 6 + 6 + 6 = 54

Find each product.

13. 2 × 26 52
14. 87 × 3 261
15. 47 × 4 188
16. 6 × 28 168
17. 3 × 19 57
18. 4 × 99 396
19. 6 × 37 222
20. 55 × 2 110
21. 68 × 4 272
22. 3 × 72 216
23. 77 × 2 154
24. 29 × 6 174

Lesson 2-2

NAME ______________ DATE ______________

Problem-Solving Practice

Solve.

1. **HEALTH** Every day Matilda and her three brothers each take a multi-vitamin. What is the total number of multi-vitamins they take in all for one week? 28
2. **ARRAYS** What multiplication problem is modeled by the array below? 6 × 5 = 30
3. **SHOPPING** Chochmo bought 3 boxes of golf balls. If each box contains 12 balls, how many balls did he buy? 36
4. **FORESTRY** Mr. Rodriquez owns a tree farm. He planted several ash trees as seen in the figure below. How many Ash trees did he plant? 14
5. **TRAVEL** Adam drove from Jacksonville, Florida to Atlanta, Georgia. If he averaged 58 miles per hour while completing the 6 hour trip, approximately how far did he travel? 348 mi
6. **GEOMETRY** Each side of a cube is called a face. What is the total number of faces shown in the figure below? 24

Chapter 2

Lesson 2-2

NAME ______________ DATE ______________

Homework Practice

Write the equation that represents each product using repeated addition.

1. 3 × 8 3 + 3 + 3 + 3 + 3 + 3 + 3 + 3 = 24
2. 6 × 5 6 + 6 + 6 + 6 + 6 = 30

Rewrite each multiplication problem in vertical format.

3. 2 × 29 29 ×2
4. 4 × 72 72 ×4

Find each product.

5. 6 × 29 174
6. 17 × 4 68
7. 75 × 3 225
8. 2 × 38 76
9. 4 × 29 116
10. 3 × 61 183

Solve.

11. **POULTRY** Harold raises chickens and sells the eggs they lay. If he packages the eggs in groups of 6 and sells on average 19 packages per day, how many eggs does he sell per day? 114
12. **COLLECTING** Melinda collects dolls. How many dolls are in her collection, if she has 13 shelves in her room each containing 2 dolls? 26

Write the vocabulary word that completes each sentence.

13. The Commutative Property of Multiplication says that the order in which two numbers are multiplied does not change the product.
14. Multiplication is an operation on two numbers to find their product.

Answer Key (Lesson 2-3)

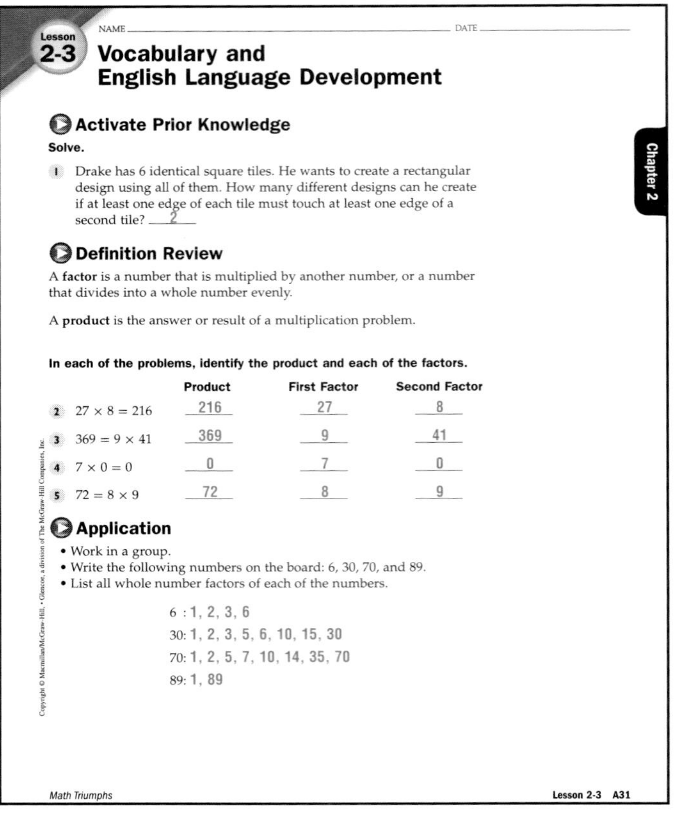

NAME ______ DATE ______

Lesson 2-3

Vocabulary and English Language Development

Chapter 2

Activate Prior Knowledge

Solve.

1. Drake has 6 identical square tiles. He wants to create a rectangular design using all of them. How many different designs can he create if at least one edge of each tile must touch at least one edge of a second tile? 2

Definition Review

A **factor** is a number that is multiplied by another number, or a number that divides into a whole number evenly.

A **product** is the answer or result of a multiplication problem.

In each of the problems, identify the product and each of the factors.

		Product	First Factor	Second Factor
2	27 × 8 = 216	216	27	8
3	369 = 9 × 41	369	9	41
4	7 × 0 = 0	0	7	0
5	72 = 8 × 9	72	8	9

Application

- Work in a group.
- Write the following numbers on the board: 6, 30, 70, and 89.
- List all whole number factors of each of the numbers.

6 : 1, 2, 3, 6
30: 1, 2, 3, 5, 6, 10, 15, 30
70: 1, 2, 5, 7, 10, 14, 35, 70
89: 1, 89

NAME ______ DATE ______

Lesson 2-3

Skills Practice

Use skip counting to fill in the blanks by the number shown.

1. 7, 14, 21, 28, 35
2. 9, 18, 27, 36, 45

Use doubling to find each product.

3. 8 × 42
   Double 42: 84
   Double the result: 168
   Double the result again: 336
4. 26 × 8
   Double 26: 52
   Double the result: 104
   Double the result again: 208
5. 91 × 8
   Double 91: 182
   Double the result: 364
   Double the result again: 728
6. 8 × 63
   Double 63: 126
   Double the result: 252
   Double the result again: 504

Use a pattern to find each product.

7. 9 × 6
   9 × 1 = 9
   9 × 2 = 18
   9 × 3 = 27
   9 × 4 = 36
   9 × 5 = 45
   9 × 6 = 54
8. 5 × 7
   5 × 1 = 5
   5 × 2 = 10
   5 × 3 = 15
   5 × 4 = 20
   5 × 5 = 25
   5 × 6 = 30
   5 × 7 = 35

Find each product.

9. 8 × 52 416
10. 65 × 7 455
11. 47 × 9 423
12. 74 × 8 592
13. 7 × 97 679
14. 9 × 24 216
15. 8 × 77 616
16. 36 × 7 252
17. 84 × 9 756
18. 8 × 8 64

NAME ______ DATE ______

Lesson 2-3

Problem-Solving Practice

Chapter 2

Solve.

1. **CHECKING ACCOUNT** Cindy's bank charges $2 per check to pay her bills from her checking account. If she wrote 9 checks last month, how much did the bank charge her? $18
2. **FENCING** Aaron is building a dog pen for his three dogs. How much fencing does he need to build the pen seen in the figure below? 80 ft

   Dog Pen
   8 feet
   8 feet 8 feet 8 feet
3. **RUNNING** Jenna has a 7 mile route that she runs each Saturday. If she runs all 52 Saturdays during the year, how many miles will she run? 364 mi
4. **TOURISM** Lake Front Tours charges $7 per person for a boat tour of Lake Michigan. Complete the table below to find the revenue generated based on the number of passengers on the tour.

Number of Passengers	1	2	3	4	5	6	7	8	9
Revenue	$7	$14	$21	$28	$35	$42	$49	$56	$63

5. **EARNINGS** Jessica earns $8 an hour working at the Ernie's pet shop. If Jessica worked 36 hours last week, how much did she earn? $288
6. **THEATER SEATING** The seating arrangement in row 1 of a movie theater is shown in the figure below. If there are 40 rows in the theater and they all contain the same number of seats, how many seats are in the theater? 360

   Row 1 □□ Aisle □□□□□ Aisle □□

NAME ______ DATE ______

Lesson 2-3

Homework Practice

Use doubling to find each product.

1. 8 × 73
   Double 73: 146
   Double the result: 292
   Double the result again: 584
2. 35 × 8
   Double 35: 70
   Double the result: 140
   Double the result again: 280

Use a pattern to find each product.

3. 8 × 7
   8 × 1 = 8
   8 × 2 = 16
   8 × 3 = 24
   8 × 4 = 32
   8 × 5 = 40
   8 × 6 = 48
   8 × 7 = 56
4. 9 × 5
   9 × 1 = 9
   9 × 2 = 18
   9 × 3 = 27
   9 × 4 = 36
   9 × 5 = 45

Find each product.

5. 9 × 71 639
6. 45 × 7 315
7. 82 × 8 656
8. 9 × 67 603

Solve.

9. **READING** Each month Heather expects to read 6 books. If she meets her expectations, how many books does she read in 9 months? 54

Write the vocabulary word that completes each sentence.

10. A number that divides into a whole number evenly is called a factor.

Answer Key (Lesson 2-4)

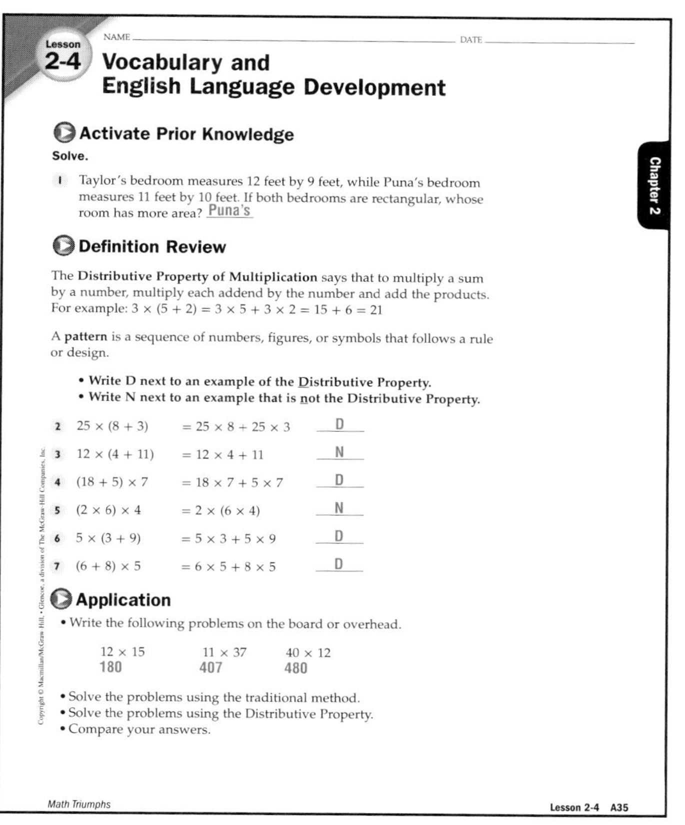

Lesson 2-4

NAME ______ DATE ______

Vocabulary and English Language Development

Chapter 2

Activate Prior Knowledge

Solve.

1 Taylor's bedroom measures 12 feet by 9 feet, while Puna's bedroom measures 11 feet by 10 feet. If both bedrooms are rectangular, whose room has more area? Puna's

Definition Review

The **Distributive Property of Multiplication** says that to multiply a sum by a number, multiply each addend by the number and add the products. For example: $3 \times (5 + 2) = 3 \times 5 + 3 \times 2 = 15 + 6 = 21$

A **pattern** is a sequence of numbers, figures, or symbols that follows a rule or design.

- **Write D next to an example of the Distributive Property.**
- **Write N next to an example that is not the Distributive Property.**

2 $25 \times (8 + 3) = 25 \times 8 + 25 \times 3$ D

3 $12 \times (4 + 11) = 12 \times 4 + 11$ N

4 $(18 + 5) \times 7 = 18 \times 7 + 5 \times 7$ D

5 $(2 \times 6) \times 4 = 2 \times (6 \times 4)$ N

6 $5 \times (3 + 9) = 5 \times 3 + 5 \times 9$ D

7 $(6 + 8) \times 5 = 6 \times 5 + 8 \times 5$ D

Application

- Write the following problems on the board or overhead.

12×15	11×37	40×12
180	407	480

- Solve the problems using the traditional method.
- Solve the problems using the Distributive Property.
- Compare your answers.

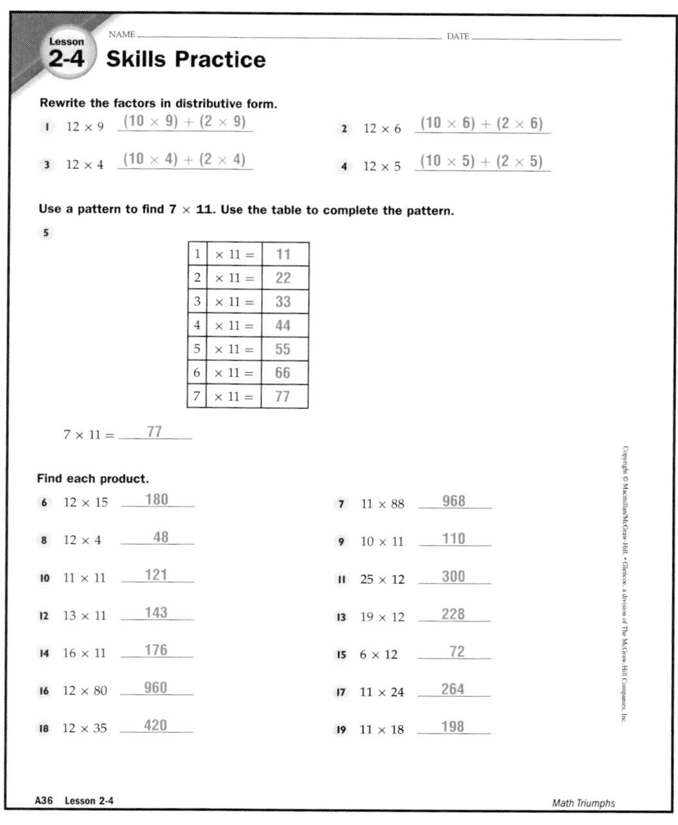

Lesson 2-4

NAME ______ DATE ______

Skills Practice

Rewrite the factors in distributive form.

1 12×9 $(10 \times 9) + (2 \times 9)$

2 12×6 $(10 \times 6) + (2 \times 6)$

3 12×4 $(10 \times 4) + (2 \times 4)$

4 12×5 $(10 \times 5) + (2 \times 5)$

Use a pattern to find 7×11. Use the table to complete the pattern.

5

1	× 11 =	11
2	× 11 =	22
3	× 11 =	33
4	× 11 =	44
5	× 11 =	55
6	× 11 =	66
7	× 11 =	77

$7 \times 11 =$ 77

Find each product.

6 12×15 180

7 11×88 968

8 12×4 48

9 10×11 110

10 11×11 121

11 25×12 300

12 13×11 143

13 19×12 228

14 16×11 176

15 6×12 72

16 12×80 960

17 11×24 264

18 12×35 420

19 11×18 198

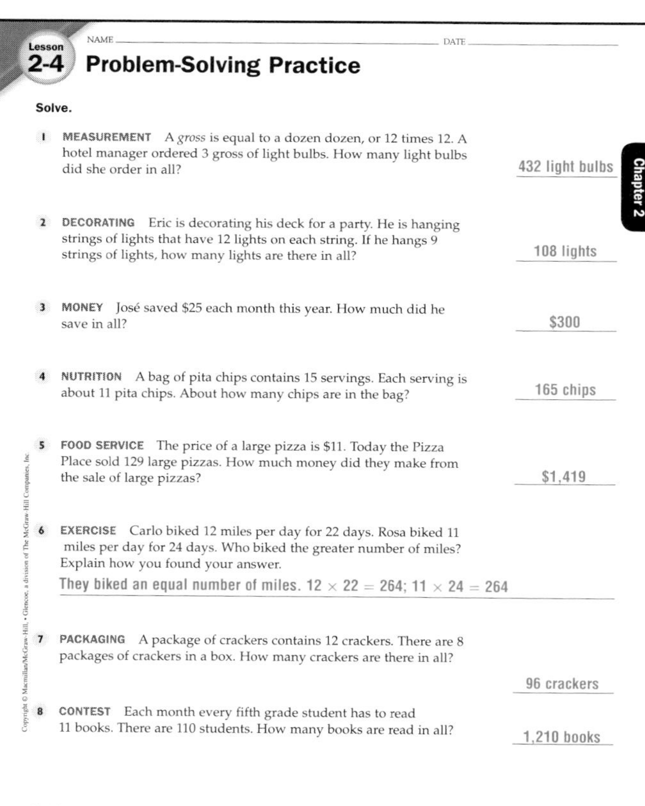

Lesson 2-4

NAME ______ DATE ______

Problem-Solving Practice

Chapter 2

Solve.

1 **MEASUREMENT** A *gross* is equal to a dozen dozen, or 12 times 12. A hotel manager ordered 3 gross of light bulbs. How many light bulbs did she order in all? 432 light bulbs

2 **DECORATING** Eric is decorating his deck for a party. He is hanging strings of lights that have 12 lights on each string. If he hangs 9 strings of lights, how many lights are there in all? 108 lights

3 **MONEY** José saved $25 each month this year. How much did he save in all? $300

4 **NUTRITION** A bag of pita chips contains 15 servings. Each serving is about 11 pita chips. About how many chips are in the bag? 165 chips

5 **FOOD SERVICE** The price of a large pizza is $11. Today the Pizza Place sold 129 large pizzas. How much money did they make from the sale of large pizzas? $1,419

6 **EXERCISE** Carlo biked 12 miles per day for 22 days. Rosa biked 11 miles per day for 24 days. Who biked the greater number of miles? Explain how you found your answer.
They biked an equal number of miles. $12 \times 22 = 264$; $11 \times 24 = 264$

7 **PACKAGING** A package of crackers contains 12 crackers. There are 8 packages of crackers in a box. How many crackers are there in all? 96 crackers

8 **CONTEST** Each month every fifth grade student has to read 11 books. There are 110 students. How many books are read in all? 1,210 books

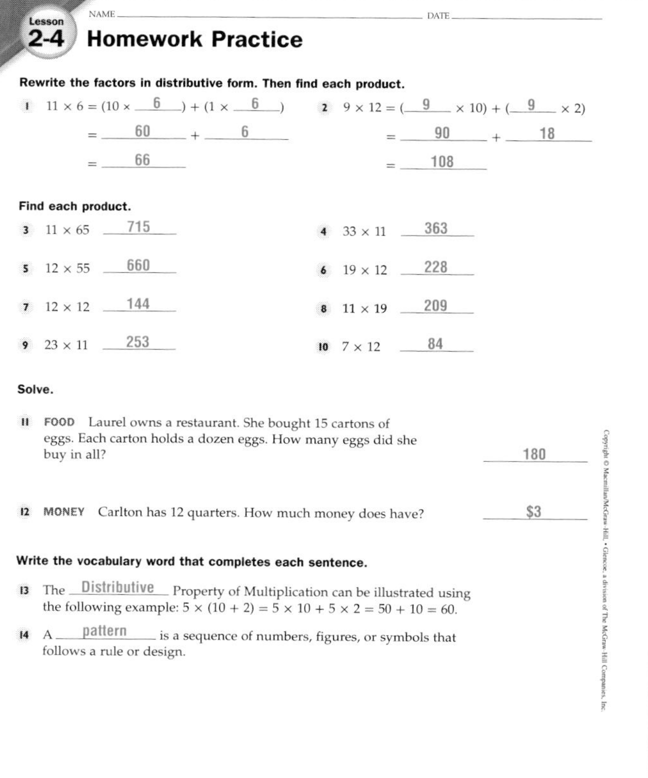

Lesson 2-4

NAME ______ DATE ______

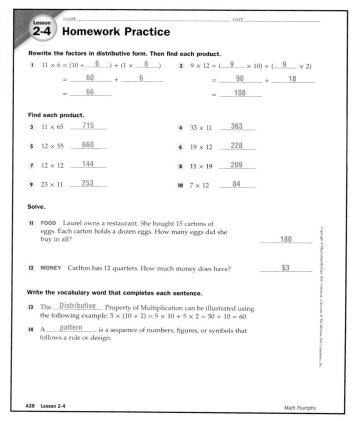

Homework Practice

Rewrite the factors in distributive form. Then find each product.

1 $11 \times 6 = (10 \times$ 6 $) + (1 \times$ 6 $)$
= 60 + 6
= 66

2 $9 \times 12 = ($ 9 $\times 10) + ($ 9 $\times 2)$
= 90 + 18
= 108

Find each product.

3 11×65 715

4 33×11 363

5 12×55 660

6 19×12 228

7 12×12 144

8 11×19 209

9 23×11 253

10 7×12 84

Solve.

11 **FOOD** Laurel owns a restaurant. She bought 15 cartons of eggs. Each carton holds a dozen eggs. How many eggs did she buy in all? 180

12 **MONEY** Carlton has 12 quarters. How much money does have? $3

Write the vocabulary word that completes each sentence.

13 The Distributive Property of Multiplication can be illustrated using the following example: $5 \times (10 + 2) = 5 \times 10 + 5 \times 2 = 50 + 10 = 60$.

14 A pattern is a sequence of numbers, figures, or symbols that follows a rule or design.

Answer Key (Lesson 2-5)

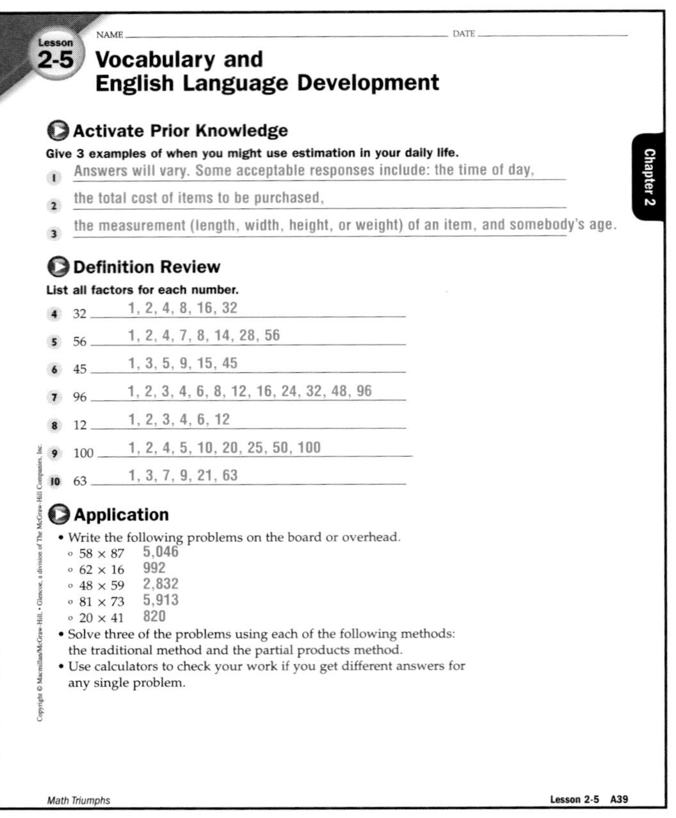

Lesson 2-5 NAME ____ DATE ____

Vocabulary and English Language Development

Chapter 2

Activate Prior Knowledge

Give 3 examples of when you might use estimation in your daily life.

1. Answers will vary. Some acceptable responses include: the time of day,
2. the total cost of items to be purchased,
3. the measurement (length, width, height, or weight) of an item, and somebody's age.

Definition Review

List all factors for each number.

4. 32 1, 2, 4, 8, 16, 32
5. 56 1, 2, 4, 7, 8, 14, 28, 56
6. 45 1, 3, 5, 9, 15, 45
7. 96 1, 2, 3, 4, 6, 8, 12, 16, 24, 32, 48, 96
8. 12 1, 2, 3, 4, 6, 12
9. 100 1, 2, 4, 5, 10, 20, 25, 50, 100
10. 63 1, 3, 7, 9, 21, 63

Application

- Write the following problems on the board or overhead.
  - 58 × 87 5,046
  - 62 × 16 992
  - 48 × 59 2,832
  - 81 × 73 5,913
  - 20 × 41 820
- Solve three of the problems using each of the following methods: the traditional method and the partial products method.
- Use calculators to check your work if you get different answers for any single problem.

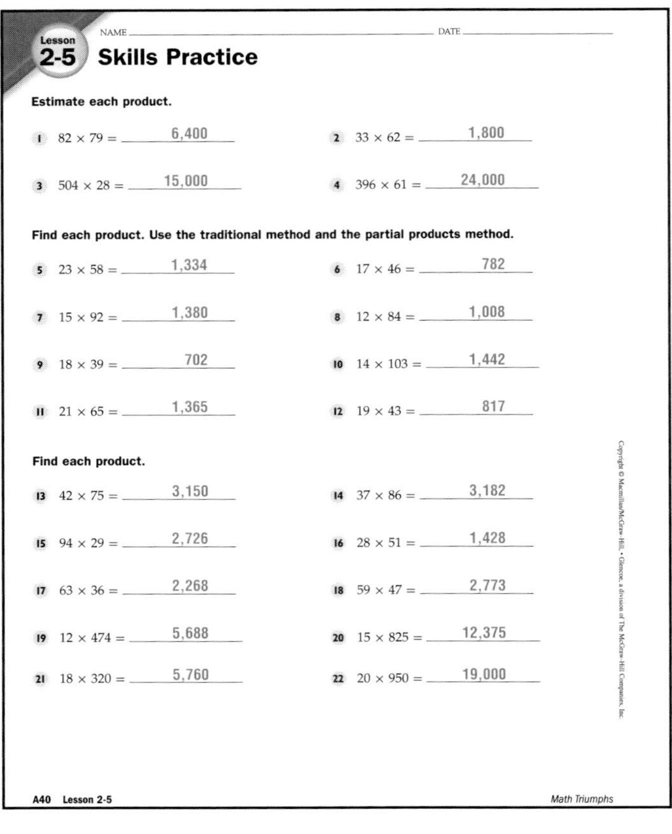

Lesson 2-5 NAME ____ DATE ____

Skills Practice

Estimate each product.

1. 82 × 79 = 6,400
2. 33 × 62 = 1,800
3. 504 × 28 = 15,000
4. 396 × 61 = 24,000

Find each product. Use the traditional method and the partial products method.

5. 23 × 58 = 1,334
6. 17 × 46 = 782
7. 15 × 92 = 1,380
8. 12 × 84 = 1,008
9. 18 × 39 = 702
10. 14 × 103 = 1,442
11. 21 × 65 = 1,365
12. 19 × 43 = 817

Find each product.

13. 42 × 75 = 3,150
14. 37 × 86 = 3,182
15. 94 × 29 = 2,726
16. 28 × 51 = 1,428
17. 63 × 36 = 2,268
18. 59 × 47 = 2,773
19. 12 × 474 = 5,688
20. 15 × 825 = 12,375
21. 18 × 320 = 5,760
22. 20 × 950 = 19,000

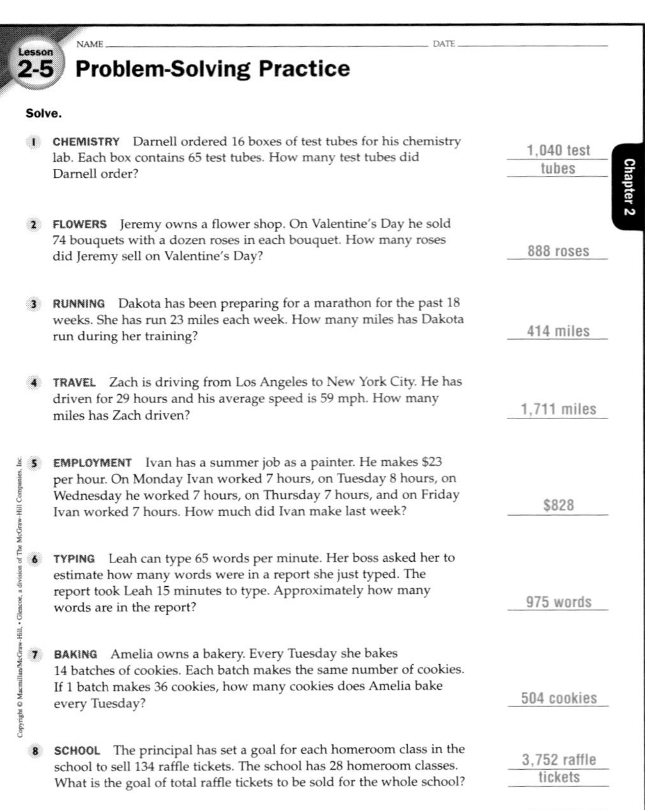

Lesson 2-5 NAME ____ DATE ____

Problem-Solving Practice

Chapter 2

Solve.

1. **CHEMISTRY** Darnell ordered 16 boxes of test tubes for his chemistry lab. Each box contains 65 test tubes. How many test tubes did Darnell order? 1,040 test tubes
2. **FLOWERS** Jeremy owns a flower shop. On Valentine's Day he sold 74 bouquets with a dozen roses in each bouquet. How many roses did Jeremy sell on Valentine's Day? 888 roses
3. **RUNNING** Dakota has been preparing for a marathon for the past 18 weeks. She has run 23 miles each week. How many miles has Dakota run during her training? 414 miles
4. **TRAVEL** Zach is driving from Los Angeles to New York City. He has driven for 29 hours and his average speed is 59 mph. How many miles has Zach driven? 1,711 miles
5. **EMPLOYMENT** Ivan has a summer job as a painter. He makes $23 per hour. On Monday Ivan worked 7 hours, on Tuesday 8 hours, on Wednesday he worked 7 hours, on Thursday 7 hours, and on Friday Ivan worked 7 hours. How much did Ivan make last week? $828
6. **TYPING** Leah can type 65 words per minute. Her boss asked her to estimate how many words were in a report she just typed. The report took Leah 15 minutes to type. Approximately how many words are in the report? 975 words
7. **BAKING** Amelia owns a bakery. Every Tuesday she bakes 14 batches of cookies. Each batch makes the same number of cookies. If 1 batch makes 36 cookies, how many cookies does Amelia bake every Tuesday? 504 cookies
8. **SCHOOL** The principal has set a goal for each homeroom class in the school to sell 134 raffle tickets. The school has 28 homeroom classes. What is the goal of total raffle tickets to be sold for the whole school? 3,752 raffle tickets

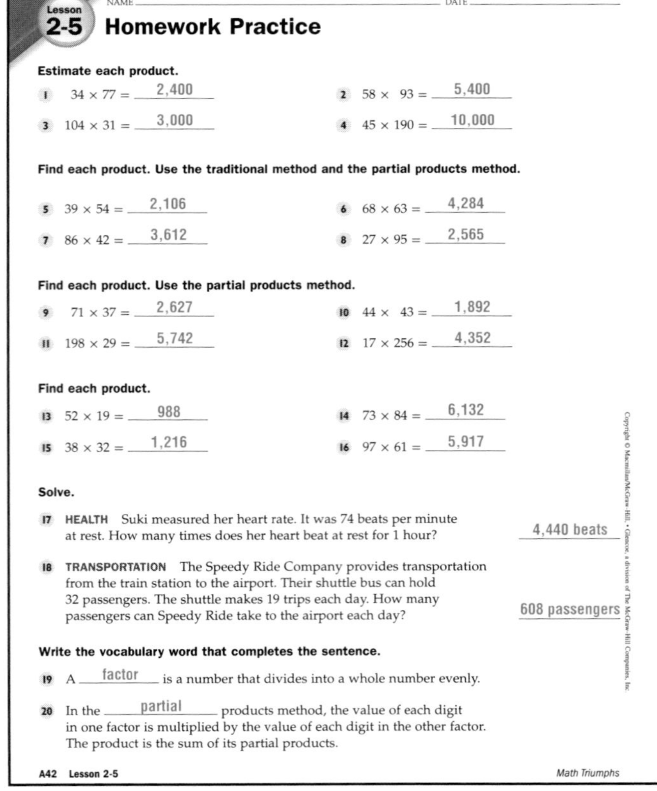

Lesson 2-5 NAME ____ DATE ____

Homework Practice

Estimate each product.

1. 34 × 77 = 2,400
2. 58 × 93 = 5,400
3. 104 × 31 = 3,000
4. 45 × 190 = 10,000

Find each product. Use the traditional method and the partial products method.

5. 39 × 54 = 2,106
6. 68 × 63 = 4,284
7. 86 × 42 = 3,612
8. 27 × 95 = 2,565

Find each product. Use the partial products method.

9. 71 × 37 = 2,627
10. 44 × 43 = 1,892
11. 198 × 29 = 5,742
12. 17 × 256 = 4,352

Find each product.

13. 52 × 19 = 988
14. 73 × 84 = 6,132
15. 38 × 32 = 1,216
16. 97 × 61 = 5,917

Solve.

17. **HEALTH** Suki measured her heart rate. It was 74 beats per minute at rest. How many times does her heart beat at rest for 1 hour? 4,440 beats
18. **TRANSPORTATION** The Speedy Ride Company provides transportation from the train station to the airport. Their shuttle bus can hold 32 passengers. The shuttle makes 19 trips each day. How many passengers can Speedy Ride take to the airport each day? 608 passengers

Write the vocabulary word that completes the sentence.

19. A factor is a number that divides into a whole number evenly.
20. In the partial products method, the value of each digit in one factor is multiplied by the value of each digit in the other factor. The product is the sum of its partial products.

Answer Key (Lesson 2-6)

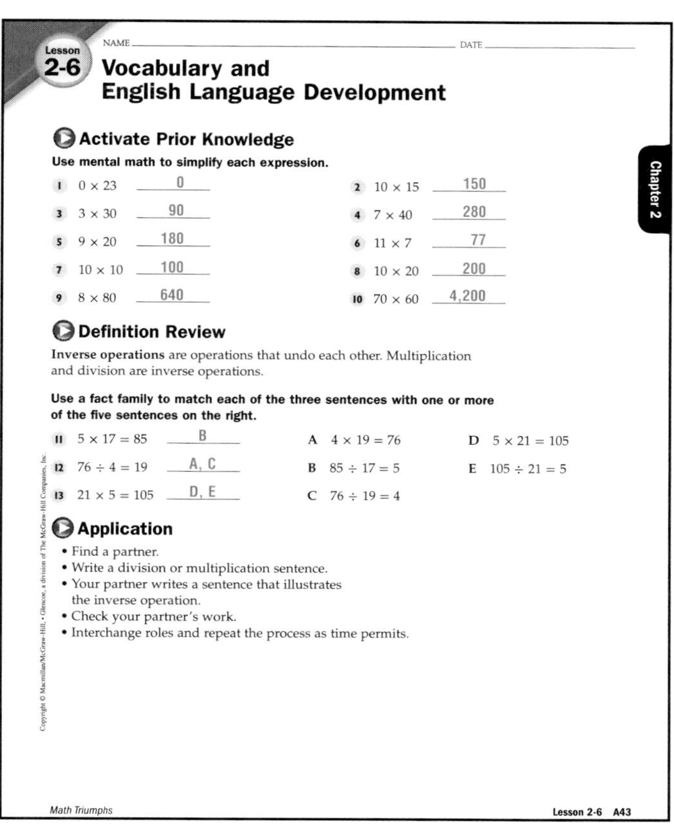

NAME ______ DATE ______

Lesson 2-6 **Vocabulary and English Language Development**

Chapter 2

Activate Prior Knowledge

Use mental math to simplify each expression.

1. 0 × 23 = 0
2. 10 × 15 = 150
3. 3 × 30 = 90
4. 7 × 40 = 280
5. 9 × 20 = 180
6. 11 × 7 = 77
7. 10 × 10 = 100
8. 10 × 20 = 200
9. 8 × 80 = 640
10. 70 × 60 = 4,200

Definition Review

Inverse operations are operations that undo each other. Multiplication and division are inverse operations.

Use a fact family to match each of the three sentences with one or more of the five sentences on the right.

11. 5 × 17 = 85 — B
12. 76 ÷ 4 = 19 — A, C
13. 21 × 5 = 105 — D, E

A 4 × 19 = 76
B 85 ÷ 17 = 5
C 76 ÷ 19 = 4
D 5 × 21 = 105
E 105 ÷ 21 = 5

Application

- Find a partner.
- Write a division or multiplication sentence.
- Your partner writes a sentence that illustrates the inverse operation.
- Check your partner's work.
- Interchange roles and repeat the process as time permits.

Math Triumphs Lesson 2-6 A43

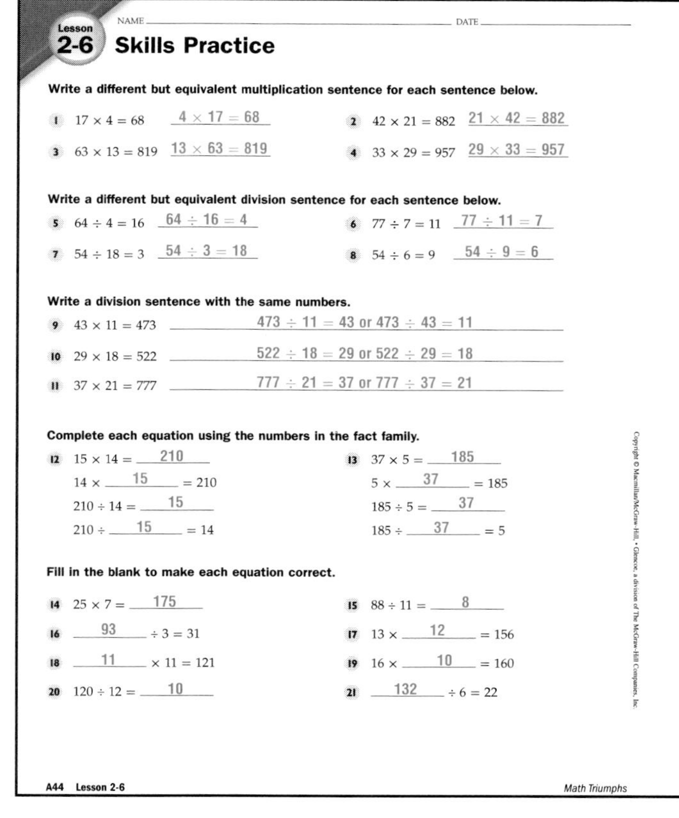

NAME ______ DATE ______

Lesson 2-6 **Skills Practice**

Write a different but equivalent multiplication sentence for each sentence below.

1. 17 × 4 = 68 — 4 × 17 = 68
2. 42 × 21 = 882 — 21 × 42 = 882
3. 63 × 13 = 819 — 13 × 63 = 819
4. 33 × 29 = 957 — 29 × 33 = 957

Write a different but equivalent division sentence for each sentence below.

5. 64 ÷ 4 = 16 — 64 ÷ 16 = 4
6. 77 ÷ 7 = 11 — 77 ÷ 11 = 7
7. 54 ÷ 18 = 3 — 54 ÷ 3 = 18
8. 54 ÷ 6 = 9 — 54 ÷ 9 = 6

Write a division sentence with the same numbers.

9. 43 × 11 = 473 — 473 ÷ 11 = 43 or 473 ÷ 43 = 11
10. 29 × 18 = 522 — 522 ÷ 18 = 29 or 522 ÷ 29 = 18
11. 37 × 21 = 777 — 777 ÷ 21 = 37 or 777 ÷ 37 = 21

Complete each equation using the numbers in the fact family.

12. 15 × 14 = 210
    14 × 15 = 210
    210 ÷ 14 = 15
    210 ÷ 15 = 14
13. 37 × 5 = 185
    5 × 37 = 185
    185 ÷ 5 = 37
    185 ÷ 37 = 5

Fill in the blank to make each equation correct.

14. 25 × 7 = 175
15. 88 ÷ 11 = 8
16. 93 ÷ 3 = 31
17. 13 × 12 = 156
18. 11 × 11 = 121
19. 16 × 10 = 160
20. 120 ÷ 12 = 10
21. 132 ÷ 6 = 22

A44 Lesson 2-6 Math Triumphs

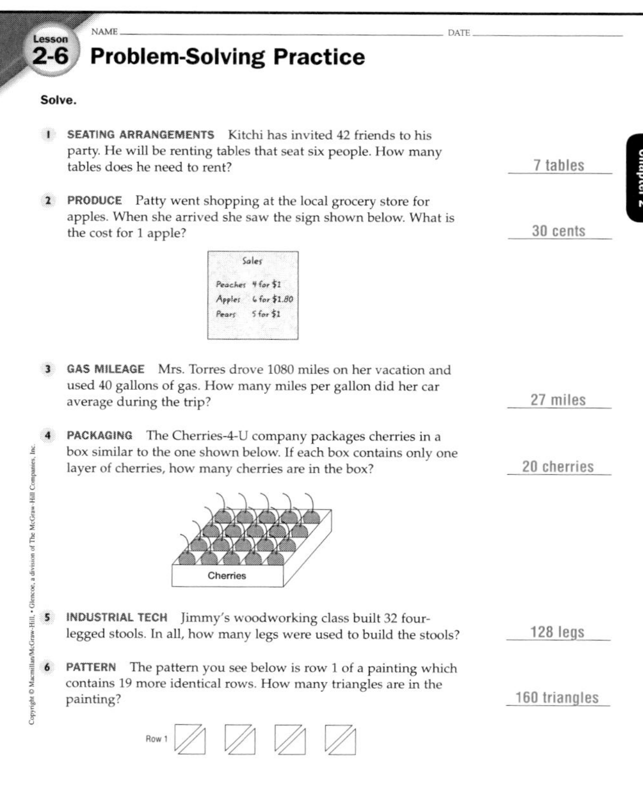

NAME ______ DATE ______

Lesson 2-6 **Problem-Solving Practice**

Chapter 2

Solve.

1. **SEATING ARRANGEMENTS** Kitchi has invited 42 friends to his party. He will be renting tables that seat six people. How many tables does he need to rent? — 7 tables
2. **PRODUCE** Patty went shopping at the local grocery store for apples. When she arrived she saw the sign shown below. What is the cost for 1 apple? — 30 cents

   Sales
   Peaches 4 for $1
   Apples 6 for $1.80
   Pears 5 for $1

3. **GAS MILEAGE** Mrs. Torres drove 1080 miles on her vacation and used 40 gallons of gas. How many miles per gallon did her car average during the trip? — 27 miles
4. **PACKAGING** The Cherries-4-U company packages cherries in a box similar to the one shown below. If each box contains only one layer of cherries, how many cherries are in the box? — 20 cherries

   Cherries

5. **INDUSTRIAL TECH** Jimmy's woodworking class built 32 four-legged stools. In all, how many legs were used to build the stools? — 128 legs
6. **PATTERN** The pattern you see below is row 1 of a painting which contains 19 more identical rows. How many triangles are in the painting? — 160 triangles

   Row 1

Math Triumphs Lesson 2-6 A45

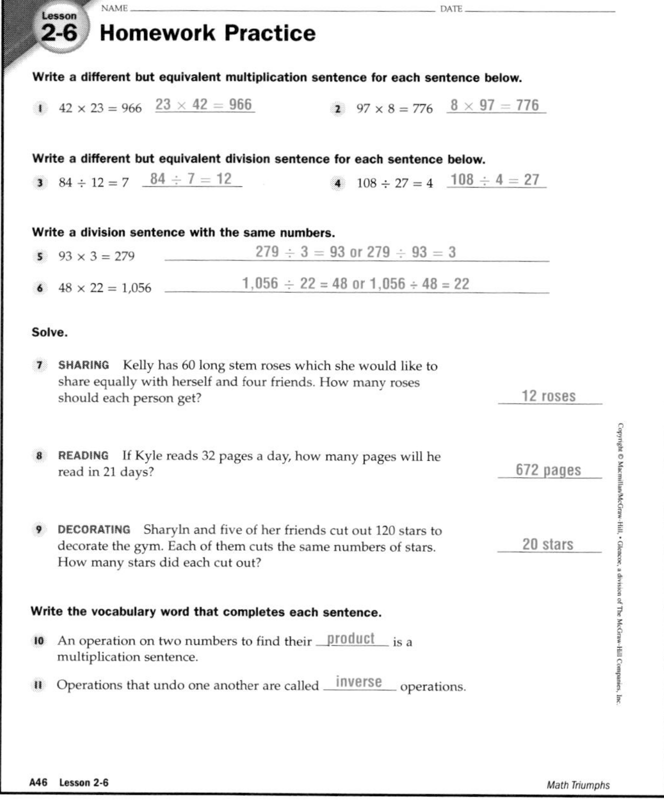

NAME ______ DATE ______

Lesson 2-6 **Homework Practice**

Write a different but equivalent multiplication sentence for each sentence below.

1. 42 × 23 = 966 — 23 × 42 = 966
2. 97 × 8 = 776 — 8 × 97 = 776

Write a different but equivalent division sentence for each sentence below.

3. 84 ÷ 12 = 7 — 84 ÷ 7 = 12
4. 108 ÷ 27 = 4 — 108 ÷ 4 = 27

Write a division sentence with the same numbers.

5. 93 × 3 = 279 — 279 ÷ 3 = 93 or 279 ÷ 93 = 3
6. 48 × 22 = 1,056 — 1,056 ÷ 22 = 48 or 1,056 ÷ 48 = 22

Solve.

7. **SHARING** Kelly has 60 long stem roses which she would like to share equally with herself and four friends. How many roses should each person get? — 12 roses
8. **READING** If Kyle reads 32 pages a day, how many pages will he read in 21 days? — 672 pages
9. **DECORATING** Sharyln and five of her friends cut out 120 stars to decorate the gym. Each of them cuts the same numbers of stars. How many stars did each cut out? — 20 stars

Write the vocabulary word that completes each sentence.

10. An operation on two numbers to find their product is a multiplication sentence.
11. Operations that undo one another are called inverse operations.

A46 Lesson 2-6 Math Triumphs

Answer Key (Lesson 3-1)

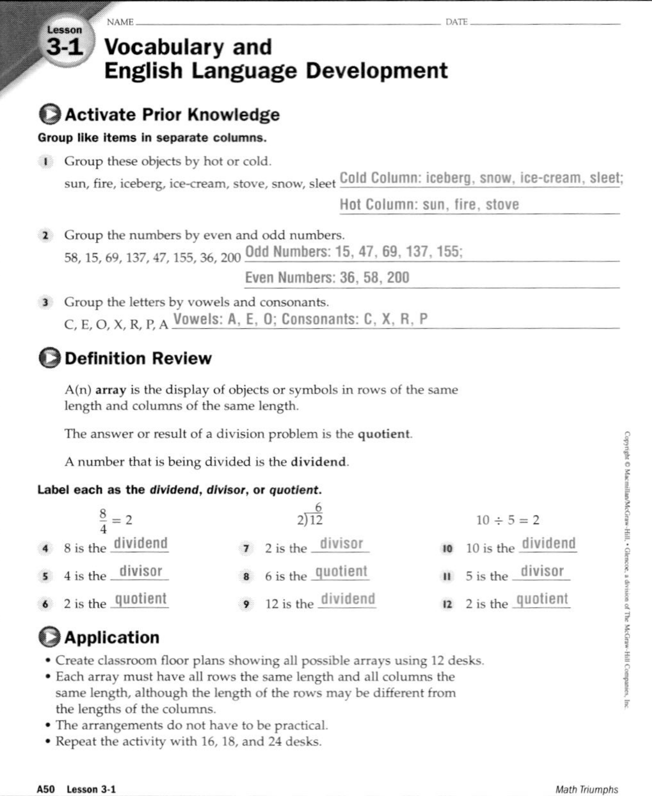

Lesson 3-1 NAME ______ DATE ______

Vocabulary and English Language Development

Activate Prior Knowledge

Group like items in separate columns.

1. Group these objects by hot or cold.
   sun, fire, iceberg, ice-cream, stove, snow, sleet Cold Column: iceberg, snow, ice-cream, sleet;
   Hot Column: sun, fire, stove
2. Group the numbers by even and odd numbers.
   58, 15, 69, 137, 47, 155, 36, 200 Odd Numbers: 15, 47, 69, 137, 155;
   Even Numbers: 36, 58, 200
3. Group the letters by vowels and consonants.
   C, E, O, X, R, P, A Vowels: A, E, O; Consonants: C, X, R, P

Definition Review

A(n) **array** is the display of objects or symbols in rows of the same length and columns of the same length.

The answer or result of a division problem is the **quotient**.

A number that is being divided is the **dividend**.

Label each as the dividend, divisor, or quotient.

$\frac{8}{4} = 2$ | $2\overline{)12}$ with quotient 6 | $10 \div 5 = 2$

4. 8 is the dividend
5. 4 is the divisor
6. 2 is the quotient
7. 2 is the divisor
8. 6 is the quotient
9. 12 is the dividend
10. 10 is the dividend
11. 5 is the divisor
12. 2 is the quotient

Application

- Create classroom floor plans showing all possible arrays using 12 desks.
- Each array must have all rows the same length and all columns the same length, although the length of the rows may be different from the lengths of the columns.
- The arrangements do not have to be practical.
- Repeat the activity with 16, 18, and 24 desks.

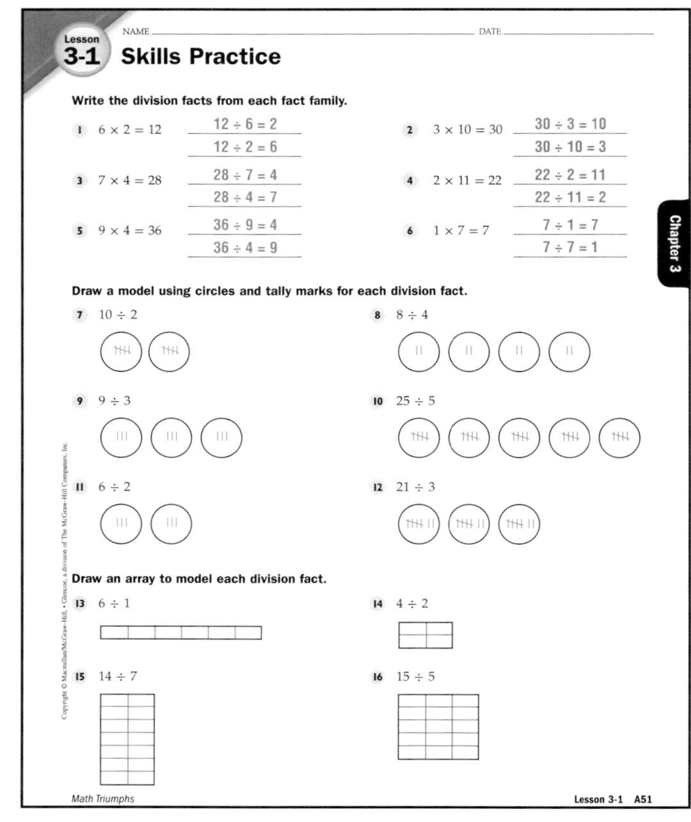

Lesson 3-1 NAME ______ DATE ______

Skills Practice

Write the division facts from each fact family.

1. $6 \times 2 = 12$ — $12 \div 6 = 2$; $12 \div 2 = 6$
2. $3 \times 10 = 30$ — $30 \div 3 = 10$; $30 \div 10 = 3$
3. $7 \times 4 = 28$ — $28 \div 7 = 4$; $28 \div 4 = 7$
4. $2 \times 11 = 22$ — $22 \div 2 = 11$; $22 \div 11 = 2$
5. $9 \times 4 = 36$ — $36 \div 9 = 4$; $36 \div 4 = 9$
6. $1 \times 7 = 7$ — $7 \div 1 = 7$; $7 \div 7 = 1$

Draw a model using circles and tally marks for each division fact.

7. $10 \div 2$
8. $8 \div 4$
9. $9 \div 3$
10. $25 \div 5$
11. $6 \div 2$
12. $21 \div 3$

Draw an array to model each division fact.

13. $6 \div 1$
14. $4 \div 2$
15. $14 \div 7$
16. $15 \div 5$

Chapter 3

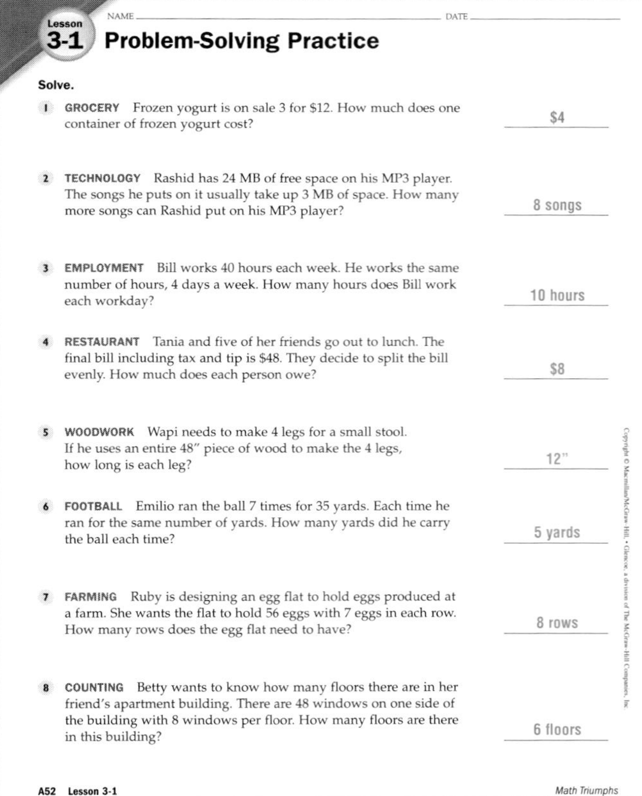

Lesson 3-1 NAME ______ DATE ______

Problem-Solving Practice

Solve.

1. **GROCERY** Frozen yogurt is on sale 3 for $12. How much does one container of frozen yogurt cost? $4
2. **TECHNOLOGY** Rashid has 24 MB of free space on his MP3 player. The songs he puts on it usually take up 3 MB of space. How many more songs can Rashid put on his MP3 player? 8 songs
3. **EMPLOYMENT** Bill works 40 hours each week. He works the same number of hours, 4 days a week. How many hours does Bill work each workday? 10 hours
4. **RESTAURANT** Tania and five of her friends go out to lunch. The final bill including tax and tip is $48. They decide to split the bill evenly. How much does each person owe? $8
5. **WOODWORK** Wapi needs to make 4 legs for a small stool. If he uses an entire 48" piece of wood to make the 4 legs, how long is each leg? 12"
6. **FOOTBALL** Emilio ran the ball 7 times for 35 yards. Each time he ran for the same number of yards. How many yards did he carry the ball each time? 5 yards
7. **FARMING** Ruby is designing an egg flat to hold eggs produced at a farm. She wants the flat to hold 56 eggs with 7 eggs in each row. How many rows does the egg flat need to have? 8 rows
8. **COUNTING** Betty wants to know how many floors there are in her friend's apartment building. There are 48 windows on one side of the building with 8 windows per floor. How many floors are there in this building? 6 floors

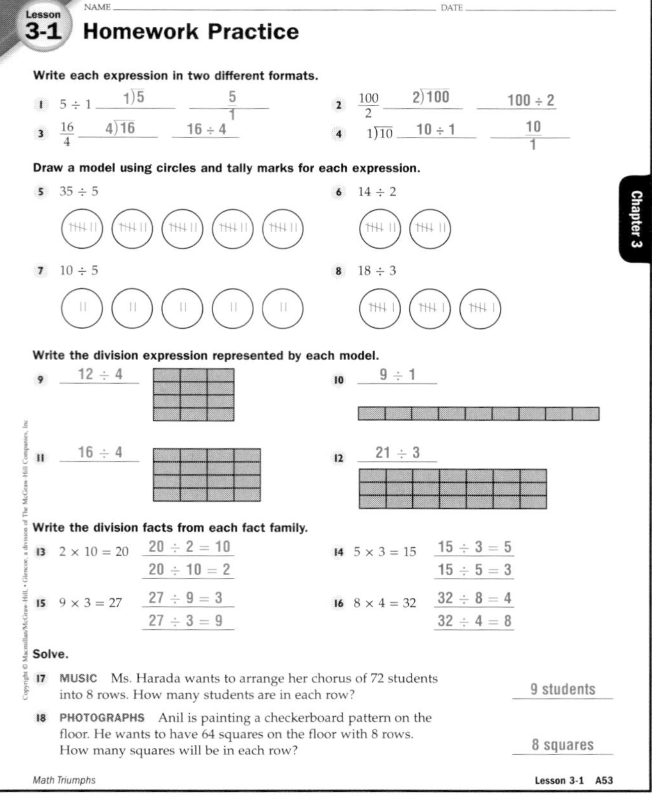

Lesson 3-1 NAME ______ DATE ______

Homework Practice

Write each expression in two different formats.

1. $5 \div 1$ — $1\overline{)5}$; $\frac{5}{1}$
2. $\frac{100}{2}$ — $2\overline{)100}$; $100 \div 2$
3. $\frac{16}{4}$ — $4\overline{)16}$; $16 \div 4$
4. $1\overline{)10}$ — $10 \div 1$; $\frac{10}{1}$

Draw a model using circles and tally marks for each expression.

5. $35 \div 5$
6. $14 \div 2$
7. $10 \div 5$
8. $18 \div 3$

Write the division expression represented by each model.

9. $12 \div 4$
10. $9 \div 1$
11. $16 \div 4$
12. $21 \div 3$

Write the division facts from each fact family.

13. $2 \times 10 = 20$ — $20 \div 2 = 10$; $20 \div 10 = 2$
14. $5 \times 3 = 15$ — $15 \div 3 = 5$; $15 \div 5 = 3$
15. $9 \times 3 = 27$ — $27 \div 9 = 3$; $27 \div 3 = 9$
16. $8 \times 4 = 32$ — $32 \div 8 = 4$; $32 \div 4 = 8$

Solve.

17. **MUSIC** Ms. Harada wants to arrange her chorus of 72 students into 8 rows. How many students are in each row? 9 students
18. **PHOTOGRAPHS** Anil is painting a checkerboard pattern on the floor. He wants to have 64 squares on the floor with 8 rows. How many squares will be in each row? 8 squares

Chapter 3

Answer Key (Lesson 3-2)

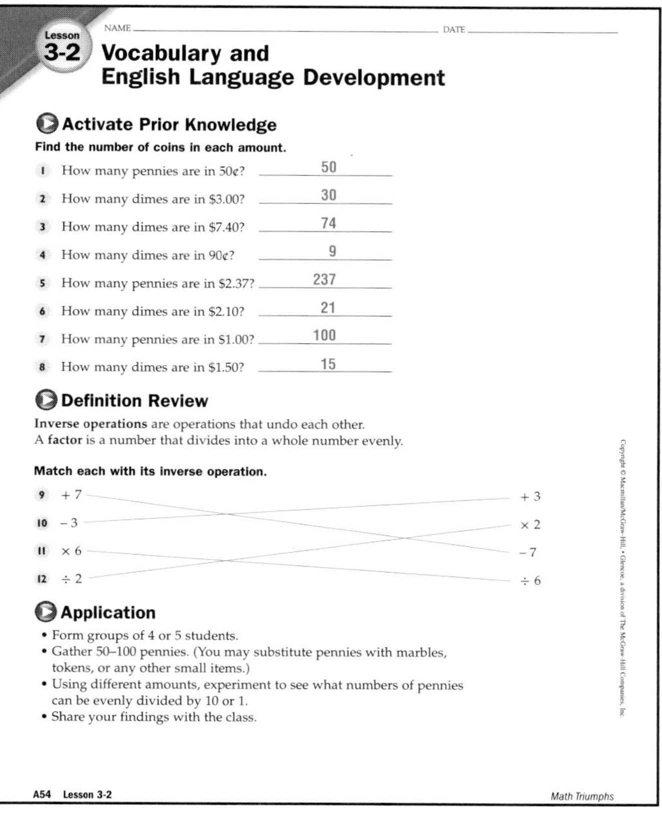

NAME ______ DATE ______

Lesson 3-2

Vocabulary and English Language Development

Activate Prior Knowledge

Find the number of coins in each amount.

1. How many pennies are in 50¢? 50
2. How many dimes are in $3.00? 30
3. How many dimes are in $7.40? 74
4. How many dimes are in 90¢? 9
5. How many pennies are in $2.37? 237
6. How many dimes are in $2.10? 21
7. How many pennies are in $1.00? 100
8. How many dimes are in $1.50? 15

Definition Review

Inverse operations are operations that undo each other.
A **factor** is a number that divides into a whole number evenly.

Match each with its inverse operation.

9 + 7	+ 3
10 − 3	× 2
11 × 6	− 7
12 ÷ 2	÷ 6

Application

- Form groups of 4 or 5 students.
- Gather 50–100 pennies. (You may substitute pennies with marbles, tokens, or any other small items.)
- Using different amounts, experiment to see what numbers of pennies can be evenly divided by 10 or 1.
- Share your findings with the class.

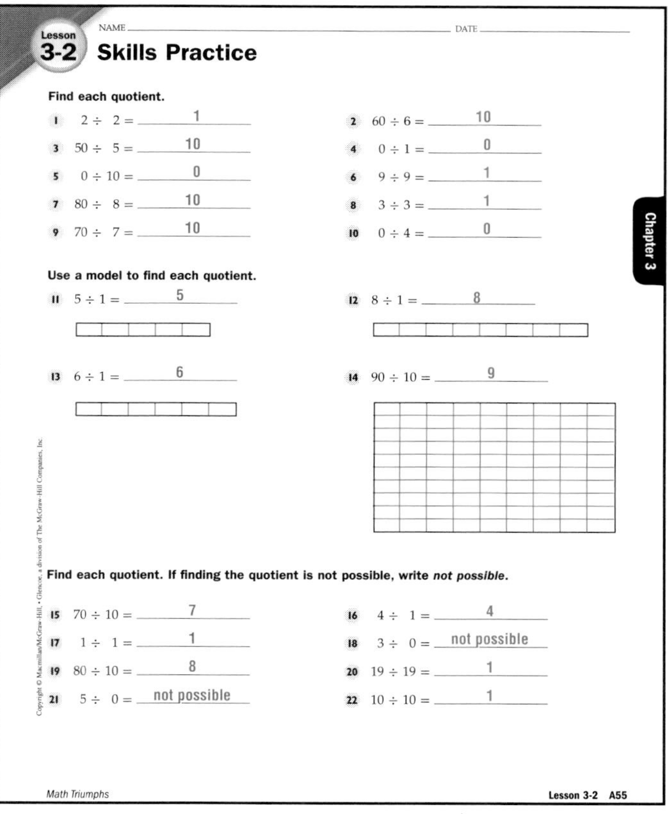

NAME ______ DATE ______

Lesson 3-2

Skills Practice

Chapter 3

Find each quotient.

1. 2 ÷ 2 = 1
2. 60 ÷ 6 = 10
3. 50 ÷ 5 = 10
4. 0 ÷ 1 = 0
5. 0 ÷ 10 = 0
6. 9 ÷ 9 = 1
7. 80 ÷ 8 = 10
8. 3 ÷ 3 = 1
9. 70 ÷ 7 = 10
10. 0 ÷ 4 = 0

Use a model to find each quotient.

11. 5 ÷ 1 = 5
12. 8 ÷ 1 = 8
13. 6 ÷ 1 = 6
14. 90 ÷ 10 = 9

Find each quotient. If finding the quotient is not possible, write *not possible*.

15. 70 ÷ 10 = 7
16. 4 ÷ 1 = 4
17. 1 ÷ 1 = 1
18. 3 ÷ 0 = not possible
19. 80 ÷ 10 = 8
20. 19 ÷ 19 = 1
21. 5 ÷ 0 = not possible
22. 10 ÷ 10 = 1

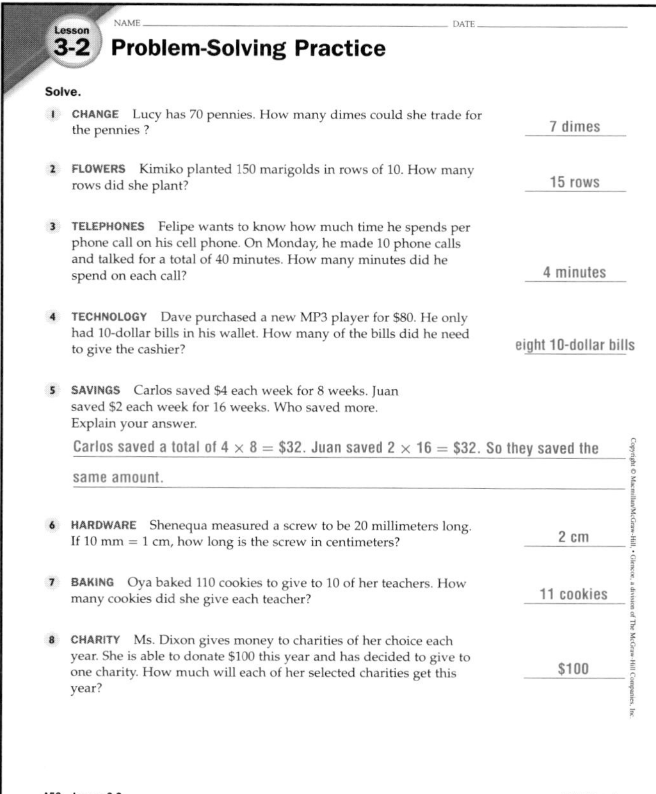

NAME ______ DATE ______

Lesson 3-2

Problem-Solving Practice

Solve.

1. **CHANGE** Lucy has 70 pennies. How many dimes could she trade for the pennies ? 7 dimes
2. **FLOWERS** Kimiko planted 150 marigolds in rows of 10. How many rows did she plant? 15 rows
3. **TELEPHONES** Felipe wants to know how much time he spends per phone call on his cell phone. On Monday, he made 10 phone calls and talked for a total of 40 minutes. How many minutes did he spend on each call? 4 minutes
4. **TECHNOLOGY** Dave purchased a new MP3 player for $80. He only had 10-dollar bills in his wallet. How many of the bills did he need to give the cashier? eight 10-dollar bills
5. **SAVINGS** Carlos saved $4 each week for 8 weeks. Juan saved $2 each week for 16 weeks. Who saved more. Explain your answer.
   Carlos saved a total of $4 \times 8 = \$32$. Juan saved $2 \times 16 = \$32$. So they saved the same amount.
6. **HARDWARE** Shenequa measured a screw to be 20 millimeters long. If 10 mm = 1 cm, how long is the screw in centimeters? 2 cm
7. **BAKING** Oya baked 110 cookies to give to 10 of her teachers. How many cookies did she give each teacher? 11 cookies
8. **CHARITY** Ms. Dixon gives money to charities of her choice each year. She is able to donate $100 this year and has decided to give to one charity. How much will each of her selected charities get this year? $100

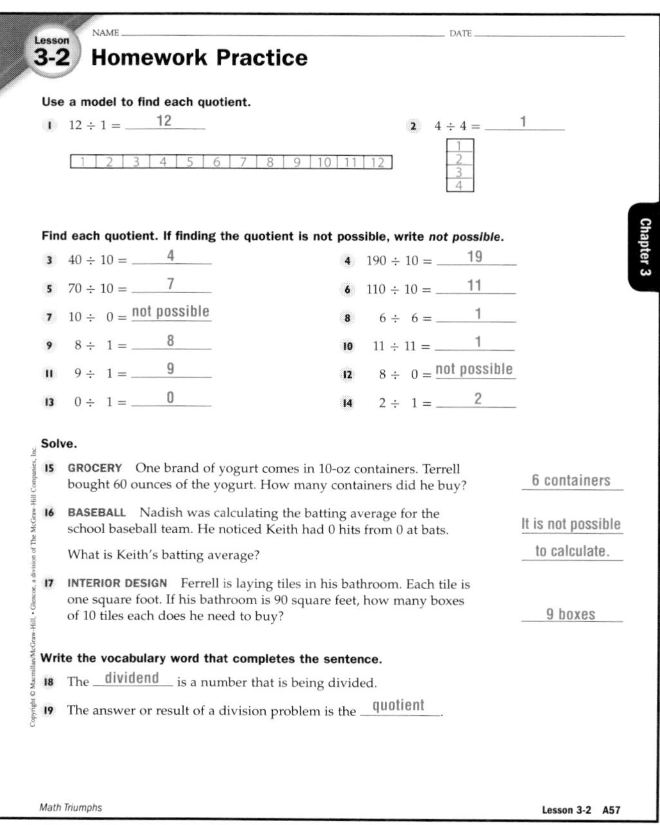

NAME ______ DATE ______

Lesson 3-2

Homework Practice

Chapter 3

Use a model to find each quotient.

1. 12 ÷ 1 = 12
2. 4 ÷ 4 = 1

Find each quotient. If finding the quotient is not possible, write *not possible*.

3. 40 ÷ 10 = 4
4. 190 ÷ 10 = 19
5. 70 ÷ 10 = 7
6. 110 ÷ 10 = 11
7. 10 ÷ 0 = not possible
8. 6 ÷ 6 = 1
9. 8 ÷ 1 = 8
10. 11 ÷ 11 = 1
11. 9 ÷ 1 = 9
12. 8 ÷ 0 = not possible
13. 0 ÷ 1 = 0
14. 2 ÷ 1 = 2

Solve.

15. **GROCERY** One brand of yogurt comes in 10-oz containers. Terrell bought 60 ounces of the yogurt. How many containers did he buy? 6 containers
16. **BASEBALL** Nadish was calculating the batting average for the school baseball team. He noticed Keith had 0 hits from 0 at bats. What is Keith's batting average? It is not possible to calculate.
17. **INTERIOR DESIGN** Ferrell is laying tiles in his bathroom. Each tile is one square foot. If his bathroom is 90 square feet, how many boxes of 10 tiles each does he need to buy? 9 boxes

Write the vocabulary word that completes the sentence.

18. The dividend is a number that is being divided.
19. The answer or result of a division problem is the quotient.

Answer Key (Lesson 3-3)

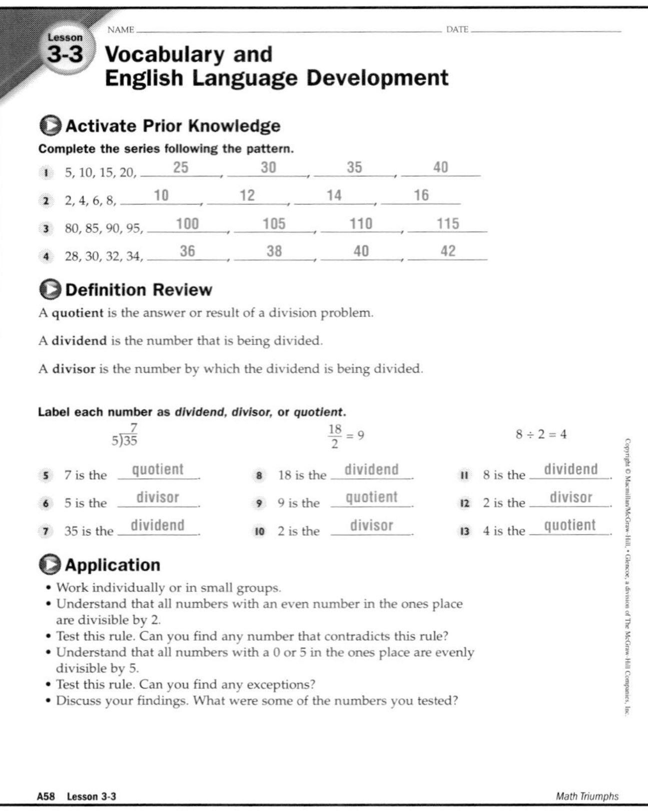

NAME ______ DATE ______

Lesson 3-3 **Vocabulary and English Language Development**

Activate Prior Knowledge

Complete the series following the pattern.

1. 5, 10, 15, 20, 25, 30, 35, 40
2. 2, 4, 6, 8, 10, 12, 14, 16
3. 80, 85, 90, 95, 100, 105, 110, 115
4. 28, 30, 32, 34, 36, 38, 40, 42

Definition Review

A **quotient** is the answer or result of a division problem.

A **dividend** is the number that is being divided.

A **divisor** is the number by which the dividend is being divided.

Label each number as *dividend, divisor,* or *quotient*.

$5\overline{)35}$ with quotient 7 $\qquad \frac{18}{2} = 9 \qquad 8 \div 2 = 4$

5. 7 is the quotient
6. 5 is the divisor
7. 35 is the dividend
8. 18 is the dividend
9. 9 is the quotient
10. 2 is the divisor
11. 8 is the dividend
12. 2 is the divisor
13. 4 is the quotient

Application

- Work individually or in small groups.
- Understand that all numbers with an even number in the ones place are divisible by 2.
- Test this rule. Can you find any number that contradicts this rule?
- Understand that all numbers with a 0 or 5 in the ones place are evenly divisible by 5.
- Test this rule. Can you find any exceptions?
- Discuss your findings. What were some of the numbers you tested?

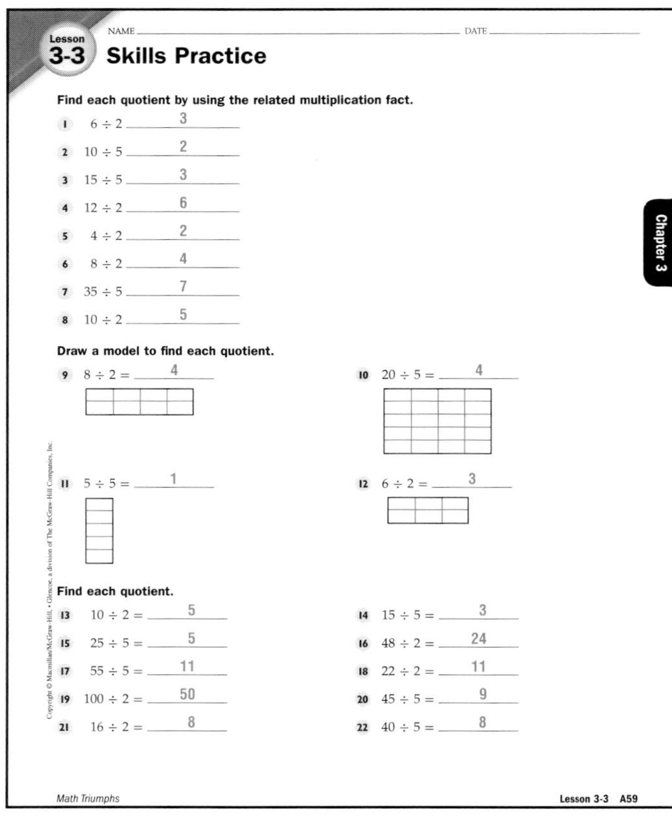

NAME ______ DATE ______

Lesson 3-3 **Skills Practice**

Find each quotient by using the related multiplication fact.

1. 6 ÷ 2 = 3
2. 10 ÷ 5 = 2
3. 15 ÷ 5 = 3
4. 12 ÷ 2 = 6
5. 4 ÷ 2 = 2
6. 8 ÷ 2 = 4
7. 35 ÷ 5 = 7
8. 10 ÷ 2 = 5

Draw a model to find each quotient.

9. 8 ÷ 2 = 4
10. 20 ÷ 5 = 4
11. 5 ÷ 5 = 1
12. 6 ÷ 2 = 3

Find each quotient.

13. 10 ÷ 2 = 5
14. 15 ÷ 5 = 3
15. 25 ÷ 5 = 5
16. 48 ÷ 2 = 24
17. 55 ÷ 5 = 11
18. 22 ÷ 2 = 11
19. 100 ÷ 2 = 50
20. 45 ÷ 5 = 9
21. 16 ÷ 2 = 8
22. 40 ÷ 5 = 8

Chapter 3

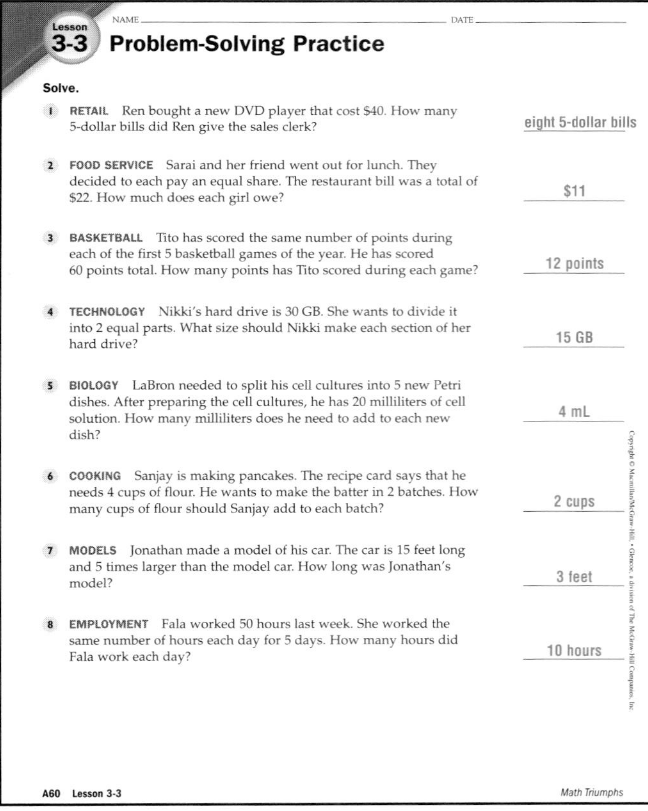

NAME ______ DATE ______

Lesson 3-3 **Problem-Solving Practice**

Solve.

1. **RETAIL** Ren bought a new DVD player that cost $40. How many 5-dollar bills did Ren give the sales clerk? eight 5-dollar bills
2. **FOOD SERVICE** Sarai and her friend went out for lunch. They decided to each pay an equal share. The restaurant bill was a total of $22. How much does each girl owe? $11
3. **BASKETBALL** Tito has scored the same number of points during each of the first 5 basketball games of the year. He has scored 60 points total. How many points has Tito scored during each game? 12 points
4. **TECHNOLOGY** Nikki's hard drive is 30 GB. She wants to divide it into 2 equal parts. What size should Nikki make each section of her hard drive? 15 GB
5. **BIOLOGY** LaBron needed to split his cell cultures into 5 new Petri dishes. After preparing the cell cultures, he has 20 milliliters of cell solution. How many milliliters does he need to add to each new dish? 4 mL
6. **COOKING** Sanjay is making pancakes. The recipe card says that he needs 4 cups of flour. He wants to make the batter in 2 batches. How many cups of flour should Sanjay add to each batch? 2 cups
7. **MODELS** Jonathan made a model of his car. The car is 15 feet long and 5 times larger than the model car. How long was Jonathan's model? 3 feet
8. **EMPLOYMENT** Fala worked 50 hours last week. She worked the same number of hours each day for 5 days. How many hours did Fala work each day? 10 hours

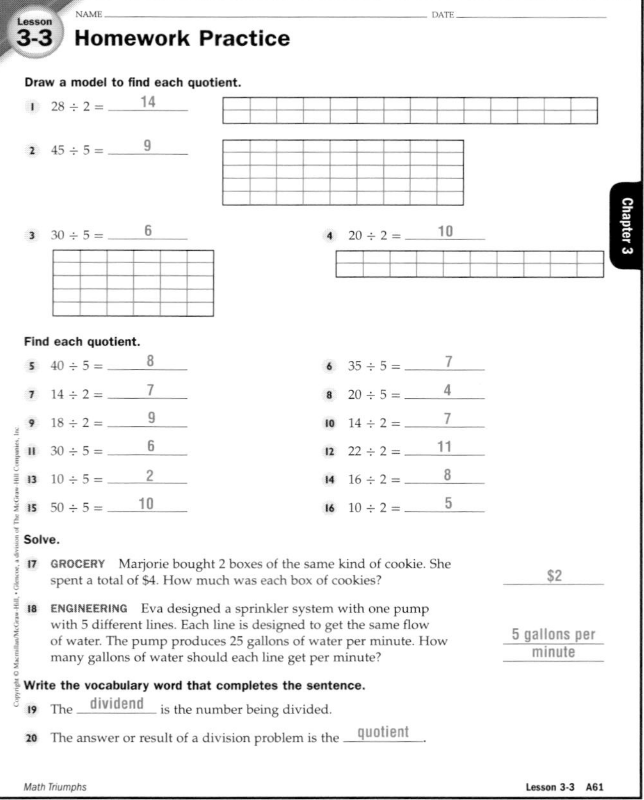

NAME ______ DATE ______

Lesson 3-3 **Homework Practice**

Draw a model to find each quotient.

1. 28 ÷ 2 = 14
2. 45 ÷ 5 = 9
3. 30 ÷ 5 = 6
4. 20 ÷ 2 = 10

Find each quotient.

5. 40 ÷ 5 = 8
6. 35 ÷ 5 = 7
7. 14 ÷ 2 = 7
8. 20 ÷ 5 = 4
9. 18 ÷ 2 = 9
10. 14 ÷ 2 = 7
11. 30 ÷ 5 = 6
12. 22 ÷ 2 = 11
13. 10 ÷ 5 = 2
14. 16 ÷ 2 = 8
15. 50 ÷ 5 = 10
16. 10 ÷ 2 = 5

Solve.

17. **GROCERY** Marjorie bought 2 boxes of the same kind of cookie. She spent a total of $4. How much was each box of cookies? $2
18. **ENGINEERING** Eva designed a sprinkler system with one pump with 5 different lines. Each line is designed to get the same flow of water. The pump produces 25 gallons of water per minute. How many gallons of water should each line get per minute? 5 gallons per minute

Write the vocabulary word that completes the sentence.

19. The dividend is the number being divided.
20. The answer or result of a division problem is the quotient.

Chapter 3

Answer Key (Lesson 3-4)

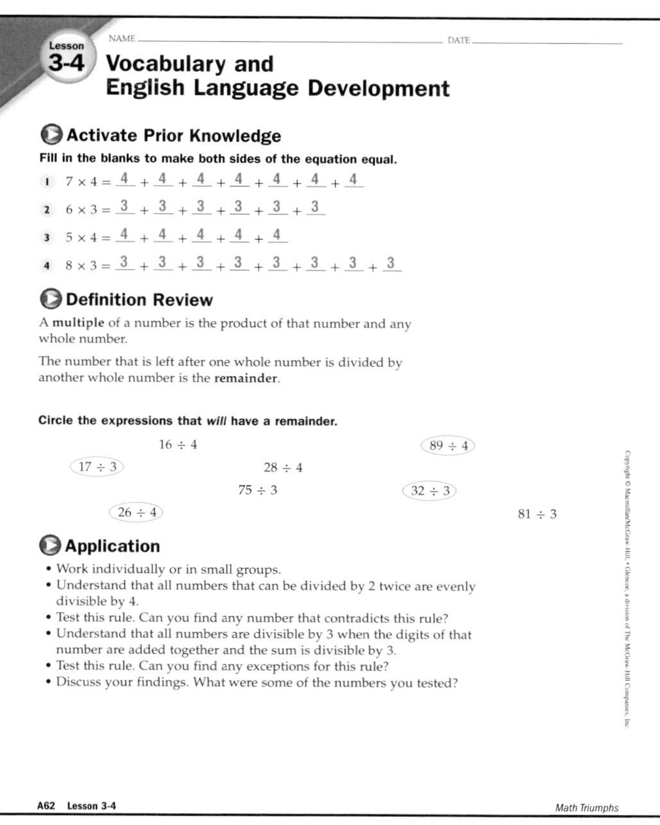

NAME ______ DATE ______

Lesson 3-4 **Vocabulary and English Language Development**

Activate Prior Knowledge

Fill in the blanks to make both sides of the equation equal.

1. 7 × 4 = 4 + 4 + 4 + 4 + 4 + 4 + 4
2. 6 × 3 = 3 + 3 + 3 + 3 + 3 + 3
3. 5 × 4 = 4 + 4 + 4 + 4 + 4
4. 8 × 3 = 3 + 3 + 3 + 3 + 3 + 3 + 3 + 3

Definition Review

A **multiple** of a number is the product of that number and any whole number.

The number that is left after one whole number is divided by another whole number is the **remainder**.

Circle the expressions that *will* have a remainder.

16 ÷ 4, (89 ÷ 4), (17 ÷ 3), 28 ÷ 4, 75 ÷ 3, (32 ÷ 3), (26 ÷ 4), 81 ÷ 3

Application

- Work individually or in small groups.
- Understand that all numbers that can be divided by 2 twice are evenly divisible by 4.
- Test this rule. Can you find any number that contradicts this rule?
- Understand that all numbers are divisible by 3 when the digits of that number are added together and the sum is divisible by 3.
- Test this rule. Can you find any exceptions for this rule?
- Discuss your findings. What were some of the numbers you tested?

A62 Lesson 3-4 *Math Triumphs*

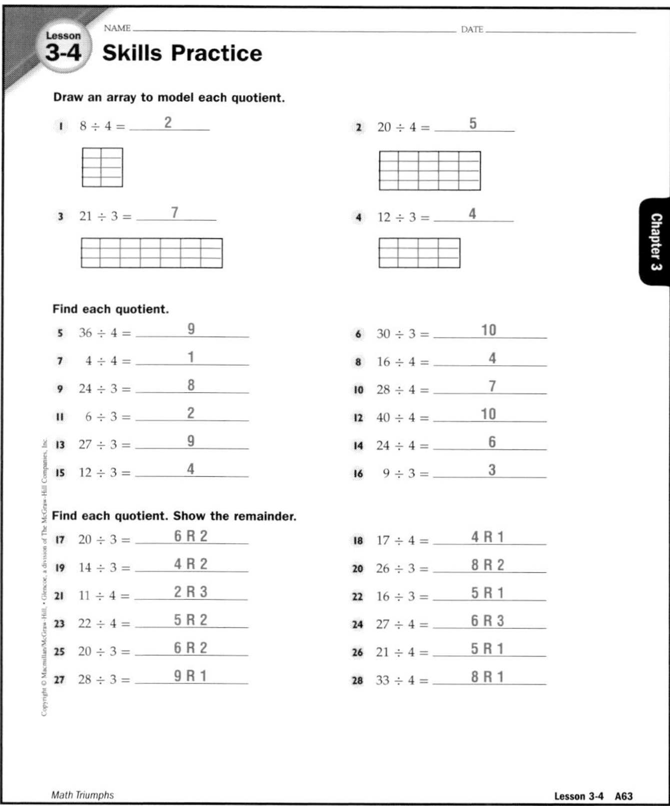

NAME ______ DATE ______

Lesson 3-4 **Skills Practice**

Draw an array to model each quotient.

1. 8 ÷ 4 = 2
2. 20 ÷ 4 = 5
3. 21 ÷ 3 = 7
4. 12 ÷ 3 = 4

Find each quotient.

5. 36 ÷ 4 = 9
6. 30 ÷ 3 = 10
7. 4 ÷ 4 = 1
8. 16 ÷ 4 = 4
9. 24 ÷ 3 = 8
10. 28 ÷ 4 = 7
11. 6 ÷ 3 = 2
12. 40 ÷ 4 = 10
13. 27 ÷ 3 = 9
14. 24 ÷ 4 = 6
15. 12 ÷ 3 = 4
16. 9 ÷ 3 = 3

Find each quotient. Show the remainder.

17. 20 ÷ 3 = 6 R 2
18. 17 ÷ 4 = 4 R 1
19. 14 ÷ 3 = 4 R 2
20. 26 ÷ 3 = 8 R 2
21. 11 ÷ 4 = 2 R 3
22. 16 ÷ 3 = 5 R 1
23. 22 ÷ 4 = 5 R 2
24. 27 ÷ 4 = 6 R 3
25. 20 ÷ 3 = 6 R 2
26. 21 ÷ 4 = 5 R 1
27. 28 ÷ 3 = 9 R 1
28. 33 ÷ 4 = 8 R 1

Chapter 3

Math Triumphs Lesson 3-4 A63

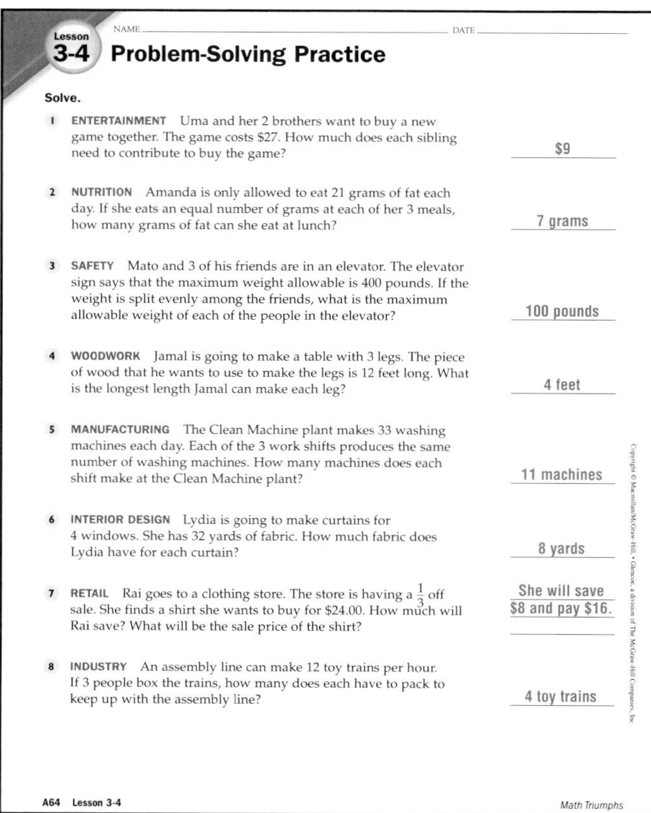

NAME ______ DATE ______

Lesson 3-4 **Problem-Solving Practice**

Solve.

1. ENTERTAINMENT Uma and her 2 brothers want to buy a new game together. The game costs $27. How much does each sibling need to contribute to buy the game? **$9**
2. NUTRITION Amanda is only allowed to eat 21 grams of fat each day. If she eats an equal number of grams at each of her 3 meals, how many grams of fat can she eat at lunch? **7 grams**
3. SAFETY Mato and 3 of his friends are in an elevator. The elevator sign says that the maximum weight allowable is 400 pounds. If the weight is split evenly among the friends, what is the maximum allowable weight of each of the people in the elevator? **100 pounds**
4. WOODWORK Jamal is going to make a table with 3 legs. The piece of wood that he wants to use to make the legs is 12 feet long. What is the longest length Jamal can make each leg? **4 feet**
5. MANUFACTURING The Clean Machine plant makes 33 washing machines each day. Each of the 3 work shifts produces the same number of washing machines. How many machines does each shift make at the Clean Machine plant? **11 machines**
6. INTERIOR DESIGN Lydia is going to make curtains for 4 windows. She has 32 yards of fabric. How much fabric does Lydia have for each curtain? **8 yards**
7. RETAIL Rai goes to a clothing store. The store is having a $\frac{1}{3}$ off sale. She finds a shirt she wants to buy for $24.00. How much will Rai save? What will be the sale price of the shirt? **She will save $8 and pay $16.**
8. INDUSTRY An assembly line can make 12 toy trains per hour. If 3 people box the trains, how many does each have to pack to keep up with the assembly line? **4 toy trains**

A64 Lesson 3-4 *Math Triumphs*

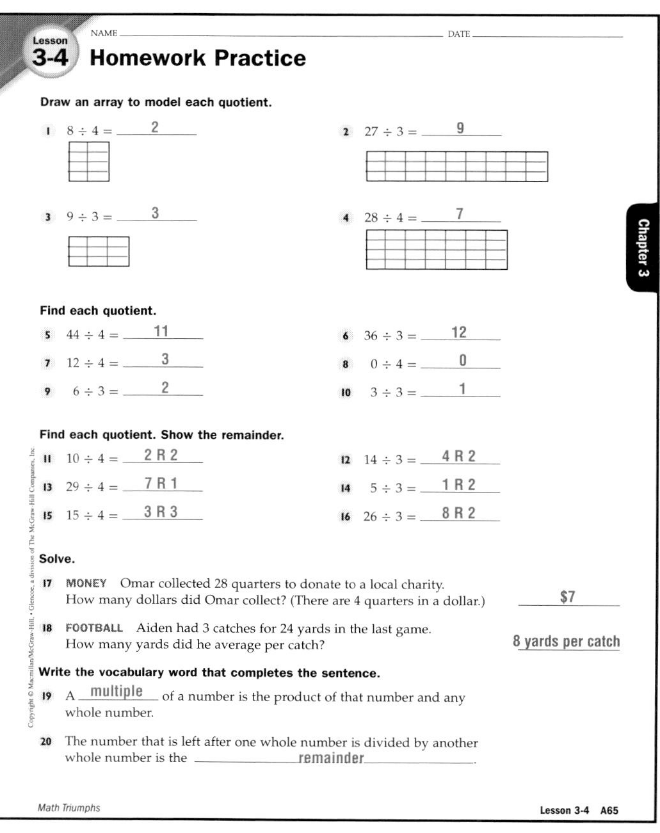

NAME ______ DATE ______

Lesson 3-4 **Homework Practice**

Draw an array to model each quotient.

1. 8 ÷ 4 = 2
2. 27 ÷ 3 = 9
3. 9 ÷ 3 = 3
4. 28 ÷ 4 = 7

Find each quotient.

5. 44 ÷ 4 = 11
6. 36 ÷ 3 = 12
7. 12 ÷ 4 = 3
8. 0 ÷ 4 = 0
9. 6 ÷ 3 = 2
10. 3 ÷ 3 = 1

Find each quotient. Show the remainder.

11. 10 ÷ 4 = 2 R 2
12. 14 ÷ 3 = 4 R 2
13. 29 ÷ 4 = 7 R 1
14. 5 ÷ 3 = 1 R 2
15. 15 ÷ 4 = 3 R 3
16. 26 ÷ 3 = 8 R 2

Solve.

17. MONEY Omar collected 28 quarters to donate to a local charity. How many dollars did Omar collect? (There are 4 quarters in a dollar.) **$7**
18. FOOTBALL Aiden had 3 catches for 24 yards in the last game. How many yards did he average per catch? **8 yards per catch**

Write the vocabulary word that completes the sentence.

19. A **multiple** of a number is the product of that number and any whole number.
20. The number that is left after one whole number is divided by another whole number is the **remainder**.

Chapter 3

Math Triumphs Lesson 3-4 A65

Answer Key (Lesson 3-5)

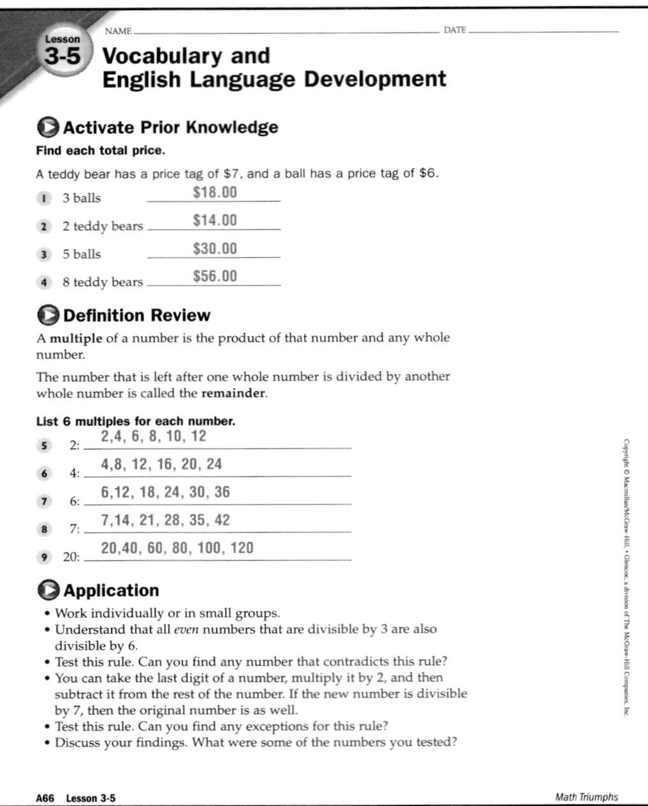

NAME ______ DATE ______

Lesson 3-5 **Vocabulary and English Language Development**

Activate Prior Knowledge

Find each total price.

A teddy bear has a price tag of $7, and a ball has a price tag of $6.

1. 3 balls $18.00
2. 2 teddy bears $14.00
3. 5 balls $30.00
4. 8 teddy bears $56.00

Definition Review

A **multiple** of a number is the product of that number and any whole number.

The number that is left after one whole number is divided by another whole number is called the **remainder**.

List 6 multiples for each number.

5. 2: 2,4, 6, 8, 10, 12
6. 4: 4,8, 12, 16, 20, 24
7. 6: 6,12, 18, 24, 30, 36
8. 7: 7,14, 21, 28, 35, 42
9. 20: 20,40, 60, 80, 100, 120

Application

- Work individually or in small groups.
- Understand that all *even* numbers that are divisible by 3 are also divisible by 6.
- Test this rule. Can you find any number that contradicts this rule?
- You can take the last digit of a number, multiply it by 2, and then subtract it from the rest of the number. If the new number is divisible by 7, then the original number is as well.
- Test this rule. Can you find any exceptions for this rule?
- Discuss your findings. What were some of the numbers you tested?

A66 Lesson 3-5 *Math Triumphs*

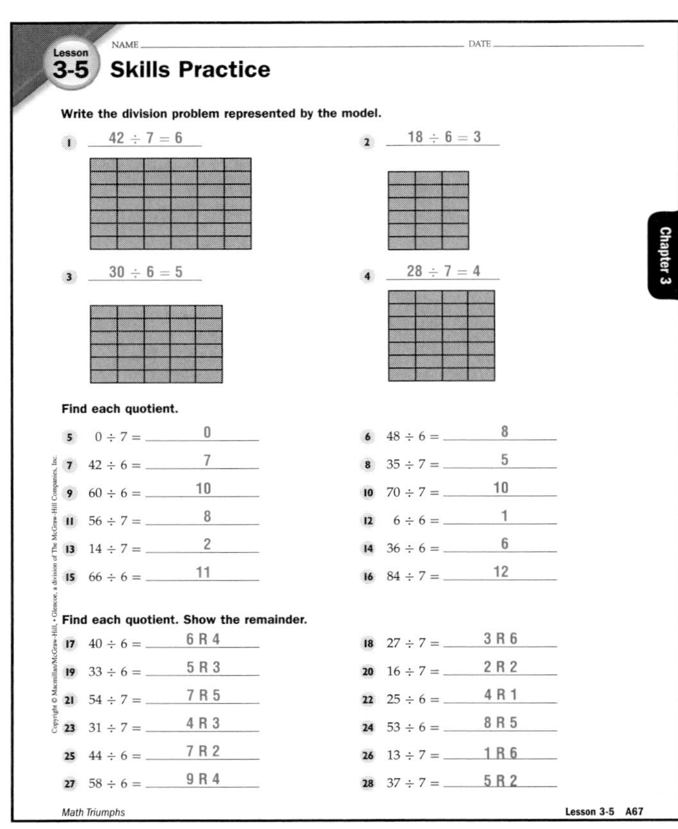

NAME ______ DATE ______

Lesson 3-5 **Skills Practice**

Write the division problem represented by the model.

1. 42 ÷ 7 = 6
2. 18 ÷ 6 = 3
3. 30 ÷ 6 = 5
4. 28 ÷ 7 = 4

Find each quotient.

5. 0 ÷ 7 = 0
6. 48 ÷ 6 = 8
7. 42 ÷ 6 = 7
8. 35 ÷ 7 = 5
9. 60 ÷ 6 = 10
10. 70 ÷ 7 = 10
11. 56 ÷ 7 = 8
12. 6 ÷ 6 = 1
13. 14 ÷ 7 = 2
14. 36 ÷ 6 = 6
15. 66 ÷ 6 = 11
16. 84 ÷ 7 = 12

Find each quotient. Show the remainder.

17. 40 ÷ 6 = 6 R 4
18. 27 ÷ 7 = 3 R 6
19. 33 ÷ 6 = 5 R 3
20. 16 ÷ 7 = 2 R 2
21. 54 ÷ 7 = 7 R 5
22. 25 ÷ 6 = 4 R 1
23. 31 ÷ 7 = 4 R 3
24. 53 ÷ 6 = 8 R 5
25. 44 ÷ 6 = 7 R 2
26. 13 ÷ 7 = 1 R 6
27. 58 ÷ 6 = 9 R 4
28. 37 ÷ 7 = 5 R 2

Chapter 3

Math Triumphs Lesson 3-5 A67

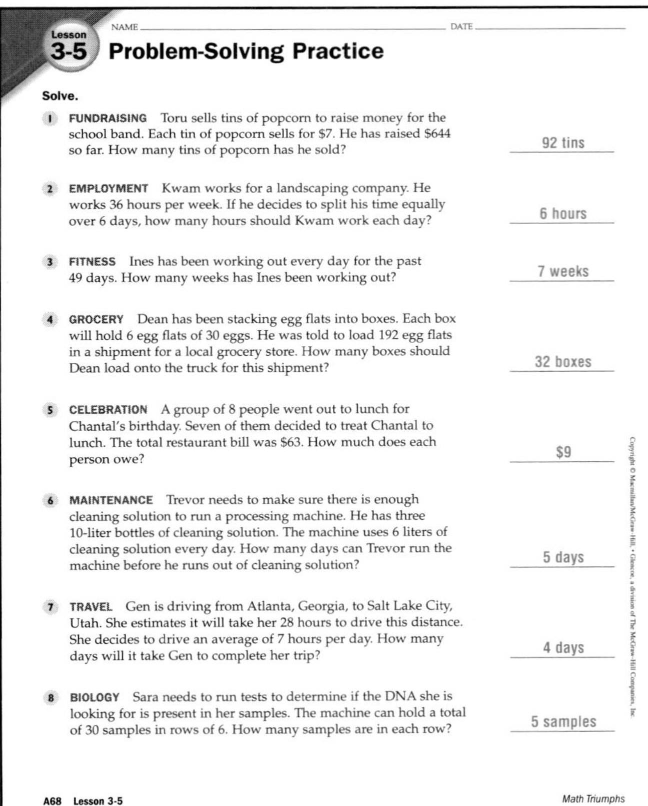

NAME ______ DATE ______

Lesson 3-5 **Problem-Solving Practice**

Solve.

1. **FUNDRAISING** Toru sells tins of popcorn to raise money for the school band. Each tin of popcorn sells for $7. He has raised $644 so far. How many tins of popcorn has he sold? 92 tins
2. **EMPLOYMENT** Kwam works for a landscaping company. He works 36 hours per week. If he decides to split his time equally over 6 days, how many hours should Kwam work each day? 6 hours
3. **FITNESS** Ines has been working out every day for the past 49 days. How many weeks has Ines been working out? 7 weeks
4. **GROCERY** Dean has been stacking egg flats into boxes. Each box will hold 6 egg flats of 30 eggs. He was told to load 192 egg flats in a shipment for a local grocery store. How many boxes should Dean load onto the truck for this shipment? 32 boxes
5. **CELEBRATION** A group of 8 people went out to lunch for Chantal's birthday. Seven of them decided to treat Chantal to lunch. The total restaurant bill was $63. How much does each person owe? $9
6. **MAINTENANCE** Trevor needs to make sure there is enough cleaning solution to run a processing machine. He has three 10-liter bottles of cleaning solution. The machine uses 6 liters of cleaning solution every day. How many days can Trevor run the machine before he runs out of cleaning solution? 5 days
7. **TRAVEL** Gen is driving from Atlanta, Georgia, to Salt Lake City, Utah. She estimates it will take her 28 hours to drive this distance. She decides to drive an average of 7 hours per day. How many days will it take Gen to complete her trip? 4 days
8. **BIOLOGY** Sara needs to run tests to determine if the DNA she is looking for is present in her samples. The machine can hold a total of 30 samples in rows of 6. How many samples are in each row? 5 samples

A68 Lesson 3-5 *Math Triumphs*

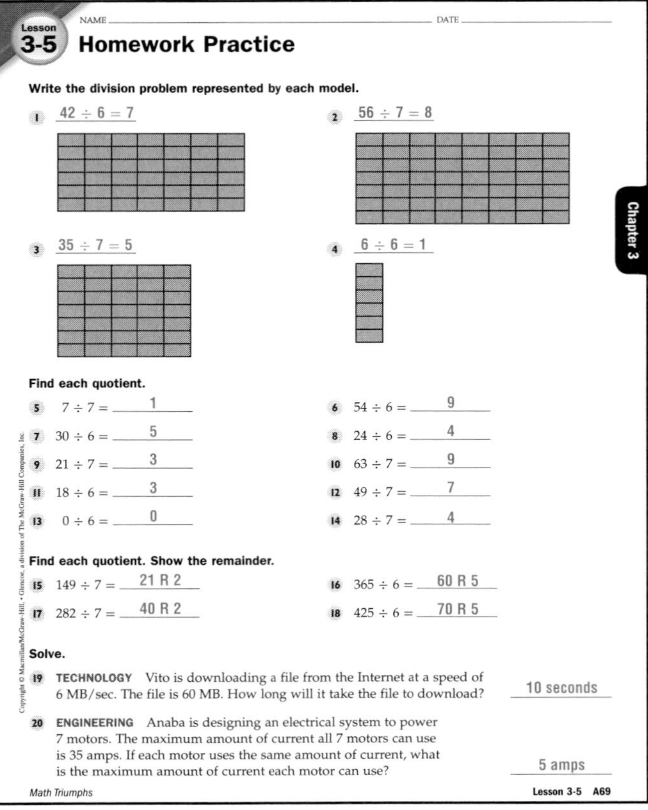

NAME ______ DATE ______

Lesson 3-5 **Homework Practice**

Write the division problem represented by each model.

1. 42 ÷ 6 = 7
2. 56 ÷ 7 = 8
3. 35 ÷ 7 = 5
4. 6 ÷ 6 = 1

Find each quotient.

5. 7 ÷ 7 = 1
6. 54 ÷ 6 = 9
7. 30 ÷ 6 = 5
8. 24 ÷ 6 = 4
9. 21 ÷ 7 = 3
10. 63 ÷ 7 = 9
11. 18 ÷ 6 = 3
12. 49 ÷ 7 = 7
13. 0 ÷ 6 = 0
14. 28 ÷ 7 = 4

Find each quotient. Show the remainder.

15. 149 ÷ 7 = 21 R 2
16. 365 ÷ 6 = 60 R 5
17. 282 ÷ 7 = 40 R 2
18. 425 ÷ 6 = 70 R 5

Solve.

19. **TECHNOLOGY** Vito is downloading a file from the Internet at a speed of 6 MB/sec. The file is 60 MB. How long will it take the file to download? 10 seconds
20. **ENGINEERING** Anaba is designing an electrical system to power 7 motors. The maximum amount of current all 7 motors can use is 35 amps. If each motor uses the same amount of current, what is the maximum amount of current each motor can use? 5 amps

Chapter 3

Math Triumphs Lesson 3-5 A69

Answer Key (Lesson 3-6)

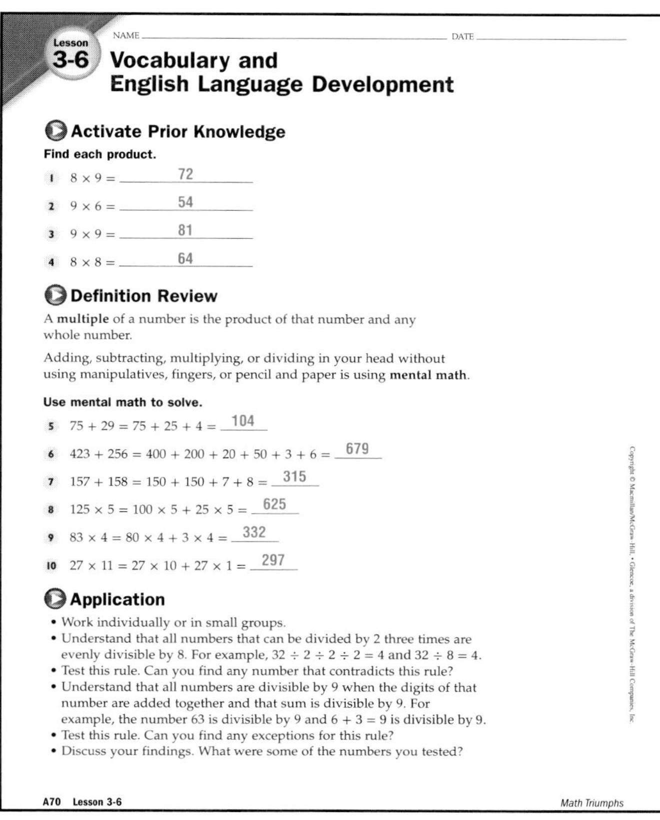

Lesson 3-6 NAME ____ DATE ____

Vocabulary and English Language Development

Activate Prior Knowledge

Find each product.

1. 8 × 9 = 72
2. 9 × 6 = 54
3. 9 × 9 = 81
4. 8 × 8 = 64

Definition Review

A **multiple** of a number is the product of that number and any whole number.

Adding, subtracting, multiplying, or dividing in your head without using manipulatives, fingers, or pencil and paper is using **mental math**.

Use mental math to solve.

5. 75 + 29 = 75 + 25 + 4 = 104
6. 423 + 256 = 400 + 200 + 20 + 50 + 3 + 6 = 679
7. 157 + 158 = 150 + 150 + 7 + 8 = 315
8. 125 × 5 = 100 × 5 + 25 × 5 = 625
9. 83 × 4 = 80 × 4 + 3 × 4 = 332
10. 27 × 11 = 27 × 10 + 27 × 1 = 297

Application

- Work individually or in small groups.
- Understand that all numbers that can be divided by 2 three times are evenly divisible by 8. For example, 32 ÷ 2 ÷ 2 ÷ 2 = 4 and 32 ÷ 8 = 4.
- Test this rule. Can you find any number that contradicts this rule?
- Understand that all numbers are divisible by 9 when the digits of that number are added together and that sum is divisible by 9. For example, the number 63 is divisible by 9 and 6 + 3 = 9 is divisible by 9.
- Test this rule. Can you find any exceptions for this rule?
- Discuss your findings. What were some of the numbers you tested?

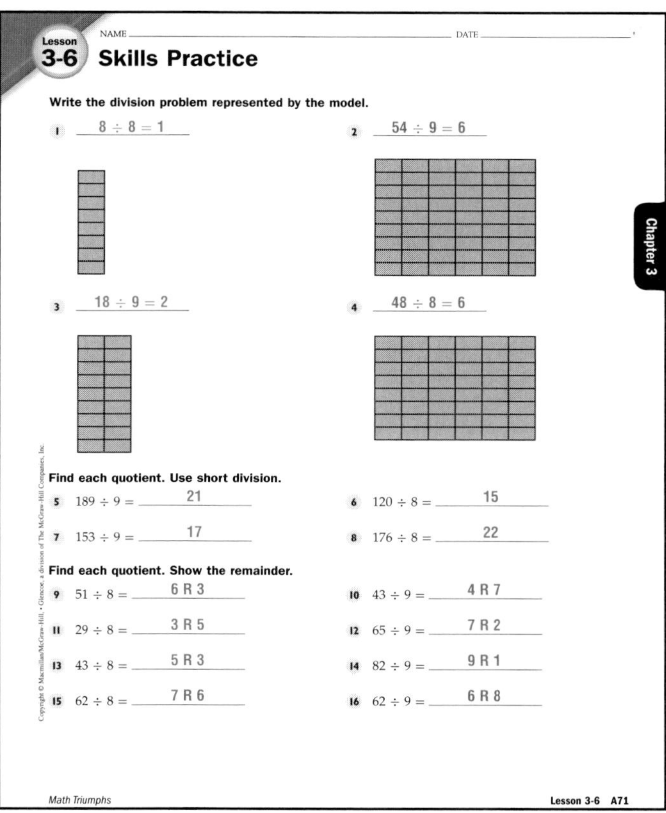

Lesson 3-6 NAME ____ DATE ____

Skills Practice

Write the division problem represented by the model.

1. 8 ÷ 8 = 1
2. 54 ÷ 9 = 6
3. 18 ÷ 9 = 2
4. 48 ÷ 8 = 6

Find each quotient. Use short division.

5. 189 ÷ 9 = 21
6. 120 ÷ 8 = 15
7. 153 ÷ 9 = 17
8. 176 ÷ 8 = 22

Find each quotient. Show the remainder.

9. 51 ÷ 8 = 6 R 3
10. 43 ÷ 9 = 4 R 7
11. 29 ÷ 8 = 3 R 5
12. 65 ÷ 9 = 7 R 2
13. 43 ÷ 8 = 5 R 3
14. 82 ÷ 9 = 9 R 1
15. 62 ÷ 8 = 7 R 6
16. 62 ÷ 9 = 6 R 8

Chapter 3

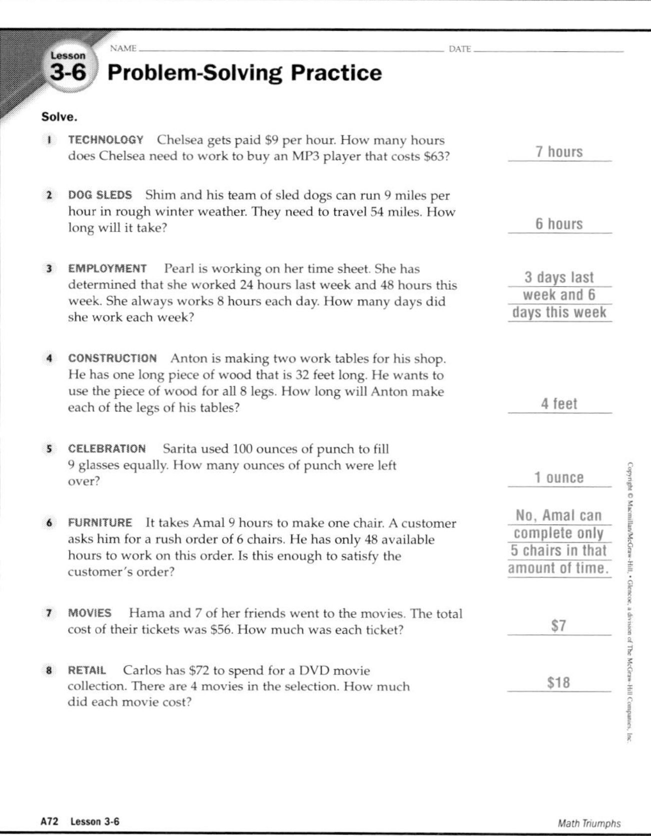

Lesson 3-6 NAME ____ DATE ____

Problem-Solving Practice

Solve.

1. **TECHNOLOGY** Chelsea gets paid $9 per hour. How many hours does Chelsea need to work to buy an MP3 player that costs $63? **7 hours**
2. **DOG SLEDS** Shim and his team of sled dogs can run 9 miles per hour in rough winter weather. They need to travel 54 miles. How long will it take? **6 hours**
3. **EMPLOYMENT** Pearl is working on her time sheet. She has determined that she worked 24 hours last week and 48 hours this week. She always works 8 hours each day. How many days did she work each week? **3 days last week and 6 days this week**
4. **CONSTRUCTION** Anton is making two work tables for his shop. He has one long piece of wood that is 32 feet long. He wants to use the piece of wood for all 8 legs. How long will Anton make each of the legs of his tables? **4 feet**
5. **CELEBRATION** Sarita used 100 ounces of punch to fill 9 glasses equally. How many ounces of punch were left over? **1 ounce**
6. **FURNITURE** It takes Amal 9 hours to make one chair. A customer asks him for a rush order of 6 chairs. He has only 48 available hours to work on this order. Is this enough to satisfy the customer's order? **No, Amal can complete only 5 chairs in that amount of time.**
7. **MOVIES** Hama and 7 of her friends went to the movies. The total cost of their tickets was $56. How much was each ticket? **$7**
8. **RETAIL** Carlos has $72 to spend for a DVD movie collection. There are 4 movies in the selection. How much did each movie cost? **$18**

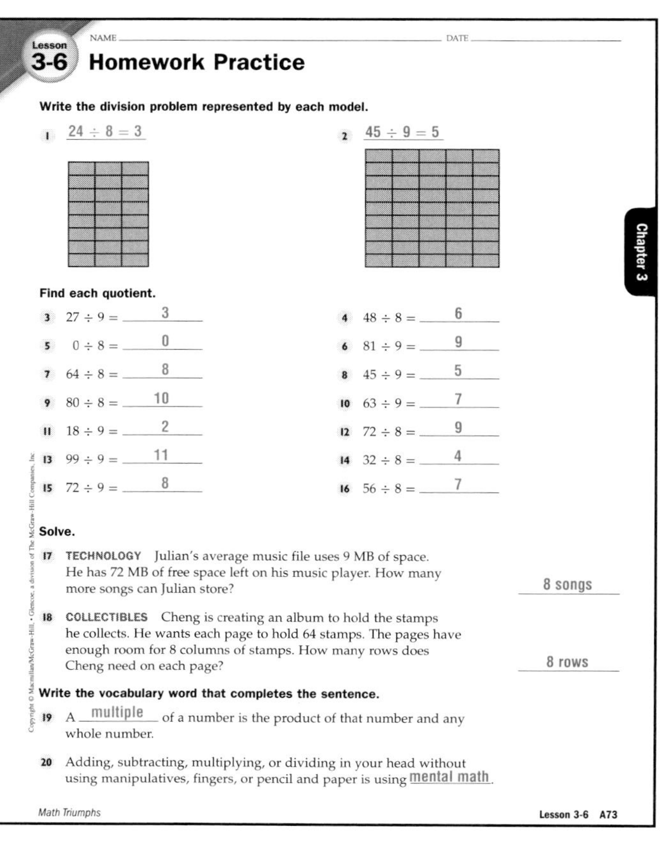

Lesson 3-6 NAME ____ DATE ____

Homework Practice

Write the division problem represented by each model.

1. 24 ÷ 8 = 3
2. 45 ÷ 9 = 5

Find each quotient.

3. 27 ÷ 9 = 3
4. 48 ÷ 8 = 6
5. 0 ÷ 8 = 0
6. 81 ÷ 9 = 9
7. 64 ÷ 8 = 8
8. 45 ÷ 9 = 5
9. 80 ÷ 8 = 10
10. 63 ÷ 9 = 7
11. 18 ÷ 9 = 2
12. 72 ÷ 8 = 9
13. 99 ÷ 9 = 11
14. 32 ÷ 8 = 4
15. 72 ÷ 9 = 8
16. 56 ÷ 8 = 7

Solve.

17. **TECHNOLOGY** Julian's average music file uses 9 MB of space. He has 72 MB of free space left on his music player. How many more songs can Julian store? **8 songs**
18. **COLLECTIBLES** Cheng is creating an album to hold the stamps he collects. He wants each page to hold 64 stamps. The pages have enough room for 8 columns of stamps. How many rows does Cheng need on each page? **8 rows**

Write the vocabulary word that completes the sentence.

19. A **multiple** of a number is the product of that number and any whole number.
20. Adding, subtracting, multiplying, or dividing in your head without using manipulatives, fingers, or pencil and paper is using **mental math**.

Chapter 3

Answer Key (Lesson 4-1)

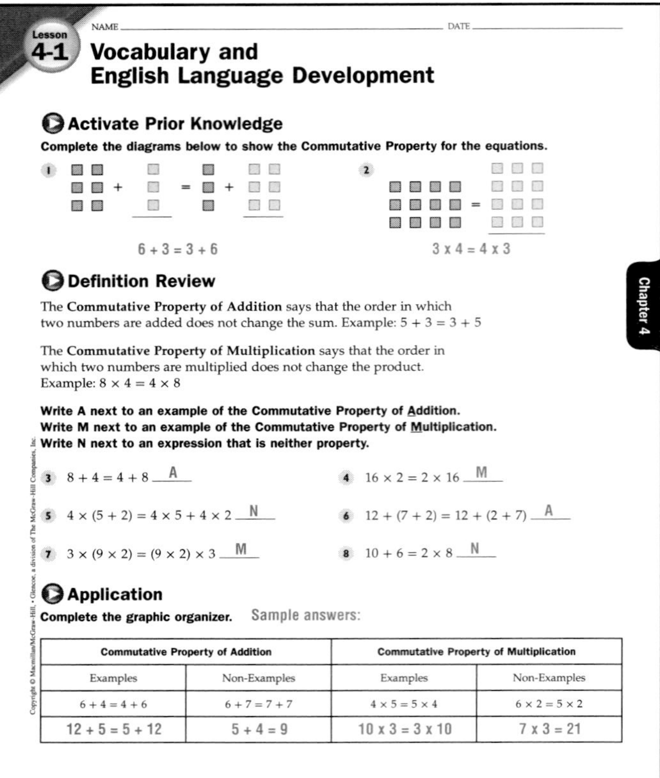

NAME ________ DATE ________

Lesson 4-1 **Vocabulary and English Language Development**

Activate Prior Knowledge

Complete the diagrams below to show the Commutative Property for the equations.

1. 6 + 3 = 3 + 6

2. 3 x 4 = 4 x 3

Definition Review

The **Commutative Property of Addition** says that the order in which two numbers are added does not change the sum. Example: 5 + 3 = 3 + 5

The **Commutative Property of Multiplication** says that the order in which two numbers are multiplied does not change the product. Example: 8 × 4 = 4 × 8

Write A next to an example of the Commutative Property of Addition.
Write M next to an example of the Commutative Property of Multiplication.
Write N next to an expression that is neither property.

3. 8 + 4 = 4 + 8 A
4. 16 × 2 = 2 × 16 M
5. 4 × (5 + 2) = 4 × 5 + 4 × 2 N
6. 12 + (7 + 2) = 12 + (2 + 7) A
7. 3 × (9 × 2) = (9 × 2) × 3 M
8. 10 + 6 = 2 × 8 N

Application

Complete the graphic organizer. Sample answers:

Commutative Property of Addition		Commutative Property of Multiplication	
Examples	Non-Examples	Examples	Non-Examples
6 + 4 = 4 + 6	6 + 7 = 7 + 7	4 × 5 = 5 × 4	6 × 2 = 5 × 2
12 + 5 = 5 + 12	5 + 4 = 9	10 x 3 = 3 x 10	7 x 3 = 21

Chapter 4

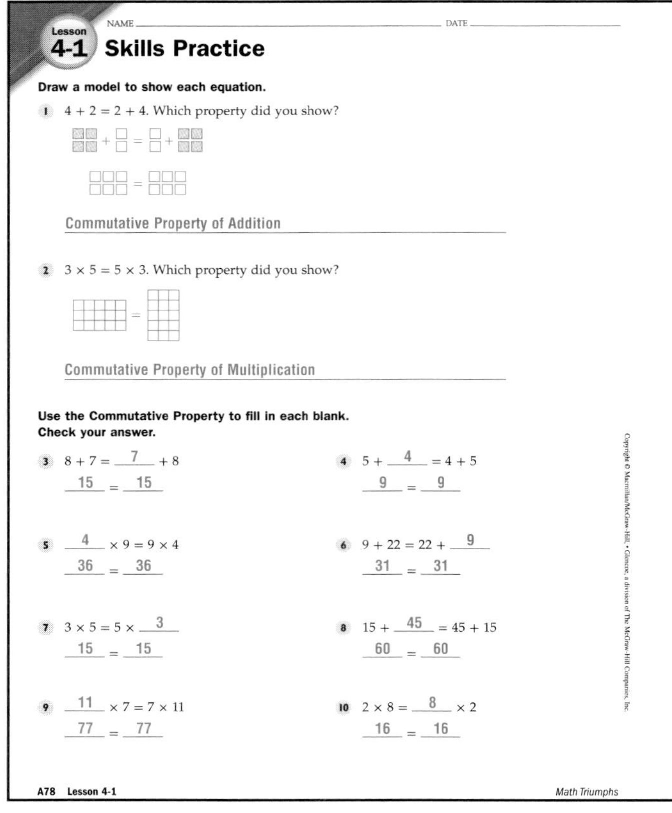

NAME ________ DATE ________

Lesson 4-1 **Skills Practice**

Draw a model to show each equation.

1. 4 + 2 = 2 + 4. Which property did you show?
Commutative Property of Addition

2. 3 × 5 = 5 × 3. Which property did you show?
Commutative Property of Multiplication

Use the Commutative Property to fill in each blank.
Check your answer.

3. 8 + 7 = 7 + 8; 15 = 15
4. 5 + 4 = 4 + 5; 9 = 9
5. 4 × 9 = 9 × 4; 36 = 36
6. 9 + 22 = 22 + 9; 31 = 31
7. 3 × 5 = 5 × 3; 15 = 15
8. 15 + 45 = 45 + 15; 60 = 60
9. 11 × 7 = 7 × 11; 77 = 77
10. 2 × 8 = 8 × 2; 16 = 16

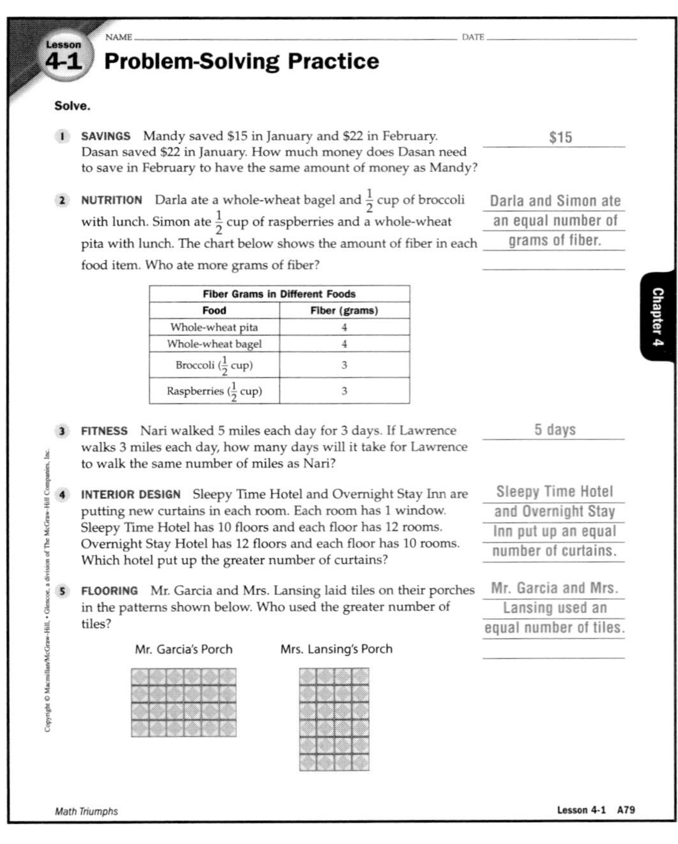

NAME ________ DATE ________

Lesson 4-1 **Problem-Solving Practice**

Solve.

1. **SAVINGS** Mandy saved \$15 in January and \$22 in February. Dasan saved \$22 in January. How much money does Dasan need to save in February to have the same amount of money as Mandy? \$15

2. **NUTRITION** Darla ate a whole-wheat bagel and $\frac{1}{2}$ cup of broccoli with lunch. Simon ate $\frac{1}{2}$ cup of raspberries and a whole-wheat pita with lunch. The chart below shows the amount of fiber in each food item. Who ate more grams of fiber? Darla and Simon ate an equal number of grams of fiber.

Fiber Grams in Different Foods	
Food	Fiber (grams)
Whole-wheat pita	4
Whole-wheat bagel	4
Broccoli ($\frac{1}{2}$ cup)	3
Raspberries ($\frac{1}{2}$ cup)	3

3. **FITNESS** Nari walked 5 miles each day for 3 days. If Lawrence walks 3 miles each day, how many days will it take for Lawrence to walk the same number of miles as Nari? 5 days

4. **INTERIOR DESIGN** Sleepy Time Hotel and Overnight Stay Inn are putting new curtains in each room. Each room has 1 window. Sleepy Time Hotel has 10 floors and each floor has 12 rooms. Overnight Stay Hotel has 12 floors and each floor has 10 rooms. Which hotel put up the greater number of curtains? Sleepy Time Hotel and Overnight Stay Inn put up an equal number of curtains.

5. **FLOORING** Mr. Garcia and Mrs. Lansing laid tiles on their porches in the patterns shown below. Who used the greater number of tiles? Mr. Garcia and Mrs. Lansing used an equal number of tiles.

Mr. Garcia's Porch Mrs. Lansing's Porch

Chapter 4

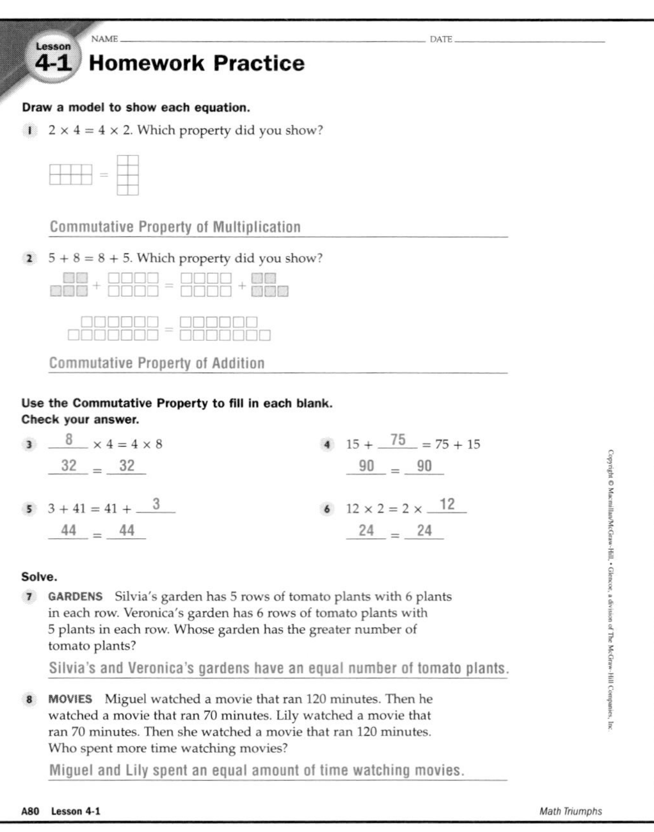

NAME ________ DATE ________

Lesson 4-1 **Homework Practice**

Draw a model to show each equation.

1. 2 × 4 = 4 × 2. Which property did you show?
Commutative Property of Multiplication

2. 5 + 8 = 8 + 5. Which property did you show?
Commutative Property of Addition

Use the Commutative Property to fill in each blank.
Check your answer.

3. 8 × 4 = 4 × 8; 32 = 32
4. 15 + 75 = 75 + 15; 90 = 90
5. 3 + 41 = 41 + 3; 44 = 44
6. 12 × 2 = 2 × 12; 24 = 24

Solve.

7. **GARDENS** Silvia's garden has 5 rows of tomato plants with 6 plants in each row. Veronica's garden has 6 rows of tomato plants with 5 plants in each row. Whose garden has the greater number of tomato plants?
Silvia's and Veronica's gardens have an equal number of tomato plants.

8. **MOVIES** Miguel watched a movie that ran 120 minutes. Then he watched a movie that ran 70 minutes. Lily watched a movie that ran 70 minutes. Then she watched a movie that ran 120 minutes. Who spent more time watching movies?
Miguel and Lily spent an equal amount of time watching movies.

Answer Key (Lesson 4-2)

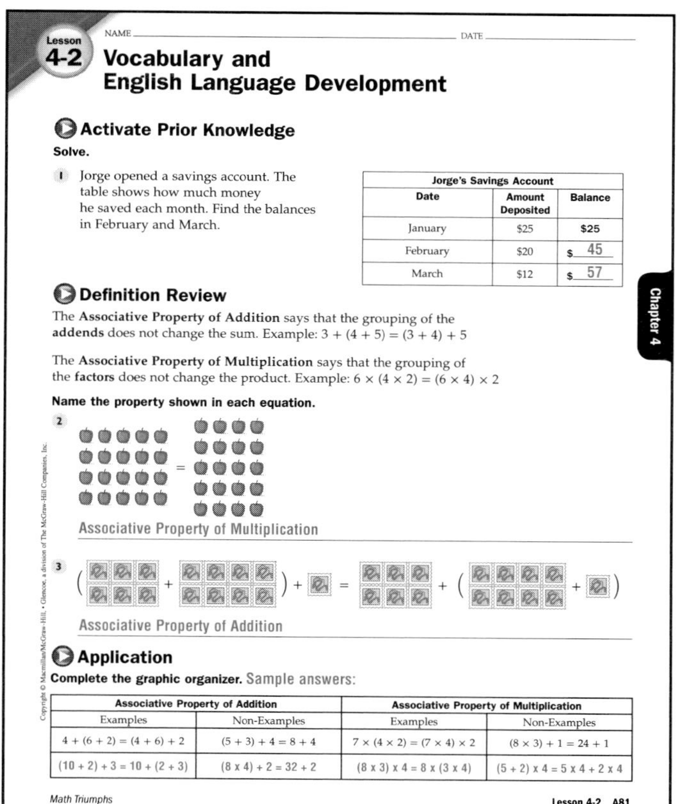

Lesson 4-2 NAME ________ DATE ________

Vocabulary and English Language Development

Activate Prior Knowledge

Solve.

1 Jorge opened a savings account. The table shows how much money he saved each month. Find the balances in February and March.

Jorge's Savings Account		
Date	Amount Deposited	Balance
January	$25	$25
February	$20	$ 45
March	$12	$ 57

Definition Review

The **Associative Property of Addition** says that the grouping of the **addends** does not change the sum. Example: 3 + (4 + 5) = (3 + 4) + 5

The **Associative Property of Multiplication** says that the grouping of the **factors** does not change the product. Example: 6 × (4 × 2) = (6 × 4) × 2

Name the property shown in each equation.

2 Associative Property of Multiplication

3 Associative Property of Addition

Application

Complete the graphic organizer. Sample answers:

Associative Property of Addition		Associative Property of Multiplication	
Examples	Non-Examples	Examples	Non-Examples
4 + (6 + 2) = (4 + 6) + 2	(5 + 3) + 4 = 8 + 4	7 × (4 × 2) = (7 × 4) × 2	(8 × 3) + 1 = 24 + 1
(10 + 2) + 3 = 10 + (2 + 3)	(8 x 4) + 2 = 32 + 2	(8 x 3) x 4 = 8 x (3 x 4)	(5 + 2) x 4 = 5 x 4 + 2 x 4

Chapter 4

Math Triumphs Lesson 4-2 A81

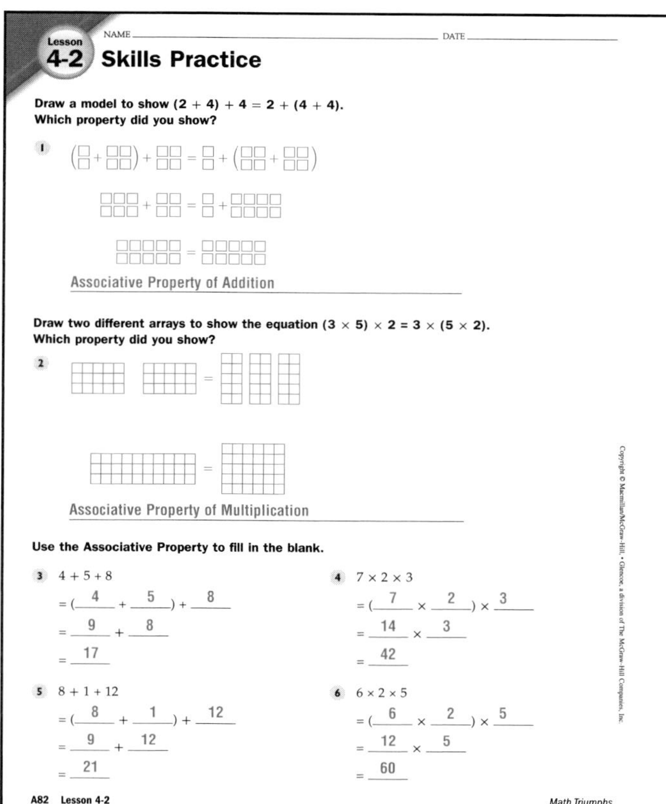

Lesson 4-2 NAME ________ DATE ________

Skills Practice

Draw a model to show (2 + 4) + 4 = 2 + (4 + 4). Which property did you show?

1 Associative Property of Addition

Draw two different arrays to show the equation (3 × 5) × 2 = 3 × (5 × 2). Which property did you show?

2 Associative Property of Multiplication

Use the Associative Property to fill in the blank.

3 4 + 5 + 8
= (4 + 5) + 8
= 9 + 8
= 17

4 7 × 2 × 3
= (7 × 2) × 3
= 14 × 3
= 42

5 8 + 1 + 12
= (8 + 1) + 12
= 9 + 12
= 21

6 6 × 2 × 5
= (6 × 2) × 5
= 12 × 5
= 60

A82 Lesson 4-2 Math Triumphs

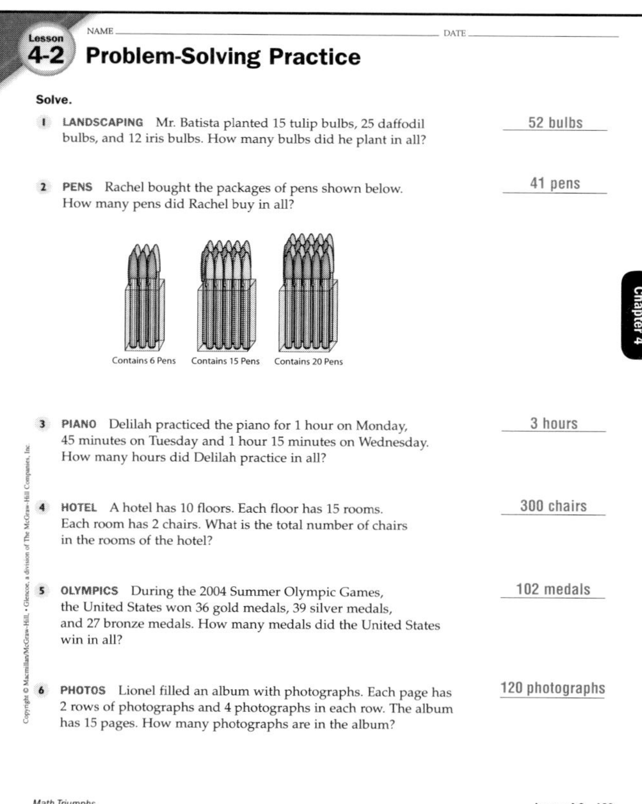

Lesson 4-2 NAME ________ DATE ________

Problem-Solving Practice

Solve.

1 **LANDSCAPING** Mr. Batista planted 15 tulip bulbs, 25 daffodil bulbs, and 12 iris bulbs. How many bulbs did he plant in all? 52 bulbs

2 **PENS** Rachel bought the packages of pens shown below. How many pens did Rachel buy in all? 41 pens

Contains 6 Pens Contains 15 Pens Contains 20 Pens

3 **PIANO** Delilah practiced the piano for 1 hour on Monday, 45 minutes on Tuesday and 1 hour 15 minutes on Wednesday. How many hours did Delilah practice in all? 3 hours

4 **HOTEL** A hotel has 10 floors. Each floor has 15 rooms. Each room has 2 chairs. What is the total number of chairs in the rooms of the hotel? 300 chairs

5 **OLYMPICS** During the 2004 Summer Olympic Games, the United States won 36 gold medals, 39 silver medals, and 27 bronze medals. How many medals did the United States win in all? 102 medals

6 **PHOTOS** Lionel filled an album with photographs. Each page has 2 rows of photographs and 4 photographs in each row. The album has 15 pages. How many photographs are in the album? 120 photographs

Chapter 4

Math Triumphs Lesson 4-2 A83

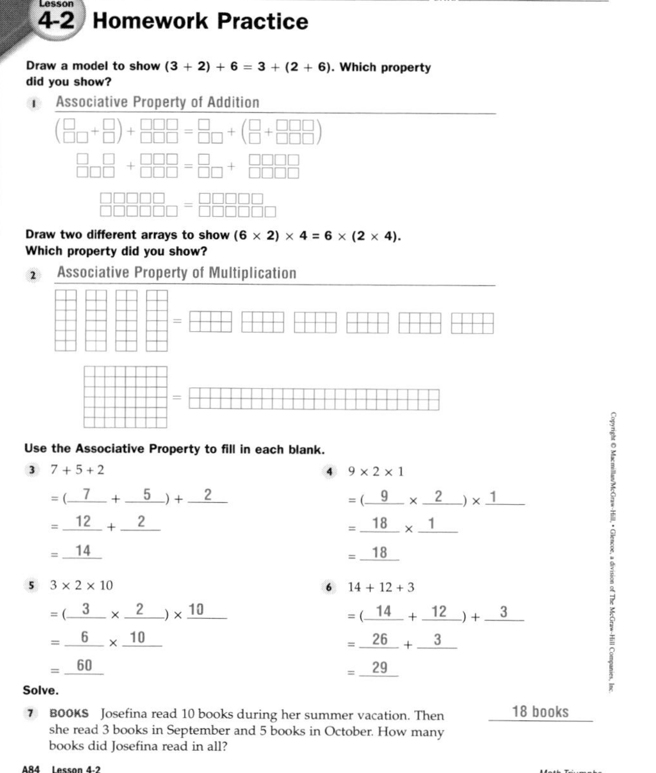

Lesson 4-2 NAME ________ DATE ________

Homework Practice

Draw a model to show (3 + 2) + 6 = 3 + (2 + 6). Which property did you show?

1 Associative Property of Addition

Draw two different arrays to show (6 × 2) × 4 = 6 × (2 × 4). Which property did you show?

2 Associative Property of Multiplication

Use the Associative Property to fill in each blank.

3 7 + 5 + 2
= (7 + 5) + 2
= 12 + 2
= 14

4 9 × 2 × 1
= (9 × 2) × 1
= 18 × 1
= 18

5 3 × 2 × 10
= (3 × 2) × 10
= 6 × 10
= 60

6 14 + 12 + 3
= (14 + 12) + 3
= 26 + 3
= 29

Solve.

7 **BOOKS** Josefina read 10 books during her summer vacation. Then she read 3 books in September and 5 books in October. How many books did Josefina read in all? 18 books

A84 Lesson 4-2 Math Triumphs

Answer Key (Lesson 4-3)

Lesson 4-3 NAME ______ DATE ______

Vocabulary and English Language Development

Activate Prior Knowledge

Complete the diagram below to model how the Distributive Property can be used to simplify 5 × (10 + 3).

10 + 3 = 13 Squares

5 × 10 + 5 × 3 = 5 × 13

50 + 15 = 65 Squares

Definition Review

The **Distributive Property of Multiplication** says that to **multiply** a **sum** by a number, you can **multiply** each addend by the number and add the products.

1 Shown below is an example of the Distributive Property.

$16 \times (6 + 2) = 128$

$16 \times 6 + 16 \times 2 = 128$

2 Fill in the blanks to show the Distributive Property.

$8 \times (9 + 6) = 120$

8 × 9 + 8 × 6 = 120

Application

- Gather 30 counters, 10 in one color and 20 in another color.
- Using the Distributive Property, arrange the counters on your desk to demonstrate the following expressions. You can use different colors to represent each addend.
  - 2 × (7 + 1)
  - 3 × (2 + 4)
  - 5 × (2 + 4)
  - 4 × (4 + 2)
  - 3 × (6 + 3)
  - 6 × (1 + 2)

Chapter 4

Lesson 4-3 NAME ______ DATE ______

Skills Practice

Use the Distributive Property and a model to find each product.

1 13 × 4 = 52

4(13) =
4(10 + 3) =
4 x 10 + 4 x 3 =
40 + 12 = 52

2 16 × 5 = 80

5(16) =
5(10 + 6) =
5 x 10 + 5 x 6 =
50 + 30 = 80

Use the Distributive Property to find each product.

3 3(4 + 8)
= 12 + 24
= 36

4 4(5 + 7)
= 20 + 28
= 48

5 10(12 + 2)
= 120 + 20
= 140

6 9(3 − 1)
= 27 − 9
= 18

7 9(11 − 5)
= 99 − 45
= 54

8 2(15 + 4)
= 30 + 8
= 38

9 8(3 + 11)
= 24 + 88
= 112

10 7(14 − 9)
= 98 − 63
= 35

Lesson 4-3 NAME ______ DATE ______

Problem-Solving Practice

Solve.

1 **GARDEN** A farmer plants tomato plants using the plan shown below. How many tomato plants does she plant in all? 90 tomato plants

2 **FOOTBALL** A football team scored 4 touchdowns (each worth 6 points) and 4 extra points (each worth 1 point). How many total points did the football team score? 28 points

3 **KNITTING** Lavelle knitted 12 scarves and 12 hats. Each scarf used 300 yards of yarn. Each hat used 150 yards of yarn. How many yards of yarn did Lavelle use in all? 5,400 yards

4 **FITNESS** Alano jogged 16 miles each week for 3 weeks, then he jogged 20 miles each week for 3 weeks. How many miles did Alano jog in all? 108 miles

5 **BASKETBALL** Willa made four 2-point baskets in the basketball game. Jenna made five 2-point baskets in the game. How many points did Willa and Jenna score in all? 18 points

6 **SAVINGS** Larisa saved $10 each month for 3 months. Then she saved $15 each month for 3 months. She wants to buy a digital camera that costs $100. How much more money does Larisa need to save? $25

7 **FLOORING** Mrs. Bateman is putting tiles on her kitchen floor in the design shown below. How many tiles does she need to buy? 65 tiles

Chapter 4

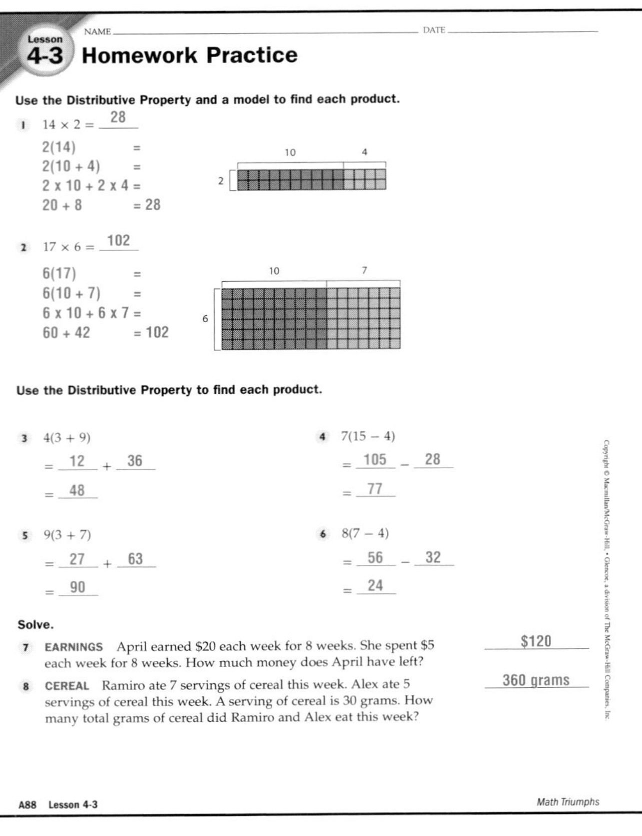

Lesson 4-3 NAME ______ DATE ______

Homework Practice

Use the Distributive Property and a model to find each product.

1 14 × 2 = 28

2(14) =
2(10 + 4) =
2 x 10 + 2 x 4 =
20 + 8 = 28

2 17 × 6 = 102

6(17) =
6(10 + 7) =
6 x 10 + 6 x 7 =
60 + 42 = 102

Use the Distributive Property to find each product.

3 4(3 + 9)
= 12 + 36
= 48

4 7(15 − 4)
= 105 − 28
= 77

5 9(3 + 7)
= 27 + 63
= 90

6 8(7 − 4)
= 56 − 32
= 24

Solve.

7 **EARNINGS** April earned $20 each week for 8 weeks. She spent $5 each week for 8 weeks. How much money does April have left? $120

8 **CEREAL** Ramiro ate 7 servings of cereal this week. Alex ate 5 servings of cereal this week. A serving of cereal is 30 grams. How many total grams of cereal did Ramiro and Alex eat this week? 360 grams

Answer Key (Lesson 4-4)

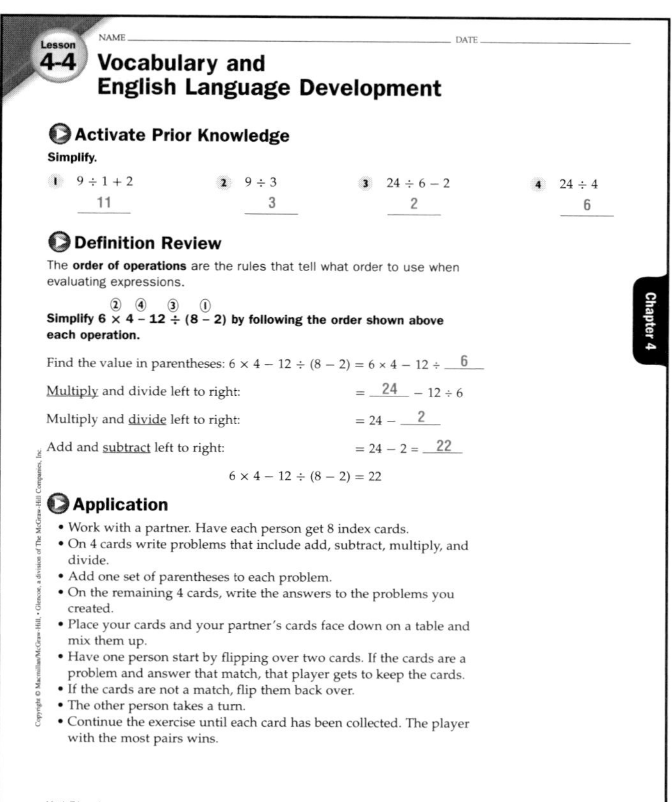

Lesson 4-4 NAME ________ DATE ________

Vocabulary and English Language Development

Activate Prior Knowledge

Simplify.

1. 9 ÷ 1 + 2 **11**
2. 9 ÷ 3 **3**
3. 24 ÷ 6 − 2 **2**
4. 24 ÷ 4 **6**

Definition Review

The **order of operations** are the rules that tell what order to use when evaluating expressions.

Simplify 6 × 4 − 12 ÷ (8 − 2) by following the order shown above each operation. (② ④ ③ ①)

Find the value in parentheses: 6 × 4 − 12 ÷ (8 − 2) = 6 × 4 − 12 ÷ **6**

Multiply and divide left to right: = **24** − 12 ÷ 6

Multiply and divide left to right: = 24 − **2**

Add and subtract left to right: = 24 − 2 = **22**

6 × 4 − 12 ÷ (8 − 2) = 22

Application

- Work with a partner. Have each person get 8 index cards.
- On 4 cards write problems that include add, subtract, multiply, and divide.
- Add one set of parentheses to each problem.
- On the remaining 4 cards, write the answers to the problems you created.
- Place your cards and your partner's cards face down on a table and mix them up.
- Have one person start by flipping over two cards. If the cards are a problem and answer that match, that player gets to keep the cards.
- If the cards are not a match, flip them back over.
- The other person takes a turn.
- Continue the exercise until each card has been collected. The player with the most pairs wins.

Chapter 4

Math Triumphs Lesson 4-4 A89

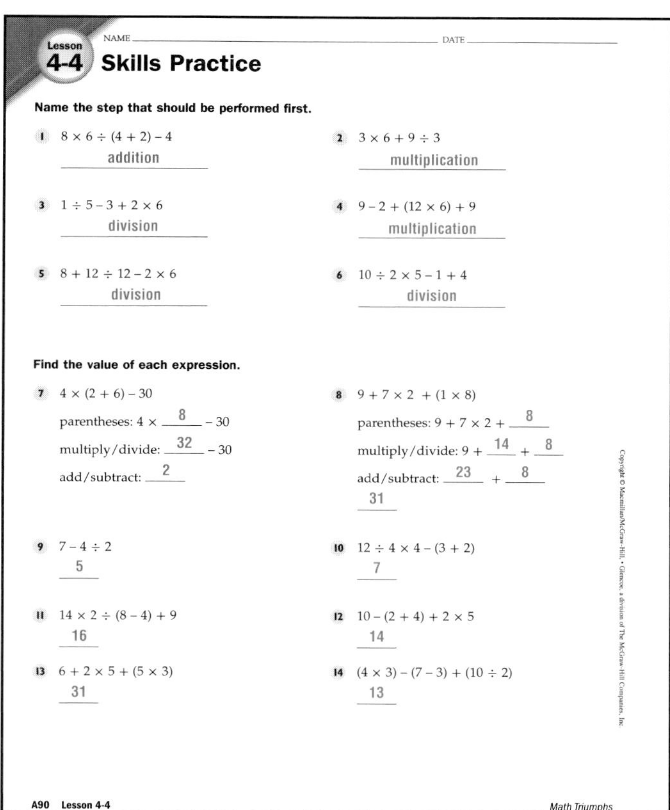

Lesson 4-4 NAME ________ DATE ________

Skills Practice

Name the step that should be performed first.

1. 8 × 6 ÷ (4 + 2) − 4 **addition**
2. 3 × 6 + 9 ÷ 3 **multiplication**
3. 1 ÷ 5 − 3 + 2 × 6 **division**
4. 9 − 2 + (12 × 6) + 9 **multiplication**
5. 8 + 12 ÷ 12 − 2 × 6 **division**
6. 10 ÷ 2 × 5 − 1 + 4 **division**

Find the value of each expression.

7. 4 × (2 + 6) − 30
   parentheses: 4 × **8** − 30
   multiply/divide: **32** − 30
   add/subtract: **2**
8. 9 + 7 × 2 + (1 × 8)
   parentheses: 9 + 7 × 2 + **8**
   multiply/divide: 9 + **14** + **8**
   add/subtract: **23** + **8**
   31
9. 7 − 4 ÷ 2 **5**
10. 12 ÷ 4 × 4 − (3 + 2) **7**
11. 14 × 2 ÷ (8 − 4) + 9 **16**
12. 10 − (2 + 4) + 2 × 5 **14**
13. 6 + 2 × 5 + (5 × 3) **31**
14. (4 × 3) − (7 − 3) + (10 ÷ 2) **13**

A90 Lesson 4-4 Math Triumphs

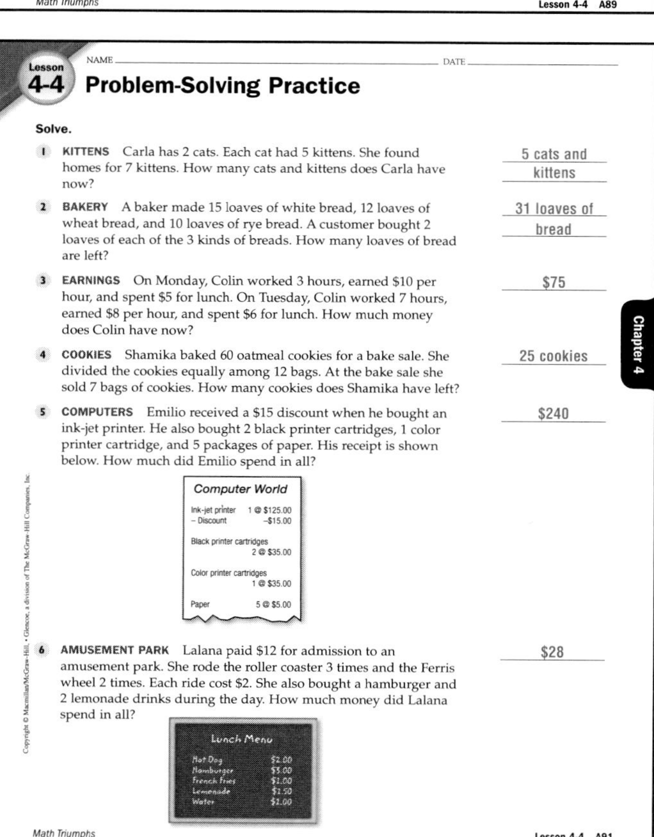

Lesson 4-4 NAME ________ DATE ________

Problem-Solving Practice

Solve.

1. **KITTENS** Carla has 2 cats. Each cat had 5 kittens. She found homes for 7 kittens. How many cats and kittens does Carla have now? **5 cats and kittens**
2. **BAKERY** A baker made 15 loaves of white bread, 12 loaves of wheat bread, and 10 loaves of rye bread. A customer bought 2 loaves of each of the 3 kinds of breads. How many loaves of bread are left? **31 loaves of bread**
3. **EARNINGS** On Monday, Colin worked 3 hours, earned $10 per hour, and spent $5 for lunch. On Tuesday, Colin worked 7 hours, earned $8 per hour, and spent $6 for lunch. How much money does Colin have now? **$75**
4. **COOKIES** Shamika baked 60 oatmeal cookies for a bake sale. She divided the cookies equally among 12 bags. At the bake sale she sold 7 bags of cookies. How many cookies does Shamika have left? **25 cookies**
5. **COMPUTERS** Emilio received a $15 discount when he bought an ink-jet printer. He also bought 2 black printer cartridges, 1 color printer cartridge, and 5 packages of paper. His receipt is shown below. How much did Emilio spend in all? **$240**

6. **AMUSEMENT PARK** Lalana paid $12 for admission to an amusement park. She rode the roller coaster 3 times and the Ferris wheel 2 times. Each ride cost $2. She also bought a hamburger and 2 lemonade drinks during the day. How much money did Lalana spend in all? **$28**

Chapter 4

Math Triumphs Lesson 4-4 A91

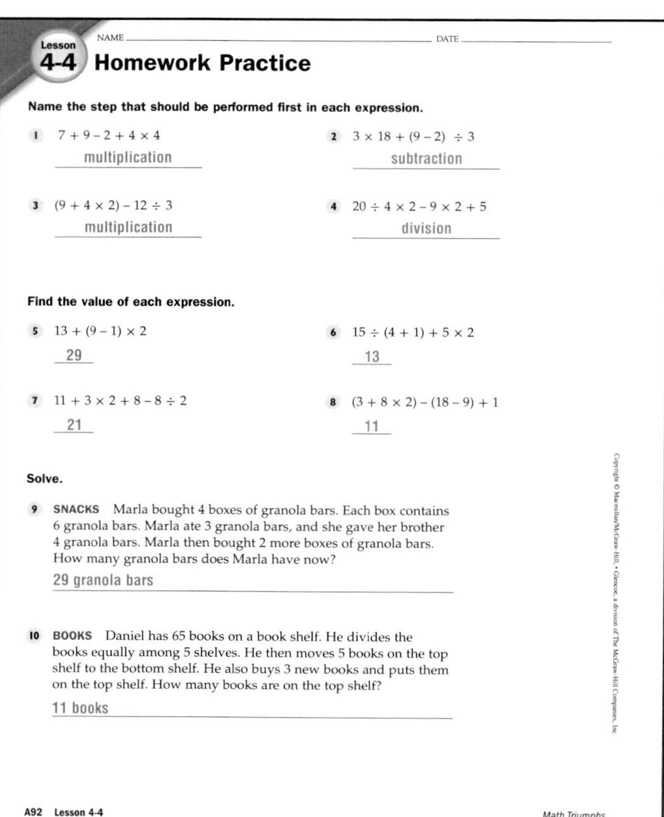

Lesson 4-4 NAME ________ DATE ________

Homework Practice

Name the step that should be performed first in each expression.

1. 7 + 9 − 2 + 4 × 4 **multiplication**
2. 3 × 18 + (9 − 2) ÷ 3 **subtraction**
3. (9 + 4 × 2) − 12 ÷ 3 **multiplication**
4. 20 ÷ 4 × 2 − 9 × 2 + 5 **division**

Find the value of each expression.

5. 13 + (9 − 1) × 2 **29**
6. 15 ÷ (4 + 1) + 5 × 2 **13**
7. 11 + 3 × 2 + 8 − 8 ÷ 2 **21**
8. (3 + 8 × 2) − (18 − 9) + 1 **11**

Solve.

9. **SNACKS** Marla bought 4 boxes of granola bars. Each box contains 6 granola bars. Marla ate 3 granola bars, and she gave her brother 4 granola bars. Marla then bought 2 more boxes of granola bars. How many granola bars does Marla have now? **29 granola bars**
10. **BOOKS** Daniel has 65 books on a book shelf. He divides the books equally among 5 shelves. He then moves 5 books on the top shelf to the bottom shelf. He also buys 3 new books and puts them on the top shelf. How many books are on the top shelf? **11 books**

A92 Lesson 4-4 Math Triumphs

Answer Key (Lesson 5-1)

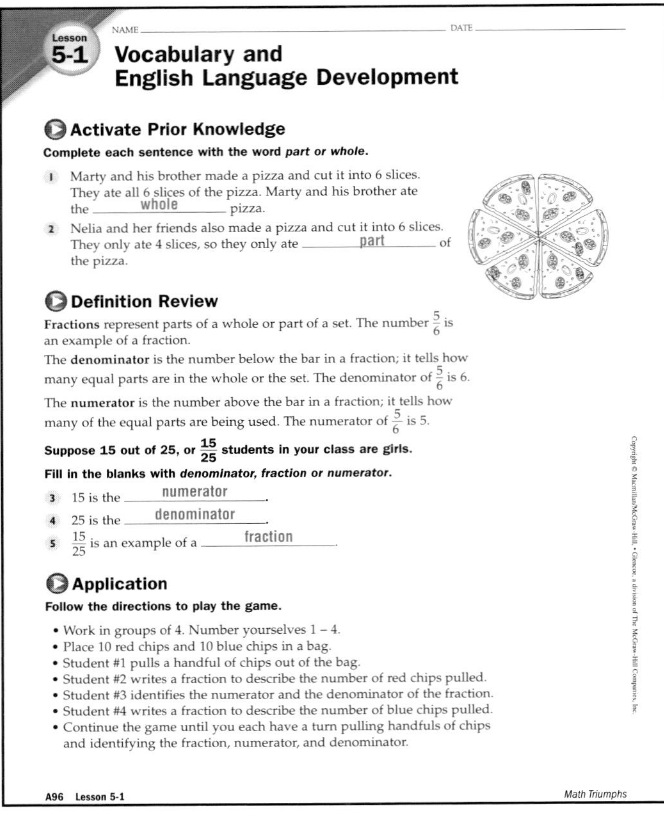

Lesson 5-1 NAME ______ DATE ______

Vocabulary and English Language Development

Activate Prior Knowledge

Complete each sentence with the word *part* or *whole*.

1 Marty and his brother made a pizza and cut it into 6 slices. They ate all 6 slices of the pizza. Marty and his brother ate the ___whole___ pizza.

2 Nelia and her friends also made a pizza and cut it into 6 slices. They only ate 4 slices, so they only ate ___part___ of the pizza.

Definition Review

Fractions represent parts of a whole or part of a set. The number $\frac{5}{6}$ is an example of a fraction.

The **denominator** is the number below the bar in a fraction; it tells how many equal parts are in the whole or the set. The denominator of $\frac{5}{6}$ is 6.

The **numerator** is the number above the bar in a fraction; it tells how many of the equal parts are being used. The numerator of $\frac{5}{6}$ is 5.

Suppose 15 out of 25, or $\frac{15}{25}$ students in your class are girls.

Fill in the blanks with *denominator, fraction or numerator.*

3 15 is the ___numerator___.

4 25 is the ___denominator___.

5 $\frac{15}{25}$ is an example of a ___fraction___.

Application

Follow the directions to play the game.

- Work in groups of 4. Number yourselves 1 – 4.
- Place 10 red chips and 10 blue chips in a bag.
- Student #1 pulls a handful of chips out of the bag.
- Student #2 writes a fraction to describe the number of red chips pulled.
- Student #3 identifies the numerator and the denominator of the fraction.
- Student #4 writes a fraction to describe the number of blue chips pulled.
- Continue the game until you each have a turn pulling handfuls of chips and identifying the fraction, numerator, and denominator.

A96 Lesson 5-1 *Math Triumphs*

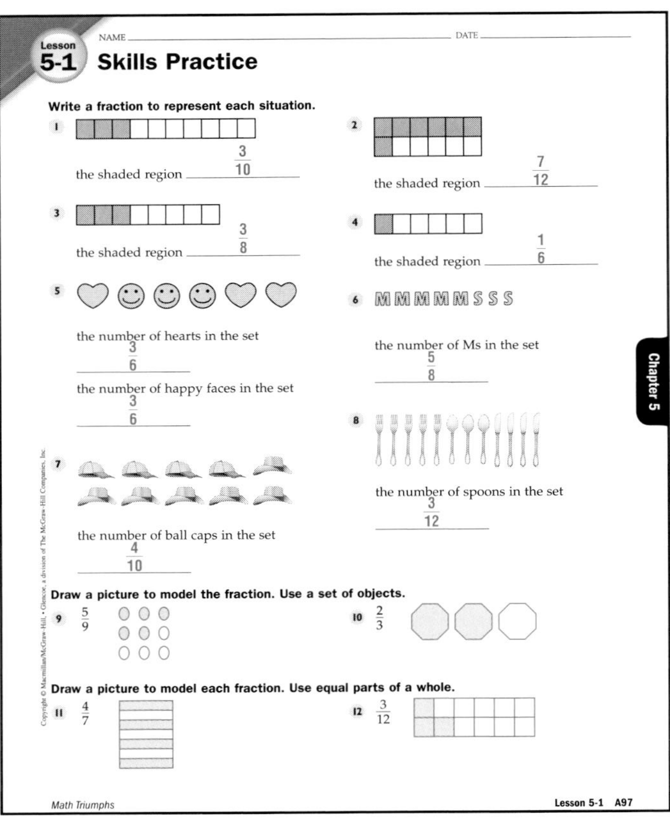

Lesson 5-1 NAME ______ DATE ______

Skills Practice

Write a fraction to represent each situation.

1 the shaded region ___$\frac{3}{10}$___

2 the shaded region ___$\frac{7}{12}$___

3 the shaded region ___$\frac{3}{8}$___

4 the shaded region ___$\frac{1}{6}$___

5 the number of hearts in the set ___$\frac{3}{6}$___

the number of happy faces in the set ___$\frac{3}{6}$___

6 M M M M M S S S

the number of Ms in the set ___$\frac{5}{8}$___

7 the number of ball caps in the set ___$\frac{4}{10}$___

8 the number of spoons in the set ___$\frac{3}{12}$___

Draw a picture to model the fraction. Use a set of objects.

9 $\frac{5}{9}$

10 $\frac{2}{3}$

Draw a picture to model each fraction. Use equal parts of a whole.

11 $\frac{4}{7}$

12 $\frac{3}{12}$

Math Triumphs Lesson 5-1 A97

Chapter 5

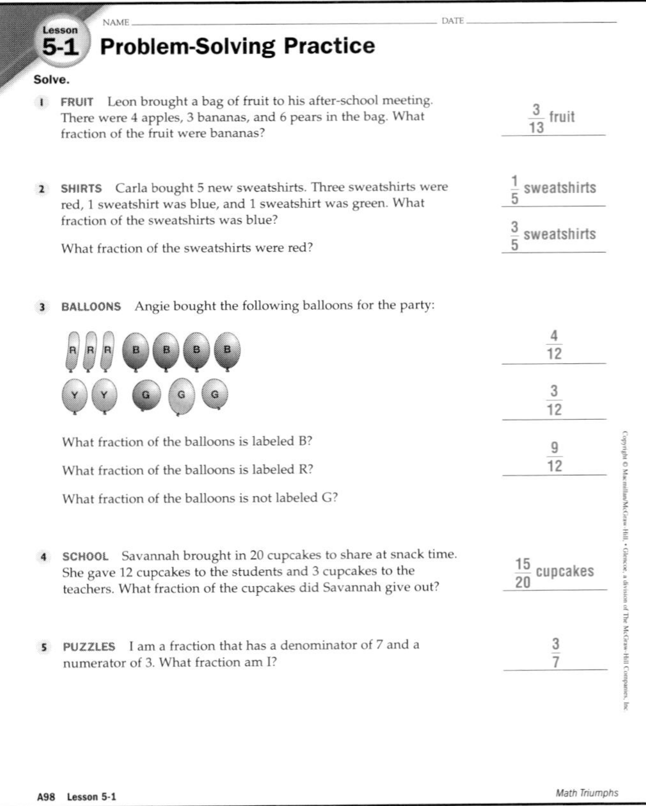

Lesson 5-1 NAME ______ DATE ______

Problem-Solving Practice

Solve.

1 **FRUIT** Leon brought a bag of fruit to his after-school meeting. There were 4 apples, 3 bananas, and 6 pears in the bag. What fraction of the fruit were bananas? ___$\frac{3}{13}$ fruit___

2 **SHIRTS** Carla bought 5 new sweatshirts. Three sweatshirts were red, 1 sweatshirt was blue, and 1 sweatshirt was green. What fraction of the sweatshirts was blue? ___$\frac{1}{5}$ sweatshirts___

What fraction of the sweatshirts were red? ___$\frac{3}{5}$ sweatshirts___

3 **BALLOONS** Angie bought the following balloons for the party:

R R R B B B B
Y Y G G G

What fraction of the balloons is labeled B? ___$\frac{4}{12}$___

What fraction of the balloons is labeled R? ___$\frac{3}{12}$___

What fraction of the balloons is not labeled G? ___$\frac{9}{12}$___

4 **SCHOOL** Savannah brought in 20 cupcakes to share at snack time. She gave 12 cupcakes to the students and 3 cupcakes to the teachers. What fraction of the cupcakes did Savannah give out? ___$\frac{15}{20}$ cupcakes___

5 **PUZZLES** I am a fraction that has a denominator of 7 and a numerator of 3. What fraction am I? ___$\frac{3}{7}$___

A98 Lesson 5-1 *Math Triumphs*

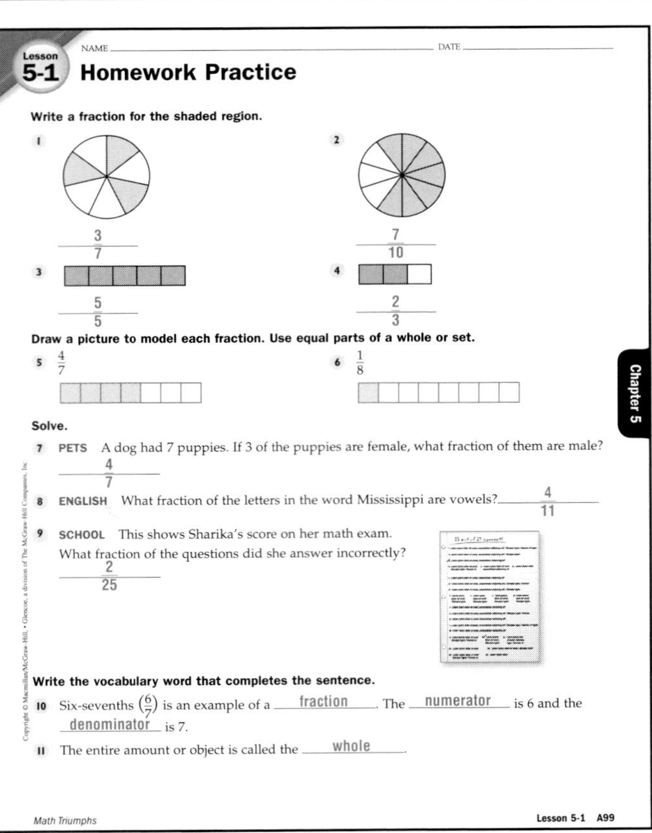

Lesson 5-1 NAME ______ DATE ______

Homework Practice

Write a fraction for the shaded region.

1 ___$\frac{3}{7}$___

2 ___$\frac{7}{10}$___

3 ___$\frac{5}{5}$___

4 ___$\frac{2}{3}$___

Draw a picture to model each fraction. Use equal parts of a whole or set.

5 $\frac{4}{7}$

6 $\frac{1}{8}$

Solve.

7 **PETS** A dog had 7 puppies. If 3 of the puppies are female, what fraction of them are male? ___$\frac{4}{7}$___

8 **ENGLISH** What fraction of the letters in the word Mississippi are vowels? ___$\frac{4}{11}$___

9 **SCHOOL** This shows Sharika's score on her math exam. What fraction of the questions did she answer incorrectly? ___$\frac{2}{25}$___

Write the vocabulary word that completes the sentence.

10 Six-sevenths $\left(\frac{6}{7}\right)$ is an example of a ___fraction___. The ___numerator___ is 6 and the ___denominator___ is 7.

11 The entire amount or object is called the ___whole___.

Math Triumphs Lesson 5-1 A99

Chapter 5

Answer Key (Lesson 5-2)

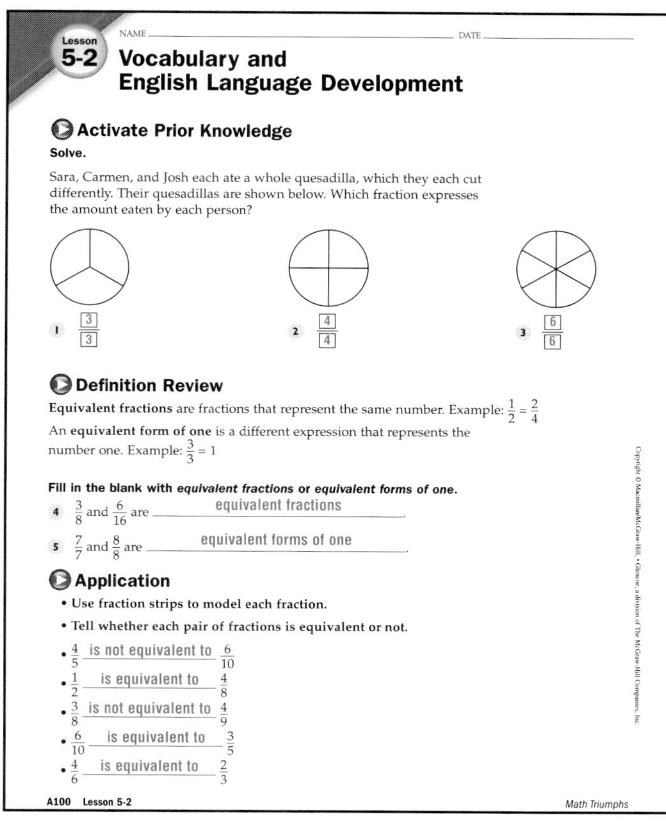

Lesson 5-2 NAME ______ DATE ______

Vocabulary and English Language Development

Activate Prior Knowledge

Solve.

Sara, Carmen, and Josh each ate a whole quesadilla, which they each cut differently. Their quesadillas are shown below. Which fraction expresses the amount eaten by each person?

1 $\frac{3}{3}$ 2 $\frac{4}{4}$ 3 $\frac{6}{6}$

Definition Review

Equivalent fractions are fractions that represent the same number. Example: $\frac{1}{2} = \frac{2}{4}$

An **equivalent form of one** is a different expression that represents the number one. Example: $\frac{3}{3} = 1$

Fill in the blank with *equivalent fractions* or *equivalent forms of one*.

4 $\frac{3}{8}$ and $\frac{6}{16}$ are equivalent fractions.

5 $\frac{7}{7}$ and $\frac{8}{8}$ are equivalent forms of one.

Application

- Use fraction strips to model each fraction.
- Tell whether each pair of fractions is equivalent or not.

- $\frac{4}{5}$ is not equivalent to $\frac{6}{10}$
- $\frac{1}{2}$ is equivalent to $\frac{4}{8}$
- $\frac{3}{8}$ is not equivalent to $\frac{4}{9}$
- $\frac{6}{10}$ is equivalent to $\frac{3}{5}$
- $\frac{4}{6}$ is equivalent to $\frac{2}{3}$

A100 Lesson 5-2 Math Triumphs

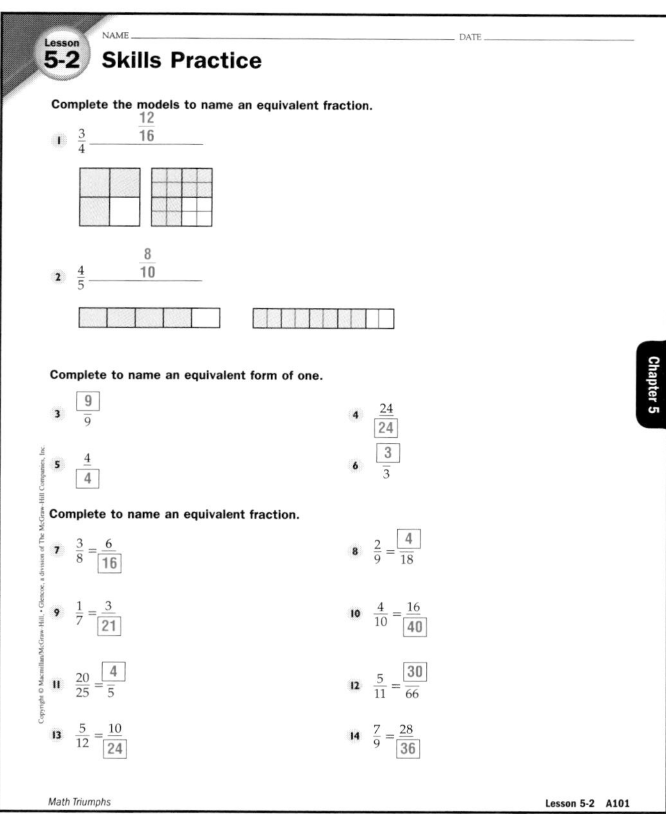

Lesson 5-2 NAME ______ DATE ______

Skills Practice

Complete the models to name an equivalent fraction.

1 $\frac{3}{4}$ $\frac{12}{16}$

2 $\frac{4}{5}$ $\frac{8}{10}$

Complete to name an equivalent form of one.

3 $\frac{9}{9}$ 4 $\frac{24}{24}$

5 $\frac{4}{4}$ 6 $\frac{3}{3}$

Complete to name an equivalent fraction.

7 $\frac{3}{8} = \frac{6}{16}$ 8 $\frac{2}{9} = \frac{4}{18}$

9 $\frac{1}{7} = \frac{3}{21}$ 10 $\frac{4}{10} = \frac{16}{40}$

11 $\frac{20}{25} = \frac{4}{5}$ 12 $\frac{5}{11} = \frac{30}{66}$

13 $\frac{5}{12} = \frac{10}{24}$ 14 $\frac{7}{9} = \frac{28}{36}$

Chapter 5

Math Triumphs Lesson 5-2 A101

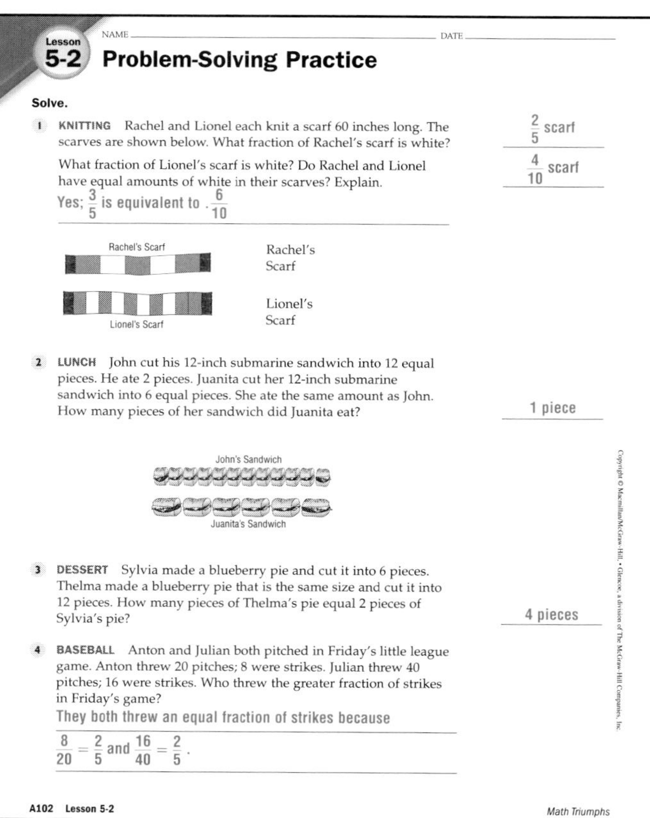

Lesson 5-2 NAME ______ DATE ______

Problem-Solving Practice

Solve.

1 **KNITTING** Rachel and Lionel each knit a scarf 60 inches long. The scarves are shown below. What fraction of Rachel's scarf is white? $\frac{2}{5}$ scarf

What fraction of Lionel's scarf is white? Do Rachel and Lionel have equal amounts of white in their scarves? Explain. $\frac{4}{10}$ scarf

Yes; $\frac{3}{5}$ is equivalent to $\frac{6}{10}$.

Rachel's Scarf

Rachel's Scarf

Lionel's Scarf

Lionel's Scarf

2 **LUNCH** John cut his 12-inch submarine sandwich into 12 equal pieces. He ate 2 pieces. Juanita cut her 12-inch submarine sandwich into 6 equal pieces. She ate the same amount as John. How many pieces of her sandwich did Juanita eat? 1 piece

John's Sandwich

Juanita's Sandwich

3 **DESSERT** Sylvia made a blueberry pie and cut it into 6 pieces. Thelma made a blueberry pie that is the same size and cut it into 12 pieces. How many pieces of Thelma's pie equal 2 pieces of Sylvia's pie? 4 pieces

4 **BASEBALL** Anton and Julian both pitched in Friday's little league game. Anton threw 20 pitches; 8 were strikes. Julian threw 40 pitches; 16 were strikes. Who threw the greater fraction of strikes in Friday's game?

They both threw an equal fraction of strikes because $\frac{8}{20} = \frac{2}{5}$ and $\frac{16}{40} = \frac{2}{5}$.

A102 Lesson 5-2 Math Triumphs

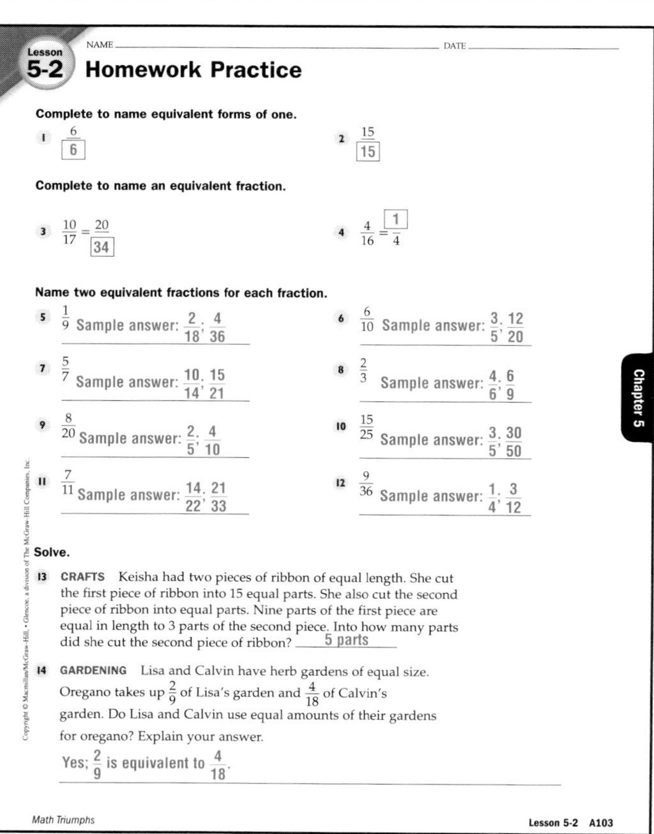

Lesson 5-2 NAME ______ DATE ______

Homework Practice

Complete to name equivalent forms of one.

1 $\frac{6}{6}$ 2 $\frac{15}{15}$

Complete to name an equivalent fraction.

3 $\frac{10}{17} = \frac{20}{34}$ 4 $\frac{4}{16} = \frac{1}{4}$

Name two equivalent fractions for each fraction.

5 $\frac{1}{9}$ Sample answer: $\frac{2}{18}, \frac{4}{36}$ 6 $\frac{6}{10}$ Sample answer: $\frac{3}{5}, \frac{12}{20}$

7 $\frac{5}{7}$ Sample answer: $\frac{10}{14}, \frac{15}{21}$ 8 $\frac{2}{3}$ Sample answer: $\frac{4}{6}, \frac{6}{9}$

9 $\frac{8}{20}$ Sample answer: $\frac{2}{5}, \frac{4}{10}$ 10 $\frac{15}{25}$ Sample answer: $\frac{3}{5}, \frac{30}{50}$

11 $\frac{7}{11}$ Sample answer: $\frac{14}{22}, \frac{21}{33}$ 12 $\frac{9}{36}$ Sample answer: $\frac{1}{4}, \frac{3}{12}$

Solve.

13 **CRAFTS** Keisha had two pieces of ribbon of equal length. She cut the first piece of ribbon into 15 equal parts. She also cut the second piece of ribbon into equal parts. Nine parts of the first piece are equal in length to 3 parts of the second piece. Into how many parts did she cut the second piece of ribbon? 5 parts

14 **GARDENING** Lisa and Calvin have herb gardens of equal size. Oregano takes up $\frac{2}{9}$ of Lisa's garden and $\frac{4}{18}$ of Calvin's garden. Do Lisa and Calvin use equal amounts of their gardens for oregano? Explain your answer.

Yes; $\frac{2}{9}$ is equivalent to $\frac{4}{18}$.

Chapter 5

Math Triumphs Lesson 5-2 A103

Answer Key (Lesson 5-3)

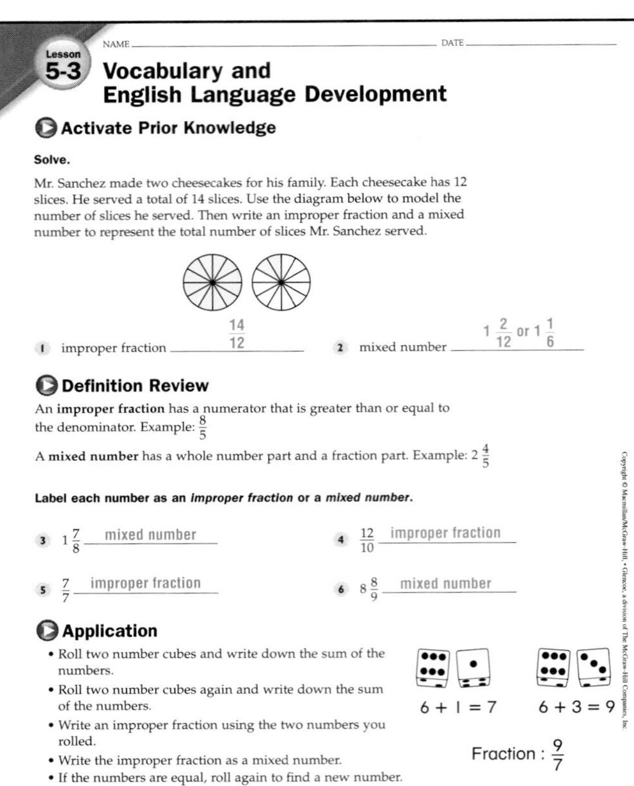

Lesson 5-3 NAME ______ DATE ______

Vocabulary and English Language Development

Activate Prior Knowledge

Solve.

Mr. Sanchez made two cheesecakes for his family. Each cheesecake has 12 slices. He served a total of 14 slices. Use the diagram below to model the number of slices he served. Then write an improper fraction and a mixed number to represent the total number of slices Mr. Sanchez served.

1 improper fraction $\frac{14}{12}$ 2 mixed number $1\frac{2}{12}$ or $1\frac{1}{6}$

Definition Review

An **improper fraction** has a numerator that is greater than or equal to the denominator. Example: $\frac{8}{5}$

A **mixed number** has a whole number part and a fraction part. Example: $2\frac{4}{5}$

Label each number as an *improper fraction* or a *mixed number*.

3 $1\frac{7}{8}$ mixed number 4 $\frac{12}{10}$ improper fraction

5 $\frac{7}{7}$ improper fraction 6 $8\frac{8}{9}$ mixed number

Application

- Roll two number cubes and write down the sum of the numbers.
- Roll two number cubes again and write down the sum of the numbers.
- Write an improper fraction using the two numbers you rolled.
- Write the improper fraction as a mixed number.
- If the numbers are equal, roll again to find a new number.

6 + 1 = 7 6 + 3 = 9

Fraction : $\frac{9}{7}$

A104 Lesson 5-3 Math Triumphs

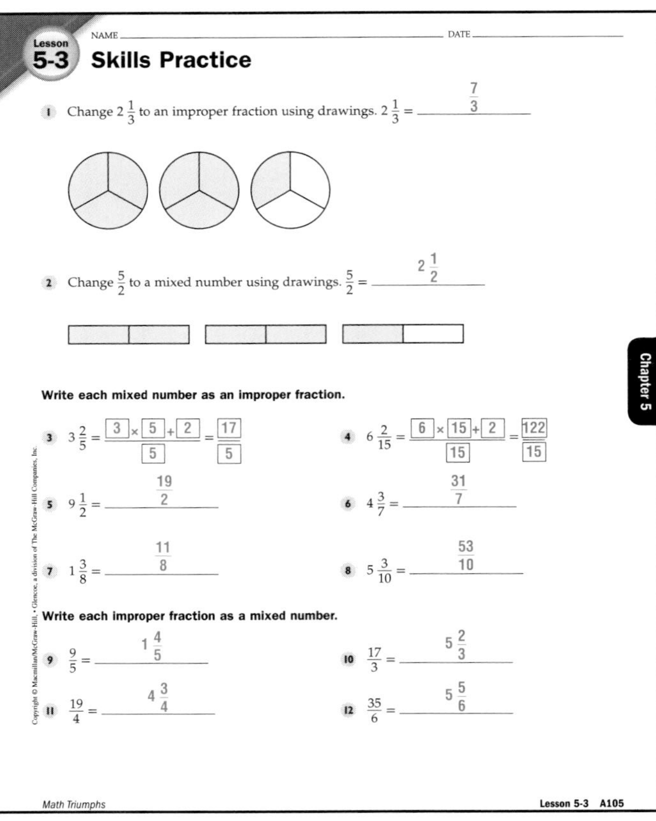

Lesson 5-3 NAME ______ DATE ______

Skills Practice

1 Change $2\frac{1}{3}$ to an improper fraction using drawings. $2\frac{1}{3} = \frac{7}{3}$

2 Change $\frac{5}{2}$ to a mixed number using drawings. $\frac{5}{2} = 2\frac{1}{2}$

Write each mixed number as an improper fraction.

3 $3\frac{2}{5} = \frac{3 \times 5 + 2}{5} = \frac{17}{5}$ 4 $6\frac{2}{15} = \frac{6 \times 15 + 2}{15} = \frac{122}{15}$

5 $9\frac{1}{2} = \frac{19}{2}$ 6 $4\frac{3}{7} = \frac{31}{7}$

7 $1\frac{3}{8} = \frac{11}{8}$ 8 $5\frac{3}{10} = \frac{53}{10}$

Write each improper fraction as a mixed number.

9 $\frac{9}{5} = 1\frac{4}{5}$ 10 $\frac{17}{3} = 5\frac{2}{3}$

11 $\frac{19}{4} = 4\frac{3}{4}$ 12 $\frac{35}{6} = 5\frac{5}{6}$

Math Triumphs Lesson 5-3 A105

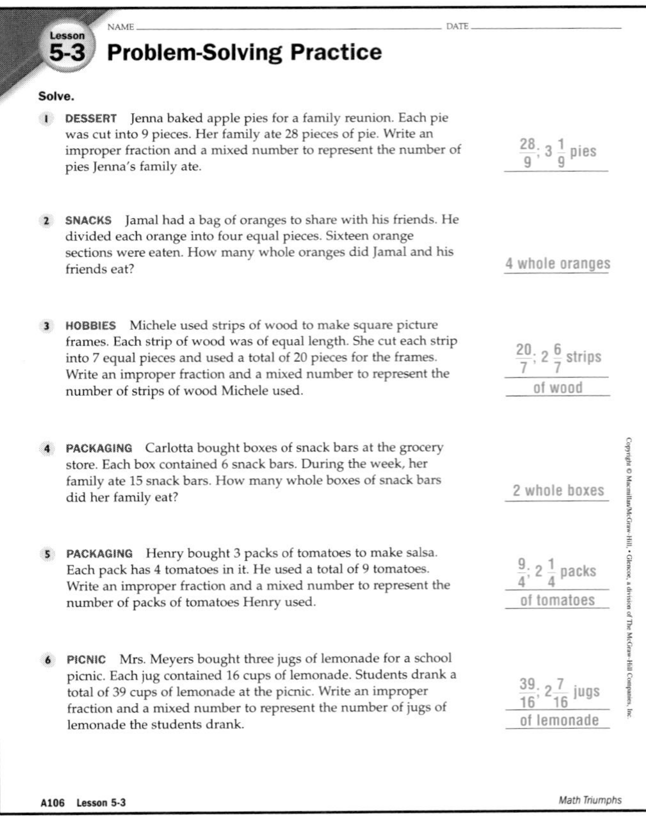

Lesson 5-3 NAME ______ DATE ______

Problem-Solving Practice

Solve.

1 **DESSERT** Jenna baked apple pies for a family reunion. Each pie was cut into 9 pieces. Her family ate 28 pieces of pie. Write an improper fraction and a mixed number to represent the number of pies Jenna's family ate. $\frac{28}{9}$; $3\frac{1}{9}$ pies

2 **SNACKS** Jamal had a bag of oranges to share with his friends. He divided each orange into four equal pieces. Sixteen orange sections were eaten. How many whole oranges did Jamal and his friends eat? 4 whole oranges

3 **HOBBIES** Michele used strips of wood to make square picture frames. Each strip of wood was of equal length. She cut each strip into 7 equal pieces and used a total of 20 pieces for the frames. Write an improper fraction and a mixed number to represent the number of strips of wood Michele used. $\frac{20}{7}$; $2\frac{6}{7}$ strips of wood

4 **PACKAGING** Carlotta bought boxes of snack bars at the grocery store. Each box contained 6 snack bars. During the week, her family ate 15 snack bars. How many whole boxes of snack bars did her family eat? 2 whole boxes

5 **PACKAGING** Henry bought 3 packs of tomatoes to make salsa. Each pack has 4 tomatoes in it. He used a total of 9 tomatoes. Write an improper fraction and a mixed number to represent the number of packs of tomatoes Henry used. $\frac{9}{4}$; $2\frac{1}{4}$ packs of tomatoes

6 **PICNIC** Mrs. Meyers bought three jugs of lemonade for a school picnic. Each jug contained 16 cups of lemonade. Students drank a total of 39 cups of lemonade at the picnic. Write an improper fraction and a mixed number to represent the number of jugs of lemonade the students drank. $\frac{39}{16}$; $2\frac{7}{16}$ jugs of lemonade

A106 Lesson 5-3 Math Triumphs

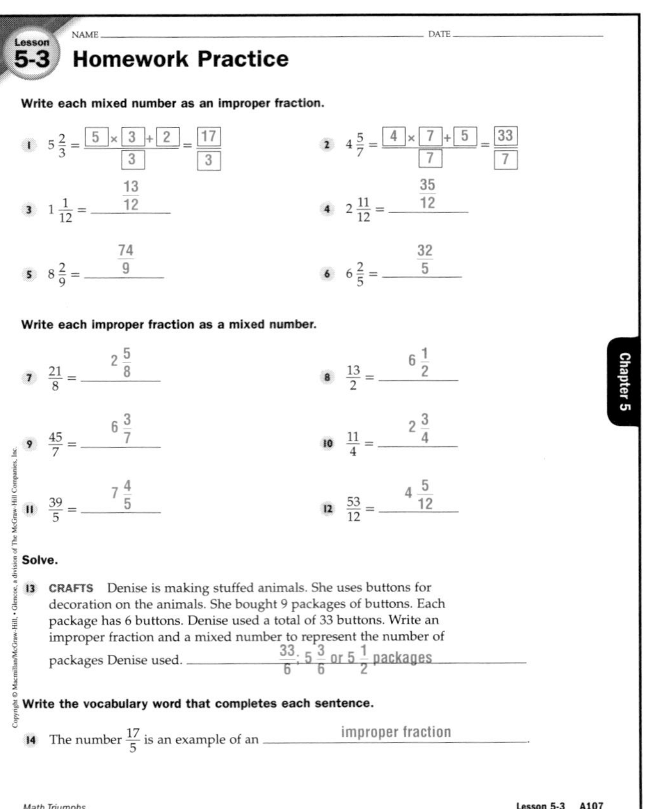

Lesson 5-3 NAME ______ DATE ______

Homework Practice

Write each mixed number as an improper fraction.

1 $5\frac{2}{3} = \frac{5 \times 3 + 2}{3} = \frac{17}{3}$ 2 $4\frac{5}{7} = \frac{4 \times 7 + 5}{7} = \frac{33}{7}$

3 $1\frac{1}{12} = \frac{13}{12}$ 4 $2\frac{11}{12} = \frac{35}{12}$

5 $8\frac{2}{9} = \frac{74}{9}$ 6 $6\frac{2}{5} = \frac{32}{5}$

Write each improper fraction as a mixed number.

7 $\frac{21}{8} = 2\frac{5}{8}$ 8 $\frac{13}{2} = 6\frac{1}{2}$

9 $\frac{45}{7} = 6\frac{3}{7}$ 10 $\frac{11}{4} = 2\frac{3}{4}$

11 $\frac{39}{5} = 7\frac{4}{5}$ 12 $\frac{53}{12} = 4\frac{5}{12}$

Solve.

13 **CRAFTS** Denise is making stuffed animals. She uses buttons for decoration on the animals. She bought 9 packages of buttons. Each package has 6 buttons. Denise used a total of 33 buttons. Write an improper fraction and a mixed number to represent the number of packages Denise used. $\frac{33}{6}$; $5\frac{3}{6}$ or $5\frac{1}{2}$ packages

Write the vocabulary word that completes each sentence.

14 The number $\frac{17}{5}$ is an example of an improper fraction.

Math Triumphs Lesson 5-3 A107

Answer Key (Lesson 5-4)

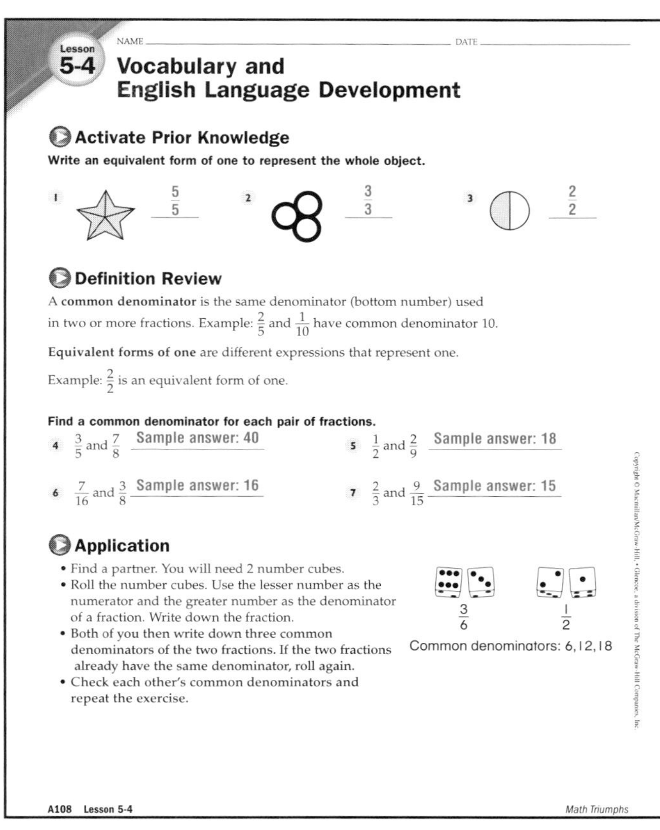

Lesson 5-4 NAME ______ DATE ______

Vocabulary and English Language Development

Activate Prior Knowledge

Write an equivalent form of one to represent the whole object.

1 $\frac{5}{5}$ 2 $\frac{3}{3}$ 3 $\frac{2}{2}$

Definition Review

A **common denominator** is the same denominator (bottom number) used in two or more fractions. Example: $\frac{2}{5}$ and $\frac{1}{10}$ have common denominator 10.

Equivalent forms of one are different expressions that represent one.

Example: $\frac{2}{2}$ is an equivalent form of one.

Find a common denominator for each pair of fractions.

4 $\frac{3}{5}$ and $\frac{7}{8}$ Sample answer: 40

5 $\frac{1}{2}$ and $\frac{2}{9}$ Sample answer: 18

6 $\frac{7}{16}$ and $\frac{3}{8}$ Sample answer: 16

7 $\frac{2}{3}$ and $\frac{9}{15}$ Sample answer: 15

Application

- Find a partner. You will need 2 number cubes.
- Roll the number cubes. Use the lesser number as the numerator and the greater number as the denominator of a fraction. Write down the fraction.
- Both of you then write down three common denominators of the two fractions. If the two fractions already have the same denominator, roll again.
- Check each other's common denominators and repeat the exercise.

$\frac{3}{6}$ $\frac{1}{2}$

Common denominators: 6, 12, 18

A108 Lesson 5-4 Math Triumphs

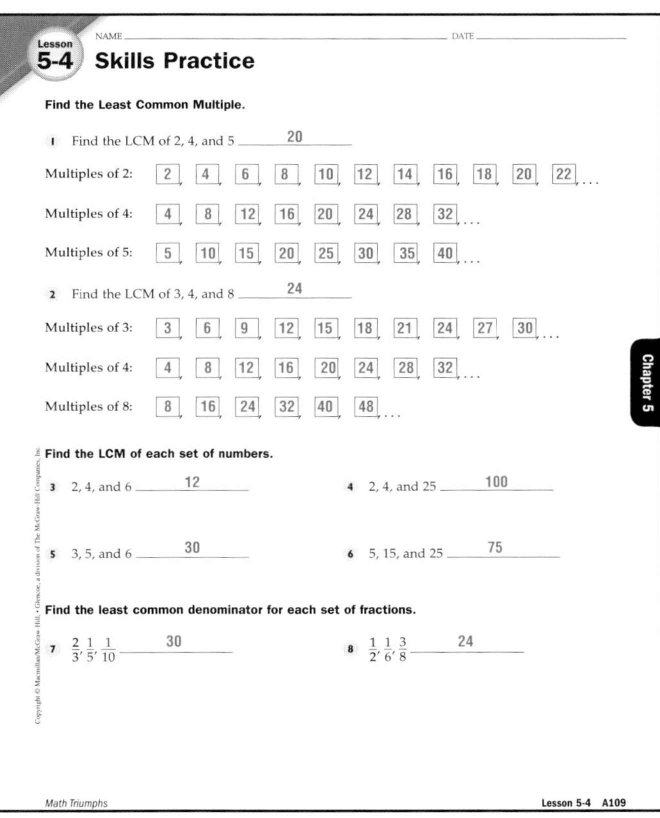

Lesson 5-4 NAME ______ DATE ______

Skills Practice

Find the Least Common Multiple.

1 Find the LCM of 2, 4, and 5 20

Multiples of 2: 2, 4, 6, 8, 10, 12, 14, 16, 18, 20, 22, ...

Multiples of 4: 4, 8, 12, 16, 20, 24, 28, 32, ...

Multiples of 5: 5, 10, 15, 20, 25, 30, 35, 40, ...

2 Find the LCM of 3, 4, and 8 24

Multiples of 3: 3, 6, 9, 12, 15, 18, 21, 24, 27, 30, ...

Multiples of 4: 4, 8, 12, 16, 20, 24, 28, 32, ...

Multiples of 8: 8, 16, 24, 32, 40, 48, ...

Find the LCM of each set of numbers.

3 2, 4, and 6 12

4 2, 4, and 25 100

5 3, 5, and 6 30

6 5, 15, and 25 75

Find the least common denominator for each set of fractions.

7 $\frac{2}{3}, \frac{1}{5}, \frac{1}{10}$ 30

8 $\frac{1}{2}, \frac{1}{6}, \frac{3}{8}$ 24

Chapter 5

Math Triumphs Lesson 5-4 A109

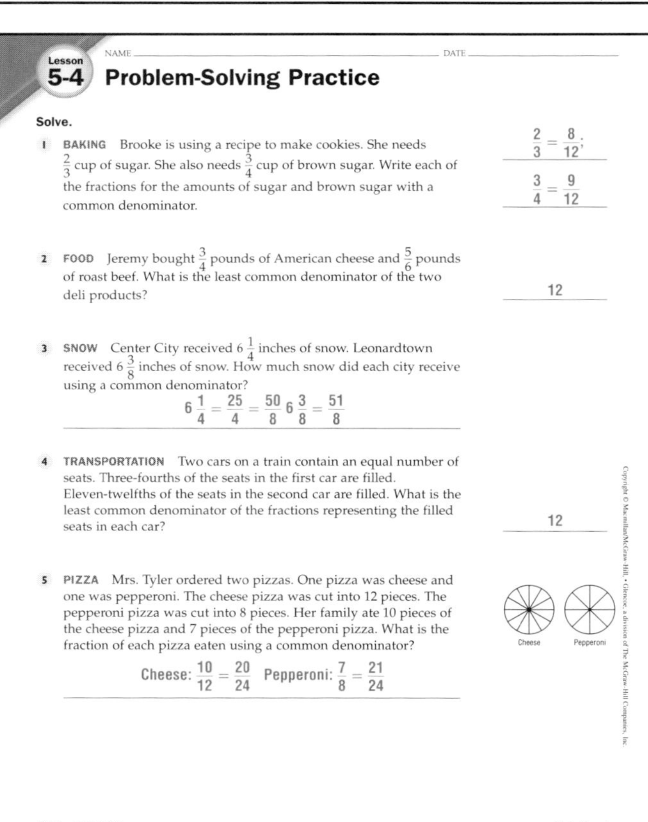

Lesson 5-4 NAME ______ DATE ______

Problem-Solving Practice

Solve.

1 BAKING Brooke is using a recipe to make cookies. She needs $\frac{2}{3}$ cup of sugar. She also needs $\frac{3}{4}$ cup of brown sugar. Write each of the fractions for the amounts of sugar and brown sugar with a common denominator.

$\frac{2}{3} = \frac{8}{12}$; $\frac{3}{4} = \frac{9}{12}$

2 FOOD Jeremy bought $\frac{3}{4}$ pounds of American cheese and $\frac{5}{6}$ pounds of roast beef. What is the least common denominator of the two deli products? 12

3 SNOW Center City received $6\frac{1}{4}$ inches of snow. Leonardtown received $6\frac{3}{8}$ inches of snow. How much snow did each city receive using a common denominator?

$6\frac{1}{4} = \frac{25}{4} = \frac{50}{8}$ $6\frac{3}{8} = \frac{51}{8}$

4 TRANSPORTATION Two cars on a train contain an equal number of seats. Three-fourths of the seats in the first car are filled. Eleven-twelfths of the seats in the second car are filled. What is the least common denominator of the fractions representing the filled seats in each car? 12

5 PIZZA Mrs. Tyler ordered two pizzas. One pizza was cheese and one was pepperoni. The cheese pizza was cut into 12 pieces. The pepperoni pizza was cut into 8 pieces. Her family ate 10 pieces of the cheese pizza and 7 pieces of the pepperoni pizza. What is the fraction of each pizza eaten using a common denominator?

Cheese Pepperoni

Cheese: $\frac{10}{12} = \frac{20}{24}$ Pepperoni: $\frac{7}{8} = \frac{21}{24}$

A110 Lesson 5-4 Math Triumphs

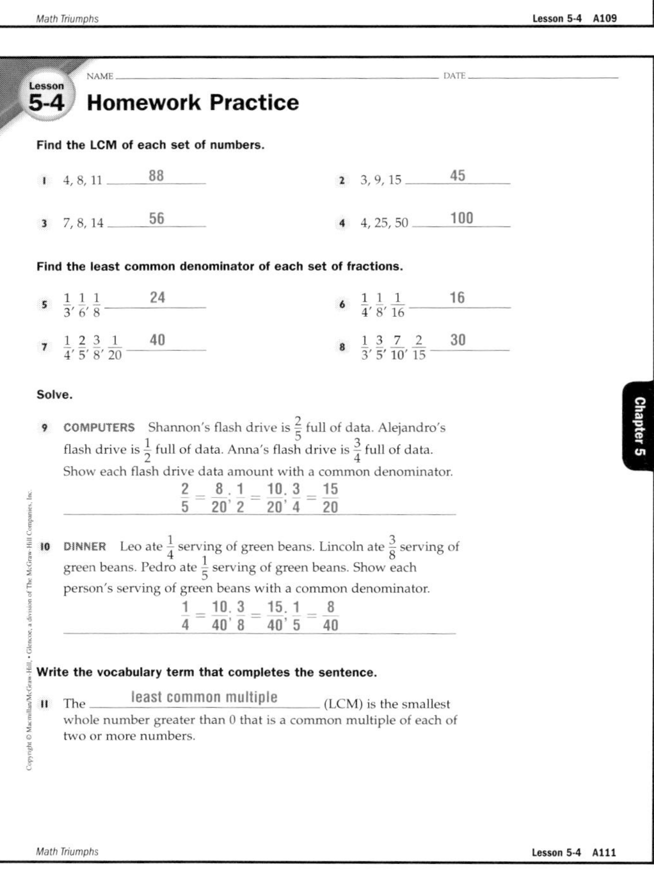

Lesson 5-4 NAME ______ DATE ______

Homework Practice

Find the LCM of each set of numbers.

1 4, 8, 11 88

2 3, 9, 15 45

3 7, 8, 14 56

4 4, 25, 50 100

Find the least common denominator of each set of fractions.

5 $\frac{1}{3}, \frac{1}{6}, \frac{1}{8}$ 24

6 $\frac{1}{4}, \frac{1}{8}, \frac{1}{16}$ 16

7 $\frac{1}{4}, \frac{2}{5}, \frac{3}{8}, \frac{1}{20}$ 40

8 $\frac{1}{3}, \frac{3}{5}, \frac{7}{10}, \frac{2}{15}$ 30

Solve.

9 COMPUTERS Shannon's flash drive is $\frac{2}{5}$ full of data. Alejandro's flash drive is $\frac{1}{2}$ full of data. Anna's flash drive is $\frac{3}{4}$ full of data. Show each flash drive data amount with a common denominator.

$\frac{2}{5} = \frac{8}{20}$, $\frac{1}{2} = \frac{10}{20}$, $\frac{3}{4} = \frac{15}{20}$

10 DINNER Leo ate $\frac{1}{4}$ serving of green beans. Lincoln ate $\frac{3}{8}$ serving of green beans. Pedro ate $\frac{1}{5}$ serving of green beans. Show each person's serving of green beans with a common denominator.

$\frac{1}{4} = \frac{10}{40}$, $\frac{3}{8} = \frac{15}{40}$, $\frac{1}{5} = \frac{8}{40}$

Write the vocabulary term that completes the sentence.

11 The least common multiple (LCM) is the smallest whole number greater than 0 that is a common multiple of each of two or more numbers.

Chapter 5

Math Triumphs Lesson 5-4 A111

Answer Key (Lesson 5-5)

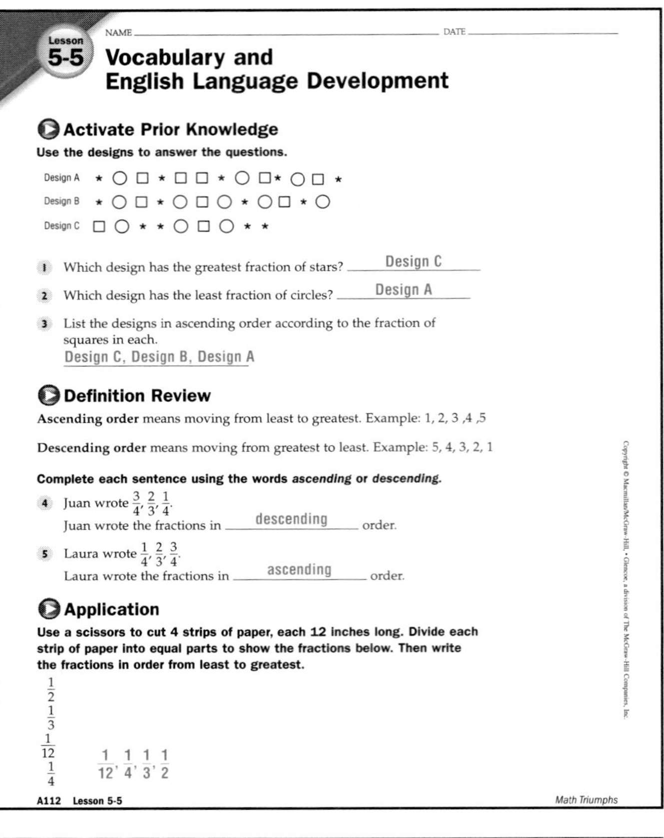

Lesson 5-5 NAME ____________ DATE ____________

Vocabulary and English Language Development

Activate Prior Knowledge

Use the designs to answer the questions.

Design A ★ ○ □ ★ □ □ ★ ○ □ ★ ○ □ ★

Design B ★ ○ □ ★ ○ □ ○ ★ ○ □ ★ ○

Design C □ ○ ★ ★ ○ □ ○ ★ ★

1 Which design has the greatest fraction of stars? Design C

2 Which design has the least fraction of circles? Design A

3 List the designs in ascending order according to the fraction of squares in each.
Design C, Design B, Design A

Definition Review

Ascending order means moving from least to greatest. Example: 1, 2, 3 ,4 ,5

Descending order means moving from greatest to least. Example: 5, 4, 3, 2, 1

Complete each sentence using the words *ascending* or *descending*.

4 Juan wrote $\frac{3}{4}, \frac{2}{3}, \frac{1}{4}$.
Juan wrote the fractions in descending order.

5 Laura wrote $\frac{1}{4}, \frac{2}{3}, \frac{3}{4}$.
Laura wrote the fractions in ascending order.

Application

Use a scissors to cut 4 strips of paper, each 12 inches long. Divide each strip of paper into equal parts to show the fractions below. Then write the fractions in order from least to greatest.

$\frac{1}{2}$

$\frac{1}{3}$

$\frac{1}{12}$

$\frac{1}{4}$ $\frac{1}{12}, \frac{1}{4}, \frac{1}{3}, \frac{1}{2}$

A112 Lesson 5-5 Math Triumphs

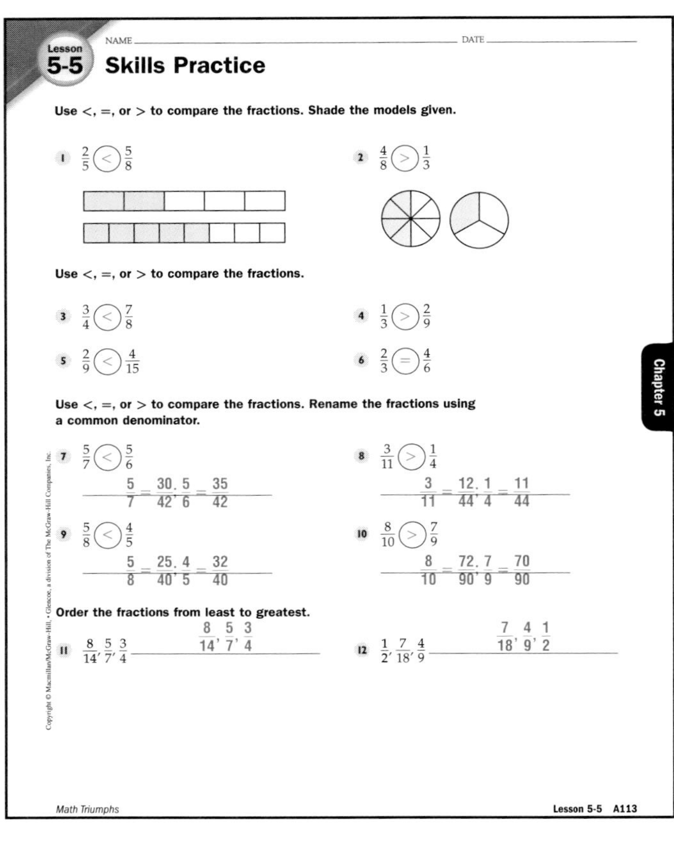

Lesson 5-5 NAME ____________ DATE ____________

Skills Practice

Use <, =, or > to compare the fractions. Shade the models given.

1 $\frac{2}{5} < \frac{5}{8}$

2 $\frac{4}{8} > \frac{1}{3}$

Use <, =, or > to compare the fractions.

3 $\frac{3}{4} < \frac{7}{8}$

4 $\frac{1}{3} > \frac{2}{9}$

5 $\frac{2}{9} < \frac{4}{15}$

6 $\frac{2}{3} = \frac{4}{6}$

Use <, =, or > to compare the fractions. Rename the fractions using a common denominator.

7 $\frac{5}{7} < \frac{5}{6}$ $\frac{5}{7} = \frac{30}{42}; \frac{5}{6} = \frac{35}{42}$

8 $\frac{3}{11} > \frac{1}{4}$ $\frac{3}{11} = \frac{12}{44}; \frac{1}{4} = \frac{11}{44}$

9 $\frac{5}{8} < \frac{4}{5}$ $\frac{5}{8} = \frac{25}{40}; \frac{4}{5} = \frac{32}{40}$

10 $\frac{8}{10} > \frac{7}{9}$ $\frac{8}{10} = \frac{72}{90}; \frac{7}{9} = \frac{70}{90}$

Order the fractions from least to greatest.

11 $\frac{8}{14}, \frac{5}{7}, \frac{3}{4}$ $\frac{8}{14}, \frac{5}{7}, \frac{3}{4}$

12 $\frac{1}{2}, \frac{7}{18}, \frac{4}{9}$ $\frac{7}{18}, \frac{4}{9}, \frac{1}{2}$

Chapter 5

Math Triumphs Lesson 5-5 A113

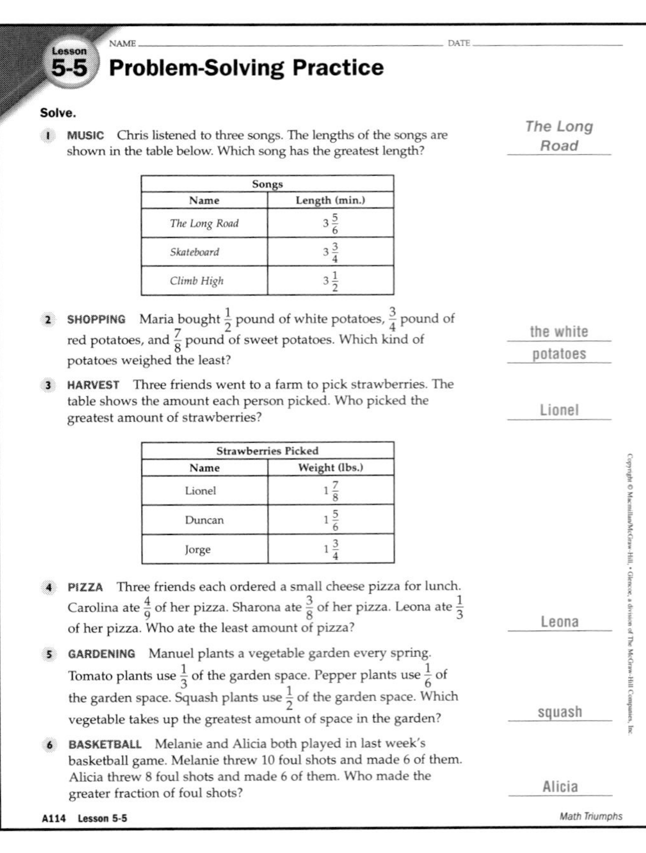

Lesson 5-5 NAME ____________ DATE ____________

Problem-Solving Practice

Solve.

1 **MUSIC** Chris listened to three songs. The lengths of the songs are shown in the table below. Which song has the greatest length? *The Long Road*

Songs	
Name	**Length (min.)**
The Long Road	$3\frac{5}{6}$
Skateboard	$3\frac{3}{4}$
Climb High	$3\frac{1}{2}$

2 **SHOPPING** Maria bought $\frac{1}{2}$ pound of white potatoes, $\frac{3}{4}$ pound of red potatoes, and $\frac{7}{8}$ pound of sweet potatoes. Which kind of potatoes weighed the least? the white potatoes

3 **HARVEST** Three friends went to a farm to pick strawberries. The table shows the amount each person picked. Who picked the greatest amount of strawberries? Lionel

Strawberries Picked	
Name	**Weight (lbs.)**
Lionel	$1\frac{7}{8}$
Duncan	$1\frac{5}{6}$
Jorge	$1\frac{3}{4}$

4 **PIZZA** Three friends each ordered a small cheese pizza for lunch. Carolina ate $\frac{4}{9}$ of her pizza. Sharona ate $\frac{3}{8}$ of her pizza. Leona ate $\frac{1}{3}$ of her pizza. Who ate the least amount of pizza? Leona

5 **GARDENING** Manuel plants a vegetable garden every spring. Tomato plants use $\frac{1}{3}$ of the garden space. Pepper plants use $\frac{1}{6}$ of the garden space. Squash plants use $\frac{1}{2}$ of the garden space. Which vegetable takes up the greatest amount of space in the garden? squash

6 **BASKETBALL** Melanie and Alicia both played in last week's basketball game. Melanie threw 10 foul shots and made 6 of them. Alicia threw 8 foul shots and made 6 of them. Who made the greater fraction of foul shots? Alicia

A114 Lesson 5-5 Math Triumphs

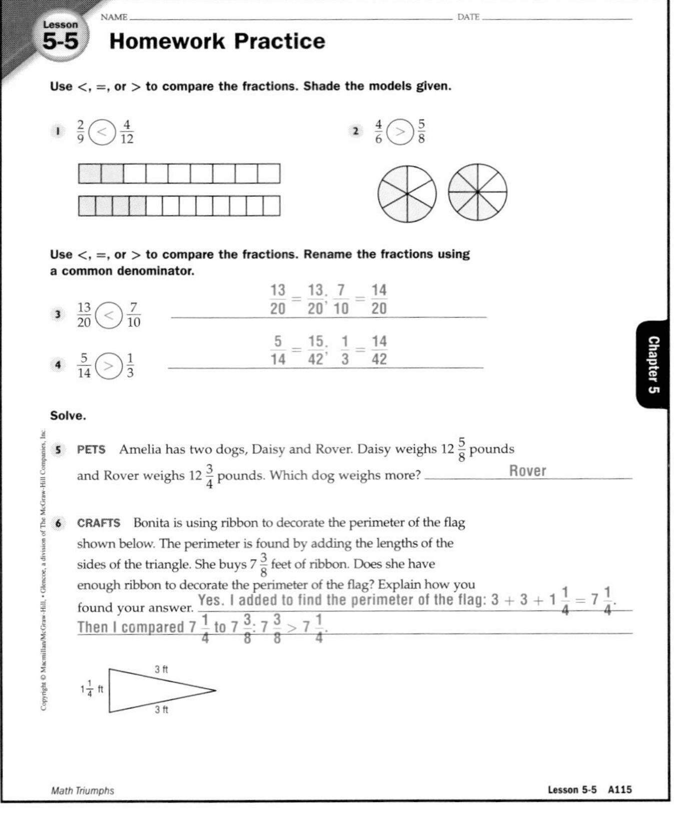

Lesson 5-5 NAME ____________ DATE ____________

Homework Practice

Use <, =, or > to compare the fractions. Shade the models given.

1 $\frac{2}{9} < \frac{4}{12}$

2 $\frac{4}{6} > \frac{5}{8}$

Use <, =, or > to compare the fractions. Rename the fractions using a common denominator.

3 $\frac{13}{20} < \frac{7}{10}$ $\frac{13}{20} = \frac{13}{20}; \frac{7}{10} = \frac{14}{20}$

4 $\frac{5}{14} > \frac{1}{3}$ $\frac{5}{14} = \frac{15}{42}; \frac{1}{3} = \frac{14}{42}$

Solve.

5 **PETS** Amelia has two dogs, Daisy and Rover. Daisy weighs $12\frac{5}{8}$ pounds and Rover weighs $12\frac{3}{4}$ pounds. Which dog weighs more? Rover

6 **CRAFTS** Bonita is using ribbon to decorate the perimeter of the flag shown below. The perimeter is found by adding the lengths of the sides of the triangle. She buys $7\frac{3}{8}$ feet of ribbon. Does she have enough ribbon to decorate the perimeter of the flag? Explain how you found your answer. Yes. I added to find the perimeter of the flag: $3 + 3 + 1\frac{1}{4} = 7\frac{1}{4}$. Then I compared $7\frac{1}{4}$ to $7\frac{3}{8}$; $7\frac{3}{8} > 7\frac{1}{4}$.

$1\frac{1}{4}$ ft 3 ft 3 ft

Chapter 5

Math Triumphs Lesson 5-5 A115

Answer Key (Lesson 5-6)

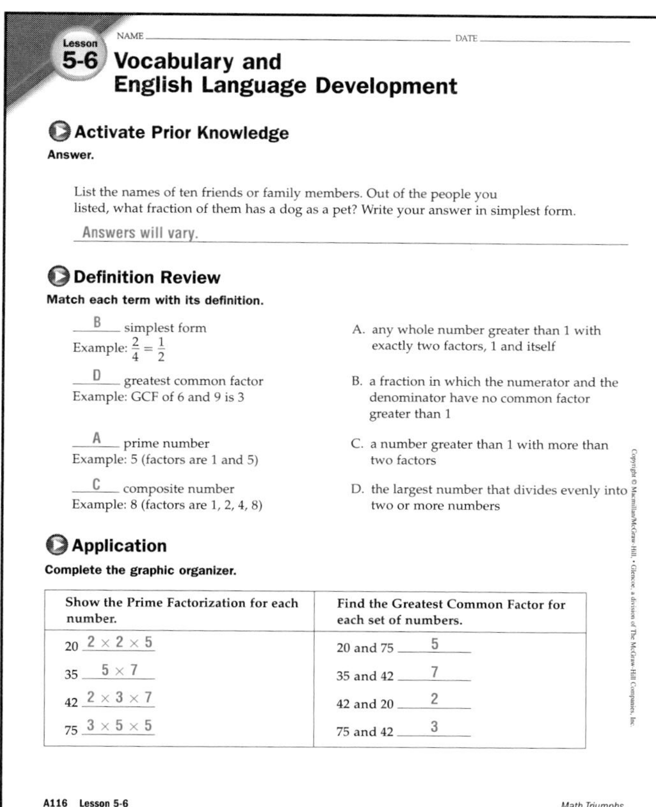

Lesson 5-6 NAME ________ DATE ________

Vocabulary and English Language Development

Activate Prior Knowledge

Answer.

List the names of ten friends or family members. Out of the people you listed, what fraction of them has a dog as a pet? Write your answer in simplest form.

Answers will vary.

Definition Review

Match each term with its definition.

B simplest form
Example: $\frac{2}{4} = \frac{1}{2}$

D greatest common factor
Example: GCF of 6 and 9 is 3

A prime number
Example: 5 (factors are 1 and 5)

C composite number
Example: 8 (factors are 1, 2, 4, 8)

A. any whole number greater than 1 with exactly two factors, 1 and itself

B. a fraction in which the numerator and the denominator have no common factor greater than 1

C. a number greater than 1 with more than two factors

D. the largest number that divides evenly into two or more numbers

Application

Complete the graphic organizer.

Show the Prime Factorization for each number.	Find the Greatest Common Factor for each set of numbers.
20 $2 \times 2 \times 5$	20 and 75 5
35 5×7	35 and 42 7
42 $2 \times 3 \times 7$	42 and 20 2
75 $3 \times 5 \times 5$	75 and 42 3

Copyright © Macmillan/McGraw-Hill, • Glencoe, a division of The McGraw-Hill Companies, Inc.

A116 Lesson 5-6 Math Triumphs

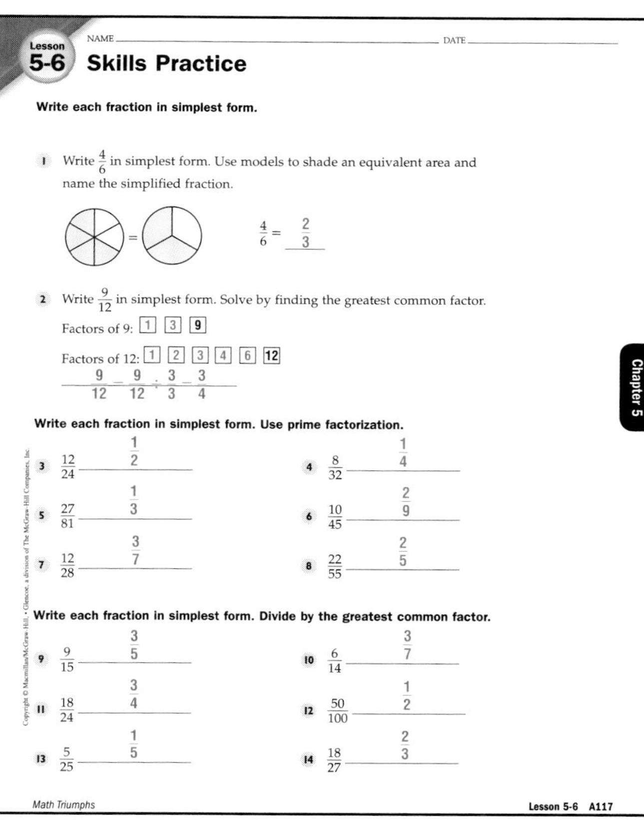

Lesson 5-6 NAME ________ DATE ________

Skills Practice

Write each fraction in simplest form.

1 Write $\frac{4}{6}$ in simplest form. Use models to shade an equivalent area and name the simplified fraction.

$\frac{4}{6} = \frac{2}{3}$

2 Write $\frac{9}{12}$ in simplest form. Solve by finding the greatest common factor.

Factors of 9: 1 3 **9**

Factors of 12: 1 2 3 4 6 **12**

$\frac{9}{12} = \frac{9}{12} \div \frac{3}{3} = \frac{3}{4}$

Write each fraction in simplest form. Use prime factorization.

3 $\frac{12}{24}$ $\frac{1}{2}$

4 $\frac{8}{32}$ $\frac{1}{4}$

5 $\frac{27}{81}$ $\frac{1}{3}$

6 $\frac{10}{45}$ $\frac{2}{9}$

7 $\frac{12}{28}$ $\frac{3}{7}$

8 $\frac{22}{55}$ $\frac{2}{5}$

Write each fraction in simplest form. Divide by the greatest common factor.

9 $\frac{9}{15}$ $\frac{3}{5}$

10 $\frac{6}{14}$ $\frac{3}{7}$

11 $\frac{18}{24}$ $\frac{3}{4}$

12 $\frac{50}{100}$ $\frac{1}{2}$

13 $\frac{5}{25}$ $\frac{1}{5}$

14 $\frac{18}{27}$ $\frac{2}{3}$

Chapter 5

Copyright © Macmillan/McGraw-Hill, • Glencoe, a division of The McGraw-Hill Companies, Inc.

Math Triumphs Lesson 5-6 A117

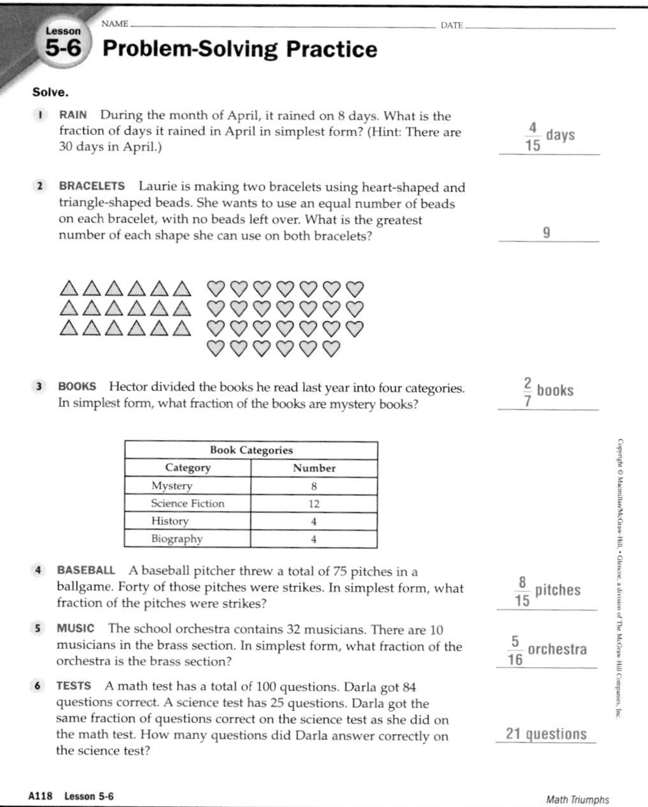

Lesson 5-6 NAME ________ DATE ________

Problem-Solving Practice

Solve.

1 **RAIN** During the month of April, it rained on 8 days. What is the fraction of days it rained in April in simplest form? (Hint: There are 30 days in April.) $\frac{4}{15}$ days

2 **BRACELETS** Laurie is making two bracelets using heart-shaped and triangle-shaped beads. She wants to use an equal number of beads on each bracelet, with no beads left over. What is the greatest number of each shape she can use on both bracelets? 9

3 **BOOKS** Hector divided the books he read last year into four categories. In simplest form, what fraction of the books are mystery books? $\frac{2}{7}$ books

Book Categories	
Category	**Number**
Mystery	8
Science Fiction	12
History	4
Biography	4

4 **BASEBALL** A baseball pitcher threw a total of 75 pitches in a ballgame. Forty of those pitches were strikes. In simplest form, what fraction of the pitches were strikes? $\frac{8}{15}$ pitches

5 **MUSIC** The school orchestra contains 32 musicians. There are 10 musicians in the brass section. In simplest form, what fraction of the orchestra is the brass section? $\frac{5}{16}$ orchestra

6 **TESTS** A math test has a total of 100 questions. Darla got 84 questions correct. A science test has 25 questions. Darla got the same fraction of questions correct on the science test as she did on the math test. How many questions did Darla answer correctly on the science test? 21 questions

Copyright © Macmillan/McGraw-Hill, • Glencoe, a division of The McGraw-Hill Companies, Inc.

A118 Lesson 5-6 Math Triumphs

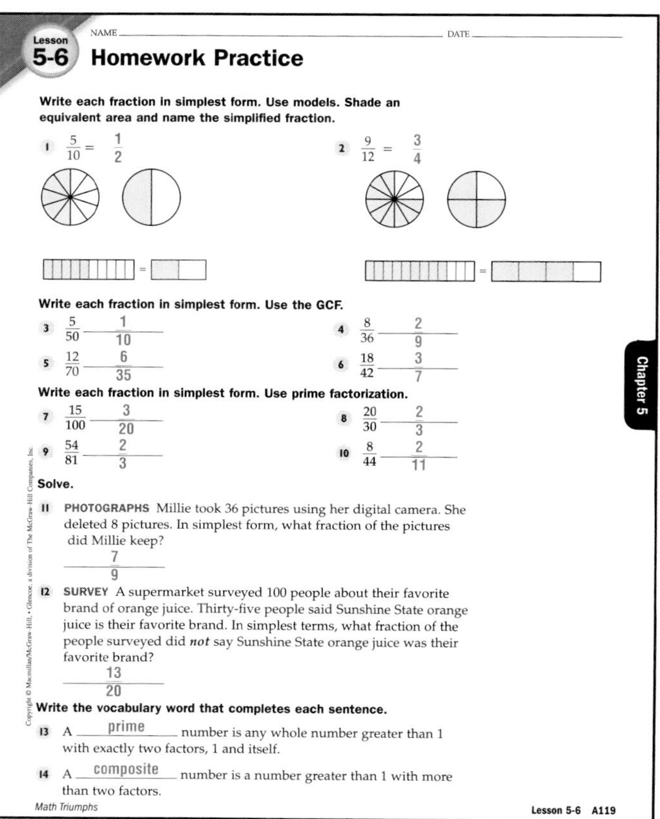

Lesson 5-6 NAME ________ DATE ________

Homework Practice

Write each fraction in simplest form. Use models. Shade an equivalent area and name the simplified fraction.

1 $\frac{5}{10} = \frac{1}{2}$

2 $\frac{9}{12} = \frac{3}{4}$

Write each fraction in simplest form. Use the GCF.

3 $\frac{5}{50}$ $\frac{1}{10}$

4 $\frac{8}{36}$ $\frac{2}{9}$

5 $\frac{12}{70}$ $\frac{6}{35}$

6 $\frac{18}{42}$ $\frac{3}{7}$

Write each fraction in simplest form. Use prime factorization.

7 $\frac{15}{100}$ $\frac{3}{20}$

8 $\frac{20}{30}$ $\frac{2}{3}$

9 $\frac{54}{81}$ $\frac{2}{3}$

10 $\frac{8}{44}$ $\frac{2}{11}$

Solve.

11 **PHOTOGRAPHS** Millie took 36 pictures using her digital camera. She deleted 8 pictures. In simplest form, what fraction of the pictures did Millie keep? $\frac{7}{9}$

12 **SURVEY** A supermarket surveyed 100 people about their favorite brand of orange juice. Thirty-five people said Sunshine State orange juice is their favorite brand. In simplest terms, what fraction of the people surveyed did *not* say Sunshine State orange juice was their favorite brand? $\frac{13}{20}$

Write the vocabulary word that completes each sentence.

13 A prime number is any whole number greater than 1 with exactly two factors, 1 and itself.

14 A composite number is a number greater than 1 with more than two factors.

Chapter 5

Copyright © Macmillan/McGraw-Hill, • Glencoe, a division of The McGraw-Hill Companies, Inc.

Math Triumphs Lesson 5-6 A119

Answer Key (Lesson 6-1)

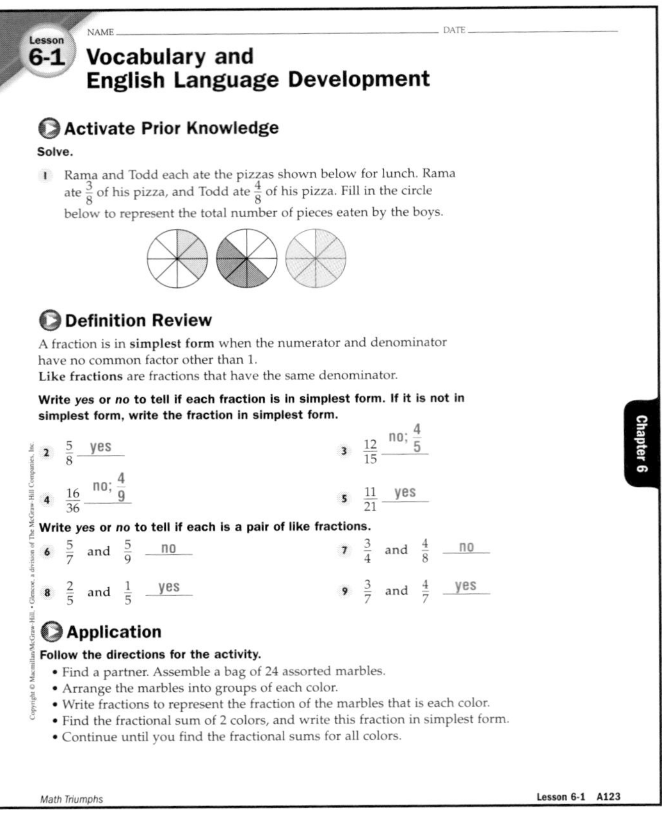

Lesson 6-1 NAME ______ DATE ______

Vocabulary and English Language Development

Activate Prior Knowledge

Solve.

1. Rama and Todd each ate the pizzas shown below for lunch. Rama ate $\frac{3}{8}$ of his pizza, and Todd ate $\frac{4}{8}$ of his pizza. Fill in the circle below to represent the total number of pieces eaten by the boys.

Definition Review

A fraction is in **simplest form** when the numerator and denominator have no common factor other than 1.
Like fractions are fractions that have the same denominator.

Write *yes* or *no* to tell if each fraction is in simplest form. If it is not in simplest form, write the fraction in simplest form.

2. $\frac{5}{8}$ yes
3. $\frac{12}{15}$ no; $\frac{4}{5}$
4. $\frac{16}{36}$ no; $\frac{4}{9}$
5. $\frac{11}{21}$ yes

Write *yes* or *no* to tell if each is a pair of like fractions.

6. $\frac{5}{7}$ and $\frac{5}{9}$ no
7. $\frac{3}{4}$ and $\frac{4}{8}$ no
8. $\frac{2}{5}$ and $\frac{1}{5}$ yes
9. $\frac{3}{7}$ and $\frac{4}{7}$ yes

Application

Follow the directions for the activity.

- Find a partner. Assemble a bag of 24 assorted marbles.
- Arrange the marbles into groups of each color.
- Write fractions to represent the fraction of the marbles that is each color.
- Find the fractional sum of 2 colors, and write this fraction in simplest form.
- Continue until you find the fractional sums for all colors.

Chapter 6

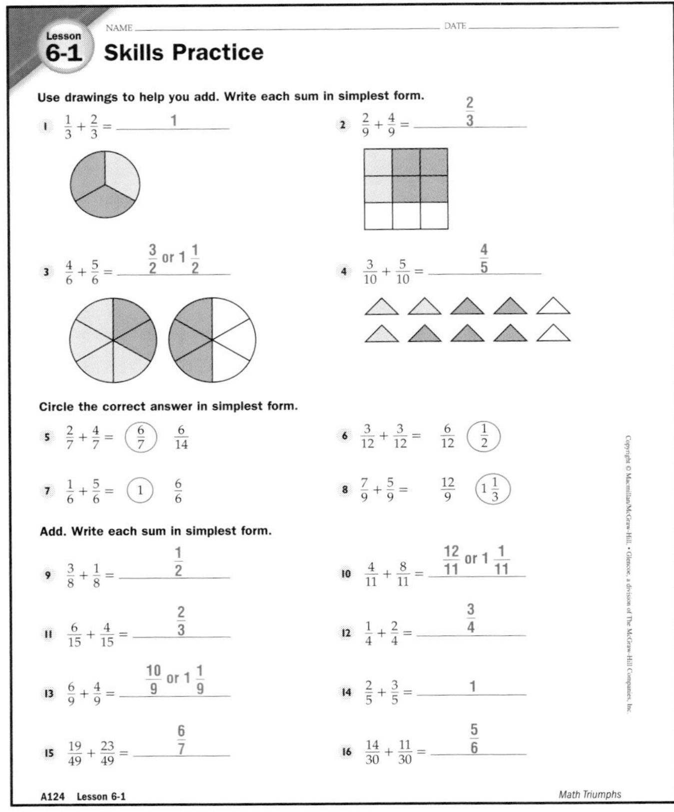

Lesson 6-1 NAME ______ DATE ______

Skills Practice

Use drawings to help you add. Write each sum in simplest form.

1. $\frac{1}{3}+\frac{2}{3}=$ 1
2. $\frac{2}{9}+\frac{4}{9}=$ $\frac{2}{3}$
3. $\frac{4}{6}+\frac{5}{6}=$ $\frac{3}{2}$ or $1\frac{1}{2}$
4. $\frac{3}{10}+\frac{5}{10}=$ $\frac{4}{5}$

Circle the correct answer in simplest form.

5. $\frac{2}{7}+\frac{4}{7}=$ ($\frac{6}{7}$) $\frac{6}{14}$
6. $\frac{3}{12}+\frac{3}{12}=$ $\frac{6}{12}$ ($\frac{1}{2}$)
7. $\frac{1}{6}+\frac{5}{6}=$ (1) $\frac{6}{6}$
8. $\frac{7}{9}+\frac{5}{9}=$ $\frac{12}{9}$ ($1\frac{1}{3}$)

Add. Write each sum in simplest form.

9. $\frac{3}{8}+\frac{1}{8}=$ $\frac{1}{2}$
10. $\frac{4}{11}+\frac{8}{11}=$ $\frac{12}{11}$ or $1\frac{1}{11}$
11. $\frac{6}{15}+\frac{4}{15}=$ $\frac{2}{3}$
12. $\frac{1}{4}+\frac{2}{4}=$ $\frac{3}{4}$
13. $\frac{6}{9}+\frac{4}{9}=$ $\frac{10}{9}$ or $1\frac{1}{9}$
14. $\frac{2}{5}+\frac{3}{5}=$ 1
15. $\frac{19}{49}+\frac{23}{49}=$ $\frac{6}{7}$
16. $\frac{14}{30}+\frac{11}{30}=$ $\frac{5}{6}$

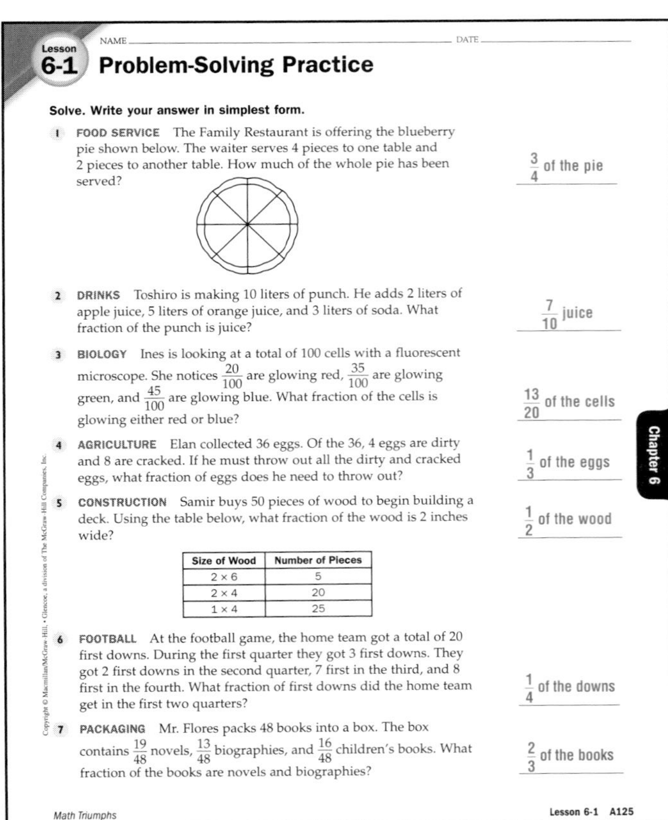

Lesson 6-1 NAME ______ DATE ______

Problem-Solving Practice

Solve. Write your answer in simplest form.

1. **FOOD SERVICE** The Family Restaurant is offering the blueberry pie shown below. The waiter serves 4 pieces to one table and 2 pieces to another table. How much of the whole pie has been served? $\frac{3}{4}$ of the pie
2. **DRINKS** Toshiro is making 10 liters of punch. He adds 2 liters of apple juice, 5 liters of orange juice, and 3 liters of soda. What fraction of the punch is juice? $\frac{7}{10}$ juice
3. **BIOLOGY** Ines is looking at a total of 100 cells with a fluorescent microscope. She notices $\frac{20}{100}$ are glowing red, $\frac{35}{100}$ are glowing green, and $\frac{45}{100}$ are glowing blue. What fraction of the cells is glowing either red or blue? $\frac{13}{20}$ of the cells
4. **AGRICULTURE** Elan collected 36 eggs. Of the 36, 4 eggs are dirty and 8 are cracked. If he must throw out all the dirty and cracked eggs, what fraction of eggs does he need to throw out? $\frac{1}{3}$ of the eggs
5. **CONSTRUCTION** Samir buys 50 pieces of wood to begin building a deck. Using the table below, what fraction of the wood is 2 inches wide? $\frac{1}{2}$ of the wood

Size of Wood	Number of Pieces
2 × 6	5
2 × 4	20
1 × 4	25

6. **FOOTBALL** At the football game, the home team got a total of 20 first downs. During the first quarter they got 3 first downs. They got 2 first downs in the second quarter, 7 first in the third, and 8 first in the fourth. What fraction of first downs did the home team get in the first two quarters? $\frac{1}{4}$ of the downs
7. **PACKAGING** Mr. Flores packs 48 books into a box. The box contains $\frac{19}{48}$ novels, $\frac{13}{48}$ biographies, and $\frac{16}{48}$ children's books. What fraction of the books are novels and biographies? $\frac{2}{3}$ of the books

Chapter 6

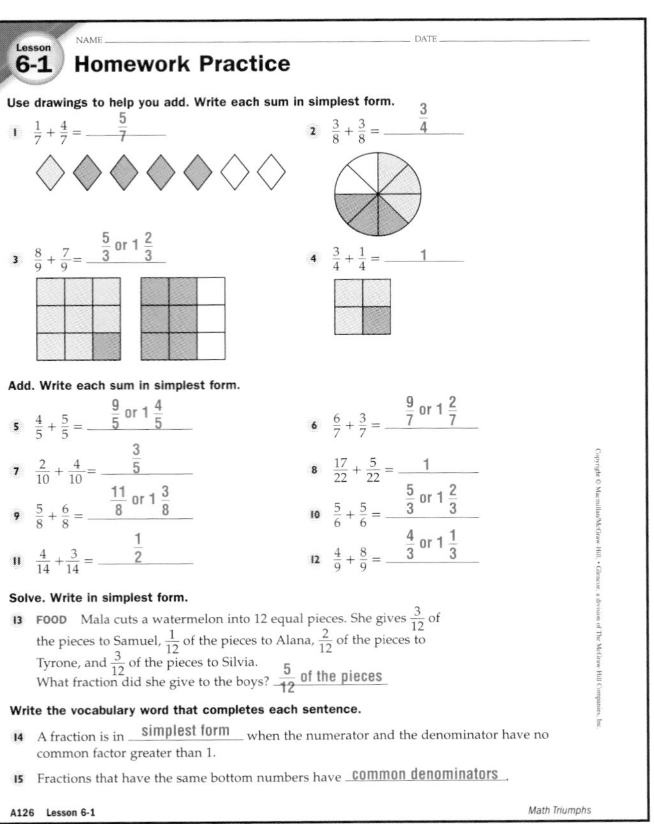

Lesson 6-1 NAME ______ DATE ______

Homework Practice

Use drawings to help you add. Write each sum in simplest form.

1. $\frac{1}{7}+\frac{4}{7}=$ $\frac{5}{7}$
2. $\frac{3}{8}+\frac{3}{8}=$ $\frac{3}{4}$
3. $\frac{8}{9}+\frac{7}{9}=$ $\frac{5}{3}$ or $1\frac{2}{3}$
4. $\frac{3}{4}+\frac{1}{4}=$ 1

Add. Write each sum in simplest form.

5. $\frac{4}{5}+\frac{5}{5}=$ $\frac{9}{5}$ or $1\frac{4}{5}$
6. $\frac{6}{7}+\frac{3}{7}=$ $\frac{9}{7}$ or $1\frac{2}{7}$
7. $\frac{2}{10}+\frac{4}{10}=$ $\frac{3}{5}$
8. $\frac{17}{22}+\frac{5}{22}=$ 1
9. $\frac{5}{8}+\frac{6}{8}=$ $\frac{11}{8}$ or $1\frac{3}{8}$
10. $\frac{5}{6}+\frac{5}{6}=$ $\frac{5}{3}$ or $1\frac{2}{3}$
11. $\frac{4}{14}+\frac{3}{14}=$ $\frac{1}{2}$
12. $\frac{4}{9}+\frac{8}{9}=$ $\frac{4}{3}$ or $1\frac{1}{3}$

Solve. Write in simplest form.

13. **FOOD** Mala cuts a watermelon into 12 equal pieces. She gives $\frac{3}{12}$ of the pieces to Samuel, $\frac{1}{12}$ of the pieces to Alana, $\frac{2}{12}$ of the pieces to Tyrone, and $\frac{3}{12}$ of the pieces to Silvia. What fraction did she give to the boys? $\frac{5}{12}$ of the pieces

Write the vocabulary word that completes each sentence.

14. A fraction is in simplest form when the numerator and the denominator have no common factor greater than 1.
15. Fractions that have the same bottom numbers have common denominators.

Answer Key (Lesson 6-2)

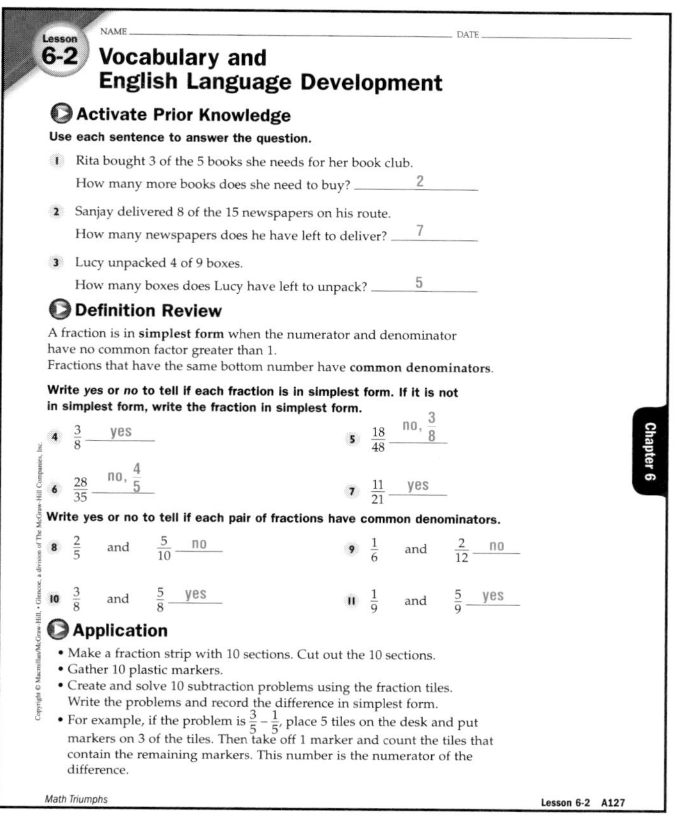

Lesson 6-2 NAME ______ DATE ______

Vocabulary and English Language Development

Activate Prior Knowledge

Use each sentence to answer the question.

1. Rita bought 3 of the 5 books she needs for her book club. How many more books does she need to buy? 2
2. Sanjay delivered 8 of the 15 newspapers on his route. How many newspapers does he have left to deliver? 7
3. Lucy unpacked 4 of 9 boxes. How many boxes does Lucy have left to unpack? 5

Definition Review

A fraction is in **simplest form** when the numerator and denominator have no common factor greater than 1.
Fractions that have the same bottom number have **common denominators**.

Write *yes* or *no* to tell if each fraction is in simplest form. If it is not in simplest form, write the fraction in simplest form.

4. $\frac{3}{8}$ yes
5. $\frac{18}{48}$ no, $\frac{3}{8}$
6. $\frac{28}{35}$ no, $\frac{4}{5}$
7. $\frac{11}{21}$ yes

Write yes or no to tell if each pair of fractions have common denominators.

8. $\frac{2}{5}$ and $\frac{5}{10}$ no
9. $\frac{1}{6}$ and $\frac{2}{12}$ no
10. $\frac{3}{8}$ and $\frac{5}{8}$ yes
11. $\frac{1}{9}$ and $\frac{5}{9}$ yes

Application

- Make a fraction strip with 10 sections. Cut out the 10 sections.
- Gather 10 plastic markers.
- Create and solve 10 subtraction problems using the fraction tiles. Write the problems and record the difference in simplest form.
- For example, if the problem is $\frac{3}{5} - \frac{1}{5}$, place 5 tiles on the desk and put markers on 3 of the tiles. Then take off 1 marker and count the tiles that contain the remaining markers. This number is the numerator of the difference.

Chapter 6

Copyright © Macmillan/McGraw-Hill, • Glencoe, a division of The McGraw-Hill Companies, Inc.

Math Triumphs Lesson 6-2 A127

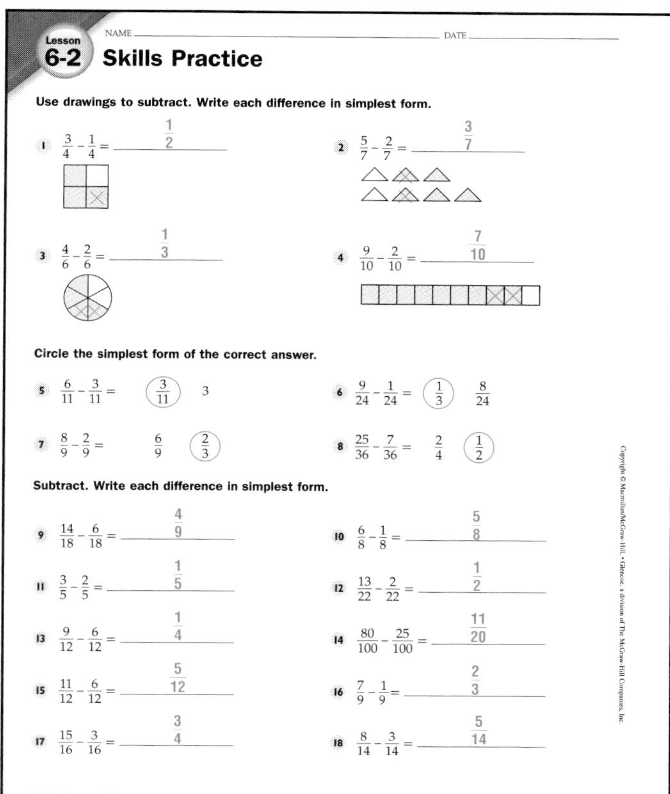

Lesson 6-2 NAME ______ DATE ______

Skills Practice

Use drawings to subtract. Write each difference in simplest form.

1. $\frac{3}{4} - \frac{1}{4} = \frac{1}{2}$
2. $\frac{5}{7} - \frac{2}{7} = \frac{3}{7}$
3. $\frac{4}{6} - \frac{2}{6} = \frac{1}{3}$
4. $\frac{9}{10} - \frac{2}{10} = \frac{7}{10}$

Circle the simplest form of the correct answer.

5. $\frac{6}{11} - \frac{3}{11} =$ (circled: $\frac{3}{11}$) 3
6. $\frac{9}{24} - \frac{1}{24} =$ (circled: $\frac{1}{3}$) $\frac{8}{24}$
7. $\frac{8}{9} - \frac{2}{9} =$ $\frac{6}{9}$ (circled: $\frac{2}{3}$)
8. $\frac{25}{36} - \frac{7}{36} =$ $\frac{2}{4}$ (circled: $\frac{1}{2}$)

Subtract. Write each difference in simplest form.

9. $\frac{14}{18} - \frac{6}{18} = \frac{4}{9}$
10. $\frac{6}{8} - \frac{1}{8} = \frac{5}{8}$
11. $\frac{3}{5} - \frac{2}{5} = \frac{1}{5}$
12. $\frac{13}{22} - \frac{2}{22} = \frac{1}{2}$
13. $\frac{9}{12} - \frac{6}{12} = \frac{1}{4}$
14. $\frac{80}{100} - \frac{25}{100} = \frac{11}{20}$
15. $\frac{11}{12} - \frac{6}{12} = \frac{5}{12}$
16. $\frac{7}{9} - \frac{1}{9} = \frac{2}{3}$
17. $\frac{15}{16} - \frac{3}{16} = \frac{3}{4}$
18. $\frac{8}{14} - \frac{3}{14} = \frac{5}{14}$

Copyright © Macmillan/McGraw-Hill, • Glencoe, a division of The McGraw-Hill Companies, Inc.

A128 Lesson 6-2 Math Triumphs

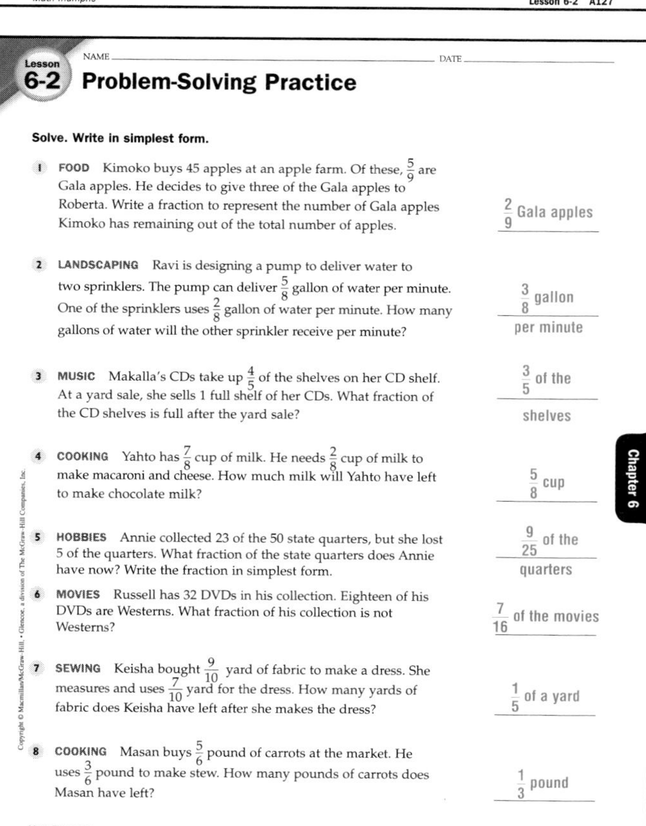

Lesson 6-2 NAME ______ DATE ______

Problem-Solving Practice

Solve. Write in simplest form.

1. **FOOD** Kimoko buys 45 apples at an apple farm. Of these, $\frac{5}{9}$ are Gala apples. He decides to give three of the Gala apples to Roberta. Write a fraction to represent the number of Gala apples Kimoko has remaining out of the total number of apples. $\frac{2}{9}$ Gala apples
2. **LANDSCAPING** Ravi is designing a pump to deliver water to two sprinklers. The pump can deliver $\frac{5}{8}$ gallon of water per minute. One of the sprinklers uses $\frac{2}{8}$ gallon of water per minute. How many gallons of water will the other sprinkler receive per minute? $\frac{3}{8}$ gallon per minute
3. **MUSIC** Makalla's CDs take up $\frac{4}{5}$ of the shelves on her CD shelf. At a yard sale, she sells 1 full shelf of her CDs. What fraction of the CD shelves is full after the yard sale? $\frac{3}{5}$ of the shelves
4. **COOKING** Yahto has $\frac{7}{8}$ cup of milk. He needs $\frac{2}{8}$ cup of milk to make macaroni and cheese. How much milk will Yahto have left to make chocolate milk? $\frac{5}{8}$ cup
5. **HOBBIES** Annie collected 23 of the 50 state quarters, but she lost 5 of the quarters. What fraction of the state quarters does Annie have now? Write the fraction in simplest form. $\frac{9}{25}$ of the quarters
6. **MOVIES** Russell has 32 DVDs in his collection. Eighteen of his DVDs are Westerns. What fraction of his collection is not Westerns? $\frac{7}{16}$ of the movies
7. **SEWING** Keisha bought $\frac{9}{10}$ yard of fabric to make a dress. She measures and uses $\frac{7}{10}$ yard for the dress. How many yards of fabric does Keisha have left after she makes the dress? $\frac{1}{5}$ of a yard
8. **COOKING** Masan buys $\frac{5}{6}$ pound of carrots at the market. He uses $\frac{3}{6}$ pound to make stew. How many pounds of carrots does Masan have left? $\frac{1}{3}$ pound

Chapter 6

Copyright © Macmillan/McGraw-Hill, • Glencoe, a division of The McGraw-Hill Companies, Inc.

Math Triumphs Lesson 6-2 A129

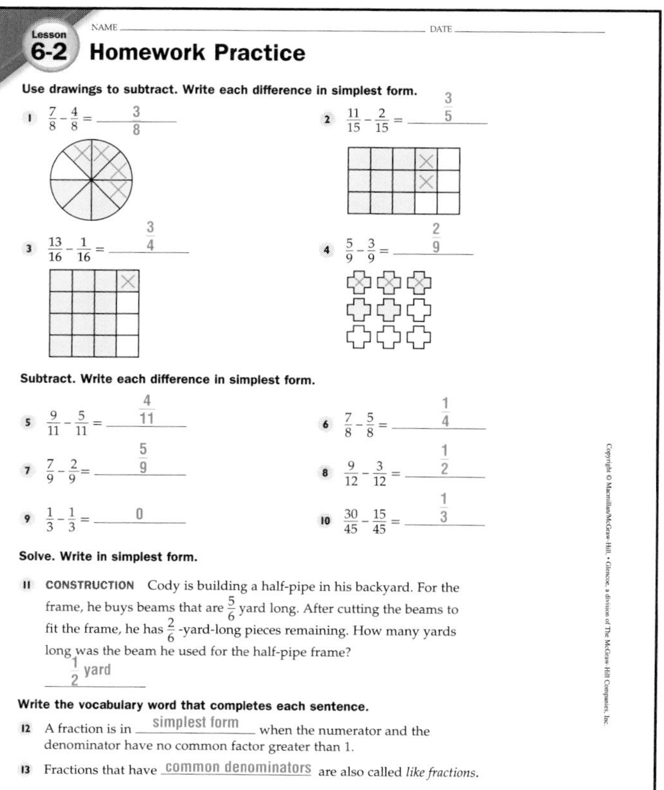

Lesson 6-2 NAME ______ DATE ______

Homework Practice

Use drawings to subtract. Write each difference in simplest form.

1. $\frac{7}{8} - \frac{4}{8} = \frac{3}{8}$
2. $\frac{11}{15} - \frac{2}{15} = \frac{3}{5}$
3. $\frac{13}{16} - \frac{1}{16} = \frac{3}{4}$
4. $\frac{5}{9} - \frac{3}{9} = \frac{2}{9}$

Subtract. Write each difference in simplest form.

5. $\frac{9}{11} - \frac{5}{11} = \frac{4}{11}$
6. $\frac{7}{8} - \frac{5}{8} = \frac{1}{4}$
7. $\frac{7}{9} - \frac{2}{9} = \frac{5}{9}$
8. $\frac{9}{12} - \frac{3}{12} = \frac{1}{2}$
9. $\frac{1}{3} - \frac{1}{3} = 0$
10. $\frac{30}{45} - \frac{15}{45} = \frac{1}{3}$

Solve. Write in simplest form.

11. **CONSTRUCTION** Cody is building a half-pipe in his backyard. For the frame, he buys beams that are $\frac{5}{6}$ yard long. After cutting the beams to fit the frame, he has $\frac{2}{6}$-yard-long pieces remaining. How many yards long was the beam he used for the half-pipe frame? $\frac{1}{2}$ yard

Write the vocabulary word that completes each sentence.

12. A fraction is in simplest form when the numerator and the denominator have no common factor greater than 1.
13. Fractions that have common denominators are also called *like fractions*.

Copyright © Macmillan/McGraw-Hill, • Glencoe, a division of The McGraw-Hill Companies, Inc.

A130 Lesson 6-2 Math Triumphs

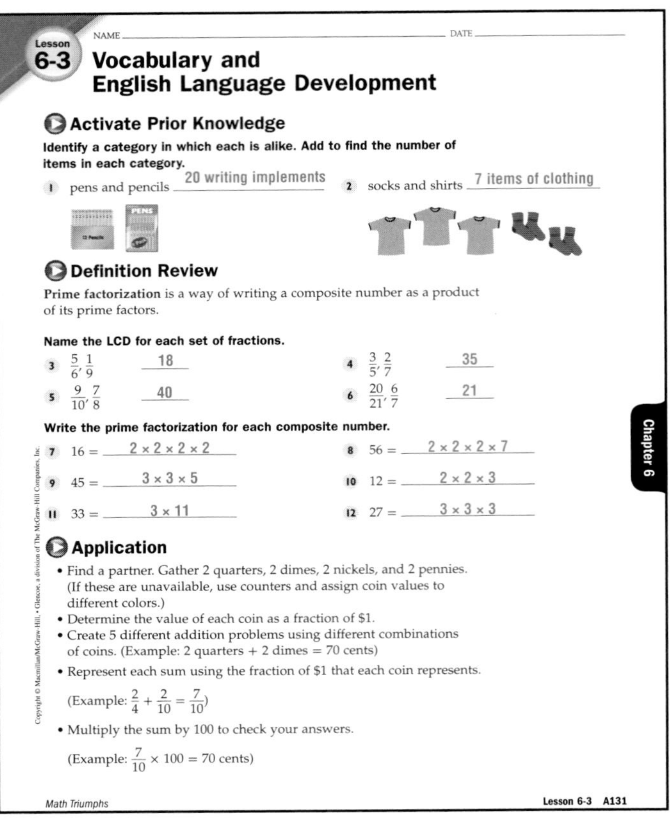

NAME ________ DATE ________

Lesson 6-3 Vocabulary and English Language Development

Activate Prior Knowledge

Identify a category in which each is alike. Add to find the number of items in each category.

1. pens and pencils **20 writing implements**
2. socks and shirts **7 items of clothing**

Definition Review

Prime factorization is a way of writing a composite number as a product of its prime factors.

Name the LCD for each set of fractions.

3. $\frac{5}{6}, \frac{1}{9}$ **18**
4. $\frac{3}{5}, \frac{2}{7}$ **35**
5. $\frac{9}{10}, \frac{7}{8}$ **40**
6. $\frac{20}{21}, \frac{6}{7}$ **21**

Write the prime factorization for each composite number.

7. 16 = **2 × 2 × 2 × 2**
8. 56 = **2 × 2 × 2 × 7**
9. 45 = **3 × 3 × 5**
10. 12 = **2 × 2 × 3**
11. 33 = **3 × 11**
12. 27 = **3 × 3 × 3**

Application

- Find a partner. Gather 2 quarters, 2 dimes, 2 nickels, and 2 pennies. (If these are unavailable, use counters and assign coin values to different colors.)
- Determine the value of each coin as a fraction of $1.
- Create 5 different addition problems using different combinations of coins. (Example: 2 quarters + 2 dimes = 70 cents)
- Represent each sum using the fraction of $1 that each coin represents. (Example: $\frac{2}{4} + \frac{2}{10} = \frac{7}{10}$)
- Multiply the sum by 100 to check your answers. (Example: $\frac{7}{10} \times 100 = 70$ cents)

Chapter 6

Copyright © Macmillan/McGraw-Hill, a division of The McGraw-Hill Companies, Inc.

Math Triumphs Lesson 6-3 A131

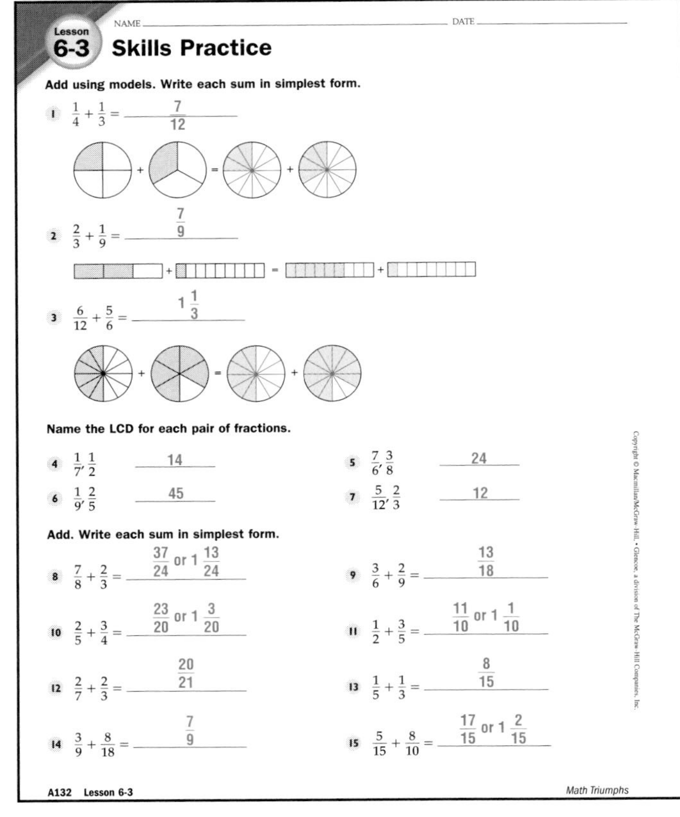

NAME ________ DATE ________

Lesson 6-3 Skills Practice

Add using models. Write each sum in simplest form.

1. $\frac{1}{4} + \frac{1}{3} =$ $\frac{7}{12}$
2. $\frac{2}{3} + \frac{1}{9} =$ $\frac{7}{9}$
3. $\frac{6}{12} + \frac{5}{6} =$ $1\frac{1}{3}$

Name the LCD for each pair of fractions.

4. $\frac{1}{7}, \frac{1}{2}$ **14**
5. $\frac{7}{6}, \frac{3}{8}$ **24**
6. $\frac{1}{9}, \frac{2}{5}$ **45**
7. $\frac{5}{12}, \frac{2}{3}$ **12**

Add. Write each sum in simplest form.

8. $\frac{7}{8} + \frac{2}{3} =$ $\frac{37}{24}$ or $1\frac{13}{24}$
9. $\frac{3}{6} + \frac{2}{9} =$ $\frac{13}{18}$
10. $\frac{2}{5} + \frac{3}{4} =$ $\frac{23}{20}$ or $1\frac{3}{20}$
11. $\frac{1}{2} + \frac{3}{5} =$ $\frac{11}{10}$ or $1\frac{1}{10}$
12. $\frac{2}{7} + \frac{2}{3} =$ $\frac{20}{21}$
13. $\frac{1}{5} + \frac{1}{3} =$ $\frac{8}{15}$
14. $\frac{3}{9} + \frac{8}{18} =$ $\frac{7}{9}$
15. $\frac{5}{15} + \frac{8}{10} =$ $\frac{17}{15}$ or $1\frac{2}{15}$

Copyright © Macmillan/McGraw-Hill, a division of The McGraw-Hill Companies, Inc.

A132 Lesson 6-3 Math Triumphs

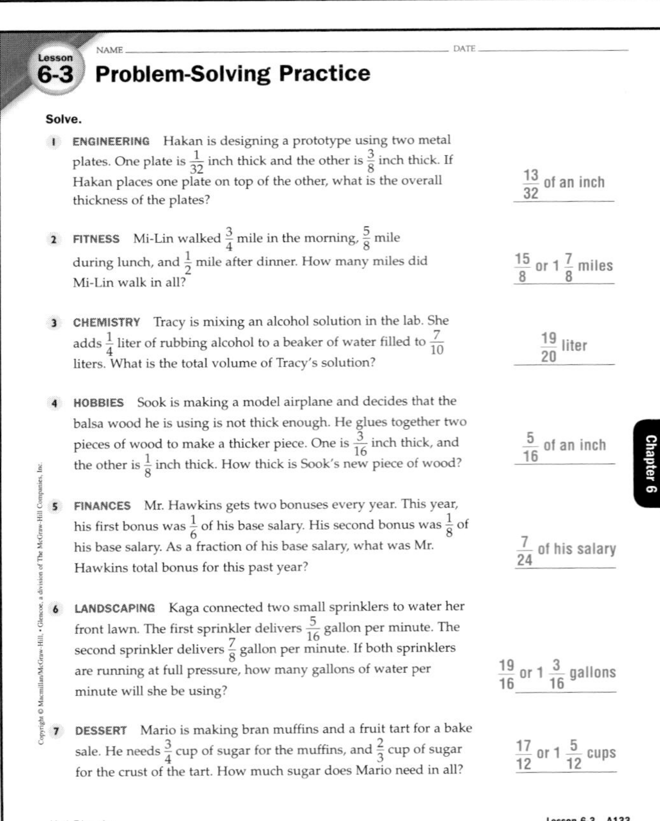

NAME ________ DATE ________

Lesson 6-3 Problem-Solving Practice

Solve.

1. **ENGINEERING** Hakan is designing a prototype using two metal plates. One plate is $\frac{1}{32}$ inch thick and the other is $\frac{3}{8}$ inch thick. If Hakan places one plate on top of the other, what is the overall thickness of the plates? **$\frac{13}{32}$ of an inch**
2. **FITNESS** Mi-Lin walked $\frac{3}{4}$ mile in the morning, $\frac{5}{8}$ mile during lunch, and $\frac{1}{2}$ mile after dinner. How many miles did Mi-Lin walk in all? **$\frac{15}{8}$ or $1\frac{7}{8}$ miles**
3. **CHEMISTRY** Tracy is mixing an alcohol solution in the lab. She adds $\frac{1}{4}$ liter of rubbing alcohol to a beaker of water filled to $\frac{7}{10}$ liters. What is the total volume of Tracy's solution? **$\frac{19}{20}$ liter**
4. **HOBBIES** Sook is making a model airplane and decides that the balsa wood he is using is not thick enough. He glues together two pieces of wood to make a thicker piece. One is $\frac{3}{16}$ inch thick, and the other is $\frac{1}{8}$ inch thick. How thick is Sook's new piece of wood? **$\frac{5}{16}$ of an inch**
5. **FINANCES** Mr. Hawkins gets two bonuses every year. This year, his first bonus was $\frac{1}{6}$ of his base salary. His second bonus was $\frac{1}{8}$ of his base salary. As a fraction of his base salary, what was Mr. Hawkins total bonus for this past year? **$\frac{7}{24}$ of his salary**
6. **LANDSCAPING** Kaga connected two small sprinklers to water her front lawn. The first sprinkler delivers $\frac{5}{16}$ gallon per minute. The second sprinkler delivers $\frac{7}{8}$ gallon per minute. If both sprinklers are running at full pressure, how many gallons of water per minute will she be using? **$\frac{19}{16}$ or $1\frac{3}{16}$ gallons**
7. **DESSERT** Mario is making bran muffins and a fruit tart for a bake sale. He needs $\frac{3}{4}$ cup of sugar for the muffins, and $\frac{2}{3}$ cup of sugar for the crust of the tart. How much sugar does Mario need in all? **$\frac{17}{12}$ or $1\frac{5}{12}$ cups**

Chapter 6

Copyright © Macmillan/McGraw-Hill, a division of The McGraw-Hill Companies, Inc.

Math Triumphs Lesson 6-3 A133

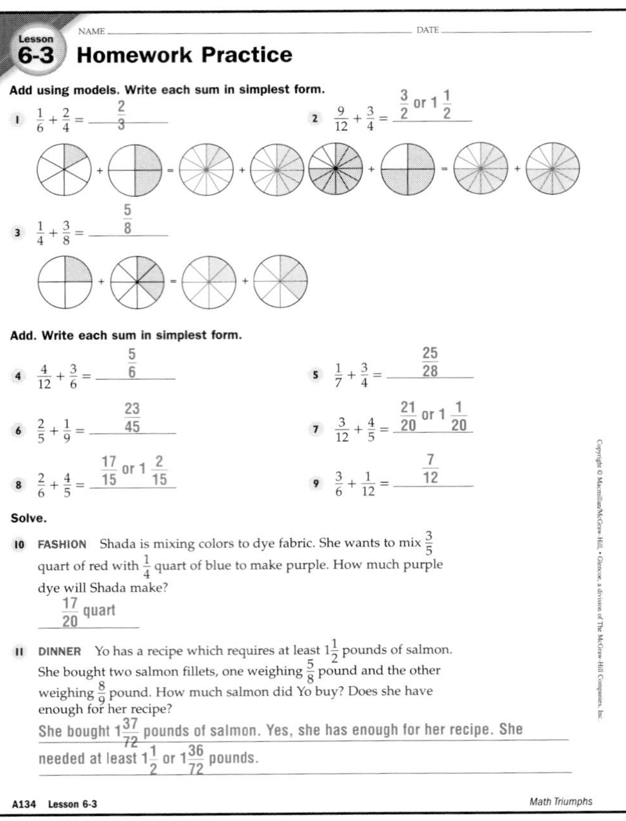

NAME ________ DATE ________

Lesson 6-3 Homework Practice

Add using models. Write each sum in simplest form.

1. $\frac{1}{6} + \frac{2}{4} =$ $\frac{2}{3}$
2. $\frac{9}{12} + \frac{3}{4} =$ $\frac{3}{2}$ or $1\frac{1}{2}$
3. $\frac{1}{4} + \frac{3}{8} =$ $\frac{5}{8}$

Add. Write each sum in simplest form.

4. $\frac{4}{12} + \frac{3}{6} =$ $\frac{5}{6}$
5. $\frac{1}{7} + \frac{3}{4} =$ $\frac{25}{28}$
6. $\frac{2}{5} + \frac{1}{9} =$ $\frac{23}{45}$
7. $\frac{3}{12} + \frac{4}{5} =$ $\frac{21}{20}$ or $1\frac{1}{20}$
8. $\frac{2}{6} + \frac{4}{5} =$ $\frac{17}{15}$ or $1\frac{2}{15}$
9. $\frac{3}{6} + \frac{1}{12} =$ $\frac{7}{12}$

Solve.

10. **FASHION** Shada is mixing colors to dye fabric. She wants to mix $\frac{3}{5}$ quart of red with $\frac{1}{4}$ quart of blue to make purple. How much purple dye will Shada make? **$\frac{17}{20}$ quart**
11. **DINNER** Yo has a recipe which requires at least $1\frac{1}{2}$ pounds of salmon. She bought two salmon fillets, one weighing $\frac{5}{8}$ pound and the other weighing $\frac{8}{9}$ pound. How much salmon did Yo buy? Does she have enough for her recipe? **She bought $1\frac{37}{72}$ pounds of salmon. Yes, she has enough for her recipe. She needed at least $1\frac{1}{2}$ or $1\frac{36}{72}$ pounds.**

Copyright © Macmillan/McGraw-Hill, a division of The McGraw-Hill Companies, Inc.

A134 Lesson 6-3 Math Triumphs

Answer Key (Lesson 6-4)

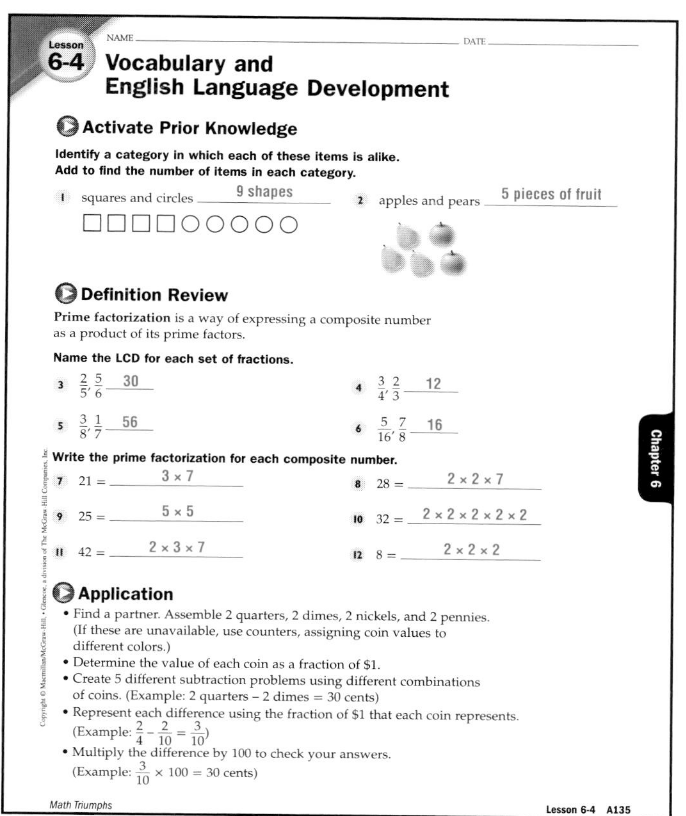

Lesson 6-4 NAME ______ DATE ______

Vocabulary and English Language Development

Activate Prior Knowledge

Identify a category in which each of these items is alike. Add to find the number of items in each category.

1 squares and circles 9 shapes

2 apples and pears 5 pieces of fruit

Definition Review

Prime factorization is a way of expressing a composite number as a product of its prime factors.

Name the LCD for each set of fractions.

3 $\frac{2}{5}, \frac{5}{6}$ 30

4 $\frac{3}{4}, \frac{2}{3}$ 12

5 $\frac{3}{8}, \frac{1}{7}$ 56

6 $\frac{5}{16}, \frac{7}{8}$ 16

Write the prime factorization for each composite number.

7 $21 = 3 \times 7$

8 $28 = 2 \times 2 \times 7$

9 $25 = 5 \times 5$

10 $32 = 2 \times 2 \times 2 \times 2 \times 2$

11 $42 = 2 \times 3 \times 7$

12 $8 = 2 \times 2 \times 2$

Application

- Find a partner. Assemble 2 quarters, 2 dimes, 2 nickels, and 2 pennies. (If these are unavailable, use counters, assigning coin values to different colors.)
- Determine the value of each coin as a fraction of $1.
- Create 5 different subtraction problems using different combinations of coins. (Example: 2 quarters – 2 dimes = 30 cents)
- Represent each difference using the fraction of $1 that each coin represents. (Example: $\frac{2}{4} - \frac{2}{10} = \frac{3}{10}$)
- Multiply the difference by 100 to check your answers. (Example: $\frac{3}{10} \times 100 = 30$ cents)

Chapter 6

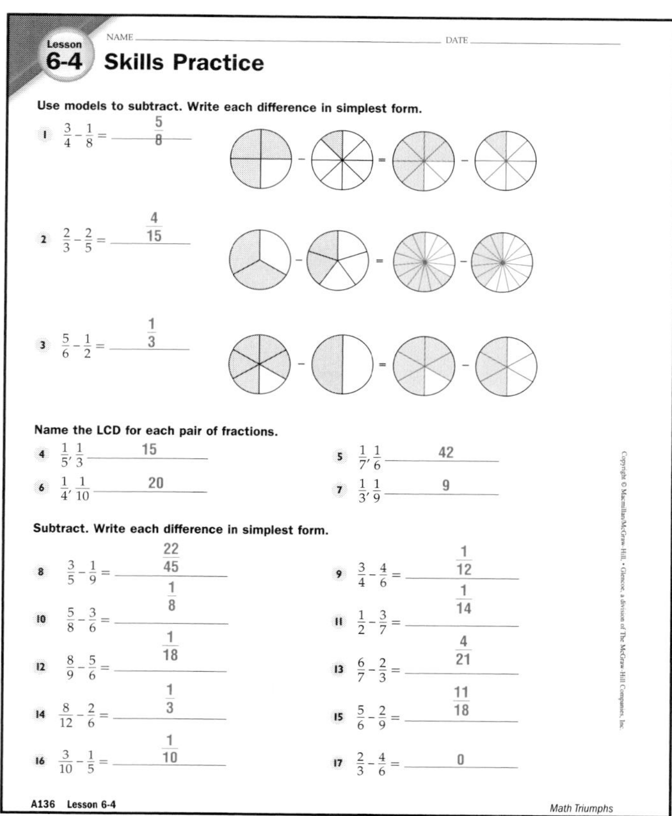

Lesson 6-4 NAME ______ DATE ______

Skills Practice

Use models to subtract. Write each difference in simplest form.

1 $\frac{3}{4} - \frac{1}{8} = \frac{5}{8}$

2 $\frac{2}{3} - \frac{2}{5} = \frac{4}{15}$

3 $\frac{5}{6} - \frac{1}{2} = \frac{1}{3}$

Name the LCD for each pair of fractions.

4 $\frac{1}{5}, \frac{1}{3}$ 15

5 $\frac{1}{7}, \frac{1}{6}$ 42

6 $\frac{1}{4}, \frac{1}{10}$ 20

7 $\frac{1}{3}, \frac{1}{9}$ 9

Subtract. Write each difference in simplest form.

8 $\frac{3}{5} - \frac{1}{9} = \frac{22}{45}$

9 $\frac{3}{4} - \frac{4}{6} = \frac{1}{12}$

10 $\frac{5}{8} - \frac{3}{6} = \frac{1}{8}$

11 $\frac{1}{2} - \frac{3}{7} = \frac{1}{14}$

12 $\frac{8}{9} - \frac{5}{6} = \frac{1}{18}$

13 $\frac{6}{7} - \frac{2}{3} = \frac{4}{21}$

14 $\frac{8}{12} - \frac{2}{6} = \frac{1}{3}$

15 $\frac{5}{6} - \frac{2}{9} = \frac{11}{18}$

16 $\frac{3}{10} - \frac{1}{5} = \frac{1}{10}$

17 $\frac{2}{3} - \frac{4}{6} = 0$

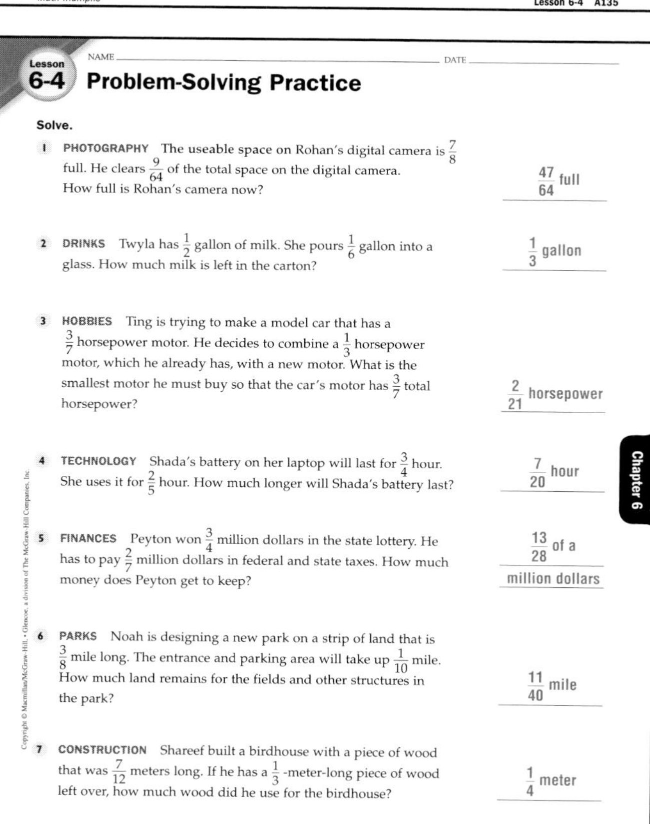

Lesson 6-4 NAME ______ DATE ______

Problem-Solving Practice

Solve.

1 **PHOTOGRAPHY** The useable space on Rohan's digital camera is $\frac{7}{8}$ full. He clears $\frac{9}{64}$ of the total space on the digital camera. How full is Rohan's camera now? $\frac{47}{64}$ full

2 **DRINKS** Twyla has $\frac{1}{2}$ gallon of milk. She pours $\frac{1}{6}$ gallon into a glass. How much milk is left in the carton? $\frac{1}{3}$ gallon

3 **HOBBIES** Ting is trying to make a model car that has a $\frac{3}{7}$ horsepower motor. He decides to combine a $\frac{1}{3}$ horsepower motor, which he already has, with a new motor. What is the smallest motor he must buy so that the car's motor has $\frac{3}{7}$ total horsepower? $\frac{2}{21}$ horsepower

4 **TECHNOLOGY** Shada's battery on her laptop will last for $\frac{3}{4}$ hour. She uses it for $\frac{2}{5}$ hour. How much longer will Shada's battery last? $\frac{7}{20}$ hour

5 **FINANCES** Peyton won $\frac{3}{4}$ million dollars in the state lottery. He has to pay $\frac{2}{7}$ million dollars in federal and state taxes. How much money does Peyton get to keep? $\frac{13}{28}$ of a million dollars

6 **PARKS** Noah is designing a new park on a strip of land that is $\frac{3}{8}$ mile long. The entrance and parking area will take up $\frac{1}{10}$ mile. How much land remains for the fields and other structures in the park? $\frac{11}{40}$ mile

7 **CONSTRUCTION** Shareef built a birdhouse with a piece of wood that was $\frac{7}{12}$ meters long. If he has a $\frac{1}{3}$-meter-long piece of wood left over, how much wood did he use for the birdhouse? $\frac{1}{4}$ meter

Chapter 6

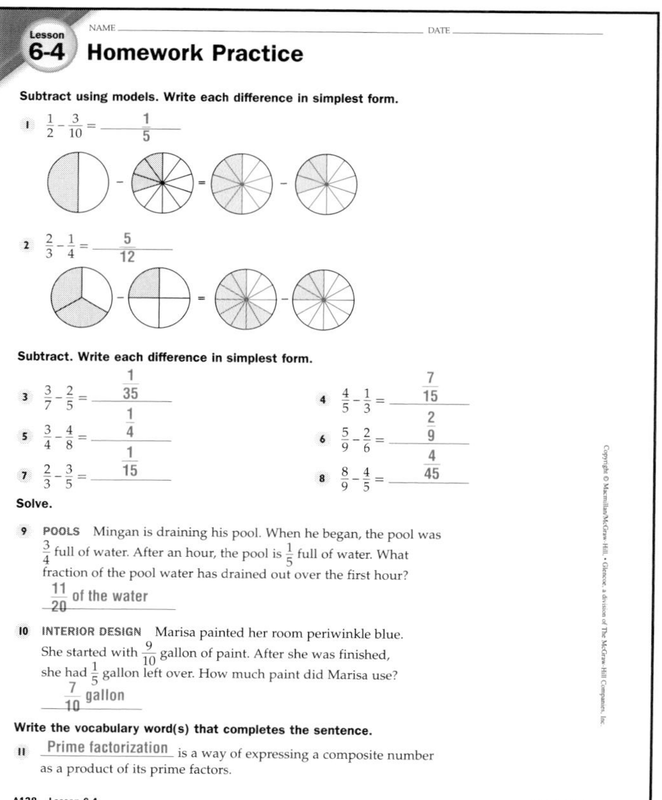

Lesson 6-4 NAME ______ DATE ______

Homework Practice

Subtract using models. Write each difference in simplest form.

1 $\frac{1}{2} - \frac{3}{10} = \frac{1}{5}$

2 $\frac{2}{3} - \frac{1}{4} = \frac{5}{12}$

Subtract. Write each difference in simplest form.

3 $\frac{3}{7} - \frac{2}{5} = \frac{1}{35}$

4 $\frac{4}{5} - \frac{1}{3} = \frac{7}{15}$

5 $\frac{3}{4} - \frac{4}{8} = \frac{1}{4}$

6 $\frac{5}{9} - \frac{2}{6} = \frac{2}{9}$

7 $\frac{2}{3} - \frac{3}{5} = \frac{1}{15}$

8 $\frac{8}{9} - \frac{4}{5} = \frac{4}{45}$

Solve.

9 **POOLS** Mingan is draining his pool. When he began, the pool was $\frac{3}{4}$ full of water. After an hour, the pool is $\frac{1}{5}$ full of water. What fraction of the pool water has drained out over the first hour? $\frac{11}{20}$ of the water

10 **INTERIOR DESIGN** Marisa painted her room periwinkle blue. She started with $\frac{9}{10}$ gallon of paint. After she was finished, she had $\frac{1}{5}$ gallon left over. How much paint did Marisa use? $\frac{7}{10}$ gallon

Write the vocabulary word(s) that completes the sentence.

11 Prime factorization is a way of expressing a composite number as a product of its prime factors.

Answer Key (Lesson 7-1)

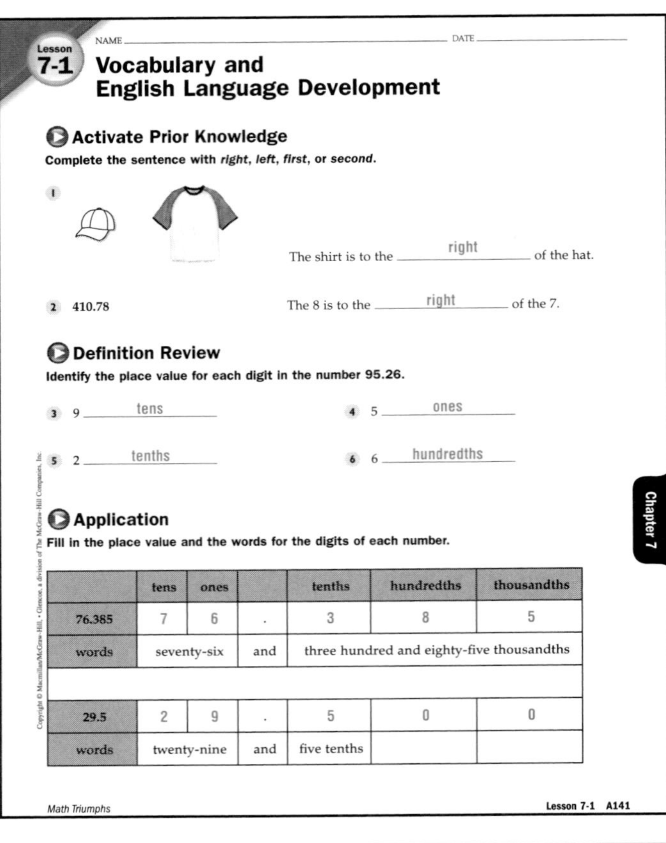

Lesson 7-1 NAME ________ DATE ________

Vocabulary and English Language Development

Activate Prior Knowledge

Complete the sentence with *right*, *left*, *first*, or *second*.

1. The shirt is to the right of the hat.
2. 410.78 The 8 is to the right of the 7.

Definition Review

Identify the place value for each digit in the number 95.26.

3. 9 tens
4. 5 ones
5. 2 tenths
6. 6 hundredths

Application

Fill in the place value and the words for the digits of each number.

	tens	ones		tenths	hundredths	thousandths
76.385	7	6	.	3	8	5
words	seventy-six		and	three hundred and eighty-five thousandths		
29.5	2	9	.	5	0	0
words	twenty-nine		and	five tenths		

Chapter 7

Lesson 7-1 NAME ________ DATE ________

Skills Practice

Write a decimal and a fraction or mixed number for each model.

1. 0.78 = $\frac{39}{50}$
2. 1.45 = $1\frac{9}{20}$

Write each number as a decimal.

3. twelve and sixty-five hundredths 12.65
4. nine tenths 0.9
5. seven and fourteen hundredths 7.14
6. eighteen and three hundredths 18.03
7. fifty-one hundredths 0.51
8. six and seven tenths 6.7

Write each number in words.

9. 20.3 twenty and three tenths
10. 0.89 eighty-nine hundredths
11. 3.078 three and seventy-eight thousandths
12. 17.4 seventeen and four tenths
13. 19.56 nineteen and fifty-six hundredths

Write the place of each underlined digit.

14. 67.4 tens
15. 13.825 thousandths
16. 5.4 tenths
17. 28.4 ones
18. 86.7 ones
19. 44.5 tens
20. 59.564 thousandths
21. 71.2 ones

Lesson 7-1 NAME ________ DATE ________

Problem-Solving Practice

Solve. Write in simplest form.

1. **RACING** Judy is racing her dragster on a $\frac{1}{4}$-mile track. If she resets her odometer to 0.00, what should her odometer read after 1 lap around the track? 0.25 mi
2. **TOOLS** Brandon needs to make a 0.625 -inch hole in a piece of wood. The drill bits he has are $\frac{3}{8}$ inch, $\frac{5}{8}$ inch, and $\frac{7}{8}$ inch in diameter. Which one should he use to drill the hole? $\frac{5}{8}$ in.
3. **TRIATHLON** Becky is training for a triathlon. To practice, she swims three-fourths of a kilometer 3 times a week. Use decimal notation to represent the number of kilometers Becky swims per week. 2.25 km
4. **HORSEBACK RIDING** Sergio rode his horse for $3\frac{14}{25}$ miles. What is the decimal equivalent of this distance? 3.56 mi
5. **RUNNING** Sabrina and Aashi raced each other in a 100m sprint. Their stop watches are shown below. Who won the race and by how many hundredths of a second? Aashi won the race by 0.08 seconds.

12:36 Sabrina

12:28 Aashi

6. **ENGINEERING** Andre is designing a power system that uses a motor with rating of $\frac{3}{4}$ hp. If his testing device reads horsepower in decimal units, what value should the testing device read? 0.75 hp
7. **TRAVEL** Tia's mother told her they would need to drive four hundred eighty-two and sixty-three hundredths miles to Mount Rushmore. What is the distance as a decimal? 482.63 mi
8. **BIOLOGY** In Biology class, Adita's frog weighed $1\frac{4}{10}$ kg. What is the decimal equivalent of the frog's weight? 1.4 kg

Chapter 7

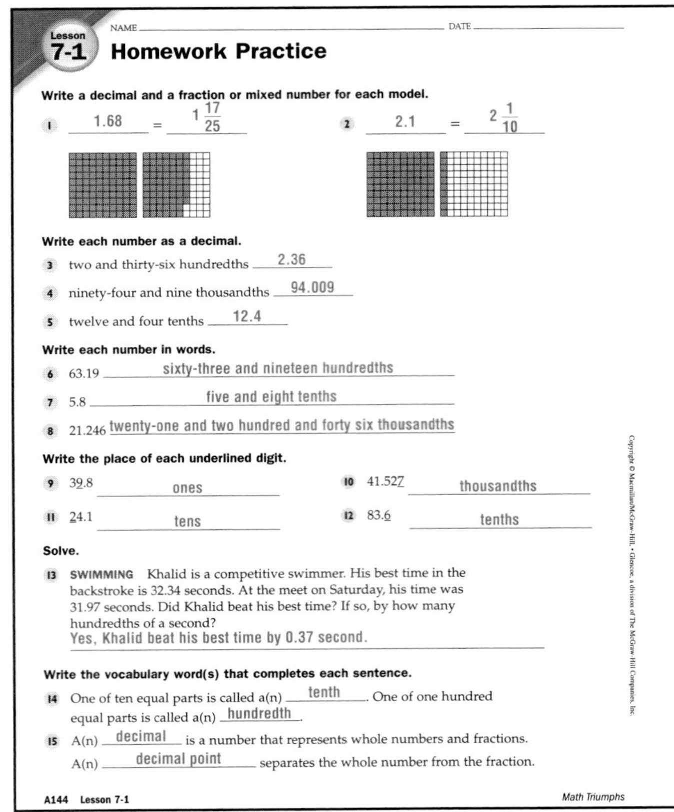

Lesson 7-1 NAME ________ DATE ________

Homework Practice

Write a decimal and a fraction or mixed number for each model.

1. 1.68 = $1\frac{17}{25}$
2. 2.1 = $2\frac{1}{10}$

Write each number as a decimal.

3. two and thirty-six hundredths 2.36
4. ninety-four and nine thousandths 94.009
5. twelve and four tenths 12.4

Write each number in words.

6. 63.19 sixty-three and nineteen hundredths
7. 5.8 five and eight tenths
8. 21.246 twenty-one and two hundred and forty six thousandths

Write the place of each underlined digit.

9. 39.8 ones
10. 41.527 thousandths
11. 24.1 tens
12. 83.6 tenths

Solve.

13. **SWIMMING** Khalid is a competitive swimmer. His best time in the backstroke is 32.34 seconds. At the meet on Saturday, his time was 31.97 seconds. Did Khalid beat his best time? If so, by how many hundredths of a second? Yes, Khalid beat his best time by 0.37 second.

Write the vocabulary word(s) that completes each sentence.

14. One of ten equal parts is called a(n) tenth. One of one hundred equal parts is called a(n) hundredth.
15. A(n) decimal is a number that represents whole numbers and fractions. A(n) decimal point separates the whole number from the fraction.

Answer Key (Lesson 7-2)

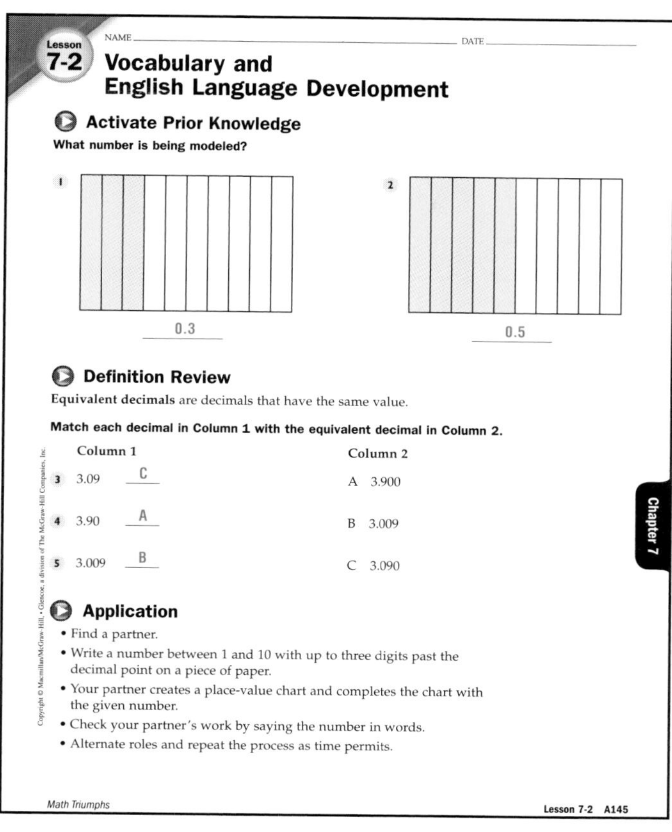

Lesson 7-2 NAME ______ DATE ______

Vocabulary and English Language Development

Activate Prior Knowledge

What number is being modeled?

1 0.3

2 0.5

Definition Review

Equivalent decimals are decimals that have the same value.

Match each decimal in Column 1 with the equivalent decimal in Column 2.

	Column 1		Column 2
3	3.09	C	A 3.900
4	3.90	A	B 3.009
5	3.009	B	C 3.090

Application

- Find a partner.
- Write a number between 1 and 10 with up to three digits past the decimal point on a piece of paper.
- Your partner creates a place-value chart and completes the chart with the given number.
- Check your partner's work by saying the number in words.
- Alternate roles and repeat the process as time permits.

Chapter 7

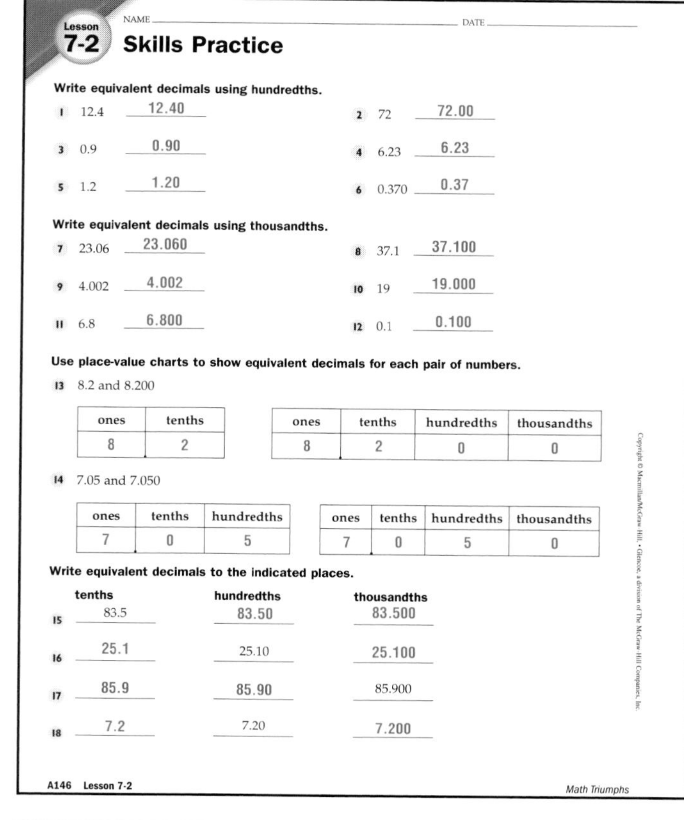

Lesson 7-2 NAME ______ DATE ______

Skills Practice

Write equivalent decimals using hundredths.

1 12.4 12.40 2 72 72.00

3 0.9 0.90 4 6.23 6.23

5 1.2 1.20 6 0.370 0.37

Write equivalent decimals using thousandths.

7 23.06 23.060 8 37.1 37.100

9 4.002 4.002 10 19 19.000

11 6.8 6.800 12 0.1 0.100

Use place-value charts to show equivalent decimals for each pair of numbers.

13 8.2 and 8.200

ones	tenths
8	2

ones	tenths	hundredths	thousandths
8	2	0	0

14 7.05 and 7.050

ones	tenths	hundredths
7	0	5

ones	tenths	hundredths	thousandths
7	0	5	0

Write equivalent decimals to the indicated places.

	tenths	hundredths	thousandths
15	83.5	83.50	83.500
16	25.1	25.10	25.100
17	85.9	85.90	85.900
18	7.2	7.20	7.200

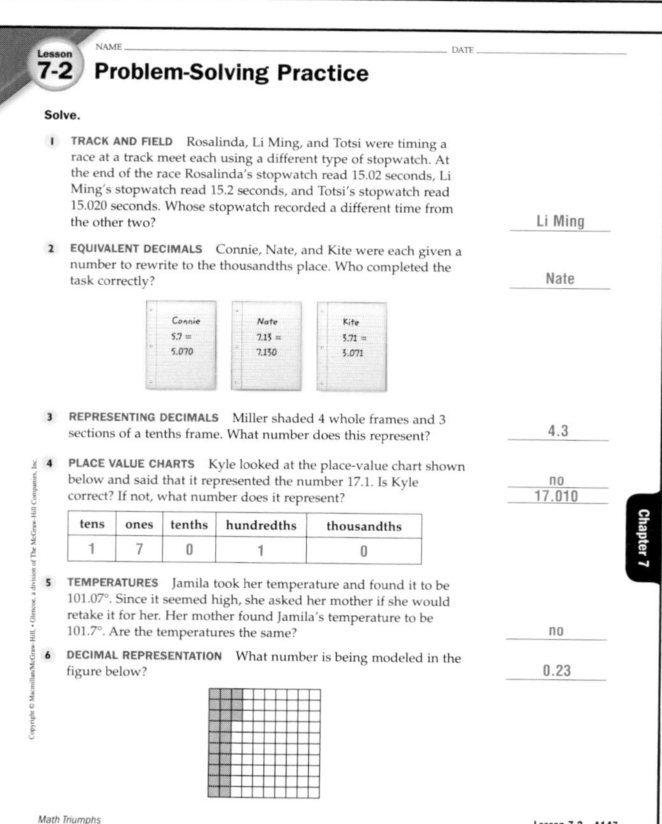

Lesson 7-2 NAME ______ DATE ______

Problem-Solving Practice

Solve.

1 TRACK AND FIELD Rosalinda, Li Ming, and Totsi were timing a race at a track meet each using a different type of stopwatch. At the end of the race Rosalinda's stopwatch read 15.02 seconds, Li Ming's stopwatch read 15.2 seconds, and Totsi's stopwatch read 15.020 seconds. Whose stopwatch recorded a different time from the other two? Li Ming

2 EQUIVALENT DECIMALS Connie, Nate, and Kite were each given a number to rewrite to the thousandths place. Who completed the task correctly? Nate

3 REPRESENTING DECIMALS Miller shaded 4 whole frames and 3 sections of a tenths frame. What number does this represent? 4.3

4 PLACE VALUE CHARTS Kyle looked at the place-value chart shown below and said that it represented the number 17.1. Is Kyle correct? If not, what number does it represent? no 17.010

tens	ones	tenths	hundredths	thousandths
1	7	0	1	0

5 TEMPERATURES Jamila took her temperature and found it to be 101.07°. Since it seemed high, she asked her mother if she would retake it for her. Her mother found Jamila's temperature to be 101.7°. Are the temperatures the same? no

6 DECIMAL REPRESENTATION What number is being modeled in the figure below? 0.23

Chapter 7

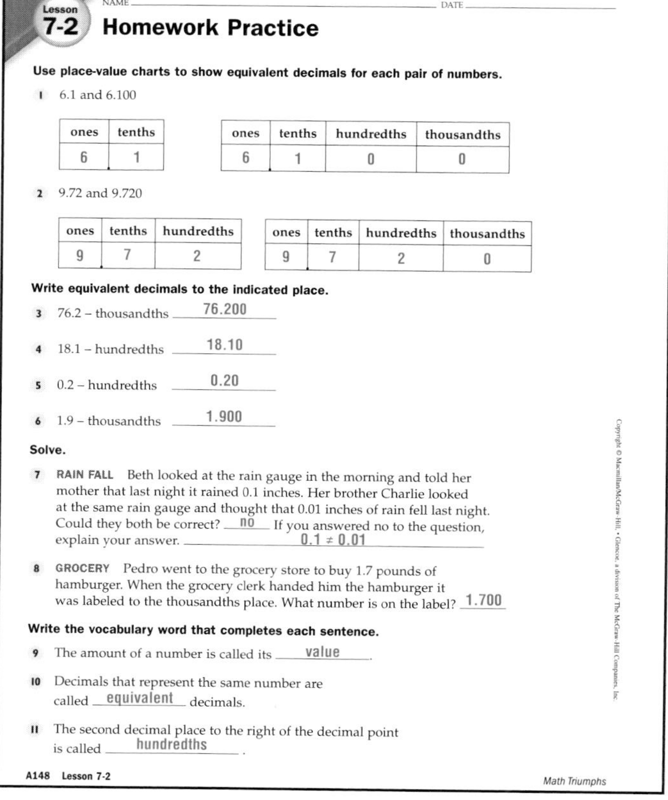

Lesson 7-2 NAME ______ DATE ______

Homework Practice

Use place-value charts to show equivalent decimals for each pair of numbers.

1 6.1 and 6.100

ones	tenths
6	1

ones	tenths	hundredths	thousandths
6	1	0	0

2 9.72 and 9.720

ones	tenths	hundredths
9	7	2

ones	tenths	hundredths	thousandths
9	7	2	0

Write equivalent decimals to the indicated place.

3 76.2 – thousandths 76.200

4 18.1 – hundredths 18.10

5 0.2 – hundredths 0.20

6 1.9 – thousandths 1.900

Solve.

7 RAIN FALL Beth looked at the rain gauge in the morning and told her mother that last night it rained 0.1 inches. Her brother Charlie looked at the same rain gauge and thought that 0.01 inches of rain fell last night. Could they both be correct? no If you answered no to the question, explain your answer. $0.1 \neq 0.01$

8 GROCERY Pedro went to the grocery store to buy 1.7 pounds of hamburger. When the grocery clerk handed him the hamburger it was labeled to the thousandths place. What number is on the label? 1.700

Write the vocabulary word that completes each sentence.

9 The amount of a number is called its value.

10 Decimals that represent the same number are called equivalent decimals.

11 The second decimal place to the right of the decimal point is called hundredths.

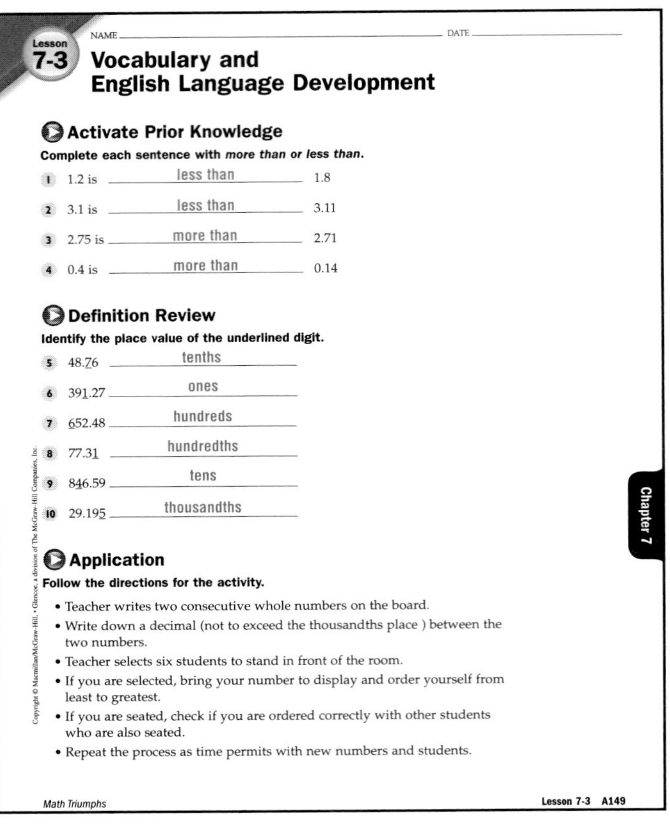

NAME ____________ DATE ____________

Lesson 7-3

Vocabulary and English Language Development

Activate Prior Knowledge

Complete each sentence with *more than* or *less than*.

1. 1.2 is less than 1.8
2. 3.1 is less than 3.11
3. 2.75 is more than 2.71
4. 0.4 is more than 0.14

Definition Review

Identify the place value of the underlined digit.

5. 48.76 tenths
6. 391.27 ones
7. 652.48 hundreds
8. 77.31 hundredths
9. 846.59 tens
10. 29.195 thousandths

Application

Follow the directions for the activity.

- Teacher writes two consecutive whole numbers on the board.
- Write down a decimal (not to exceed the thousandths place) between the two numbers.
- Teacher selects six students to stand in front of the room.
- If you are selected, bring your number to display and order yourself from least to greatest.
- If you are seated, check if you are ordered correctly with other students who are also seated.
- Repeat the process as time permits with new numbers and students.

Chapter 7

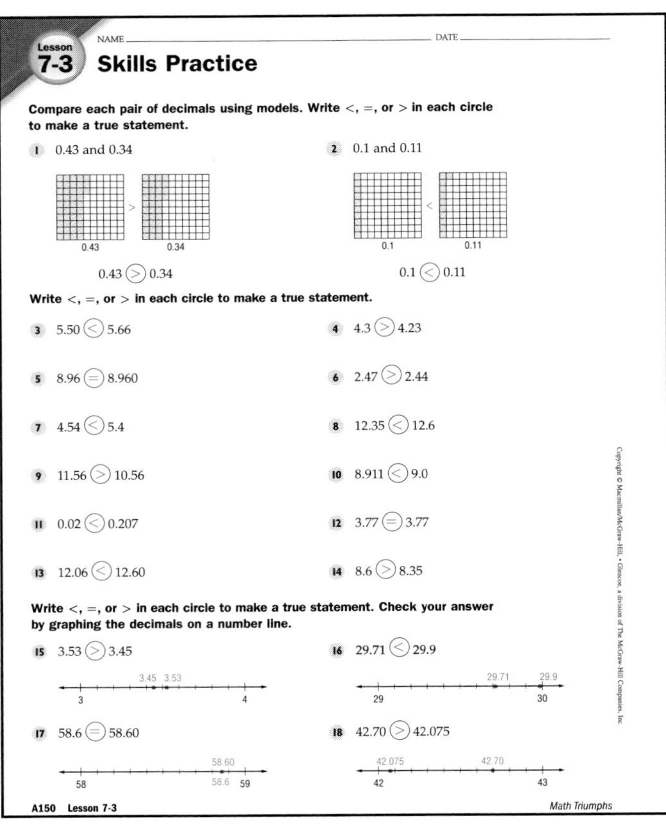

NAME ____________ DATE ____________

Lesson 7-3

Skills Practice

Compare each pair of decimals using models. Write <, =, or > in each circle to make a true statement.

1. 0.43 and 0.34 — 0.43 (>) 0.34
2. 0.1 and 0.11 — 0.1 (<) 0.11

Write <, =, or > in each circle to make a true statement.

3. 5.50 (<) 5.66
4. 4.3 (>) 4.23
5. 8.96 (=) 8.960
6. 2.47 (>) 2.44
7. 4.54 (<) 5.4
8. 12.35 (<) 12.6
9. 11.56 (>) 10.56
10. 8.911 (<) 9.0
11. 0.02 (<) 0.207
12. 3.77 (=) 3.77
13. 12.06 (<) 12.60
14. 8.6 (>) 8.35

Write <, =, or > in each circle to make a true statement. Check your answer by graphing the decimals on a number line.

15. 3.53 (>) 3.45
16. 29.71 (<) 29.9
17. 58.6 (=) 58.60
18. 42.70 (>) 42.075

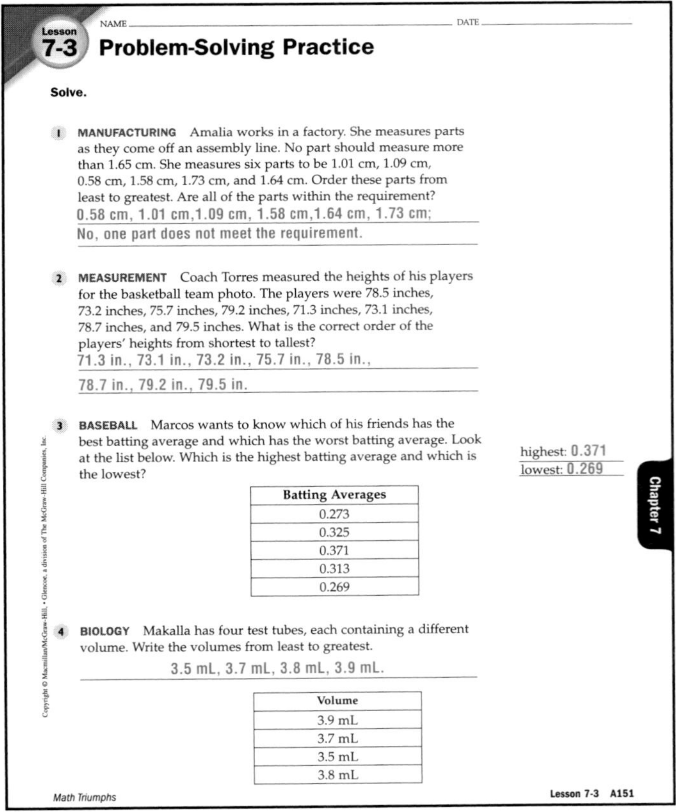

NAME ____________ DATE ____________

Lesson 7-3

Problem-Solving Practice

Solve.

1. MANUFACTURING Amalia works in a factory. She measures parts as they come off an assembly line. No part should measure more than 1.65 cm. She measures six parts to be 1.01 cm, 1.09 cm, 0.58 cm, 1.58 cm, 1.73 cm, and 1.64 cm. Order these parts from least to greatest. Are all of the parts within the requirement?
   0.58 cm, 1.01 cm,1.09 cm, 1.58 cm,1.64 cm, 1.73 cm;
   No, one part does not meet the requirement.

2. MEASUREMENT Coach Torres measured the heights of his players for the basketball team photo. The players were 78.5 inches, 73.2 inches, 75.7 inches, 79.2 inches, 71.3 inches, 73.1 inches, 78.7 inches, and 79.5 inches. What is the correct order of the players' heights from shortest to tallest?
   71.3 in., 73.1 in., 73.2 in., 75.7 in., 78.5 in.,
   78.7 in., 79.2 in., 79.5 in.

3. BASEBALL Marcos wants to know which of his friends has the best batting average and which has the worst batting average. Look at the list below. Which is the highest batting average and which is the lowest?
   highest: 0.371
   lowest: 0.269

Batting Averages
0.273
0.325
0.371
0.313
0.269

4. BIOLOGY Makalla has four test tubes, each containing a different volume. Write the volumes from least to greatest.
   3.5 mL, 3.7 mL, 3.8 mL, 3.9 mL.

Volume
3.9 mL
3.7 mL
3.5 mL
3.8 mL

Chapter 7

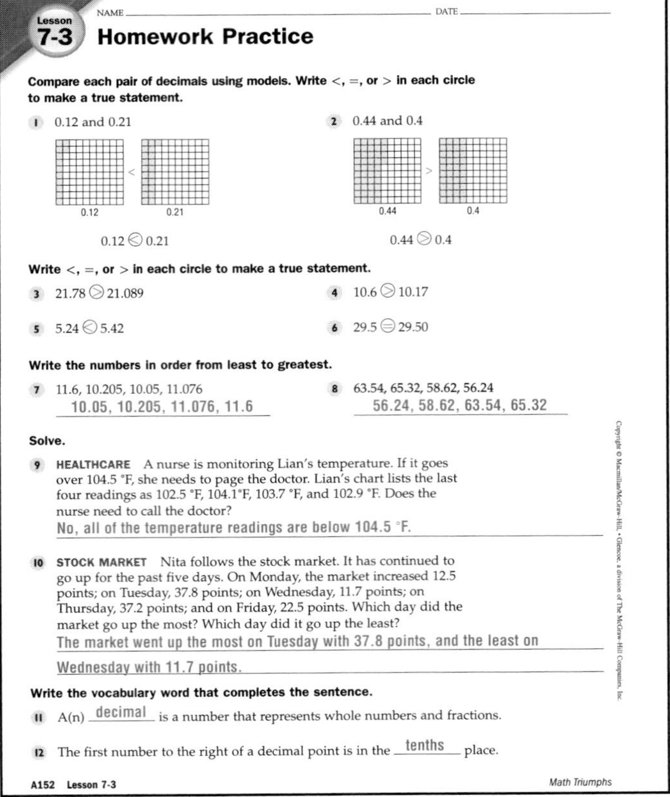

NAME ____________ DATE ____________

Lesson 7-3

Homework Practice

Compare each pair of decimals using models. Write <, =, or > in each circle to make a true statement.

1. 0.12 and 0.21 — 0.12 (<) 0.21
2. 0.44 and 0.4 — 0.44 (>) 0.4

Write <, =, or > in each circle to make a true statement.

3. 21.78 (>) 21.089
4. 10.6 (>) 10.17
5. 5.24 (<) 5.42
6. 29.5 (=) 29.50

Write the numbers in order from least to greatest.

7. 11.6, 10.205, 10.05, 11.076
   10.05, 10.205, 11.076, 11.6
8. 63.54, 65.32, 58.62, 56.24
   56.24, 58.62, 63.54, 65.32

Solve.

9. HEALTHCARE A nurse is monitoring Lian's temperature. If it goes over 104.5 °F, she needs to page the doctor. Lian's chart lists the last four readings as 102.5 °F, 104.1°F, 103.7 °F, and 102.9 °F. Does the nurse need to call the doctor?
   No, all of the temperature readings are below 104.5 °F.

10. STOCK MARKET Nita follows the stock market. It has continued to go up for the past five days. On Monday, the market increased 12.5 points; on Tuesday, 37.8 points; on Wednesday, 11.7 points; on Thursday, 37.2 points; and on Friday, 22.5 points. Which day did the market go up the most? Which day did it go up the least?
    The market went up the most on Tuesday with 37.8 points, and the least on Wednesday with 11.7 points.

Write the vocabulary word that completes the sentence.

11. A(n) decimal is a number that represents whole numbers and fractions.
12. The first number to the right of a decimal point is in the tenths place.

Answer Key (Lesson 7-4)

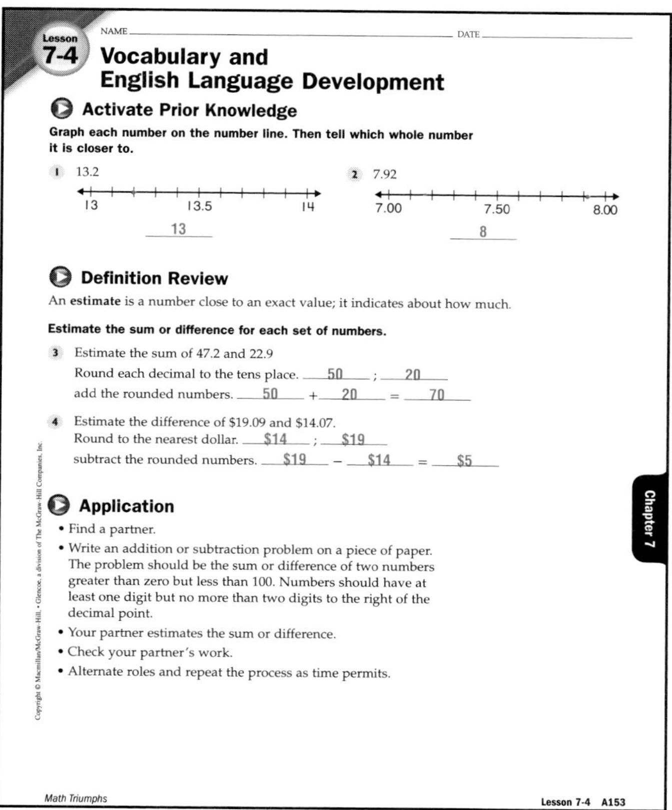

Lesson 7-4 NAME ______ DATE ______

Vocabulary and English Language Development

Activate Prior Knowledge

Graph each number on the number line. Then tell which whole number it is closer to.

1. 13.2 (number line: 13, 13.5, 14) **13**
2. 7.92 (number line: 7.00, 7.50, 8.00) **8**

Definition Review

An **estimate** is a number close to an exact value; it indicates about how much.

Estimate the sum or difference for each set of numbers.

3. Estimate the sum of 47.2 and 22.9
   Round each decimal to the tens place. **50** ; **20**
   add the rounded numbers. **50** + **20** = **70**
4. Estimate the difference of $19.09 and $14.07.
   Round to the nearest dollar. **$14** ; **$19**
   subtract the rounded numbers. **$19** − **$14** = **$5**

Application

- Find a partner.
- Write an addition or subtraction problem on a piece of paper. The problem should be the sum or difference of two numbers greater than zero but less than 100. Numbers should have at least one digit but no more than two digits to the right of the decimal point.
- Your partner estimates the sum or difference.
- Check your partner's work.
- Alternate roles and repeat the process as time permits.

Chapter 7

Math Triumphs Lesson 7-4 A153

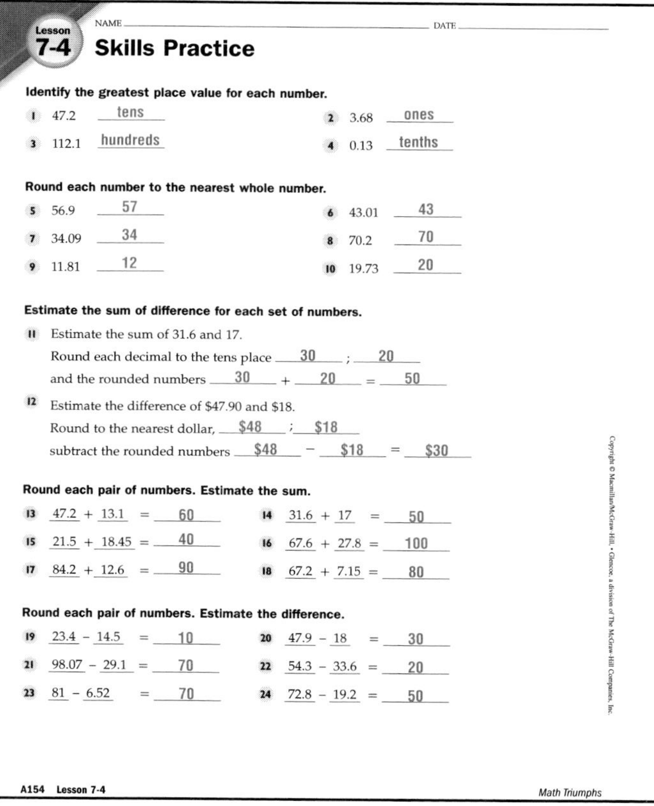

Lesson 7-4 NAME ______ DATE ______

Skills Practice

Identify the greatest place value for each number.

1. 47.2 **tens**
2. 3.68 **ones**
3. 112.1 **hundreds**
4. 0.13 **tenths**

Round each number to the nearest whole number.

5. 56.9 **57**
6. 43.01 **43**
7. 34.09 **34**
8. 70.2 **70**
9. 11.81 **12**
10. 19.73 **20**

Estimate the sum of difference for each set of numbers.

11. Estimate the sum of 31.6 and 17.
    Round each decimal to the tens place **30** ; **20**
    and the rounded numbers **30** + **20** = **50**
12. Estimate the difference of $47.90 and $18.
    Round to the nearest dollar, **$48** ; **$18**
    subtract the rounded numbers **$48** − **$18** = **$30**

Round each pair of numbers. Estimate the sum.

13. 47.2 + 13.1 = **60**
14. 31.6 + 17 = **50**
15. 21.5 + 18.45 = **40**
16. 67.6 + 27.8 = **100**
17. 84.2 + 12.6 = **90**
18. 67.2 + 7.15 = **80**

Round each pair of numbers. Estimate the difference.

19. 23.4 − 14.5 = **10**
20. 47.9 − 18 = **30**
21. 98.07 − 29.1 = **70**
22. 54.3 − 33.6 = **20**
23. 81 − 6.52 = **70**
24. 72.8 − 19.2 = **50**

A154 Lesson 7-4 Math Triumphs

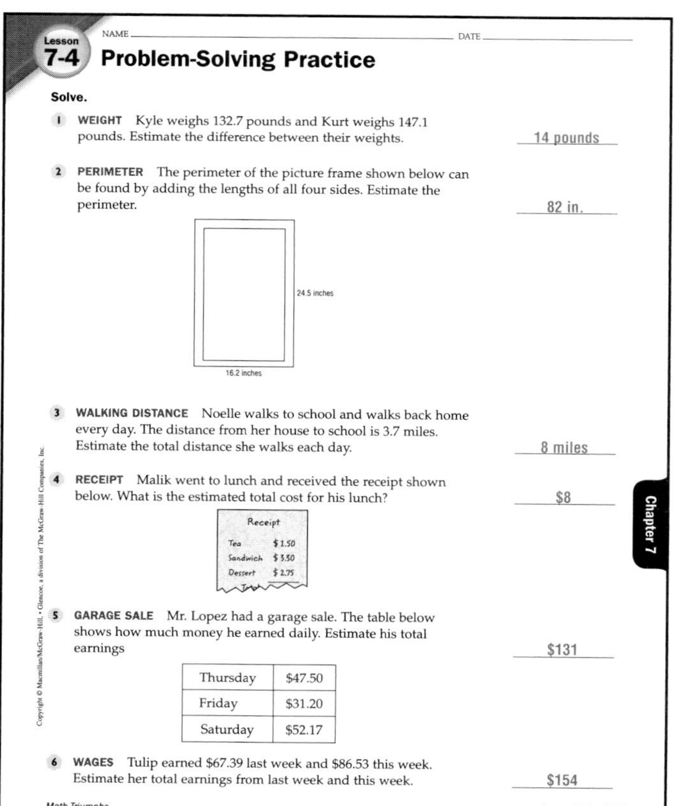

Lesson 7-4 NAME ______ DATE ______

Problem-Solving Practice

Solve.

1. **WEIGHT** Kyle weighs 132.7 pounds and Kurt weighs 147.1 pounds. Estimate the difference between their weights. **14 pounds**
2. **PERIMETER** The perimeter of the picture frame shown below can be found by adding the lengths of all four sides. Estimate the perimeter. **82 in.**

3. **WALKING DISTANCE** Noelle walks to school and walks back home every day. The distance from her house to school is 3.7 miles. Estimate the total distance she walks each day. **8 miles**
4. **RECEIPT** Malik went to lunch and received the receipt shown below. What is the estimated total cost for his lunch? **$8**

5. **GARAGE SALE** Mr. Lopez had a garage sale. The table below shows how much money he earned daily. Estimate his total earnings **$131**

Thursday	$47.50
Friday	$31.20
Saturday	$52.17

6. **WAGES** Tulip earned $67.39 last week and $86.53 this week. Estimate her total earnings from last week and this week. **$154**

Chapter 7

Math Triumphs Lesson 7-4 A155

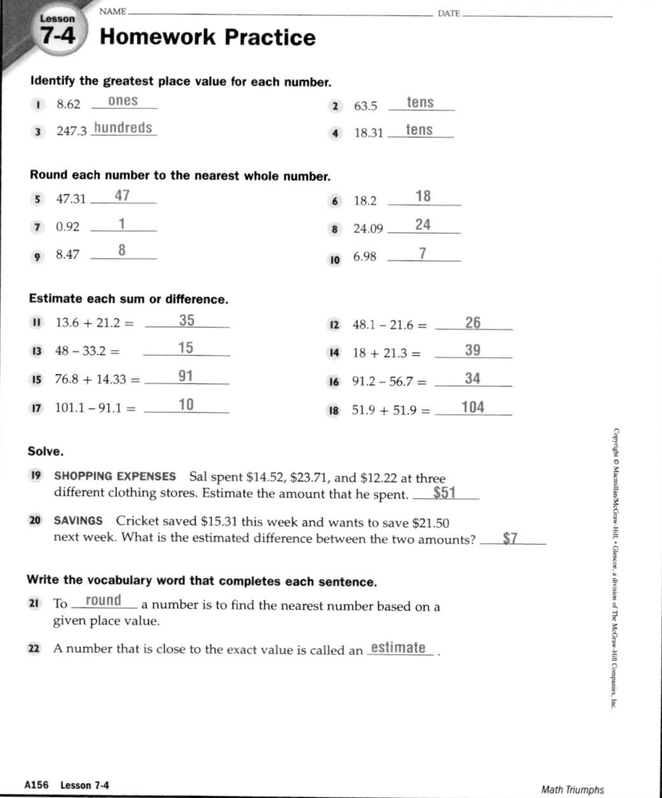

Lesson 7-4 NAME ______ DATE ______

Homework Practice

Identify the greatest place value for each number.

1. 8.62 **ones**
2. 63.5 **tens**
3. 247.3 **hundreds**
4. 18.31 **tens**

Round each number to the nearest whole number.

5. 47.31 **47**
6. 18.2 **18**
7. 0.92 **1**
8. 24.09 **24**
9. 8.47 **8**
10. 6.98 **7**

Estimate each sum or difference.

11. 13.6 + 21.2 = **35**
12. 48.1 − 21.6 = **26**
13. 48 − 33.2 = **15**
14. 18 + 21.3 = **39**
15. 76.8 + 14.33 = **91**
16. 91.2 − 56.7 = **34**
17. 101.1 − 91.1 = **10**
18. 51.9 + 51.9 = **104**

Solve.

19. **SHOPPING EXPENSES** Sal spent $14.52, $23.71, and $12.22 at three different clothing stores. Estimate the amount that he spent. **$51**
20. **SAVINGS** Cricket saved $15.31 this week and wants to save $21.50 next week. What is the estimated difference between the two amounts? **$7**

Write the vocabulary word that completes each sentence.

21. To **round** a number is to find the nearest number based on a given place value.
22. A number that is close to the exact value is called an **estimate**.

A156 Lesson 7-4 Math Triumphs

Answer Key (Lesson 7-5)

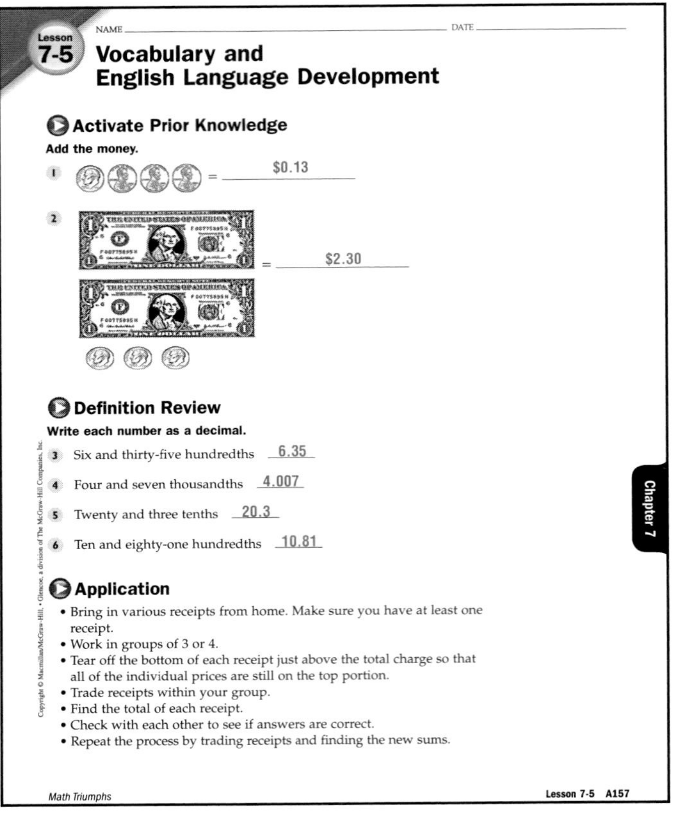

NAME ____________ DATE ____________

Lesson 7-5

Vocabulary and English Language Development

Activate Prior Knowledge

Add the money.

1. = $0.13

2. = $2.30

Definition Review

Write each number as a decimal.

3. Six and thirty-five hundredths 6.35
4. Four and seven thousandths 4.007
5. Twenty and three tenths 20.3
6. Ten and eighty-one hundredths 10.81

Application

- Bring in various receipts from home. Make sure you have at least one receipt.
- Work in groups of 3 or 4.
- Tear off the bottom of each receipt just above the total charge so that all of the individual prices are still on the top portion.
- Trade receipts within your group.
- Find the total of each receipt.
- Check with each other to see if answers are correct.
- Repeat the process by trading receipts and finding the new sums.

Chapter 7

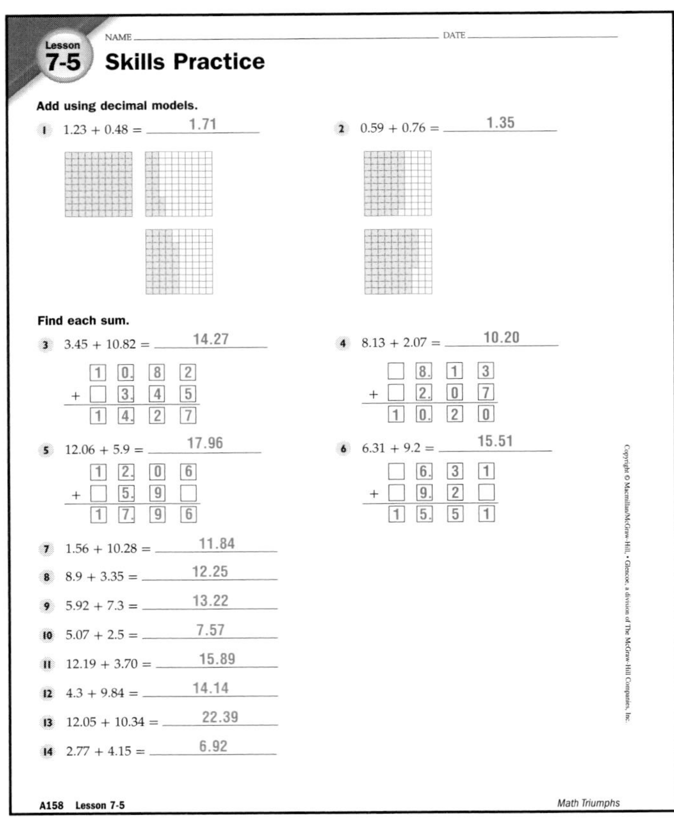

NAME ____________ DATE ____________

Lesson 7-5

Skills Practice

Add using decimal models.

1. 1.23 + 0.48 = 1.71
2. 0.59 + 0.76 = 1.35

Find each sum.

3. 3.45 + 10.82 = 14.27

   10.82 + 3.45 = 14.27

4. 8.13 + 2.07 = 10.20

   8.13 + 2.07 = 10.20

5. 12.06 + 5.9 = 17.96

   12.06 + 5.9 = 17.96

6. 6.31 + 9.2 = 15.51

   6.31 + 9.2 = 15.51

7. 1.56 + 10.28 = 11.84
8. 8.9 + 3.35 = 12.25
9. 5.92 + 7.3 = 13.22
10. 5.07 + 2.5 = 7.57
11. 12.19 + 3.70 = 15.89
12. 4.3 + 9.84 = 14.14
13. 12.05 + 10.34 = 22.39
14. 2.77 + 4.15 = 6.92

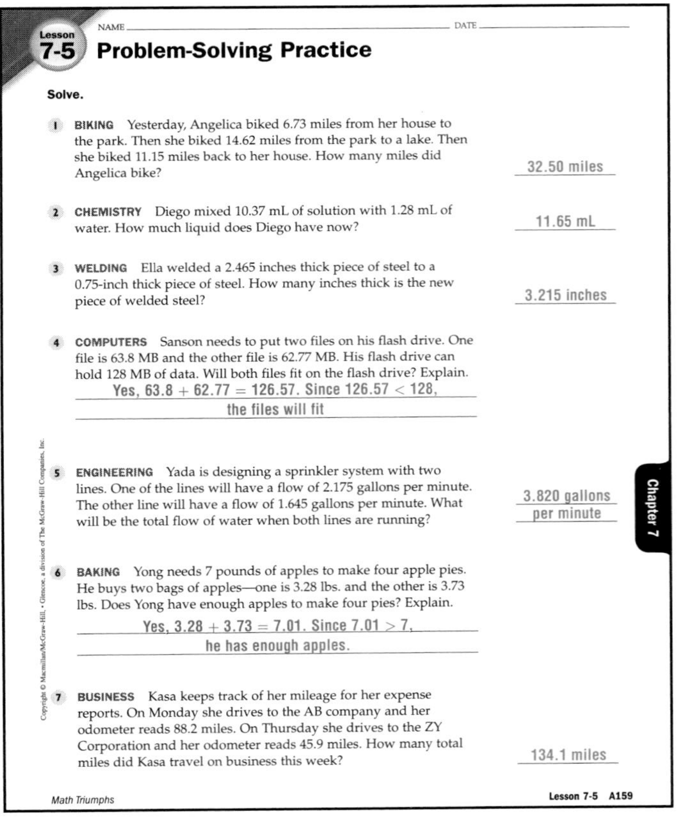

NAME ____________ DATE ____________

Lesson 7-5

Problem-Solving Practice

Solve.

1. **BIKING** Yesterday, Angelica biked 6.73 miles from her house to the park. Then she biked 14.62 miles from the park to a lake. Then she biked 11.15 miles back to her house. How many miles did Angelica bike? 32.50 miles

2. **CHEMISTRY** Diego mixed 10.37 mL of solution with 1.28 mL of water. How much liquid does Diego have now? 11.65 mL

3. **WELDING** Ella welded a 2.465 inches thick piece of steel to a 0.75-inch thick piece of steel. How many inches thick is the new piece of welded steel? 3.215 inches

4. **COMPUTERS** Sanson needs to put two files on his flash drive. One file is 63.8 MB and the other file is 62.77 MB. His flash drive can hold 128 MB of data. Will both files fit on the flash drive? Explain.
   Yes, 63.8 + 62.77 = 126.57. Since $126.57 < 128$, the files will fit

5. **ENGINEERING** Yada is designing a sprinkler system with two lines. One of the lines will have a flow of 2.175 gallons per minute. The other line will have a flow of 1.645 gallons per minute. What will be the total flow of water when both lines are running? 3.820 gallons per minute

6. **BAKING** Yong needs 7 pounds of apples to make four apple pies. He buys two bags of apples—one is 3.28 lbs. and the other is 3.73 lbs. Does Yong have enough apples to make four pies? Explain.
   Yes, 3.28 + 3.73 = 7.01. Since $7.01 > 7$, he has enough apples.

7. **BUSINESS** Kasa keeps track of her mileage for her expense reports. On Monday she drives to the AB company and her odometer reads 88.2 miles. On Thursday she drives to the ZY Corporation and her odometer reads 45.9 miles. How many total miles did Kasa travel on business this week? 134.1 miles

Chapter 7

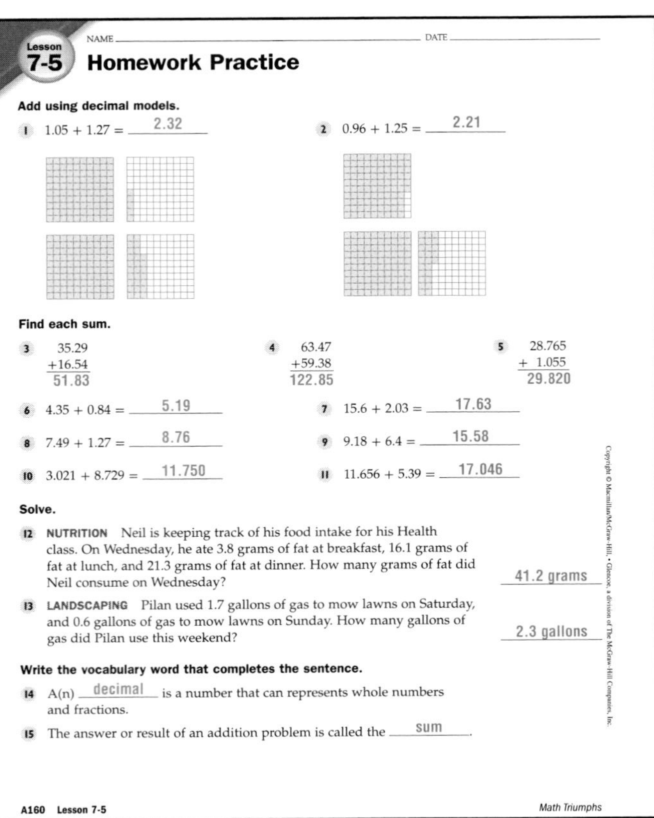

NAME ____________ DATE ____________

Lesson 7-5

Homework Practice

Add using decimal models.

1. 1.05 + 1.27 = 2.32
2. 0.96 + 1.25 = 2.21

Find each sum.

3. 35.29 + 16.54 = 51.83
4. 63.47 + 59.38 = 122.85
5. 28.765 + 1.055 = 29.820
6. 4.35 + 0.84 = 5.19
7. 15.6 + 2.03 = 17.63
8. 7.49 + 1.27 = 8.76
9. 9.18 + 6.4 = 15.58
10. 3.021 + 8.729 = 11.750
11. 11.656 + 5.39 = 17.046

Solve.

12. **NUTRITION** Neil is keeping track of his food intake for his Health class. On Wednesday, he ate 3.8 grams of fat at breakfast, 16.1 grams of fat at lunch, and 21.3 grams of fat at dinner. How many grams of fat did Neil consume on Wednesday? 41.2 grams

13. **LANDSCAPING** Pilan used 1.7 gallons of gas to mow lawns on Saturday, and 0.6 gallons of gas to mow lawns on Sunday. How many gallons of gas did Pilan use this weekend? 2.3 gallons

Write the vocabulary word that completes the sentence.

14. A(n) decimal is a number that can represents whole numbers and fractions.

15. The answer or result of an addition problem is called the sum.

Answer Key (Lesson 7-6)

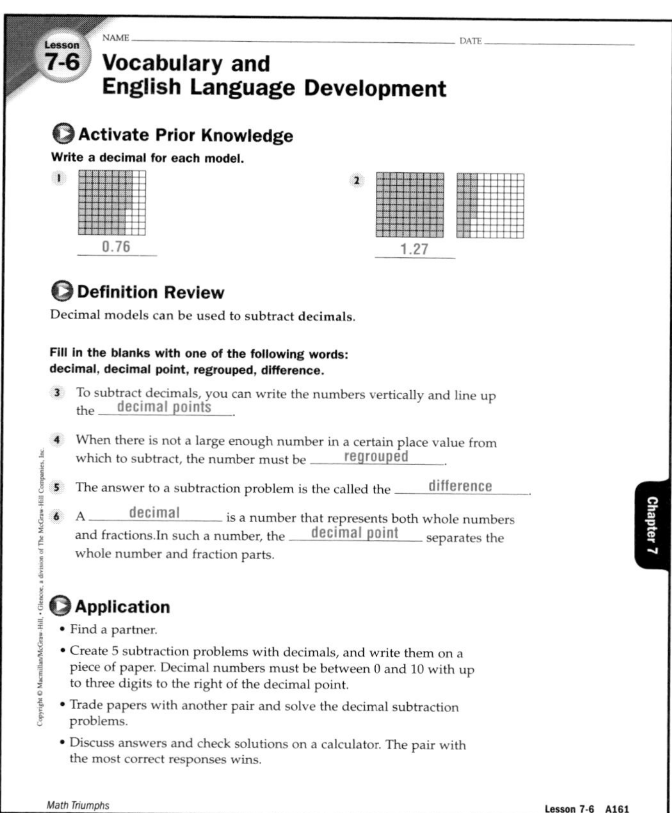

Lesson 7-6 Vocabulary and English Language Development

NAME ____ DATE ____

Activate Prior Knowledge

Write a decimal for each model.

1 0.76

2 1.27

Definition Review

Decimal models can be used to subtract decimals.

Fill in the blanks with one of the following words: decimal, decimal point, regrouped, difference.

3 To subtract decimals, you can write the numbers vertically and line up the decimal points.

4 When there is not a large enough number in a certain place value from which to subtract, the number must be regrouped.

5 The answer to a subtraction problem is the called the difference.

6 A decimal is a number that represents both whole numbers and fractions.In such a number, the decimal point separates the whole number and fraction parts.

Application

- Find a partner.
- Create 5 subtraction problems with decimals, and write them on a piece of paper. Decimal numbers must be between 0 and 10 with up to three digits to the right of the decimal point.
- Trade papers with another pair and solve the decimal subtraction problems.
- Discuss answers and check solutions on a calculator. The pair with the most correct responses wins.

Math Triumphs Lesson 7-6 A161

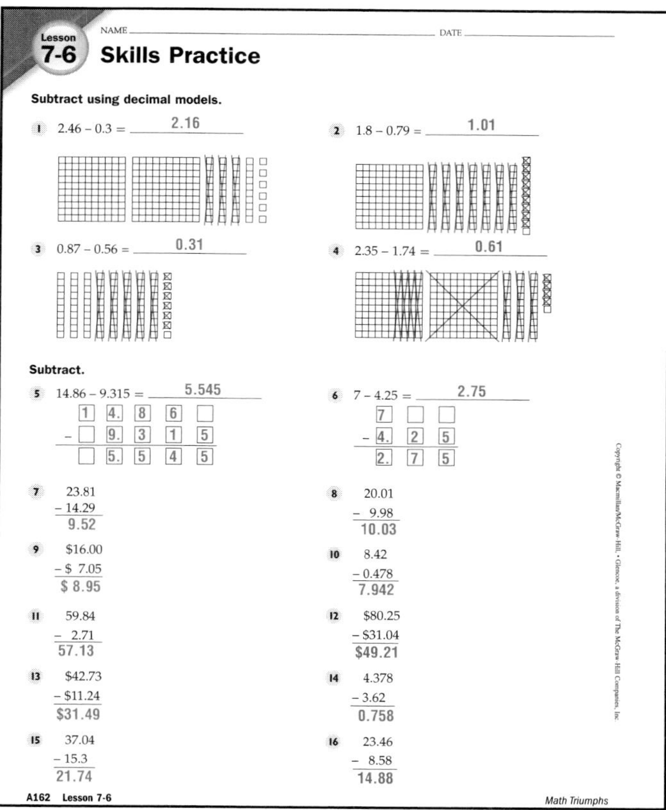

Lesson 7-6 Skills Practice

Subtract using decimal models.

1 2.46 − 0.3 = 2.16

2 1.8 − 0.79 = 1.01

3 0.87 − 0.56 = 0.31

4 2.35 − 1.74 = 0.61

Subtract.

5 14.86 − 9.315 = 5.545

6 7 − 4.25 = 2.75

7 23.81 − 14.29 = 9.52

8 20.01 − 9.98 = 10.03

9 $16.00 − $7.05 = $8.95

10 8.42 − 0.478 = 7.942

11 59.84 − 2.71 = 57.13

12 $80.25 − $31.04 = $49.21

13 $42.73 − $11.24 = $31.49

14 4.378 − 3.62 = 0.758

15 37.04 − 15.3 = 21.74

16 23.46 − 8.58 = 14.88

A162 Lesson 7-6 Math Triumphs

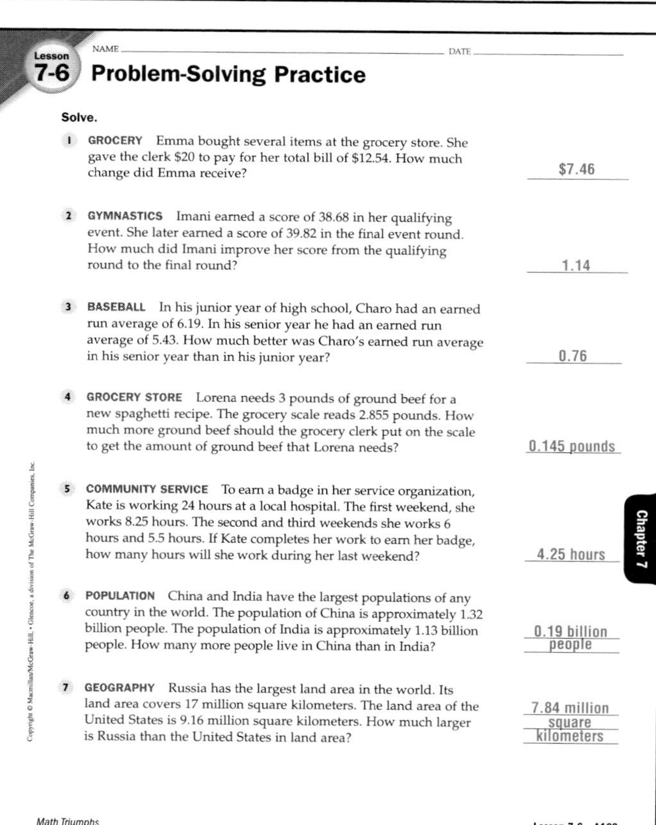

Lesson 7-6 Problem-Solving Practice

Solve.

1 GROCERY Emma bought several items at the grocery store. She gave the clerk $20 to pay for her total bill of $12.54. How much change did Emma receive? $7.46

2 GYMNASTICS Imani earned a score of 38.68 in her qualifying event. She later earned a score of 39.82 in the final event round. How much did Imani improve her score from the qualifying round to the final round? 1.14

3 BASEBALL In his junior year of high school, Charo had an earned run average of 6.19. In his senior year he had an earned run average of 5.43. How much better was Charo's earned run average in his senior year than in his junior year? 0.76

4 GROCERY STORE Lorena needs 3 pounds of ground beef for a new spaghetti recipe. The grocery scale reads 2.855 pounds. How much more ground beef should the grocery clerk put on the scale to get the amount of ground beef that Lorena needs? 0.145 pounds

5 COMMUNITY SERVICE To earn a badge in her service organization, Kate is working 24 hours at a local hospital. The first weekend, she works 8.25 hours. The second and third weekends she works 6 hours and 5.5 hours. If Kate completes her work to earn her badge, how many hours will she work during her last weekend? 4.25 hours

6 POPULATION China and India have the largest populations of any country in the world. The population of China is approximately 1.32 billion people. The population of India is approximately 1.13 billion people. How many more people live in China than in India? 0.19 billion people

7 GEOGRAPHY Russia has the largest land area in the world. Its land area covers 17 million square kilometers. The land area of the United States is 9.16 million square kilometers. How much larger is Russia than the United States in land area? 7.84 million square kilometers

Math Triumphs Lesson 7-6 A163

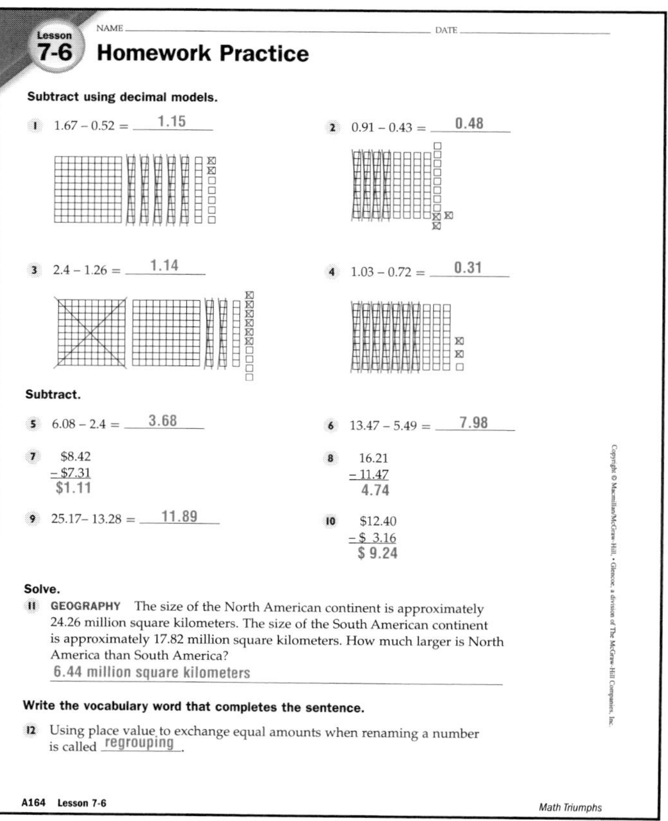

Lesson 7-6 Homework Practice

Subtract using decimal models.

1 1.67 − 0.52 = 1.15

2 0.91 − 0.43 = 0.48

3 2.4 − 1.26 = 1.14

4 1.03 − 0.72 = 0.31

Subtract.

5 6.08 − 2.4 = 3.68

6 13.47 − 5.49 = 7.98

7 $8.42 − $7.31 = $1.11

8 16.21 − 11.47 = 4.74

9 25.17 − 13.28 = 11.89

10 $12.40 − $3.16 = $9.24

Solve.

11 GEOGRAPHY The size of the North American continent is approximately 24.26 million square kilometers. The size of the South American continent is approximately 17.82 million square kilometers. How much larger is North America than South America? 6.44 million square kilometers

Write the vocabulary word that completes the sentence.

12 Using place value to exchange equal amounts when renaming a number is called regrouping.

A164 Lesson 7-6 Math Triumphs

Answer Key (Lesson 8-1)

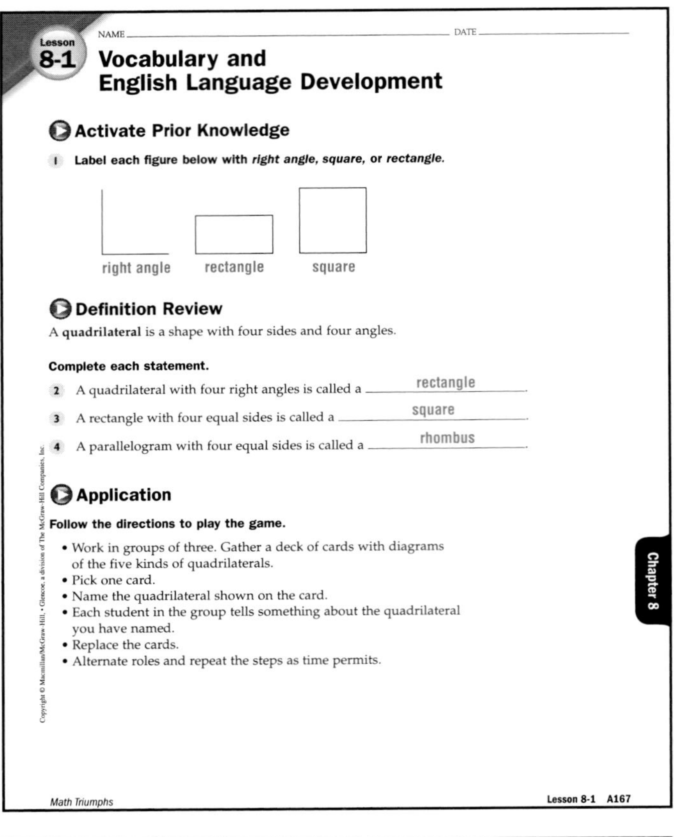
Lesson 8-1

NAME ______ DATE ______

Vocabulary and English Language Development

Activate Prior Knowledge

1 Label each figure below with *right angle, square,* or *rectangle.*

right angle rectangle square

Definition Review

A **quadrilateral** is a shape with four sides and four angles.

Complete each statement.

2 A quadrilateral with four right angles is called a rectangle.

3 A rectangle with four equal sides is called a square.

4 A parallelogram with four equal sides is called a rhombus.

Application

Follow the directions to play the game.

- Work in groups of three. Gather a deck of cards with diagrams of the five kinds of quadrilaterals.
- Pick one card.
- Name the quadrilateral shown on the card.
- Each student in the group tells something about the quadrilateral you have named.
- Replace the cards.
- Alternate roles and repeat the steps as time permits.

Chapter 8

Copyright © Macmillan/McGraw-Hill, • Glencoe, a division of The McGraw-Hill Companies, Inc.

Math Triumphs Lesson 8-1 A167

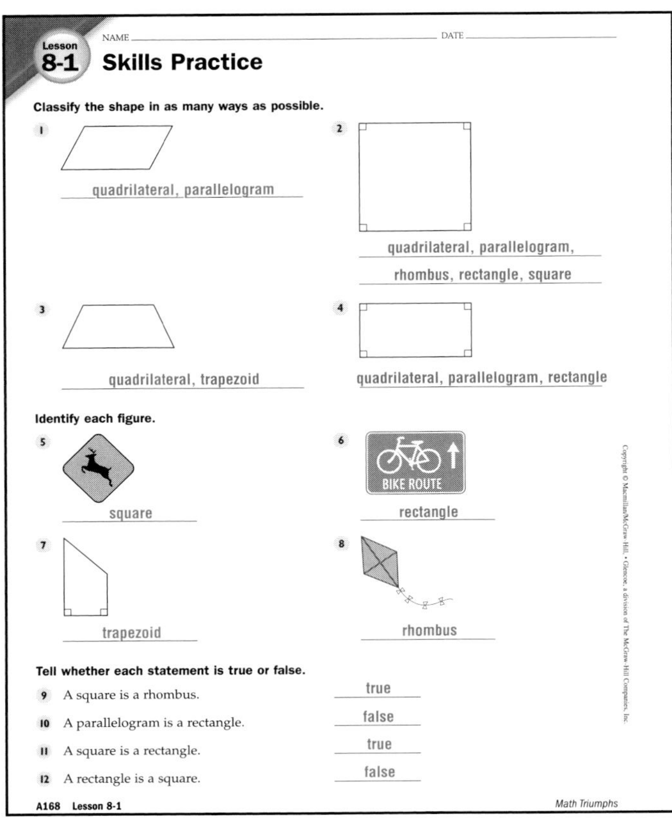
Lesson 8-1

NAME ______ DATE ______

Skills Practice

Classify the shape in as many ways as possible.

1 quadrilateral, parallelogram

2 quadrilateral, parallelogram, rhombus, rectangle, square

3 quadrilateral, trapezoid

4 quadrilateral, parallelogram, rectangle

Identify each figure.

5 square

6 BIKE ROUTE rectangle

7 trapezoid

8 rhombus

Tell whether each statement is true or false.

9 A square is a rhombus. true

10 A parallelogram is a rectangle. false

11 A square is a rectangle. true

12 A rectangle is a square. false

Copyright © Macmillan/McGraw-Hill, • Glencoe, a division of The McGraw-Hill Companies, Inc.

A168 Lesson 8-1 Math Triumphs

Lesson 8-1

NAME ______ DATE ______

Problem-Solving Practice

Solve.

1 **QUADRILATERAL** A quadrilateral has four equal sides and four right angles. What is the quadrilateral? square

2 **RECTANGLE** Circle all the rectangles.

3 **QUADRILATERAL** Gregg draws a quadrilateral. Each pair of opposite sides are parallel. Two sides are longer than the other two. What is the quadrilateral? parallelogram

4 **WINDOW** Marsha found these shapes in a stained glass window. She said three were parallelograms. Bill said four were parallelograms. Who is correct? Bill

5 **MAP** What shape is the state of Colorado? rectangle

Denver

COLORADO

6 **TABLE** What shape is the table shown? trapezoid

Chapter 8

Math Triumphs Lesson 8-1 A169

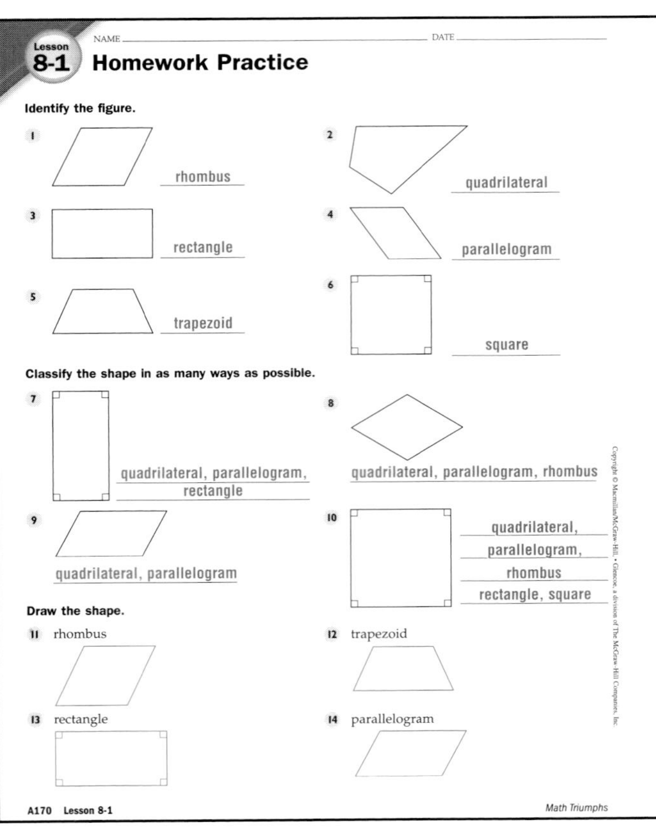
Lesson 8-1

NAME ______ DATE ______

Homework Practice

Identify the figure.

1 rhombus

2 quadrilateral

3 rectangle

4 parallelogram

5 trapezoid

6 square

Classify the shape in as many ways as possible.

7 quadrilateral, parallelogram, rectangle

8 quadrilateral, parallelogram, rhombus

9 quadrilateral, parallelogram

10 quadrilateral, parallelogram, rhombus, rectangle, square

Draw the shape.

11 rhombus

12 trapezoid

13 rectangle

14 parallelogram

Copyright © Macmillan/McGraw-Hill, • Glencoe, a division of The McGraw-Hill Companies, Inc.

A170 Lesson 8-1 Math Triumphs

Answer Key (Lesson 8-2)

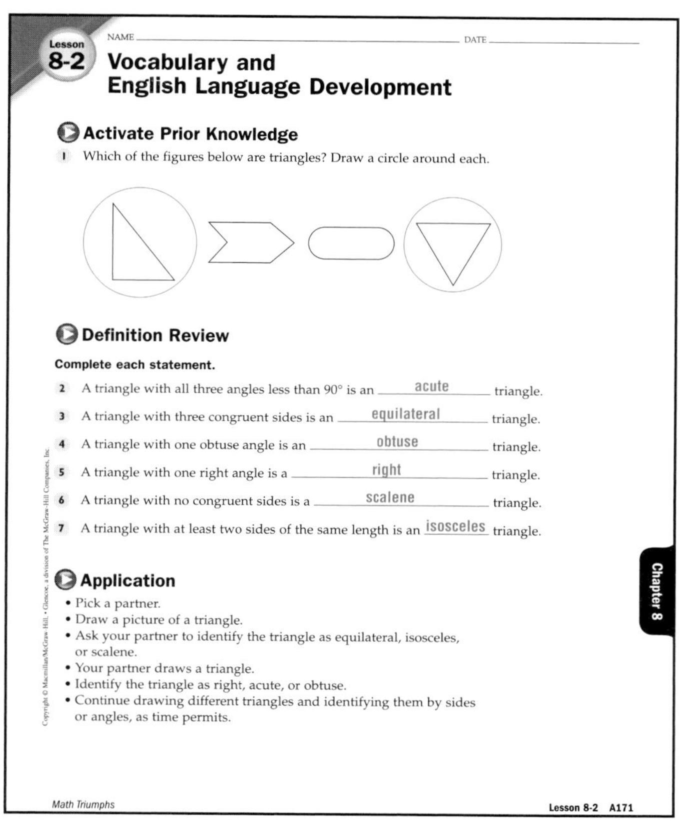
Lesson 8-2 NAME ____ DATE ____

Vocabulary and English Language Development

Activate Prior Knowledge

1 Which of the figures below are triangles? Draw a circle around each.

Definition Review

Complete each statement.

2 A triangle with all three angles less than 90° is an ___acute___ triangle.
3 A triangle with three congruent sides is an ___equilateral___ triangle.
4 A triangle with one obtuse angle is an ___obtuse___ triangle.
5 A triangle with one right angle is a ___right___ triangle.
6 A triangle with no congruent sides is a ___scalene___ triangle.
7 A triangle with at least two sides of the same length is an ___isosceles___ triangle.

Application

- Pick a partner.
- Draw a picture of a triangle.
- Ask your partner to identify the triangle as equilateral, isosceles, or scalene.
- Your partner draws a triangle.
- Identify the triangle as right, acute, or obtuse.
- Continue drawing different triangles and identifying them by sides or angles, as time permits.

Chapter 8

Math Triumphs Lesson 8-2 A171

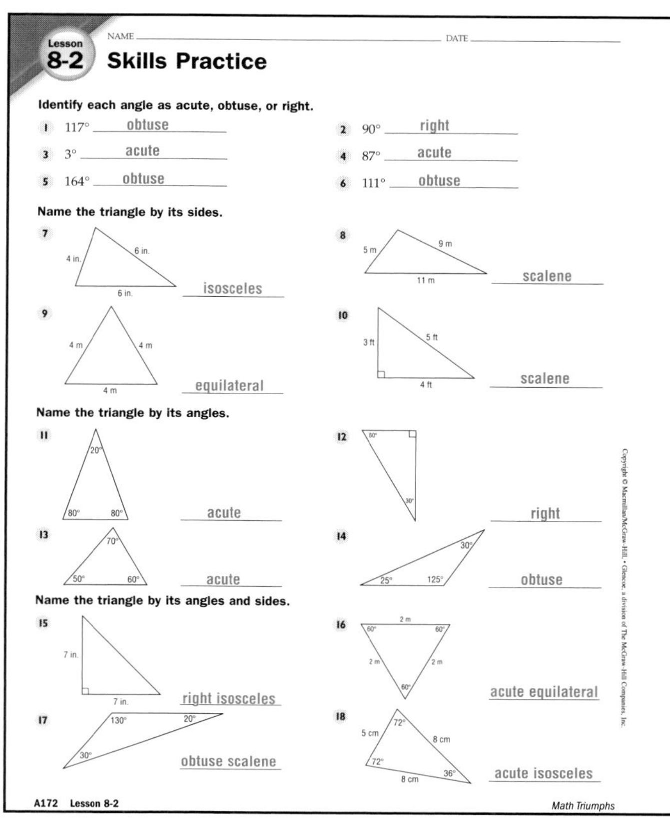
Lesson 8-2 NAME ____ DATE ____

Skills Practice

Identify each angle as acute, obtuse, or right.

1 117° ___obtuse___
2 90° ___right___
3 3° ___acute___
4 87° ___acute___
5 164° ___obtuse___
6 111° ___obtuse___

Name the triangle by its sides.

7 (4 in., 6 in., 6 in.) ___isosceles___
8 (5 m, 9 m, 11 m) ___scalene___
9 (4 m, 4 m, 4 m) ___equilateral___
10 (3 ft, 5 ft, 4 ft) ___scalene___

Name the triangle by its angles.

11 (20°, 80°, 80°) ___acute___
12 (60°, 30°) ___right___
13 (70°, 50°, 60°) ___acute___
14 (30°, 25°, 125°) ___obtuse___

Name the triangle by its angles and sides.

15 (7 in., 7 in.) ___right isosceles___
16 (2 m, 60°, 60°, 2 m, 2 m, 60°) ___acute equilateral___
17 (130°, 20°, 30°) ___obtuse scalene___
18 (72°, 5 cm, 8 cm, 72°, 8 cm, 36°) ___acute isosceles___

A172 Lesson 8-2 *Math Triumphs*

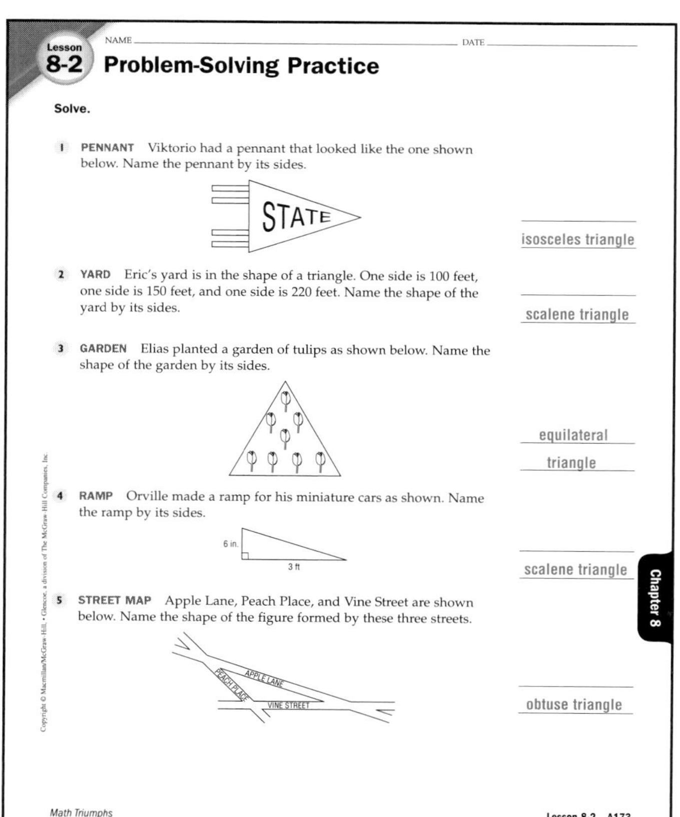
Lesson 8-2 NAME ____ DATE ____

Problem-Solving Practice

Solve.

1 **PENNANT** Viktorio had a pennant that looked like the one shown below. Name the pennant by its sides. ___isosceles triangle___

2 **YARD** Eric's yard is in the shape of a triangle. One side is 100 feet, one side is 150 feet, and one side is 220 feet. Name the shape of the yard by its sides. ___scalene triangle___

3 **GARDEN** Elias planted a garden of tulips as shown below. Name the shape of the garden by its sides. ___equilateral triangle___

4 **RAMP** Orville made a ramp for his miniature cars as shown. Name the ramp by its sides. (6 in., 3 ft) ___scalene triangle___

5 **STREET MAP** Apple Lane, Peach Place, and Vine Street are shown below. Name the shape of the figure formed by these three streets. ___obtuse triangle___

Chapter 8

Math Triumphs Lesson 8-2 A173

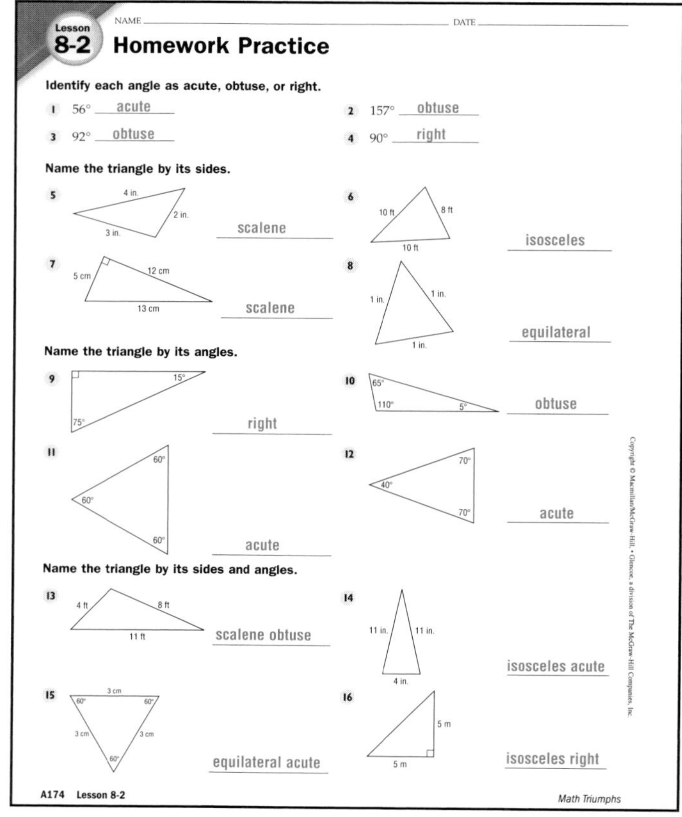
Lesson 8-2 NAME ____ DATE ____

Homework Practice

Identify each angle as acute, obtuse, or right.

1 56° ___acute___
2 157° ___obtuse___
3 92° ___obtuse___
4 90° ___right___

Name the triangle by its sides.

5 (4 in., 2 in., 3 in.) ___scalene___
6 (10 ft, 8 ft, 10 ft) ___isosceles___
7 (5 cm, 12 cm, 13 cm) ___scalene___
8 (1 in., 1 in., 1 in.) ___equilateral___

Name the triangle by its angles.

9 (15°, 75°) ___right___
10 (65°, 110°, 5°) ___obtuse___
11 (60°, 60°, 60°) ___acute___
12 (70°, 40°, 70°) ___acute___

Name the triangle by its sides and angles.

13 (4 ft, 8 ft, 11 ft) ___scalene obtuse___
14 (11 in., 11 in., 4 in.) ___isosceles acute___
15 (3 cm, 60°, 60°, 3 cm, 3 cm, 60°) ___equilateral acute___
16 (5 m, 5 m) ___isosceles right___

A174 Lesson 8-2 *Math Triumphs*

Answer Key (Lesson 8-3)

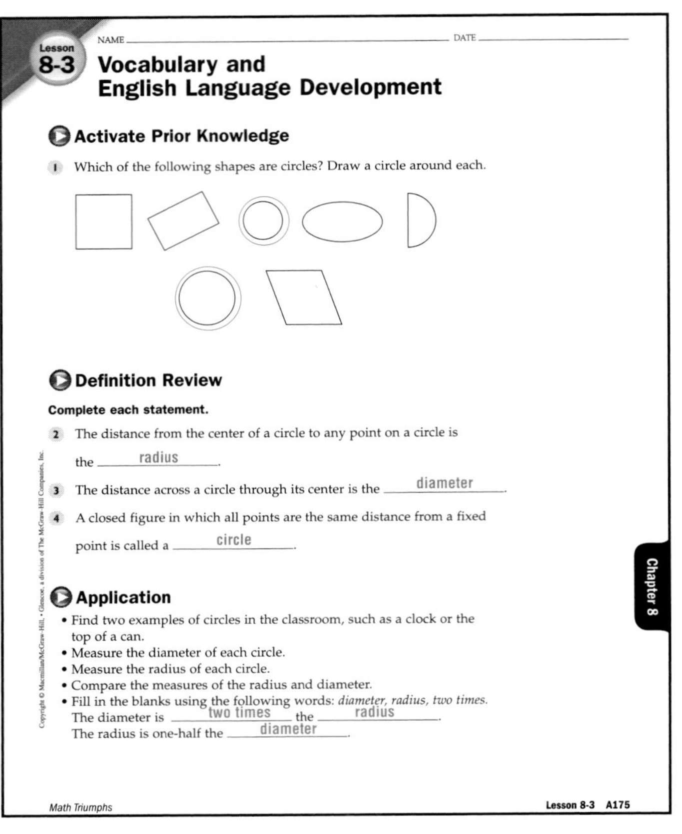

NAME ______ DATE ______

Lesson 8-3

Vocabulary and English Language Development

Activate Prior Knowledge

1 Which of the following shapes are circles? Draw a circle around each.

Definition Review

Complete each statement.

2 The distance from the center of a circle to any point on a circle is the radius.

3 The distance across a circle through its center is the diameter.

4 A closed figure in which all points are the same distance from a fixed point is called a circle.

Application

- Find two examples of circles in the classroom, such as a clock or the top of a can.
- Measure the diameter of each circle.
- Measure the radius of each circle.
- Compare the measures of the radius and diameter.
- Fill in the blanks using the following words: *diameter, radius, two times.*
  The diameter is two times the radius.
  The radius is one-half the diameter.

Chapter 8

Copyright © Macmillan/McGraw-Hill, • Glencoe, a division of The McGraw-Hill Companies, Inc.

Math Triumphs Lesson 8-3 A175

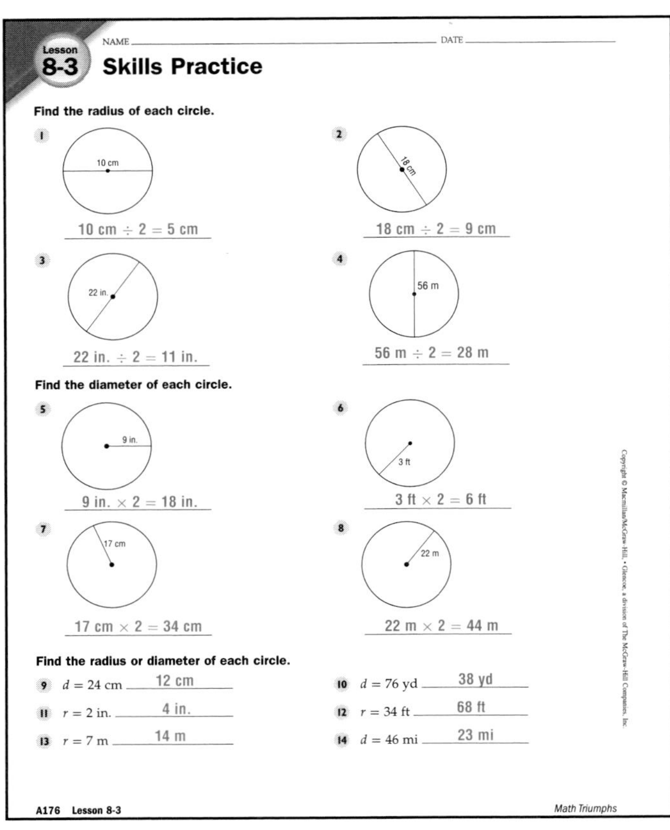

NAME ______ DATE ______

Lesson 8-3

Skills Practice

Find the radius of each circle.

1 (10 cm) 10 cm ÷ 2 = 5 cm

2 (18 cm) 18 cm ÷ 2 = 9 cm

3 (22 in.) 22 in. ÷ 2 = 11 in.

4 (56 m) 56 m ÷ 2 = 28 m

Find the diameter of each circle.

5 (9 in.) 9 in. × 2 = 18 in.

6 (3 ft) 3 ft × 2 = 6 ft

7 (17 cm) 17 cm × 2 = 34 cm

8 (22 m) 22 m × 2 = 44 m

Find the radius or diameter of each circle.

9 $d = 24$ cm 12 cm

10 $d = 76$ yd 38 yd

11 $r = 2$ in. 4 in.

12 $r = 34$ ft 68 ft

13 $r = 7$ m 14 m

14 $d = 46$ mi 23 mi

Copyright © Macmillan/McGraw-Hill, • Glencoe, a division of The McGraw-Hill Companies, Inc.

A176 Lesson 8-3 Math Triumphs

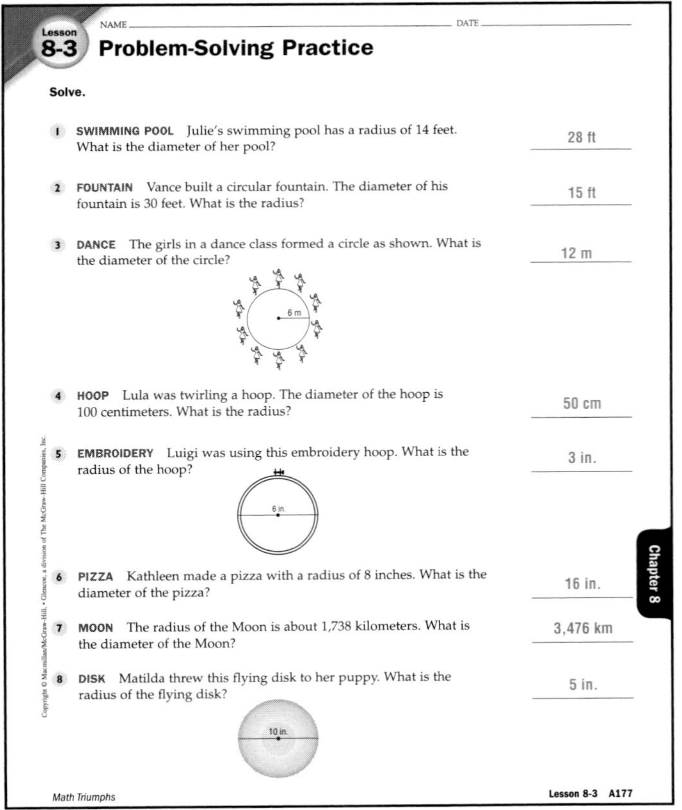

NAME ______ DATE ______

Lesson 8-3

Problem-Solving Practice

Solve.

1 **SWIMMING POOL** Julie's swimming pool has a radius of 14 feet. What is the diameter of her pool? 28 ft

2 **FOUNTAIN** Vance built a circular fountain. The diameter of his fountain is 30 feet. What is the radius? 15 ft

3 **DANCE** The girls in a dance class formed a circle as shown. What is the diameter of the circle? 12 m

(6 m)

4 **HOOP** Lula was twirling a hoop. The diameter of the hoop is 100 centimeters. What is the radius? 50 cm

5 **EMBROIDERY** Luigi was using this embroidery hoop. What is the radius of the hoop? 3 in.

(6 in.)

6 **PIZZA** Kathleen made a pizza with a radius of 8 inches. What is the diameter of the pizza? 16 in.

7 **MOON** The radius of the Moon is about 1,738 kilometers. What is the diameter of the Moon? 3,476 km

8 **DISK** Matilda threw this flying disk to her puppy. What is the radius of the flying disk? 5 in.

(10 in.)

Chapter 8

Copyright © Macmillan/McGraw-Hill, • Glencoe, a division of The McGraw-Hill Companies, Inc.

Math Triumphs Lesson 8-3 A177

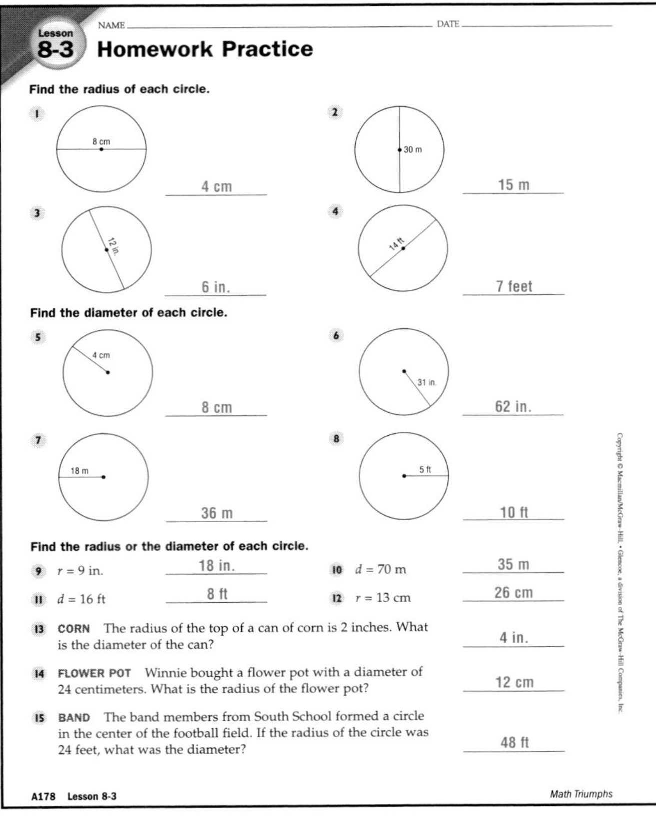

NAME ______ DATE ______

Lesson 8-3

Homework Practice

Find the radius of each circle.

1 (8 cm) 4 cm

2 (30 m) 15 m

3 (12 in.) 6 in.

4 (14 ft) 7 feet

Find the diameter of each circle.

5 (4 cm) 8 cm

6 (31 in.) 62 in.

7 (18 m) 36 m

8 (5 ft) 10 ft

Find the radius or the diameter of each circle.

9 $r = 9$ in. 18 in.

10 $d = 70$ m 35 m

11 $d = 16$ ft 8 ft

12 $r = 13$ cm 26 cm

13 **CORN** The radius of the top of a can of corn is 2 inches. What is the diameter of the can? 4 in.

14 **FLOWER POT** Winnie bought a flower pot with a diameter of 24 centimeters. What is the radius of the flower pot? 12 cm

15 **BAND** The band members from South School formed a circle in the center of the football field. If the radius of the circle was 24 feet, what was the diameter? 48 ft

Copyright © Macmillan/McGraw-Hill, • Glencoe, a division of The McGraw-Hill Companies, Inc.

A178 Lesson 8-3 Math Triumphs

Answer Key (Lesson 8-4)

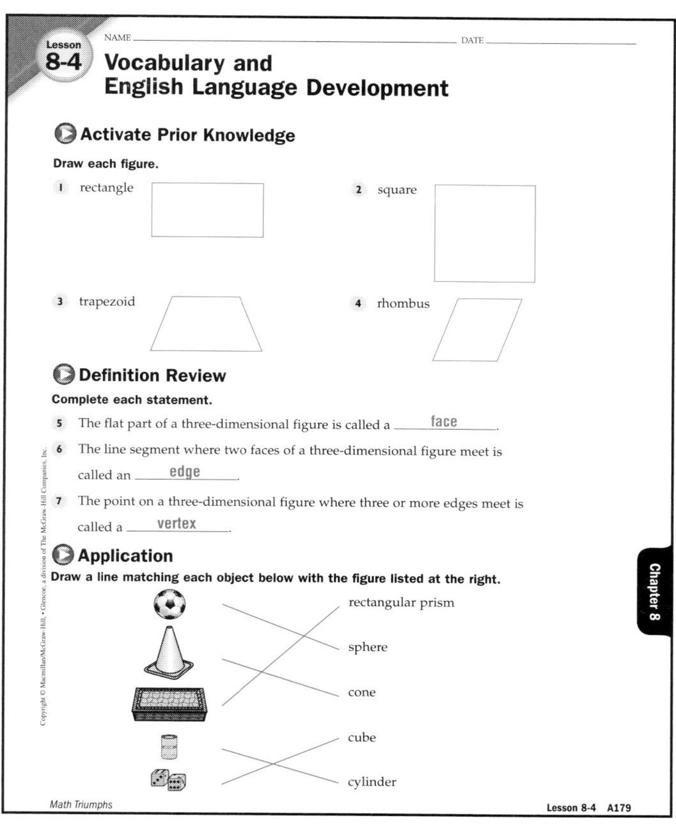

Lesson 8-4 NAME ______ DATE ______

Vocabulary and English Language Development

Activate Prior Knowledge

Draw each figure.

1 rectangle

2 square

3 trapezoid

4 rhombus

Definition Review

Complete each statement.

5 The flat part of a three-dimensional figure is called a face.

6 The line segment where two faces of a three-dimensional figure meet is called an edge.

7 The point on a three-dimensional figure where three or more edges meet is called a vertex.

Application

Draw a line matching each object below with the figure listed at the right.

rectangular prism

sphere

cone

cube

cylinder

Chapter 8

Copyright © Macmillan/McGraw-Hill, • Glencoe, a division of The McGraw-Hill Companies, Inc.

Math Triumphs   Lesson 8-4 A179

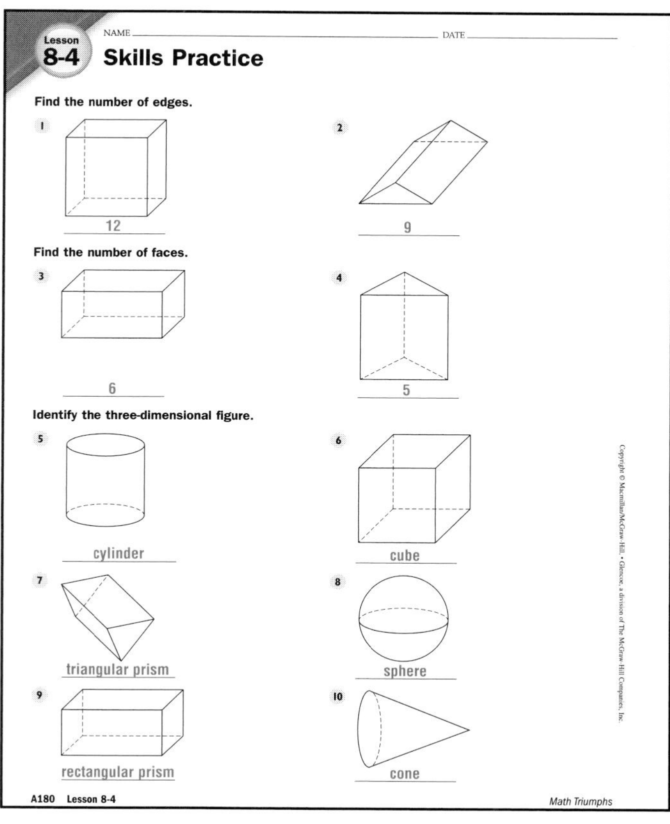

Lesson 8-4 NAME ______ DATE ______

Skills Practice

Find the number of edges.

1 12

2 9

Find the number of faces.

3 6

4 5

Identify the three-dimensional figure.

5 cylinder

6 cube

7 triangular prism

8 sphere

9 rectangular prism

10 cone

Copyright © Macmillan/McGraw-Hill, • Glencoe, a division of The McGraw-Hill Companies, Inc.

A180 Lesson 8-4   Math Triumphs

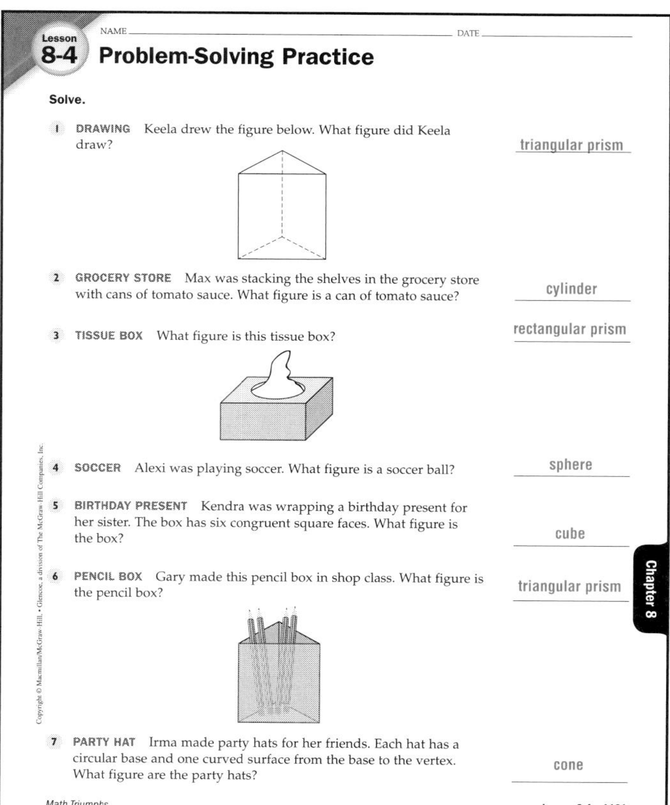

Lesson 8-4 NAME ______ DATE ______

Problem-Solving Practice

Solve.

1 DRAWING Keela drew the figure below. What figure did Keela draw? triangular prism

2 GROCERY STORE Max was stacking the shelves in the grocery store with cans of tomato sauce. What figure is a can of tomato sauce? cylinder

3 TISSUE BOX What figure is this tissue box? rectangular prism

4 SOCCER Alexi was playing soccer. What figure is a soccer ball? sphere

5 BIRTHDAY PRESENT Kendra was wrapping a birthday present for her sister. The box has six congruent square faces. What figure is the box? cube

6 PENCIL BOX Gary made this pencil box in shop class. What figure is the pencil box? triangular prism

7 PARTY HAT Irma made party hats for her friends. Each hat has a circular base and one curved surface from the base to the vertex. What figure are the party hats? cone

Chapter 8

Copyright © Macmillan/McGraw-Hill, • Glencoe, a division of The McGraw-Hill Companies, Inc.

Math Triumphs   Lesson 8-4 A181

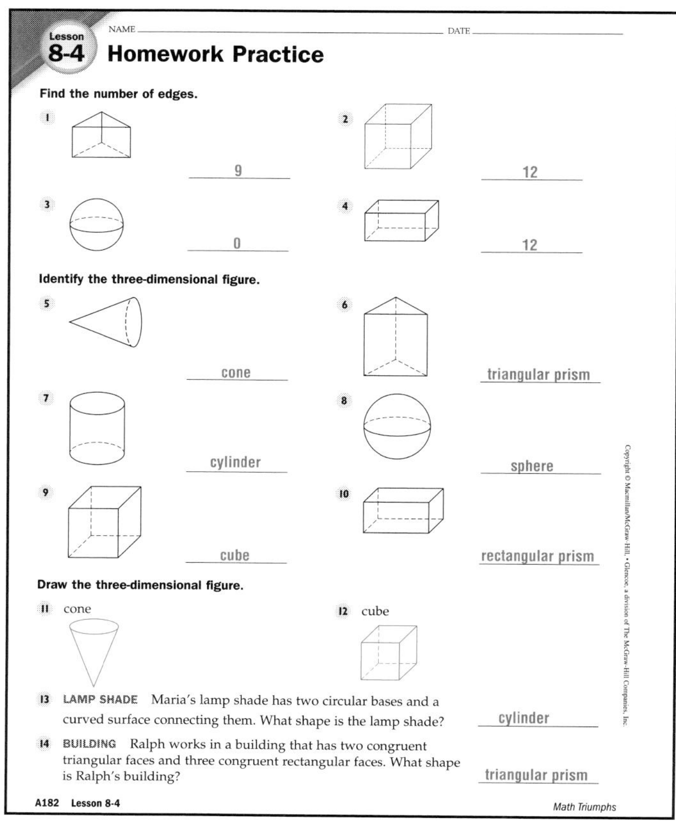

Lesson 8-4 NAME ______ DATE ______

Homework Practice

Find the number of edges.

1 9

2 12

3 0

4 12

Identify the three-dimensional figure.

5 cone

6 triangular prism

7 cylinder

8 sphere

9 cube

10 rectangular prism

Draw the three-dimensional figure.

11 cone

12 cube

13 LAMP SHADE Maria's lamp shade has two circular bases and a curved surface connecting them. What shape is the lamp shade? cylinder

14 BUILDING Ralph works in a building that has two congruent triangular faces and three congruent rectangular faces. What shape is Ralph's building? triangular prism

Copyright © Macmillan/McGraw-Hill, • Glencoe, a division of The McGraw-Hill Companies, Inc.

A182 Lesson 8-4   Math Triumphs

Answer Key (Lesson 9-1)

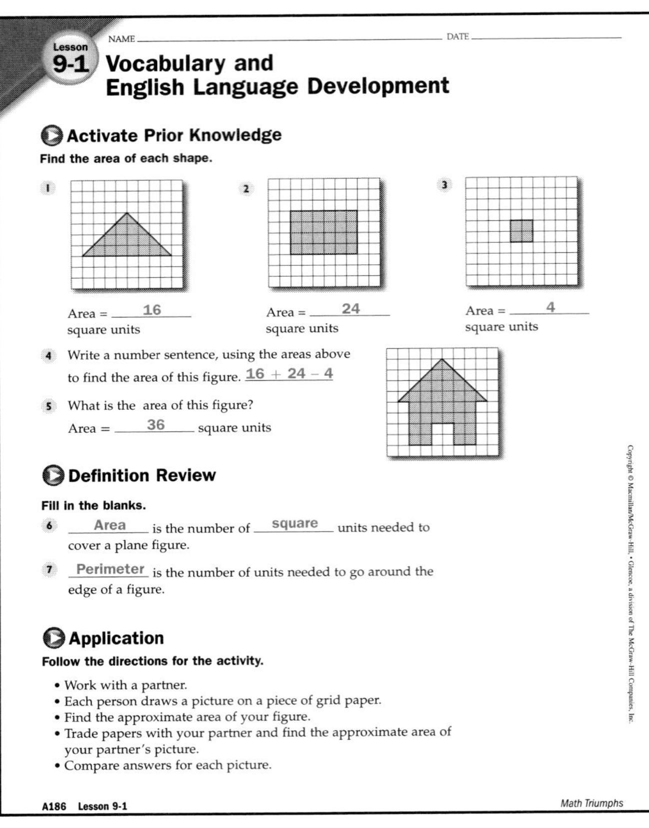

Lesson 9-1 NAME ______ DATE ______

Vocabulary and English Language Development

Activate Prior Knowledge

Find the area of each shape.

1. Area = 16 square units
2. Area = 24 square units
3. Area = 4 square units
4. Write a number sentence, using the areas above to find the area of this figure. 16 + 24 − 4
5. What is the area of this figure? Area = 36 square units

Definition Review

Fill in the blanks.

6. Area is the number of square units needed to cover a plane figure.
7. Perimeter is the number of units needed to go around the edge of a figure.

Application

Follow the directions for the activity.

- Work with a partner.
- Each person draws a picture on a piece of grid paper.
- Find the approximate area of your figure.
- Trade papers with your partner and find the approximate area of your partner's picture.
- Compare answers for each picture.

A186 Lesson 9-1 *Math Triumphs*

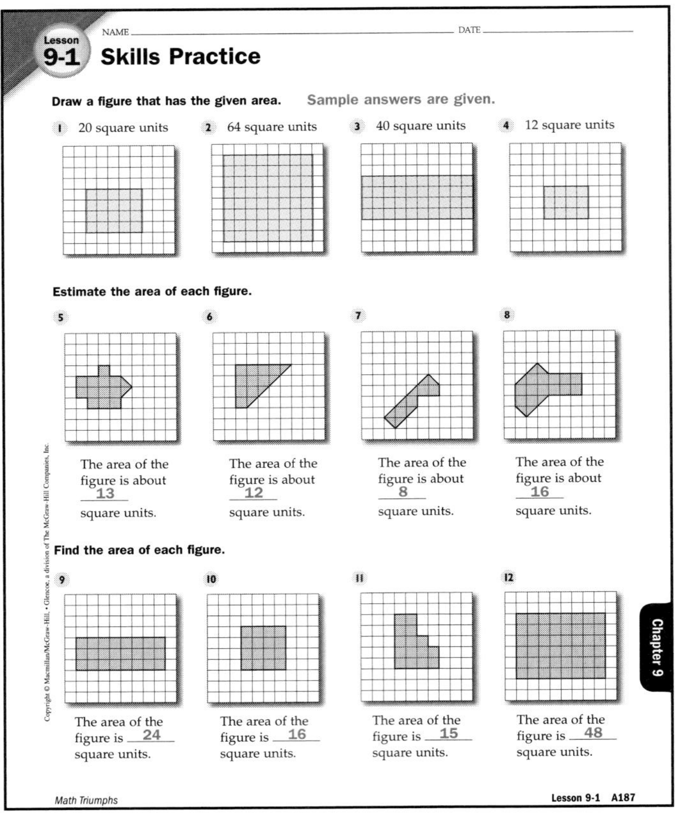

Lesson 9-1 NAME ______ DATE ______

Skills Practice

Draw a figure that has the given area. Sample answers are given.

1. 20 square units
2. 64 square units
3. 40 square units
4. 12 square units

Estimate the area of each figure.

5. The area of the figure is about 13 square units.
6. The area of the figure is about 12 square units.
7. The area of the figure is about 8 square units.
8. The area of the figure is about 16 square units.

Find the area of each figure.

9. The area of the figure is 24 square units.
10. The area of the figure is 16 square units.
11. The area of the figure is 15 square units.
12. The area of the figure is 48 square units.

Chapter 9

Math Triumphs Lesson 9-1 A187

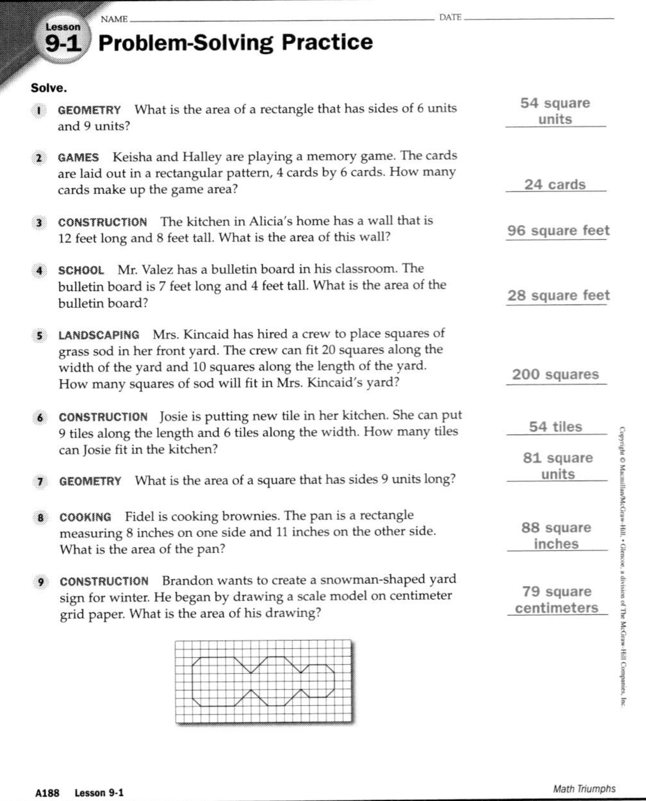

Lesson 9-1 NAME ______ DATE ______

Problem-Solving Practice

Solve.

1. **GEOMETRY** What is the area of a rectangle that has sides of 6 units and 9 units? 54 square units
2. **GAMES** Keisha and Halley are playing a memory game. The cards are laid out in a rectangular pattern, 4 cards by 6 cards. How many cards make up the game area? 24 cards
3. **CONSTRUCTION** The kitchen in Alicia's home has a wall that is 12 feet long and 8 feet tall. What is the area of this wall? 96 square feet
4. **SCHOOL** Mr. Valez has a bulletin board in his classroom. The bulletin board is 7 feet long and 4 feet tall. What is the area of the bulletin board? 28 square feet
5. **LANDSCAPING** Mrs. Kincaid has hired a crew to place squares of grass sod in her front yard. The crew can fit 20 squares along the width of the yard and 10 squares along the length of the yard. How many squares of sod will fit in Mrs. Kincaid's yard? 200 squares
6. **CONSTRUCTION** Josie is putting new tile in her kitchen. She can put 9 tiles along the length and 6 tiles along the width. How many tiles can Josie fit in the kitchen? 54 tiles
7. **GEOMETRY** What is the area of a square that has sides 9 units long? 81 square units
8. **COOKING** Fidel is cooking brownies. The pan is a rectangle measuring 8 inches on one side and 11 inches on the other side. What is the area of the pan? 88 square inches
9. **CONSTRUCTION** Brandon wants to create a snowman-shaped yard sign for winter. He began by drawing a scale model on centimeter grid paper. What is the area of his drawing? 79 square centimeters

A188 Lesson 9-1 *Math Triumphs*

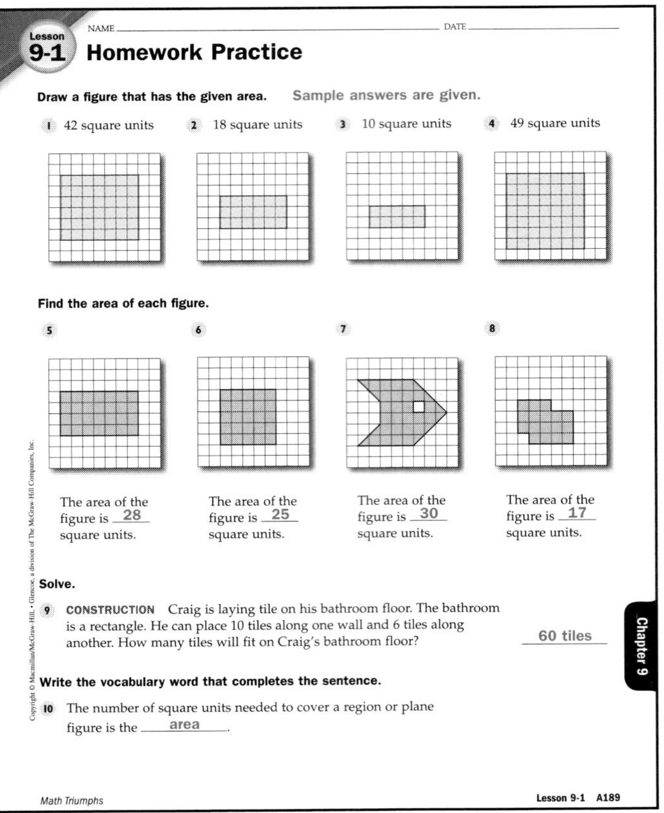

Lesson 9-1 NAME ______ DATE ______

Homework Practice

Draw a figure that has the given area. Sample answers are given.

1. 42 square units
2. 18 square units
3. 10 square units
4. 49 square units

Find the area of each figure.

5. The area of the figure is 28 square units.
6. The area of the figure is 25 square units.
7. The area of the figure is 30 square units.
8. The area of the figure is 17 square units.

Solve.

9. **CONSTRUCTION** Craig is laying tile on his bathroom floor. The bathroom is a rectangle. He can place 10 tiles along one wall and 6 tiles along another. How many tiles will fit on Craig's bathroom floor? 60 tiles

Write the vocabulary word that completes the sentence.

10. The number of square units needed to cover a region or plane figure is the area.

Chapter 9

Math Triumphs Lesson 9-1 A189

Answer Key (Lesson 9-2)

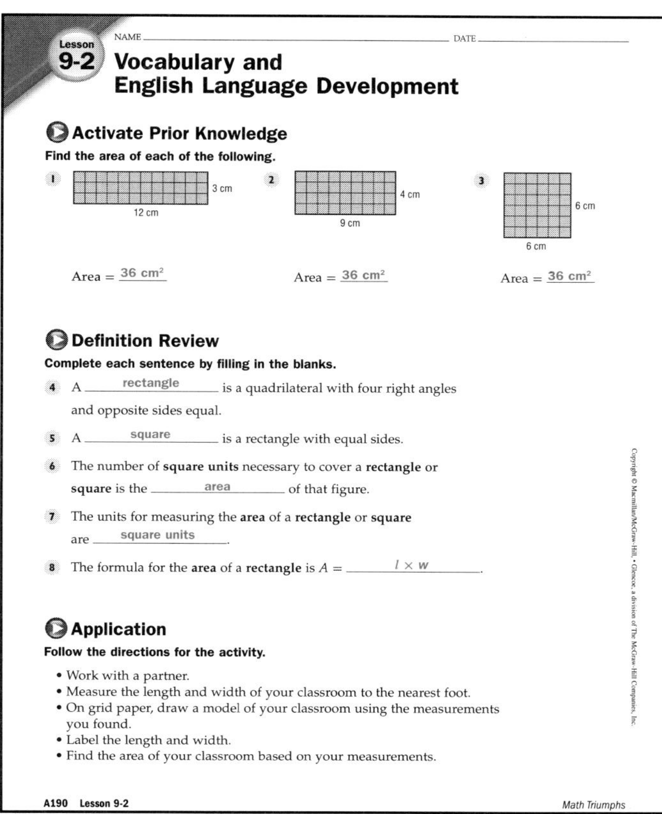

NAME ______ DATE ______

Lesson 9-2

Vocabulary and English Language Development

Activate Prior Knowledge

Find the area of each of the following.

1 12 cm by 3 cm — Area = 36 cm²

2 9 cm by 4 cm — Area = 36 cm²

3 6 cm by 6 cm — Area = 36 cm²

Definition Review

Complete each sentence by filling in the blanks.

4 A rectangle is a quadrilateral with four right angles and opposite sides equal.

5 A square is a rectangle with equal sides.

6 The number of **square units** necessary to cover a **rectangle** or **square** is the area of that figure.

7 The units for measuring the **area** of a **rectangle** or **square** are square units.

8 The formula for the **area** of a **rectangle** is $A =$ $l \times w$.

Application

Follow the directions for the activity.

- Work with a partner.
- Measure the length and width of your classroom to the nearest foot.
- On grid paper, draw a model of your classroom using the measurements you found.
- Label the length and width.
- Find the area of your classroom based on your measurements.

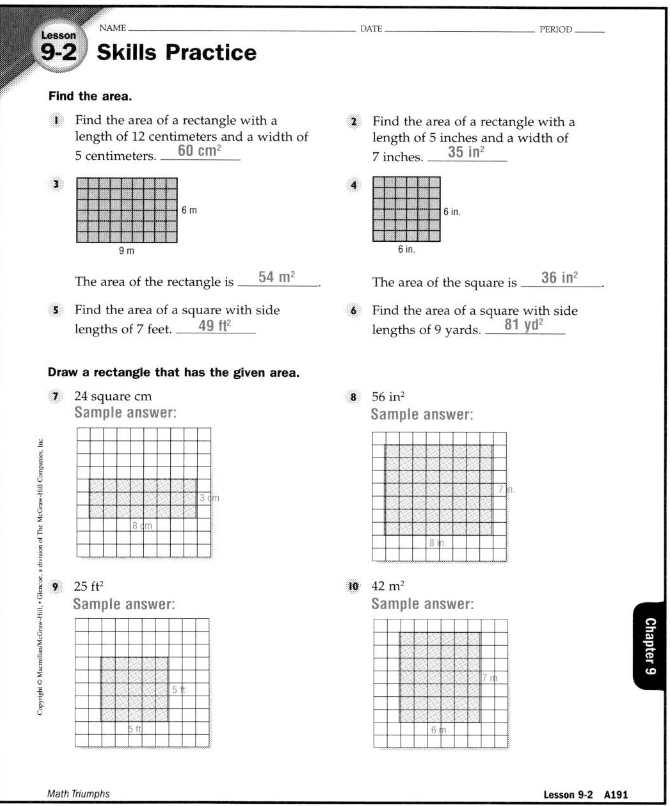

NAME ______ DATE ______ PERIOD ______

Lesson 9-2

Skills Practice

Find the area.

1 Find the area of a rectangle with a length of 12 centimeters and a width of 5 centimeters. 60 cm²

2 Find the area of a rectangle with a length of 5 inches and a width of 7 inches. 35 in²

3 (9 m by 6 m) The area of the rectangle is 54 m².

4 (6 in. by 6 in.) The area of the square is 36 in².

5 Find the area of a square with side lengths of 7 feet. 49 ft²

6 Find the area of a square with side lengths of 9 yards. 81 yd²

Draw a rectangle that has the given area.

7 24 square cm
Sample answer: (8 cm by 3 cm)

8 56 in²
Sample answer: (8 in. by 7 in.)

9 25 ft²
Sample answer: (5 ft by 5 ft)

10 42 m²
Sample answer: (6 m by 7 m)

Chapter 9

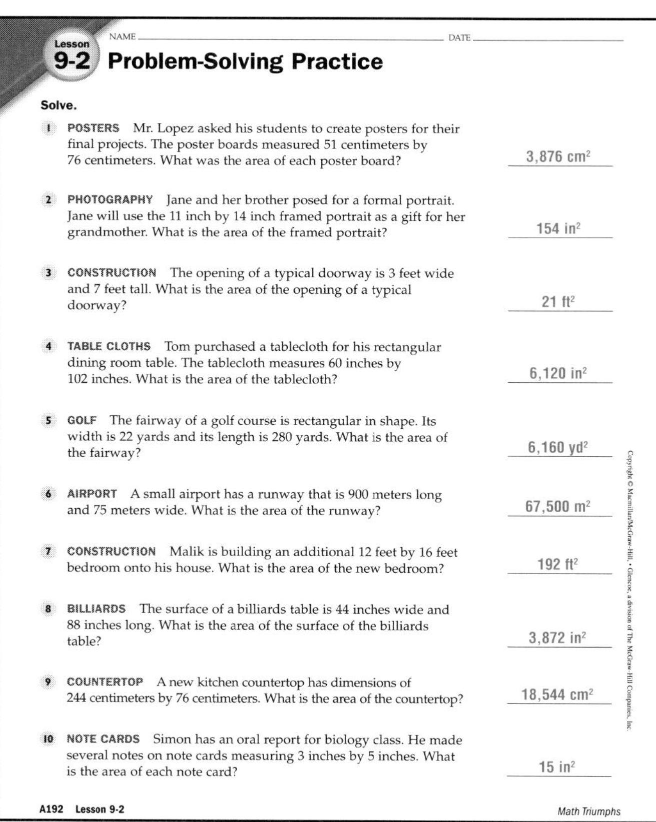

NAME ______ DATE ______

Lesson 9-2

Problem-Solving Practice

Solve.

1 **POSTERS** Mr. Lopez asked his students to create posters for their final projects. The poster boards measured 51 centimeters by 76 centimeters. What was the area of each poster board? 3,876 cm²

2 **PHOTOGRAPHY** Jane and her brother posed for a formal portrait. Jane will use the 11 inch by 14 inch framed portrait as a gift for her grandmother. What is the area of the framed portrait? 154 in²

3 **CONSTRUCTION** The opening of a typical doorway is 3 feet wide and 7 feet tall. What is the area of the opening of a typical doorway? 21 ft²

4 **TABLE CLOTHS** Tom purchased a tablecloth for his rectangular dining room table. The tablecloth measures 60 inches by 102 inches. What is the area of the tablecloth? 6,120 in²

5 **GOLF** The fairway of a golf course is rectangular in shape. Its width is 22 yards and its length is 280 yards. What is the area of the fairway? 6,160 yd²

6 **AIRPORT** A small airport has a runway that is 900 meters long and 75 meters wide. What is the area of the runway? 67,500 m²

7 **CONSTRUCTION** Malik is building an additional 12 feet by 16 feet bedroom onto his house. What is the area of the new bedroom? 192 ft²

8 **BILLIARDS** The surface of a billiards table is 44 inches wide and 88 inches long. What is the area of the surface of the billiards table? 3,872 in²

9 **COUNTERTOP** A new kitchen countertop has dimensions of 244 centimeters by 76 centimeters. What is the area of the countertop? 18,544 cm²

10 **NOTE CARDS** Simon has an oral report for biology class. He made several notes on note cards measuring 3 inches by 5 inches. What is the area of each note card? 15 in²

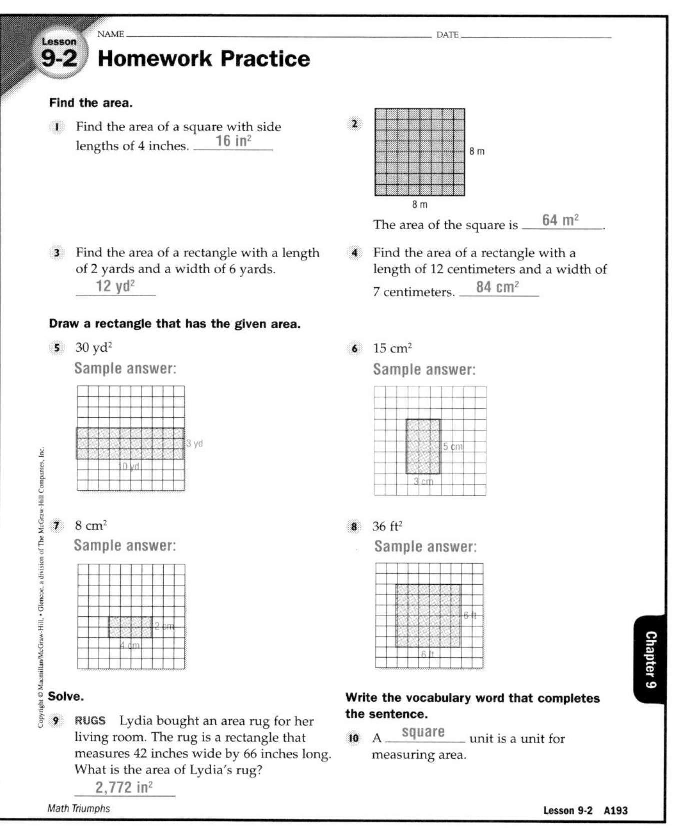

NAME ______ DATE ______

Lesson 9-2

Homework Practice

Find the area.

1 Find the area of a square with side lengths of 4 inches. 16 in²

2 (8 m by 8 m) The area of the square is 64 m².

3 Find the area of a rectangle with a length of 2 yards and a width of 6 yards. 12 yd²

4 Find the area of a rectangle with a length of 12 centimeters and a width of 7 centimeters. 84 cm²

Draw a rectangle that has the given area.

5 30 yd²
Sample answer: (10 yd by 3 yd)

6 15 cm²
Sample answer: (3 cm by 5 cm)

7 8 cm²
Sample answer: (4 cm by 2 cm)

8 36 ft²
Sample answer: (6 ft by 6 ft)

Solve.

9 **RUGS** Lydia bought an area rug for her living room. The rug is a rectangle that measures 42 inches wide by 66 inches long. What is the area of Lydia's rug? 2,772 in²

Write the vocabulary word that completes the sentence.

10 A square unit is a unit for measuring area.

Chapter 9

Answer Key (Lesson 9-3)

Lesson 9-3 Vocabulary and English Language Development

NAME ______ DATE ______

Activate Prior Knowledge

Use the points on the grid to complete the following.

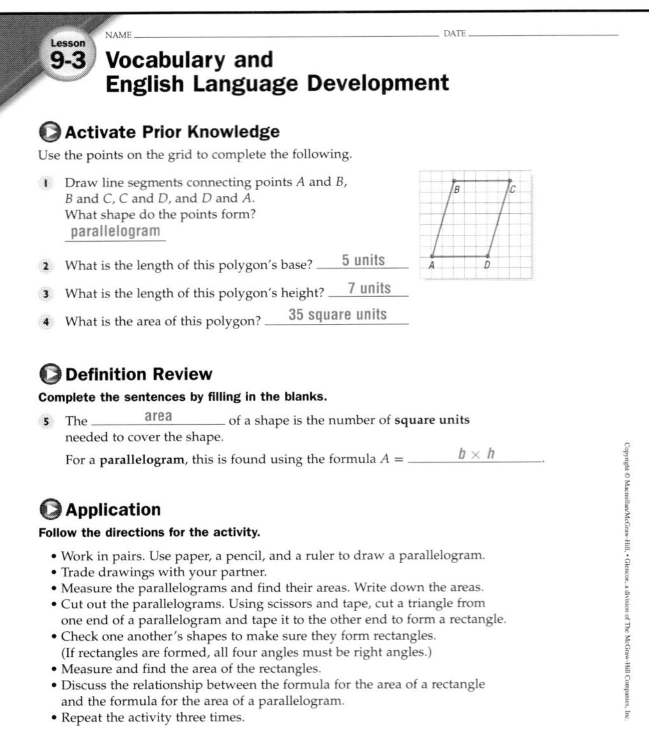

1. Draw line segments connecting points A and B, B and C, C and D, and D and A. What shape do the points form? parallelogram
2. What is the length of this polygon's base? 5 units
3. What is the length of this polygon's height? 7 units
4. What is the area of this polygon? 35 square units

Definition Review

Complete the sentences by filling in the blanks.

5. The area of a shape is the number of **square units** needed to cover the shape. For a **parallelogram**, this is found using the formula $A = b \times h$.

Application

Follow the directions for the activity.

- Work in pairs. Use paper, a pencil, and a ruler to draw a parallelogram.
- Trade drawings with your partner.
- Measure the parallelograms and find their areas. Write down the areas.
- Cut out the parallelograms. Using scissors and tape, cut a triangle from one end of a parallelogram and tape it to the other end to form a rectangle.
- Check one another's shapes to make sure they form rectangles. (If rectangles are formed, all four angles must be right angles.)
- Measure and find the area of the rectangles.
- Discuss the relationship between the formula for the area of a rectangle and the formula for the area of a parallelogram.
- Repeat the activity three times.

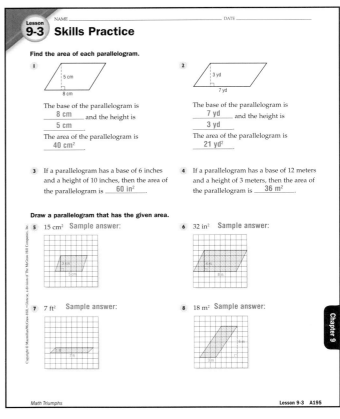

Lesson 9-3 Skills Practice

NAME ______ DATE ______

Find the area of each parallelogram.

1. (5 cm, 8 cm) The base of the parallelogram is 8 cm and the height is 5 cm. The area of the parallelogram is 40 cm².
2. (3 yd, 7 yd) The base of the parallelogram is 7 yd and the height is 3 yd. The area of the parallelogram is 21 yd².
3. If a parallelogram has a base of 6 inches and a height of 10 inches, then the area of the parallelogram is 60 in².
4. If a parallelogram has a base of 12 meters and a height of 3 meters, then the area of the parallelogram is 36 m².

Draw a parallelogram that has the given area.

5. 15 cm² Sample answer: (3 cm, 5 cm)
6. 32 in² Sample answer: (4 in., 8 in.)
7. 7 ft² Sample answer: (1 ft, 7 ft)
8. 18 m² Sample answer: (6 m, 3 m)

Chapter 9

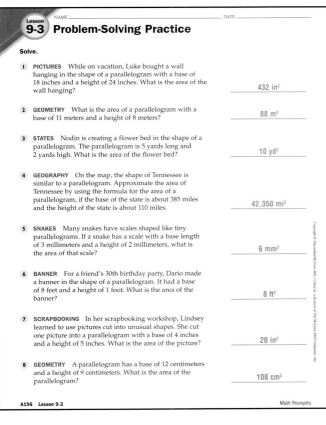

Lesson 9-3 Problem-Solving Practice

NAME ______ DATE ______

Solve.

1. **PICTURES** While on vacation, Luke bought a wall hanging in the shape of a parallelogram with a base of 18 inches and a height of 24 inches. What is the area of the wall hanging? 432 in²
2. **GEOMETRY** What is the area of a parallelogram with a base of 11 meters and a height of 8 meters? 88 m²
3. **STATES** Nodin is creating a flower bed in the shape of a parallelogram. The parallelogram is 5 yards long and 2 yards high. What is the area of the flower bed? 10 yd²
4. **GEOGRAPHY** On the map, the shape of Tennessee is similar to a parallelogram. Approximate the area of Tennessee by using the formula for the area of a parallelogram, if the base of the state is about 385 miles and the height of the state is about 110 miles. 42,350 mi²
5. **SNAKES** Many snakes have scales shaped like tiny parallelograms. If a snake has a scale with a base length of 3 millimeters and a height of 2 millimeters, what is the area of that scale? 6 mm²
6. **BANNER** For a friend's 30th birthday party, Dario made a banner in the shape of a parallelogram. It had a base of 8 feet and a height of 1 foot. What is the area of the banner? 8 ft²
7. **SCRAPBOOKING** In her scrapbooking workshop, Lindsey learned to use pictures cut into unusual shapes. She cut one picture into a parallelogram with a base of 4 inches and a height of 5 inches. What is the area of the picture? 20 in²
8. **GEOMETRY** A parallelogram has a base of 12 centimeters and a height of 9 centimeters. What is the area of the parallelogram? 108 cm²

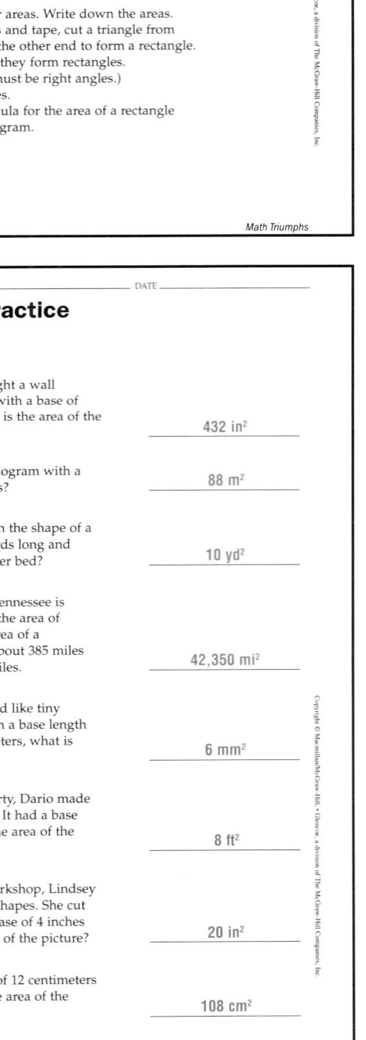

Lesson 9-3 Homework Practice

NAME ______ DATE ______

Find the area of each parallelogram.

1. (4 cm, 3 cm) The base of the parallelogram is 3 cm and the height is 4 cm. The area of the parallelogram is 12 cm².
2. (7 ft, 12 ft) The base of the parallelogram is 12 ft and the height is 7 ft. The area of the parallelogram is 84 ft².
3. (6 m, 6 m) The area of the parallelogram is 36 m².
4. (3 in., 10 in.) The area of the parallelogram is 30 in².

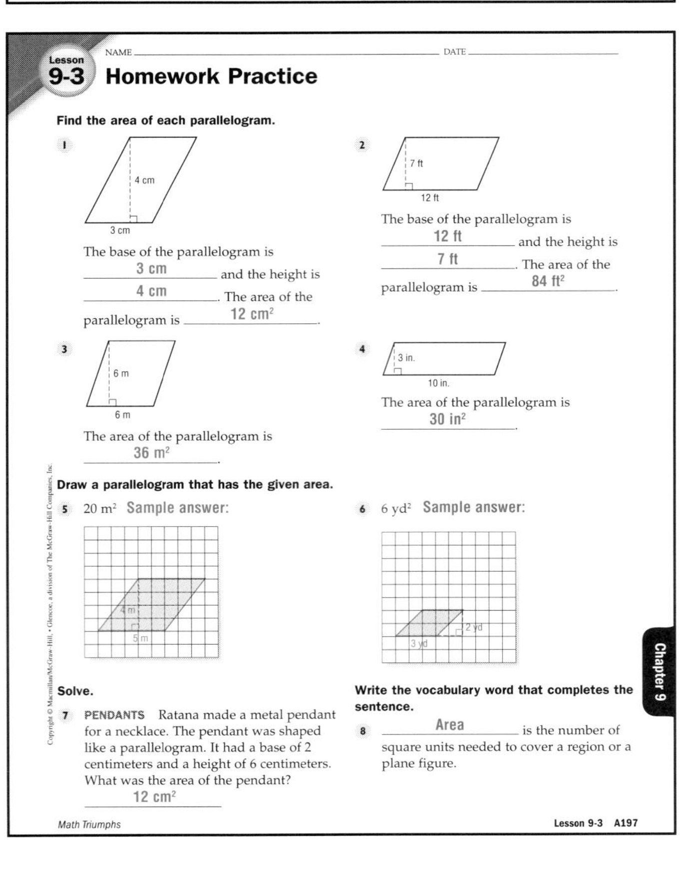

Draw a parallelogram that has the given area.

5. 20 m² Sample answer: (4 m, 5 m)
6. 6 yd² Sample answer: (2 yd, 3 yd)

Solve.

7. **PENDANTS** Ratana made a metal pendant for a necklace. The pendant was shaped like a parallelogram. It had a base of 2 centimeters and a height of 6 centimeters. What was the area of the pendant? 12 cm²

Write the vocabulary word that completes the sentence.

8. Area is the number of square units needed to cover a region or a plane figure.

Chapter 9

Answer Key (Lesson 9-4)

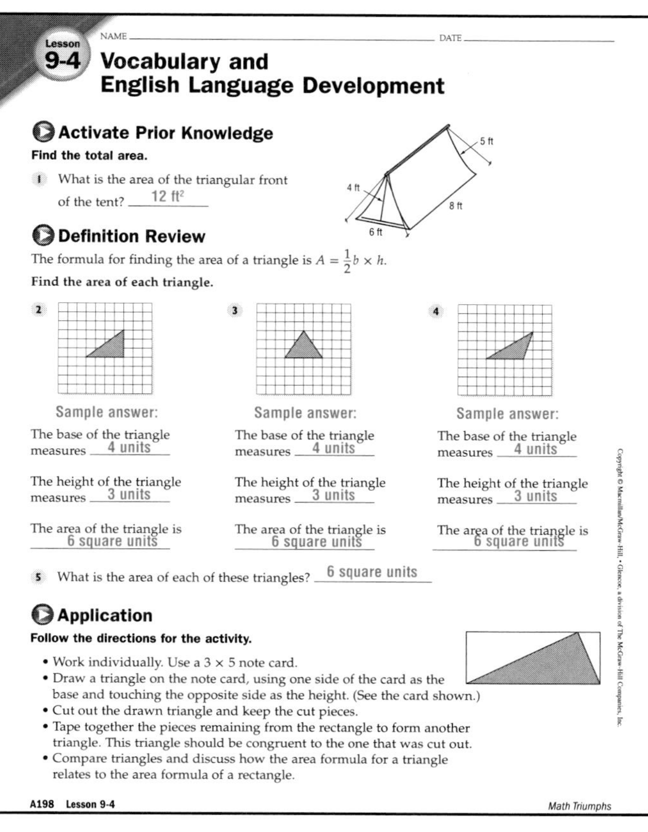

Lesson 9-4

NAME ______________________ DATE ____________

Vocabulary and English Language Development

Activate Prior Knowledge

Find the total area.

1 What is the area of the triangular front of the tent? 12 ft²

Definition Review

The formula for finding the area of a triangle is $A = \frac{1}{2}b \times h$.

Find the area of each triangle.

2 Sample answer:
The base of the triangle measures 4 units
The height of the triangle measures 3 units
The area of the triangle is 6 square units

3 Sample answer:
The base of the triangle measures 4 units
The height of the triangle measures 3 units
The area of the triangle is 6 square units

4 Sample answer:
The base of the triangle measures 4 units
The height of the triangle measures 3 units
The area of the triangle is 6 square units

5 What is the area of each of these triangles? 6 square units

Application

Follow the directions for the activity.

- Work individually. Use a 3 × 5 note card.
- Draw a triangle on the note card, using one side of the card as the base and touching the opposite side as the height. (See the card shown.)
- Cut out the drawn triangle and keep the cut pieces.
- Tape together the pieces remaining from the rectangle to form another triangle. This triangle should be congruent to the one that was cut out.
- Compare triangles and discuss how the area formula for a triangle relates to the area formula of a rectangle.

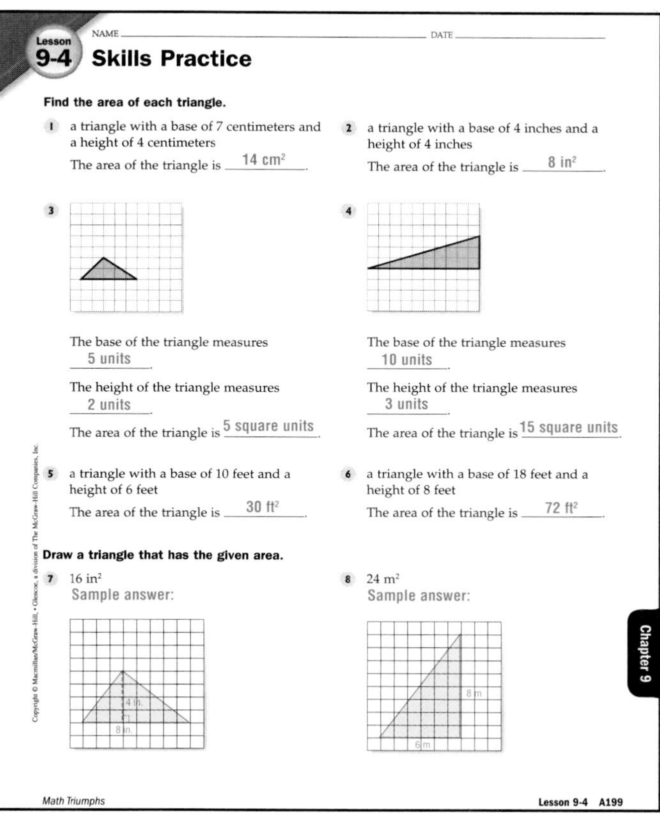

Lesson 9-4

NAME ______________________ DATE ____________

Skills Practice

Find the area of each triangle.

1 a triangle with a base of 7 centimeters and a height of 4 centimeters
The area of the triangle is 14 cm².

2 a triangle with a base of 4 inches and a height of 4 inches
The area of the triangle is 8 in².

3
The base of the triangle measures 5 units.
The height of the triangle measures 2 units.
The area of the triangle is 5 square units.

4
The base of the triangle measures 10 units.
The height of the triangle measures 3 units.
The area of the triangle is 15 square units.

5 a triangle with a base of 10 feet and a height of 6 feet
The area of the triangle is 30 ft².

6 a triangle with a base of 18 feet and a height of 8 feet
The area of the triangle is 72 ft².

Draw a triangle that has the given area.

7 16 in²
Sample answer:

8 24 m²
Sample answer:

Chapter 9

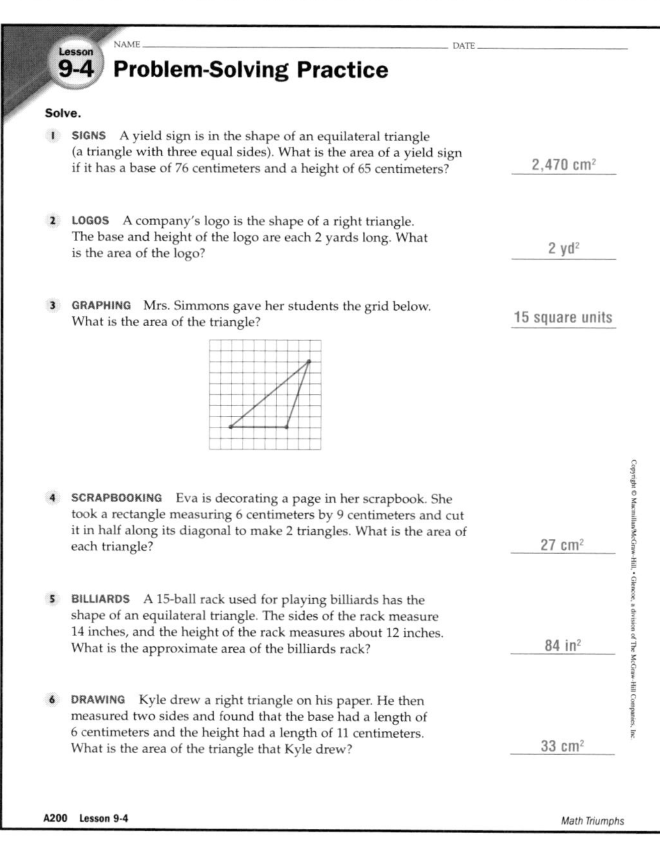

Lesson 9-4

NAME ______________________ DATE ____________

Problem-Solving Practice

Solve.

1 SIGNS A yield sign is in the shape of an equilateral triangle (a triangle with three equal sides). What is the area of a yield sign if it has a base of 76 centimeters and a height of 65 centimeters? 2,470 cm²

2 LOGOS A company's logo is the shape of a right triangle. The base and height of the logo are each 2 yards long. What is the area of the logo? 2 yd²

3 GRAPHING Mrs. Simmons gave her students the grid below. What is the area of the triangle? 15 square units

4 SCRAPBOOKING Eva is decorating a page in her scrapbook. She took a rectangle measuring 6 centimeters by 9 centimeters and cut it in half along its diagonal to make 2 triangles. What is the area of each triangle? 27 cm²

5 BILLIARDS A 15-ball rack used for playing billiards has the shape of an equilateral triangle. The sides of the rack measure 14 inches, and the height of the rack measures about 12 inches. What is the approximate area of the billiards rack? 84 in²

6 DRAWING Kyle drew a right triangle on his paper. He then measured two sides and found that the base had a length of 6 centimeters and the height had a length of 11 centimeters. What is the area of the triangle that Kyle drew? 33 cm²

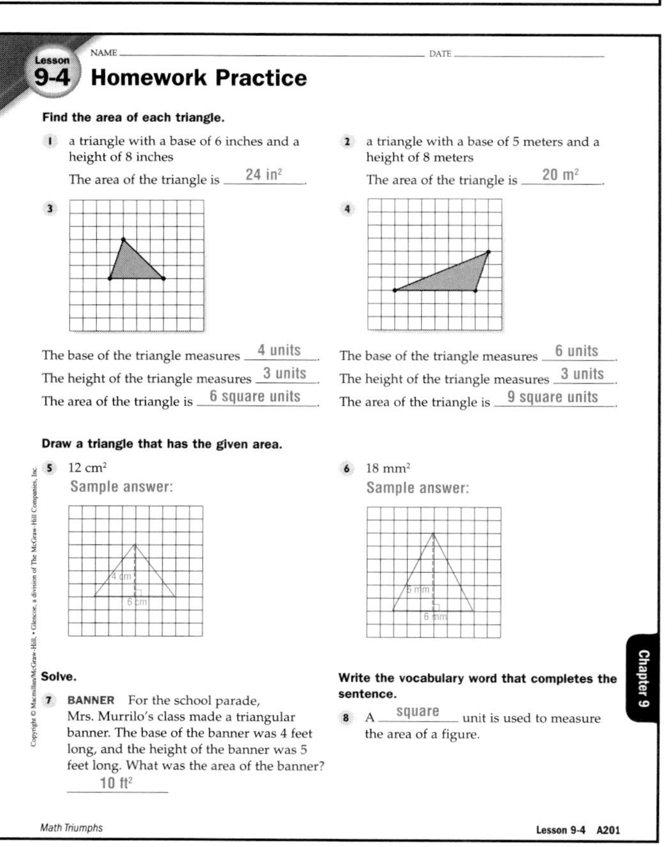

Lesson 9-4

NAME ______________________ DATE ____________

Homework Practice

Find the area of each triangle.

1 a triangle with a base of 6 inches and a height of 8 inches
The area of the triangle is 24 in².

2 a triangle with a base of 5 meters and a height of 8 meters
The area of the triangle is 20 m².

3
The base of the triangle measures 4 units.
The height of the triangle measures 3 units.
The area of the triangle is 6 square units.

4
The base of the triangle measures 6 units.
The height of the triangle measures 3 units.
The area of the triangle is 9 square units.

Draw a triangle that has the given area.

5 12 cm²
Sample answer:

6 18 mm²
Sample answer:

Solve.

7 BANNER For the school parade, Mrs. Murrilo's class made a triangular banner. The base of the banner was 4 feet long, and the height of the banner was 5 feet long. What was the area of the banner? 10 ft²

Write the vocabulary word that completes the sentence.

8 A square unit is used to measure the area of a figure.

Chapter 9

Answer Key (Lesson 10-1)

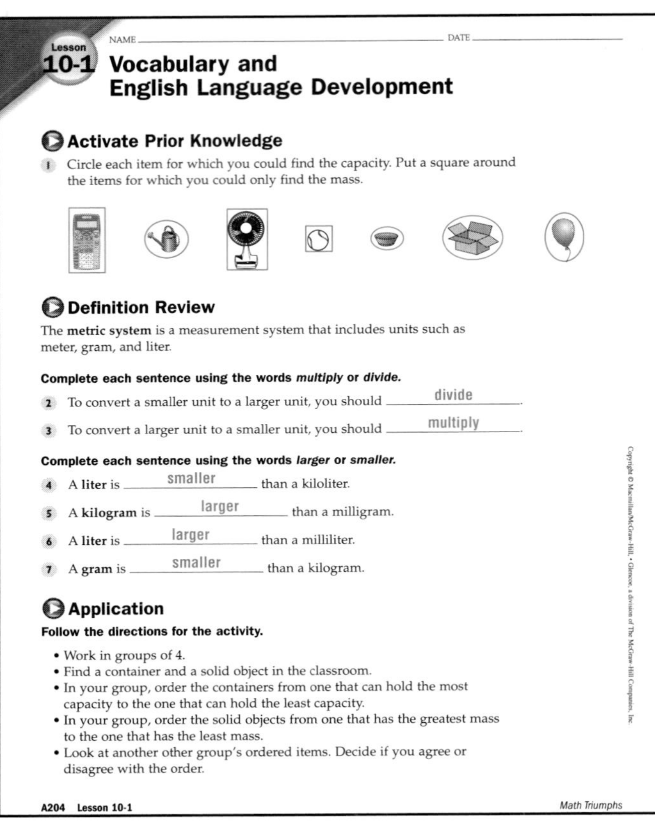

NAME ______________________ DATE ____________

Lesson 10-1 Vocabulary and English Language Development

Activate Prior Knowledge

1. Circle each item for which you could find the capacity. Put a square around the items for which you could only find the mass.

Definition Review

The **metric system** is a measurement system that includes units such as meter, gram, and liter.

Complete each sentence using the words *multiply* or *divide*.

2. To convert a smaller unit to a larger unit, you should divide.
3. To convert a larger unit to a smaller unit, you should multiply.

Complete each sentence using the words *larger* or *smaller*.

4. A **liter** is smaller than a kiloliter.
5. A **kilogram** is larger than a milligram.
6. A **liter** is larger than a milliliter.
7. A **gram** is smaller than a kilogram.

Application

Follow the directions for the activity.

- Work in groups of 4.
- Find a container and a solid object in the classroom.
- In your group, order the containers from one that can hold the most capacity to the one that can hold the least capacity.
- In your group, order the solid objects from one that has the greatest mass to the one that has the least mass.
- Look at another other group's ordered items. Decide if you agree or disagree with the order.

A204 Lesson 10-1 *Math Triumphs*

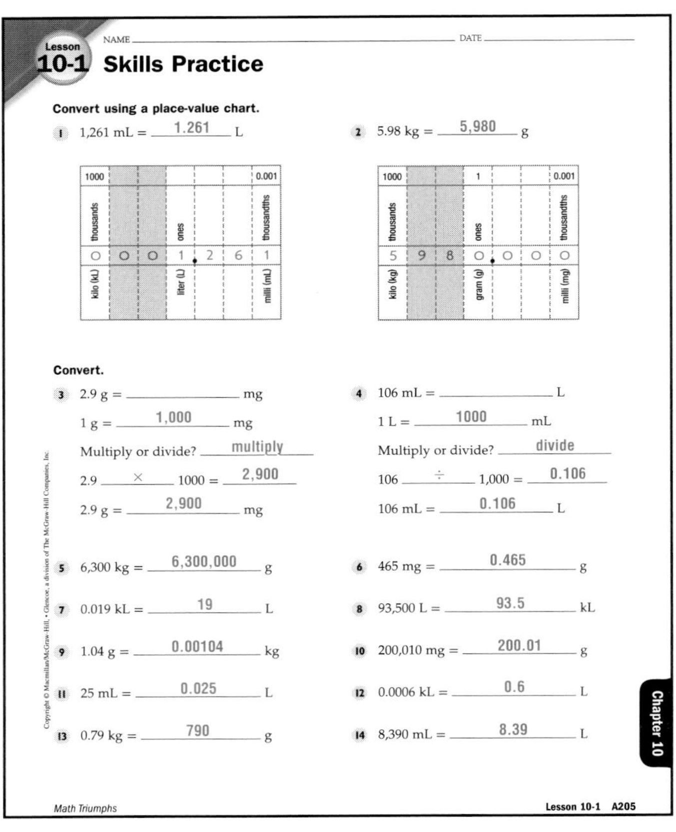

NAME ______________________ DATE ____________

Lesson 10-1 Skills Practice

Convert using a place-value chart.

1. 1,261 mL = 1.261 L

1000						0.001
thousands			ones			thousandths
0	0	0	1.	2	6	1
kilo (kL)			liter (L)			milli (mL)

2. 5.98 kg = 5,980 g

1000			1			0.001
thousands			ones			thousandths
5	9	8	0.	0	0	0
kilo (kg)			gram (g)			milli (mg)

Convert.

3. 2.9 g = ______ mg
   1 g = 1,000 mg
   Multiply or divide? multiply
   2.9 × 1000 = 2,900
   2.9 g = 2,900 mg

4. 106 mL = ______ L
   1 L = 1000 mL
   Multiply or divide? divide
   106 ÷ 1,000 = 0.106
   106 mL = 0.106 L

5. 6,300 kg = 6,300,000 g
6. 465 mg = 0.465 g
7. 0.019 kL = 19 L
8. 93,500 L = 93.5 kL
9. 1.04 g = 0.00104 kg
10. 200,010 mg = 200.01 g
11. 25 mL = 0.025 L
12. 0.0006 kL = 0.6 L
13. 0.79 kg = 790 g
14. 8,390 mL = 8.39 L

Chapter 10

Math Triumphs Lesson 10-1 A205

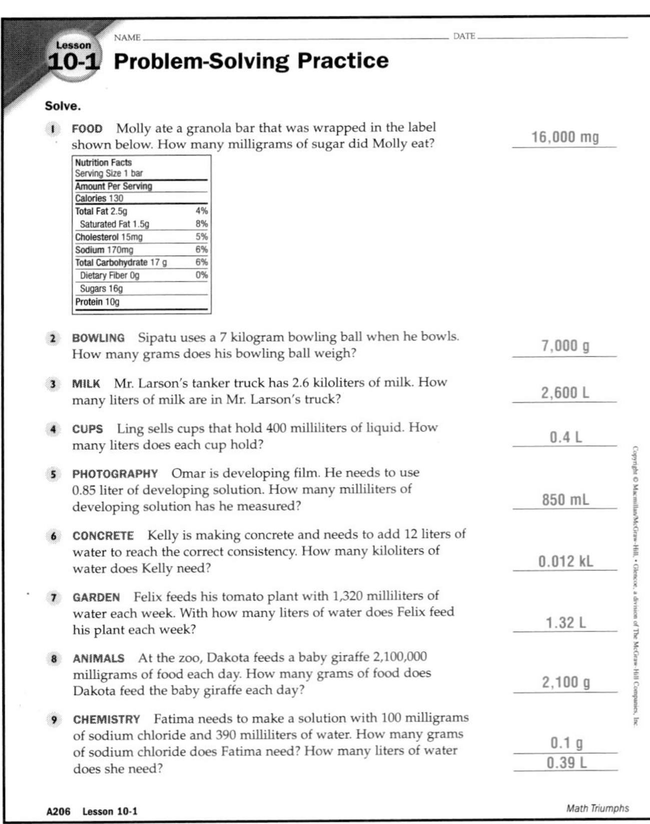

NAME ______________________ DATE ____________

Lesson 10-1 Problem-Solving Practice

Solve.

1. **FOOD** Molly ate a granola bar that was wrapped in the label shown below. How many milligrams of sugar did Molly eat? 16,000 mg

Nutrition Facts	
Serving Size 1 bar	
Amount Per Serving	
Calories 130	
Total Fat 2.5g	4%
Saturated Fat 1.5g	8%
Cholesterol 15mg	5%
Sodium 170mg	6%
Total Carbohydrate 17 g	6%
Dietary Fiber 0g	0%
Sugars 16g	
Protein 10g	

2. **BOWLING** Sipatu uses a 7 kilogram bowling ball when he bowls. How many grams does his bowling ball weigh? 7,000 g
3. **MILK** Mr. Larson's tanker truck has 2.6 kiloliters of milk. How many liters of milk are in Mr. Larson's truck? 2,600 L
4. **CUPS** Ling sells cups that hold 400 milliliters of liquid. How many liters does each cup hold? 0.4 L
5. **PHOTOGRAPHY** Omar is developing film. He needs to use 0.85 liter of developing solution. How many milliliters of developing solution has he measured? 850 mL
6. **CONCRETE** Kelly is making concrete and needs to add 12 liters of water to reach the correct consistency. How many kiloliters of water does Kelly need? 0.012 kL
7. **GARDEN** Felix feeds his tomato plant with 1,320 milliliters of water each week. With how many liters of water does Felix feed his plant each week? 1.32 L
8. **ANIMALS** At the zoo, Dakota feeds a baby giraffe 2,100,000 milligrams of food each day. How many grams of food does Dakota feed the baby giraffe each day? 2,100 g
9. **CHEMISTRY** Fatima needs to make a solution with 100 milligrams of sodium chloride and 390 milliliters of water. How many grams of sodium chloride does Fatima need? How many liters of water does she need? 0.1 g; 0.39 L

A206 Lesson 10-1 *Math Triumphs*

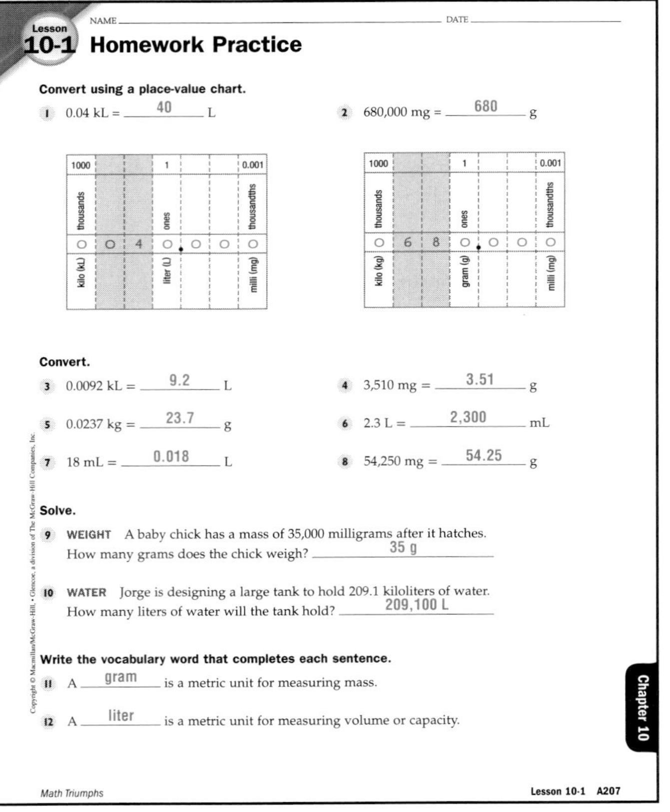

NAME ______________________ DATE ____________

Lesson 10-1 Homework Practice

Convert using a place-value chart.

1. 0.04 kL = 40 L

1000			1			0.001
thousands			ones			thousandths
0	0	4	0.	0	0	0
kilo (kL)			liter (L)			milli (mg)

2. 680,000 mg = 680 g

1000			1			0.001
thousands			ones			thousandths
0	6	8	0.	0	0	0
kilo (kg)			gram (g)			milli (mg)

Convert.

3. 0.0092 kL = 9.2 L
4. 3,510 mg = 3.51 g
5. 0.0237 kg = 23.7 g
6. 2.3 L = 2,300 mL
7. 18 mL = 0.018 L
8. 54,250 mg = 54.25 g

Solve.

9. **WEIGHT** A baby chick has a mass of 35,000 milligrams after it hatches. How many grams does the chick weigh? 35 g
10. **WATER** Jorge is designing a large tank to hold 209.1 kiloliters of water. How many liters of water will the tank hold? 209,100 L

Write the vocabulary word that completes each sentence.

11. A gram is a metric unit for measuring mass.
12. A liter is a metric unit for measuring volume or capacity.

Chapter 10

Math Triumphs Lesson 10-1 A207

Answer Key (Lesson 10-2)

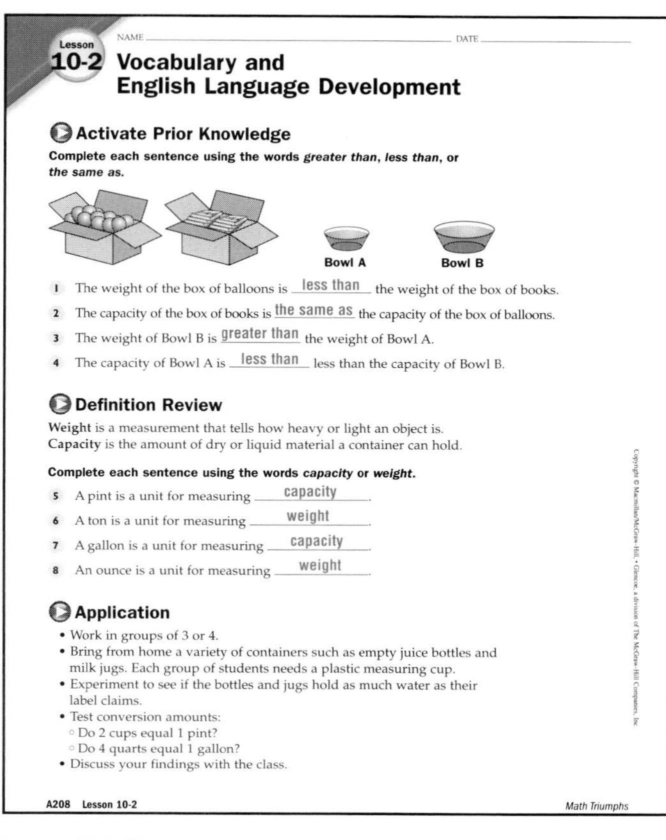

NAME ______________ DATE ______________

Lesson 10-2 Vocabulary and English Language Development

Activate Prior Knowledge

Complete each sentence using the words *greater than, less than,* or *the same as.*

Bowl A Bowl B

1. The weight of the box of balloons is less than the weight of the box of books.
2. The capacity of the box of books is the same as the capacity of the box of balloons.
3. The weight of Bowl B is greater than the weight of Bowl A.
4. The capacity of Bowl A is less than less than the capacity of Bowl B.

Definition Review

Weight is a measurement that tells how heavy or light an object is.
Capacity is the amount of dry or liquid material a container can hold.

Complete each sentence using the words *capacity* or *weight*.

5. A pint is a unit for measuring capacity.
6. A ton is a unit for measuring weight.
7. A gallon is a unit for measuring capacity.
8. An ounce is a unit for measuring weight.

Application

- Work in groups of 3 or 4.
- Bring from home a variety of containers such as empty juice bottles and milk jugs. Each group of students needs a plastic measuring cup.
- Experiment to see if the bottles and jugs hold as much water as their label claims.
- Test conversion amounts:
  - Do 2 cups equal 1 pint?
  - Do 4 quarts equal 1 gallon?
- Discuss your findings with the class.

A208 Lesson 10-2 *Math Triumphs*

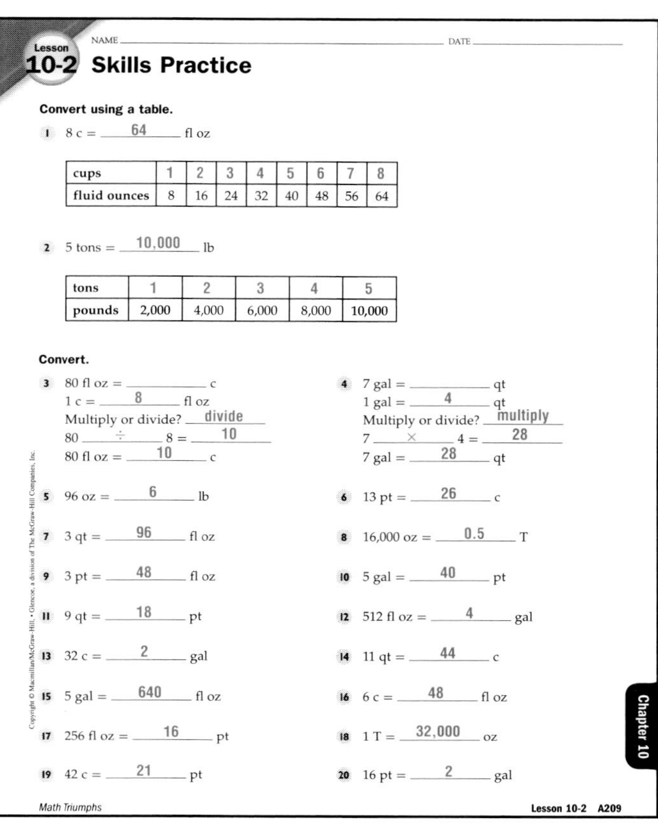

NAME ______________ DATE ______________

Lesson 10-2 Skills Practice

Convert using a table.

1. 8 c = 64 fl oz

cups	1	2	3	4	5	6	7	8
fluid ounces	8	16	24	32	40	48	56	64

2. 5 tons = 10,000 lb

tons	1	2	3	4	5
pounds	2,000	4,000	6,000	8,000	10,000

Convert.

3. 80 fl oz = ______ c
   1 c = 8 fl oz
   Multiply or divide? divide
   80 ÷ 8 = 10
   80 fl oz = 10 c
4. 7 gal = ______ qt
   1 gal = 4 qt
   Multiply or divide? multiply
   7 × 4 = 28
   7 gal = 28 qt
5. 96 oz = 6 lb
6. 13 pt = 26 c
7. 3 qt = 96 fl oz
8. 16,000 oz = 0.5 T
9. 3 pt = 48 fl oz
10. 5 gal = 40 pt
11. 9 qt = 18 pt
12. 512 fl oz = 4 gal
13. 32 c = 2 gal
14. 11 qt = 44 c
15. 5 gal = 640 fl oz
16. 6 c = 48 fl oz
17. 256 fl oz = 16 pt
18. 1 T = 32,000 oz
19. 42 c = 21 pt
20. 16 pt = 2 gal

Chapter 10

Math Triumphs Lesson 10-2 A209

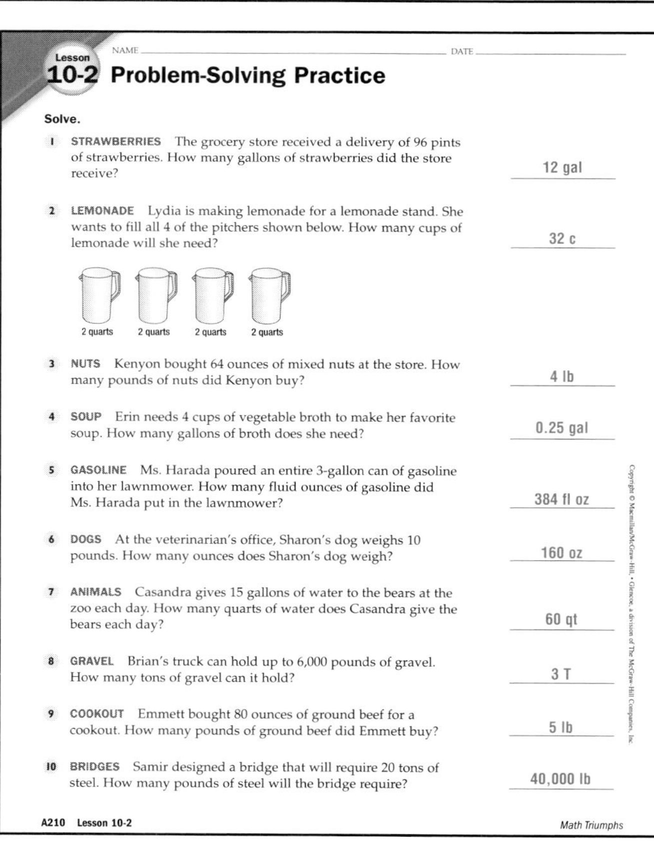

NAME ______________ DATE ______________

Lesson 10-2 Problem-Solving Practice

Solve.

1. **STRAWBERRIES** The grocery store received a delivery of 96 pints of strawberries. How many gallons of strawberries did the store receive? 12 gal
2. **LEMONADE** Lydia is making lemonade for a lemonade stand. She wants to fill all 4 of the pitchers shown below. How many cups of lemonade will she need? 32 c

2 quarts 2 quarts 2 quarts 2 quarts

3. **NUTS** Kenyon bought 64 ounces of mixed nuts at the store. How many pounds of nuts did Kenyon buy? 4 lb
4. **SOUP** Erin needs 4 cups of vegetable broth to make her favorite soup. How many gallons of broth does she need? 0.25 gal
5. **GASOLINE** Ms. Harada poured an entire 3-gallon can of gasoline into her lawnmower. How many fluid ounces of gasoline did Ms. Harada put in the lawnmower? 384 fl oz
6. **DOGS** At the veterinarian's office, Sharon's dog weighs 10 pounds. How many ounces does Sharon's dog weigh? 160 oz
7. **ANIMALS** Casandra gives 15 gallons of water to the bears at the zoo each day. How many quarts of water does Casandra give the bears each day? 60 qt
8. **GRAVEL** Brian's truck can hold up to 6,000 pounds of gravel. How many tons of gravel can it hold? 3 T
9. **COOKOUT** Emmett bought 80 ounces of ground beef for a cookout. How many pounds of ground beef did Emmett buy? 5 lb
10. **BRIDGES** Samir designed a bridge that will require 20 tons of steel. How many pounds of steel will the bridge require? 40,000 lb

A210 Lesson 10-2 *Math Triumphs*

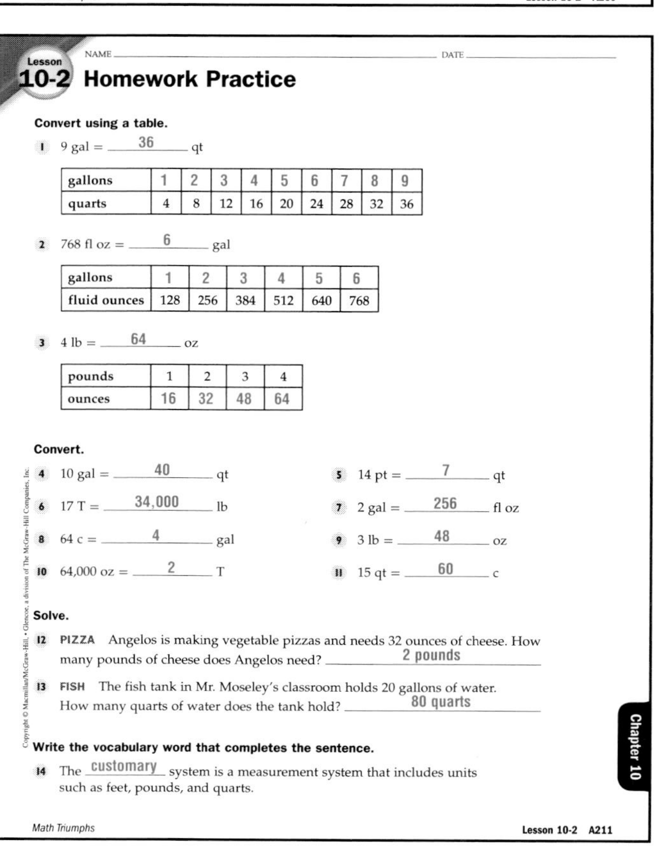

NAME ______________ DATE ______________

Lesson 10-2 Homework Practice

Convert using a table.

1. 9 gal = 36 qt

gallons	1	2	3	4	5	6	7	8	9
quarts	4	8	12	16	20	24	28	32	36

2. 768 fl oz = 6 gal

gallons	1	2	3	4	5	6
fluid ounces	128	256	384	512	640	768

3. 4 lb = 64 oz

pounds	1	2	3	4
ounces	16	32	48	64

Convert.

4. 10 gal = 40 qt
5. 14 pt = 7 qt
6. 17 T = 34,000 lb
7. 2 gal = 256 fl oz
8. 64 c = 4 gal
9. 3 lb = 48 oz
10. 64,000 oz = 2 T
11. 15 qt = 60 c

Solve.

12. **PIZZA** Angelos is making vegetable pizzas and needs 32 ounces of cheese. How many pounds of cheese does Angelos need? 2 pounds
13. **FISH** The fish tank in Mr. Moseley's classroom holds 20 gallons of water. How many quarts of water does the tank hold? 80 quarts

Write the vocabulary word that completes the sentence.

14. The customary system is a measurement system that includes units such as feet, pounds, and quarts.

Chapter 10

Math Triumphs Lesson 10-2 A211

Answer Key (Lesson 10-3)

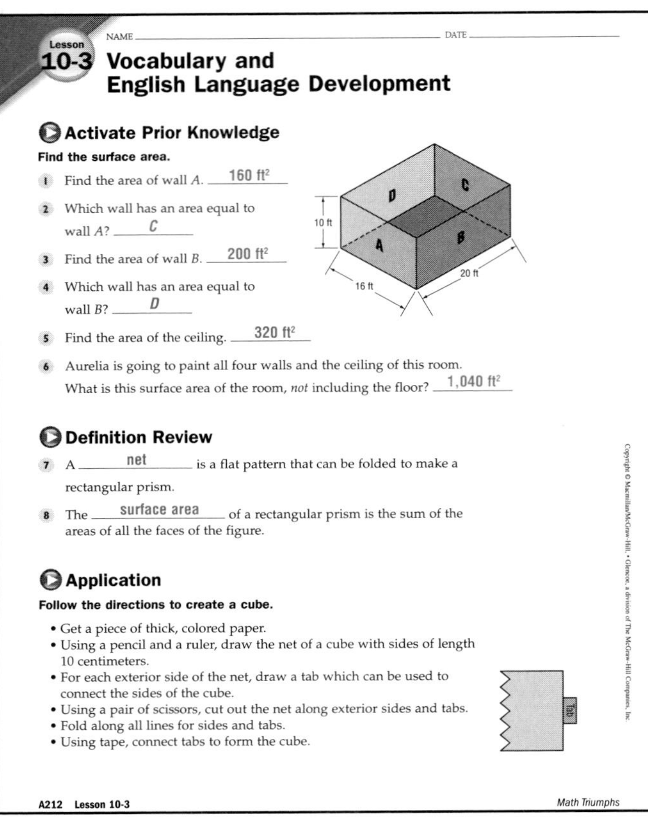

Lesson 10-3 NAME ______ DATE ______

Vocabulary and English Language Development

Activate Prior Knowledge

Find the surface area.

1. Find the area of wall *A*. 160 ft²
2. Which wall has an area equal to wall *A*? C
3. Find the area of wall *B*. 200 ft²
4. Which wall has an area equal to wall *B*? D
5. Find the area of the ceiling. 320 ft²
6. Aurelia is going to paint all four walls and the ceiling of this room. What is this surface area of the room, *not* including the floor? 1,040 ft²

Definition Review

7. A net is a flat pattern that can be folded to make a rectangular prism.
8. The surface area of a rectangular prism is the sum of the areas of all the faces of the figure.

Application

Follow the directions to create a cube.

- Get a piece of thick, colored paper.
- Using a pencil and a ruler, draw the net of a cube with sides of length 10 centimeters.
- For each exterior side of the net, draw a tab which can be used to connect the sides of the cube.
- Using a pair of scissors, cut out the net along exterior sides and tabs.
- Fold along all lines for sides and tabs.
- Using tape, connect tabs to form the cube.

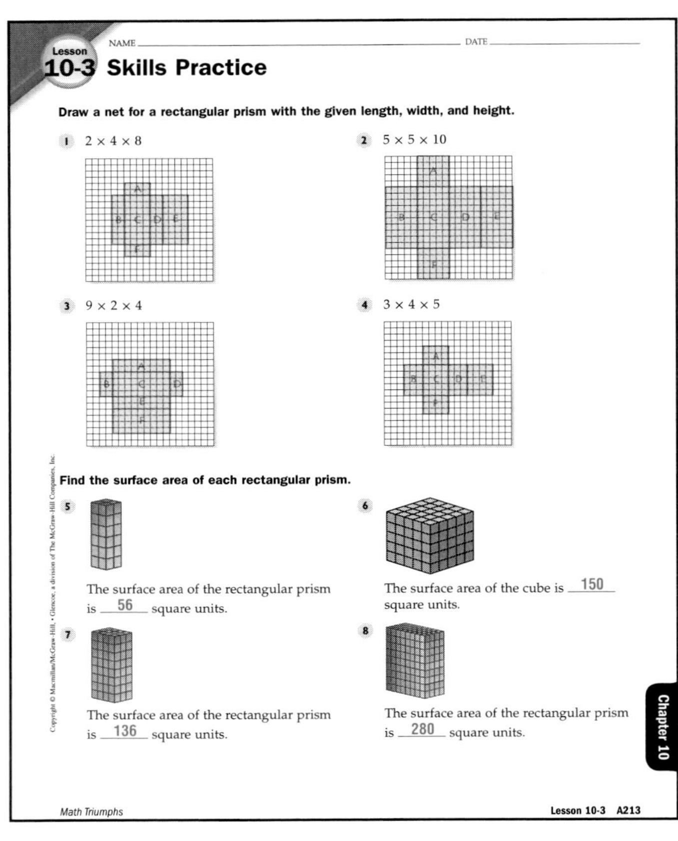

Lesson 10-3 NAME ______ DATE ______

Skills Practice

Draw a net for a rectangular prism with the given length, width, and height.

1. $2 \times 4 \times 8$
2. $5 \times 5 \times 10$
3. $9 \times 2 \times 4$
4. $3 \times 4 \times 5$

Find the surface area of each rectangular prism.

5. The surface area of the rectangular prism is 56 square units.
6. The surface area of the cube is 150 square units.
7. The surface area of the rectangular prism is 136 square units.
8. The surface area of the rectangular prism is 280 square units.

Chapter 10

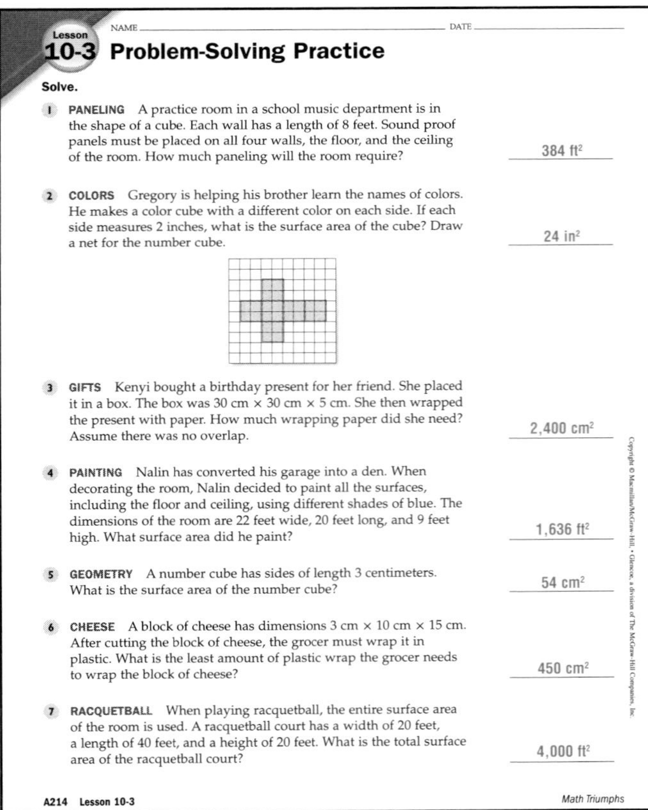

Lesson 10-3 NAME ______ DATE ______

Problem-Solving Practice

Solve.

1. **PANELING** A practice room in a school music department is in the shape of a cube. Each wall has a length of 8 feet. Sound proof panels must be placed on all four walls, the floor, and the ceiling of the room. How much paneling will the room require? 384 ft²
2. **COLORS** Gregory is helping his brother learn the names of colors. He makes a color cube with a different color on each side. If each side measures 2 inches, what is the surface area of the cube? Draw a net for the number cube. 24 in²
3. **GIFTS** Kenyi bought a birthday present for her friend. She placed it in a box. The box was 30 cm × 30 cm × 5 cm. She then wrapped the present with paper. How much wrapping paper did she need? Assume there was no overlap. 2,400 cm²
4. **PAINTING** Nalin has converted his garage into a den. When decorating the room, Nalin decided to paint all the surfaces, including the floor and ceiling, using different shades of blue. The dimensions of the room are 22 feet wide, 20 feet long, and 9 feet high. What surface area did he paint? 1,636 ft²
5. **GEOMETRY** A number cube has sides of length 3 centimeters. What is the surface area of the number cube? 54 cm²
6. **CHEESE** A block of cheese has dimensions 3 cm × 10 cm × 15 cm. After cutting the block of cheese, the grocer must wrap it in plastic. What is the least amount of plastic wrap the grocer needs to wrap the block of cheese? 450 cm²
7. **RACQUETBALL** When playing racquetball, the entire surface area of the room is used. A racquetball court has a width of 20 feet, a length of 40 feet, and a height of 20 feet. What is the total surface area of the racquetball court? 4,000 ft²

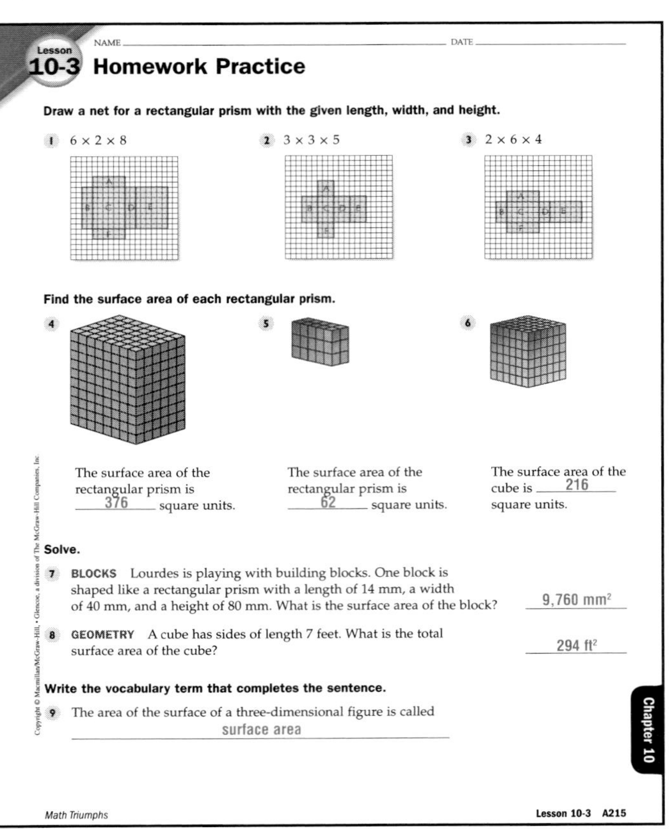

Lesson 10-3 NAME ______ DATE ______

Homework Practice

Draw a net for a rectangular prism with the given length, width, and height.

1. $6 \times 2 \times 8$
2. $3 \times 3 \times 5$
3. $2 \times 6 \times 4$

Find the surface area of each rectangular prism.

4. The surface area of the rectangular prism is 376 square units.
5. The surface area of the rectangular prism is 62 square units.
6. The surface area of the cube is 216 square units.

Solve.

7. **BLOCKS** Lourdes is playing with building blocks. One block is shaped like a rectangular prism with a length of 14 mm, a width of 40 mm, and a height of 80 mm. What is the surface area of the block? 9,760 mm²
8. **GEOMETRY** A cube has sides of length 7 feet. What is the total surface area of the cube? 294 ft²

Write the vocabulary term that completes the sentence.

9. The area of the surface of a three-dimensional figure is called surface area

Chapter 10

Answer Key (Lesson 10-4)

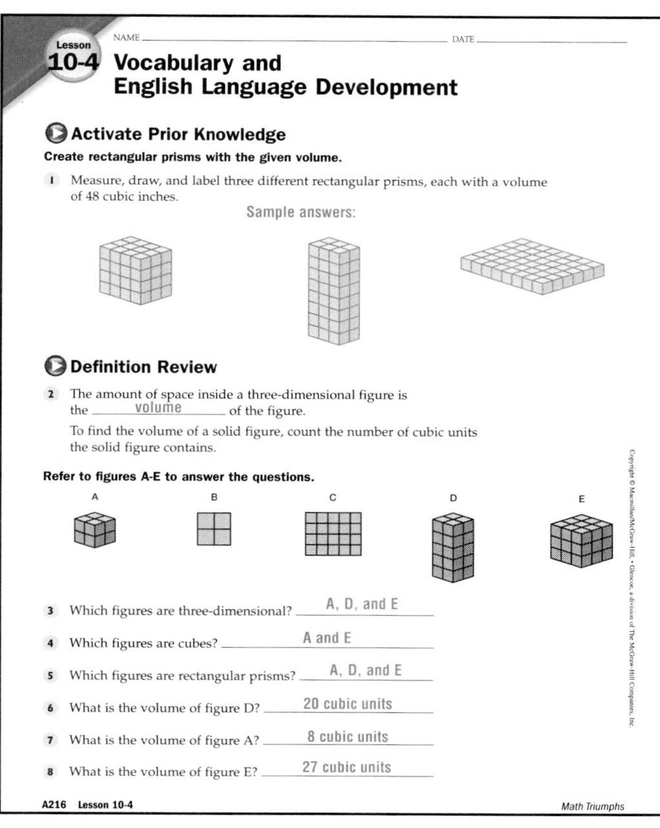

NAME ____________ DATE ____________

Lesson 10-4 **Vocabulary and English Language Development**

Activate Prior Knowledge

Create rectangular prisms with the given volume.

1 Measure, draw, and label three different rectangular prisms, each with a volume of 48 cubic inches.

Sample answers:

Definition Review

2 The amount of space inside a three-dimensional figure is the ___volume___ of the figure.

To find the volume of a solid figure, count the number of cubic units the solid figure contains.

Refer to figures A-E to answer the questions.

A B C D E

3 Which figures are three-dimensional? ___A, D, and E___

4 Which figures are cubes? ___A and E___

5 Which figures are rectangular prisms? ___A, D, and E___

6 What is the volume of figure D? ___20 cubic units___

7 What is the volume of figure A? ___8 cubic units___

8 What is the volume of figure E? ___27 cubic units___

A216 Lesson 10-4 *Math Triumphs*

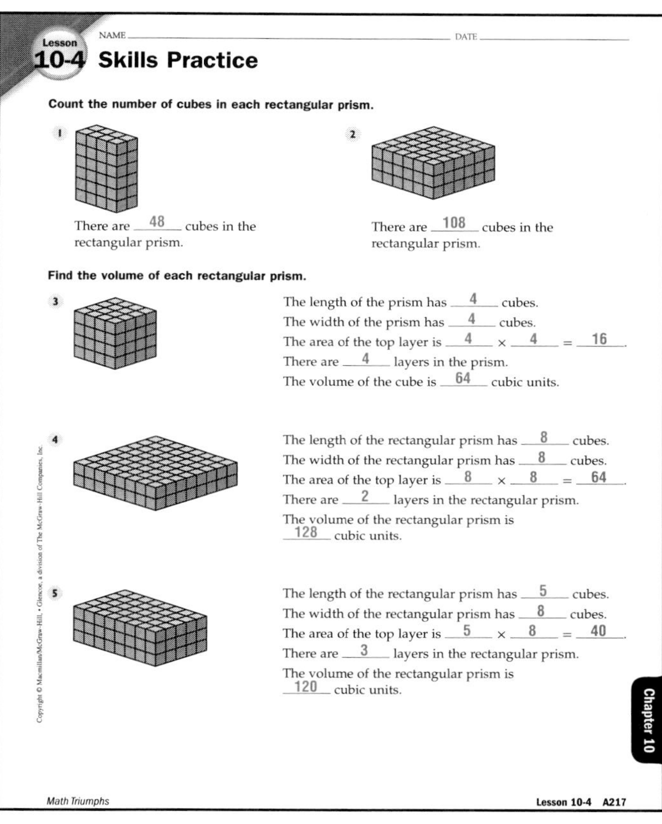

NAME ____________ DATE ____________

Lesson 10-4 **Skills Practice**

Count the number of cubes in each rectangular prism.

1 There are ___48___ cubes in the rectangular prism.

2 There are ___108___ cubes in the rectangular prism.

Find the volume of each rectangular prism.

3 The length of the prism has ___4___ cubes.
The width of the prism has ___4___ cubes.
The area of the top layer is ___4___ × ___4___ = ___16___.
There are ___4___ layers in the prism.
The volume of the cube is ___64___ cubic units.

4 The length of the rectangular prism has ___8___ cubes.
The width of the rectangular prism has ___8___ cubes.
The area of the top layer is ___8___ × ___8___ = ___64___.
There are ___2___ layers in the rectangular prism.
The volume of the rectangular prism is ___128___ cubic units.

5 The length of the rectangular prism has ___5___ cubes.
The width of the rectangular prism has ___8___ cubes.
The area of the top layer is ___5___ × ___8___ = ___40___.
There are ___3___ layers in the rectangular prism.
The volume of the rectangular prism is ___120___ cubic units.

Chapter 10

Math Triumphs Lesson 10-4 A217

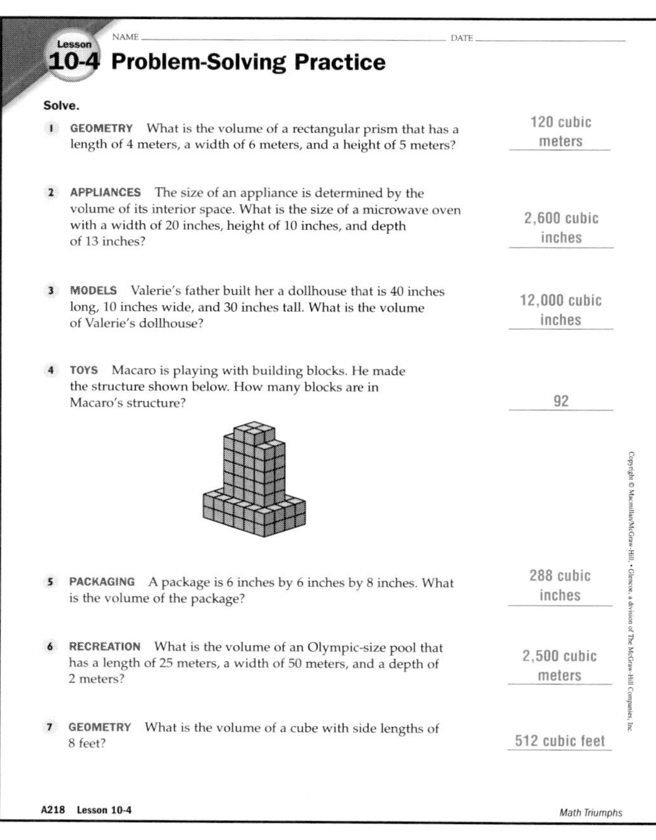

NAME ____________ DATE ____________

Lesson 10-4 **Problem-Solving Practice**

Solve.

1 **GEOMETRY** What is the volume of a rectangular prism that has a length of 4 meters, a width of 6 meters, and a height of 5 meters? ___120 cubic meters___

2 **APPLIANCES** The size of an appliance is determined by the volume of its interior space. What is the size of a microwave oven with a width of 20 inches, height of 10 inches, and depth of 13 inches? ___2,600 cubic inches___

3 **MODELS** Valerie's father built her a dollhouse that is 40 inches long, 10 inches wide, and 30 inches tall. What is the volume of Valerie's dollhouse? ___12,000 cubic inches___

4 **TOYS** Macaro is playing with building blocks. He made the structure shown below. How many blocks are in Macaro's structure? ___92___

5 **PACKAGING** A package is 6 inches by 6 inches by 8 inches. What is the volume of the package? ___288 cubic inches___

6 **RECREATION** What is the volume of an Olympic-size pool that has a length of 25 meters, a width of 50 meters, and a depth of 2 meters? ___2,500 cubic meters___

7 **GEOMETRY** What is the volume of a cube with side lengths of 8 feet? ___512 cubic feet___

A218 Lesson 10-4 *Math Triumphs*

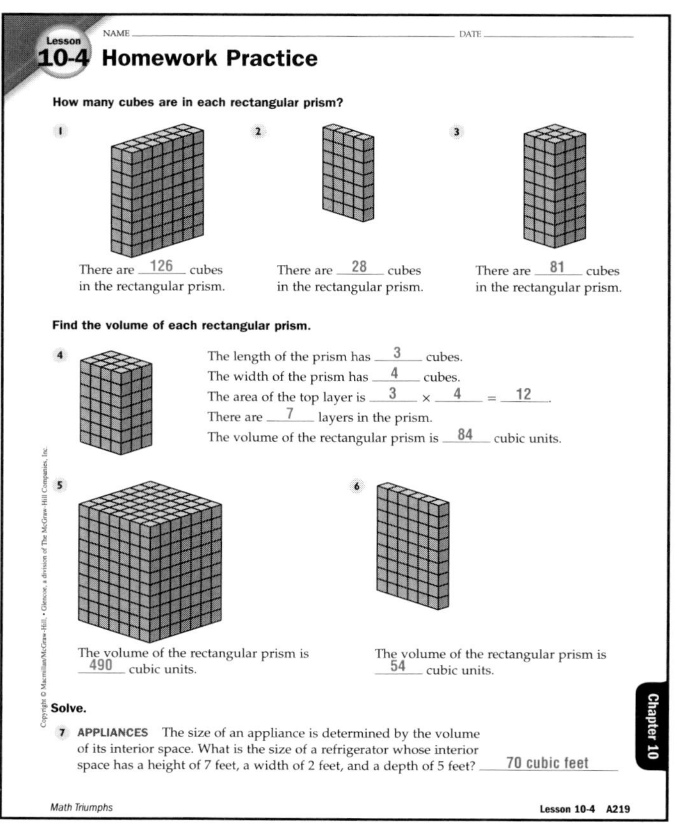

NAME ____________ DATE ____________

Lesson 10-4 **Homework Practice**

How many cubes are in each rectangular prism?

1 There are ___126___ cubes in the rectangular prism.

2 There are ___28___ cubes in the rectangular prism.

3 There are ___81___ cubes in the rectangular prism.

Find the volume of each rectangular prism.

4 The length of the prism has ___3___ cubes.
The width of the prism has ___4___ cubes.
The area of the top layer is ___3___ × ___4___ = ___12___.
There are ___7___ layers in the prism.
The volume of the rectangular prism is ___84___ cubic units.

5 The volume of the rectangular prism is ___490___ cubic units.

6 The volume of the rectangular prism is ___54___ cubic units.

Solve.

7 **APPLIANCES** The size of an appliance is determined by the volume of its interior space. What is the size of a refrigerator whose interior space has a height of 7 feet, a width of 2 feet, and a depth of 5 feet? ___70 cubic feet___

Chapter 10

Math Triumphs Lesson 10-4 A219

Answer Key (Lesson 10-5)

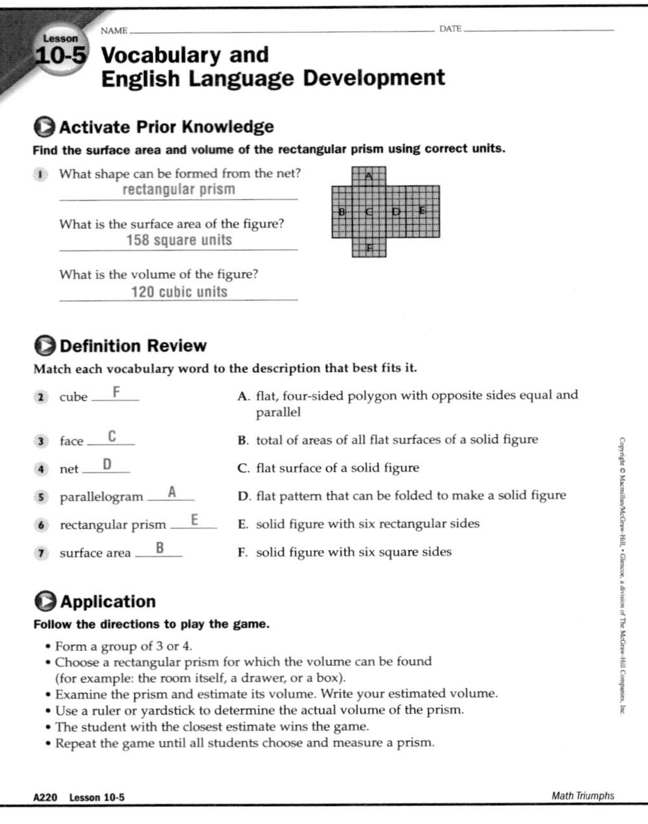

NAME ____________ DATE ____________

Lesson 10-5 Vocabulary and English Language Development

Activate Prior Knowledge

Find the surface area and volume of the rectangular prism using correct units.

1. What shape can be formed from the net? rectangular prism

   What is the surface area of the figure? 158 square units

   What is the volume of the figure? 120 cubic units

Definition Review

Match each vocabulary word to the description that best fits it.

2. cube F
3. face C
4. net D
5. parallelogram A
6. rectangular prism E
7. surface area B

A. flat, four-sided polygon with opposite sides equal and parallel
B. total of areas of all flat surfaces of a solid figure
C. flat surface of a solid figure
D. flat pattern that can be folded to make a solid figure
E. solid figure with six rectangular sides
F. solid figure with six square sides

Application

Follow the directions to play the game.

- Form a group of 3 or 4.
- Choose a rectangular prism for which the volume can be found (for example: the room itself, a drawer, or a box).
- Examine the prism and estimate its volume. Write your estimated volume.
- Use a ruler or yardstick to determine the actual volume of the prism.
- The student with the closest estimate wins the game.
- Repeat the game until all students choose and measure a prism.

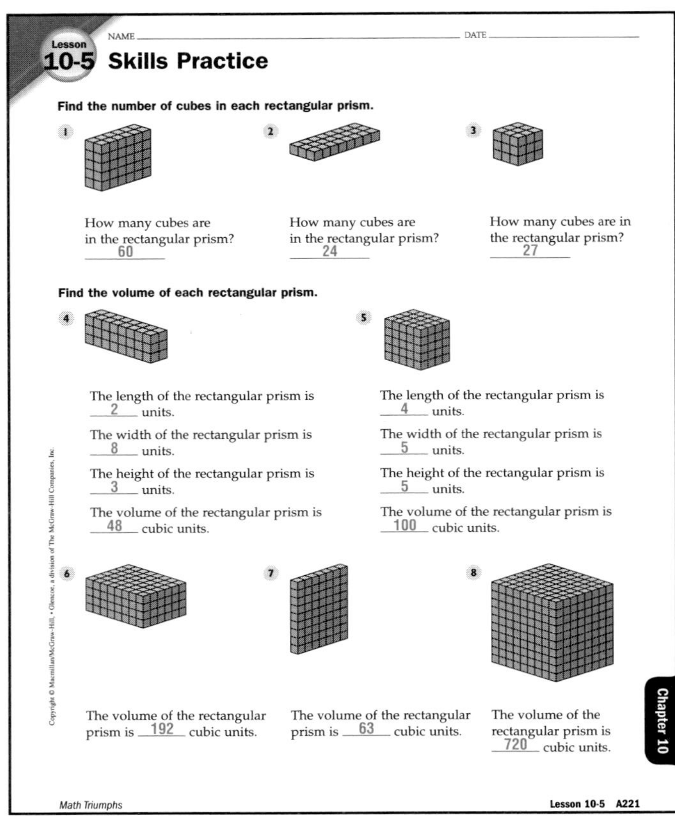

NAME ____________ DATE ____________

Lesson 10-5 Skills Practice

Find the number of cubes in each rectangular prism.

1. How many cubes are in the rectangular prism? 60
2. How many cubes are in the rectangular prism? 24
3. How many cubes are in the rectangular prism? 27

Find the volume of each rectangular prism.

4. The length of the rectangular prism is 2 units.
   The width of the rectangular prism is 8 units.
   The height of the rectangular prism is 3 units.
   The volume of the rectangular prism is 48 cubic units.
5. The length of the rectangular prism is 4 units.
   The width of the rectangular prism is 5 units.
   The height of the rectangular prism is 5 units.
   The volume of the rectangular prism is 100 cubic units.
6. The volume of the rectangular prism is 192 cubic units.
7. The volume of the rectangular prism is 63 cubic units.
8. The volume of the rectangular prism is 720 cubic units.

Chapter 10

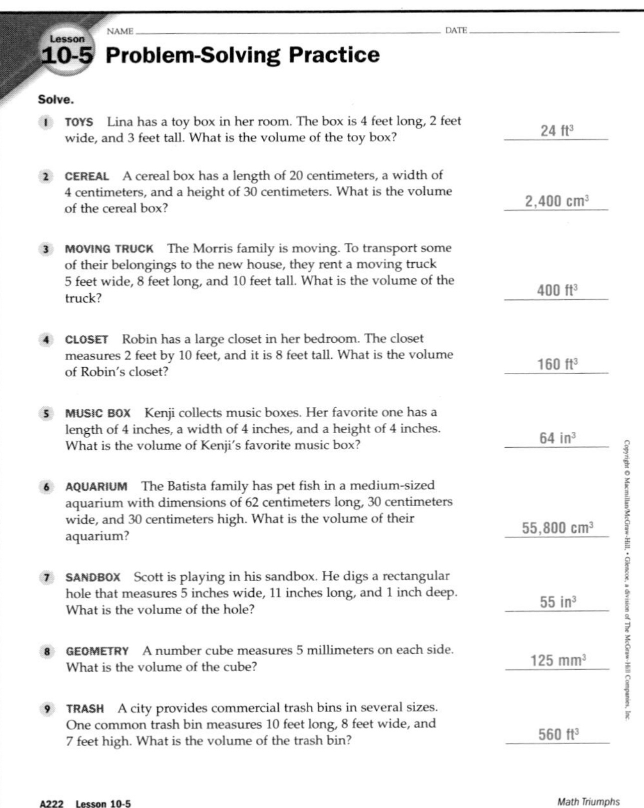

NAME ____________ DATE ____________

Lesson 10-5 Problem-Solving Practice

Solve.

1. **TOYS** Lina has a toy box in her room. The box is 4 feet long, 2 feet wide, and 3 feet tall. What is the volume of the toy box? 24 ft^3
2. **CEREAL** A cereal box has a length of 20 centimeters, a width of 4 centimeters, and a height of 30 centimeters. What is the volume of the cereal box? 2,400 cm^3
3. **MOVING TRUCK** The Morris family is moving. To transport some of their belongings to the new house, they rent a moving truck 5 feet wide, 8 feet long, and 10 feet tall. What is the volume of the truck? 400 ft^3
4. **CLOSET** Robin has a large closet in her bedroom. The closet measures 2 feet by 10 feet, and it is 8 feet tall. What is the volume of Robin's closet? 160 ft^3
5. **MUSIC BOX** Kenji collects music boxes. Her favorite one has a length of 4 inches, a width of 4 inches, and a height of 4 inches. What is the volume of Kenji's favorite music box? 64 in^3
6. **AQUARIUM** The Batista family has pet fish in a medium-sized aquarium with dimensions of 62 centimeters long, 30 centimeters wide, and 30 centimeters high. What is the volume of their aquarium? 55,800 cm^3
7. **SANDBOX** Scott is playing in his sandbox. He digs a rectangular hole that measures 5 inches wide, 11 inches long, and 1 inch deep. What is the volume of the hole? 55 in^3
8. **GEOMETRY** A number cube measures 5 millimeters on each side. What is the volume of the cube? 125 mm^3
9. **TRASH** A city provides commercial trash bins in several sizes. One common trash bin measures 10 feet long, 8 feet wide, and 7 feet high. What is the volume of the trash bin? 560 ft^3

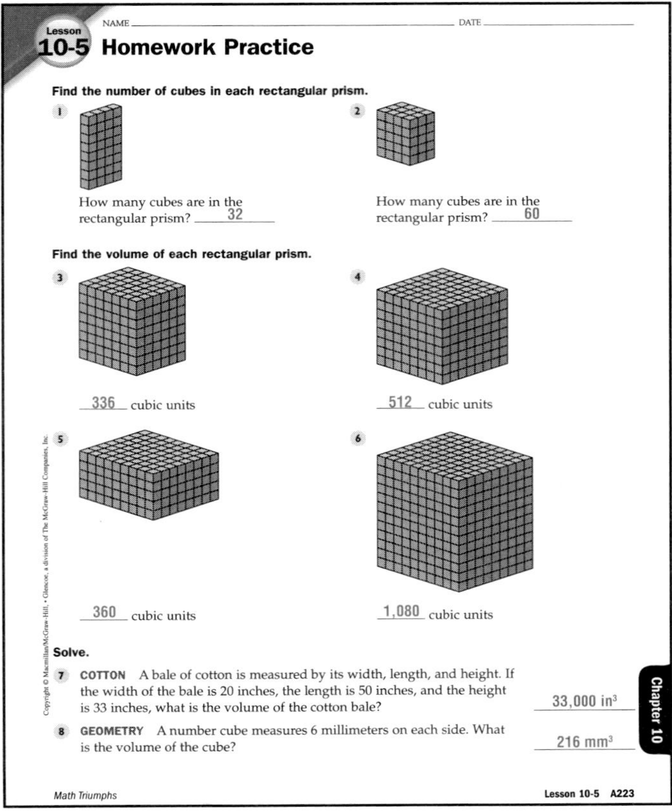

NAME ____________ DATE ____________

Lesson 10-5 Homework Practice

Find the number of cubes in each rectangular prism.

1. How many cubes are in the rectangular prism? 32
2. How many cubes are in the rectangular prism? 60

Find the volume of each rectangular prism.

3. 336 cubic units
4. 512 cubic units
5. 360 cubic units
6. 1,080 cubic units

Solve.

7. **COTTON** A bale of cotton is measured by its width, length, and height. If the width of the bale is 20 inches, the length is 50 inches, and the height is 33 inches, what is the volume of the cotton bale? 33,000 in^3
8. **GEOMETRY** A number cube measures 6 millimeters on each side. What is the volume of the cube? 216 mm^3

Chapter 10